# Visit classzone.com and get connected

## Online resources for students and parents

*ClassZone* resources provide instruction, practice, and learning support.

### eEdition Plus ONLINE

This interactive version of the text encourages students to explore science.

### Content Review Online

Interactive review reinforces the big idea and key concepts of each chapter.

### SciLinks

NSTA-selected links provide relevant Web resources correlated to the text.

### Chapter-Based Support

Math tutorials, news, resources, test practice, and a misconceptions database help students succeed.

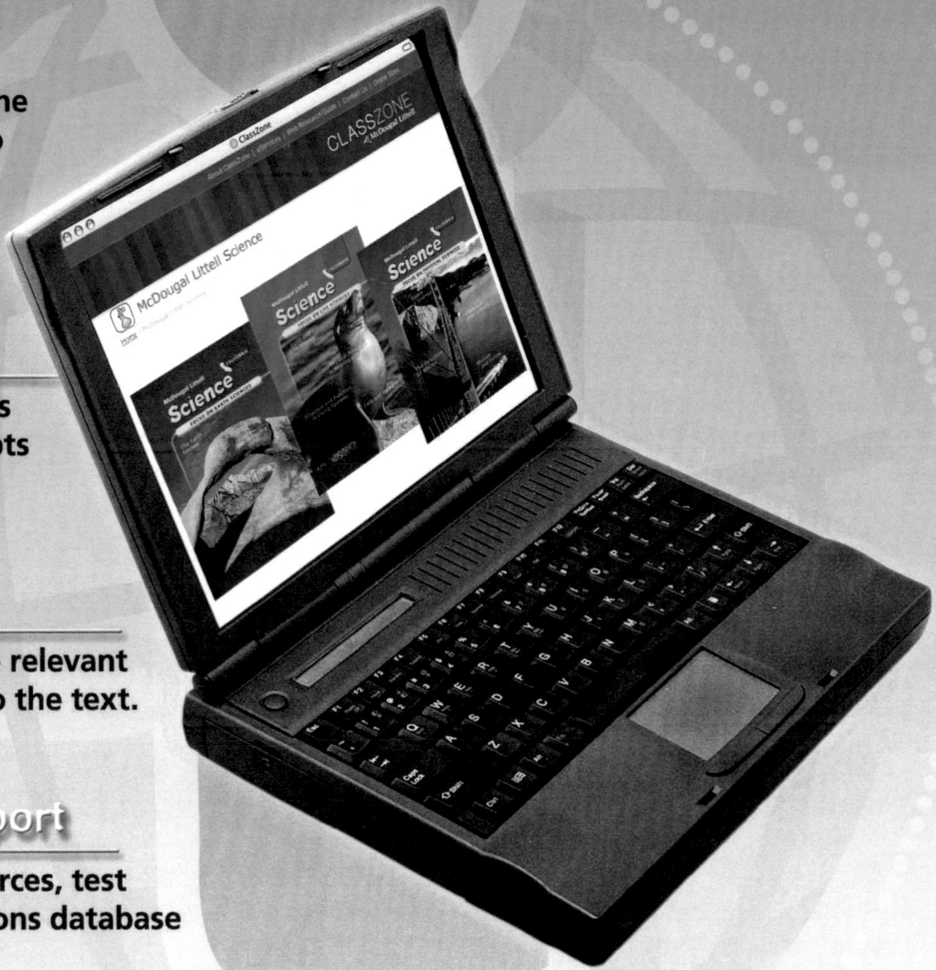


**Now it all clicks!™**

CLASSZONE.COM

McDougal Littell

McDougal Littell

CALIFORNIA

# Science

## FOCUS ON EARTH SCIENCES

The Earth System

The Changing Earth

Earth's Surface

Ecology and Resources

Science Content Standards for California Public Schools reproduced by permission, California Department of Education, CDE Press, 1430 N Street, Suite 3207, Sacramento, CA 95814.



Printed in the U.S.A.

ISBN 13: 978-0-618-64094-2 7 8 0930 15
ISBN 10: 0-618-64094-0 4500563186

Internet Web Site: http://www.mcdougallittell.com

## Science Consultants

### Chief Science Consultant

**James Trefil, Ph.D.** is the Clarence J. Robinson Professor of Physics at George Mason University. He is the author or co-author of more than 25 books, including *Science Matters* and *The Nature of Science*. Dr. Trefil is a member of the American Association for the Advancement of Science's Committee on the Public Understanding of Science and Technology. He is also a fellow of the World Economic Forum and a frequent contributor to *Smithsonian* magazine.

**Rita Ann Calvo, Ph.D.** is Senior Lecturer in Molecular Biology and Genetics at Cornell University, where for 12 years she also directed the Cornell Institute for Biology Teachers. Dr. Calvo is the 1999 recipient of the College and University Teaching Award from the National Association of Biology Teachers.

**Kenneth Cutler, M.S.** is the Education Coordinator for the Julius L. Chambers Biomedical Biotechnology Research Institute at North Carolina Central University. A former middle school and high school science teacher, he received a 1999 Presidential Award for Excellence in Science Teaching.

## Instructional Design Consultants

**Douglas Carnine, Ph.D.** is Professor of Education and Director of the National Center for Improving the Tools of Educators at the University of Oregon. He is the author of seven books and over 100 other scholarly publications, primarily in the areas of instructional design and effective instructional strategies and tools for diverse learners. Dr. Carnine also serves as a member of the National Institute for Literacy Advisory Board.

**Linda Carnine, Ph.D.** consults with school districts on curriculum development and effective instruction for students struggling academically. A former teacher and school administrator, Dr. Carnine also co-authored a popular remedial reading program.

**Sam Miller, Ph.D.** is a middle school science teacher and the Teacher Development Liaison for the Eugene, Oregon, Public Schools. He is the author of curricula for teaching science, mathematics, computer skills, and language arts.

**Donald Steely, Ph.D.** serves as principal investigator at the Oregon Center for Applied Science (ORCAS) on federal grants for science and language arts programs. His background also includes teaching and authoring of print and multimedia programs in science, mathematics, history, and spelling.

**Vicky Vachon, Ph.D.** consults with school districts throughout the United States and Canada on improving overall academic achievement with a focus on literacy. She is also co-author of a widely used program for remedial readers.

# Content Reviewers

**John Beaver, Ph.D.**
*Ecology*
Professor, Director of Science Education Center
College of Education and Human Services
Western Illinois University
Macomb, IL

**Donald J. DeCoste, Ph.D.**
*Matter and Energy, Chemical Interactions*
Chemistry Instructor
University of Illinois
Urbana-Champaign, IL

**Dorothy Ann Fallows, Ph.D., MSc**
*Diversity of Living Things, Microbiology*
Partners in Health
Boston, MA

**Michael Foote, Ph.D.**
*The Changing Earth, Life Over Time*
Associate Professor
Department of the Geophysical Sciences
The University of Chicago
Chicago, IL

**Lucy Fortson, Ph.D.**
*Space Science*
Director of Astronomy
Adler Planetarium and Astronomy Museum
Chicago, IL

**Elizabeth Godrick, Ph.D.**
*Human Biology*
Professor, CAS Biology
Boston University
Boston, MA

**Isabelle Sacramento Grilo, M.S.**
*The Changing Earth*
Lecturer, Department of the Geological Sciences
San Diego State University
San Diego, CA

**David Harbster, MSc**
*Diversity of Living Things*
Professor of Biology
Paradise Valley Community College
Phoenix, AZ

**Richard D. Norris, Ph.D.**
*Earth's Waters*
Professor of Paleobiology
Scripps Institution of Oceanography
University of California, San Diego
La Jolla, CA

**Donald B. Peck, M.S.**
*Motion and Forces; Waves, Sound, and Light; Electricity and Magnetism*
Director of the Center for Science Education (retired)
Fairleigh Dickinson University
Madison, NJ

**Javier Penalosa, Ph.D.**
*Diversity of Living Things, Plants*
Associate Professor, Biology Department
Buffalo State College
Buffalo, NY

**Raymond T. Pierrehumbert, Ph.D.**
*Earth's Atmosphere*
Professor in Geophysical Sciences (Atmospheric Science)
The University of Chicago
Chicago, IL

**Brian J. Skinner, Ph.D.**
*Earth's Surface*
Eugene Higgins Professor of Geology and Geophysics
Yale University
New Haven, CT

**Nancy E. Spaulding, M.S.**
*Earth's Surface, The Changing Earth, Earth's Waters*
Earth Science Teacher (retired)
Elmira Free Academy
Elmira, NY

**Steven S. Zumdahl, Ph.D.**
*Matter and Energy, Chemical Interactions*
Professor Emeritus of Chemistry
University of Illinois
Urbana-Champaign, IL

**Susan L. Zumdahl, M.S.**
*Matter and Energy, Chemical Interactions*
Chemistry Education Specialist
University of Illinois
Urbana-Champaign, IL

# Safety Consultant

**Juliana Texley, Ph.D.**
Former K–12 Science Teacher and School Superintendent
Boca Raton, FL

# English Language Advisor

**Judy Lewis, M.A.**
Director, State and Federal Programs for reading proficiency and high risk populations
Rancho Cordova, CA

## California Teacher Reviewers

**Bill Bruce**
Tenaya Middle School
Fresno, CA

**Mark J. Handwerker, Ph.D.**
Erle Stanley Gardner Middle School
Temecula, CA

**Jack Castro**
William Sheppard Middle School
San Jose, CA

**Sandy Steinburg**
Winston Churchill Middle School
Carmichael, CA

**Bernice Filerman, Ph.D.**
Bell Gardens High School
Bell Gardens, CA

## California Panel Members and Lab Evaluators

**Al Brofman**
Tehipite Middle School,
Fresno, CA

**Jenifer Cox**
Sylvan Middle School,
Citrus Heights, CA

**Ann Marie Lynn**
Amelia Earhart Middle School,
Riverside, CA

**Barbara Newell**
Charles Evans Hughes Middle School,
Long Beach, CA

**Greg Pirolo**
Golden Valley Middle School,
San Bernardino, CA

**Nancy Stubbs**
Sweetwater Union Unified
School District,
Chula Vista, CA

**Lori Walker**
Audubon Middle School &
Magnet Center,
Los Angeles, CA

## Teacher Panel Members

**Carol Arbour**
Tallmadge Middle School,
Tallmadge, OH

**Patty Belcher**
Goodrich Middle School,
Akron, OH

**Gwen Broestl**
Luis Munoz Marin Middle School,
Cleveland, OH

**John Cockrell**
Clinton Middle School,
Columbus, OH

**Linda Culpepper**
Martin Middle School,
Charlotte, NC

**Melvin Figueroa**
New River Middle School,
Ft. Lauderdale, FL

**Doretha Grier**
Kannapolis Middle School,
Kannapolis, NC

**Robert Hood**
Alexander Hamilton Middle School,
Cleveland, OH

**Scott Hudson**
Covedale Elementary School,
Cincinnati, OH

**Loretta Langdon**
Princeton Middle School,
Princeton, NC

**Carlyn Little**
Glades Middle School,
Miami, FL

**James Minogue**
Lowe's Grove Middle School,
Durham, NC

**Kathleen Montagnino-DeMatteo**
Jefferson Davis Middle School,
West Palm Beach, FL

**Joann Myers**
Buchanan Middle School,
Tampa, FL

**Anita Parker**
Kannapolis Middle School,
Kannapolis, NC

**Laura Pottmyer**
Apex Middle School,
Apex, NC

**Lynn Prichard**
Williams Middle Magnet School,
Tampa, FL

**Jacque Quick**
Walter Williams High School,
Burlington, NC

**Robert Glenn Reynolds**
Hillman Middle School,
Youngstown, OH

**Stacy Rinehart**
Lufkin Road Middle School,
Apex, NC

**Theresa Short**
Abbott Middle School,
Fayetteville, NC

**Rita Slivka**
Alexander Hamilton Middle School,
Cleveland, OH

**Marie Sofsak**
B F Stanton Middle School,
Alliance, OH

**Sharon Stull**
Quail Hollow Middle School,
Charlotte, NC

**Donna Taylor**
Bak Middle School of the Arts,
West Palm Beach, FL

**Sandi Thompson**
Harding Middle School,
Lakewood, OH

## Teacher Lab Evaluators

**Andrew Boy**
W.E.B. DuBois Academy,
Cincinnati, OH

**Jill Brimm-Byrne**
Albany Park Academy,
Chicago, IL

**Gwen Broestl**
Luis Munoz Marin Middle School,
Cleveland, OH

**Michael A. Burstein**
The Rashi School,
Newton, MA

**Trudi Coutts**
Madison Middle School,
Naperville, IL

**Larry Cwik**
Madison Middle School,
Naperville, IL

**Esther Dabagyan**
Le Conte Middle School,
Los Angeles, CA

**Jennifer Donatelli**
Kennedy Junior High School,
Lisle, IL

**Melissa Dupree**
Lakeside Middle School,
Evans, GA

**Carl Fechko**
Luis Munoz Marin Middle School,
Cleveland, OH

**Paige Fullhart**
Highland Middle School,
Libertyville, IL

**Sue Hood**
Glen Crest Middle School,
Glen Ellyn, IL

**William Luzader**
Plymouth Community Intermediate School,
Plymouth, MA

**Ann Min**
Beardsley Middle School,
Crystal Lake, IL

**Aileen Mueller**
Kennedy Junior High School,
Lisle, IL

**Nancy Nega**
Churchville Middle School,
Elmhurst, IL

**Oscar Newman**
Sumner Math and Science Academy,
Chicago, IL

**Lynn Prichard**
Willimas Middle Magnet School,
Tampa, FL

**Jacque Quick**
Walter Williams High School,
Burlington, NC

**Stacy Rinehart**
Lufkin Road Middle School,
Apex, NC

**Seth Robey**
Gwendolyn Brooks Middle School,
Oak Park, IL

**Kevin Steele**
Grissom Middle School,
Tinley Park, IL

MCDOUGAL LITTELL SCIENCE

# Focus on Earth Sciences

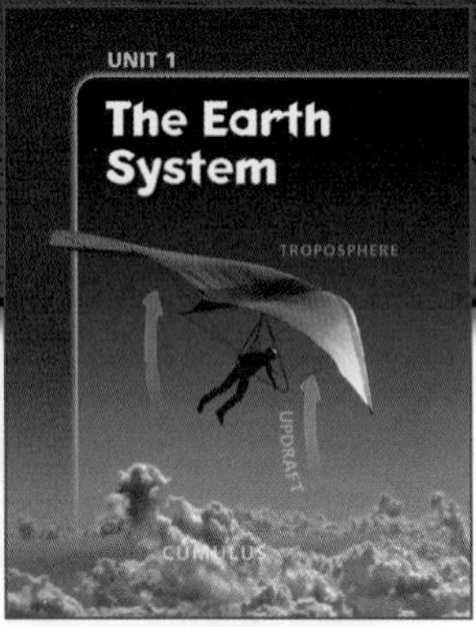


UNIT 1
# The Earth System

eEdition

## Unit Features



*What different forms of energy are shown in this photograph?* *page 6*

## 3 Weather Patterns 76

**the BIG idea**

Some features of weather have predictable patterns.



## 4 Weather Fronts and Storms 112

**the BIG idea**

The interaction of air masses causes changes in weather.

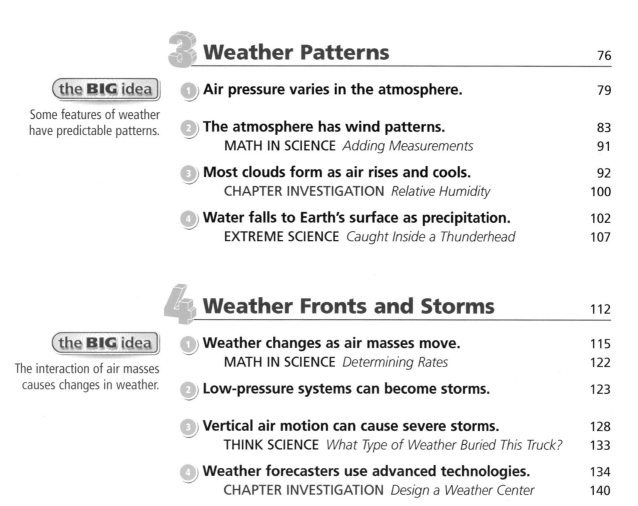

## Visual Highlights

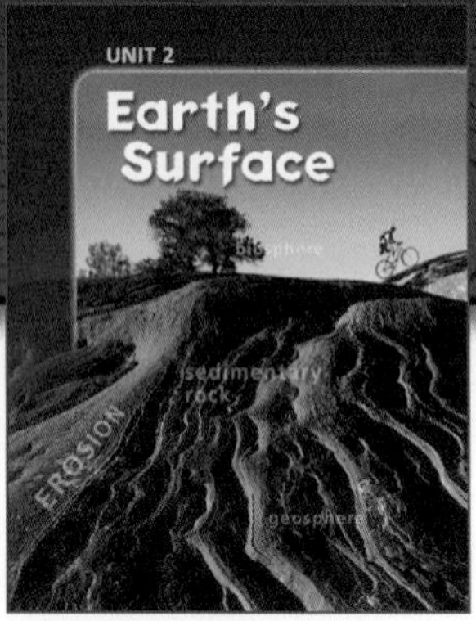


UNIT 2
# Earth's Surface

eEdition

## Unit Features

*How can gold be separated from other minerals and rocks in a river?* *page 180*

## 6 Minerals and Rocks 180

**the BIG idea**

Minerals and rocks are basic building blocks of Earth.



## 7 Erosion and Deposition 222

**the BIG idea**

Water, wind, and ice shape Earth's surface.

## Visual Highlights

eEdition

UNIT 3
# The Changing Earth

## Unit Features



## 8 Plate Tectonics 262

the BIG idea

The movement of tectonic plates causes geological changes on Earth.

*What might have made this huge crack in Earth's surface? page 262*

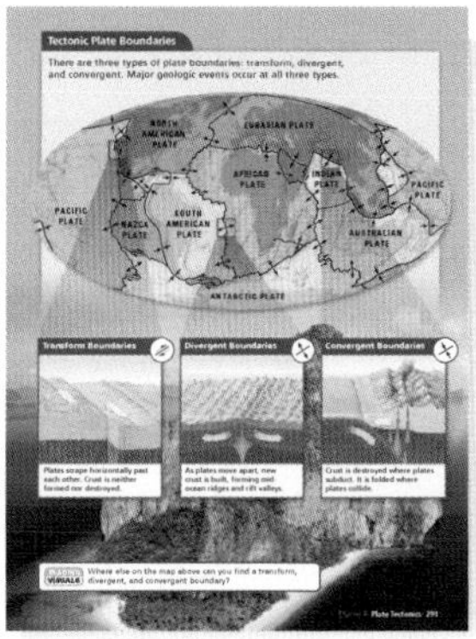

## Visual Highlights

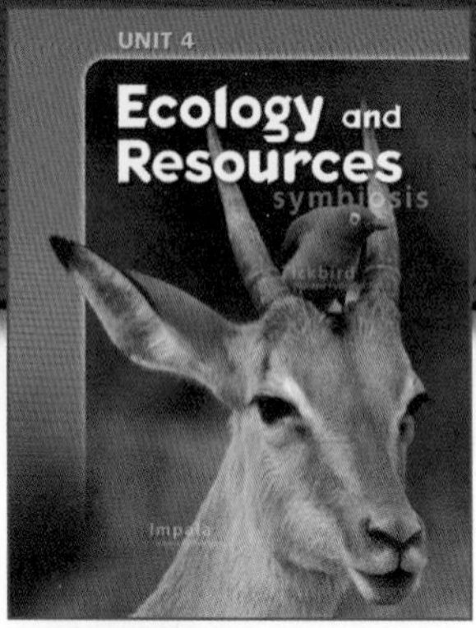


eEdition

UNIT 4
# Ecology and Resources

## Unit Features



*How many living and nonliving things can you identify in this photograph?* *page 374*

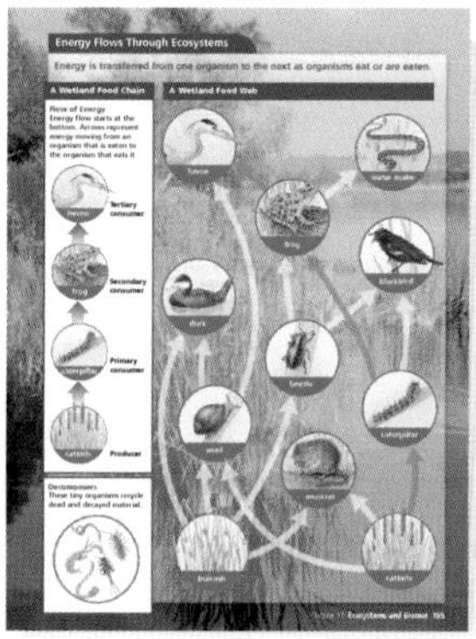

## Visual Highlights

# Features

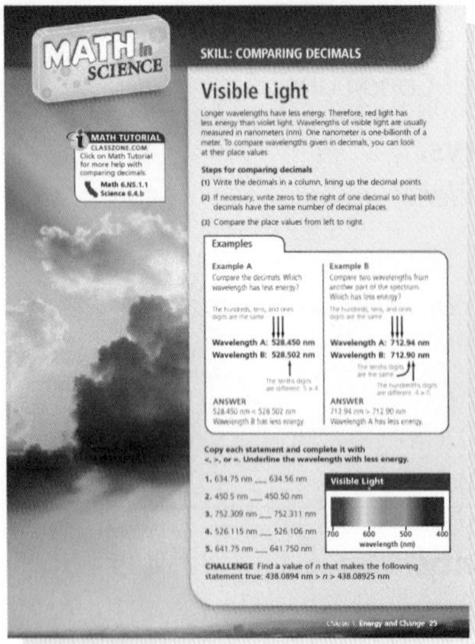


## Math in Science



## Think Science



## Connecting Sciences



## Science on the Job



## Extreme Science

## California Close-Up



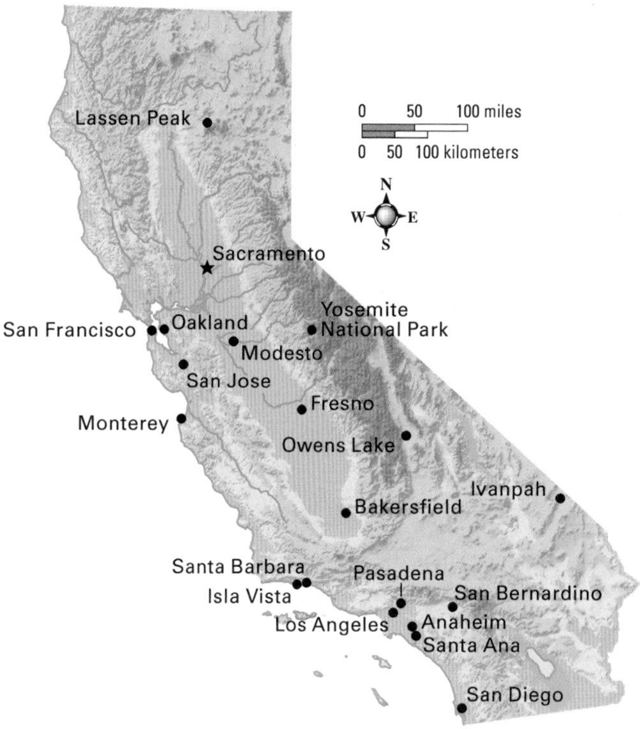


## Frontiers in Science



## Timelines in Science



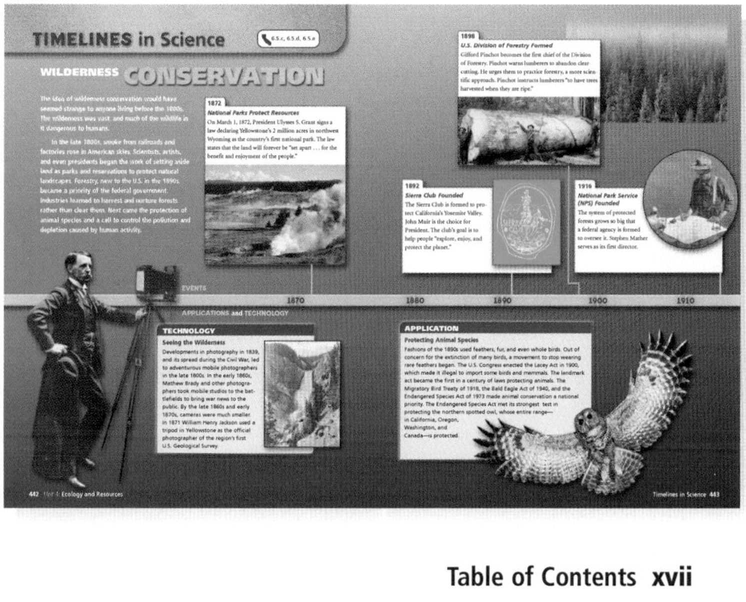

# Internet Resources @ ClassZone.com

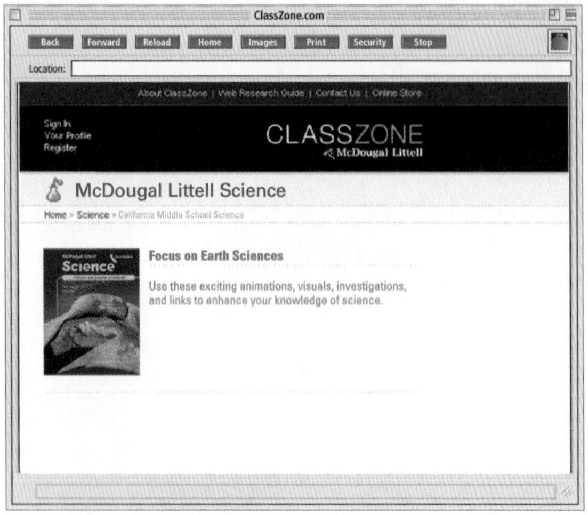


## Simulations



## Visualizations



## Career Centers

## Resource Centers

**THE EARTH SYSTEM**
Resources for the following topics may be found at ClassZone.com: *Uses of Energy; Electromagnetic Spectrum; Convection Currents; Earth System Science; Solar Energy; Ocean Currents; Temperature and Heat Research; Air Pressure; Global Winds; Lightning; Clouds; Weather and Weather Forecasting.*

**EARTH'S SURFACE**
Resources for the following topics may be found at ClassZone.com: *Satellite Mapping; Map Projections; GIS; Minerals; Igneous, Sedimentary, and Metamorphic Rock; Weathering; Geologic Maps; Fossil Research and Excavation; Mudflows; River Erosion; Glaciers.*

**THE CHANGING EARTH**
Resources for the following topics may be found at ClassZone.com: *Earth's Interior; Plate Movement; Recent Earthquakes; Seismology; Tsunamis; Earth System Research; Historic and Current Volcanic Eruptions; Effects of Volcanic Eruptions.*

**ECOLOGY AND RESOURCES**
Resources for the following topics may be found at ClassZone.com: *Prairie Ecosystems; Ecosystems; Cycles in Nature; Land and Aquatic Biomes; Symbiotic Relationships; Succession; Conservation Efforts; Natural Resources; Gems; Renewable Energy Resources; The Environment; Urban Expansion; Ecosystem Recovery.*

## Math Tutorials



## NSTA SciLinks

*Codes for use with the NSTA SciLinks site may be found on every chapter opener.*

## Content Reviews

*There is content review for every chapter at ClassZone.com.*

## Test Practice

*There is test practice for every chapter at ClassZone.com.*

# Explore the Big Idea

*Chapter Opening Inquiry*

Each chapter opens with hands-on explorations that introduce the chapter's Big Idea.

# Chapter Investigations

*Full-Period Labs*

The Chapter Investigations are in-depth labs that let you form and test a hypothesis, build a model, or sometimes design your own investigation.

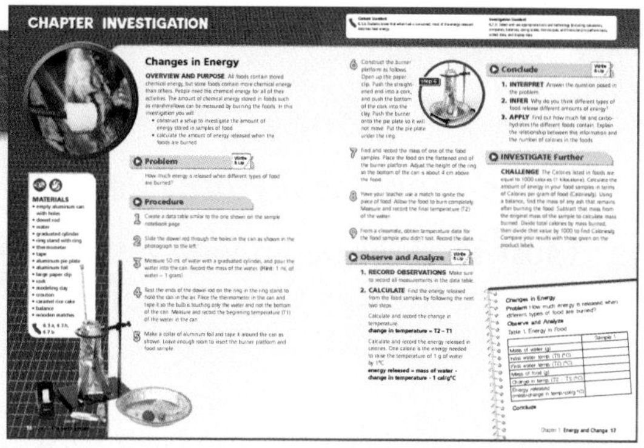

# Explore

*Introductory Inquiry Activities*

Most sections begin with a simple activity that lets you explore the Key Concept before you read the section.

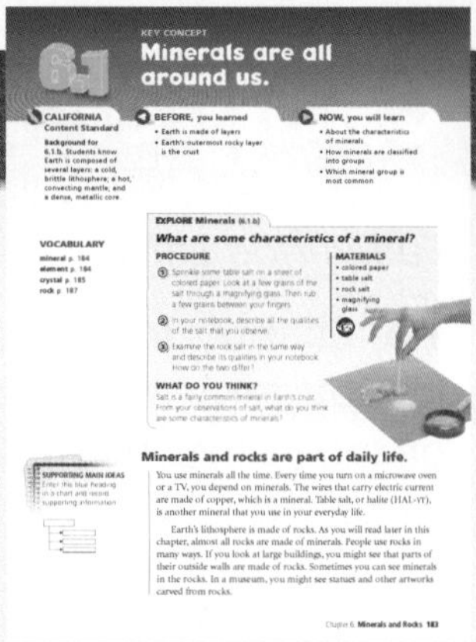
KEY CONCEPT

6.1 Minerals are all around us.

CALIFORNIA Content Standard

Background for 6.1.b. Students know Earth is composed of several layers: a cold, brittle lithosphere; a hot, convecting mantle; and a dense, metallic core.

BEFORE, you learned
- Earth is made of layers
- Earth's outermost rocky layer is the crust

NOW, you will learn
- About the characteristics of minerals
- How minerals are classified into groups
- Which mineral group is most common

VOCABULARY
mineral p. 184
element p. 184
crystal p. 185
rock p. 187

EXPLORE Minerals (6.1.b)

What are some characteristics of a mineral?

PROCEDURE
1. Sprinkle some table salt on a sheet of colored paper. Look at a few grains of the salt through a magnifying glass. Then rub a few grains between your fingers.
2. In your notebook, describe all the qualities of the salt that you observe.
3. Examine the rock salt in the same way and describe its qualities in your notebook. How do the two differ?

MATERIALS
- colored paper
- table salt
- rock salt
- magnifying glass

WHAT DO YOU THINK?
Salt is a fairly common mineral in Earth's crust. From your observations of salt, what do you think are some characteristics of minerals?

SUPPORTING MAIN IDEAS
Enter this blue heading in a chart and record supporting information.

Minerals and rocks are part of daily life.

You use minerals all the time. Every time you turn on a microwave oven or a TV, you depend on minerals. The wires that carry electric current are made of copper, which is a mineral. Table salt, or halite (HAL-YT), is another mineral that you use in your everyday life.

Earth's lithosphere is made of rocks. As you will read later in this chapter, almost all rocks are made of minerals. People use rocks in many ways. If you look at large buildings, you might see that parts of their outside walls are made of rocks. Sometimes you can see minerals in the rocks. In a museum, you might see statues and other artworks carved from rocks.

Chapter 6: Minerals and Rocks 183

## The Earth System



## Earth's Surface



## The Changing Earth



## Ecology and Resources

# Investigate

*Skill Labs*

Each Investigate activity gives you a chance to practice a specific science skill related to the content that you're studying.

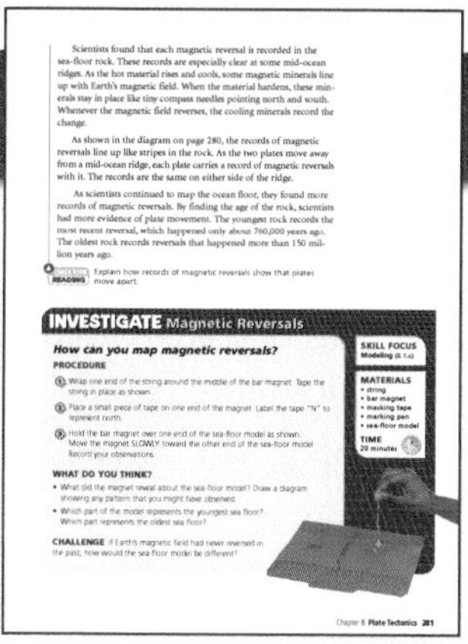

Scientists found that each magnetic reversal is recorded in the sea-floor rock. These records are especially clear at some mid-ocean ridges. As the hot material rises and cools, some magnetic minerals line up with Earth's magnetic field. When the material hardens, these minerals stay in place like tiny compass needles pointing north and south. Whenever the magnetic field reverses, the cooling minerals record the change.

As shown in the diagram on page 280, the records of magnetic reversals line up like stripes in the rock. As the two plates move away from a mid-ocean ridge, each plate carries a record of magnetic reversals with it. The records are the same on either side of the ridge.

As scientists continued to map the ocean floor, they found more records of magnetic reversals. By finding the age of the rock, scientists had more evidence of plate movement. The youngest rock records the most recent reversal, which happened only about 760,000 years ago. The oldest rock records reversals that happened more than 150 million years ago.

READING Explain how records of magnetic reversals show that plates move apart.

**INVESTIGATE** Magnetic Reversals

***How can you map magnetic reversals?***

**PROCEDURE**

1. Wrap one end of the string around the middle of the bar magnet. Tape the string in place as shown.
2. Place a small piece of tape on one end of the magnet. Label the tape "N" to represent north.
3. Hold the bar magnet over one end of the sea-floor model as shown. Move the magnet SLOWLY toward the other end of the sea-floor model. Record your observations.

**WHAT DO YOU THINK?**

- What did the magnet reveal about the sea-floor model? Draw a diagram showing any pattern that you might have observed.
- Which part of the model represents the youngest sea floor? Which part represents the oldest sea floor?

**CHALLENGE** If Earth's magnetic field had never reversed in the past, how would the sea-floor model be different?

**SKILL FOCUS** Modeling (6.1.a)

**MATERIALS**
- string
- bar magnet
- masking tape
- marking pen
- sea-floor model

**TIME** 20 minutes

Chapter 8 **Plate Tectonics 281**

## The Earth System



## Earth's Surface



## The Changing Earth



## Ecology and Resources

# California Science Standards

As you read and study your science book this year, you'll be learning many of the ideas described in the California Science Standards. The standards that you will concentrate on are listed here.

Following each standard is an explanation of what it means and how you will learn about it. References to chapters tell you where you'll begin to study the content in the standard. Many standards refer to several chapters. That's because you will read and study information presented in several chapters in order to understand a standard fully. By the end of the year, you will have learned the content of these California Science Standards.

## Focus on Earth Sciences

### Plate Tectonics and Earth's Structure

**Standard 6.1: Plate tectonics accounts for important features of Earth's surface and major geologic events.**

| Standard 6.1.a | What It Means to You |
|---|---|
| Students know evidence of plate tectonics is derived from the fit of the continents; the location of earthquakes, volcanoes, and midocean ridges; and the distribution of fossils, rock types, and ancient climatic zones. | The theory of plate tectonics explains how the major features on Earth's surface formed and why geologic events such as earthquakes happen. It states that Earth's lithosphere is broken into huge plates that move and change in size over time. You will learn how scientists developed this theory by noticing evidence such as the shapes of the continents and how they appear to fit together. **(Chapters 8, 9, and 10)** |

| Standard 6.1.b | What It Means to You |
|---|---|
| Students know Earth is composed of several layers: a cold, brittle lithosphere; a hot, convecting mantle; and a dense, metallic core. | You will learn the properties of Earth's layers. The lithosphere is made up of Earth's crust, a thin layer of cool rock, and the top of the mantle. The top of the mantle is cool and hard. The rest of the mantle is made of rock that is hot and soft enough to flow slowly. Below the mantle is the outer core, a layer of molten metals. The inner core, which is at Earth's center, is made up of very hot but solid metals. **(Chapters 2, 6, 8, 9, and 10)** |

| Standard 6.1.c | What It Means to You |
|---|---|
| Students know lithospheric plates the size of continents and ocean move at rates of centimeters per year in response to movement in the mantle. | The lithosphere is broken into slabs of rock called plates. They fit together like a jigsaw puzzle on Earth's surface. Underneath the plates is the asthenosphere, a layer of soft, hot rock. You will learn that rock in the asthenosphere moves slowly by convection, a motion that transfers heat energy. Convection in the asthenosphere allows the plates to move over Earth's surface. **(Chapters 8 and 10)** |

| Standard 6.1.d | What It Means to You |
|---|---|
| Students know that earthquakes are sudden motions along breaks in the crust called faults and that volcanoes and fissures are locations where magma reaches the surface. | A fault is a break in the lithosphere where blocks of rock move past each other. An earthquake is a shaking of the ground caused by a sudden movement along a fault. You will learn that magma is rock that is so hot it is molten and can flow. A volcano is an opening in Earth's crust through which magma can erupt. **(Chapter 10)** |

| Standard 6.1.e | What It Means to You |
|---|---|
| Students know major geologic events, such as earthquakes, volcanic eruptions, and mountain building, result from plate motions. | Most major earthquakes, volcanic eruptions, and mountain-building events happen where one tectonic plate meets another. Plates can move apart, push together, or scrape past each other. One plate can sink beneath another plate. Mountains can form as rocks crumple and fold. **(Chapters 8, 9, and 10)** |

| Standard 6.1.f | What It Means to You |
|---|---|
| Students know how to explain major features of California geology (including mountains, faults, volcanoes) in terms of plate tectonics. | You will learn how the movement of tectonic plates has shaped the geologic features of California. For example, the San Andreas Fault is where the Pacific Plate and the North American Plate are scraping past each other. Mount Shasta is a volcano that has formed in an area where the Pacific Plate is sinking underneath the edge of the North American Plate. **(Chapters 8, 9, and 10)** |

| Standard 6.1.g | What It Means to You |
|---|---|
| Students know how to determine the epicenter of an earthquake and know that the effects of an earthquake on any region vary, depending on the size of the earthquake, the distance of the region from the epicenter, the local geology, and the type of construction in the region. | The focus of an earthquake is the place underground where rocks first begin to move. The epicenter is the place on the surface directly above the focus. You will learn that scientists can locate an earthquake's epicenter by analyzing seismic waves recorded at three locations. **(Chapter 9)** |

## Shaping Earth's Surface

**Standard 6.2: Topography is reshaped by the weathering of rock and soil and by the transportation and deposition of sediment.**

| Standard 6.2.a | What It Means to You |
|---|---|
| Students know water running downhill is the dominant process in shaping the landscape, including California's landscape. | Running water is the major force shaping the landscape on Earth. You will use a stream table to demonstrate how water erodes land and deposits sediment. You will learn about water's ability to shape shorelines and form drainage basins, divides, floodplains, deltas, and caverns. **(Chapters 6 and 7)** |

| Standard 6.2.b | What It Means to You |
|---|---|
| Students know rivers and streams are dynamic systems that erode, transport sediment, change course, and flood their banks in natural and recurring patterns. | Flowing water picks up sediment and deposits it in a new place. You will learn that streams form complex drainage systems as they flow toward the ocean. **(Chapters 2 and 7)** |

| Standard 6.2.c | What It Means to You |
|---|---|
| Students know beaches are dynamic systems in which the sand is supplied by rivers and moved along the coast by the action of waves. | Streams deposit sediment as they slow down when they flow into the ocean. Waves and ocean currents move this sediment along the shore, forming sandy beaches. Shorelines are shaped by the action of water, currents, and wind. **(Chapter 7)** |

| Standard 6.2.d | What It Means to You |
|---|---|
| Students know earthquakes, volcanic eruptions, landslides, and floods change human and wildlife habitats. | Powerful natural processes can cause earthquakes, volcanic eruptions, landslides, and floods. These events in turn can cause severe damage and loss of life. You will learn how people can reduce the damage caused by these natural events by learning to predict where they are likely to happen and by building different types of structures. **(Chapters 1, 2, 7, 9, and 10)** |

## Heat (Thermal Energy) (Physical Sciences)

**Standard 6.3: Heat moves in a predictable flow from warmer objects to cooler objects until all the objects are at the same temperature.**

| Standard 6.3.a | What It Means to You |
|---|---|
| Students know energy can be carried from one place to another by heat flow or by waves, including water, light and sound waves, or by moving objects. | Energy is the ability to cause change. Energy moves from one place to another when objects change in temperature. It also travels in waves, such as radiation from the Sun. You will learn how energy moves through the Earth system, making it possible for organisms to live and grow. **(Chapters 1, 2, 9, 10, and 13)** |

| Standard 6.3.b | What It Means to You |
|---|---|
| Students know that when fuel is consumed, most of the energy released becomes heat energy. | Every time energy changes form, some of it changes into heat. For example, in a light bulb, not all of the electrical energy is changed into light. Some useful energy is lost as heat. **(Chapters 1 and 13)** |

| Standard 6.3.c | What It Means to You |
|---|---|
| Students know heat flows in solids by conduction (which involves no flow of matter) and in fluids by conduction and convection (which involves flow of matter). | Conduction is the process that moves energy from one object to another when they are touching. Convection is also a process that moves energy from place to place, but it occurs in materials that are able to flow, such as gases and liquids. **(Chapters 1, 2, 8, 10, and 13)** |

| Standard 6.3.d | What It Means to You |
|---|---|
| Students know heat energy is also transferred between objects by radiation (radiation can travel through space). | Energy in the form of electromagnetic waves is called radiation. You will learn about different forms of radiation, such as visible light, microwaves, and x-rays, and how people use them to improve everyday life. **(Chapters 1, 2, and 13)** |

**Energy in the Earth System**

**Standard 6.4: Many phenomena on Earth's surface are affected by the transfer of energy through radiation and convection currents.**

| Standard 6.4.a | What It Means to You |
|---|---|
| Students know the sun is the major source of energy for phenomena on Earth's surface; it powers winds, ocean currents, and the water cycle. | Almost all of the energy around you comes from the Sun. This energy can be transferred within the Earth system. You will learn that solar energy powers the water cycle, weather, and climate. **(Chapters 2 and 3)** |

| Standard 6.4.b | What It Means to You |
|---|---|
| Students know solar energy reaches Earth through radiation, mostly in the form of visible light. | The Sun's energy travels to Earth in electromagnetic waves called radiation. You will learn that visible light—light that the eye can see—is only a small part of the electromagnetic spectrum. **(Chapters 1 and 2)** |

| Standard 6.4.c | What It Means to You |
|---|---|
| Students know heat from Earth's interior reaches the surface primarily through convection. | Heat is generated deep inside Earth. You will learn that convection currents transfer heat from the Earth's interior toward the surface. Evidence of this internal heat can be seen at hot springs, geysers, and erupting volcanoes. **(Chapters 2 and 13)** |

| Standard 6.4.d | What It Means to You |
|---|---|
| Students know convection currents distribute heat in the atmosphere and oceans. | A convection current is a pattern of circulation in which a material is heated and rises in one area, and then sinks in another area. You will learn the effects of convection currents on weather, ocean currents, and tectonic plate movement. **(Chapters 1, 2, and 4)** |

| Standard 6.4.e | What It Means to You |
|---|---|
| Students know differences in pressure, heat, air movement, and humidity result in changes of weather. | Weather is the condition of Earth's atmosphere at a particular time and place. You will learn that moving air masses cause changes in weather. High-pressure systems bring fair weather, while low-pressure systems tend to bring stormy weather. **(Chapters 2, 3, and 4)** |

**Ecology (Life Sciences)**

**Standard 6.5: Organisms in ecosystems exchange energy and nutrients among themselves and with the environment.**

| Standard 6.5.a | What It Means to You |
|---|---|
| Students know energy entering ecosystems as sunlight is transferred by producers into chemical energy through photosynthesis and then from organism to organism through food webs. | A producer is any organism that takes in energy from the Sun and stores it in food as chemical energy. You will learn that food webs and food chains are models that show feeding relationships among organisms in an ecosystem. **(Chapter 11)** |

| Standard 6.5.b | What It Means to You |
|---|---|
| Students know matter is transferred over time from one organism to others in the food web and between organisms and the physical environment. | In an ecosystem, energy is transferred from one organism to the next as organisms eat or are eaten. You will learn that the remains of dead plants and animals become the organic matter in soil. The process of decay adds valuable raw materials to the ecosystem. **(Chapter 11)** |

| Standard 6.5.c | What It Means to You |
|---|---|
| Students know populations of organisms can be categorized by the functions they serve in an ecosystem. | Scientists group living things according to shared characteristics. Organisms can also be grouped according to the functions they perform in an ecosystem. You will learn about predators and prey, along with other ways in which organisms interact. **(Chapter 12)** |

| Standard 6.5.d | What It Means to You |
|---|---|
| Students know different kinds of organisms may play similar ecological roles in similar biomes. | Biomes are large geographic regions that have similar climates, plants, and animals. You will learn about both land and marine biomes and the organisms that live there. **(Chapter 11)** |

| Standard 6.5.e | What It Means to You |
|---|---|
| Students know the number and types of organisms an ecosystem can support depends on the resources available and on abiotic factors, such as quantities of light and water, a range of temperatures, and soil composition. | Abiotic factors are nonliving parts of an ecosystem. The combination of different abiotic factors in an ecosystem determines the types of organisms that the ecosystem can support. **(Chapters 11 and 12)** |

## Resources

**Standard 6.6: Sources of energy and materials differ in amounts, distribution, usefulness, and the time required for their formation.**

| Standard 6.6.a | What It Means to You |
|---|---|
| Students know the utility of energy sources is determined by factors that are involved in converting these sources to useful forms and the consequences of the conversion process. | Natural resources are energy sources, organisms, or substances found in nature that people use. You will learn the benefits and costs of using certain resources, such as fossil fuels. For example, burning coal produces heat but also releases material that pollutes the air. **(Chapters 10, 13, and 14)** |

| Standard 6.6.b | What It Means to You |
|---|---|
| Students know different natural energy and material resources, include air, soil, rocks, minerals, petroleum, fresh water, wildlife, and forests, and know how to classify them as renewable or nonrenewable. | Renewable resources can be replaced in nature at about the same rate that they are used. Nonrenewable resources exist in fixed amounts or are used up faster than they can be replaced. You will learn how scientists are developing alternative energy sources, such as solar and wind energy. **(Chapters 13 and 14)** |

| Standard 6.6.c | What It Means to You |
|---|---|
| Students know the natural origin of the materials used to make common objects. | Fossil fuels, minerals, and plants are used in many everyday items, such as cars, glass, clothing, toothpaste, and paint. You will learn the common uses of many natural materials in technology, industry, and the arts. **(Chapters 13 and 14)** |

## Investigation and Experimentation

**Standard 6.7: Scientific progress is made by asking meaningful questions and conducting careful investigations.**

| Standard 6.7.a | What It Means to You |
|---|---|
| Develop a hypothesis. | A hypothesis is a tentative explanation for something you observe. You will perform investigations to test hypotheses. Your findings will either support or not support your original hypothesis. **(Chapters 2, 3, 8, 9, 10, 13, and 14)** |

| Standard 6.7.b | What It Means to You |
|---|---|
| Select and use appropriate tools and technology (including calculators, computer, balances, spring scales, microscopes, and binoculars) to perform tests, collect data, and display data. | Design Your Own and other investigations allow you to choose the materials and procedures for testing an idea. This will help you develop scientific habits of mind, such as asking questions and sharing results. **(Unit projects and investigations throughout)** |

| Standard 6.7.c | What It Means to You |
|---|---|
| Construct appropriate graphs from data and develop qualitative statements about the relationships between variables. | Scientists must choose the best way to record and communicate their data. You will show the results of your investigations as drawings, narratives, graphs, or tables. The type of graph you choose depends on your independent variable. **(Investigations throughout)** |

| Standard 6.7.d | What It Means to You |
|---|---|
| Communicate the steps and results from an investigation in written reports and oral presentations. | Scientists must describe their findings so others are able to reproduce them. As part of interpreting the results of an investigation, you will write an answer to a problem statement. **(Investigations throughout)** |

| Standard 6.7.e | What It Means to You |
|---|---|
| Recognize whether evidence is consistent with a proposed explanation. | After performing an investigation, scientists interpret the results to determine if they support the hypothesis. You will do the same in the conclusion stage of an investigation. **(Chapters and investigations throughout)** |

| Standard 6.7.f | What It Means to You |
|---|---|
| Read a topographic map and a geologic map for evidence provided on the maps and construct and interpret a simple scale map. | A scale map relates distances on the map to actual distances on Earth's surface. A topographic map shows the shape of land using contour lines. A geologic map shows geologic features of Earth's surface, including rock types. You will learn to read and interpret all three types of maps. **(Chapters 5 and 6)** |

| Standard 6.7.g | What It Means to You |
|---|---|
| Interpret events by sequence and time from natural phenomena (e.g., the relative ages of rocks and intrusions). | Some natural events leave evidence about the order in which they happened. You will learn how to interpret such evidence. For example, older layers of sediment are covered by younger layers. The types of plants and animals in an area change as environmental conditions change. **(Chapters throughout)** |

| Standard 6.7.h | What It Means to You |
|---|---|
| Identify changes in natural phenomena over time without manipulating the phenomena (e.g., a tree limb, a grove of trees, a stream, a hillslope). | Natural processes change landscapes and landforms. For example, you will learn how waves and currents shape rock formations and shorelines over time. You will learn how the movement of energy causes change. **(Chapters throughout)** |

# Introducing Science

Scientists are curious. Since ancient times, they have been asking and answering questions about the world around them. Scientists are also very skeptical of the answers they get. They carefully collect evidence and test their answers many times before accepting an idea as correct.

In this book you will see how scientific knowledge keeps growing and changing as scientists ask new questions and rethink what was known before. The following sections will help you get started.

# What Is Science?

Science is the systematic study of all of nature, from particles too small to see to the human body to the entire universe. However, no individual scientist can study all of nature. Therefore science is divided into many different fields. For example, some scientists are biologists, others are geologists, and still others are chemists or astronomers.

All the different scientific fields can be grouped into three broad categories: earth science, life science, and physical science.

- Earth science focuses on the study of our planet and its place in the universe; it includes the fields of geology, oceanography, meteorology, and astronomy.
- Life science focuses on the study of living things; it includes the fields of cell biology, botany, ecology, zoology, and human biology.
- Physical science focuses on the study of what things are made of and how they change; it includes the fields of chemistry and physics.

## McDougal Littell Science, Focus on Earth Sciences

*McDougal Littell Science, Focus on Earth Sciences,* explores the Earth where you live but includes some life science and physical science as well. In this book you will first learn about where Earth gets its energy and how that energy appears—in sunshine, wind, and storms for example. Then you'll learn about Earth's surface, what it's made of, and how land and water structures get built up and worn down. You will see how Earth's surface can change suddenly, through earthquakes, mountain building, and volcanoes. Finally you will see how living things together with Earth make up ecosystems, and how humans fit into the whole Earth system.

## Unifying Principles

As you learn, it helps to have a big picture of science as a framework for new information. *McDougal Littell Science* has identified unifying principles from each of the three broad categories of science: earth science, life science, and physical science. These unifying principles are described on the following pages. However, keep in mind that the broad categories of science do not have fixed borders. Earth science shades into life science, which shades into physical science, which shades back into earth science.

On the next few pages, look for the four unifying principles of earth science:

- Heat energy inside Earth and radiation from the Sun provide energy for Earth's processes.
- Physical forces, such as gravity, affect the movement of all matter on Earth and throughout the universe.
- Matter and energy move among Earth's rocks and soil, atmosphere, waters, and living things.
- Earth has changed over time and continues to change.

**the BIG idea**

Each chapter begins with a big idea. Keep in mind that each big idea relates to one or more of the unifying principles.

# What is Earth Science?

Earth science is the study of Earth's interior, its rocks and soil, its atmosphere, its oceans, and outer space. For many years scientists studied each of these topics separately. Recently, however, they have started to look more and more at the connections among the different parts of Earth—its oceans, atmosphere, living things, rocks and soil, even other planets in the solar system and stars and galaxies far away. Through these studies scientists have learned more about Earth and its place in the universe.

The lava pouring out of this volcano in Hawaii is liquid rock that was melted by heat energy under Earth's surface.

# UNIFYING PRINCIPLES of Earth Science

## Heat energy inside Earth and radiation from the Sun provide energy for Earth's processes.

You are always surrounded by different forms of energy, such as heat energy or light. **Energy** is the ability to cause change. All of Earth's processes need energy to occur. A process is a set of changes that leads to a particular result. For example, **evaporation** is the process by which liquid changes into gas. A puddle on a sidewalk dries up through the process of evaporation. The energy needed for the puddle to dry up comes from the Sun.

Earth's interior is very hot. It is so hot that the solid rock there is able to flow very slowly—a few centimeters each year. In a process called **convection**, hot material rises, cools, then sinks until it is heated enough to rise again. Convection of hot rock carries heat energy up to Earth's surface. There it provides the energy to build mountains, cause earthquakes, and make volcanoes erupt.

Earth receives energy from the Sun as **radiation**—the energy that moves in the form of certain types of waves. Visible light is one type of radiation. Energy from the Sun causes winds to blow, ocean currents to flow, and water to move from the ground to the atmosphere and back again.

## Physical forces, such as gravity, affect the movement of all matter on Earth and throughout the universe.

What do the stars in a galaxy, the planet Earth, and your body have in common? For one thing, they are all made of matter. **Matter** is anything that has mass and takes up space. Rocks are matter. You are matter. Even the air around you is matter. Matter is made of tiny particles called atoms that are too small to see through an ordinary microscope.

Everything in the universe is also affected by the same physical forces. A **force** is a push or a pull. Forces affect how matter moves everywhere in the universe. One force you experience every moment is **gravity**, which is the attraction, or pull, between two objects. Gravity pulls you to Earth and Earth to you; gravity is the force that causes objects to fall downward toward the center of Earth, and the force that keeps objects in orbit around planets and stars.

**Friction** is the force that resists motion between two surfaces that are pressed together. You feel friction when you rub your finger across a table or a piece of sandpaper. There are many other forces at work on Earth and throughout the universe. Magnetic fields exert forces. A contact force occurs when one object pushes or pulls on another object by touching it.

You see Earth changing all of the time. Rain turns dirt to mud, and a dry wind turns the mud to dust. Many changes are small and can take hundreds, thousands, or even millions of years to add up to much. Other changes are sudden and can destroy in minutes a house that had stood for many years.

# UNIFYING PRINCIPLES of Earth Science, continued

## Matter and energy move among Earth's rocks and soil, atmosphere, waters, and living things.

Think of Earth as a huge system, or an organized group of parts that work together. Within this system, matter and energy move among the different parts. The four major parts of Earth's system are the

- **atmosphere,** which includes all the air surrounding the solid planet
- **geosphere,** which includes all of Earth's rocks and minerals, as well as Earth's interior
- **hydrosphere,** which includes oceans, rivers, lakes, every drop of water on or under Earth's surface, and water in the air
- **biosphere,** which includes all living things on Earth.

It's easy to see how matter moves within the Earth system. When water in the atmosphere falls as rain, it becomes part of the hydrosphere. When an animal drinks water from a puddle, the water becomes part of the biosphere. When rainwater soaks into the ground, it moves through the geosphere. As the puddle dries up, the water becomes part of the atmosphere again.

## Earth has changed over time and continues to change.

Events are always changing Earth's surface. Some events, such as the building or wearing away of mountains, occur over millions of years. Others, such as earthquakes, occur within seconds. A change can affect a small area or an entire continent, such as North America.

Scientists learn about Earth's past by examining the evidence they find in rock layers and by observing processes now occurring. Evidence from rocks and fossils along the edges of continents shows that all continents were once joined and then moved apart over time. A **fossil** is the trace of a once-living organism. Fossils show that new types of plants and animals develop, and others, such as dinosaurs, die out. **Climate**—the long-term weather patterns of an area—may also change. Scientists are studying how changes in climates around the world might affect Earth in this century.

# What is Life Science?

Life science is the study of living things. As you study life science, you will observe and read about a variety of organisms, from huge redwood trees to the tiny bacteria that cause sore throats. But life science is not simply about learning the names of millions of organisms. It includes big ideas to help us understand how all these living things interact with their environment. Life science is the study of characteristics and needs that all living things have in common. It's also a study of changes, both daily changes and changes that take place over millions of years. It's the study of how living things depend on Earth and its resources.

A moose chomps on the leaves of a plant. This ordinary event involves many interactions among living and nonliving things within the forest.

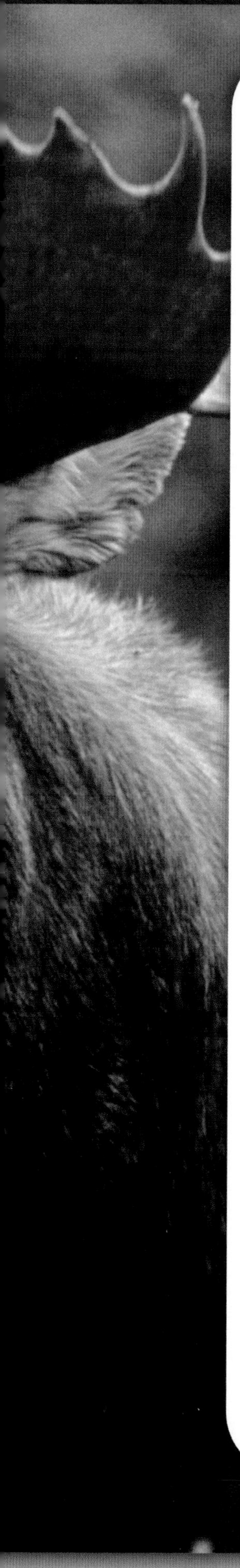

# UNIFYING PRINCIPLES of Life Science

## All living things share common characteristics.

Despite the variety of living things on Earth, there are certain characteristics common to all. The basic unit of life is the **cell**. Any living thing, whether it has one cell or many, is described as an **organism**. All organisms are characterized by

- organization—the way the organism's body is arranged
- growth—the way that an organism grows and develops over its lifetime
- reproduction—the way that an organism produces offspring like itself
- response—the ways an organism interacts with its surroundings

## All living things share common needs.

All living things have three basic needs: energy, materials, and living space. These needs must be met for the organism to stay alive. Energy enables an organism to carry out all the activities of life. The body of every organism needs water and other materials. Water is important because most of the chemical reactions in a cell take place in water. Organisms also require other materials. Plants, for example, need carbon dioxide to make energy-rich sugars, and most living things need oxygen. Living space is the environment in which an organism gets the energy and materials it needs.

## Living things meet their needs through interactions with the environment.

The **environment** is everything that surrounds a living thing. This includes other organisms as well as nonliving factors, such as rainfall, sunlight, and soil. Any exchange of energy or materials between the living and nonliving parts of the environment is an interaction. Plants interact with the environment by capturing energy from sunlight and changing that energy into chemical energy that is stored in sugar. Animals can interact with plants by eating the plants and getting energy from the sugars that plants have made.

## The types and numbers of living things change over time.

A **species** is a group of living things so closely related that they can produce offspring together that can also reproduce. Scientists have named about 1.4 million different species. The great variety of species on Earth today is called **biodiversity**. Different species have different characteristics, or **adaptations**, that allow the members of that species to get their needs met in a particular environment. Over the millions of years that life has existed on Earth, new species have come into being and others have disappeared. The disappearance of a species is called **extinction**. Studying fossils of extinct organisms is one way that scientists have of seeing how living things have changed over time.

# What is Physical Science?

Physical science is the study of what things are made of and how they change. It combines the studies of both physics and chemistry. Physics is the science of matter, energy, and forces. It includes the study of topics such as motion, light, and electricity and magnetism. Chemistry is the study of the structure and properties of matter. It especially focuses on how substances change into different substances.

You cannot "use up" energy. Even though a camp stove's fuel may be gone and a flashlight's battery is no longer functioning, the energy they provided has not disappeared. It has only changed forms.

# UNIFYING PRINCIPLES of Physical Science

## Matter is made of particles too small to see.

The tiny particles that make up all matter are called **atoms**. Atoms are so tiny that they are far too small to see even through a powerful microscope. In fact, an atom is more than a million times smaller than the period at the end of this sentence. There are more than 100 basic kinds of matter called **elements**. The atoms of any element are all alike but different from the atoms of any other element.

## Matter changes form and moves from place to place.

You see objects moving and changing all around you. All changes in matter are results of atoms moving and combining in different ways. Regardless of how much matter may change, however, under ordinary conditions it is never created or destroyed. Matter that seems to disappear merely changes into another form of matter.

## Energy changes from one form to another, but it cannot be created or destroyed.

All the changes you see around you depend on energy. **Energy**, in fact, means the ability to cause change. Using energy means changing energy. But energy is never created or destroyed, no matter how often it changes form. This fact is known as the **law of conservation of energy**. The energy you may think you've lost when a match has burned out has only been changed into other forms of energy.

## Physical forces affect the movement of all matter on Earth and throughout the universe.

A **force** is a push or a pull. Every time you push or pull an object, you are applying a force to that object, whether or not the object moves. There are several forces—several pushes or pulls—acting on you right now. All these forces are necessary for you to do the things you do, even sitting and reading. **Gravity** keeps you on the ground. Gravity also keeps the Moon moving around Earth, and Earth moving around the Sun. **Friction** is the force that opposes motion. The friction between the bottoms of your shoes and the floor makes it possible for you to walk without slipping. Too much friction between a heavy box and the floor makes it hard to push the box across the floor.

# The Nature of Science

You may think of science as a body of knowledge or a collection of facts. More important, however, science is an active process that involves certain ways of looking at the world.

## Scientific Habits of Mind

**Scientists are curious.** They ask questions. A scientist who finds an unusual rock by the side of a river would ask questions such as, "Did this rock form in this area?" or "Did this rock form elsewhere and get moved here?" Questions like these make a scientist want to investigate.

**Scientists are observant.** They look closely at the world around them. A scientist who studies rocks can learn a lot about a rock just by picking it up, looking at its color, and feeling how heavy it is.

**Scientists are creative.** They draw on what they know to form possible explanations for a pattern, an event, or an interesting phenomenon that they have observed. Then scientists put together a plan for testing their ideas.

**Scientists are skeptical.** Scientists don't accept an explanation or answer unless it is based on evidence and logical reasoning. They continually question their own conclusions as well as the conclusions suggested by other scientists. Scientists only trust evidence that can be confirmed by other people or other methods.

Scientists use seismographs to observe and measure vibrations that move through the ground.

This scientist is collecting a sample of melted rock from a hot lava flow in Hawaii.

## Science Processes at Work

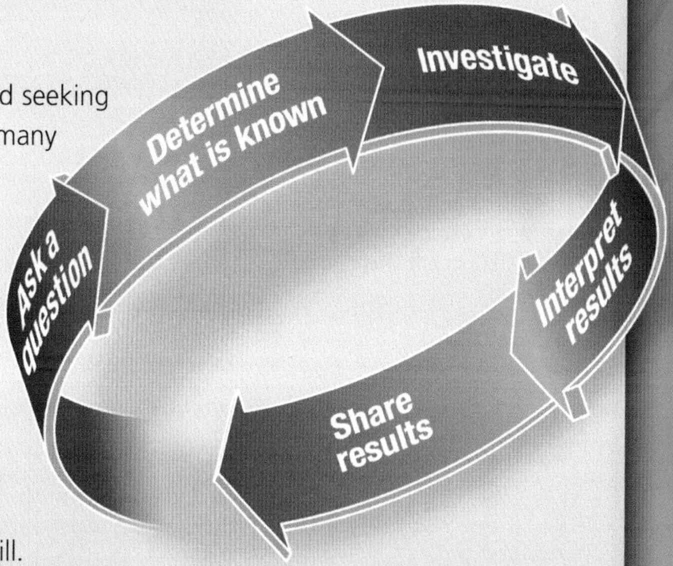


You can think of science as a continuous cycle of asking and seeking answers to questions about the world. Although there are many processes that scientists use, all scientists typically do the following:

- Observe and ask a question
- Determine what is known
- Investigate
- Interpret results
- Share results

### Observe and Ask a Question

It may surprise you that asking questions is an important skill. A scientific investigation may start when a scientist asks a question. Perhaps scientists observe an event or a process that they don't understand, or perhaps answering one question leads to another.

### Determine What Is Known

When beginning an inquiry, scientists find out what is already known about a question. They study results from other scientific investigations, read journals, and talk with other scientists. The scientist who is trying to figure out where an unusual rock came from will study maps that show what types of rocks are already known to be in the area where the rock was found.

## Investigate

Investigating is the process of collecting evidence. Two important ways of doing this are experimenting and observing.

An **experiment** is an organized procedure to study something under controlled conditions. For example, the scientist who found the rock by the river might notice that it is lighter in color where it is chipped. The scientist might design an experiment to determine why the rock is a different color on the inside. The scientist could break off a small piece of the inside of the rock and heat it up to see if it becomes the same color as the outside. The scientist would need to use a piece of the same rock that is being studied. A different rock might react differently to heat.

A scientist may use photography to study fast events, such as multiple flashes of lightning.

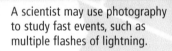

Rocks, such as this one from the Moon, can be subjected to different conditions in a laboratory.

**Observing** is the act of noting and recording an event, characteristic, or anything else detected with an instrument or with the senses. A scientist makes observations while performing an experiment. However, some things cannot be studied using experiments. For example, streaks of light called meteors occur when small rocks from outer space hit Earth's atmosphere. A scientist might study meteors by taking pictures of the sky at a time when meteors are likely to occur.

Forming hypotheses and making predictions are two other skills involved in scientific investigations. A **hypothesis** is a tentative explanation for an observation or a scientific problem that can be tested by further investigation. For example, the scientist might make the following hypothesis about the rock from the beach:

The rock is a meteorite, which is a rock that fell to the ground from outer space. The outside of the rock changed color because it was heated up from passing through Earth's atmosphere.

A **prediction** is an expectation of what will be observed or what will happen. To test the hypothesis that the rock's outside is black because it is a meteorite, the scientist might predict that a close examination of the rock will show that it has many characteristics in common with rocks that are already known to be meteorites.

## Interpret Results

As scientists investigate, they analyze their evidence, or data, and begin to draw conclusions. **Analyzing data** involves looking at the evidence gathered through observations or experiments and trying to identify any patterns that might exist in the data. Scientists often need to make additional observations or perform more experiments before they are sure of their conclusions. Many times scientists make new predictions or revise their hypotheses.

Scientists use computers to gather and interpret data.

Scientists make images such as this computer drawing of a landscape to help share their results with others.

## Share Results

An important part of scientific investigation is sharing results of experiments. Scientists read and publish in journals and attend conferences to communicate with other scientists around the world. Sharing data and procedures gives scientists a way to test each others' results. They also share results with the public through newspapers, television, and other media.

# The Nature of Technology

When you think of technology, you may think of cars, computers, and cell phones. Imagine having no refrigerator or radio. It's difficult to think of a world without the products of what we call technology. Technology, however, is more than just devices that make our daily activities easier. Technology is the process of using scientific knowledge to design solutions to real-world problems.

## Science and Technology

Science and technology go hand in hand. Each depends upon the other. Even a device as simple as a thermometer is designed using knowledge of the ways different materials respond to changes in temperature. In turn, thermometers have allowed scientists to learn more about the world. Greater knowledge of how materials respond to changes in temperature helped engineers to build items such as refrigerators. They have also built thermometers that could be read automatically by computers. New technologies lead to new scientific knowledge and new scientific knowledge leads to even better technologies.

## The Process of Technological Design

The process of technological design involves many choices. What, for example, should be done to protect the residents of an area prone to severe storms such as tornadoes and hurricanes? Build stronger homes that can withstand the winds? Try to develop a way to detect the storms long before they occur? Or learn more about hurricanes in order to find new ways to protect people from the dangers? The steps people take to solve the problem depend a great deal on what they already know about the problem as well as what can reasonably be done. As you learn about the steps in the process of technological design, think about the different choices that could be made at each step.

## Identify a Need

To study hurricanes, scientists needed to know what happens inside the most dangerous parts of the storm. However, it was not safe for scientists to go near the centers of hurricanes because the winds were too strong and changed direction too fast. Scientists needed a way to measure conditions deep inside the storm without putting themselves in danger.

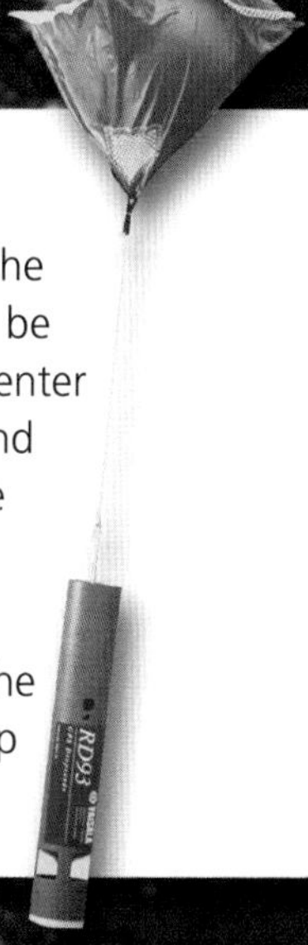


## Design and Develop

One approach was to design a robotic probe to take the measurements. The probe and instruments needed to be strong enough to withstand the fast winds near the center of a hurricane. The scientists also needed a way to send the probe into the storm and to get the data from the instruments quickly.

Scientists designed a device called a dropsonde, which could be dropped from an airplane flying over the hurricane. A dropsonde takes measurements from deep inside the storm and radios data back to the scientists.

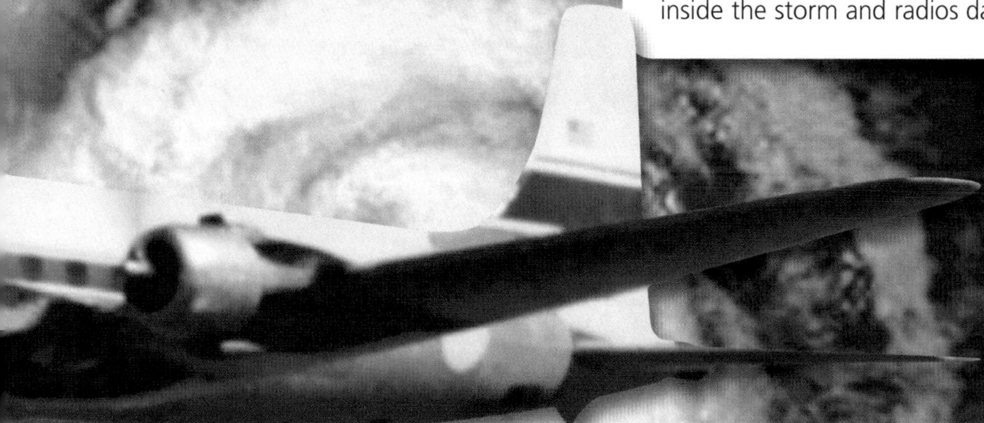

## Test and Improve

Even good technology can usually be improved. When scientists first used dropsondes, they learned about hurricanes. They also learned what things about the dropsondes worked well and what did not. For example, the scientists wanted better ways to keep track of where the probe moved. Newer dropsondes make use of the Global Positioning System, which is a way of pinpointing any position on Earth by using satellite signals.

# Using the Tools of Science

You can learn about science by doing it. Doing science includes trying experiments or making observations so that you see for yourself what happens. For example, activities such as growing plants, measuring acid in rainwater, looking at live cells under a microscope, and trying to make an object fly are the exciting parts of science. These are the reasons people become scientists.

## Safety First!

To do any experiments, think safety first! You may think it is unnecessary to wear goggles or plastic gloves—and sometimes it is unnecessary. But beakers break and spill, even if the materials are not dangerous. Why take a chance? You can prevent injuries or ruined clothes by taking simple precautions. Remember, we never plan for things to go wrong, but accidents happen!

The investigations and explorations in this book have safety symbols next to them when needed. Some have to do with what you wear—goggles, apron, gloves. Some warn of fire and heat dangers; some concern safety when working with electricity. Others caution you about chemicals, sharp objects, disposing of materials, or working with animals. Look at the safety rules and symbols on page R10. Become familiar with them. Look for them before you do an activity, and take the necessary precautions.

## Measuring

Scientists use the International System (SI) for measurements of length, volume, mass, and temperature. The units in the SI system are metric, based on multiples of ten. These are different from the units we use in the United States, but most countries and all scientists use them. Once you learn the SI system, you will become part of the international community.

**Measuring Length** In science, meters and centimeters, not yards, feet, and inches, are used to measure length. A meter is about a yard. Within the metric system you change units by multiplying or dividing by powers of 10. For example,

1 centimeter (cm) = .01 meter (m), or 1/100 of a meter

1 millimeter (mm) = .001 meter (m), or 1/1000 of a meter

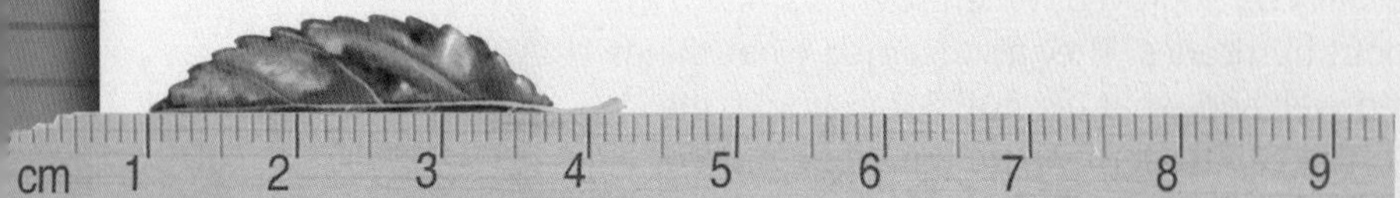


The prefix tells you how large or small each measurement is. You can easily change units to and from the SI units. See page R20 for help in changing units of the metric system.

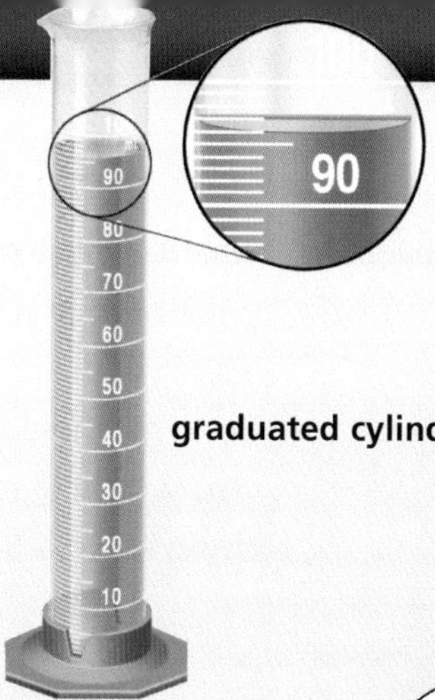


graduated cylinder

**Measuring Volume** The metric system measures volume in liters, not gallons. If you buy a 2 liter bottle of soda, it is about half a gallon in U.S. units. In a lab, it is more precise to measure 20 milliliters than to measure 1 teaspoon. Remember that 1 liter (L) = 1000 milliliters (mL). The prefix *milli-* means "one thousandth." When you measure the volume of a liquid, use a graduated cylinder and read the volume in mL, or milliliters. Each milliliter equals 1 $cm^3$.

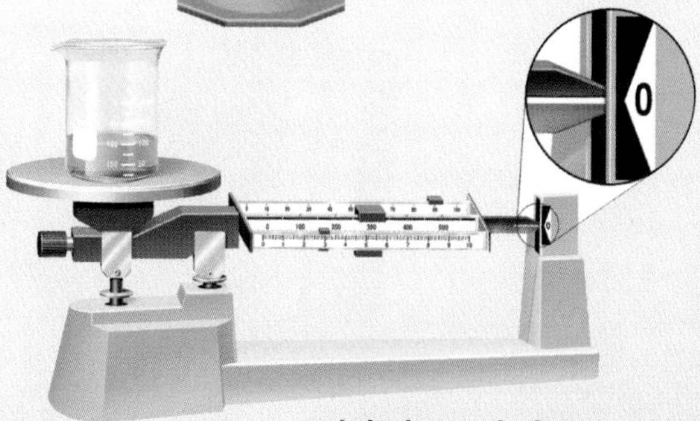


triple-beam balance

**Measuring Mass** Mass is measured in grams, not pounds. By now you can guess that 1 kilogram (kg) = 1000 grams (g). A pound is a measure of weight, and weight is not the same as mass. In SI units, weight is measured in newtons. To measure mass, you use a double-pan balance or a triple-beam balance.

**Measuring Temperature** There are three systems of temperature measurement in the International System: Kelvin, Celsius, and Fahrenheit. Usually in science class you will use Celsius, not Fahrenheit or Kelvin. The Celsius system uses one hundred degrees between the freezing and the boiling point of water, 0–100° C. The Fahrenheit system, which we commonly use in the United States, goes from 32° to 212° F freezing to boiling point. Again, since it's based on 10's, the Celsius scale is easier to use.

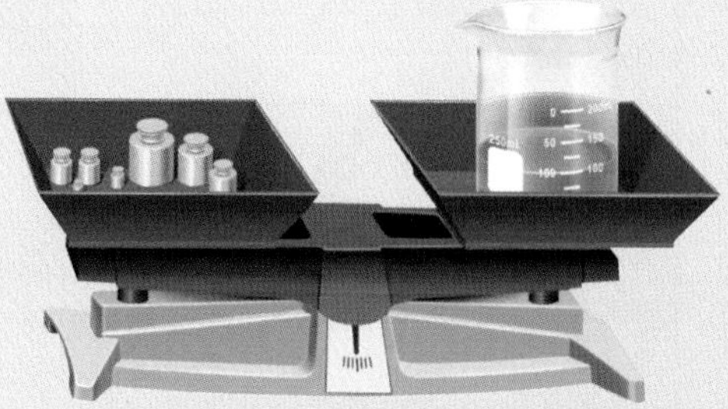

double-pan balance

## Why Bother?

Why do all scientists need to use standard tools and measurements? They do this so that others can reproduce their experiments. Remember that scientists are a skeptical bunch—they don't believe what they hear until they try it themselves. To try an experiment that someone else has done, you have to have exact measurements. One drop more of a solution can make a huge difference in the results! One temperature degree higher and the whole experiment might fail!

Reproducibility is the only way scientists accept each other's work. Hypotheses have to be tested over and over again. If the results are different every time the experiment is done, then the hypothesis is not supported.

You need to use the scientific method every time you do an investigation. The scientific method varies according to the kind of investigation you're doing. The next two pages walk you through a lab. How do you make a hypothesis? How do you set up a test for it? How do you interpret your results? **Turn the page to find out.**

# Conducting an Investigation

The fun part of science is "doing" science. You "do" science when you conduct your own investigations, collect your own data, and reach your own conclusions. You will practice using scientific methods whenever you do an investigation. Your method will change depending on what you are investigating. Sometimes you will observe and collect data. Sometimes you will make a model to see how things work. Sometimes you will conduct an experiment.

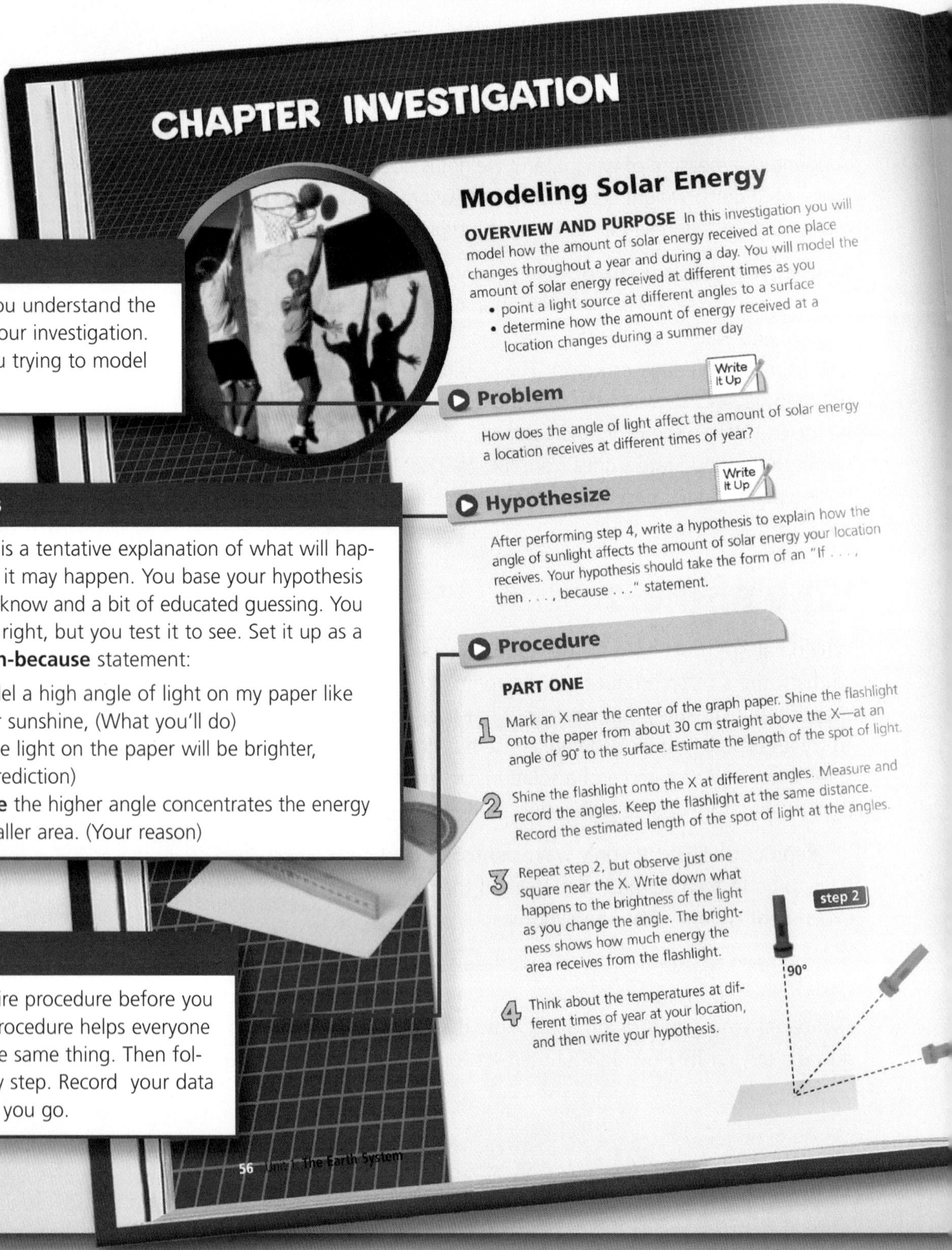

CHAPTER INVESTIGATION

## Modeling Solar Energy

**OVERVIEW AND PURPOSE** In this investigation you will model how the amount of solar energy received at one place changes throughout a year and during a day. You will model the amount of solar energy received at different times as you
- point a light source at different angles to a surface
- determine how the amount of energy received at a location changes during a summer day

### Problem

How does the angle of light affect the amount of solar energy a location receives at different times of year?

### Hypothesize

After performing step 4, write a hypothesis to explain how the angle of sunlight affects the amount of solar energy your location receives. Your hypothesis should take the form of an "If . . . , then . . . , because . . ." statement.

### Procedure

**PART ONE**

1. Mark an X near the center of the graph paper. Shine the flashlight onto the paper from about 30 cm straight above the X—at an angle of 90° to the surface. Estimate the length of the spot of light.
2. Shine the flashlight onto the X at different angles. Measure and record the angles. Keep the flashlight at the same distance. Record the estimated length of the spot of light at the angles.
3. Repeat step 2, but observe just one square near the X. Write down what happens to the brightness of the light as you change the angle. The brightness shows how much energy the area receives from the flashlight.
4. Think about the temperatures at different times of year at your location, and then write your hypothesis.



**Problem**

Make sure you understand the purpose of your investigation. What are you trying to model or find out?

**Hypothesis**

A hypothesis is a tentative explanation of what will happen and why it may happen. You base your hypothesis on what you know and a bit of educated guessing. You might not be right, but you test it to see. Set it up as a 3-part **if-then-because** statement:

1. **If** I model a high angle of light on my paper like summer sunshine, (What you'll do)
2. **then** the light on the paper will be brighter, (Your prediction)
3. **because** the higher angle concentrates the energy in a smaller area. (Your reason)

**Procedure**

Read the entire procedure before you begin. This procedure helps everyone do exactly the same thing. Then follow it step by step. Record your data accurately as you go.

## Measure and Calculate

In order to collect data in this experiment, you need to use a protractor and subtraction. You will figure out your latitude and the angle that you need to shine the flashlight.

**Content Standard**
6.4.b Students know solar energy reaches Earth through radiation, mostly in the form of visible light.

**Investigation Standard**
6.7.a Develop a hypothesis.

### PART TWO

5 Find from your teacher the latitude of your location. You will use this information to calculate the Sun's noontime elevation at your location on June 21, the first day of summer.

6 Subtract the latitude of the tropic of Cancer, which is at 23.5° north, from your latitude.

7 Subtract the number you calculated in step 6 from 90°. Your result is the Sun's noontime elevation in degrees above the horizon in your location on the first day of summer.

8 Point the light at the X on the graph paper. Move the flashlight in an arc from one side of the graph paper to the other. The maximum angle of the flashlight above the paper should be the angle you calculated in step 7. The movement of the flashlight represents the apparent movement of the Sun across the sky.

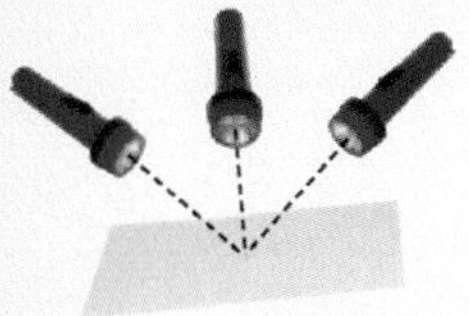

9 Observe how the brightness of the light near the X changes as you move the flashlight through the arc.

### Observe and Analyze

Write It Up

1. **RECORD** Draw the setup of your materials in each part of the investigation. Organize your notes.
2. **ANALYZE** Describe how the angle of the flashlight in step 2 affected the spot of light. Which angle concentrated the light into the smallest area?
3. **EVALUATE** In Part Two, what part of the flashlight arc represented sunrise? noon? sunset?
4. **COMPARE** Compare the brightness of light your area receives during a day at noon and at sunset.

### Conclude

Write It Up

1. **EVALUATE** Why do areas closer to the equator receive more solar energy?
2. **APPLY** Why are you more likely to get a sunburn at noon than at sunrise?
3. **INTERPRET** Do your results support your hypothesis? Explain why or why not.

### INVESTIGATE Further

**CHALLENGE** Compare the brightness of a day in summer and a day in winter at your location. Determine the total difference in latitude between your location and the latitude of the tropic of Capricorn (23.5° south). Subtract the total from 90°. The result is the noontime elevation of the Sun in your area on the first day of winter. Repeat Part Two using this maximum angle.

Modeling Solar Energy

Problem How does the angle of light affect the amount of solar energy a location receives at different times of year?

Hypothesize

Observe and Analyze

Table 1. Angle of Light and Brightness

| Angle of Light (°) | Length of Spot (cm) | Brightness |
|---|---|---|
| | | |
| 15 | | |
| 30 | | |
| 45 | | |

Chapter 2: **Energy in the Earth System** 57

## Conclude

Draw conclusions from your experiment. Was your hypothesis supported? What did you learn from the experiment?

## Record Observations

Write all your data so others can copy your experiment. Draw your setup. Measure your angles and the length of the spot. In some experiments, you can graph your data.

UNIT 1

# The Earth System

## Contents Overview

# FRONTIERS in Science

# DUST in the AIR

**What happens around this beautiful island in the Caribbean when dust from an African storm travels thousands of kilometers across the ocean?**

**California Content Standards**

**6.4.e** Students know differences in pressure, heat, **air movement,** and humidity result in changes of weather.

**6.5.b** Students know matter is transferred over time from one organism to others in the food web and **between organisms and the physical environment.**

**SCIENTIFIC AMERICAN FRONTIERS**

Learn more about the scientists studying dust in the atmosphere. See the video "Dust Busting."

This map shows the path that dust travels from Africa, across the Atlantic Ocean, to the Caribbean—a distance of about 5000 kilometers (3000 mi).

## A Problem to Solve

Images from space show gigantic clouds of dust traveling from Africa thousands of kilometers across the Atlantic Ocean. Weather reports in the Caribbean warn listeners about African dust storms. Coral and manatees in Caribbean waters show signs of disease. Are these events connected?

Each year, natural events and human activities together send as much as 2 billion metric tons of material into the skies. Once dust enters the atmosphere, it moves with the other materials in the air.

But how do Earth's surface processes and the movement of air relate to diseased coral? Teams of scientists studied diseases in living things around the Caribbean. In addition, they examined satellite photographs and recorded when dust storms occurred. After analyzing these data, they hypothesized that materials in African dust were affecting living things in the Caribbean.

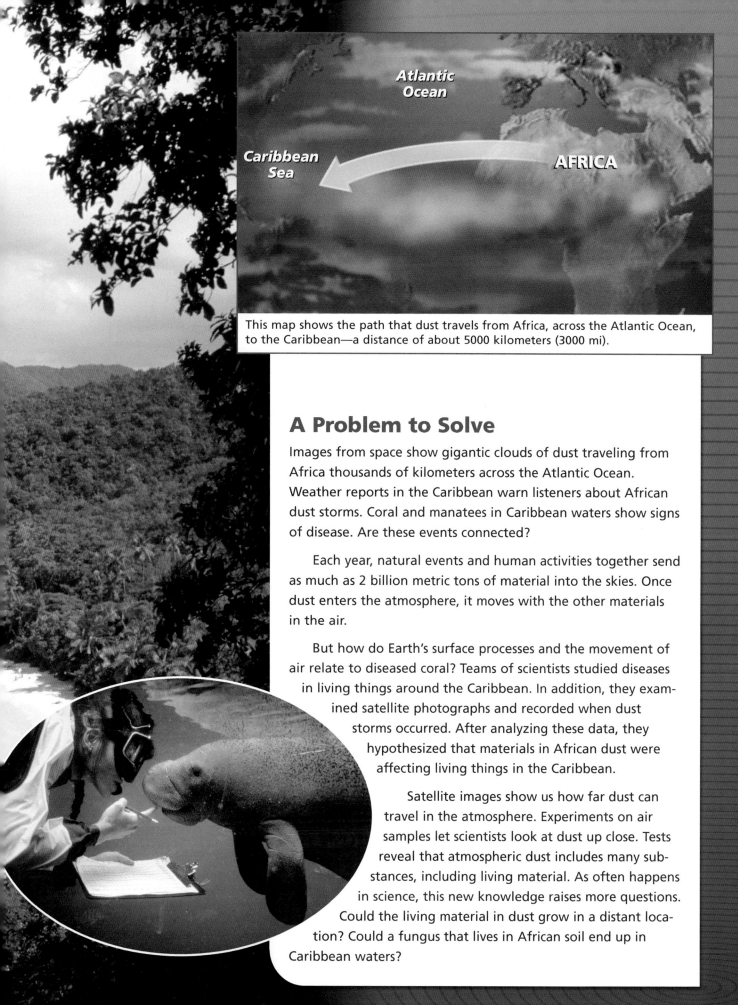

Satellite images show us how far dust can travel in the atmosphere. Experiments on air samples let scientists look at dust up close. Tests reveal that atmospheric dust includes many substances, including living material. As often happens in science, this new knowledge raises more questions. Could the living material in dust grow in a distant location? Could a fungus that lives in African soil end up in Caribbean waters?

Wind-borne dust provides nutrients for this bromeliad plant growing on a tree trunk high in the rain forest of South America.

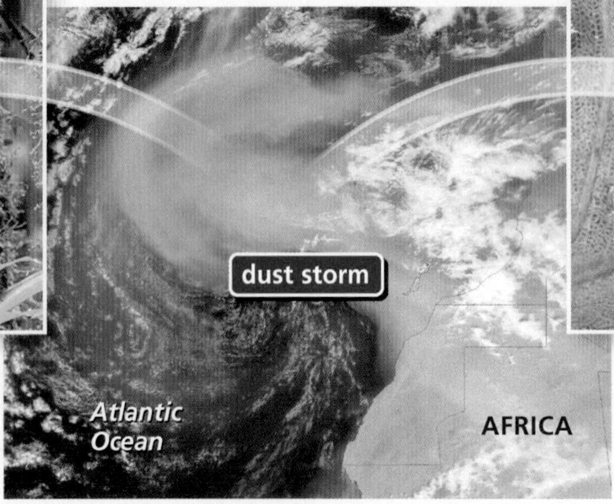


The huge dust storm shown in this satellite image carries both destructive fungus spores and life-sustaining nutrients across the Atlantic.

Fungus spores carried on dust particles have infected sea-fan corals growing on this reef near the island of St. John in the Caribbean Sea.

## Answers Hidden in Dust

To explore these questions, scientists in the Caribbean gather air samples during dust storms. They collect dust from high in the air and from locations closer to Earth's surface. To collect the samples, scientists pull air through a paper filter, trapping the dust. Once they have caught the dust, the scientists are ready to perform tests to see what's really in the tiny particles.

In the laboratory, researchers place dust samples on top of nutrients in petri dishes. Then they see if anything in the dust grows. Recent studies have shown that dust samples collected over the Caribbean contained African fungi and bacteria. More importantly, scientists saw that, even after their long voyage through the atmosphere, the living materials were able to grow.

### SCIENTIFIC AMERICAN FRONTIERS

**View the "Dust Busting" segment of your *Scientific American Frontiers* video to learn about the detective work that went into solving the mystery of sea-fan disease.**

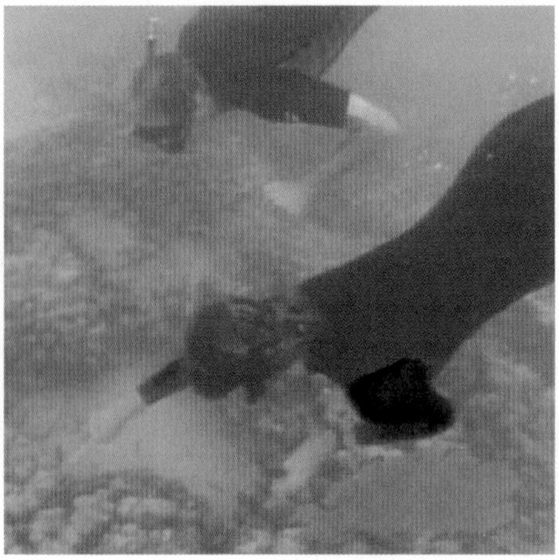

**IN THIS SCENE FROM THE VIDEO** **Biologist Ginger Garrison shows diseased coral to host Alan Alda.**

**MYSTERY SOLVED** Sea fans are an important part of the Caribbean coral-reef community, but in the 1970s they began to die off. Recently marine biologist Garriet Smith was surprised to discover that a common soil fungus, called aspergillus, was killing the sea fans. But how could a soil fungus reach an undersea reef?

The answer came from geologist Gene Shinn, who knew that global winds carry dust from Africa to the Caribbean. When Shinn read about Smith's research, he hypothesized that aspergillus might be arriving with African dust. Shinn teamed up with Smith and biologist Ginger Garrison to test the hypothesis. They collected Caribbean air samples during an African dust event and cultured dust from the samples. Aspergillus grew in their very first cultures.

Dust from Africa also contains tiny bits of metals, such as iron. The soil and atmosphere in the Caribbean are enriched by iron carried in African dust. Beautiful plants called bromeliads get the iron they need directly from the atmosphere.

Unfortunately, some of the materials found in the dust samples could be harmful to living things, such as manatees and corals. One of the fungi found in Caribbean dust samples is *Aspergillus sydowii,* which may cause diseases in sea fans and other corals. In addition, the dust contains bacteria that may speed the growth of toxic red algae, which can be harmful to manatees and other ocean animals.

## Strong Connections

Dust storms affect the entire planet. On April 6–8, 2001, soils from the Gobi Desert in Mongolia and China blew into the air, creating a massive dust cloud. Satellite images showed the cloud traveling eastward. A few days later people in the western United States saw the sky turn a chalky white.

Such observations of atmospheric dust show us how events in one part of the planet can affect living and nonliving things thousands of kilometers away in ways we might not have imagined.

### UNANSWERED Questions

Tiny particles of atmospheric dust may have huge effects. Yet the more we learn about the makeup and nature of dust, the more questions we have.

- How do dust storms affect human health?
- What can dust tell us about climate change?
- How can we use information about dust storms to predict climate change?
- How do materials in dust change ecosystems?

## UNIT PROJECTS

**As you study this unit, work alone or with a group on one of these projects.**

### TV News Report (6.4.e)

Prepare a brief news report on recent dust storms, using visuals and a script.

- Research dust storms that have occurred recently. Find out how they were related to the weather.
- Copy or print visuals, and write and practice delivering your report. Then make your presentation.

### Map the Dust (6.7.f)

Make a map showing how dust arrives in your area or another location.

- Find out what the dust contains and how it moved there. Collect information from atlases, the Internet, newspapers, and magazines.
- Prepare your map, including all the areas you need to show. Include a key, a title, and a compass rose.

### Design an Experiment (6.7.a, 6.7.d)

Design an experiment to explore how the atmosphere has changed. Research the forms of evidence scientists gather about the state of our atmosphere.

- Pick one question to investigate in an experiment. Write a hypothesis.
- List and assemble materials for your experiment. Create a data table and write up your procedure.
- Demonstrate or describe your experiment for the class.

**CAREER CENTER**
CLASSZONE.COM

Learn about careers in meteorology.

CHAPTER 1

# Energy and Change

## the BIG idea

**Waves and heat flow transfer energy.**

## Key Concepts

SECTION 1
**Change occurs as energy is transferred.**
Learn about different forms of energy and how energy can change from one form to another.

SECTION 2
**Radiation transfers energy.**
Learn about radiation and the electromagnetic spectrum.

SECTION 3
**Heat energy flows from warmer to cooler areas.**
Learn how the processes of conduction and convection transfer heat.

**California ClassZone**

CLASSZONE.COM

Chapter 1 online resources: Content Review, two Simulations, three Resource Centers, Math Tutorial, Test Practice

***What different forms of energy are shown in this photograph?***

# EXPLORE the BIG idea

## A Penny for Your Energy

6.3.a Students know energy can be carried from one place to another by heat flow or by waves, including water, light and sound waves, or by moving objects.

Chill an empty glass bottle. Immediately complete the following steps. Rub a drop of cooking oil around the rim of the bottle. Place a coin on the rim so the oil forms a seal between the coin and the bottle. Wrap your hands around the bottle.

**Observe and Think** What happened to the coin? What do you think caused this to happen?

## Hot Dog!

6.3.a Students know energy can be carried from one place to another by heat flow or by waves, including water, light and sound waves, or by moving objects.

Cover a piece of cardboard with aluminum foil. Bend it into the shape of a U. Poke a wooden skewer through a hot dog and through each side of the cardboard. Push corks over both ends of the skewer so the cardboard does not flatten out. Place your setup in direct sunlight for 30 minutes.

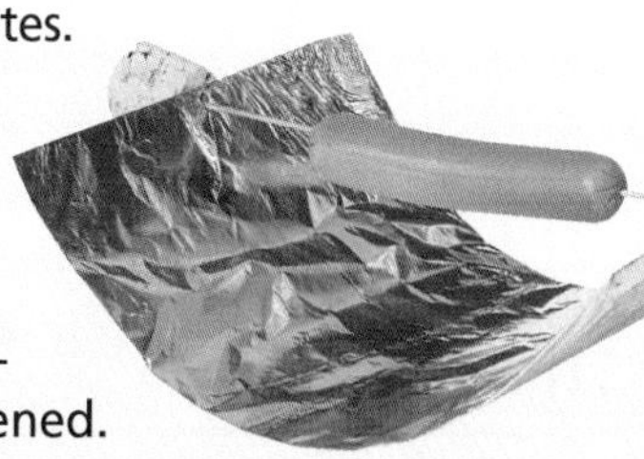

**Observe and Think**
What happened to the hot dog? Propose an explanation for what happened.

NSTA scilinks.org SCILINKS
Forms of Energy **Code: MDL063**

CHAPTER 1

# Getting Ready to Learn

## CONCEPT REVIEW

- All matter is made of tiny particles called atoms.
- Earth receives energy from the Sun.
- All of Earth's processes need energy to occur.

## VOCABULARY REVIEW

*See Glossary for definitions.*

**atom**

**force**

**matter**

**molecule**

**CONTENT REVIEW**
CLASSZONE.COM

Review concepts and vocabulary.

## TAKING NOTES

### SUPPORTING MAIN IDEAS

Make a chart to show each main idea and the information that supports it. Copy each blue heading, which is a main idea. Below it, add supporting information, such as reasons, explanations, and examples.

### VOCABULARY STRATEGY

Draw a **magnet word** diagram for each new vocabulary term. Around the magnet write words and ideas related to the term.

See the Note-Taking Handbook on pages R45–R51.

### SCIENCE NOTEBOOK

Energy has many forms.

- Mechanical energy is the energy an object has due to its motion or position.
- Sound energy moves through matter.
- Chemical energy holds atoms together in molecules.
- Electromagnetic energy includes visible light, x-rays, and microwaves.

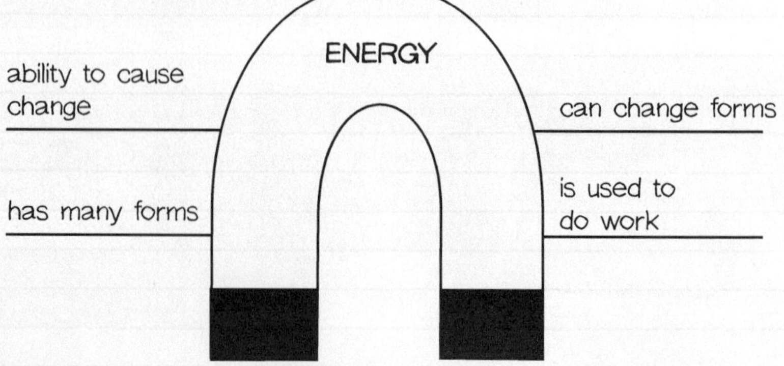

KEY CONCEPT

# 1.1 Change occurs as energy is transferred.

**CALIFORNIA Content Standards**

**6.3.a** Students know energy can be carried from one place to another by heat flow or by waves, including water, light and sound waves, or by moving objects.

**6.3.b** Students know that when fuel is consumed, most of the energy released becomes heat energy.

**BEFORE, you learned**

- Matter is made of atoms, which may combine to make molecules
- Volume refers to the amount of space an object takes up
- Mass is a measure of how much matter an object contains

**NOW, you will learn**

- About some forms of energy
- How energy moves from place to place
- How energy can change from one form to another

**VOCABULARY**

**energy** p. 9
**heat energy** p. 10
**temperature** p. 10
**heat flow** p. 11
**conservation of energy** p. 14
**work** p. 15

**THINK ABOUT**

***From what source do animals get their energy?***

The California dogface butterfly *(Zerene eurydice)* is the state insect of California. When the butterfly is an adult, it feeds on flower nectar. Where do you think the butterfly gets the energy it needs to fly from flower to flower?

## Life requires energy.

SUPPORTING MAIN IDEAS
Support the main idea about life and energy with details and examples.

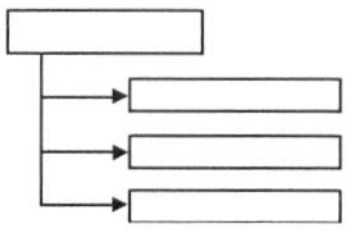

All living things need energy to live and grow. **Energy** is the ability to cause change. A redwood tree needs energy to produce new branches and leaves. A whale needs energy to swim through the ocean. You need energy for all of your activities, including eating, exercising, and even sleeping.

All living things get energy from food. Plants use energy from sunlight to make their own food. Using this energy, plants combine carbon dioxide from the air, and water from the soil, into sugars. Plants store these sugars for future use. Animals, including people, get energy by eating plants or by eating other animals that ate plants. When you eat a baked potato or a slice of chicken, you are gaining energy that originally came from sunlight.

**CHECK YOUR READING** Where does the energy you need for talking or for playing basketball originally come from?

## Energy has many forms.

Drummers use mechanical energy to produce sound, which is another form of energy.

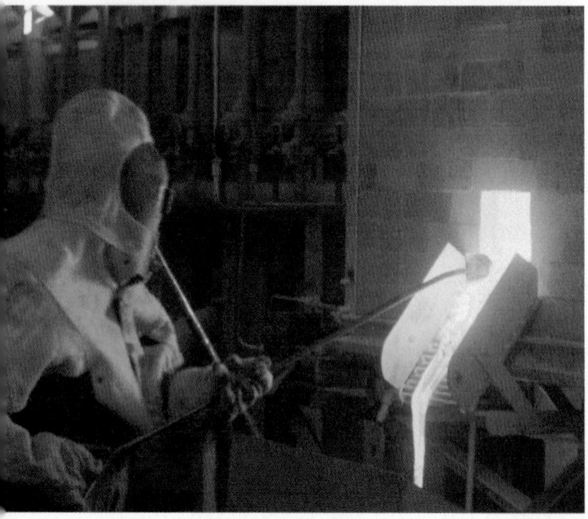

In this fiberglass factory, chemical energy from fuel is used to produce heat energy, which, in turn, melts the materials used to make glass. The melted glass releases electro-magnetic energy and heat energy.

Energy takes many forms and has many different effects. For example, a bird uses energy to fly. The energy of wind causes leaves to flutter. All forms of energy have one important point in common: they cause changes to occur. Some of the many types of energy are described below.

**Mechanical Energy** The energy that an object has due to its motion or position is mechanical energy. For example, a basketball tossed in the air has mechanical energy as a result of its motion and its position above the ground.

**Sound Energy** Sound energy moves through matter such as air and water. When sound energy reaches you, your ears change it to electrical signals that are sent to your brain. You hear a sound when your brain processes the signals.

**Chemical Energy** Recall that matter is made up of atoms and molecules. The energy that holds atoms together in molecules is chemical energy. Your body uses chemical energy stored in food. As you digest food, its molecules break apart. They release chemical energy. Chemical energy is also released when wood or gasoline burns.

**Electromagnetic Energy** Electromagnetic energy includes visible light, x-rays, and microwaves. The energy that comes from the Sun is electromagnetic energy. Unlike sound energy, electromagnetic energy can move through empty space. You will read more about electromagnetic energy later in this chapter.

**Heat Energy** The atoms and molecules in matter are always moving. Even the atoms and molecules in a solid object are always moving back and forth over tiny distances. An object's **heat energy** is the total energy of the motion of particles in the object. Heat energy is also called thermal energy.

Heat energy and temperature are closely related. But they are not the same. **Temperature** is a measure of the average amount of energy of motion of the particles in an object. Temperature is measured using a thermometer.

Consider a liquid, such as hot cocoa, that has a high temperature. The particles that make up the liquid are moving very fast. On average, their energy of motion is high. The cocoa feels hot. Now consider a drink, such as a fruit smoothie, that has a low temperature. The particles in the liquid are moving more slowly. On average, their energy of motion is lower. The smoothie feels cold.

**CHECK YOUR READING** What is the relationship between temperature and heat energy?

## Movement of Energy

**Energy from the Sun can be transferred to plants and then to animals. Living things require this movement of energy.**

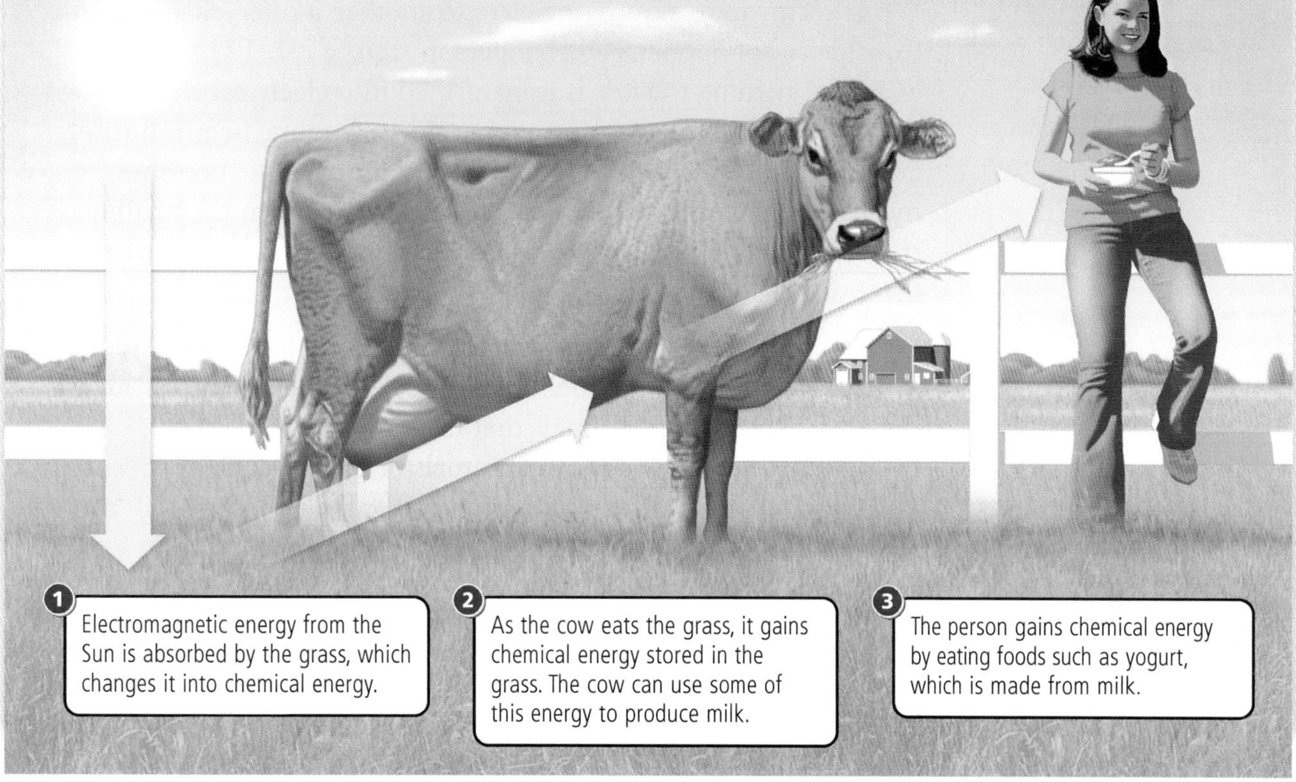

1
Electromagnetic energy from the Sun is absorbed by the grass, which changes it into chemical energy.
2
As the cow eats the grass, it gains chemical energy stored in the grass. The cow can use some of this energy to produce milk.
3
The person gains chemical energy by eating foods such as yogurt, which is made from milk.

## Energy moves from one place to another.

The illustration above shows some of the ways that energy moves. Energy from the Sun is transferred to plants on Earth's surface. When animals such as cows eat the plants, some of the plants' energy is transferred to them. Milk from the cows can be turned into dairy products such as yogurt, ice cream, and cheese. Some of the energy in the food is transferred to the person who eats it.

Energy can also move from one object to another because of differences in temperature. The movement of heat energy is called **heat flow.** Suppose ice cubes are placed in a pitcher of warm lemonade. At first, the lemonade and the ice cubes have different temperatures. But the warm lemonade transfers heat energy to the cold ice cubes. The lemonade loses heat energy, so its temperature decreases. The ice gains energy, so its temperature rises. Eventually, the temperature of everything in the pitcher is the same. Heat energy always flows from warmer to cooler objects. If energy flowed in the opposite direction—from cooler to warmer—the ice would get colder and the lemonade would get hotter.

**CHECK YOUR READING** In which direction does heat flow always transfer energy?

## Energy can change from one form to another.

RESOURCE CENTER
CLASSZONE.COM

Learn about ways in which people use energy.

When energy moves from one place to another, it often changes form. Consider what happens when a person starts a car. The mechanical energy of turning the key is transformed into electrical energy that starts the engine. As the car's engine starts, gasoline begins burning. Some of the chemical energy released by the gasoline becomes mechanical energy used to make the car move. From the turning of the key to the movement of the car, energy has changed form at least three times.

Gasoline contains energy that changed form long ago. Gasoline is made from oil, a fossil fuel. A fossil fuel is a fuel formed from the remains of plants and animals that lived millions of years ago. The energy stored in the plants and animals originally came from sunlight. The remains of the plants and animals eventually became oil. You will read more about how fossil fuels form in Chapter 13.

**CHECK YOUR READING** Provide your own example of energy changing form.

### Uses of Energy

People have developed ways to change energy from one form to another for many purposes. Some ways that energy changes form are described below. As you read each description, follow the process in the illustrations on page 13. You will see how energy that is stored in water held behind a dam is changed into electrical energy.

1. The water behind the dam has mechanical energy because of its position above Earth's surface. The water flows downward in response to the pull of gravity.
2. Some of the water flows through a tunnel within the dam.
3. Some of the mechanical energy of the moving water is transferred to the turbines, causing them to turn. Mechanical energy of the moving turbines is changed into electrical energy by electrical generators.
4. Electrical energy is transported away from the dam through wires. The electrical energy is changed into different forms of energy and is used in many different ways. For example, at a concert or a play, electrical energy is changed into light and heat by lighting systems. It is changed into sound energy by sound systems.

As you can see, energy changes form several times in the production of electrical energy. Every time that energy changes form, some of it becomes heat energy. The energy that becomes heat energy is usually not useful. Therefore, every time energy in the dam changes form, some useful energy is lost because it has become heat energy.

**CALIFORNIA Focus**

Shasta Dam, shown above, is on the Sacramento River. Water passing through the dam is used to produce some of the electricity supplied to California.

## Changes in Forms of Energy

**Energy is often changed from one form to another in order to meet everyday needs.**

1 Water held behind the dam has **mechanical energy.**
2 The water moves through the tunnel in response to gravity.
3 The water causes the turbines to turn. This **mechanical energy** is converted into **electrical energy** by generators.
4 **Electrical energy** is transmitted through wires, and then converted into many other forms of energy.

### Transfer of Mechanical Energy

Some of the mechanical energy of water is transferred to turbines inside the dam.

### Mechanical Energy to Electrical Energy

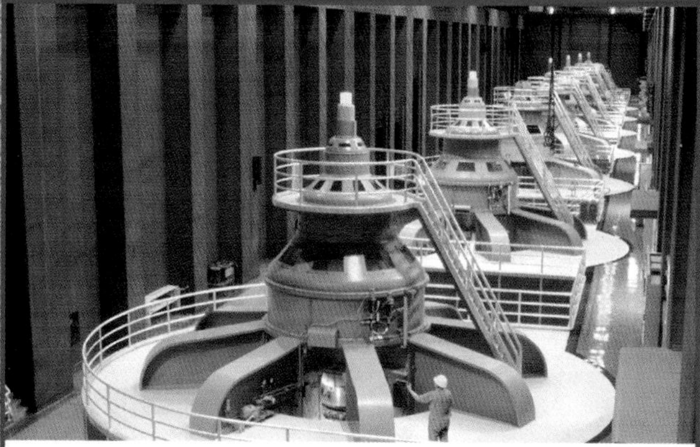

The mechanical energy of turning turbines becomes electrical energy in these generators.

**READING VISUALS** How many different transfers of energy are described in this diagram?

## INVESTIGATE Energy

### *How can you observe energy changing form?*

**PROCEDURE**

1. Mark and cut a spiral pattern in a piece of paper.
2. Cut a 15 cm piece of thread and tape one end to the center of the spiral.
3. Adjust the lamp to shine straight at the ceiling.
4. Fasten the thread to an object above the lamp so that the spiral hangs about 10 cm above the light bulb. Wait for the spiral to stop moving. Then turn on the lamp. **CAUTION: Don't let the paper touch the bulb!**

**WHAT DO YOU THINK?**

- What happened to the spiral after you turned on the light?
- In what sense has the energy changed form?

**CHALLENGE** In addition to the heat from the lamp, what conditions in the room might affect the spiral?

**SKILL FOCUS**
Observing (6.3.a)

**MATERIALS**
- paper
- marker
- scissors
- thread
- tape
- desk lamp

**TIME**
15 minutes

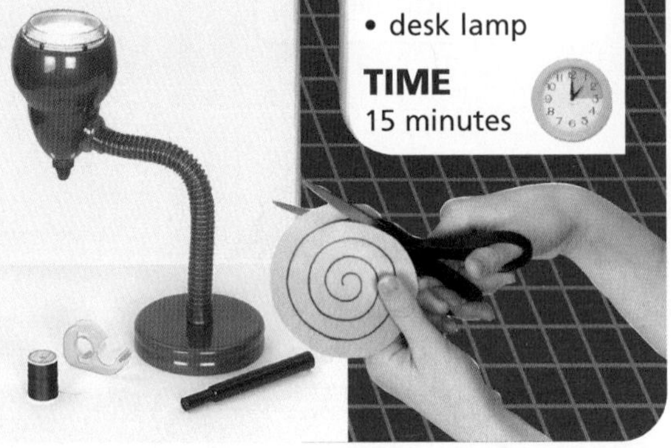

## Conservation of Energy

No matter how energy is transferred or changes form, all of the energy is still present. The total amount of energy never changes. This fact is described by the law of **conservation of energy,** which states that energy can change from one form to another, but it is never created or destroyed. For example, in a light bulb, electrical energy is changed into light and heat. The heat given off by a light bulb is usually not useful energy. So the amount of useful energy is less. But the total amount of energy is still the same.

Recall what happens when a car is started. Gasoline begins to burn in the car's engine. The car gains energy as some of the chemical energy from the fuel becomes mechanical energy. The energy from the fuel is used to make the car move. If more gas is not sent to the engine, the car soon stops moving.

The car also slows down or stops when the driver uses the brake system. This causes the car's mechanical energy to change form. There is friction between the car's wheels and the ground and also between the brake system and the wheels. Friction causes mechanical energy to change into heat energy. Eventually, most of the energy released by the fuel becomes heat energy. But the overall amount of energy is still the same. It has just changed form or moved to a different place.

## Energy and Work

In science, **work** is the use of force to move an object some distance. A force is a push or a pull. In scientific terms, solving a crossword puzzle does not require work. However, filling out the puzzle with a pencil is work, because you are moving the pencil.

**SIMULATION**
CLASSZONE.COM
Explore work by lifting virtual weights.

Work transfers energy. You do work on objects when you move them. For example, you do work when you pick up a piece of paper. When you pick up the paper, you transfer some of your energy to it. Objects can also do work. Water in a river does work as it carries fallen leaves downstream. A bowling ball does work when it knocks down bowling pins.

In the photograph, the woman is holding a large box. When she lifted the box, she did work on it. She applied a force that acted in the same direction as the motion of the box. The force was applied in an upward direction, and the box moved upward. What if she stood still while holding the box? She would not be doing work on the box, even if her muscles got tired. She must be moving the box to do work on it.

**CHECK YOUR READING** Give an example of applying a force to do work.

# 1.1 Review

**KEY CONCEPTS**

1. Give an example of how energy causes change.
2. What is heat energy? How is it different from temperature? (6.3.a)
3. Describe the changes in energy that take place when a person starts a car.

**CRITICAL THINKING**

4. **Synthesize** Describe two of the types of energy that are involved when a person beats on a drum with drumsticks.
5. **Apply** Is work being done by a person who is reading a book? Explain.

**CHALLENGE**

6. **Analyze** Explain how the heat and light produced by burning wood originally come from the Sun.

# CHAPTER INVESTIGATION

## Changes in Energy

**OVERVIEW AND PURPOSE** All foods contain stored chemical energy, but some foods contain more chemical energy than others. People need this chemical energy for all of their activities. The amount of chemical energy stored in foods such as marshmallows can be measured by burning the foods. In this investigation you will

- construct a setup to investigate the amount of energy stored in samples of food
- calculate the amount of energy released when the foods are burned

### Problem

Write It Up

How much energy is released when different types of food are burned?

**MATERIALS**

- empty aluminum can with holes
- dowel rod
- water
- graduated cylinder
- ring stand with ring
- thermometer
- tape
- aluminum pie plate
- aluminum foil
- large paper clip
- cork
- modeling clay
- crouton
- caramel rice cake
- balance
- wooden matches

6.3.a, 6.3.b, 6.7.b

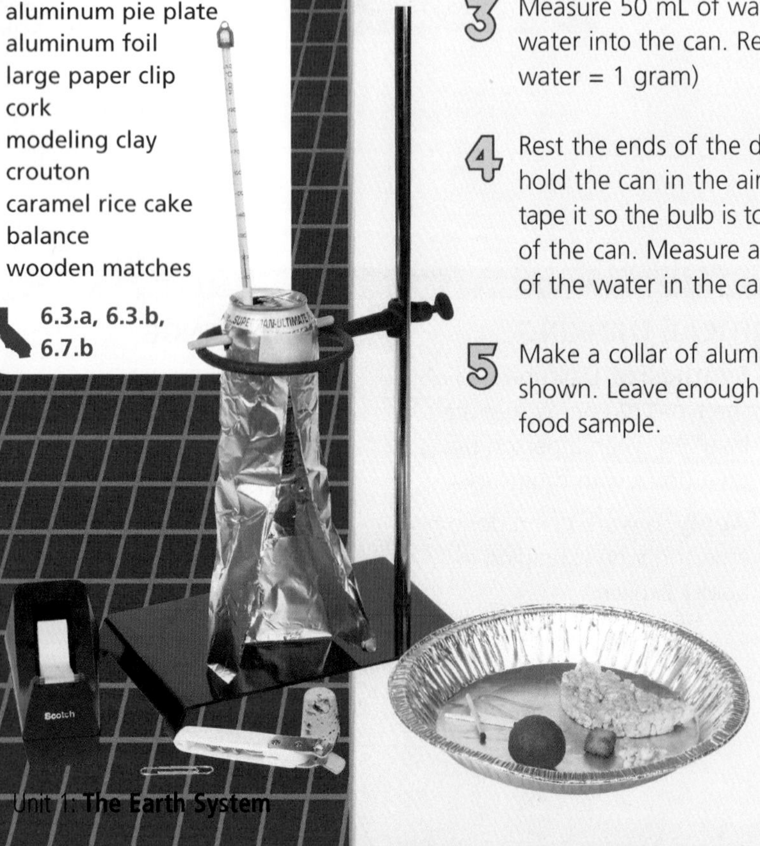

### Procedure

1. Create a data table similar to the one shown on the sample notebook page.

2. Slide the dowel rod through the holes in the can as shown in the photograph to the left.

3. Measure 50 mL of water with a graduated cylinder, and pour the water into the can. Record the mass of the water. (**Hint:** 1 mL of water = 1 gram)

4. Rest the ends of the dowel rod on the ring in the ring stand to hold the can in the air. Place the thermometer in the can and tape it so the bulb is touching only the water and not the bottom of the can. Measure and record the beginning temperature (T1) of the water in the can.

5. Make a collar of aluminum foil and tape it around the can as shown. Leave enough room to insert the burner platform and food sample.

**Content Standard**
6.3.b Students know that when fuel is consumed, most of the energy released becomes heat energy.

**Investigation Standard**
6.7.b Select and use appropriate tools and technology (including calculators, computers, balances, spring scales, microscopes, and binoculars) to perform tests, collect data, and display data.

6 Construct the burner platform as follows. Open up the paper clip. Push the straightened end into a cork, and push the bottom of the cork into the clay. Push the burner onto the pie plate so it will not move. Put the pie plate under the ring.

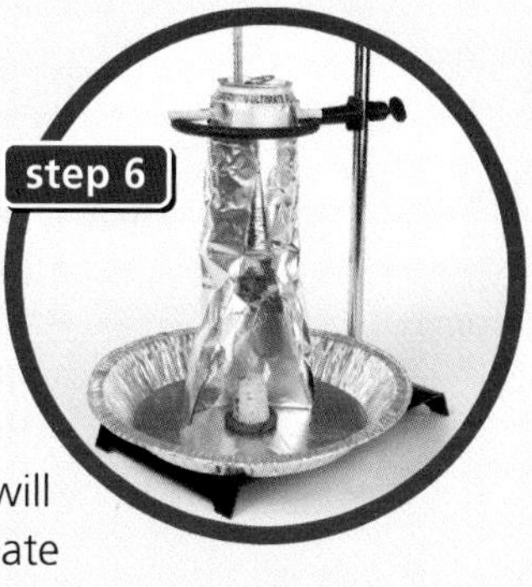


7 Find and record the mass of one of the food samples. Place the food on the flattened end of the burner platform. Adjust the height of the ring so the bottom of the can is about 4 cm above the food.

8 Have your teacher use a match to ignite the piece of food. Allow the food to burn completely. Measure and record the final temperature (T2) of the water.

9 From a classmate, obtain temperature data for the food sample you didn't test. Record the data.

## Observe and Analyze

Write It Up

1. **RECORD OBSERVATIONS** Make sure to record all measurements in the data table.
2. **CALCULATE** Find the energy released from the food samples by following the next two steps.

   Calculate and record the change in temperature.
   **change in temperature = T2 – T1**

   Calculate and record the energy released in calories. One calorie is the energy needed to raise the temperature of 1 g of water by 1°C.
   **energy released = mass of water • change in temperature • 1 cal/g°C**

## Conclude

Write It Up

1. **INTERPRET** Answer the question posed in the problem.
2. **INFER** Why do you think different types of food release different amounts of energy?
3. **APPLY** Find out how much fat and carbohydrates the different foods contain. Explain the relationship between this information and the number of calories in the foods.

## INVESTIGATE Further

**CHALLENGE** The Calories listed in foods are equal to 1000 calories (1 kilocalorie). Calculate the amount of energy in your food samples in terms of Calories per gram of food (Calories/g). Using a balance, find the mass of any ash that remains after burning the food. Subtract that mass from the original mass of the sample to calculate mass burned. Divide total calories by mass burned, then divide that value by 1000 to find Calories/g. Compare your results with those given on the product labels.

Changes in Energy

Problem How much energy is released when different types of food are burned?

Observe and Analyze

Table 1. Energy in Food

| | Sample 1 |
|---|---|
| Mass of water (g) | |
| Initial water temp. (T1) (°C) | |
| Final water temp. (T2) (°C) | |
| Mass of food (g) | |
| Change in temp. (T2 - T1) (°C) | |
| Energy released (mass•change in temp.•cal/g °C) | |

Conclude

KEY CONCEPT

# 1.2 Radiation transfers energy.

**CALIFORNIA Content Standards**

**6.3.a** Students know energy can be carried from one place to another by heat flow or by waves, including water, light and sound waves, or by moving objects.

**6.3.d** Students know heat energy is also transferred between objects by radiation (radiation can travel through space).

**6.4.b** Students know solar energy reaches Earth through radiation, mostly in the form of visible light.

**BEFORE, you learned**

- Energy causes change
- Energy exists in many forms
- Energy can change from one form to another

**NOW, you will learn**

- How radiation travels
- About the electromagnetic spectrum
- How radiation transfers energy

**VOCABULARY**

**radiation** p. 18
**wave** p. 19
**wavelength** p. 20
**electromagnetic spectrum** p. 21

**EXPLORE Radiation** (6.3.d)

### *Can you feel radiation?*

**PROCEDURE**

1. Turn on the lamp and wait for it to become warm. It gives off energy in the form of radiation.
2. Hold one hand a short distance from the bulb. Record your observations.
3. Turn the lamp off. The bulb continues to give off energy. Hold your other hand a short distance from the bulb.

**MATERIALS**

- lamp

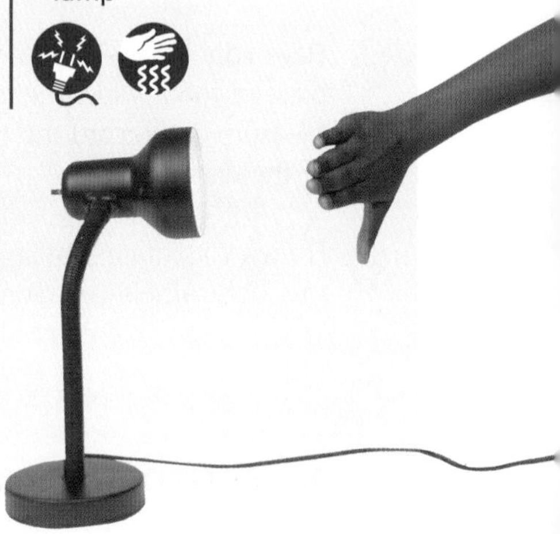

**WHAT DO YOU THINK?**

- What did you see and feel?
- How did radiation affect each hand?

## Radiation travels in waves.

On a bright day, sunlight sparkles on water, the windows of buildings, and cars. You can feel sunlight as warmth on your face. If a cloud comes between your face and the Sun, you feel cooler. But how does sunlight travel through empty space to Earth's surface?

The Sun's energy travels to Earth in the form of radiation. **Radiation** is energy that travels across distances in the form of electromagnetic waves. These waves transmit energy that is partly electric and partly magnetic. Types of radiation include visible light, microwaves, and infrared radiation (IHN-fruh-REHD).

**CHECK YOUR READING** How does energy from the Sun travel to Earth?

You have learned that energy can move from one place to another. A **wave** is a disturbance that carries energy from one place to another. Consider what happens when you shake one end of a rope. The rope wiggles up and down or from side to side. This motion, or disturbance, travels in a wave. Energy from the wave travels along the rope. However, the particles that make up the rope do not travel from one end of the rope to the other. A wave transfers energy, but not matter, over long distances.

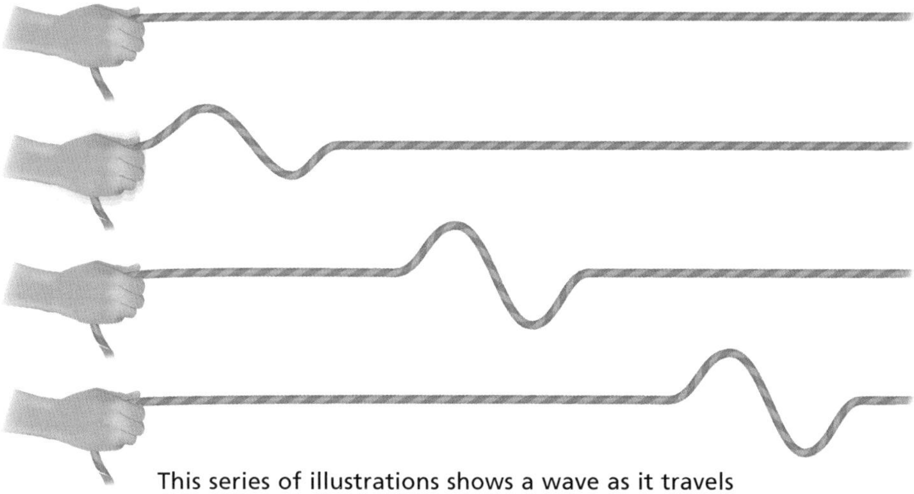

This series of illustrations shows a wave as it travels through a rope. The rope returns to its original position after the energy from the wave has passed through it.

In the rope example, a wave is traveling through matter. However, electromagnetic waves can travel through empty space. If electromagnetic waves could not travel through empty space, then Earth would receive no energy from the Sun.

CHECK YOUR READING How are electromagnetic waves different from the waves illustrated above?

## Energy and Wavelengths

Much of the Sun's energy that reaches Earth is in the form of visible light waves. Your eyes can detect visible light. But there are types of radiation that humans cannot see.

Many types of radiation have less energy than the light you can see. Others have more. For example, infrared radiation has less energy than visible light. Infrared radiation usually warms the materials that absorb it. When you feel heat from a light bulb or from sunlight, you are sensing infrared radiation. Ultraviolet radiation has more energy than visible light. Ultraviolet radiation can cause sunburns.

Different types of radiation have different wavelengths. A **wavelength** is the distance between one wave crest and the next crest. As shown in the illustration below, a wave crest is the highest point on a wave. A trough is the lowest point on the wave. A wavelength can also be measured from trough to trough. Every type of wave has a wavelength that can be measured.

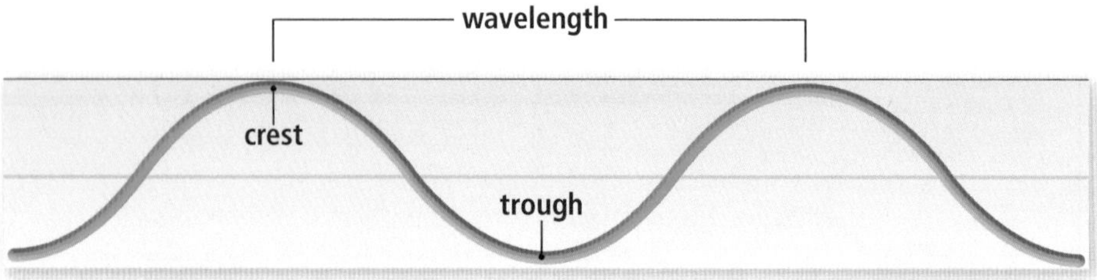


Electromagnetic waves that have longer wavelengths have less energy. For example, infrared radiation has longer wavelengths and less energy than does visible light. Waves with shorter wavelengths have more energy.

**CHECK YOUR READING** In electromagnetic waves, what is the relationship between wavelength and energy?

## The Electromagnetic Spectrum

**The different forms of electromagnetic radiation vary in their wavelengths.**

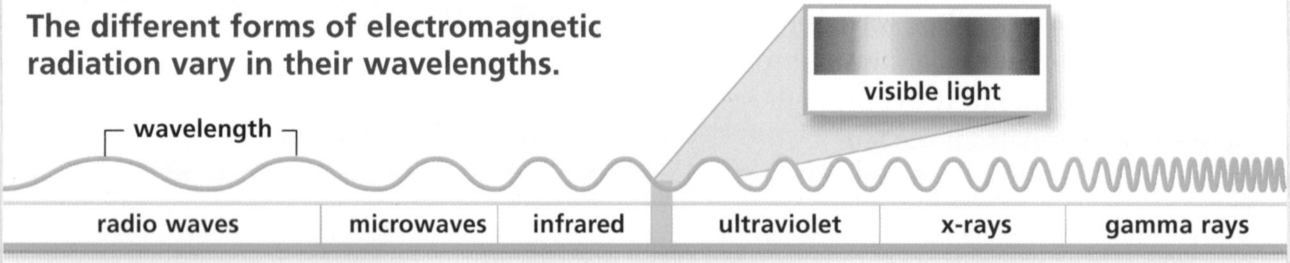


### Radio Waves

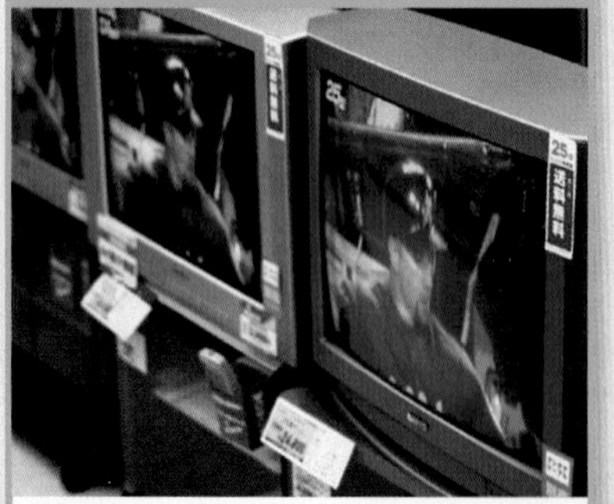

Radio waves are used for radio and television broadcasts.

### Microwaves

Microwaves are used to send cellular phone signals.

### X-Rays

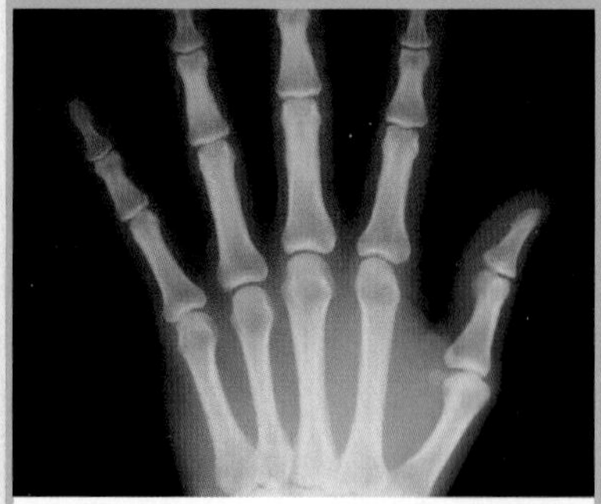

X-rays are used to show hard tissues, such as bones, inside the body.

**READING VISUALS** Which form of electromagnetic energy has the longest wavelengths? Which has the lowest energy?

## Electromagnetic Spectrum

The **electromagnetic spectrum** is the entire range of electromagnetic energy, from radiation that has the shortest wavelengths to radiation that has the longest wavelengths. Visible light is only a small part of the electromagnetic spectrum.

The illustration on page 20 shows the names of each type of electromagnetic energy. On the left-hand side of the illustration are the waves with the longest wavelengths and the lowest energy. Toward the right, the wavelengths become shorter and the energy becomes higher.

People use electromagnetic energy in many ways. Radio waves are used to carry radio signals and television signals. Microwaves are used in microwave ovens to cook food. They are also used to transmit cellular phone signals. X-rays and gamma rays are very high-energy waves that are used in medical technologies. And, of course, people use many kinds of devices that give off visible light.

READING TIP

*Spectrum* comes from the Latin word *specere,* meaning "to look at." A spectrum is a broad, continuous range of related qualities, ideas, or activities.

RESOURCE CENTER
CLASSZONE.COM
Learn more about the electromagnetic spectrum.

## Visible Light

The light that comes from the Sun is made up of all colors of visible light blended together. Each color in visible light has its own range of wavelengths. Of the colors of visible light, red light has the longest wavelength and violet light has the shortest wavelength.

You can divide visible light into colors by passing it through a prism, as shown in the photograph at right. Light bends as it passes through the prism. The amount that each color of light bends depends on its wavelength. A rainbow shows the colors of visible light in the order of their wavelengths. A rainbow appears when light bends as it passes through droplets of water in the atmosphere. The droplets of water act like prisms.

CHECK YOUR READING How are the colors of visible light similar? different?

## Earth receives radiation from the Sun.

Earth is extremely small compared with the Sun. It is also far away from the Sun. Therefore, Earth receives only a tiny amount of the energy given off by the Sun. However, the Sun is the major source of energy for processes that occur in Earth's atmosphere and on Earth's surface. You will read more about these processes in Chapter 2.

Electromagnetic energy from the Sun reaches Earth in a little over eight minutes. This energy undergoes no significant change as it travels the 150 million kilometers (93 million miles) through space. However, energy from the Sun goes through many changes as it passes through Earth's atmosphere.

### Reflection and Absorption in the Atmosphere

**READING TIP**

Reflection occurs when something is thrown back or bent back. Absorption occurs when something is taken in or soaked up.

The Sun gives off the full range of energy in the electromagnetic spectrum. Energy from the Sun is called solar energy. All types of electromagnetic energy from the Sun reach the top of Earth's atmosphere. But much of this solar energy does not reach Earth's surface. Some of it is reflected back into space. And some of it is absorbed by the atoms and molecules of the atmosphere.

Almost all of the visible light from the Sun passes through the atmosphere to Earth's surface. However, most of the electromagnetic energy with wavelengths shorter than visible light is absorbed by the atmosphere. A great deal of ultraviolet radiation (UHL-truh-VY-uh-liht), which can cause sunburns and damage plants, is absorbed before it reaches the ground. X-rays and gamma rays are completely absorbed in the atmosphere at heights greater than 100 kilometers (60 miles) above Earth's surface.

### Reflection and Absorption

**Much of the solar energy that reaches the top of Earth's atmosphere is reflected or absorbed before it reaches Earth's surface.**

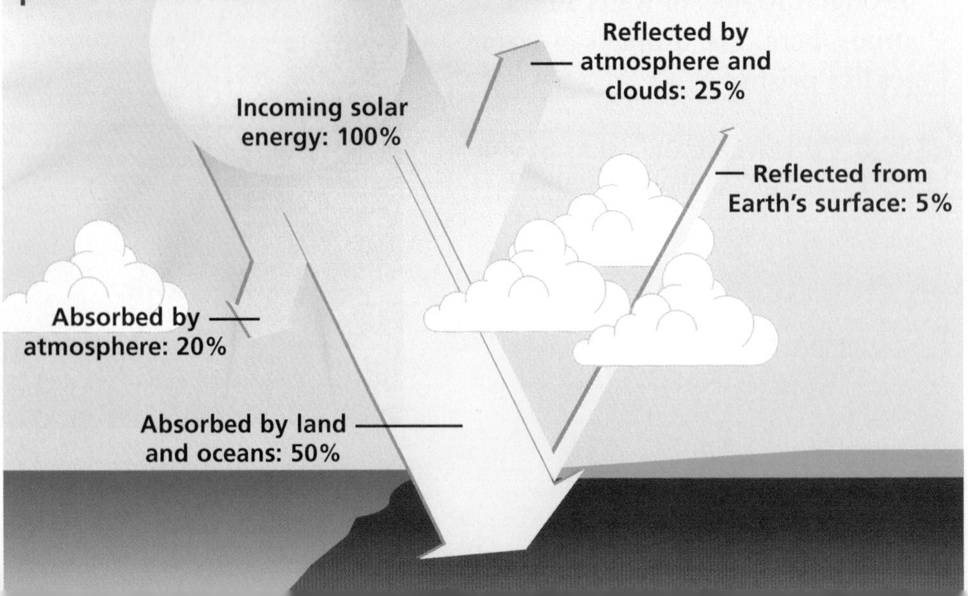

Infrared radiation, microwaves, and radio waves have wavelengths longer than those of visible light. Infrared radiation, which helps keep the planet's surface warm, is mostly absorbed by the atmosphere. Microwaves are mostly absorbed by the atmosphere too. Radio waves are not absorbed. They pass through the atmosphere to Earth's surface, but they have little effect on Earth. The radio waves used to send television and radio signals are generated by devices that people make.

## Reflection and Absorption at Earth's Surface

Two main things happen to the solar energy that reaches Earth's surface. Some is reflected, or sent in a new direction. Some is absorbed. When radiation is absorbed, it changes into heat energy. Earth's surface is heated when it absorbs energy from the Sun.

Dark-colored surfaces absorb more solar energy. Therefore, they gain more heat energy. Light-colored surfaces reflect more solar energy, so they gain less heat energy. Consider the clothing you might wear on a sunny summer day. You would feel cooler if you wore light-colored clothes than if you wore similar, dark-colored clothes. The light-colored clothes reflect more solar energy. In the same way, light-colored materials on Earth's surface, such as ice and snow, reflect more solar energy. Dark-colored rocks absorb more solar energy, and they gain more heat energy.

## INVESTIGATE Energy Transfer

### *What improves the collection of solar energy?*

**PROCEDURE**

1. Cover the top of one cup with white plastic, and cover the top of the other cup with black plastic. Secure the plastic with a rubber band.
2. Use the scissors to make a small hole in the center of each cup's plastic lid. Insert a thermometer through each opening.
3. Place the cups in direct sunlight, and record their temperatures every minute for ten minutes.

**WHAT DO YOU THINK?**

- Which cup showed a greater temperature change? Why do you think this happened?
- Make a line graph of your results to show the change in temperature in each cup.

**CHALLENGE** Try the experiment again, using aluminum foil instead of white plastic. How do the results differ with the aluminum foil? Why might this be the case?

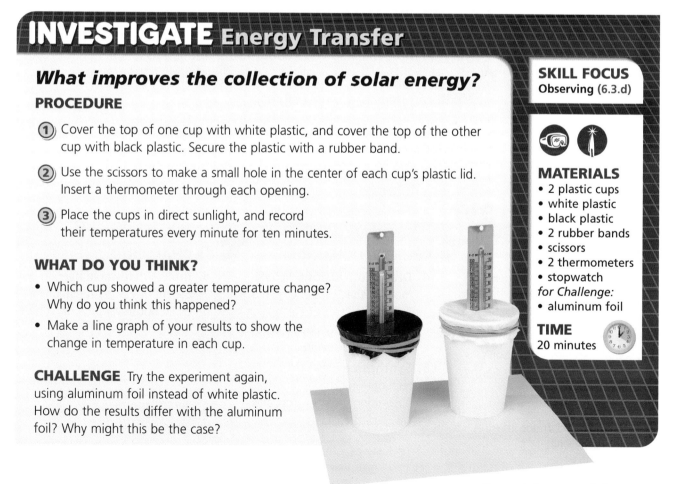

**SKILL FOCUS**
Observing (6.3.d)

**MATERIALS**
- 2 plastic cups
- white plastic
- black plastic
- 2 rubber bands
- scissors
- 2 thermometers
- stopwatch

*for Challenge:*
- aluminum foil

**TIME**
20 minutes

## The Sun as an Energy Resource

Much of the energy used on Earth comes from fossil fuels such as coal, oil, and natural gas. However, the supply of fossil fuels is limited. As a result, people are exploring ways to use other energy sources, including sunlight, to generate electricity. For example, modern solar cells are made of materials that change sunlight into electrical energy. Solar cells are used to provide electrical energy for such things as satellites in orbit around Earth, calculators, and experimental cars.

Solar energy can be used in homes to provide heat and electrical energy.

In addition to changing sunlight into electrical energy, people use the Sun's radiation for heating. The photograph shows a house that uses energy from sunlight. The solar panels on the roof hold solar cells that provide electrical energy, and the large windows help trap the warmth in sunlight.

Energy from the Sun has several advantages compared with fossil fuels. Its supply is not limited, and it does not produce the same harmful waste products that fossil fuels do. But solar cells are not yet commonly used because the materials used to make them are very expensive. Also, solar cells are not very efficient. Large numbers of solar cells produce only a relatively small amount of electrical energy. You will read more in Chapter 13 about using sunlight as an energy source.

**CHECK YOUR READING** What is an advantage of using solar energy as an energy resource? a disadvantage?

# 1.2 Review

### KEY CONCEPTS

1. How does the Sun's energy travel to Earth? (6.4.b)
2. What is the electromagnetic spectrum? (6.4.b)
3. What happens to the Sun's energy when it reaches Earth? (6.3.a)

### CRITICAL THINKING

4. **Draw Conclusions** Would more of the Sun's energy reach a particular part of Earth's surface on a sunny day or on a cloudy day? Explain.
5. **Synthesize** Describe the relationships among energy absorption, heat energy, and temperature.

### CHALLENGE

6. **Infer** What would happen on Earth if the Sun's radiation could not travel through space?

MATH in SCIENCE

MATH TUTORIAL
CLASSZONE.COM
Click on Math Tutorial for more help with comparing decimals.

Math 6.NS.1.1
Science 6.4.b

## SKILL: COMPARING DECIMALS

# Visible Light

Longer wavelengths have less energy. Therefore, red light has less energy than violet light. Wavelengths of visible light are usually measured in nanometers (nm). One nanometer is one-billionth of a meter. To compare wavelengths given in decimals, you can look at their place values.

**Steps for comparing decimals**

**(1)** Write the decimals in a column, lining up the decimal points.

**(2)** If necessary, write zeros to the right of one decimal so that both decimals have the same number of decimal places.

**(3)** Compare the place values from left to right.

### Examples

**Example A**

Compare the decimals. Which wavelength has less energy?

The hundreds, tens, and ones digits are the same.

**Wavelength A: 528.450 nm**
**Wavelength B: 528.502 nm**

The tenths digits are different: 5 > 4.

**ANSWER**
528.450 nm < 528.502 nm
Wavelength B has less energy.

**Example B**

Compare two wavelengths from another part of the spectrum. Which has less energy?

The hundreds, tens, and ones digits are the same.

**Wavelength A: 712.94 nm**
**Wavelength B: 712.90 nm**

The tenths digits are the same.

The hundredths digits are different: 4 > 0.

**ANSWER**
712.94 nm > 712.90 nm
Wavelength A has less energy.

**Copy each statement and complete it with <, >, or =. Underline the wavelength with less energy.**

**1.** 634.75 nm ___ 634.56 nm

**2.** 450.5 nm ___ 450.50 nm

**3.** 752.309 nm ___ 752.311 nm

**4.** 526.115 nm ___ 526.106 nm

**5.** 641.75 nm ___ 641.750 nm

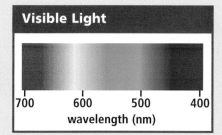

**Visible Light**

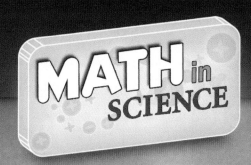

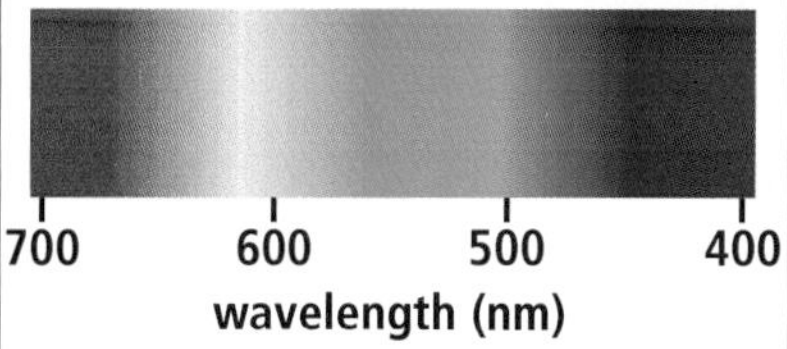


**CHALLENGE** Find a value of *n* that makes the following statement true: 438.0894 nm > *n* > 438.08925 nm

KEY CONCEPT

# 1.3 Heat energy flows from warmer to cooler areas.

**CALIFORNIA Content Standards**

**6.3.c** Students know heat flows in solids by conduction (which involves no flow of matter) and in fluids by conduction and by convection (which involves flow of matter).

**6.4.d** Students know convection currents distribute heat in the atmosphere and oceans.

**BEFORE, you learned**

- Radiation travels through empty space
- The electromagnetic spectrum includes all the forms of electromagnetic energy
- Radiation transfers energy as heat

**NOW, you will learn**

- How heat is transferred in matter
- How the process of conduction transfers heat
- How the process of convection transfers heat

**VOCABULARY**

**conduction** p. 27
**convection** p. 28
**density** p. 28
**convection current** p. 30

**EXPLORE Conduction** (6.3.c)

### *How can you observe a flow of energy?*

**PROCEDURE**

1. Fill the large beaker halfway with hot tap water. Fill the small beaker halfway with cold water. Place a thermometer in each beaker. Record the temperature of the water in each beaker.
2. Without removing the water in either beaker, place the small beaker inside the large beaker. Record the temperature in each beaker every 30 seconds for 2 minutes.

**MATERIALS**

- 500 mL beaker
- hot tap water
- 200 mL beaker
- cold water
- 2 thermometers
- stopwatch

**WHAT DO YOU THINK?**

- How did the water temperature in each beaker change?
- In which direction did energy flow? How do you know?

## Heat flow is a transfer of energy.

Think about what you might do to keep warm on a cold day. You might sit next to a heater. You might also avoid being near a door that opens to the outside and lets in cold air. Now think about what you might do to keep cool on a hot day. You might wear light clothing and sit in the shade of a tree. In all of these situations, you are trying to control the flow of heat between yourself and your surroundings.

Recall that heat energy moves from a warmer object to a cooler object. You have read about how radiation transfers heat energy. There are two other ways that heat energy is transferred. One is called conduction. The other is called convection.

## Heat flow by conduction requires contact.

One way that energy is transferred as heat is through direct contact between objects. **Conduction** is the process that moves energy from one object to another when they are touching. The heat energy moves from one object to another. But there is no flow of matter.

Recall that the atoms and molecules in matter are always moving. The average energy of motion of particles in the warmer object is greater than that of the particles in the cooler object. When particles collide, or bump into each other, some of the energy of motion of faster-moving particles is transferred to slower-moving particles. Therefore, energy is transferred from the warmer object to the cooler object. As long as the objects are touching, conduction continues until the temperatures of the objects are equal.

Conduction can also occur within a single object. In this case, energy is transferred from the warmer part of the object to the cooler part of the object by heat flow. Suppose you put a metal spoon into a cup of hot cocoa. Energy will be conducted from the warm end of the spoon in the cocoa to the cool end until the temperature of the entire spoon is the same.

**SUPPORTING MAIN IDEAS** Use this diagram to help you take note on how heat flows by conduction.

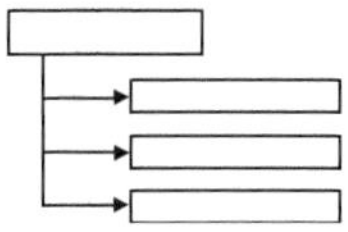

**CHECK YOUR READING** How is energy transferred by conduction?

Conduction transfers energy from the cocoa to the mug and through the gloves to the person's hands.

Some materials transfer heat flow by conduction better than others. Materials that transfer energy easily are called conductors. Metals are typically good conductors. You know that when one end of a metal object gets hot, the other end quickly becomes hot as well. Consider a saucepan that has a metal handle. After the pan has been placed on a stove that has been turned on, the handle might become quite hot. You would use something to protect your hand when you held the handle.

Materials that are poor conductors are called insulators. Some examples of insulators are wood and paper. Air is also a poor conductor of heat energy. Many materials that are insulators have a large amount of trapped air inside them. Consider a cup made of plastic foam. It contains many open spaces within it that are filled with trapped air. A plastic foam cup will not easily transfer energy by conduction. As a result, plastic foam is often used to keep cold drinks cold and hot drinks hot.

Think about the handle of the pan mentioned above. Often, the handle is not made of metal, a good conductor. Instead, it is made of a material that is an insulator, such as wood or plastic. Although a wood or plastic handle will get hot when the pan is on a stove, it takes a much longer time for wood or plastic to get hot compared with a metal handle.

## Heat flow by convection involves a flow of matter.

Energy can also be transferred through the movement of gases or liquids. **Convection** is the process that transfers energy from place to place by the motion of a gas or liquid. Recall that in conduction, atoms and molecules in objects move over tiny distances and transfer energy by touching other atoms and molecules. The particles themselves do not flow. In convection, the atoms and molecules do move, and they transfer energy over much greater distances. That is why convection occurs only in materials that are able to flow. Materials that are able to flow are called fluids.

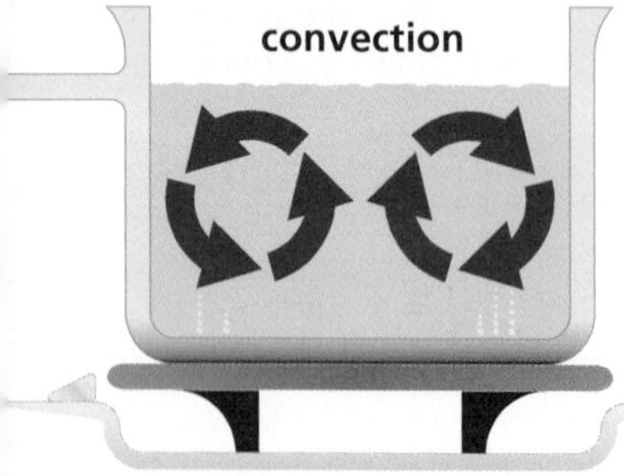


Liquid is heated at the bottom of a pan. The hot liquid rises, carrying heat energy with it in the process of convection. Cooler liquid sinks to take the place of the rising liquid.

You can see convection when you watch a boiling pan of soup on a stove. The stove heats the bottom of the pan, which then heats the soup that is in contact with it by conduction. But then the hot soup rises toward the top of the pan, carrying heat energy with it. It's easy to see small pieces of vegetables or other soup ingredients being carried by the movement of the soup. The movement of hot soup is an example of energy transfer by convection.

**CHECK YOUR READING** How is convection different from conduction?

### Density

What causes the hot soup to rise toward the top of the pan? The answer involves density. Before you can continue to explore convection, you need to understand density.

A substance's **density** is a measure of the amount of mass it contains per unit volume. A substance that has a higher density has more mass in a particular volume, or amount of space. Consider a tennis ball and a baseball. They are about the same size—they have a similar volume. But the baseball weighs more than the tennis ball. The baseball has more mass and so is more dense.

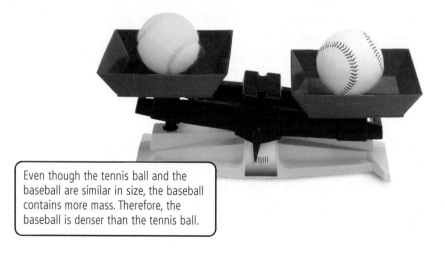

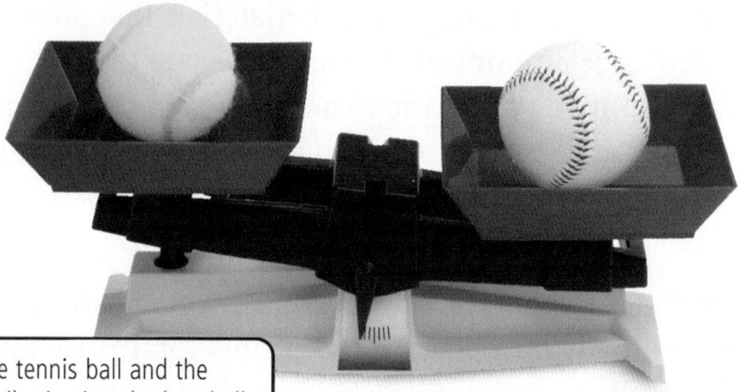

Even though the tennis ball and the baseball are similar in size, the baseball contains more mass. Therefore, the baseball is denser than the tennis ball.

You can use a simple method to compare the densities of a solid and a liquid, or two liquids. You can check to see which one floats on the other. Suppose you drop a small piece of wood and a small piece of rock into a bowl of water. The wood floats because it is less dense than water. The rock sinks because it is more dense than water. Similarly, oil floats on water because oil is less dense than water.

## Changes in Density

The density of a substance changes as its temperature changes. The density of a solid object does not change much when the object gets warmer or cooler. Because the atoms and molecules of a solid object are tightly held together, the object's volume cannot change much. But the atoms and molecules of a liquid are more free to move. The density of a liquid can change quite a bit as its temperature changes.

Consider what happens as a liquid changes in temperature. When the liquid becomes warmer, its molecules move faster. The motion makes the molecules collide more, so they stay farther apart. When there is more space between molecules, the liquid is less dense. When the liquid becomes cooler, its molecules move more slowly. The molecules collide less, so they stay closer together. The liquid becomes more dense.

## INVESTIGATE Density

### *Why do liquids form layers?*

**PROCEDURE**

1. Insert the straw into one of the solutions. Cover the top of the straw with your finger and then remove the straw from the solution.The liquid should stay in the straw.
2. Using this method, try to layer the three liquids in your straw so that you can see three separate layers.
3. Experiment with the order in which you place the liquids into the straw. Between trials, empty the contents of the straw into the waste cup.

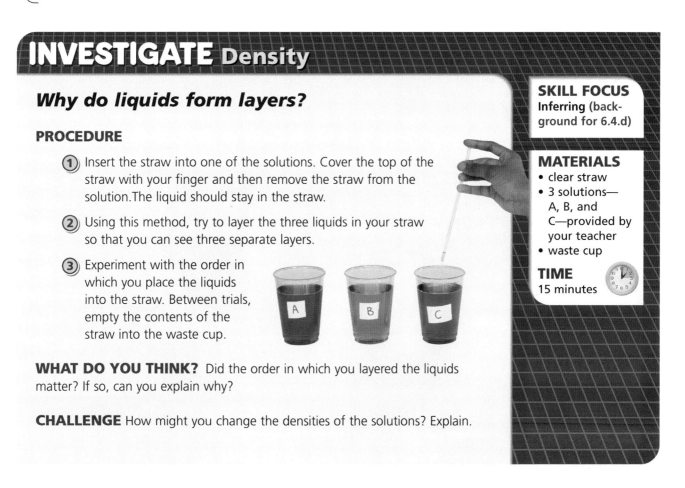

**WHAT DO YOU THINK?** Did the order in which you layered the liquids matter? If so, can you explain why?

**CHALLENGE** How might you change the densities of the solutions? Explain.

**SKILL FOCUS**
Inferring (background for 6.4.d)

**MATERIALS**
- clear straw
- 3 solutions—A, B, and C—provided by your teacher
- waste cup

**TIME**
15 minutes

## Density and Convection Currents

RESOURCE CENTER
CLASSZONE.COM
Find out more about convection currents.

Differences in density within a liquid or gas can produce the motion of convection. As a gas or liquid becomes warmer and less dense, it tends to rise. As it becomes cooler and more dense, it tends to sink. This motion can form a convection current. A **convection current** is a pattern of movement that occurs when a gas or liquid rises as it becomes warmer in one area and sinks as it becomes cooler in another area. The current flows in a continuous loop.

The illustration below shows a convection current in the atmosphere. During the day, energy from the Sun heats Earth's surface. The warm surface heats the air in contact with it by conduction.

**READING TIP**

As you read about the cycle that causes a convection current to form, follow the steps in the illustration below. Note that ● = particle of air.

1. As the air is heated, its molecules move farther apart. The warm air becomes less dense, so it rises. As the air rises into the atmosphere, it begins to cool. It will stop rising when it is no longer warmer and less dense than the air above it.
2. As the air continues to cool, its molecules get closer together. The cool air begins to sink when it becomes denser than the warmer air beneath it.
3. Cool, dense air sinks and flows sideways to replace the warm, rising air. When the cooler air becomes warmed by contact with Earth's surface, it will rise too.

### Convection

**A convection current flows in a continuous loop.**

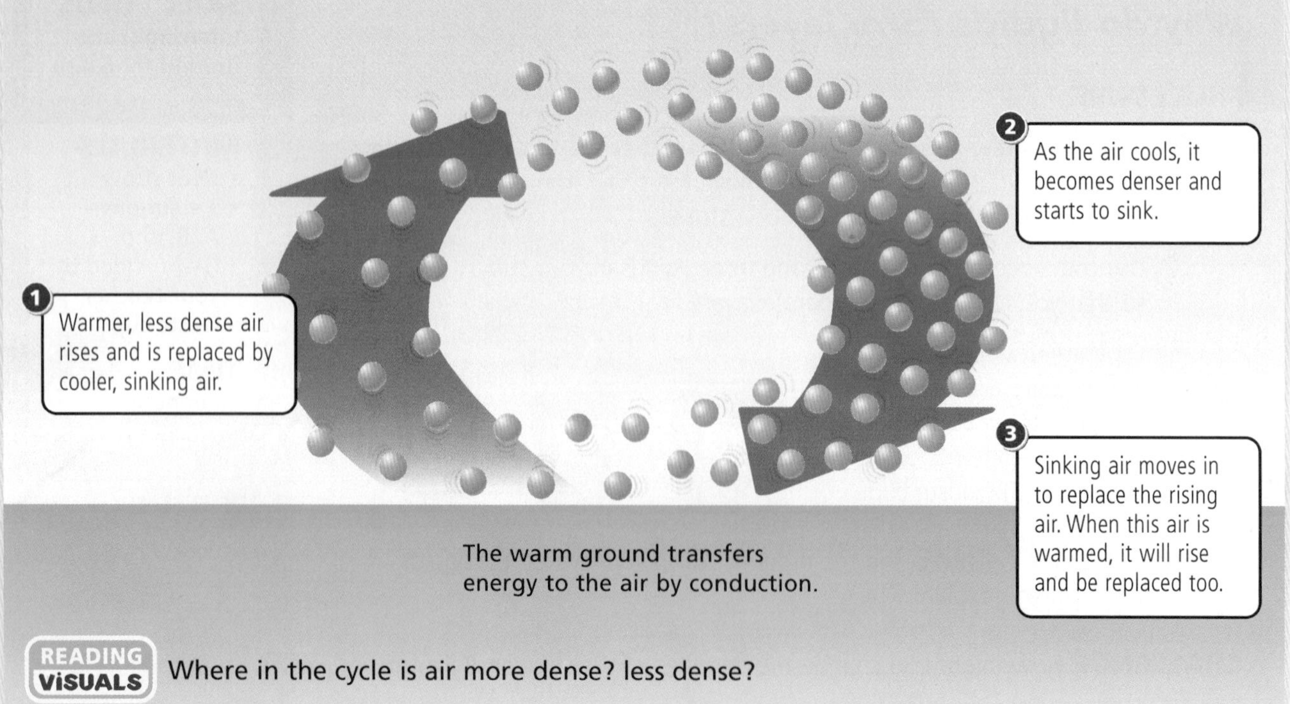

1 Warmer, less dense air rises and is replaced by cooler, sinking air.
2 As the air cools, it becomes denser and starts to sink.
3 Sinking air moves in to replace the rising air. When this air is warmed, it will rise and be replaced too.
The warm ground transfers energy to the air by conduction.

**READING VISUALS** Where in the cycle is air more dense? less dense?

Convection currents in liquids are similar to those in the atmosphere. Warm water is less dense than cold water, so warm water tends to rise and cold water tends to sink. Consider what happens in a lake as the seasons change throughout a year.

## Lake Turnover

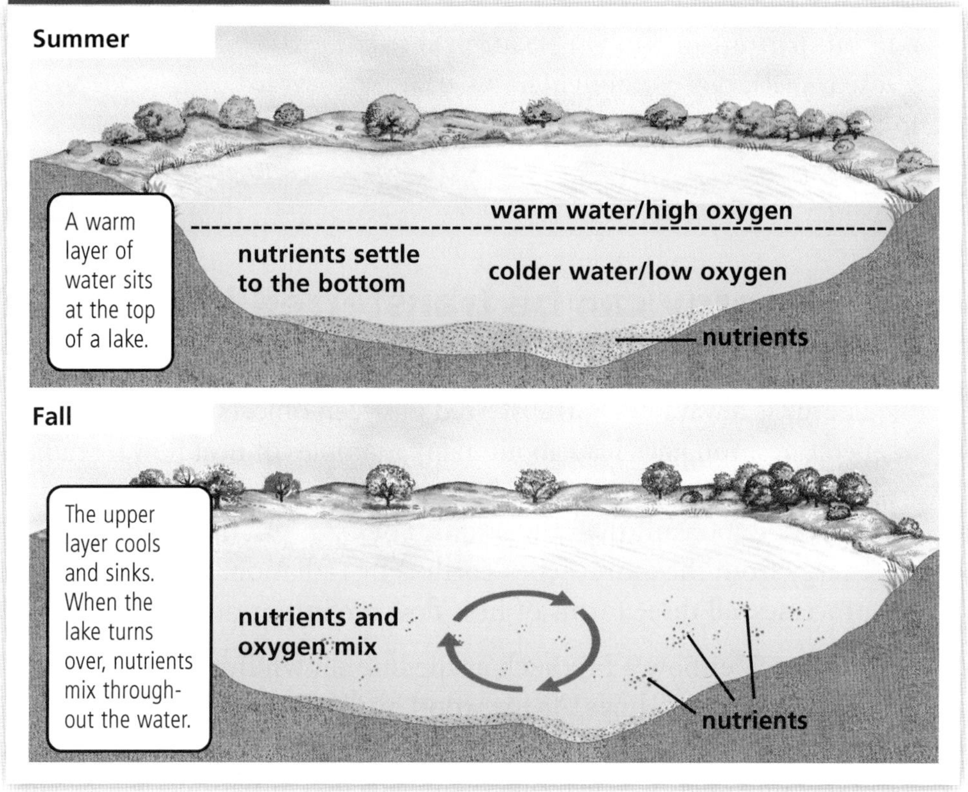
Summer
A warm layer of water sits at the top of a lake.
warm water/high oxygen
nutrients settle to the bottom
colder water/low oxygen
nutrients
Fall
The upper layer cools and sinks. When the lake turns over, nutrients mix throughout the water.
nutrients and oxygen mix
nutrients

In the spring and summer, sunlight can warm a layer of water at the surface of the lake. The layer of warm water is less dense than the layer of cooler water beneath it. The layers of water do not mix easily, and no convection currents form.

The layering of water in the lake affects the organisms that live in it. The layer of warm water is likely to be high in oxygen because it is in contact with the air. Fish may be more plentiful in the upper part of the lake. The layer of cold water is likely to be low in oxygen. But it is likely to be higher in nutrients needed by many of the organisms.

In the fall, the air becomes cooler. The water in contact with the air becomes cooler too. The water loses heat energy to the air above it through conduction. The upper layer of water becomes denser than the water underneath it. As the dense water sinks, warmer water rises to the top of the lake. It too becomes cool and sinks. Convection currents form, and the water of the lake mixes. Oxygen and nutrients become more evenly distributed. Convection stops when the water at the top of the lake is about the same temperature as the air.

The fire warms its surroundings in three ways. It gives off infrared radiation. It warms the air around it by conduction. The warmed air helps heat the room by convection.

## Heat energy can be transferred in different ways at the same time.

**SIMULATION**
CLASSZONE.COM
Find out more about convection currents.

Energy is always being transferred between objects at different temperatures. You have read about many examples of heat flow by radiation, conduction, and convection. In some processes, one type of heat flow is more important than the others. For example, the only way that energy from the Sun reaches Earth is by radiation. However, in many processes, all three forms of heat flow are important.

Consider how a fire, such as the one shown in the photograph, heats its surroundings. As the wood burns, it gives off energy in the form of radiation. Some of this energy is light energy, and some of it is infrared energy. When objects absorb this radiation, they become warmer. Heat from the fire is also transferred by conduction. The hot coals that fall through the grate warm the stone they are in contact with. The fire also warms the air around it by conduction. This warmed air then moves through the room and heats it by convection.

## 1.3 Review

### KEY CONCEPTS

1. What are three ways in which energy can be transferred as heat? Give an example of each. (6.3.c, 6.3.d)
2. How is heat transferred by conduction? (6.3.c)
3. Explain how density is involved in convection. (6.4.d)

### CRITICAL THINKING

4. **Analyze** A wool sweater traps air against your body. Is wool a good conductor? Explain.
5. **Synthesize** If you pour out some of the water in a bucket, does the density of the remaining water change? Explain.

### CHALLENGE

6. **Infer** Explain why it is incorrect to say that insulation "keeps out the cold."

SCIENCE on the JOB

# CHEF

## Cooking and Heat

6.3.c Students know heat flows in solids by conduction (which involves no flow of matter) and in fluids by conduction and by convection (which involves flow of matter).

A chef makes many decisions about cooking a meal based on heat and temperature. The appropriate temperature and cooking method must be used. A chef must calculate the cooking time of each part of the meal so that everything is finished at the same time. A chef also needs to understand how heat moves through food. For example, if an oven temperature is too hot, meat can be overcooked on the outside and undercooked on the inside.

### Bread vs. Meat

Chefs have to understand how heat energy is transferred to different foods. For example, the fluffy texture of bread comes from pockets of gas that separate its fibers. The gas is a poor conductor of energy. Therefore, more energy and a longer cooking time are needed to cook bread than to cook an equal amount of meat.

### What Temperature?

Eggs cook very differently under different temperatures. For example, temperature is important when baking meringue, which is made of egg whites and sugar. A Key lime pie topped with meringue is baked at 400°F to make a meringue that is soft. However, meringue baked at 275°F makes light and crisp dessert shells.

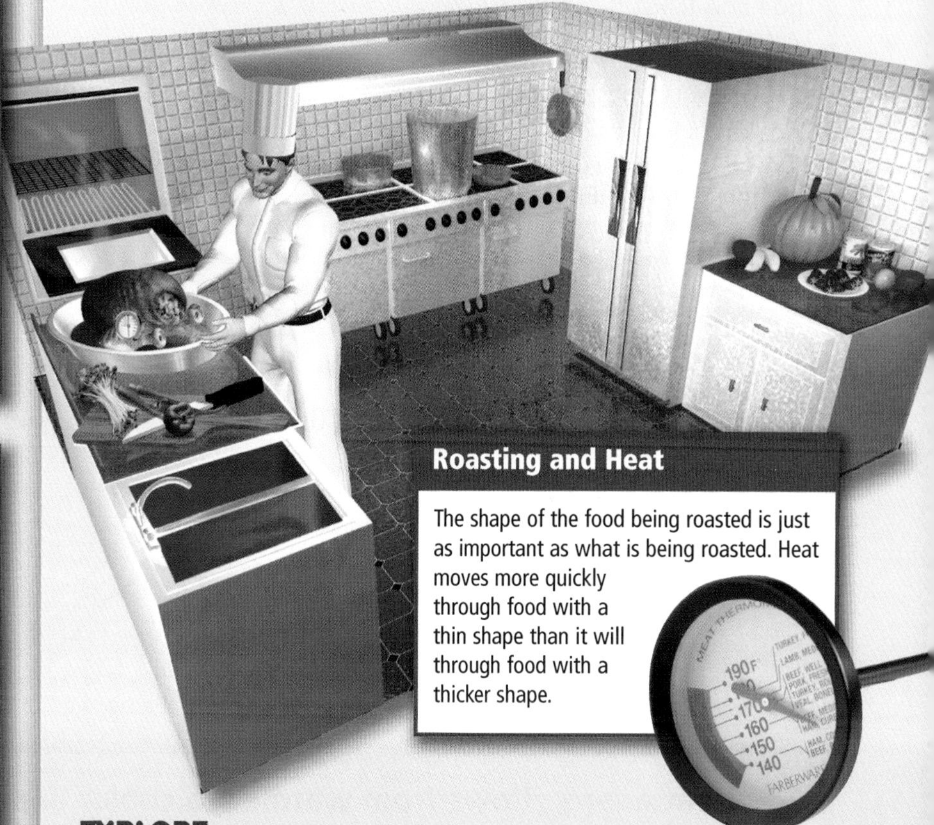


### Roasting and Heat

The shape of the food being roasted is just as important as what is being roasted. Heat moves more quickly through food with a thin shape than it will through food with a thicker shape.

### EXPLORE

1. **COMPARE** Using a cookbook, find the oven temperatures for baking biscuits, potatoes, and beef. Could you successfully cook a roast and biscuits in the oven at the same time?
2. **CHALLENGE** Crack open three eggs. Lightly beat one egg in each of three separate bowls. Follow the steps below.
   1. Heat about two cups of water to 75°C in a small pan.
   2. Pour one of the eggs into the water in the pan.
   3. Observe the egg and record your observations.
   4. Repeat steps 1–3 twice, once with boiling water and then with room-temperature water.

   Describe the differences that you observed among the three eggs. What may account for these differences?

# 1 Chapter Review

## the BIG idea

**Waves and heat flow transfer energy.**

CONTENT REVIEW
CLASSZONE.COM

## KEY CONCEPTS SUMMARY

### 1 Change occurs as energy is transferred.

- Energy is the ability to cause a change.
- Different forms of energy produce changes in different ways.
- All living things require energy.
- Work transfers energy.

Energy from sunlight is transferred to plants and then to animals.

**VOCABULARY**
**energy** p. 9
**heat energy** p. 10
**temperature** p. 10
**heat flow** p. 11
**conservation of energy** p. 14
**work** p. 15

### 2 Radiation transfers energy.

Radiation is energy that travels in the form of electromagnetic waves. A wavelength is the distance between one wave crest or trough and the next.

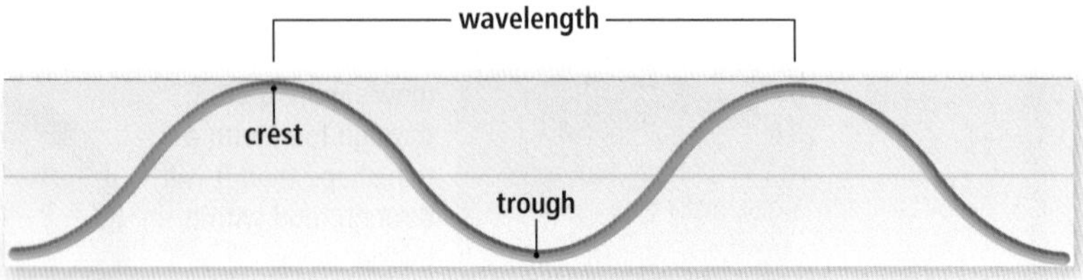


**VOCABULARY**
**radiation** p. 18
**wave** p. 19
**wavelength** p. 20
**electromagnetic spectrum** p. 21

### 3 Heat energy flows from warmer to cooler areas.

Conduction transfers energy by direct contact. Energy from the cocoa is transferred to the mug, to the gloves, and then to the person's hands.

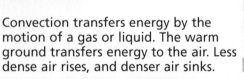

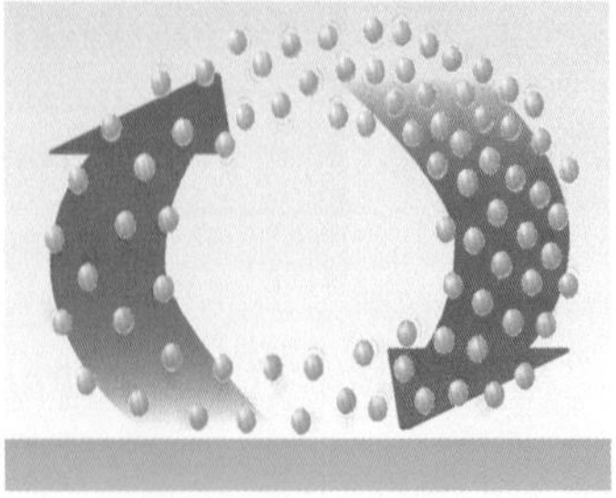

Convection transfers energy by the motion of a gas or liquid. The warm ground transfers energy to the air. Less dense air rises, and denser air sinks.

**VOCABULARY**
**conduction** p. 27
**convection** p. 28
**density** p. 28
**convection current** p. 30

## Reviewing Vocabulary

*Copy and complete the chart below. If the right column is blank, give a brief description or definition. If the left column is blank, give the correct term.*

| Term | Description |
|---|---|
| **1.** temperature | |
| **2.** | the ability to cause change |
| **3.** heat energy | |
| **4.** | a disturbance that carries energy from one place to another |
| **5.** conduction | |
| **6.** | law stating energy can change form but is never created or destroyed |
| **7.** | the use of force to move an object some distance |
| **8.** radiation | |
| **9.** | a measure of the amount of mass a substance contains |
| **10.** convection current | |
| **11.** | the distance between one wave crest and the next |
| **12.** | the range of all types of electromagnetic energy |
| **13.** convection | |

## Reviewing Key Concepts

**Multiple Choice** *Choose the letter of the best answer.*

**14.** When energy changes from one form to another, what is usually produced?

**a.** chemical energy
**b.** sound energy
**c.** heat energy
**d.** mechanical energy

**15.** Energy from the Sun travels to Earth as (6.3.d)

**a.** radiation
**b.** sound energy
**c.** conduction
**d.** mechanical energy

**16.** Which type of energy is stored in food?

**a.** sound
**b.** mechanical
**c.** chemical
**d.** electromagnetic

**17.** Which type of energy includes visible light, x-rays, and microwaves? (6.4.b)

**a.** sound
**b.** mechanical
**c.** chemical
**d.** electromagnetic

**Short Answer** *Write a short answer to each question.*

**18.** What is the difference between heat and temperature?

**19.** Explain why energy cannot travel by conduction through empty space. (6.3.c)

**20.** What are the parts of a wave? Copy the drawing below onto your paper, and label each part.

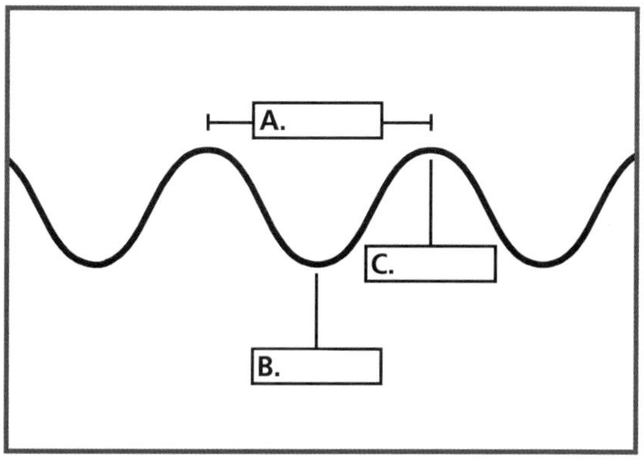

## Thinking Critically

*The illustration below shows heat energy being transferred as a pot is heated on a stove. Use the illustration to answer the next five questions.*

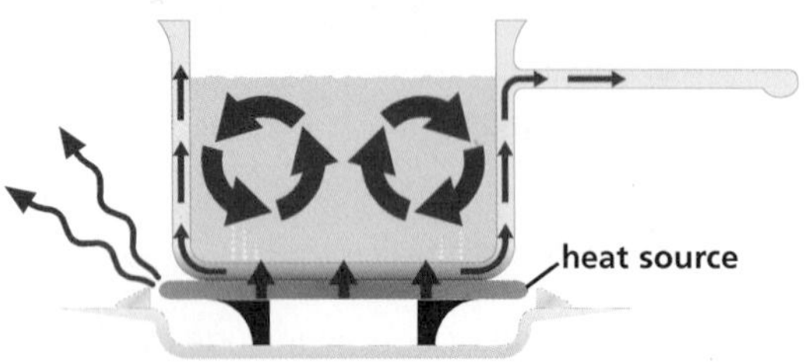


21. **OBSERVE** What process do the thick arrows in the liquid show? (6.3.c)

22. **OBSERVE** What process do the thin arrows along the sides of the pot show? (6.3.c)

23. **APPLY** By what process is heat energy being transferred from the stove to the pot? (6.3.c)

24. **APPLY** Use your understanding of density to explain the motion of the liquid inside the pot. (6.3.c)

25. **COMPARE AND CONTRAST** How is the radiation from the hot stove similar to radiation from the Sun? (6.3.d)

26. **DRAW CONCLUSIONS** Suppose you are outdoors on a hot day and you move into the shade of a tree. Which form of energy transfer are you avoiding? Which type of energy transfer might still cause you to feel hot? Explain. (6.3.d, 6.4.d)

27. **COMPARE AND CONTRAST** Draw a Venn diagram to compare and contrast conduction and convection. (6.3.c)

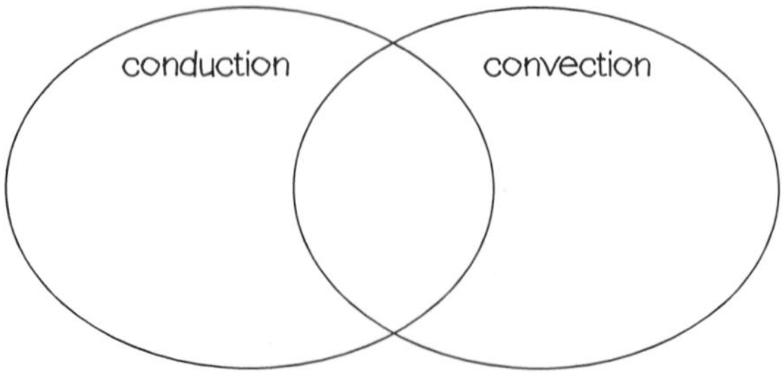


28. **COMMUNICATE** Draw a sketch that shows how visible light can be separated into different colors. (6.4.b)

29. **SYNTHESIZE** Explain how the energy stored in wood, corn, and the muscles of an animal all came originally from the Sun. (6.4.a)

30. **COMMUNICATE** Describe a process in which energy changes forms at least twice. Draw and label a diagram that shows these energy changes.

31. **SYNTHESIZE** How are plants and solar cells similar? How are the ways in which they capture sunlight and change it into other forms of energy different? Explain.

32. **INFER** Suppose you live in a hot climate. How would it help to make the roof of your home a light color?

## the BIG idea

33. **APPLY** Look again at the photograph on pages 6 and 7 and consider the opening question. How might your answer have changed after reading the chapter?

34. **COMMUNICATE** Explain the law of conservation of energy in your own words. What, if anything, about the law of conservation of energy surprised you?

## UNIT PROJECTS

If you are doing a unit project, make a folder for your project. Include in your folder a list of the resources you will need, the date on which the project is due, and a schedule to track your progress. Begin gathering data.

## Interpreting Diagrams

6.3.c

The diagrams below illustrate the process that occurs in sea and land breezes.

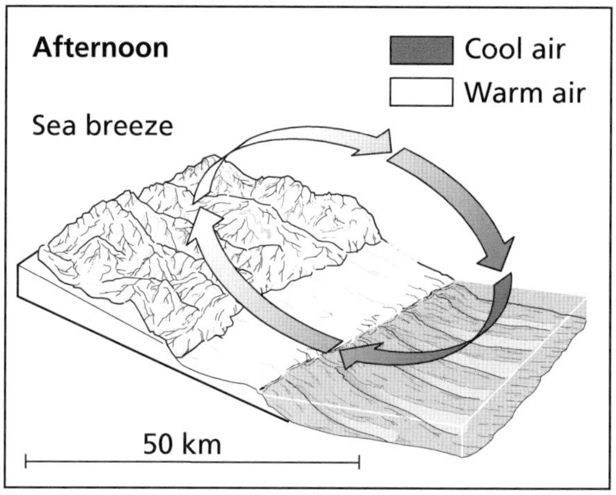


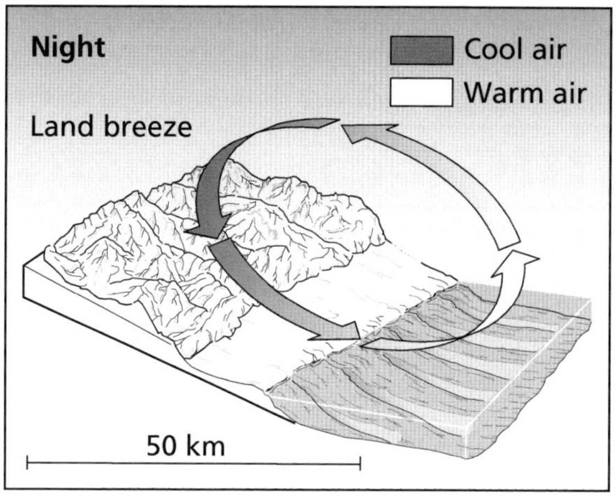


*Use the diagrams to answer the next five questions.*

1. What is a major difference between the two diagrams?
   - **a.** They show conditions in different areas.
   - **b.** They show conditions during different times of day.
   - **c.** They show conditions that transfer different types of energy.
   - **d.** They show conditions in summer and winter.
2. What happens as the surface of the land becomes warmer?
   - **a.** Its energy decreases.
   - **b.** Its particles move faster.
   - **c.** Its density increases.
   - **d.** Its rate of convection increases.
3. What process transfers energy from the warm ground to the air in contact with it?
   - **a.** convection
   - **b.** condensation
   - **c.** evaporation
   - **d.** conduction
4. Cooler air moves in to replace warmer, rising air during convection because the cooler air
   - **a.** is more dense
   - **b.** has more energy
   - **c.** is less dense
   - **d.** has less energy
5. About how far over water does this land breeze extend?
   - **a.** 1 kilometer
   - **b.** 10 kilometers
   - **c.** 25 kilometers
   - **d.** 50 kilometers

## Extended Response

*Answer the two questions below in detail.*

6. If a puddle of water is frozen, do particles in the ice have any heat energy? Explain.
7. Suppose you place two spoons—one of metal and one of wood—into a cup filled with hot water. The bowl end of the spoon is inside the cup and the handle is sticking up into the air. On each handle, you place a bead, held to the spoon by a dab of margarine. From which spoon will the bead fall first, and why?

CHAPTER 2

# Energy in the Earth System

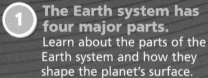

## the BIG idea

**The Sun is the major source of energy for Earth's atmosphere and surface.**

## Key Concepts

SECTION 1
**The Earth system has four major parts.**
Learn about the parts of the Earth system and how they shape the planet's surface.

SECTION 2
**The Sun provides energy to the Earth system.**
Learn how uneven heating of Earth by the Sun is one cause of the seasons.

SECTION 3
**Energy is transferred within the Earth system.**
Learn how solar energy powers the water cycle and affects weather and climate.

**California ClassZone**

CLASSZONE.COM

Chapter 2 online resources: Content Review, three Visualizations, three Resource Centers, Math Tutorial, Test Practice

**Which parts of the Earth system are shown here? How does energy from the Sun affect them?**

# EXPLORE the BIG idea

## How Does Heating Affect Air?

6.3.c Students know heat flows in solids by conduction (which involves no flow of matter) and in fluids by conduction and by convection (which involves flow of matter).

Stretch the lip of a balloon over the neck of a small bottle. Next, fill a bowl with ice water and a second bowl with hot tap water. Place the bottle upright in the hot water. After 5 minutes, move the bottle to the cold water.

**Observe and Think** What changes did you observe in the balloon? What might have caused these changes?

## How Fast Does It Chill?

6.3.a Students know energy can be carried from one place to another by heat flow or by waves, including water, light and sound waves, or by moving objects.

Place an outdoor thermometer in an empty paper cup, and place the cup in a freezer. Check the thermometer every three minutes and record the time it takes for the temperature to reach 0°C (32°F). Remove the cup from the freezer. After it returns to room temperature, fill the cup with soil and repeat the experiment.

**Observe and Think** How long did it take for the temperature to reach 0°C each time? Why might there have been a difference?

NSTA scilinks.org SCILINKS
What Is Climate? **Code: MDL012**

CHAPTER 2

# Getting Ready to Learn

## CONCEPT REVIEW

- Energy is the ability to cause change.
- There are different forms of energy.
- Energy flows from warmer areas to cooler areas.

## VOCABULARY REVIEW

**energy** p. 9
**temperature** p. 10
**heat energy** p. 10
**radiation** p. 18
**conduction** p. 27
**convection** p. 28

**CONTENT REVIEW**
CLASSZONE.COM

Review concepts and vocabulary.

## TAKING NOTES

### OUTLINE

As you read, copy the headings onto your paper in the form of an outline. Then add notes in your own words that summarize what you read.

### VOCABULARY STRATEGY

Write each new vocabulary term in the center of a **frame game** diagram. Decide what information to frame the term with. Use examples, descriptions, pictures, or sentences that use the term in context.

See the Note-Taking Handbook on pages R45–R51.

SCIENCE NOTEBOOK

I. The Earth system has four major parts.
  A. The parts of the Earth system are connected.
    1. Atmosphere
      a.
      b.
    2. Hydrosphere
      a.
      b.
    3. Biosphere
      a.
      b.

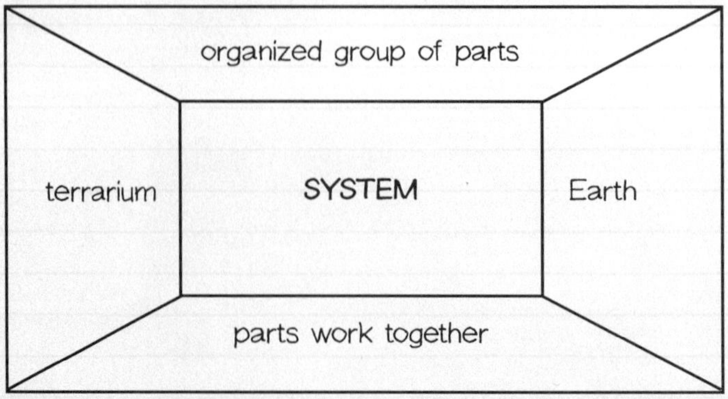

KEY CONCEPT

# 2.1 The Earth system has four major parts.

**CALIFORNIA Content Standards**

**6.1.b** Students know Earth is composed of several layers: a cold, brittle lithosphere; a hot, convecting mantle; and a dense, metallic core.

**6.2.d** Students know earthquakes, volcanic eruptions, landslides, and floods change human and wildlife habitats.

**BEFORE, you learned**

- Waves, heat flow, and the movement of matter transfer energy
- Radiation can travel through matter and empty space
- Conduction transfers heat between objects in contact

**NOW, you will learn**

- About the parts of the Earth system
- How the parts of the Earth system interact
- How the parts of the Earth system shape the planet's surface

**VOCABULARY**

**system** p. 41
**cycle** p. 44

**THINK ABOUT**

***How do these parts work together?***

Look closely at this terrarium. Notice that the bowl and its cover form a boundary between the terrarium and the outside world. What might happen to the entire terrarium if any part were taken away? What might happen if you placed the terrarium in a dark closet?

## The parts of the Earth system are connected.

**VOCABULARY**
Remember to make a frame game diagram for each vocabulary term.

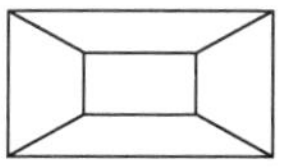

A terrarium is a simple example of a **system**—an organized group of parts that work together to form a whole. To understand a system, you need to see how all its parts work together. This is true for a small terrarium, and it is true for planet Earth.

Both a terrarium and Earth are closed systems. They are closed because matter, such as soil or water, cannot enter or leave. However, energy can flow into or out of the systems. Light and heat can pass through the glass of the terrarium. In the same way, sunlight and heat enter and leave the Earth system through the atmosphere.

The Earth system is made up of four connected parts. These parts are the atmosphere (Earth's air), the hydrosphere (Earth's waters), the biosphere (Earth's living things), and the geosphere (Earth's interior and its rocks and sediments). Each of these parts is an open system because both matter and energy move into and out of it. The four open systems work together to form one large, closed system called Earth.

## Atmosphere

**READING TIP**

The names of the Earth system's four parts contain Greek prefixes. *Atmo-* refers to vapor or gas. *Hydro-* refers to water. *Bio-* refers to life, and *geo-* refers to earth.

The atmosphere (AT-muh-SFEER) is the mixture of gases and particles that surrounds and protects the surface of Earth. Nitrogen makes up about 78 percent of the gases. Oxygen makes up nearly 21 percent. The atmosphere also contains carbon dioxide, water vapor, and other gases.

Understanding the atmosphere can help people in their everyday lives. This is because weather, which occurs in the lower atmosphere, affects many things around us. Scientists collect data about what is happening in the atmosphere. The data show that the atmosphere interacts with the other parts of the Earth system to form weather patterns. The more scientists learn about these patterns, the better they can predict local weather.

## Hydrosphere

The hydrosphere (HY-druh-SFEER) is made up of all the water on Earth in the air, the ocean, lakes, glaciers, rivers and streams, and underground. Water covers nearly three-fourths of Earth's surface. Ocean water is salt water. Only about 3 percent of the hydrosphere is fresh water. About 80 percent of the fresh water is frozen in glaciers and polar ice caps.

### Parts of the Earth System

**Atmosphere**

Over 400 cones make this weather balloon more stable as it gathers data about the atmosphere.

**Hydrosphere**

This scuba diver uses special equipment to study a kelp forest off the coast of California.

Scientists use deep-sea vehicles, special buoys, and satellite images to study the ocean. They have discovered that the ocean contains many currents. Currents at the surface of the ocean are set in motion by winds blowing over the water. Surface currents affect weather patterns. An example of this is when a warm-water current brings heat to nearby land. A current can also carry nutrients long distances. It can provide resources to fish and other ocean organisms.

**CHECK YOUR READING** How does the hydrosphere affect the atmosphere?

**OUTLINE**
As you read, remember to take notes in outline form.

I. Main idea
  A. Supporting idea
    1. Detail
    2. Detail
  B. Supporting idea

## Biosphere

The biosphere (BY-uh-SFEER) includes all life on Earth—in the air, on the land, and in the waters. Most animals need oxygen from the atmosphere and water from the hydrosphere. Plants need nutrients from the soil or the geosphere, water from the hydrosphere, and carbon dioxide and oxygen from the atmosphere.

Scientists have learned a lot about how the biosphere interacts with the other parts of the Earth system. For example, large forests act as Earth's "lungs." Trees absorb carbon dioxide and release oxygen into the atmosphere. When dead trees decay, they return nutrients to the soil.

**CHECK YOUR READING** Name one way the biosphere and the atmosphere act together.

**Biosphere**

These platforms, built in treetops, are used to observe forest plants and animals.

**Geosphere**

In mines dug deep underground, scientists can explore Earth's minerals and rocks.

## Geosphere

RESOURCE CENTER
CLASSZONE.COM

Find out more about the Earth system.

The geosphere (JEE-uh-SFEER) includes all the features on Earth's surface—the continents, islands, and sea floor. It also includes everything below the surface. As the diagram shows, the geosphere is made up of several layers: crust, mantle, outer core, and inner core. The lithosphere is made up of the crust and the uppermost mantle. You will read more about the lithosphere in Chapter 8.

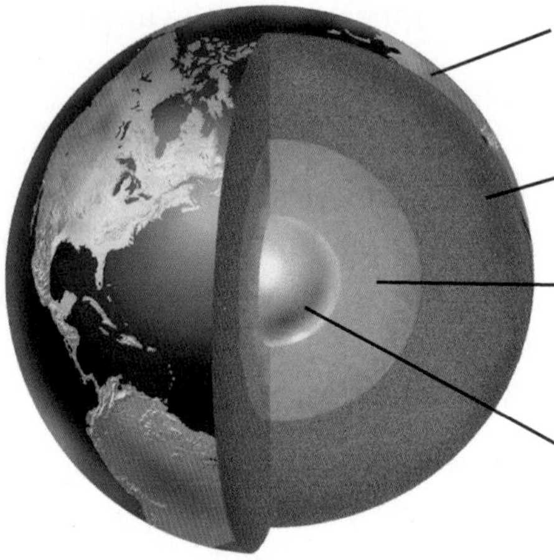
**crust:** thin, rocky shell that includes continents and sea floor
**mantle:** thick layer of hot rock
**outer core:** molten metal, mostly iron
**inner core:** solid metal, mostly iron

Earth is constantly changing. Some changes, such as the pushing up of mountain ranges, happen over millions of years. Other changes are sudden. An example is when a volcano erupts, sends gases into the air, and covers nearby land with lava. Some changes happen in a repeating pattern, or cycle. A **cycle** is a series of events or actions that repeats over and over. For example, rocks are slowly forming, changing, breaking apart, and re-forming in a set of processes called the rock cycle.

CHECK YOUR READING Give an example of matter moving from the geosphere to the atmosphere.

Earth's surface has many landforms, such as these rock formations in Joshua Tree National Park in California.

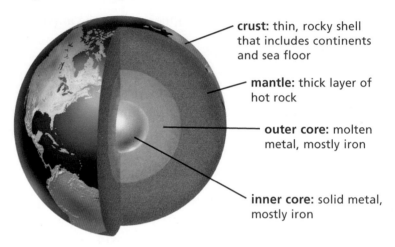

# INVESTIGATE The Geosphere's Layers

### *How can you model the geosphere's layers?*

**PROCEDURE**

1. You will be using a piece of apple that your teacher has cut to model the layers of the geosphere. Note: Never eat food in the science classroom.
2. Hold the apple slice and observe it carefully. Compare it with the diagram of the geosphere's layers on page 44.
3. Draw a diagram of the apple and label it with the names of the layers of the geosphere.

**WHAT DO YOU THINK?**

- What are the four parts of the apple slice?
- What major layer of the geosphere does each part of the apple resemble?

**CHALLENGE** What other object do you think would make a good model of the geosphere's layers? What model could you build or make yourself?

**SKILL FOCUS**
Modeling (6.1.b)

**MATERIALS**
apple slice

**TIME**
15 minutes

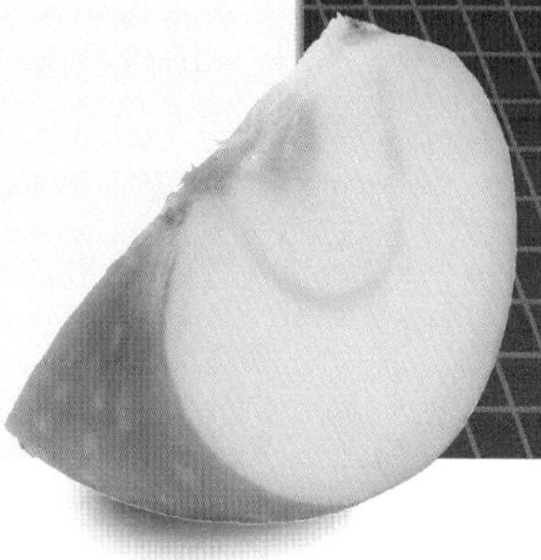

## All four parts of the Earth system shape the planet's surface.

Earth's surface is worn away, built up, and reshaped every day. The atmosphere, the hydrosphere, the biosphere, and the geosphere all shape the surface. Here are some of the ways the four parts affect the surface.

**Atmosphere and Hydrosphere** Not even the hardest rock can stand up to wind and water over time. Over millions of years, rain, wind, and flowing water carve huge formations. You can see an example of this in the photograph of Joshua Tree National Park on page 44.

**Geosphere** Landmasses pushing together have set off earthquakes and formed volcanoes and mountain ranges around the world.

**Biosphere** Plants, animals, and human beings have also changed Earth's surface. For example, earthworms help make soil richer. And throughout human history, people have dammed rivers and cleared forests for farmland.

You are part of this process too. Every time you walk or ride a bike across open land, you are changing Earth's surface. Your feet or the bike's tires dig into the ground. This can wear away plants and expose soil to sunlight, wind, and water. If you take the same route every day, over time you will wear a path in the land.

**READING TIP**
The word *landmass* is a compound word made up of the words *land* and *mass*. It means "a large area of land."

Landslide in California
Atmosphere and Hydrosphere Heavy winter rains soak the ground until it cannot absorb any more water.
Geosphere With nothing to hold the water-soaked ground, it slides downhill, leaving a deep trench.
Biosphere Homes built on hillsides replace plants whose roots help hold the soil in place.

The photograph above shows a good example of how the four parts of the Earth system can suddenly change Earth's surface. A landslide like this one can happen in a matter of minutes. Sometimes a steep slope may collapse after heavy rains. The slope can become a river of mud that can move or even bury many buildings. The landslide shown above took place in Laguna Beach, California, in 2005.

The four parts of the Earth system continue to shape the surface with every passing year. Scientists study these changes to help them understand the planet's related systems.

**CHECK YOUR READING** Give three examples of how the parts of the Earth system shape the planet's surface.

## 2.1 Review

### KEY CONCEPTS

1. Give your own example of a system and describe its parts.
2. Name the four parts of the Earth system. List one feature from each of the four parts.
3. Give two examples of your own of how Earth systems interact to shape Earth's surface. (6.2.d)

### CRITICAL THINKING

4. **Apply** Suppose you see that plants are dying in the class terrarium. What might be missing from its system?
5. **Infer** You visit a state park and see a thin rock wall with a hole, like a window, worn through it. Which of the four parts of the Earth system might have made the hole? Explain.

### CHALLENGE

6. **Predict** Imagine that a volcano erupts in a forested area. There is also a small town a few miles away from the base of the volcano. Describe one way that this event would affect the biosphere or the geosphere.

California Close-Up

EARTHQUAKE ENERGY

# An Earth-Moving Force

6.1.g Students know how to determine the epicenter of an earthquake and know that the **effects of an earthquake** on any region vary, depending on the size of the earthquake, the distance of the region from the epicenter, the local geology, and the type of construction in the region.

You've probably seen evidence of the damage done by a big earthquake in a movie or maybe even in real life. The earthquake that shook Northridge, California, in 1994 was so strong that it caused some freeway bridges and buildings to collapse.

Earthquakes aren't rare events. Thousands of earthquakes occur around the world each day. However, the shaking of the ground is usually so minor that only the most sensitive instruments can detect it.

The 1989 Loma Prieta earthquake caused the collapse of this part of Interstate 880 in Oakland.

## It All Adds Up

Hundreds of small earthquakes occur in California in a typical week. Over several years, the small earthquakes may release as much energy as one large earthquake. But if it's the same amount of energy, why are the effects so different?

Many years of frequent, small earthquakes produced the offset in this roadside curb and gutter in Hayward.

## Stress Release

An earthquake occurs when underground rocks slip against each other. If the rocks slide easily, many small slips occur. Waves called seismic waves carry the energy outward. However, small waves lose much of their energy to the rocks they move through before the waves reach the surface. Little energy is left to cause damage. But if the rocks get stuck, energy builds up until the rocks give way suddenly. The larger slip produces larger waves that shake the surface with more energy and do more damage.

Small earthquakes release underground energy a little at a time. Think of what happens if you drop a bottle of soda. If you open it quickly, the liquid bubbles and sprays out. But if you turn the cap just a little, you release the energy slowly. Small earthquakes allow energy to be released slowly, causing less damage than energy released all at once.

## WRITING ABOUT SCIENCE

Think of another example where energy can be released. It can be in small amounts over a long period of time or in large amounts in a short period of time. Your example might come from nature or everyday life. Describe the example and its effects.

KEY CONCEPT

# 2.2 The Sun provides energy to the Earth system.

**CALIFORNIA Content Standards**

**6.3.d** Students know heat energy is also transferred between objects by radiation (radiation can travel through space).

**6.4.a** Students know the sun is the major source of energy for phenomena on Earth's surface; it powers winds, ocean currents, and the water cycle.

**6.4.b** Students know solar energy reaches Earth through radiation, mostly in the form of visible light.

**BEFORE, you learned**

- The Earth system has four main parts: atmosphere, hydrosphere, biosphere, and geosphere
- The parts of the Earth system continually interact with each other
- The Earth system's parts interact to shape Earth's surface

**NOW, you will learn**

- How Earth receives energy from the Sun
- Why Earth is heated unevenly by the Sun
- Why Earth has seasons

**VOCABULARY**

**axis** p. 52

**THINK ABOUT**

***Can you feel sunlight?***

If you have been on a hot beach, you have felt energy from sunlight. Perhaps you felt sunlight warming your skin or hot sand underneath your feet. It is easy to notice the energy of sunlight when it makes the ground or your skin warm. Where else does the energy from sunlight go?

## Earth receives energy from the Sun.

**OUTLINE**
Remember to include this heading in your outline of this section.

I. Main idea
  A. Supporting idea
    1. Detail
    2. Detail
  B. Supporting idea

As you read in Chapter 1, almost all the energy around you comes from the Sun. That means food energy, fires, and even the warmth of your own body can be traced back to energy from the Sun. A lot of this energy reaches Earth in a form you can see—visible light.

Recall that some of the solar radiation that reaches Earth is reflected, or sent in a new direction. You see most of the objects around you by reflected light. The sand in the picture above looks light in color because it reflects much of the sunlight that hits it. Earth's surface also absorbs some of the sunlight that reaches it. The substance that absorbs the light energy from the Sun is heated by the energy. The sand can become warm or even hot as it absorbs some of the sunlight that hits it.

Color makes a difference in how much energy an object will absorb and how much it will reflect. Light-colored objects, such as the white shirts in the picture above, reflect more light than dark objects. The dark shirts absorb more light.

**CHECK YOUR READING** What happens to the sunlight that reaches Earth's surface?

## Reflected Solar Energy

Some surfaces reflect more sunlight than others. Lighter surfaces and objects reflect more light. For example, clouds, snow, and light-colored buildings reflect a lot of solar radiation. Dust particles and gases in the atmosphere reflect some sunlight. About 25 percent of the Sun's energy is reflected by clouds and particles in the atmosphere. Another 5 percent of solar energy is reflected by Earth's surface. The energy from the Sun that is reflected goes back into outer space.

**RESOURCE CENTER**
CLASSZONE.COM
Find out more about solar energy.

## Absorbed Solar Energy

If 30 percent of the solar energy that reaches Earth is sent back out into space, what happens to the other 70 percent? It is absorbed by Earth's atmosphere and surface. Darker objects or surfaces absorb more sunlight. About 20 percent of the solar energy is absorbed by clouds, particles, and gases in the atmosphere. This energy heats the atmosphere.

About 50 percent of the Sun's energy is absorbed by Earth's surface, as shown in the graph below. Landforms, living things, and the ocean absorb most of this energy. Energy that is absorbed by Earth's atmosphere and surface is later released and is lost to outer space. The amount of energy being absorbed by the Earth system is balanced by the amount of energy being lost. If these amounts were not balanced, Earth's average surface temperature would change over time.

### Reflected and Absorbed Energy

**This photograph of Lake Tahoe, California, shows that more sunlight is reflected from clouds, snow, and water than from trees, grass, and dark-colored rocks.**

**READING VISUALS** How much of the Sun's energy is absorbed by Earth's atmosphere and surface?

## Energy from the Sun heats Earth's surface unevenly.

**READING TIP**

A perpendicular angle is a 90° angle. A 90° angle is also called a right angle. A higher angle is closer to 90° than a lower angle is.

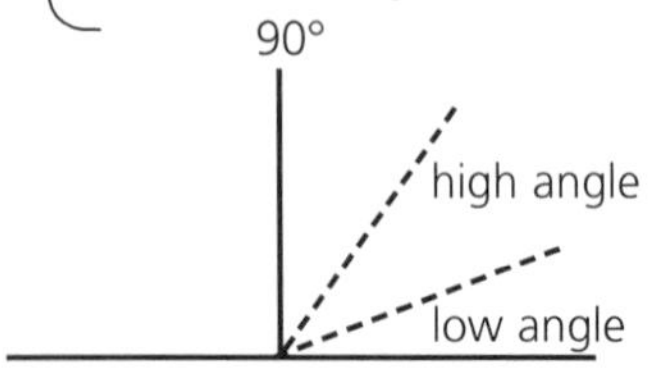
90°
high angle
low angle

Not all parts of Earth receive equal amounts of the Sun's energy. Light from the Sun hits Earth's curved surface at different angles. Sunlight hits Earth's surface at an angle that is close to perpendicular at the equator, as shown in the diagram below. Near the north and south poles, sunlight hits the surface at a much lower angle. The parts of the surface that receive sunlight at a lower angle receive less solar energy. It's like shining a flashlight on a building. Where the light from the flashlight hits the building straight on, or at a 90° angle, the light is brighter. If you shine the flashlight higher up on the building, the light hits the building at a lower angle. The light beam that hits at an angle spreads out over a larger area. A spread-out beam does not light up the surface as brightly. The same thing happens on Earth's surface because of its curved shape.

The areas on Earth's surface that receive sunlight at high angles heat up more. These areas receive more solar energy. For the same reason, you can get a sunburn faster at noon, when the Sun is highest in the sky.

**CHECK YOUR READING** Where does sunlight hit Earth at the highest angle?

### Uneven Heating

**Earth's surface receives more heat from the Sun in areas where sunlight hits the surface at high angles.**

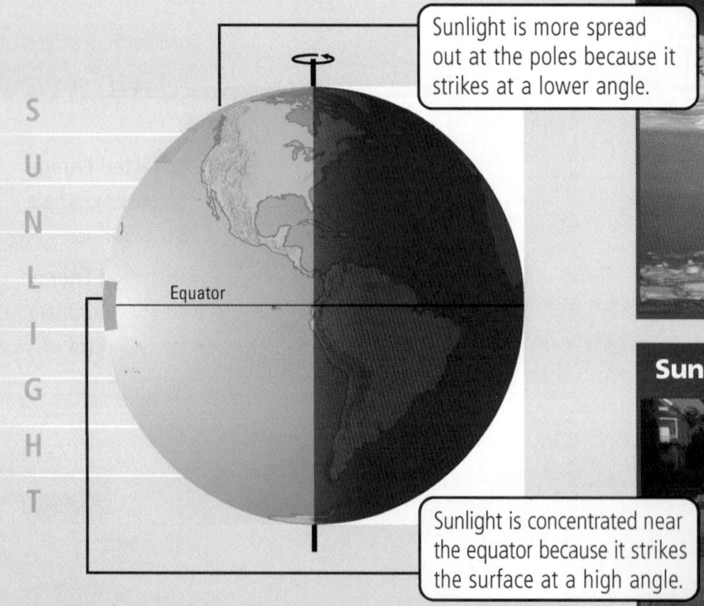
S
U
N
L
I
G
H
T
Equator
Sunlight is more spread out at the poles because it strikes at a lower angle.
Sunlight is concentrated near the equator because it strikes the surface at a high angle.

**Sunlight near the poles is spread out.**

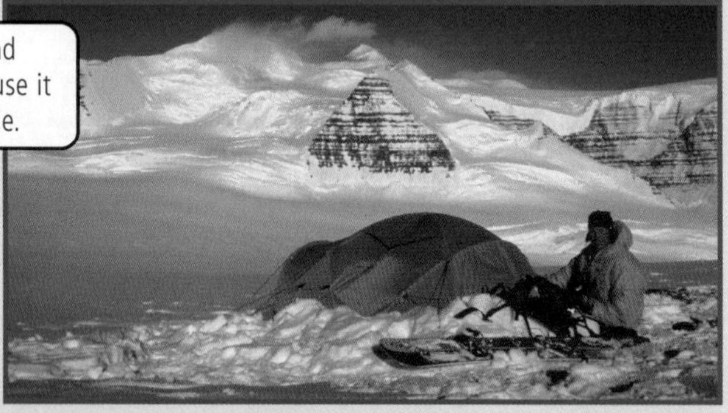

**Sunlight near the equator is concentrated.**

**READING VISUALS** How does the angle of sunlight affect the heating of Earth's surface?

# INVESTIGATE Solar Energy

### *How does the angle of light affect heating?*

**SKILL FOCUS**
Comparing (6.3.d)

**PROCEDURE**

1. Tape a black square over the bulb of each thermometer. Then tape the thermometers to the cardboard tube as shown.
2. Place the setup on a sunny windowsill or under a lamp. One square should face the light at a 90° angle. Record the temperatures.
3. Wait 10 minutes. Record the temperatures again.

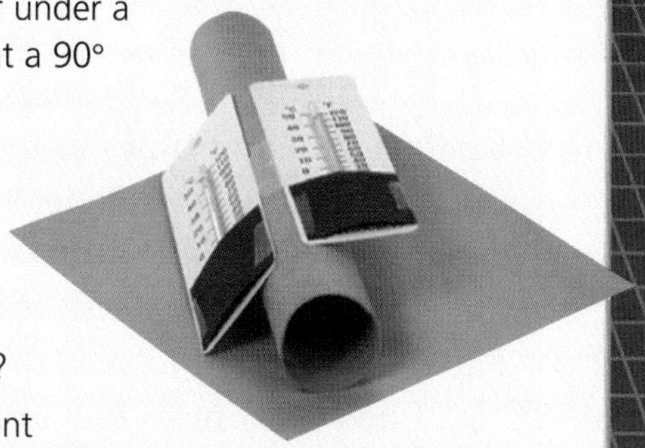

**WHAT DO YOU THINK?**

- How did the temperature readings change?
- How did the angle of light affect the amount of heat absorbed?

**CHALLENGE** How could you use the angle of light to model how the amount of solar radiation that hits Earth's surface changes with distance from the equator?

**MATERIALS**
- tape
- 2 black paper squares
- 2 thermometers
- 1 cardboard tube from a paper towel roll
- sunny windowsill or lamp

**TIME**
20 minutes

## Uneven heating is a cause of the seasons.

The unequal heating of Earth's surface by the Sun is one cause of the seasons. The four seasons are spring, summer, fall, and winter. The range of temperatures and the weather patterns are different in most places during each season. There are fewer seasonal changes near the equator. The temperature stays about the same all year. Near the poles, seasonal changes are much greater. In the winter, temperatures are much lower than during the summer. These temperature changes are caused by differences in the amount of solar energy received throughout the year.

As you have read, it is warmer in areas where sunlight hits Earth's surface at high angles. Also, it is warmer during the summer, because the amount of solar energy received is greater. What causes the amount of solar energy received from the Sun to change at different times of the year? The total amount of energy that Earth receives from the Sun does not change throughout the year. However, the areas where the most solar energy strikes Earth's surface do change. Because the amount of solar energy received by an area changes during the year, average daily temperatures also change.

**VISUALIZATION**
CLASSZONE.COM
See a visualization of why there are seasons.

**CHECK YOUR READING** What changes mark the seasons?

## Tilt of Earth's Axis

**VOCABULARY**
Remember to make a frame game diagram for *axis*.

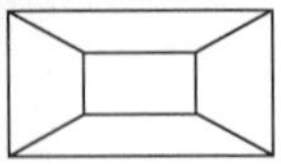

As you know, Earth rotates, or turns. The rotation causes day and night. At any time, half of Earth is facing the Sun. On the part of Earth facing the Sun, it is daylight. On the half of Earth facing away from the Sun, it is night. Earth rotates around its axis. Earth's **axis** is an imaginary line running through the center of the planet. As you can see in the illustrations on page 53, Earth's axis is not perpendicular to the plane of its orbit around the Sun. Instead, it is tilted at an angle of about 23 degrees.

This tilt of the axis causes different amounts of solar energy to hit Earth at different times of the year. As Earth revolves around the Sun, different areas of the planet are tilted toward the Sun. This results in sunlight hitting Earth's surface at different angles at different times of the year. This tilt of Earth's axis is a cause of the seasons. The part of Earth that is tilted toward the Sun receives more solar energy than the part tilted away from the Sun.

When the Northern Hemisphere is tilted toward the Sun, it is summer there. At the same time, it is winter in the Southern Hemisphere. This is because the Southern Hemisphere is tilted away from the Sun. In the same way, when it is summer in the Southern Hemisphere, it is winter in the Northern Hemisphere.

## Tropic of Cancer

In June the Northern Hemisphere is tilted toward the Sun. As a result, the Sun appears to be higher in the sky. The first day of summer in the Northern Hemisphere is June 21. This day is also the first day of winter in the Southern Hemisphere. At noon on June 21, solar energy strikes Earth's surface at right angles along an imaginary line in the Northern Hemisphere called the tropic of Cancer. You can find the tropic of Cancer in the illustrations on page 53. At all times other than June 21, the perpendicular rays of the Sun hit Earth south of the tropic of Cancer.

## Tropic of Capricorn

In December the Northern Hemisphere is tilted away from the Sun. As a result, the Sun appears to be lower in the sky. The first day of winter in the Northern Hemisphere is December 21. This is also the first day of summer in the Southern Hemisphere. At noon on December 21, solar energy strikes Earth's surface at right angles along an imaginary line in the Southern Hemisphere called the tropic of Capricorn. At all other times, the perpendicular rays of the Sun hit Earth north of the tropic of Capricorn.

## Tilt of Earth's Axis and the Seasons

**Earth's axis points in a constant direction as Earth orbits the Sun. The tilt of Earth's axis is a cause of the seasons.**

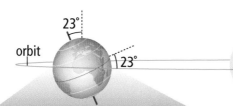

### Winter in the Northern Hemisphere and Summer in the Southern Hemisphere

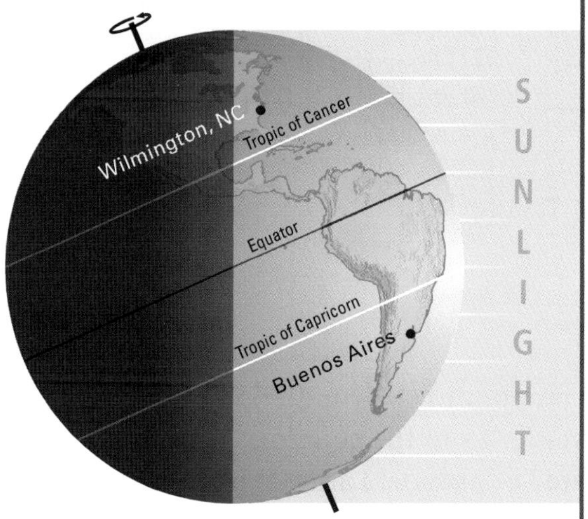


The hemisphere in which it is winter is tilted away from the Sun. When it is winter in the Northern Hemisphere, it is summer in the Southern Hemisphere.

### Summer in the Northern Hemisphere and Winter in the Southern Hemisphere

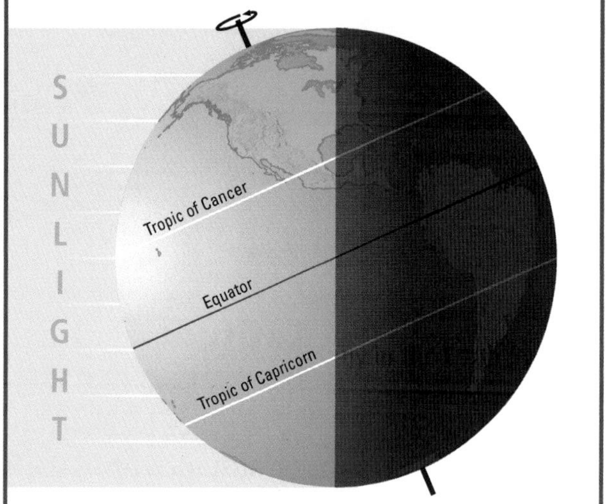


The hemisphere in which it is summer is tilted toward the Sun. When it is summer in the Northern Hemisphere, it is winter in the Southern Hemisphere.

Buenos Aires, Argentina, is in the Southern Hemisphere. Wilmington, North Carolina, is in the Northern Hemisphere. These cities are about the same distance from the equator, but their seasons are reversed. The warmest months in Buenos Aires are the coldest months in Wilmington.

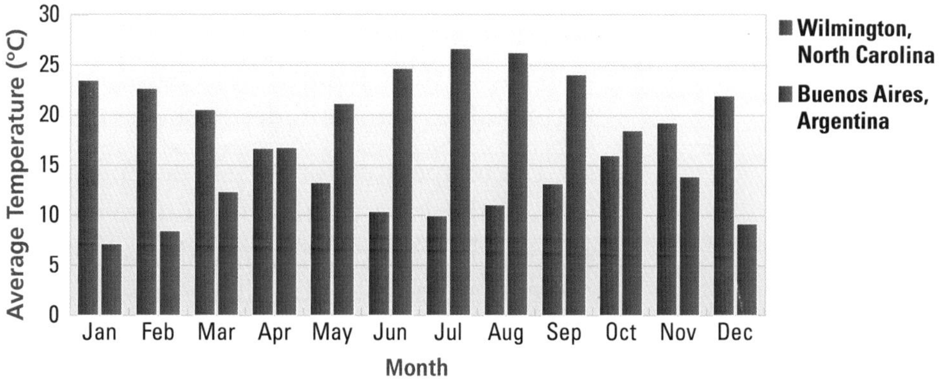


**READING VISUALS** How does the tilt of Earth's axis cause temperatures to be higher in the Northern Hemisphere during July and lower during January?

## Latitude and Temperature

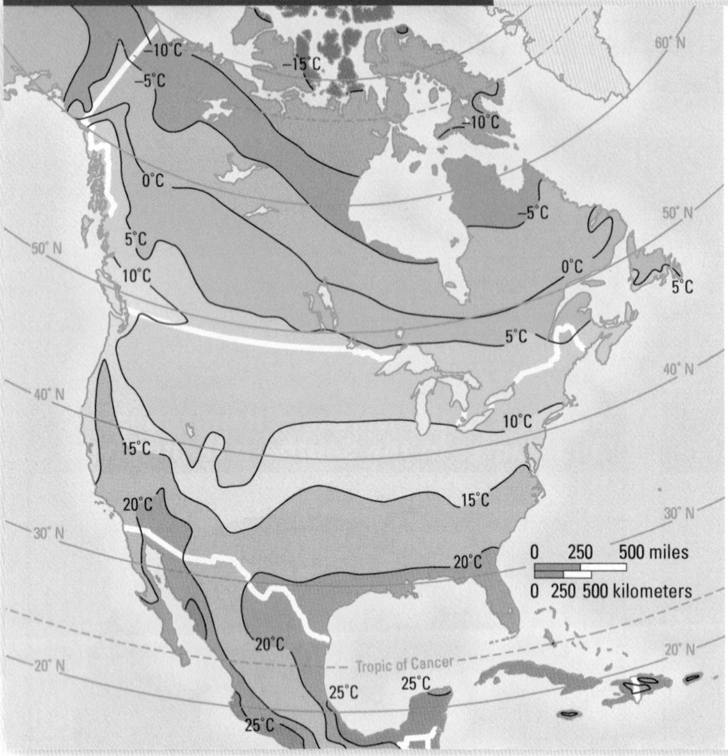


This map shows average annual temperatures in North America. Average temperatures generally decrease as you move away from the equator into higher latitudes.

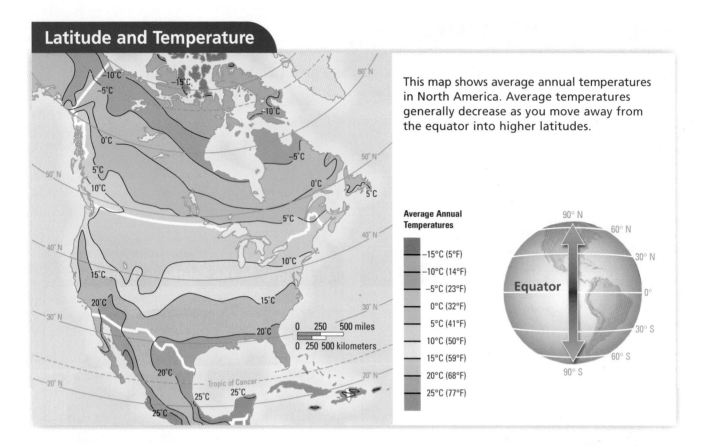

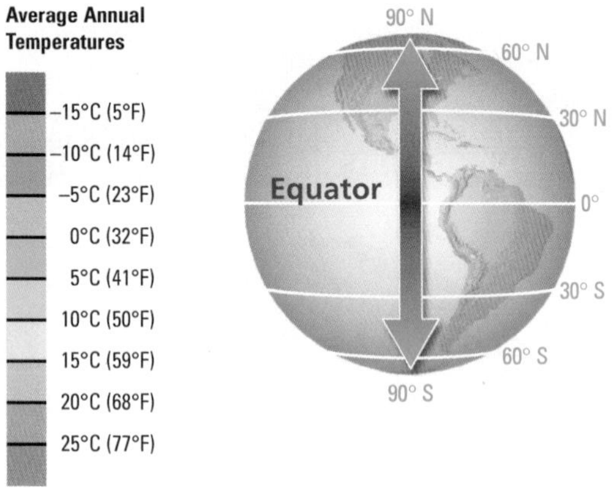


## Latitude

**READING TIP**

Notice on the globe in the illustration that latitude numbers get higher as you move away from the equator.

You have read that the amount of solar radiation received at Earth's surface is related to distance from the equator. One way to measure distance from the equator is latitude. Latitude is the distance in degrees north or south of the equator. The equator is at 0 degrees latitude. Each degree equals 1/360 of the distance around the planet. You will read more about latitude in Chapter 5.

Because of the unequal heating caused by Earth's curved shape, temperatures usually go down as you move away from the equator toward either the North Pole or the South Pole. As you can see in the map above, these temperature changes do not follow lines of latitude. Factors other than latitude affect average annual temperatures.

The temperature of an area depends in part on its height above sea level. In the atmosphere, temperature normally goes down as height goes up. Therefore, the temperatures high on a mountain are usually cooler than those in the valley below. Also, the temperature of an area depends in part on how close it is to a large lake or the ocean. Water heats and cools more slowly than land. Large bodies of water cause areas along a coast to be cooler in summer and warmer in winter than land at the same latitude in the middle of a continent.

**CHECK YOUR READING** What is the connection between latitude and temperature?

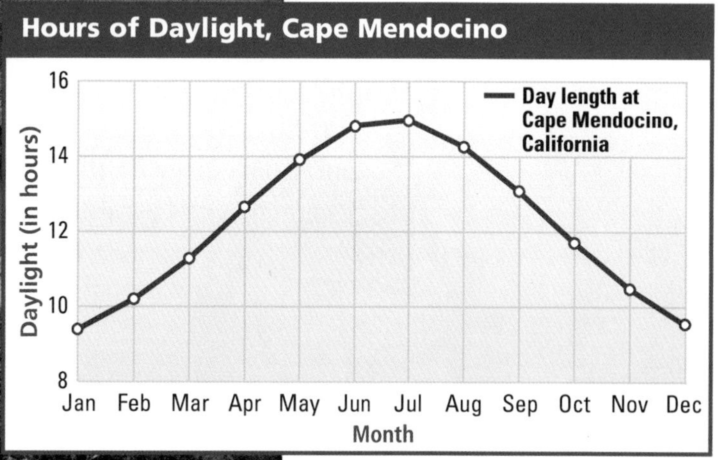


Source: U.S. Naval Observatory

## Hours of Daylight

The temperatures in the different seasons are also affected by the length of the days. For example, at Cape Mendocino, California, the summer sunlight heats the ground for about 15 hours per day on June 21. But, on December 21, the day is only about 9 hours long. In the winter, solar energy does not heat Earth's surface as much as in the summer. The greater the hours of daylight, the more the Sun's energy heats Earth's surface. Therefore, another reason it is warmer in the summer is that the days are longer.

The closer you are to the poles, the more the day length varies. Near the poles, there is sunlight for 18 hours or more during the summer. At the north and south poles, the Sun does not set at all for six months of the year. And during the winter at the poles, there is no sunlight. The winter at the poles is cold and dark. Close to the equator, the lengths of the day and night are almost equal all year round. Areas near the equator have about 12 hours of daylight all year. That's one reason why the seasons near the equator do not have large changes in temperature.

# 2.2 Review

### KEY CONCEPTS

1. What two things happen to the solar radiation that reaches Earth? (6.3.d)
2. What part of Earth's surface receives the most solar energy? Explain. (6.3.d)
3. What causes the amount of solar energy received in a particular area to change throughout the year? (6.3.d)

### CRITICAL THINKING

4. **Apply** On June 21 are there more hours of daylight in San Francisco or at the equator? Explain.
5. **Infer** If Earth's axis were not tilted, how would the seasons be affected?

### CHALLENGE

6. **Predict** Which would likely be hotter in the Northern Hemisphere, a cloudy day in July or a sunny day in July? Explain.

# CHAPTER INVESTIGATION

## Modeling Solar Energy

**OVERVIEW AND PURPOSE** In this investigation you will model how the amount of solar energy received at one place changes throughout a year and during a day. You will model the amount of solar energy received at different times as you

- point a light source at different angles to a surface
- determine how the amount of energy received at a location changes during a summer day

### Problem

Write It Up

How does the angle of light affect the amount of solar energy a location receives at different times of year?

### Hypothesize

Write It Up

After performing step 4, write a hypothesis to explain how the angle of sunlight affects the amount of solar energy your location receives. Your hypothesis should take the form of an "If . . . , then . . . , because . . ." statement.

**MATERIALS**
- graph paper
- flashlight
- meter stick
- protractor

6.3.d, 6.4.b, 6.7.a, 6.7.e

### Procedure

**PART ONE**

1. Mark an X near the center of the graph paper. Shine the flashlight onto the paper from about 30 cm straight above the X—at an angle of 90° to the surface. Estimate the length of the spot of light.

2. Shine the flashlight onto the X at different angles. Measure and record the angles. Keep the flashlight at the same distance. Record the estimated length of the spot of light at the angles.

3. Repeat step 2, but observe just one square near the X. Write down what happens to the brightness of the light as you change the angle. The brightness shows how much energy the area receives from the flashlight.

4. Think about the temperatures at different times of year at your location, and then write your hypothesis.

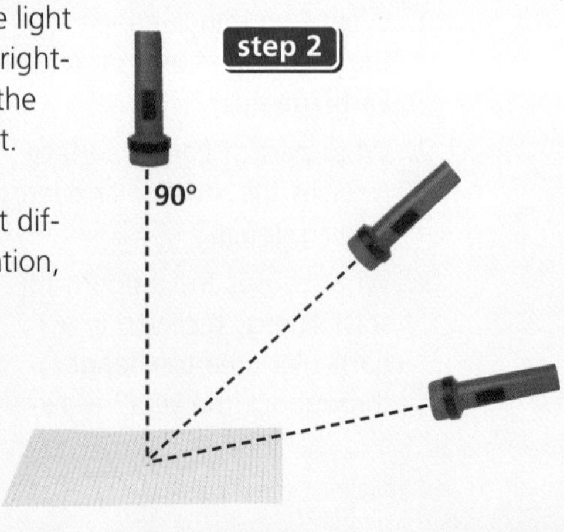

**Content Standard**
6.4.b Students know solar energy reaches Earth through radiation, mostly in the form of visible light.

**Investigation Standard**
6.7.a Develop a hypothesis.

## PART TWO

5 Find from your teacher the latitude of your location. You will use this information to calculate the Sun's noontime elevation at your location on June 21, the first day of summer.

6 Subtract the latitude of the tropic of Cancer, which is at 23.5° north, from your latitude.

7 Subtract the number you calculated in step 6 from 90°. Your result is the Sun's noontime elevation in degrees above the horizon in your location on the first day of summer.

8 Point the light at the X on the graph paper. Move the flashlight in an arc from one side of the graph paper to the other. The maximum angle of the flashlight above the paper should be the angle you calculated in step 7. The movement of the flashlight represents the apparent movement of the Sun across the sky.

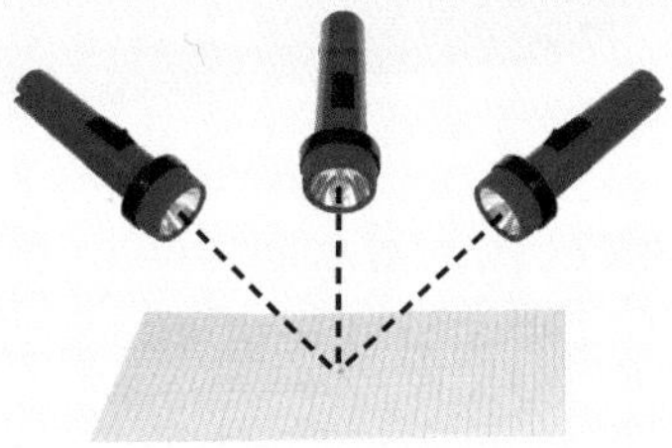

9 Observe how the brightness of the light near the X changes as you move the flashlight through the arc.

## Observe and Analyze

Write It Up

1. **RECORD** Draw the setup of your materials in each part of the investigation. Organize your notes.
2. **ANALYZE** Describe how the angle of the flashlight in step 2 affected the spot of light. Which angle concentrated the light into the smallest area?
3. **EVALUATE** In Part Two, what part of the flashlight arc represented sunrise? noon? sunset?
4. **COMPARE** Compare the brightness of light your area receives during a day at noon and at sunset.

## Conclude

Write It Up

1. **EVALUATE** Why do areas closer to the equator receive more solar energy?
2. **APPLY** Why are you more likely to get a sunburn at noon than at sunrise?
3. **INTERPRET** Do your results support your hypothesis? Explain why or why not.

## INVESTIGATE Further

**CHALLENGE** Compare the brightness of a day in summer and a day in winter at your location. Determine the total difference in latitude between your location and the latitude of the tropic of Capricorn (23.5° south). Subtract the total from 90°. The result is the noontime elevation of the Sun in your area on the first day of winter. Repeat Part Two using this maximum angle.

Modeling Solar Energy

Problem How does the angle of light affect the amount of solar energy a location receives at different times of year?

Hypothesize

Observe and Analyze

Table 1. Angle of Light and Brightness

| Angle of Light (°) | Length of Spot (cm) | Brightness |
|---|---|---|
| | | |
| 15 | | |
| 30 | | |
| 45 | | |

KEY CONCEPT

# 2.3 Energy is transferred within the Earth system.

**CALIFORNIA Content Standards**

**6.4.a** Students know the sun is the major source of energy for phenomena on Earth's surface; it powers winds, ocean currents, and the water cycle.

**6.4.c** Students know heat from Earth's interior reaches the surface primarily through convection.

**6.4.d** Students know convection currents distribute heat in the atmosphere and oceans.

**BEFORE, you learned**

- Earth receives energy from the Sun as radiation
- The curve of Earth's surface causes it to be heated unequally
- One cause of the seasons is the unequal heating of Earth's surface

**NOW, you will learn**

- How heat is transferred over Earth's surface
- How solar energy powers the water cycle
- How solar energy affects weather and climate

**VOCABULARY**

**water cycle** p. 60
**weather** p. 62
**ocean current** p. 62
**greenhouse effect** p. 63
**climate** p. 65

**THINK ABOUT**

***Where does most of Earth's energy come from?***

Look at the photograph of an erupting volcano. Where is the energy that fuels the volcano coming from? A huge amount of energy is released from Earth's interior by an erupting volcano. How does the amount of energy released by an eruption from Earth's interior compare with the amount of energy that comes to Earth from the Sun every day?

**OUTLINE**
Remember to take notes in the form of an outline as you read.

I. Main idea
  A. Supporting idea
    1. Detail
    2. Detail
  B. Supporting idea

## Little of Earth's internal heat reaches the surface.

Almost all of the energy that reaches Earth's surface comes from the Sun. Earth's interior is very hot. But very little of the heat in Earth's interior reaches the surface. Convection currents carry some heat from inside Earth toward the surface. You will read more about this in Chapter 8. But the rock that makes up Earth's outer layers does not conduct heat easily. Therefore, only a small amount of heat is carried from Earth's interior to the atmosphere. You can see signs of Earth's internal heat in a few places. Volcanoes, hot springs, and geysers are places where Earth's internal heat reaches the surface. The amount of energy released by an erupting volcano is huge. But that amount is tiny compared with the amount of energy Earth receives from the Sun.

## Energy from the Sun moves through the Earth system.

As you read in Chapter 1, energy from the Sun reaches Earth through radiation. Life on Earth depends on solar radiation. Plants change sunlight to stored energy. Humans and other animals that eat plants use this stored energy. Therefore, the Sun provides both plants and animals with the energy they need to live.

When solar radiation is absorbed by the atmosphere or by Earth's surface, it changes into heat energy. Recall that heat energy can be transferred in three ways—radiation, conduction, and convection.

The illustration below shows each of these processes. Solar radiation heats Earth's surface. Energy is carried by conduction from Earth's surface to the air molecules touching it. The warm air then carries energy upward by convection.

The Sun provides energy for many processes that take place at Earth's surface. It causes winds to blow and currents to move across the surface of the ocean. Energy from the Sun also causes water to move in a cycle between the atmosphere and Earth's surface.

**VISUALIZATION** CLASSZONE.COM

See radiation, conduction, and convection in action.

**CHECK YOUR READING** What questions do you have about how energy from the Sun moves through the four parts of the Earth system?

### Transfer of Energy

**Radiation, conduction, and convection move energy from place to place.**

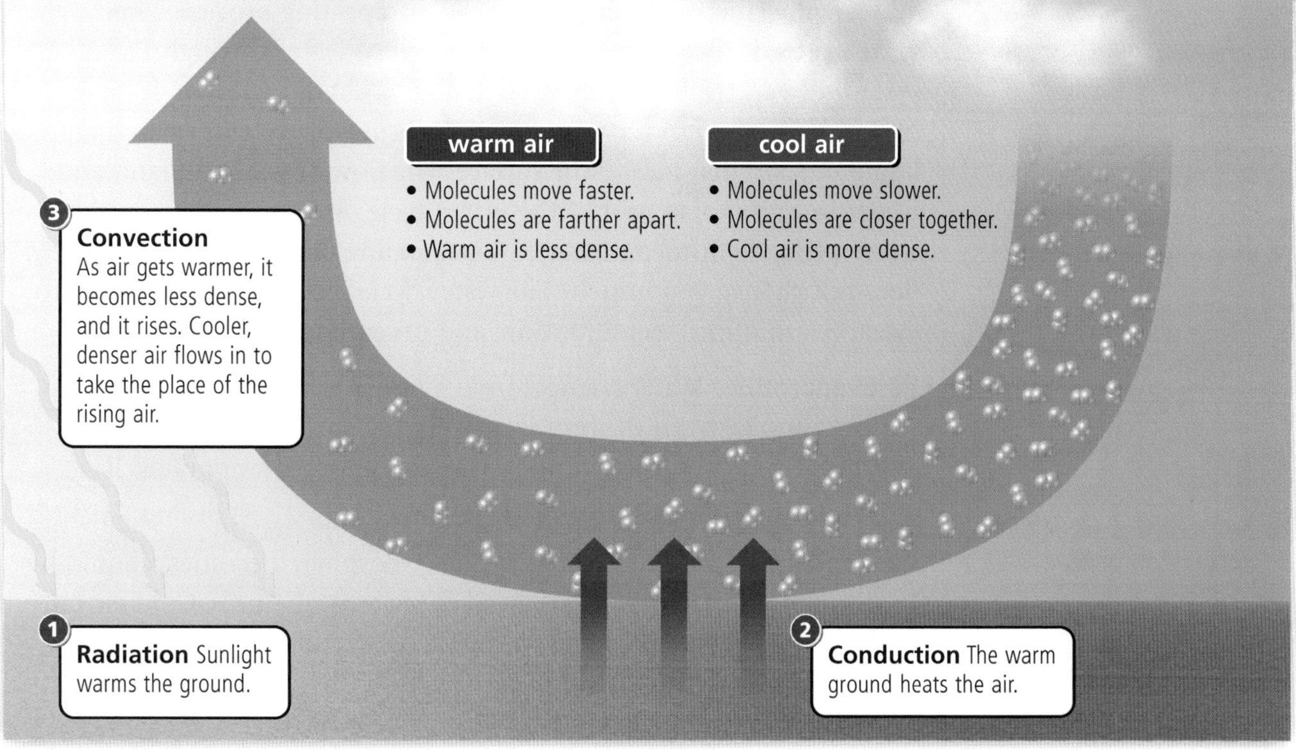

warm air
• Molecules move faster.
• Molecules are farther apart.
• Warm air is less dense.
cool air
• Molecules move slower.
• Molecules are closer together.
• Cool air is more dense.
3 Convection As air gets warmer, it becomes less dense, and it rises. Cooler, denser air flows in to take the place of the rising air.
1 Radiation Sunlight warms the ground.
2 Conduction The warm ground heats the air.

## The Water Cycle

**Water on Earth moves in a repeating cycle.**

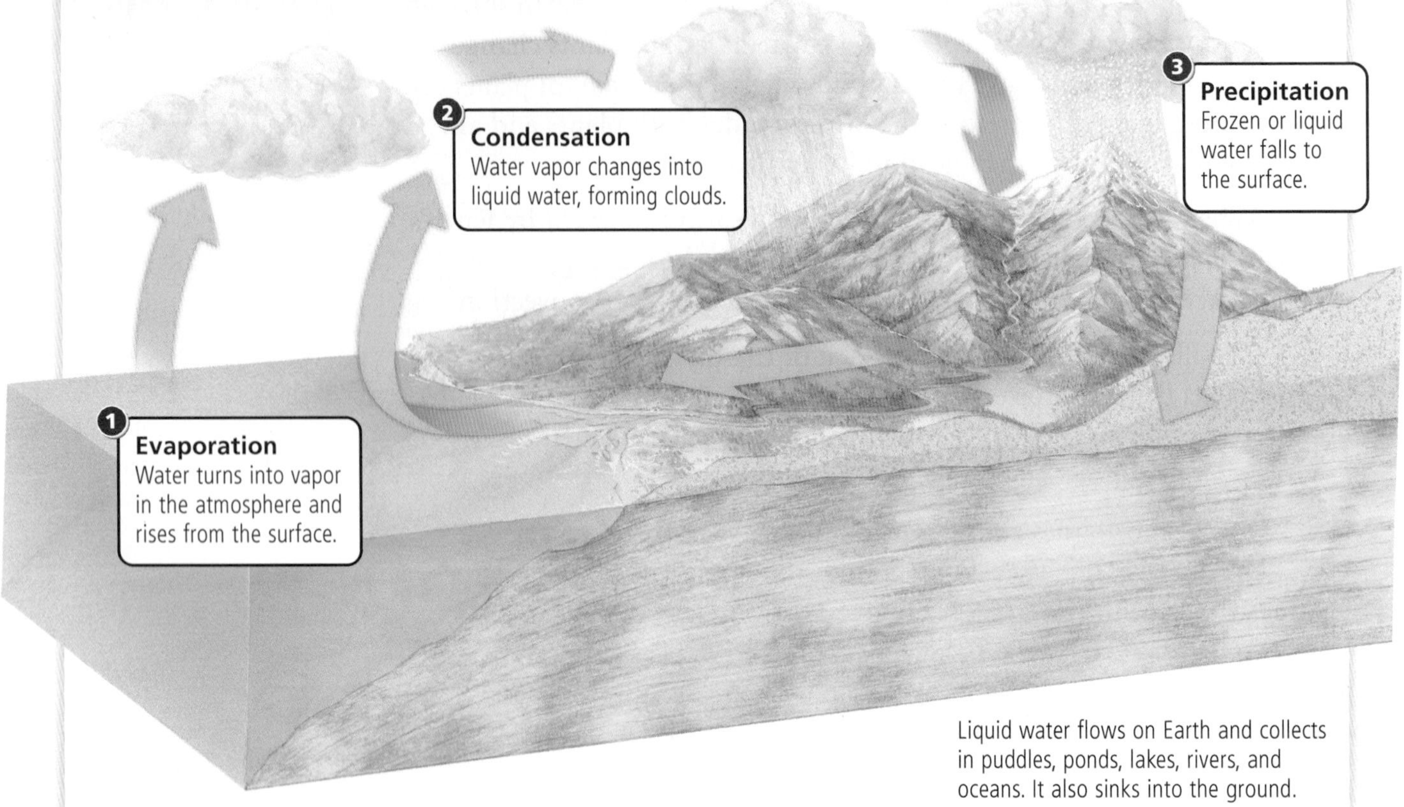

2 Condensation
Water vapor changes into liquid water, forming clouds.
3 Precipitation
Frozen or liquid water falls to the surface.
1 Evaporation
Water turns into vapor in the atmosphere and rises from the surface.
Liquid water flows on Earth and collects in puddles, ponds, lakes, rivers, and oceans. It also sinks into the ground.


**VOCABULARY**
Remember to make a frame game diagram in your notebook for *water cycle*.



## Water Cycle

Water's movement on Earth is a cycle, or repeating process. The **water cycle** is the continuous movement of water through Earth's systems. In the water cycle, water is always changing form. It changes from a liquid on land to a vapor in the atmosphere and again to a liquid or solid that falls to the surface. The flow of water on land and underground is also part of the water cycle. As water moves in the water cycle, the total amount of water in any part of the Earth system does not change very much. The water cycle includes three major processes: evaporation, condensation, and precipitation.

1 **Evaporation** Water changes from a liquid to vapor by evaporation. Heat energy from the Sun warms up the surface of the ocean or another body of water. Some of the liquid water evaporates. It becomes water vapor, an invisible gas.

2 **Condensation** Water vapor in the atmosphere becomes a liquid by condensation. Condensation takes place as air cools. Cold air can hold less water vapor than warm air. As a result, some of the vapor condenses. This means that it turns into droplets of liquid water. These droplets form clouds.

**3 Precipitation** Water or ice that falls from clouds is precipitation. Inside a cloud, water droplets or bits of ice bump together and join to become larger. They finally become heavy enough to fall as precipitation, such as rain or snow. The water from precipitation sinks into the soil or flows into streams and rivers.

Plants also play a role in the water cycle. They pull water up from the ground through their roots. Then they release much of it into the air through their leaves. How does the water move when it is released into the atmosphere? Water moves through the lower atmosphere by convection currents. Warm, moist air rises. When the water vapor in the air cools, it condenses to form clouds. Water falls back to the surface as rain or snow.

Heat energy is absorbed when water evaporates. This energy changes the liquid water to water vapor. When water condenses, heat energy is released. In this way, the water cycle moves both water and heat energy through the atmosphere.

**CHECK YOUR READING** How does water enter the atmosphere?

This photograph shows Yosemite National Park in winter. How does it show each part of the water cycle in action?

## Winds and Ocean Currents

RESOURCE CENTER
CLASSZONE.COM
Learn more about ocean currents.

**Weather** is the condition of the atmosphere at a certain time and place. On a TV news program, forecasters predict what the weather will be like over the next few days. Wind direction and wind speed are important in forecasting the weather. Wind is air that is moving parallel to the ground. Global winds blow steadily from a certain direction over large distances. Earth's major wind patterns carry heat energy through the atmosphere by convection. You will read more about winds in Chapter 3.

Global winds circulate heat around Earth in the atmosphere. Heat energy also flows around Earth in the ocean. An **ocean current** is a mass of moving water. Many different currents move water through the oceans. As ocean currents move water, they carry heat around the globe. Convection is the main process by which currents transfer heat around the planet.

**CALIFORNIA Focus**

The California Current carries cool water south from the Gulf of Alaska. Because the current flows close to the coastline of northern California, this region has cooler coastal waters than southern California.

**CHECK YOUR READING** What is an ocean current?

## Global Surface Currents

**Surface currents are caused by winds. Currents move warm water away from the equator and cool water away from the poles.**

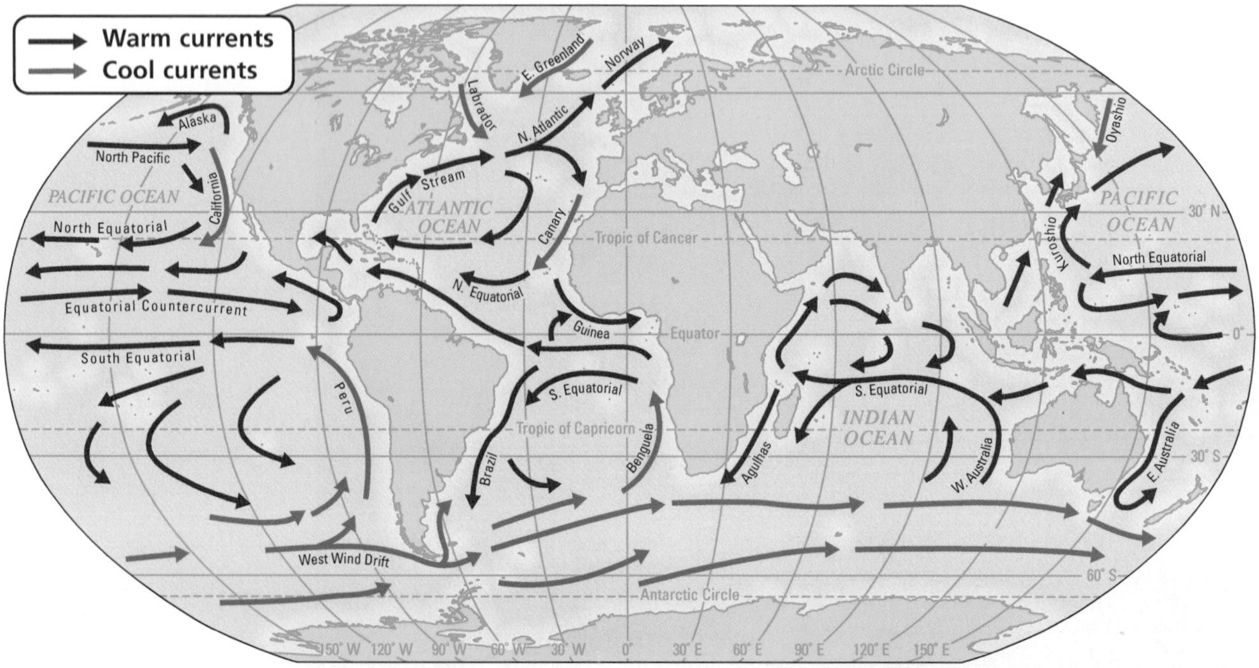


**READING VISUALS** Which currents could be used for sailing east across the Atlantic Ocean?

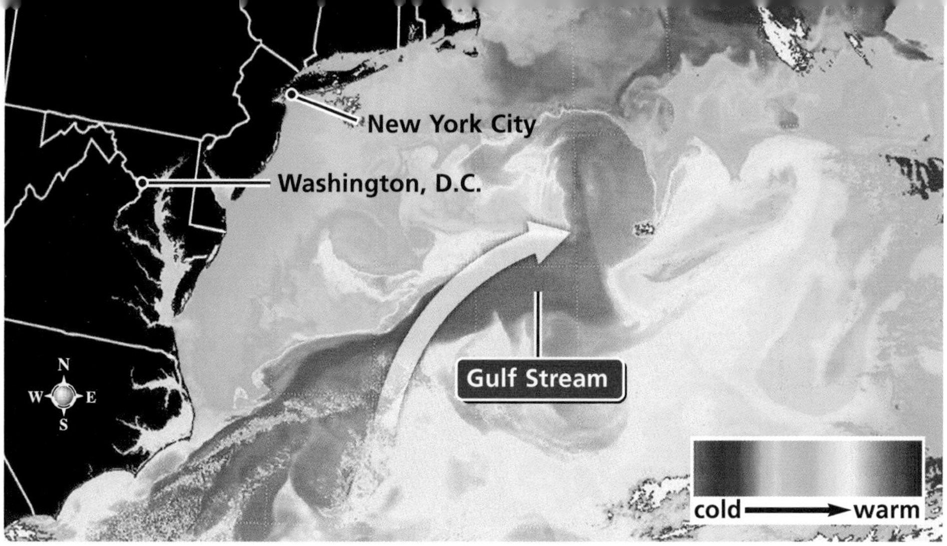


This satellite image uses false colors to show the Gulf Stream, a surface current that flows along the eastern coast of the United States. The colors show the temperature of the water.

The uneven heating of Earth's surface causes winds to blow. As winds blow over the ocean surface, they cause surface currents to flow. The currents usually reach only about 100 to 200 meters (300–500 ft) down into the ocean, but they cover large areas. The map on page 62 shows major ocean currents.

Earth's rotation causes surface currents to flow into giant clockwise patterns in the Northern Hemisphere. In the Southern Hemisphere, currents flow counterclockwise. The shapes of the continents also affect the paths of surface currents.

Surface currents carry warm water away from the equator and cool water away from the poles. In this way, surface currents help make temperatures on Earth more even. Global winds and ocean currents keep areas near the equator from getting hotter and hotter. They also spread some of the energy from the Sun around the planet.

The ocean and the atmosphere also act together to affect weather. Wind causes surface water to move. At the same time, the water changes the temperature of the air above it. Areas that are affected by warm ocean currents have warmer climates. Look at the Gulf Stream, shown above. It carries warm water toward northern Europe. The climate in that area is milder because of the Gulf Stream.

**CHECK YOUR READING** What causes ocean surface currents?

## Greenhouse Effect

A coat helps keep you warm by slowing the movement of heat away from your body. In a similar way, certain gases in the atmosphere slow the movement of heat energy away from Earth's surface. This process is known as the **greenhouse effect.** The gases absorb and give off infrared radiation. This process slows the loss of energy from the atmosphere to outer space. You cannot see infrared radiation, but you can feel it as heat. The greenhouse effect got its name because both a greenhouse and Earth's atmosphere act to trap heat, even though they do it in different ways.

## The Greenhouse Effect

**Greenhouse gas molecules absorb and emit infrared radiation.**

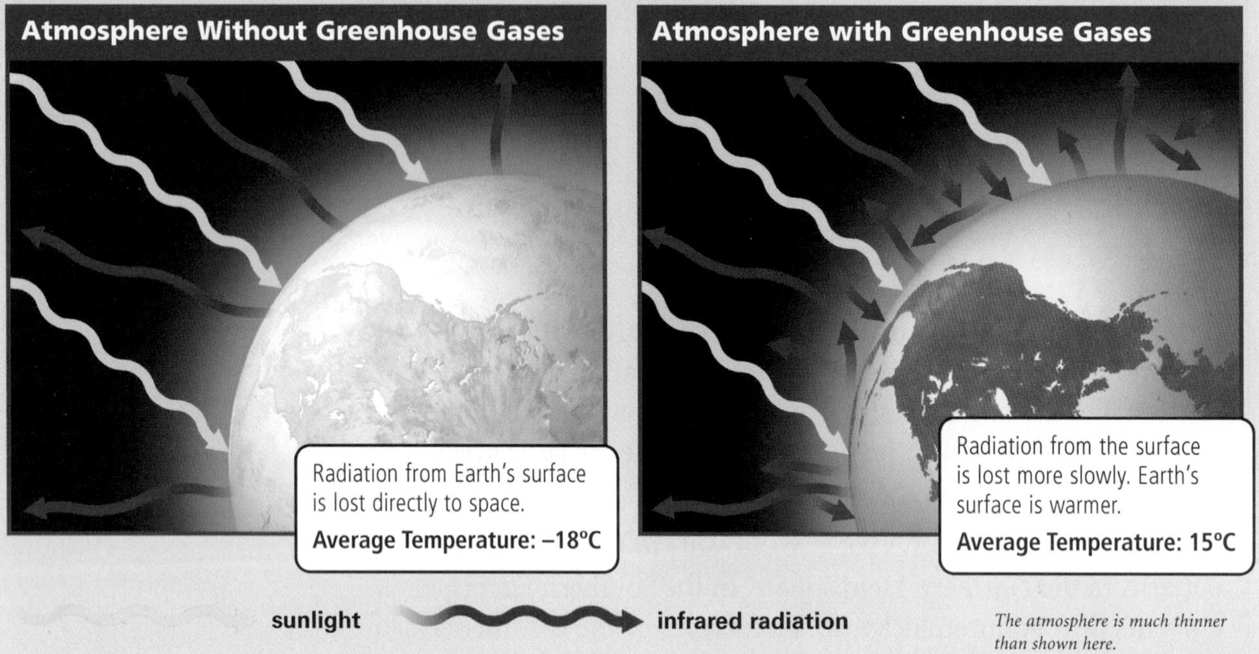
Atmosphere Without Greenhouse Gases
Radiation from Earth's surface is lost directly to space.
Average Temperature: –18°C
Atmosphere with Greenhouse Gases
Radiation from the surface is lost more slowly. Earth's surface is warmer.
Average Temperature: 15°C
sunlight
infrared radiation

*The atmosphere is much thinner than shown here.*

Greenhouse gases include carbon dioxide, methane, and water vapor. Greenhouse gases do not form a single layer. They are mixed together with nitrogen, oxygen, and other gases in the air.

Radiation from the Sun, including visible light, warms Earth's surface. The surface absorbs some energy. The surface also releases some of the energy back into the atmosphere as infrared radiation. If the atmosphere had no greenhouse gases, the infrared radiation would be lost to outer space. Earth's average surface temperature would be only about –18°C (0°F). Water would freeze, and it would be too cold for most life forms on Earth to survive.

**VISUALIZATION** CLASSZONE.COM

See how the greenhouse effect works.

Greenhouse gases absorb some of the infrared radiation given off by Earth's surface. The gases then give off this energy as infrared radiation. Some of the energy is absorbed again by the surface, while some of the energy goes out into space. The greenhouse effect keeps Earth's average surface temperature around 15°C (59°F). Human activities add more greenhouse gases to the atmosphere. Earth is getting warmer. Many people are concerned that these extra gases are adding to this warmth. Even a small increase in average temperature could affect climates around the planet.

**CHECK YOUR READING** How do greenhouse gases affect Earth's atmosphere?

## Solar energy drives weather and climate.

Weather conditions can change daily or even hourly. But the climate of an area changes over much longer periods. **Climate** describes the weather conditions in a place over a long time. Scientists often focus on patterns of precipitation and temperature when they classify climates. Four factors affect these patterns: latitude, distance from large bodies of water, ocean currents, and land elevation. You read about each of these factors earlier in this chapter.

**Latitude** Latitude affects temperature because solar radiation heats Earth's surface unevenly. It is usually warmer closer to the equator and cooler toward the poles.

**Distance from Water** Land heats up and cools off faster than water. The ocean and large lakes slow down heating and cooling of the air. For this reason, areas along coasts usually have milder temperatures than areas far inland. Large bodies of water also affect precipitation.

**Ocean Currents** Ocean currents carry energy from one part of the ocean to another. In general, warm-water currents carry warmth toward the poles. Warm-water currents help keep areas along coasts warm. Cold-water currents cool these areas. Moving heat from warm areas to cooler areas helps even out extremes in Earth's surface temperatures.

## INVESTIGATE Heating and Cooling Rates

### *How quickly do soil and water heat and cool?*

**SKILL FOCUS**
Comparing (6.3.c)

**PROCEDURE**

1. Mark a line 3 centimeters from the bottom of each cup. Fill one cup to the line with water and the other with soil. Place a thermometer into the contents of each cup. Wait 2 minutes. Record the temperature in each cup.
2. Place the cups side by side in bright sunlight or under a lamp. Wait 10 minutes. Record the temperature in each cup.
3. Move the cups into a shaded area to cool. Wait 10 minutes. Record the temperature in each cup.

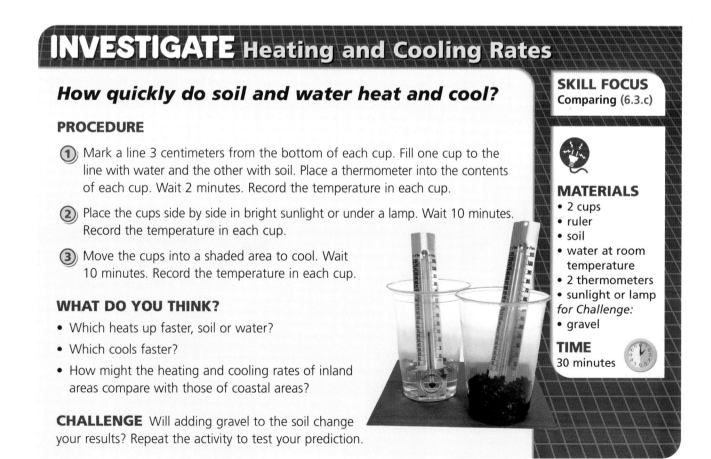

**WHAT DO YOU THINK?**

- Which heats up faster, soil or water?
- Which cools faster?
- How might the heating and cooling rates of inland areas compare with those of coastal areas?

**CHALLENGE** Will adding gravel to the soil change your results? Repeat the activity to test your prediction.

**MATERIALS**
- 2 cups
- ruler
- soil
- water at room temperature
- 2 thermometers
- sunlight or lamp

*for Challenge:*
- gravel

**TIME**
30 minutes

## Mountain Climates

**Because altitude changes sharply on a mountain, different climates can exist within a small area.**

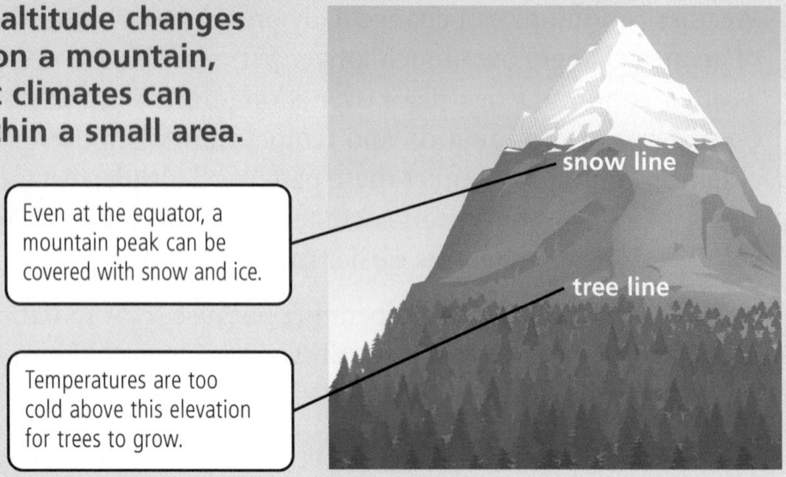

Even at the equator, a mountain peak can be covered with snow and ice.
Temperatures are too cold above this elevation for trees to grow.
snow line
tree line

**Land Elevation** Recall that elevation is the height of land above sea level. Elevation affects temperature. If you rode a cable car up a mountain, the temperature would decrease by about 6.5°C (11.7°F) for every kilometer you rose in elevation. Why does it get colder as you move higher up? The lowest layer of the atmosphere is warmed mainly by conduction from Earth's surface and by convection currents. As convection lifts the warmed air to higher altitudes, the air cools.

The effect of elevation on temperature can cause an area near the equator to be cold. One example is Mount Stanley, a tall mountain near the border of Uganda and the Democratic Republic of the Congo in Africa. Mount Stanley lies a short distance from the equator. However, it has ice sheets at its top and is always covered with snow. Notice in the illustration how one mountain can have several types of climates.

**CHECK YOUR READING** What four factors influence temperature and precipitation patterns?

# 2.3 Review

### KEY CONCEPTS

1. Describe the three processes that transfer energy over Earth's surface. (6.3)
2. Explain the three processes that make up the water cycle. (6.4.a)
3. How do ocean currents carry heat around the globe? (6.4.d)

### CRITICAL THINKING

4. **Predict** How could a region's climate change if a cold-water ocean current stopped flowing past it?
5. **Infer** What would happen to Earth's climates if all ocean currents and global winds stopped?

### CHALLENGE

6. **Draw Conclusions** What effect would an increase in greenhouse gases in the atmosphere have on Earth's overall temperature?

MATH in SCIENCE

## SKILL: INTERPRETING LINE GRAPHS

# Carbon Dioxide Levels

**MATH TUTORIAL**
CLASSZONE.COM
Click on Math Tutorial for more help with interpreting line graphs.

**Math** 6.MS.1.1

Since the 1950s, carbon dioxide levels have been measured in air samples collected at the Mauna Loa Observatory in Hawaii. Carbon dioxide is an important greenhouse gas. The graphs below show the carbon dioxide data plotted in two different ways. In the graph on the left, the scale showing carbon dioxide levels starts at 0 parts per million (ppm) and goes up to 400 ppm. The graph on the right offers a close-up view of the same data. The vertical scale on the right-hand graph is broken to focus on the values from 310 ppm to 380 ppm.

**Amount of Carbon Dioxide in the Air**

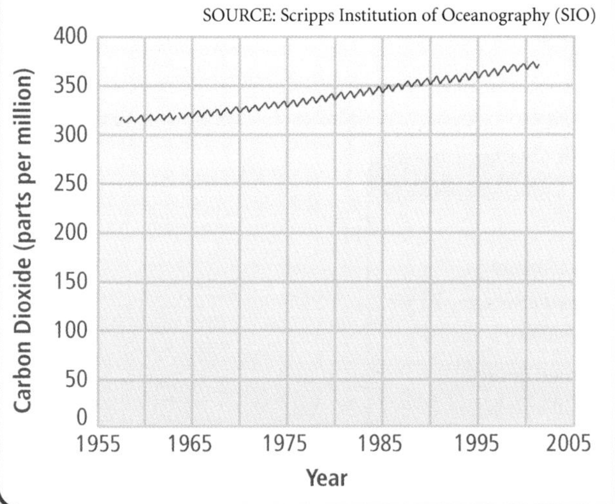


**Amount of Carbon Dioxide in the Air**

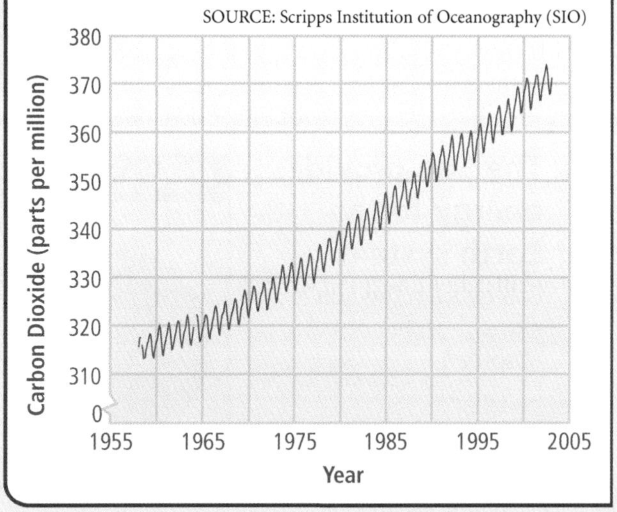


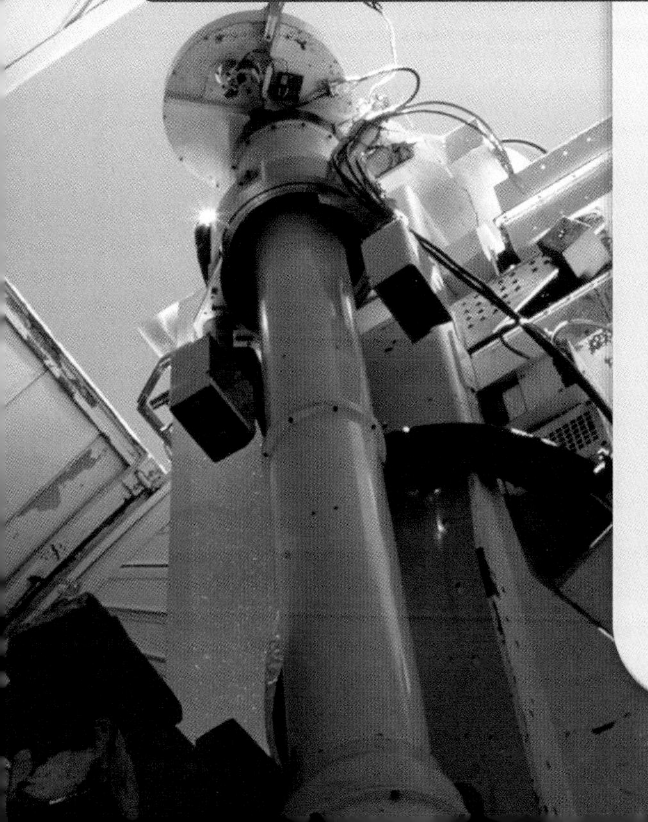

**Use the graphs to answer the following questions.**

1. What was the carbon dioxide level at the beginning of 1995?

2. The data show a 17 percent increase in the carbon dioxide level in the air from 1958 through 2001. Which graph shows this increase more clearly? Why?

3. In both graphs, the line that shows carbon dioxide levels is jagged, because carbon dioxide levels rise and fall regularly as the seasons change. In some years, the seasonal rise and fall is greater than in other years. Which graph emphasizes these variations more? Why?

**CHALLENGE** The carbon dioxide level in the air in the Northern Hemisphere starts falling in May or June each year and continues to fall through October. What do you think causes this change to occur? Hint: Consider the relationship between plants and carbon dioxide.

# 2 Chapter Review

## the BIG idea

**The Sun is the major source of energy for Earth's atmosphere and surface.**

CONTENT REVIEW
CLASSZONE.COM

## KEY CONCEPTS SUMMARY

### 1 The Earth system has four major parts.

The atmosphere, hydrosphere, biosphere, and geosphere work together to form one large Earth system.

**VOCABULARY**
**system** p. 41
**cycle** p. 44

### 2 The Sun provides energy to the Earth system.

Energy from the Sun is either reflected or absorbed.

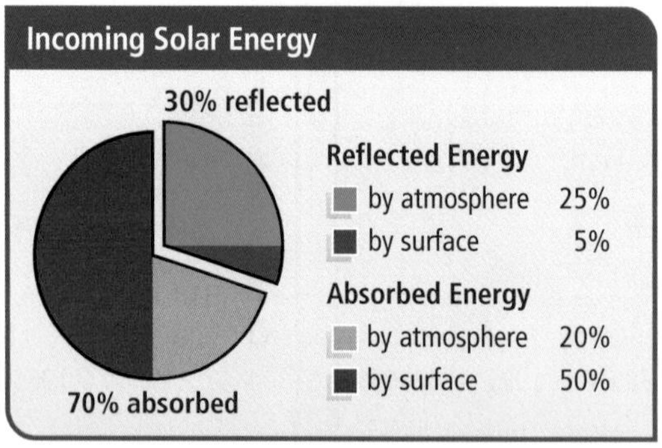


**VOCABULARY**
**axis** p. 52

### 3 Energy is transferred within the Earth system.

Radiation, conduction, and convection move energy from place to place.

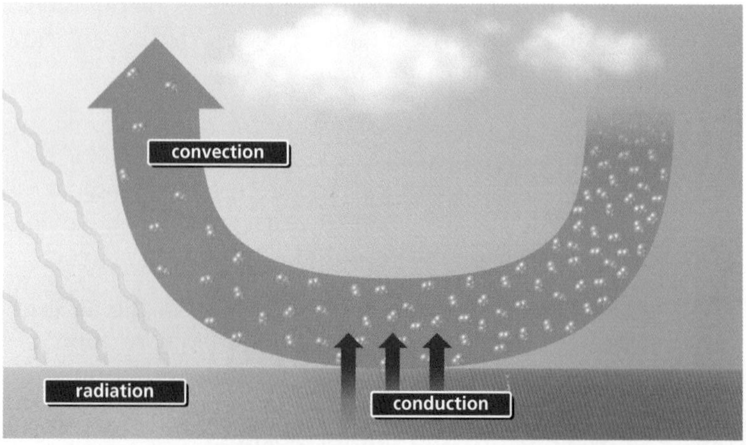


**VOCABULARY**
**water cycle** p. 60
**weather** p. 62
**ocean current** p. 62
**greenhouse effect** p. 63
**climate** p. 65

## Reviewing Vocabulary

*Draw a word triangle for each of the vocabulary terms listed below. Define the term, use it in a sentence, and draw a picture to help you remember the term. A sample is shown below.*

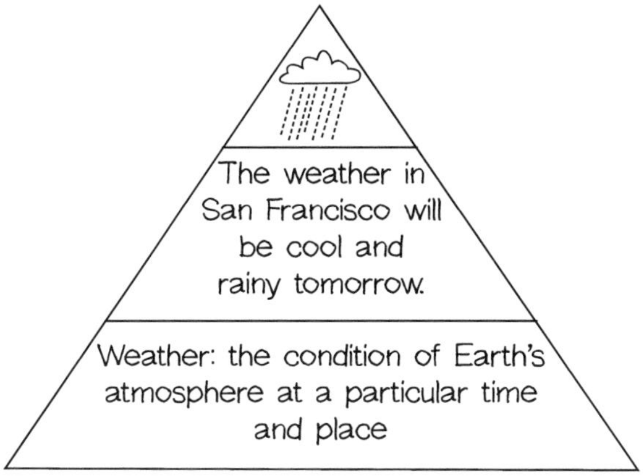

The weather in San Francisco will be cool and rainy tomorrow.
Weather: the condition of Earth's atmosphere at a particular time and place


1. system
2. cycle
3. axis
4. water cycle
5. greenhouse effect

## Reviewing Key Concepts

**Multiple Choice** *Choose the letter of the best answer.*

6. Which process forms clouds?
   **a.** evaporation **c.** condensation
   **b.** precipitation **d.** runoff

7. Continents, islands, mountains, and the ocean floor form part of the
   **a.** biosphere **c.** hydrosphere
   **b.** atmosphere **d.** geosphere

8. Compared with weather patterns, climate patterns are more
   **a.** long-term **c.** short-term
   **b.** severe **d.** local

9. Most of the heat energy at Earth's surface comes from (6.4.a)
   **a.** Earth's interior **c.** the Sun
   **b.** volcanic eruptions **d.** oil and gas

10. What area of Earth's surface receives more solar energy? (6.3.d)
    **a.** North Pole **c.** Northern Hemisphere
    **b.** South Pole **d.** equator

11. What causes different amounts of solar energy to strike Earth's surface at different times of the year? (6.3.d)
    **a.** the tilt of Earth's axis
    **b.** the distance between the Sun and Earth
    **c.** the revolution of the Sun around Earth
    **d.** the curve of Earth's surface

12. What is the main process by which ocean currents transfer heat energy around Earth? (6.4.d)
    **a.** conduction **c.** precipitation
    **b.** convection **d.** radiation

13. What keeps Earth's surface warm?
    **a.** conduction
    **b.** the water cycle
    **c.** convection
    **d.** the greenhouse effect

**Short Answer** *Write a short answer to each question.*

14. Give an example of a feature from each of the four parts of the Earth system.
15. Describe how the northern and southern hemispheres are tilted with respect to the Sun in December. What season is it in each hemisphere?
16. What three processes transfer heat over Earth's surface? (6.3)
17. Describe how water moves through the atmosphere in the water cycle. (6.4.a)

## Thinking Critically

*Use the diagram to answer the next five questions.*

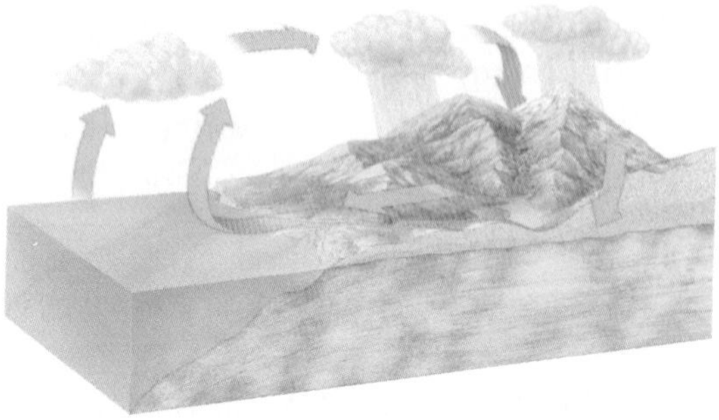

18. **CLASSIFY** What series of processes is shown in the diagram above? (6.4.a)

19. **OBSERVE** What process results in rain and snow falling on Earth's surface? Which arrow in the diagram represents this process? (6.4.a)

20. **INFER** What process results in water vapor becoming part of the atmosphere? Does this process absorb or release heat energy? (6.4.a)

21. **DRAW CONCLUSIONS** How are plants involved in this cycle? (6.4.a)

22. **EXPLAIN** Explain why this cycle is important to humans, plants, and animals. (6.4.a)

23. **APPLY** Why is the transfer of energy by radiation important to life on Earth? (6.4.b)

24. **PREDICT** What would you expect the climate at the top of a tall mountain located at the equator to be like?

25. **SYNTHESIZE** Give an example of how the four parts of the Earth system interact.

26. **CLASSIFY** Classify the following according to which part of the Earth system each belongs: a horse, a cloud, a glacier, a rock, water vapor.

27. **DRAW CONCLUSIONS** What would happen if all of the solar energy that reached Earth was reflected by the atmosphere? (6.3.d)

28. **ANALYZE** Which would be heated more by the Sun—a white, snow-covered area or a dark-colored area of bare soil? Explain. (6.3.d)

29. **SYNTHESIZE** What features of the Earth system distribute heat around the planet? (6.4.d)

30. **INFER** What would happen if the amounts of carbon dioxide, methane, and water vapor in the atmosphere decreased greatly? Explain.

31. **COMMUNICATE** Describe how temperature patterns change as distance from the equator increases.

32. **EVALUATE** Describe a place that has what you consider to be a perfect climate. Explain how the following factors affect the temperature of that place:
    - latitude
    - elevation
    - distance from large bodies of water
    - ocean currents

## the BIG idea

33. **SYNTHESIZE** Explain how energy from the Sun is related to rain and other types of precipitation. (6.4.a)

34. **APPLY** Look again at the photograph on pages 38–39. Give an example from the photograph of each part of the Earth system. Then give an example of how energy affects that part. (6.4.a)

## UNIT PROJECTS

If you need to create graphs or other visuals for your project, be sure you have grid paper, poster board, markers, and other supplies.

For more practice, go to . . .
TEST PRACTICE
CLASSZONE.COM

## Analyzing a Diagram

6.4.a

*This diagram shows the four major parts of the Earth system. Use it to answer the questions below.*

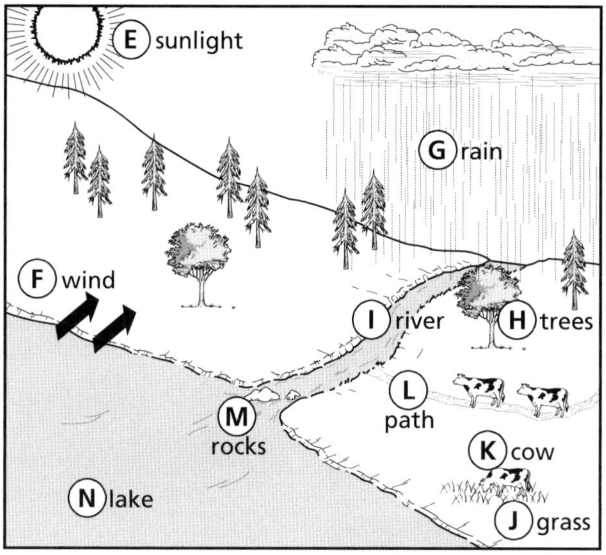


1. Where is the main source of energy for the Earth system?
   - a. E
   - b. F
   - c. G
   - d. L
2. Where is the biosphere shaping the geosphere?
   - a. E
   - b. F
   - c. L
   - d. M
3. Where is matter moving from one part of the hydrosphere to another?
   - a. I to N
   - b. G to H
   - c. J to H
   - d. N to M
4. Which items belong to the geosphere?
   - a. F and G
   - b. H and J
   - c. I and N
   - d. M and L
5. Which process is occurring at M, where water is running over the rocks?
   - a. The geosphere is shaping the atmosphere.
   - b. The atmosphere is shaping the biosphere.
   - c. The hydrosphere is shaping the geosphere.
   - d. The biosphere is shaping the geosphere.
6. Where is matter moving from the atmosphere to the biosphere?
   - a. E to F
   - b. F to M
   - c. G to H
   - d. I to G
7. At K, the cow is eating grass. What kind of movement in the Earth system does this represent?
   - a. from the atmosphere to the hydrosphere
   - b. from the hydrosphere to the biosphere
   - c. between two parts of the geosphere
   - d. between two parts of the biosphere
8. Which is an example of how the hydrosphere is supported by the geosphere?
   - a. I, because the river receives the rain
   - b. H, because the trees are rooted in the ground
   - c. M, because the river drains into the lake
   - d. N, because the lake is contained by a basin

## Extended Response

*Answer the two questions below in detail. Include some of the terms shown in the word box. In your answers, underline each term you use.*

| | | |
|---|---|---|
| geosphere | surface | system |
| atmosphere | hydrosphere | biosphere |

9. Rain falls and soaks into the soil. Plants and animals use some of the water. More of the water drains into a river, and then enters the ocean. Describe this process as movements among the major parts of the Earth system.

10. Describe an example of how people can shape the surface of the geosphere.

# TIMELINES in Science

6.3.a, 6.3.c, 6.3.d, 6.7.d

## ABOUT TEMPERATURE AND HEAT

Most likely, the first fires early people saw were caused by lightning. Eventually, people realized that fire provided warmth and light, and they learned how to make it themselves. During the Stone Age 25,000 years ago, people used firewood to cook food as well as to warm and light their shelters. Wood was the first fuel.

This timeline shows a few of the many steps on the path toward understanding temperature and heat. Notice how the observations and ideas of previous thinkers sparked new theories by later scientists. The boxes below the timeline show how technology has led to new insights and to applications related to temperature and heat.

**445 B.C.**

***Four Basic Substances Named***

Greek philosopher Empedocles says that everything on Earth is made of some combination of four basic substances: earth, air, fire, and water. Different types of matter have different qualities depending on how they combine these substances.

**350 B.C.**

***Aristotle Expands Theory of Matter***

Greek philosopher Aristotle names four basic qualities of matter: dryness, wetness, hotness, and coldness. Each of the four basic substances has two of these qualities.

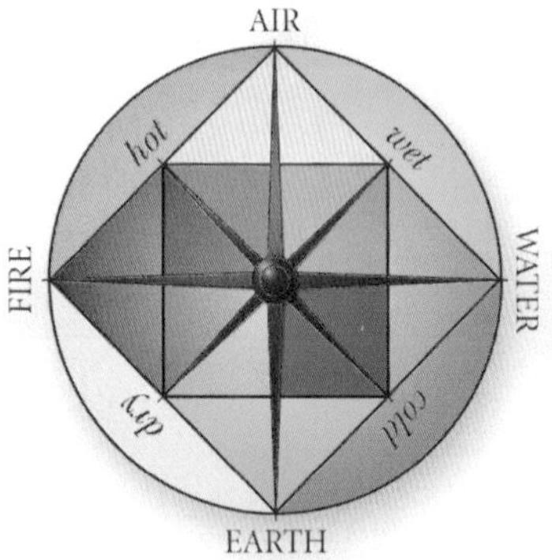


EVENTS

480 B.C. | 440 B.C. | 400 B.C. | 360 B.C. | 320 B.C.

APPLICATIONS AND TECHNOLOGY

People have been trying to understand and control heat since early times.

**A.D. 1617**

***Heat Is Motion***

English philosopher Francis Bacon uses observation and experimentation to demonstrate that heat is a form of motion. Most people remain unconvinced. They consider heat to be a fluid, which they call caloric.

**1724**

***Mercury Used for Thermometer***

Gabriel Fahrenheit, a German instrument maker, reports that mercury works well for measuring temperature. It expands evenly as temperature rises, and its silvery appearance makes it easy to see inside a glass tube. On Fahrenheit's scale, the boiling point of pure water is 212 degrees and the freezing point is 32 degrees.

**1742**

***New Temperature Scale Used***

Swedish astronomer Anders Celsius devises a scale for measuring temperature in which the freezing point of water is 0 degrees. The boiling point of pure water is 100 degrees. He calls this the Centigrade scale, from Latin words meaning "one hundred steps."

**1762**

***Calorimetry Founded***

Scottish chemist Joseph Black founds the science of calorimetry, which describes the amount of energy as heat a substance can hold. His research in boiling and evaporation is valuable to his friend James Watt, who is making improvements to the steam engine.

A.D. 1600 | 1640 | 1680 | 1720 | 1760

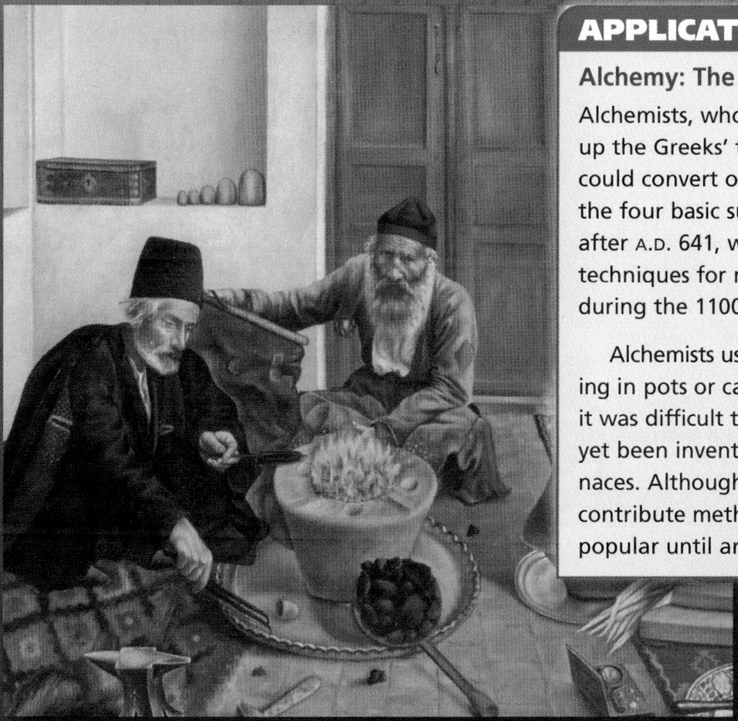

## APPLICATION

### Alchemy: The Quest to Create Gold

Alchemists, who hoped to turn less valuable metals into gold, took up the Greeks' theory of the four basic substances. They thought they could convert one substance into another by changing the balance of the four basic substances. Their ideas spread to the Byzantine Empire after A.D. 641, where these concepts were combined with advances in techniques for manipulating heat. Alchemy spread to Western Europe during the 1100s and 1200s.

Alchemists used chemical processes such as heating in furnaces, boiling in pots or cauldrons, distillation, pounding, and grinding. Because it was difficult to control the temperature, and thermometers had not yet been invented, alchemists usually had many different kinds of furnaces. Although alchemy is not considered a true science today, it did contribute methods and processes still used by chemists. It remained popular until around 1700.

## 1798

### *Heat and Friction Linked*

While observing cannons at a weapons factory, American-born scientist Benjamin Thompson (Count Rumford) notices that friction between the cutting tools and the metal cannon barrels generates large amounts of heat. He concludes that friction is an unending source of heat. This observation helps put an end to the theory that heat is a fluid.

## 1824

### *Heat Moves from Warmer to Cooler Objects*

French physicist Nicolas Sadi Carnot shows that heat is a flow of energy from an object with a higher temperature to an object with a lower temperature. This explains why ice placed in a hot liquid melts and becomes a liquid rather than the liquid becoming ice.

## 1845

### *Various Energies Produce Heat*

British physicist James Joule shows that mechanical energy can be converted to heat. Using a paddle-wheel device, he shows that the various forms of energy, such as mechanical and thermal, are basically the same and can change from one form to another. Joule also states that a given amount of energy of whatever form always yields that same amount of heat.

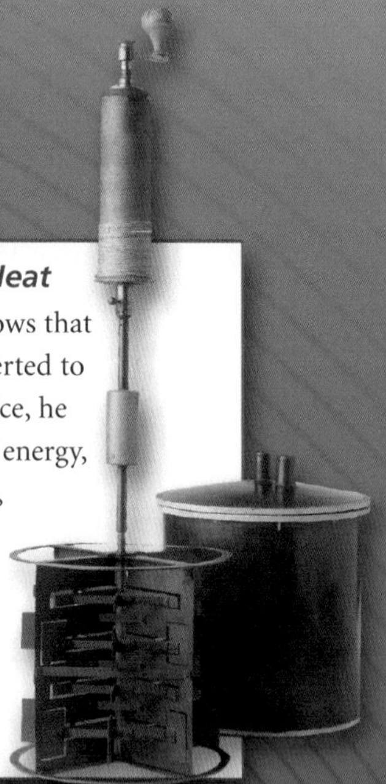

## 1906

### *Absolute Zero Identified*

German physicist Walther Nernst suggests that absolute zero is the temperature at which the individual particles in an object would be practically motionless. Absolute zero, equivalent to –273°C, is the lowest temperature any object can reach. This limit was identified by British physicist Lord Kelvin in 1848. However, this temperature can never actually be reached by any real object.

## TECHNOLOGY

### Keeping Heat In or Out

In 1892 Scottish physicist James Dewar invented the vacuum flask—a container in which warm fluids could be kept warm and cool fluids cool. A vacuum between the inner and outer walls of the container reduced conduction, which is the transfer of heat between two objects that are touching each other. Because a vacuum contains no matter, it does not conduct heat. Dewar's flask had silver walls to reflect radiated energy. As long as the flask was sealed, the vacuum was maintained and the temperature of a liquid inside the flask did not change much. A variation on Dewar's flask was produced in the early 1900s under the trade name Thermos. Today we call any vacuum container used for keeping beverages hot or cold a thermos.

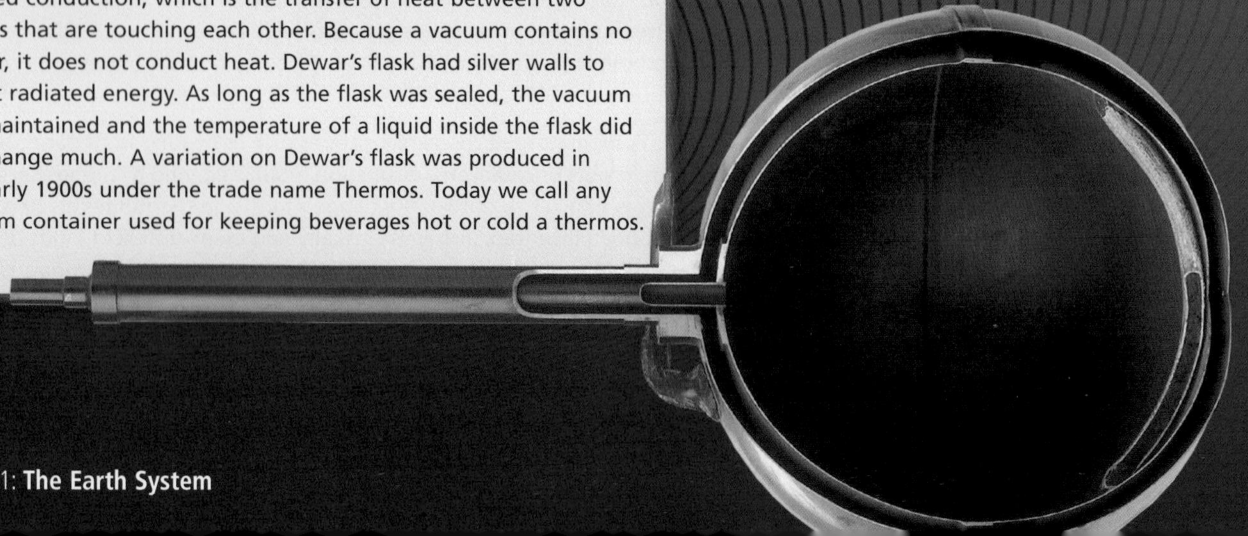

This cutaway shows the inside of one of Dewar's experimental flasks.

**2003**

### *Wasps Stay Cool*

Scientists in Israel have found evidence that some wasps have an internal air-conditioning system. Like a refrigerator, the wasp uses energy to stay cooler than the air around it. The energy may come from several sources, such as the energy generated by an electric current produced when the wasp's shell is exposed to sunlight. This ability to stay cool allows wasps to hunt for food even on very hot days.

**RESOURCE CENTER**
CLASSZONE.COM

Learn about current temperature and heat research.

1960 2000

## APPLICATION

### Using Thermal Energy from Ponds

Ponds can be used to store solar energy. The goal is to turn the solar energy into energy people can use. Salt must be added to the ponds, however, so that the water at the bottom is denser than the water at the top. This prevents thermal energy stored on the bottom from moving up to the surface, where it would be lost to the air through evaporation. A net on the surface helps prevent wind from mixing the water layers.

## SPOTLIGHT on DAVID CROSTHWAIT

David Crosthwait (1898–1976) was a leader in the United States in the field of heat transfer. He received 39 U.S. patents for his inventions related to heating, ventilating, and air-conditioning. He was an expert on methods of heating and cooling with water.

In the 1920s and 1930s, huge skyscrapers were being built. Crosthwait was hired to design the heating system for Radio City Music Hall in New York City's Rockefeller Center.

Crosthwait's inventions improved heating systems in large buildings. His innovations include an improved boiler, a new thermostat control, and a new vacuum pump. Crosthwait's influence lives on, as steam is still used to heat and cool many skyscrapers in the United States.

## ACTIVITIES

### Design a Procedure

Many people claim that it is possible to determine the temperature by listening to the chirping of crickets. Crickets are sensitive to changes in air temperature and chirp more quickly when the temperature rises. To calculate the temperature in degrees Celsius, count the number of chirps in 7 seconds and add 5.

Write a procedure for an experiment that would test this claim. What factors would you consider testing? What range of temperatures would you test?

### Writing About Science

Alchemy has fascinated people for centuries. Research its influence on both the technology and procedures of modern chemistry. Write a short report.

CHAPTER 3

# Weather Patterns

## the BIG idea

**Some features of weather have predictable patterns.**

What weather conditions do you see in the distance?

## Key Concepts

SECTION 1
**Air pressure varies in the atmosphere.**
Learn how air pressure changes and how it is measured.

SECTION 2
**The atmosphere has wind patterns.**
Learn how wind develops and about different types of wind.

SECTION 3
**Most clouds form as air rises and cools.**
Learn how water changes form in the atmosphere and about different types of clouds.

SECTION 4
**Water falls to Earth's surface as precipitation.**
Learn about the different types of precipitation and about acid rain.

**California ClassZone**

CLASSZONE.COM

Chapter 3 online resources: Content Review, two Visualizations, four Resource Centers, Math Tutorial, Test Practice

# EXPLORE the BIG idea

## How Does Air Motion Affect Balloons?

6.4.e Students know differences in pressure, heat, air movement, and humidity result in changes of weather.

Inflate two small balloons. Tie them to a pencil so that they are separated by about 5 centimeters, as shown in the photograph. Gently blow air between the balloons.

**Observe and Think**
How did the balloons move? Why did the air make them move this way?

## Internet Activity: Wind

6.4.e Students know differences in pressure, heat, air movement, and humidity result in changes of weather.

Go to **ClassZone.com** to explore how breezes blowing over land and water change over the course of an entire day. Examine how changing patterns of temperature during the day affect the winds.

**Observe and Think**
What patterns can you see in winds that occur near water?

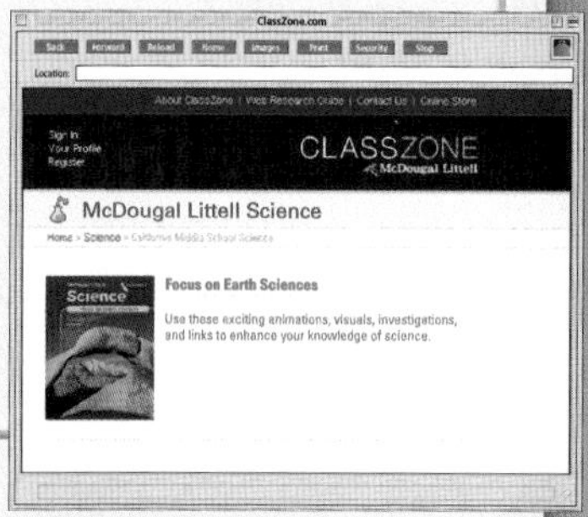


NSTA scilinks.org SCILINKS
Atmospheric Pressure and Winds **Code: MDL010**

CHAPTER 3

# Getting Ready to Learn

## CONCEPT REVIEW

- The Sun supplies the atmosphere's energy.
- Energy moves throughout the Earth system.
- Heat energy flows from warmer to cooler areas.

## VOCABULARY REVIEW

**convection** p. 28

**density** p. 28

**water cycle** p. 60

*See Glossary for definitions.*

**altitude, atmosphere**

**CONTENT REVIEW**
CLASSZONE.COM

Review concepts and vocabulary.

## TAKING NOTES

### COMBINATION NOTES

To take notes about a new concept, first make an informal outline of the information. Then make a sketch of the concept and label it so that you can study it later.

### VOCABULARY STRATEGY

Place each vocabulary term at the center of a **description wheel.** Write some words describing it on the spokes.

See the Note-Taking Handbook on pages R45–R51.

SCIENCE NOTEBOOK

NOTES

Air pressure

- is the force of air molecules pushing on an area
- pushes in all directions

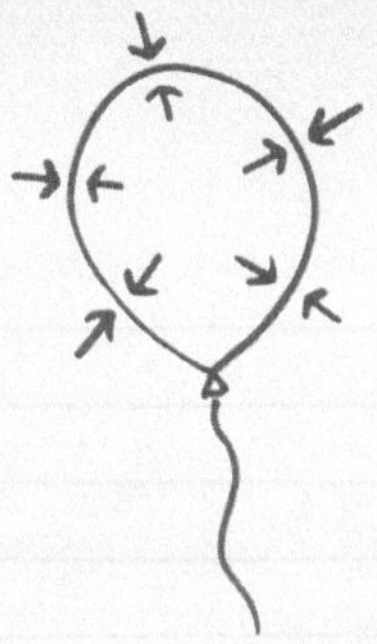

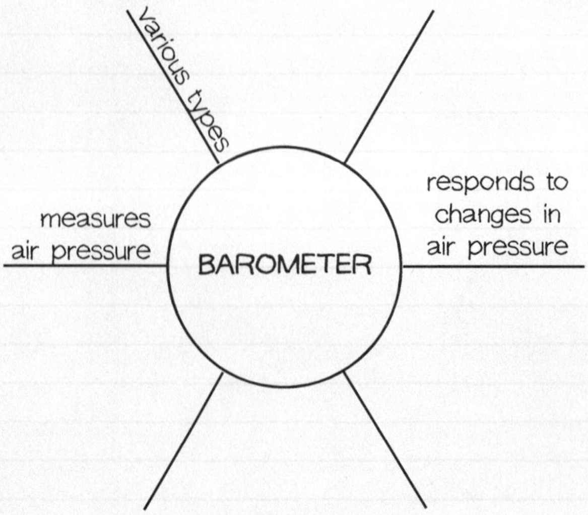

KEY CONCEPT

# 3.1 Air pressure varies in the atmosphere.

**CALIFORNIA Content Standard**

6.4.e Students know differences in pressure, heat, air movement, and humidity result in changes of weather.

**BEFORE, you learned**

- Density is the amount of mass in a given volume of a substance
- Air becomes less dense as temperature increases
- Differences in density cause air to rise and sink

**NOW, you will learn**

- How the movement of air molecules causes air pressure
- How air pressure varies
- How differences in air pressure affect the atmosphere

**VOCABULARY**

**air pressure** p. 79
**barometer** p. 82

**EXPLORE Air Pressure** (6.4.e)

### *What does air do to the egg?*

**PROCEDURE**

1. Set a peeled hard-boiled egg in the mouth of a bottle. Make sure that the egg can't slip through.
2. Light the matches. Remove the egg, and drop the matches into the bottle. Quickly replace the egg.
3. Watch carefully, and record your observations.

**MATERIALS**

- peeled hard-boiled egg
- glass bottle
- 2 wooden matches

**WHAT DO YOU THINK?**

- What happened when you placed the egg back on top of the bottle?
- What can your observations tell you about the air in the bottle?

## Air exerts pressure.

Air molecules move constantly. As they move, they bounce off each other like rubber balls. They also bounce off every surface they hit. As you read this book, billions of air molecules are bouncing off your body, the book, and everything else around you.

Each time an air molecule bounces off an object, it pushes, or exerts a force, on that object. When billions of air molecules bounce off a surface, the force is spread over the area of that surface. **Air pressure** is the force of air molecules pushing on an area. The greater the force, the higher the air pressure. Because air molecules move in all directions, air pressure pushes in all directions.

**VOCABULARY**
Add a description wheel for *air pressure* to your notebook.

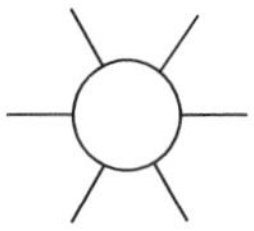

**CHECK YOUR READING** How does the number of air molecules relate to air pressure?

## Air pressure is related to altitude and density.

COMBINATION NOTES
Record details about how air pressure varies.

The air pressure at any area on Earth depends on the weight of the air above that area. If you hold out your hand, the force of air pushing down on your hand is greater than the weight of a bowling ball. So why don't you feel the air pushing down on your hand? Remember that air pushes in all directions. The pressure of air pushing down is balanced by the pressure of air pushing up from below.

Air pressure decreases as you move higher in the atmosphere. Think of a column of air directly over your body. If you stood at sea level, this column would stretch from where you stood to the top of the atmosphere. The air pressure on your body would be equal to the weight of all the air in the column. But if you stood on a mountain, the column of air would be shorter. With less air above you, the pressure would be lower. At an altitude of 5.5 kilometers (3.4 mi), air pressure is about half what it is at sea level.

REMINDER
Density is the amount of mass in a given volume of a substance.

Air pressure and density are related. Just as air pressure decreases with altitude, so does the density of air. Notice in the illustration that air molecules at sea level are closer together than air molecules over the mountain. Since the pressure is greater at sea level, the air molecules are pushed closer together. Therefore, the air at sea level is denser than air at high altitudes.

### Air Pressure and Density

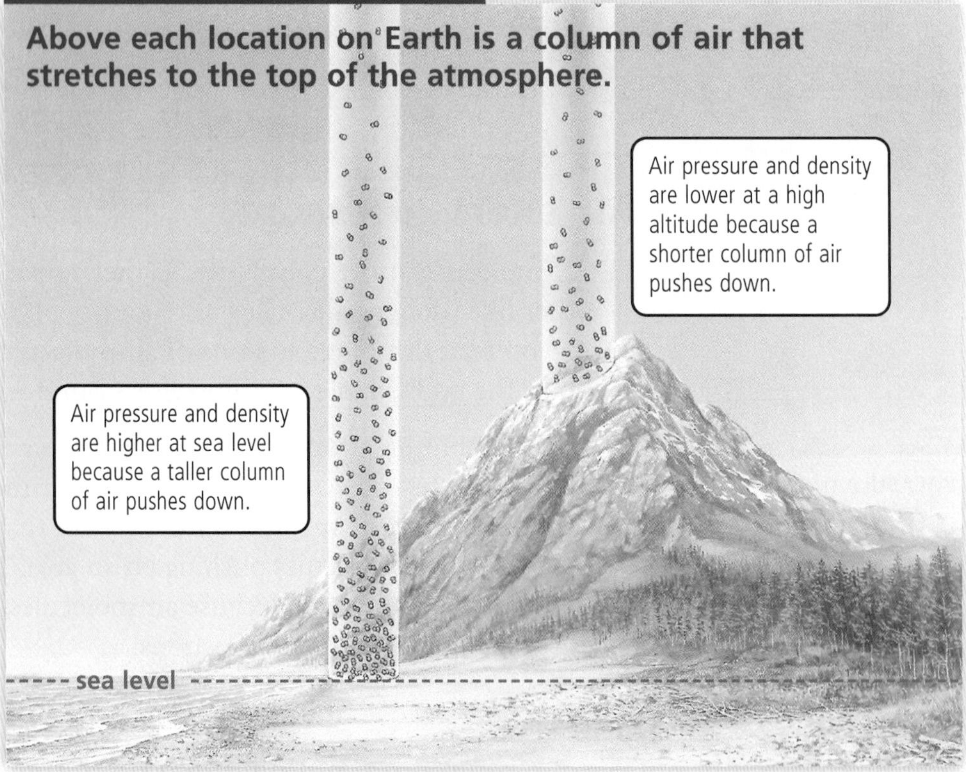

Above each location on Earth is a column of air that stretches to the top of the atmosphere.
Air pressure and density are lower at a high altitude because a shorter column of air pushes down.
Air pressure and density are higher at sea level because a taller column of air pushes down.
sea level

## Pressure and Air Motion

You've read that air pressure decreases as you move to higher altitudes. Air pressure also often varies in two locations at the same altitude. You can observe how such pressure differences affect air when you open a new can of tennis balls. You may hear a hiss as air rushes into the can. The air inside the sealed can of tennis balls is at a lower pressure than the air outside the can. When you break the seal, air moves from outside the can toward the lower pressure inside it.

Air pressure differences in the atmosphere affect air in a similar way. If the air pressure were the same at all locations, air wouldn't move much. Because of differences in pressure, air starts to move from areas of higher pressure toward areas of lower pressure. The air may move only a short distance, or it may travel many kilometers. You will learn more about how air moves in response to pressure differences in Section 3.2.

**RESOURCE CENTER**
CLASSZONE.COM
Find out more about air pressure.

**CHECK YOUR READING** How do differences in air pressure affect the movement of air?

## INVESTIGATE Air Pressure

### *How can you measure changes in air pressure?*

**PROCEDURE**

1. Cut open a balloon along one side until you get close to the end. Stretch the balloon across the open top of the can. Secure it tightly in place with a rubber band.
2. Cut the straw on an angle to make a pointer. Tape the other end of the straw to the center of the balloon.
3. Tape a ruler against a wall or a box so that the end of the pointer almost touches the ruler. Record the position of the pointer against the ruler.
4. Record the position of the pointer at least once a day for the next five days. Look for small changes in its position. For each day, record the air pressure printed in a local newspaper.

**WHAT DO YOU THINK?**

- In what direction did the pointer move when the air pressure went up? when the air pressure went down?
- Explain how your instrument worked.

**CHALLENGE** Predict what would happen to the pointer if you repeated this experiment but poked some small holes in the balloon.

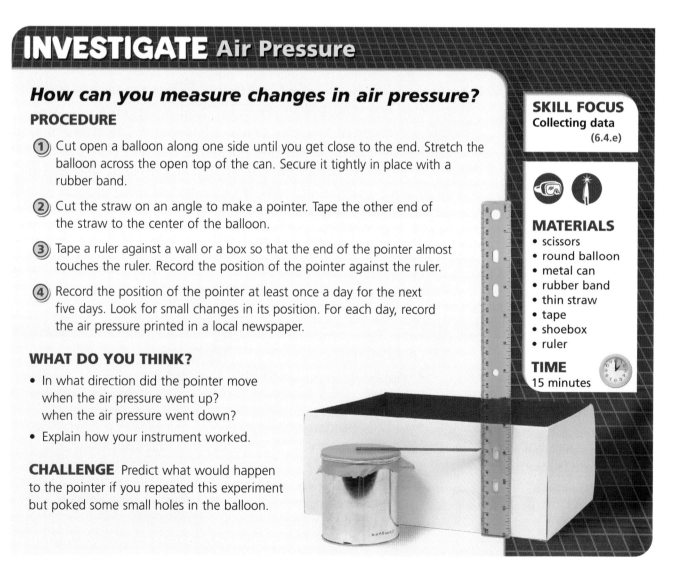

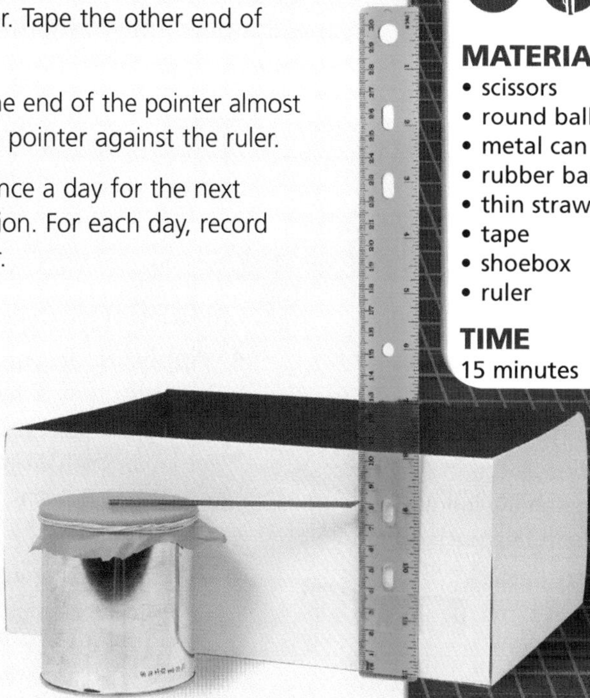

**SKILL FOCUS**
**Collecting data**
(6.4.e)

**MATERIALS**
- scissors
- round balloon
- metal can
- rubber band
- thin straw
- tape
- shoebox
- ruler

**TIME**
15 minutes

## How a Barometer Works

### High Air Pressure

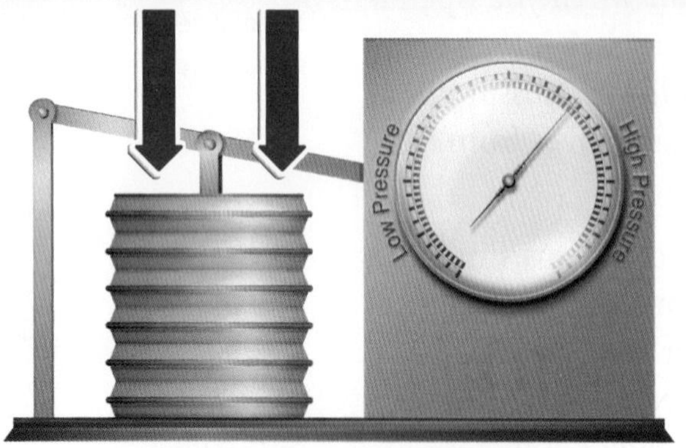


The flexible chamber on the barometer contracts when the air pressure increases.

### Low Air Pressure

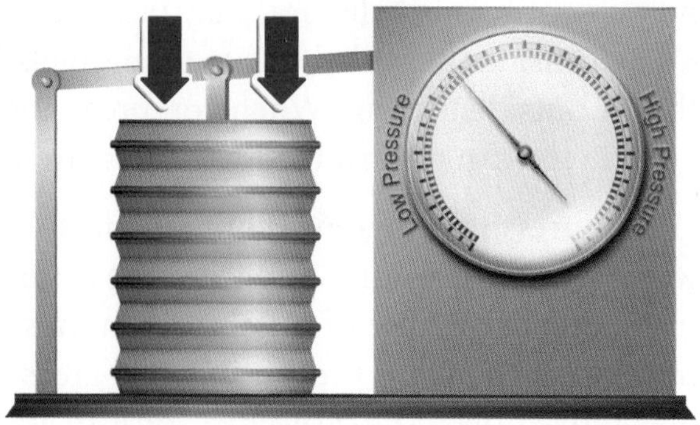


The chamber expands when the air pressure decreases.

**READING VISUALS** Which of these barometer readings would be the more likely one on a mountain? Explain why.

## Barometers and Air Pressure

Air pressure can be measured in different ways. A **barometer** is any instrument that measures air pressure. The illustrations above show a simplified version of a common type of barometer. This type contains a sealed flexible chamber that has little air inside. The chamber contracts when the outside air pressure is high and expands when the air pressure is low. A series of levers or other devices turns the motion of the chamber into something that can be read—the movement of a needle on a dial or a jagged line on a strip of graph paper.

# 3.1 Review

### KEY CONCEPTS

1. How does the movement of air molecules cause pressure? (6.4.e)
2. How does altitude affect air pressure? (6.4.e)
3. How is air density related to air pressure? (6.4.e)

### CRITICAL THINKING

4. **Apply** Would you expect the air pressure in a valley that's below sea level to be higher or lower than air pressure at sea level? Explain.
5. **Predict** Two barometers are placed one kilometer apart. One shows higher pressure than the other. What will happen to air between them?

### CHALLENGE

6. **Infer** The eardrum is a thin sheet of tissue that separates air in the middle part of your ear from air outside your ear. What could cause your eardrum to make a popping sound as you ride up a tall building in an elevator?

KEY CONCEPT

# 3.2 The atmosphere has wind patterns.

**CALIFORNIA Content Standards**

**6.4.a** Students know the sun is the major source of energy for phenomena on Earth's surface; it powers winds, ocean currents, and the water cycle.

**6.4.e** Students know differences in pressure, heat, air movement, and humidity result in changes of weather.

**BEFORE, you learned**

- Solar energy heats Earth's surface and atmosphere
- Differences in density cause air to move
- Air pressure differences set air in motion

**NOW, you will learn**

- About forces that affect wind
- About global winds
- About patterns of heating and cooling

**VOCABULARY**

**wind** p. 83
**global wind** p. 84
**Coriolis effect** p. 85
**jet stream** p. 88
**monsoon** p. 90

**EXPLORE Solar Energy** (6.4.a)

***How does Earth's shape affect solar heating?***

**PROCEDURE**

1. Place a globe on a desk in a darkened room.
2. Point a flashlight at the equator on the globe from a distance of about 15 centimeters. Keep the flashlight level. Observe the lighted area on the globe.
3. Keeping the flashlight level, raise it up and point it at the United States. Observe the lighted area.

**MATERIALS**

- globe
- flashlight
- ruler

**WHAT DO YOU THINK?**

- How were the two lighted areas different?
- What might have caused the difference?

## Uneven heating causes air to move.

On local news broadcasts, weather forecasters often spend several minutes discussing what the weather will be like over the next few days. Recall that weather is the condition of Earth's atmosphere at a particular time and place. Wind is an important part of weather. You will read about other weather factors later in this chapter.

**Wind** is air that moves horizontally, or parallel to the ground. Remember that air pressure can differ from place to place at the same altitude. Uneven heating of Earth's surface causes such pressure differences, which set air in motion. Over a short distance, wind moves directly from higher pressure toward lower pressure.

**REMINDER**

Remember that air pressure is the force that air molecules exert on an area.

**CHECK YOUR READING** What is the relationship between air pressure and wind?

## How Wind Forms

**Wind moves from an area of high pressure toward an area of low pressure.**

❶ Warmer air rises.

❷ Cooler air sinks.

low pressure

high pressure

❸ Wind moves across surface.

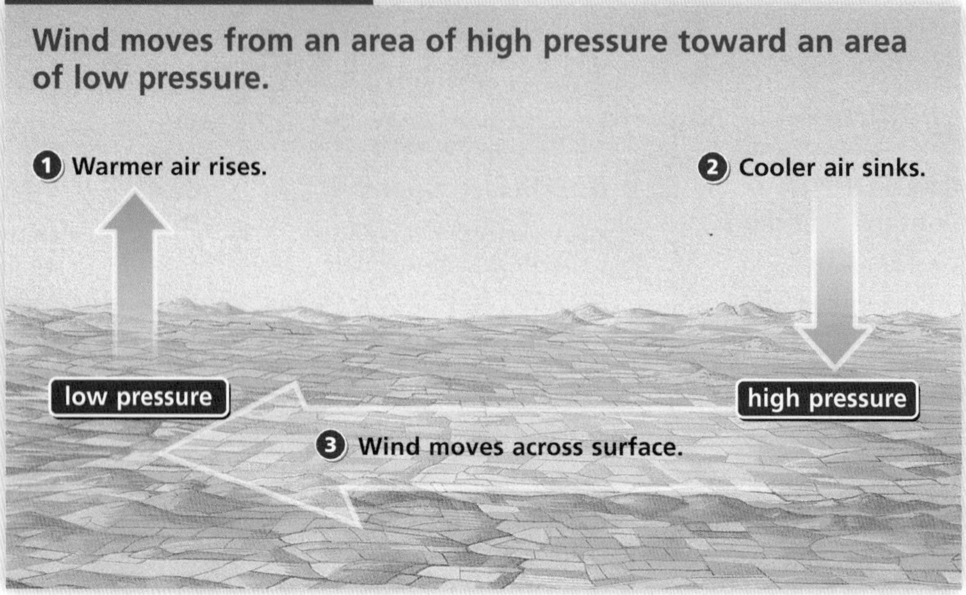

The illustration above shows a common pattern of air circulation caused by uneven heating of Earth's surface:

❶ Sunlight strongly heats an area of ground. The ground heats the air. The warm air rises, and an area of low pressure forms.

❷ Sunlight heats an area of ground less strongly. The cooler, denser air sinks slowly, and an area of high pressure forms.

❸ Air moves as wind across the surface, from higher toward lower pressure.

When the difference in pressure between two areas is small, the wind may move too slowly to be noticeable. A very large pressure difference can produce wind strong enough to uproot trees.

**CHECK YOUR READING** What factor determines the strength of wind?

Sunlight is concentrated near the equator because it strikes the surface directly.

North Pole

Arctic Circle

Tropic of Cancer

Equator

Tropic of Capricorn

Sunlight is more spread out near the poles because it strikes at a lower angle.

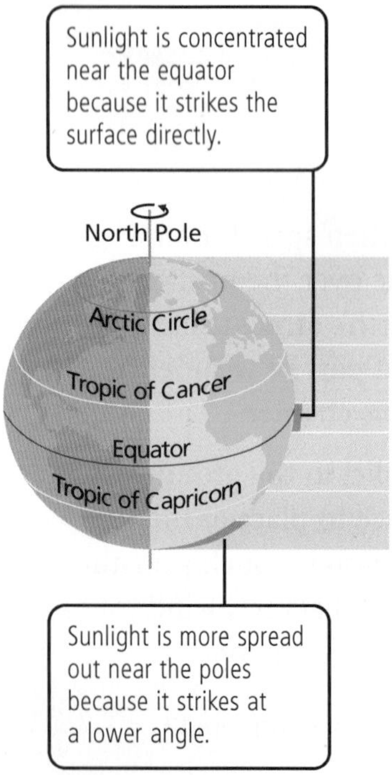

The distance winds travel varies. Some winds die out quickly after blowing a few meters. In contrast, **global winds** travel thousands of kilometers in steady patterns. Global winds last for weeks.

Uneven heating between the equator and the north and south poles causes global winds. Notice in the illustration at left how sunlight strikes Earth's curved surface. Near the equator, concentrated sunlight heats the surface to a high temperature. Warm air rises, producing low pressure.

In regions closer to the poles, the sunlight is more spread out. Because less of the Sun's energy reaches these regions, the air above them is cooler and denser. The sinking dense air produces high pressure that sets global winds in motion.

## Earth's rotation affects wind direction.

If Earth did not rotate, global winds would flow directly from the poles to the equator. However, Earth's rotation changes the direction of winds and other objects moving over Earth. The influence of Earth's rotation is called the **Coriolis effect** (KAWR-ee-OH-lihs). Global winds curve as Earth turns beneath them. In the Northern Hemisphere, winds curve to the right of the direction of motion. Winds in the Southern Hemisphere curve to the left. The Coriolis effect is noticeable only for winds that travel long distances.

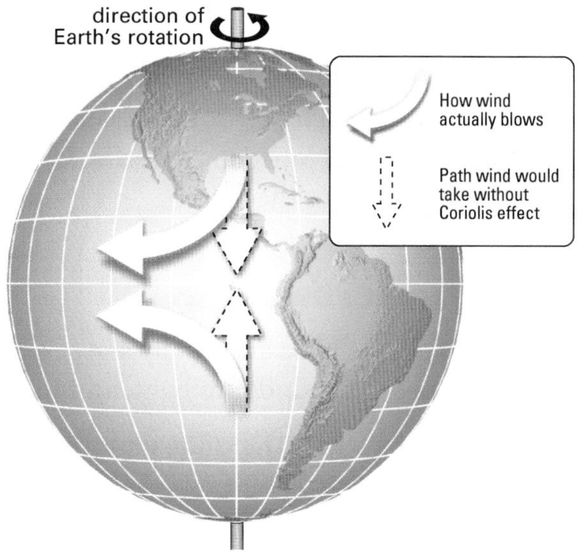


Because the Coriolis effect causes global winds to curve, they cannot flow directly from the poles to the equator. Instead, global winds travel along three routes in each hemisphere. These routes, which circle the world, are called global wind belts.

**CHECK YOUR READING** In which direction do winds curve in the Northern Hemisphere?

## INVESTIGATE Coriolis Effect

### *How does Earth's rotation affect wind?*

**PROCEDURE**

1. Blow up a balloon and tie it off.
2. Have a classmate slowly rotate the balloon to the right. Draw a line straight down from the top of the balloon to the center as the balloon rotates.
3. Now draw a line from the bottom of the balloon straight up to the center as the balloon rotates.

**WHAT DO YOU THINK?**

- How did the rotation affect the lines that you drew?
- How does this activity demonstrate the Coriolis effect?

**CHALLENGE** How might changing the speed at which the balloon is rotated affect your results? Repeat the activity to test your prediction.

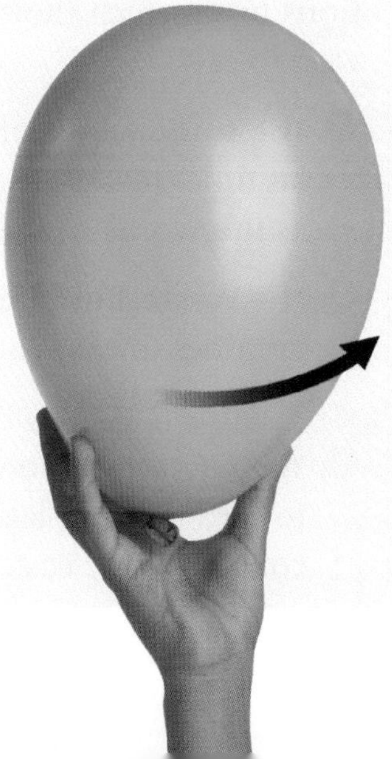

**SKILL FOCUS**
Modeling (6.4.e)

**MATERIALS**
- round balloon
- felt-tip pen

**TIME**
10 minutes

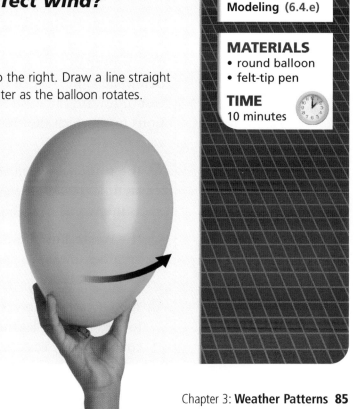

## Bands of calm air separate global wind belts.

RESOURCE CENTER
CLASSZONE.COM

Learn more about global winds.

Earth's rotation and the uneven heating of its surface cause a pattern of wind belts separated by calm regions. Each calm region is a zone of either high pressure or low pressure. The illustration on page 87 shows how each wind belt and the calm regions that border it form a giant loop of moving air. These loops are called circulation cells. The section of a cell that flows along Earth's surface is global wind. Notice that the direction of airflow changes from one circulation cell to the next.

### Calm Regions

The air usually stays calm in high-pressure and low-pressure zones. Winds are light, and they often change direction.

READING TIP

As you read about each region or wind belt, locate it in the diagram on page 87.

1. **The doldrums** are a low-pressure zone near the equator. There, warm air rises to the top of the troposphere, which is the atmosphere's lowest layer. Then the air spreads out toward the poles. The rising, moist air produces clouds and heavy rain. During the hottest months, heavy evaporation from warm ocean water in the region fuels tropical storms.
2. **The horse latitudes** are high-pressure zones located about 30° north and 30° south of the equator. Warm air traveling away from the equator cools and sinks in these regions. The weather tends to be clear and dry.

### Wind Belts

As dense air sinks to Earth's surface in the horse latitudes and other high-pressure zones, it flows out toward regions of low pressure. This pattern of air movement produces three global wind belts in each hemisphere. Because of the Coriolis effect, the winds curve toward the east or toward the west. Some global winds are named for the directions from which they blow. The westerlies, for example, blow from west to east.

3. **The trade winds** blow from the east, moving from the horse latitudes toward the equator. These strong, steady winds die out as they come near the equator.
4. **The westerlies** blow from the west, moving from the horse latitudes toward the poles. They bring storms across much of the United States.
5. **The easterlies** blow from the east, moving from the polar regions toward the mid-latitudes. Stormy weather often occurs when the cold air of the easterlies meets the warmer air of the westerlies.

## Global Winds

**Belts of global wind circle Earth. Because of the Coriolis effect, the winds in these belts curve to the east or the west. Between the global wind belts are calm areas of rising or falling air.**

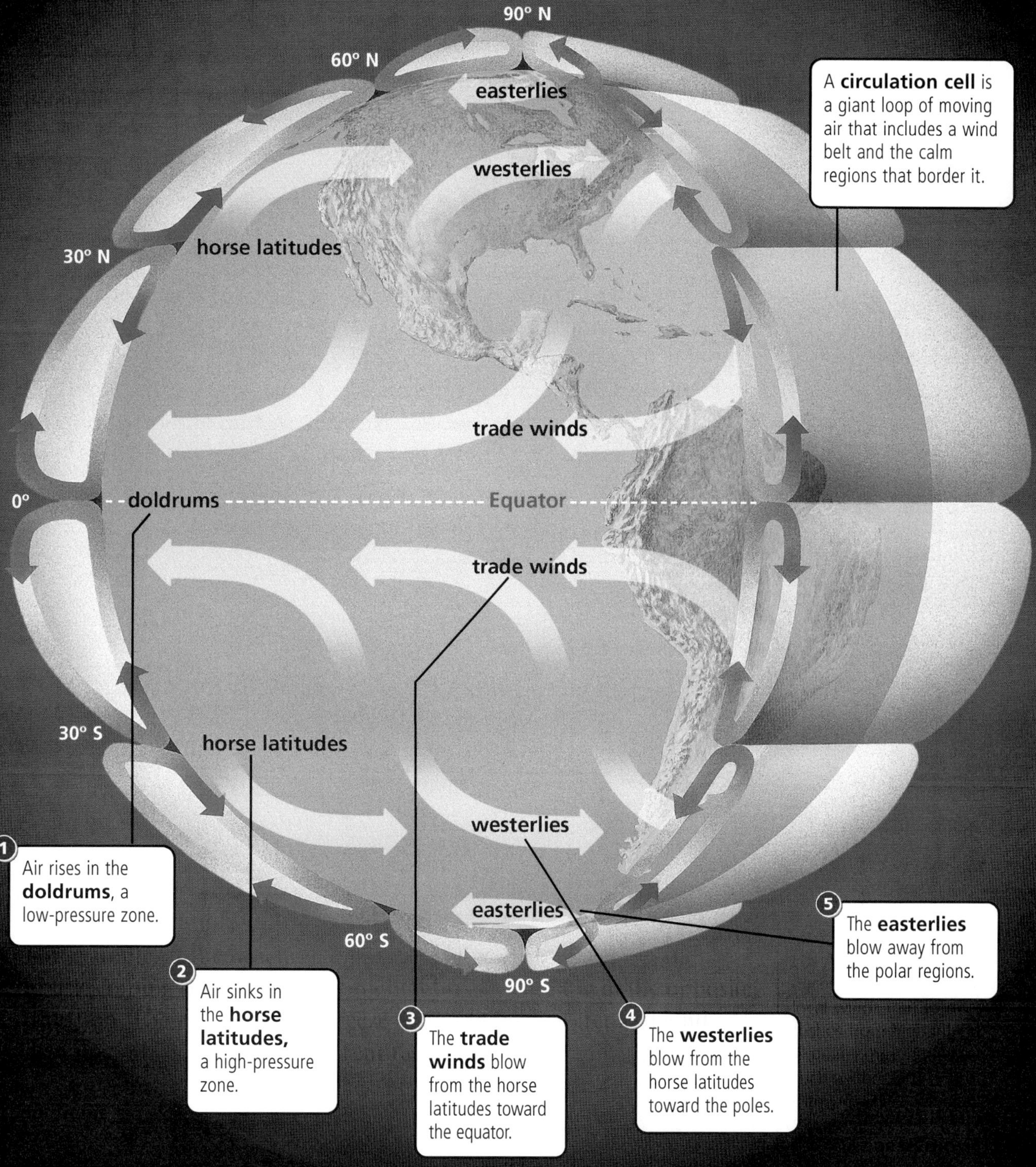

90° N
60° N
easterlies
westerlies
30° N
horse latitudes
trade winds
0°
doldrums
Equator
trade winds
30° S
horse latitudes
westerlies
easterlies
60° S
90° S
A **circulation cell** is a giant loop of moving air that includes a wind belt and the calm regions that border it.
1 Air rises in the **doldrums**, a low-pressure zone.
2 Air sinks in the **horse latitudes,** a high-pressure zone.
3 The **trade winds** blow from the horse latitudes toward the equator.
4 The **westerlies** blow from the horse latitudes toward the poles.
5 The **easterlies** blow away from the polar regions.

READING VISUALS What are the positions of the calm regions and the wind belts in the circulation cells?

## Effects of Wind on Travel

Before the invention of steam engines, sailors used to dread traveling through the doldrums and the horse latitudes. There often wasn't enough wind to move their sailing ships. A ship might stall for days or even weeks, wasting precious supplies of food and fresh water.

To avoid the calm regions, sailors sought out global wind belts. The trade winds got their name because traders used them to sail from east to west. For centuries, sailors relied on the trade winds to reach North America from Europe. They would return by sailing north to catch the westerlies and ride them across the Atlantic.

# Jet streams flow high above Earth's surface.

**COMBINATION NOTES**
Record information about how jet streams flow and their effects on weather and travel.

Not all long-distance winds travel along Earth's surface. **Jet streams** are fast-moving winds that circle Earth from west to east at high altitudes. Air often moves in jet streams at speeds greater than 200 kilometers per hour (125 mi/hr). Like global winds, jet streams form because Earth's surface is heated unevenly. Instead of following a straight line, jet streams curve north and south, as shown on the globe below.

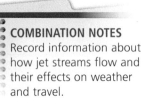

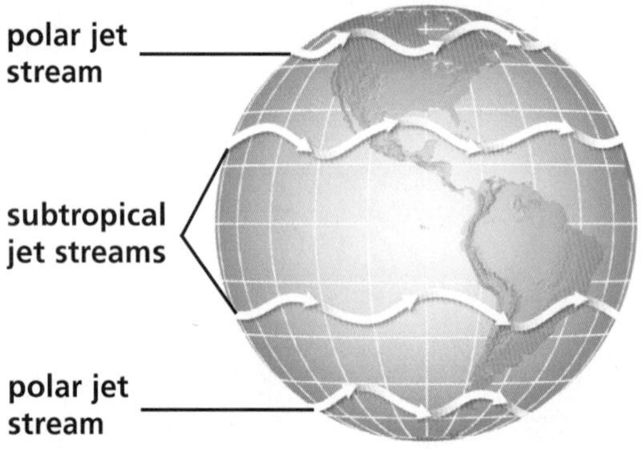


Jet streams flow in a wavy pattern from west to east around the world. They change positions during the year.

Each hemisphere usually has two jet streams, a polar jet stream and a subtropical jet stream. The polar jet streams flow closer to the poles in summer than in winter.

The polar jet stream has a strong influence on weather in North America. It can pull cold air down from Canada into the United States and pull warm air up toward Canada. In addition, strong storms tend to form along its curves. Scientists must know where the jet stream is flowing to make accurate weather predictions.

Jet streams also affect air-travel times. They usually flow 10 to 15 kilometers (6–9 mi) above Earth's surface. Since airplanes often fly at these altitudes, their travel times can be lengthened or shortened by the strong wind of a jet stream.

## Patterns of heating and cooling cause local winds and monsoons.

Have you ever noticed how the wind can change in predictable ways? For example, at the beach on a hot day you will often feel a cool breeze coming off the water. At night a breeze will flow in the opposite direction. The change in the breeze occurs because water and land heat up and cool down at different rates.

**CALIFORNIA Focus**

Los Angeles often experiences Santa Ana winds, local winds that form as air rushes from high inland plateaus through low areas such as the Santa Ana Canyon. These winds blow toward an area of low pressure over the ocean.

### Local Winds

Some winds change daily in a regular pattern. These local winds blow within small areas.

- Sea breezes and land breezes occur near shorelines. During the day, land heats up faster than water. The air over the land rises and expands. Denser ocean air moves into the area of low pressure, producing a sea breeze. As the illustration below shows, this pattern is reversed at night, when land cools faster than water. Warm air rises over the ocean, and cooler air flows in, producing a land breeze.

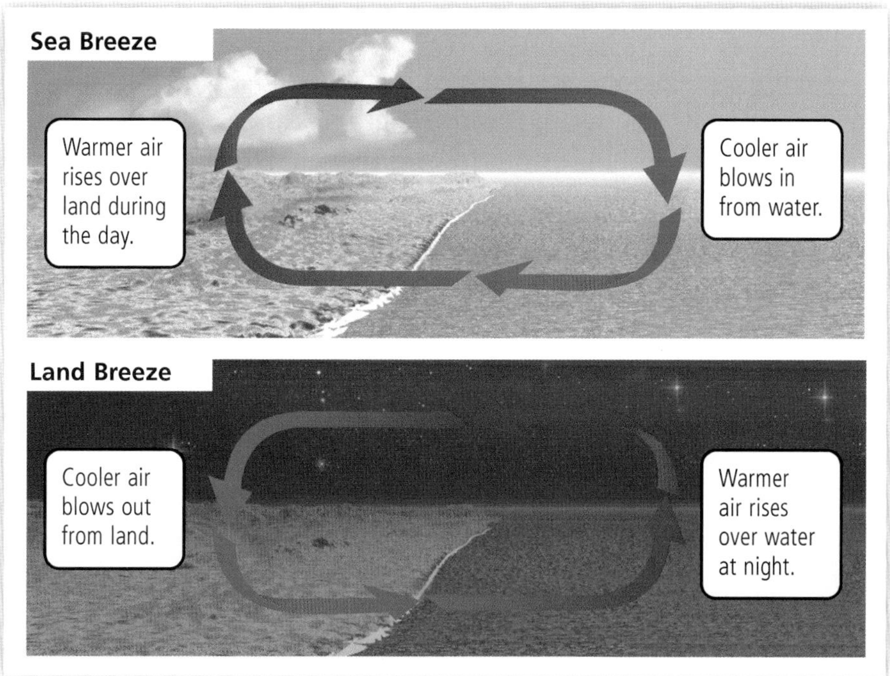
Sea Breeze
Warmer air rises over land during the day.
Cooler air blows in from water.
Land Breeze
Cooler air blows out from land.
Warmer air rises over water at night.

**REMINDER**

Red arrows stand for warmer air. Blue arrows stand for cooler air.

- Valley breezes and mountain breezes are caused by a similar process. Mountain slopes heat up and cool faster than the valleys below them. During the day, valley breezes flow up mountains. At night mountain breezes flow down into valleys.

**CHECK YOUR READING** How do mountains and bodies of water affect patterns of heating and cooling?

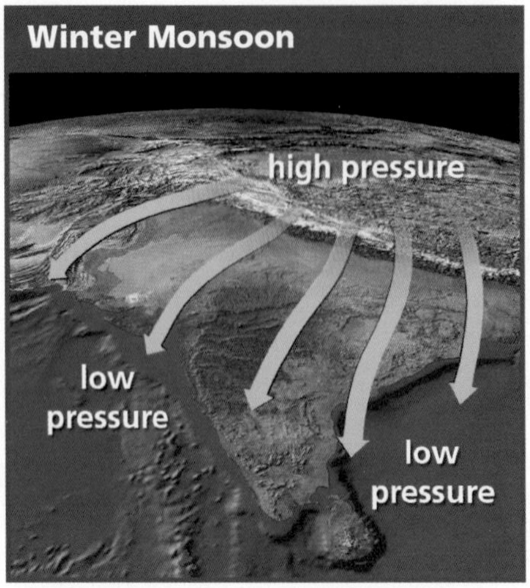


Dry air blows from the high-pressure area over the continent to the low-pressure areas over the ocean.

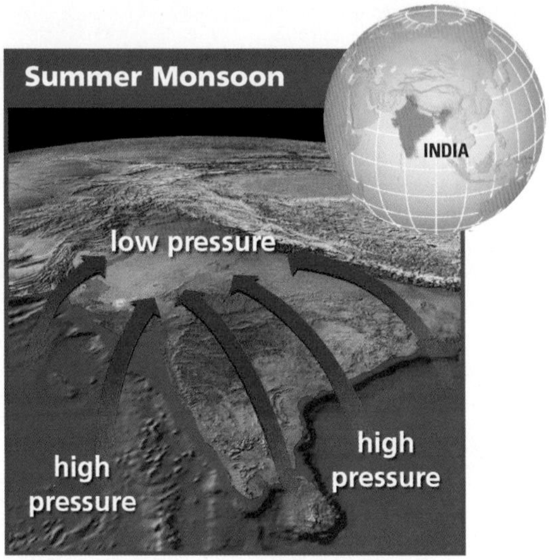


Moist air blows from the high-pressure areas over the ocean to the low-pressure area over the continent.

## Monsoons

**VOCABULARY**
Add a description wheel for *monsoon* to your notebook.

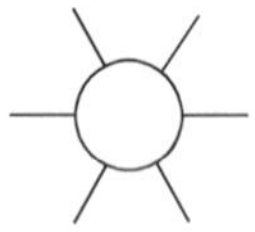

Winds that change direction with the seasons are called **monsoons.** Like sea breezes and land breezes, monsoons are caused by the different heating and cooling rates of land and sea. However, monsoons flow longer distances and affect much larger areas.

Winter monsoons occur in regions where the land becomes much cooler than the sea during winter. High pressure builds over the land, and cool, dry wind blows out toward the sea. During summer this pattern reverses as the land becomes much warmer than the sea. Moist wind flows inland, often bringing heavy rains. The most extreme monsoons occur in South Asia and Southeast Asia. Farmers there depend on rain from the summer monsoon to grow crops.

**CHECK YOUR READING** How do monsoon winds affect rainfall?

# 3.2 Review

### KEY CONCEPTS

1. How does the uneven heating of Earth's surface cause winds to flow? (6.4.a)
2. How does Earth's rotation influence the movement of global winds? (6.4.e)
3. Why do some winds change direction in areas where land is near water? (6.4.e)

### CRITICAL THINKING

4. **Compare and Contrast** How are global winds and local winds similar? How are they different?
5. **Analyze** Make a table that shows the causes and effects of local winds and monsoons.

### CHALLENGE

6. **Predict** Suppose that a city is located in a valley between the sea and a mountain range. What kind of wind pattern would you predict for this area?

MATH in SCIENCE

## SKILL: ADDING MEASUREMENTS

# Navigate the Jet Stream

When an airplane flies in the same direction as a jet stream, the airplane gets a boost in its speed. Pilots can save time if they fly with the jet stream. But flying against the jet stream slows an airplane down.

**MATH TUTORIAL**
CLASSZONE.COM
Click on Math Tutorial for more help with adding measures of time.

**Math** 6.NS.2.3
**Science** 6.4.d, 6.4.e

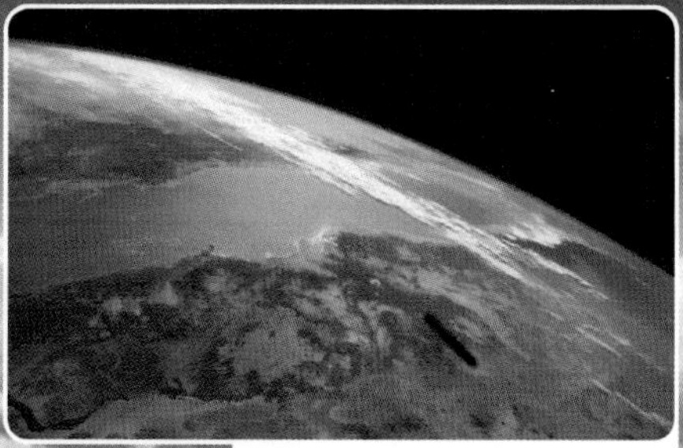

High clouds show the location of the jet stream in this satellite image.

### Example

To determine the total flight time between San Francisco and Chicago, with a stop in Denver, you need to add the hours and minutes separately. Set up the problem like this:

| | | |
|---|---|---|
| San Francisco to Denver: | 2 h | 10 min |
| Denver to Chicago: | 1 h | 45 min |
| Total flight time: | 3 h | 55 min |

**ANSWER** The total flight time is 3 hours 55 minutes.

**Flight Times**

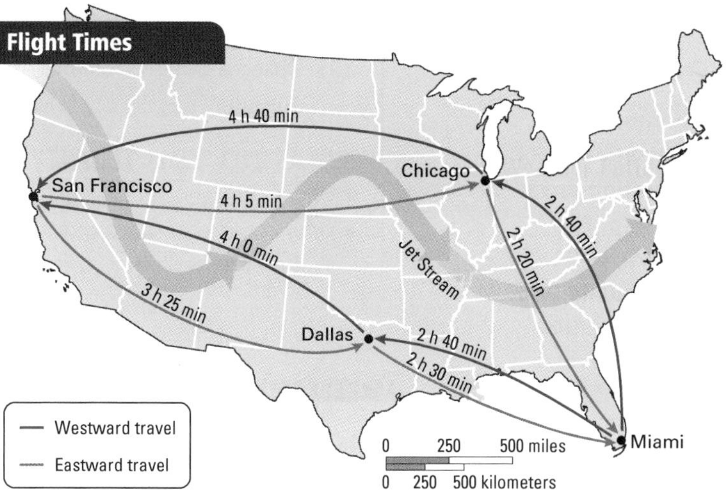

**Use the map to answer the following questions.**

1. What is the total flight time for an airplane flying from San Francisco to Miami through Chicago?

2. What is the total flight time for an airplane flying from San Francisco to Miami through Dallas?

3. Which route from Miami to San Francisco is faster? What is the time difference between the routes?

4. Compare the flight time from Chicago to San Francisco with the flight time from San Francisco to Chicago.

**CHALLENGE** Use the map scale to find the approximate distance between San Francisco and Chicago. What is the average air speed of an airplane that flies the route in 4 hours?

KEY CONCEPT

# 3.3 Most clouds form as air rises and cools.

**CALIFORNIA Content Standards**

**6.4.a** Students know the sun is the major source of energy for phenomena on Earth's surface; it powers winds, ocean currents, and the water cycle.

**6.4.e** Students know differences in pressure, heat, air movement, and humidity result in changes of weather.

**BEFORE, you learned**

- Water vapor circulates from Earth to the atmosphere
- Warm air is less dense than cool air and tends to rise

**NOW, you will learn**

- How water in the atmosphere changes
- How clouds form
- About the types of clouds

**VOCABULARY**

**evaporation** p. 92
**condensation** p. 92
**precipitation** p. 93
**humidity** p. 94
**saturation** p. 94
**relative humidity** p. 94
**dew point** p. 94

**EXPLORE Condensation** (6.4.e)

### *How does condensation occur?*

**PROCEDURE**

1. Observe the air as a classmate breathes out.
2. Observe a mirror as a classmate breathes onto it.

**MATERIALS**

hand mirror

**WHAT DO YOU THINK?**

- What changes did you observe on the mirror?
- Why could you see water on the mirror but not in the air when your classmate breathed out?

## Temperature affects water in the air.

Water is always in the atmosphere. You may see water in solid form, such as falling snow. Water may also be present as liquid water droplets. Even if you can't see any water, it is still part of the air as water vapor, an invisible gas. When temperatures change, water changes its form.

- **Evaporation** is the process by which a liquid changes into a gas. For water to evaporate, it needs extra energy.
- **Condensation** is the process by which a gas, such as water vapor, changes into a liquid. Condensation occurs when moist air cools.

The picture on the left shows the processes of evaporation and condensation at work. Water in a teakettle absorbs heat. It gets enough energy to evaporate into water vapor. The invisible water vapor rises and escapes from the kettle. When the vapor hits the cooler air outside the kettle, it cools and condenses into tiny but visible water droplets.

## Water in the Air

Vast amounts of Earth's water are recycled. The oceans hold most of the water. Water is also stored in lakes, rivers, and ice sheets; in plants; and underground. Energy from sunlight causes molecules to evaporate from the surface of a body of water. These molecules become part of the air in the form of water vapor.

As air rises in the atmosphere, it cools. The loss of heat causes water vapor to condense into tiny water droplets or ice crystals. If the droplets or crystals grow and become heavy enough, they fall as rain, snow, sleet, or hail. Any type of liquid or solid water that falls to Earth's surface is called **precipitation.** Earth's water goes through a never-ending cycle of evaporation, condensation, and precipitation.

**VOCABULARY**
Add a description wheel for *precipitation* to your notebook.

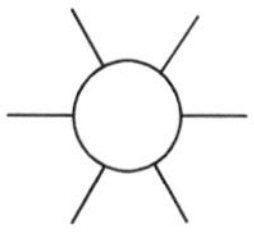

Water vapor can also condense on solid surfaces. Have you ever gotten your shoes wet while walking on grass in the early morning? The grass was covered with dew, which is water that has condensed on cool surfaces at night. If the temperature is cold enough, water vapor can change directly into a covering of ice, called frost.

**CHECK YOUR READING** Summarize the way water moves in the water cycle. For each part of the cycle, specify whether water exists as a gas, liquid, or solid.

### Water Cycle

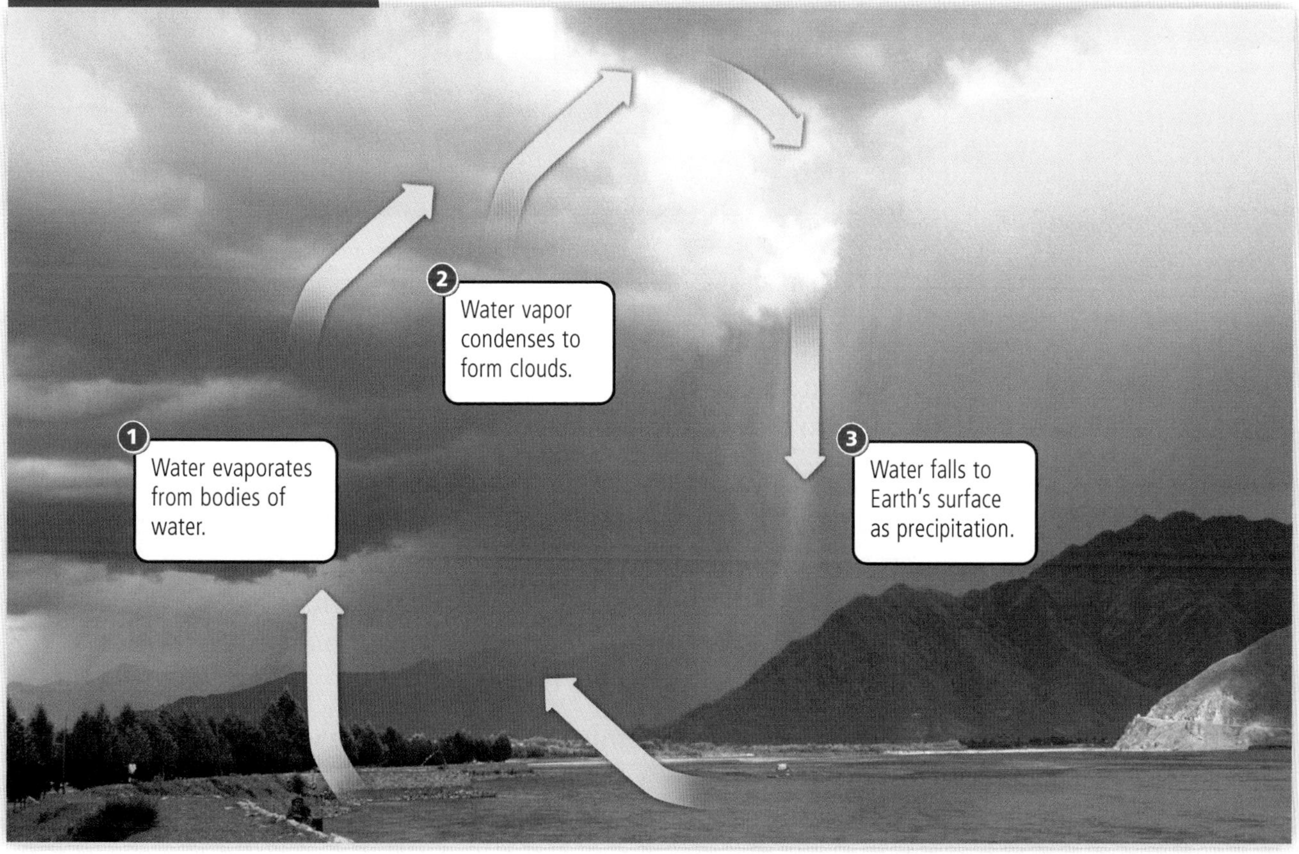
1
Water evaporates from bodies of water.
2
Water vapor condenses to form clouds.
3
Water falls to Earth's surface as precipitation.

## Humidity and Relative Humidity

On a warm summer day, evaporation of moisture from your skin can help you feel comfortable. However, a lot of water vapor in the air can cause less moisture to evaporate from your skin. With less evaporation, the air will seem hotter and damper. **Humidity** is the amount of water vapor in air. Humidity varies from place to place and from time to time.

The illustration shows how humidity increases in a sealed container. As water molecules evaporate into the air, some start to condense and return to the water. For a while the air gains water vapor because more water evaporates than condenses. But eventually the air reaches **saturation,** a condition in which the rates of evaporation and condensation are equal. Any additional water that evaporates is balanced by water that condenses.

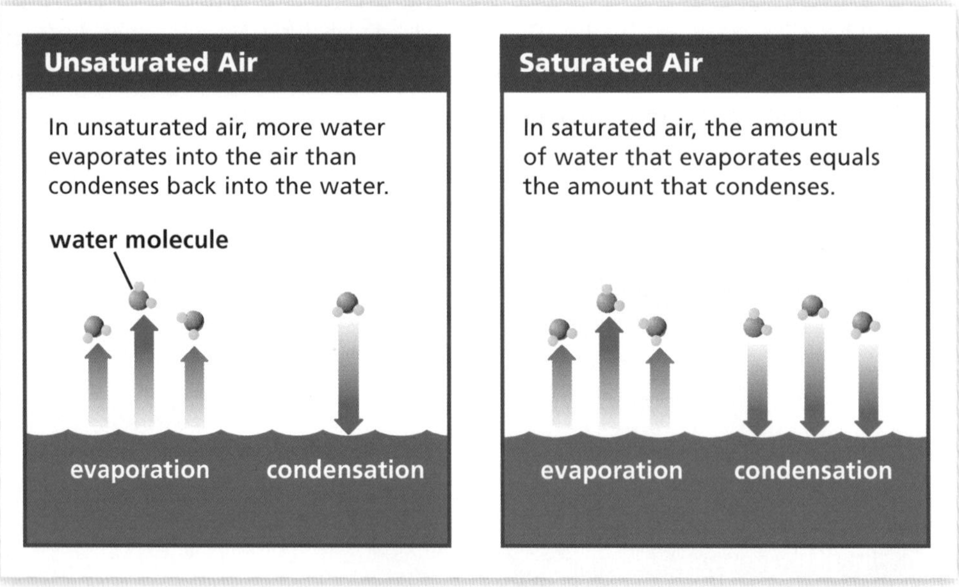

Unsaturated Air
In unsaturated air, more water evaporates into the air than condenses back into the water.
water molecule
evaporation
condensation
Saturated Air
In saturated air, the amount of water that evaporates equals the amount that condenses.
evaporation
condensation

**READING TIP**

*Relative* means "considered in comparison with something else."

The amount of water vapor in air at saturation depends on the temperature of the air. The warmer air is, the more water vapor it takes to saturate it. Scientists use this principle to describe the humidity of air in two different ways: relative humidity and dew point.

**Relative humidity** compares the amount of water vapor in air with the maximum amount of water vapor that can be present at that temperature. For example, air with 50 percent relative humidity has half the amount of water needed for saturation. If the amount of water vapor in air stays the same, relative humidity will decrease as the air heats up and increase as the air cools.

**Dew point** is the temperature at which air with a given amount of water vapor will reach saturation. For example, air with a dew point of 26°C (79°F) will become saturated if it cools to 26°C. The higher the dew point of air, the more water vapor the air contains.

## Water vapor condenses and forms clouds.

Clouds are made of condensed water vapor. As warm air rises in the atmosphere, it cools. When the air cools to its dew point—the temperature at which air reaches saturation—water vapor condenses into tiny droplets or ice crystals. These droplets and crystals are so light that they either float as clouds on rising air or fall very slowly.

Rising warm air can produce clouds. Water vapor begins to condense when the air cools to its dew point.

Recall how dew condenses on grass. Water vapor condenses on liquid water or on something solid. There are no large solid surfaces in the air. However, the air is filled with tiny particles such as dust, smoke, and salt from the ocean. Water vapor condenses on these particles.

## INVESTIGATE Condensation

### *How does a cloud form?*

**PROCEDURE**

1. Add a spoonful of water to the bottle to increase the humidity inside it.
2. Lay the bottle on its side. Light a match, blow it out, and then stick the match into the bottle for a few seconds to let smoke flow in. Replace the cap.
3. Squeeze the bottle quickly and then release it. Observe what happens when the bottle is allowed to expand.

**WHAT DO YOU THINK?**

- What happened to the water vapor inside the bottle when you squeezed the bottle and then let it expand?
- How did the smoke affect what happened to the water vapor?

**CHALLENGE** How would the cloud change if you raised or lowered the temperature inside the bottle?

**SKILL FOCUS**
Observing (6.4.e)

**MATERIALS**
- clear 1-liter plastic bottle with cap
- water at room temperature
- tablespoon
- matches

**TIME**
10 minutes

RESOURCE CENTER
CLASSZONE.COM

Observe different types of clouds.

## Characteristics of Clouds

If you watch the sky over a period of time, you will probably observe clouds that do not look alike. Clouds have different characteristics because they form under different conditions. The shapes and sizes of clouds are mainly determined by air movement. For example, puffy clouds form in air that rises sharply or moves straight up and down. Flat, smooth clouds covering large areas form in air that rises gradually.

Location affects the composition of clouds. Since the troposphere gets colder with altitude, clouds that form at high altitudes are made of tiny ice crystals. Closer to Earth's surface, clouds are made of water droplets or a mixture of ice crystals and water droplets.

**CHECK YOUR READING** How are clouds that form at high altitudes different from clouds that form close to Earth's surface?

**COMBINATION NOTES**
Record information about the three main cloud types.

In the illustration on page 97, notice that some cloud names share word parts. That is because clouds are classified and named according to their altitudes, the ways they form, and their general characteristics. The three main types of clouds are cirrus, cumulus, and stratus. These names come from Latin words that suggest the clouds' appearances.

- ***Cirrus*** (SEER-uhs) means "curl of hair." Cirrus clouds appear feathery or wispy.
- ***Cumulus*** (KYOOM-yuh-luhs) means "heap" or "pile." Cumulus-type clouds can grow to be very tall.
- ***Stratus*** (STRAT-uhs) means "spread out." Stratus-type clouds form in flat layers.

Word parts are used to tell more about clouds. For example, names of clouds that produce precipitation contain the word part *nimbo-* or *nimbus.* Names of clouds that form at a medium altitude have the prefix *alto-*.

cirrus clouds

## Cirrus Clouds

Cirrus clouds form in very cold air at high altitudes. Made of ice crystals, they have a wispy or feathery appearance. Strong winds often blow streamers or "tails" off cirrus clouds. These features show the direction of the wind in the upper troposphere. You will usually see cirrus clouds in fair weather. However, they can be a sign that a storm is approaching.

## Cloud Types

**The three main cloud types are cirrus, cumulus, and stratus. These names can be combined with each other and with other word parts to identify more specific cloud types.**

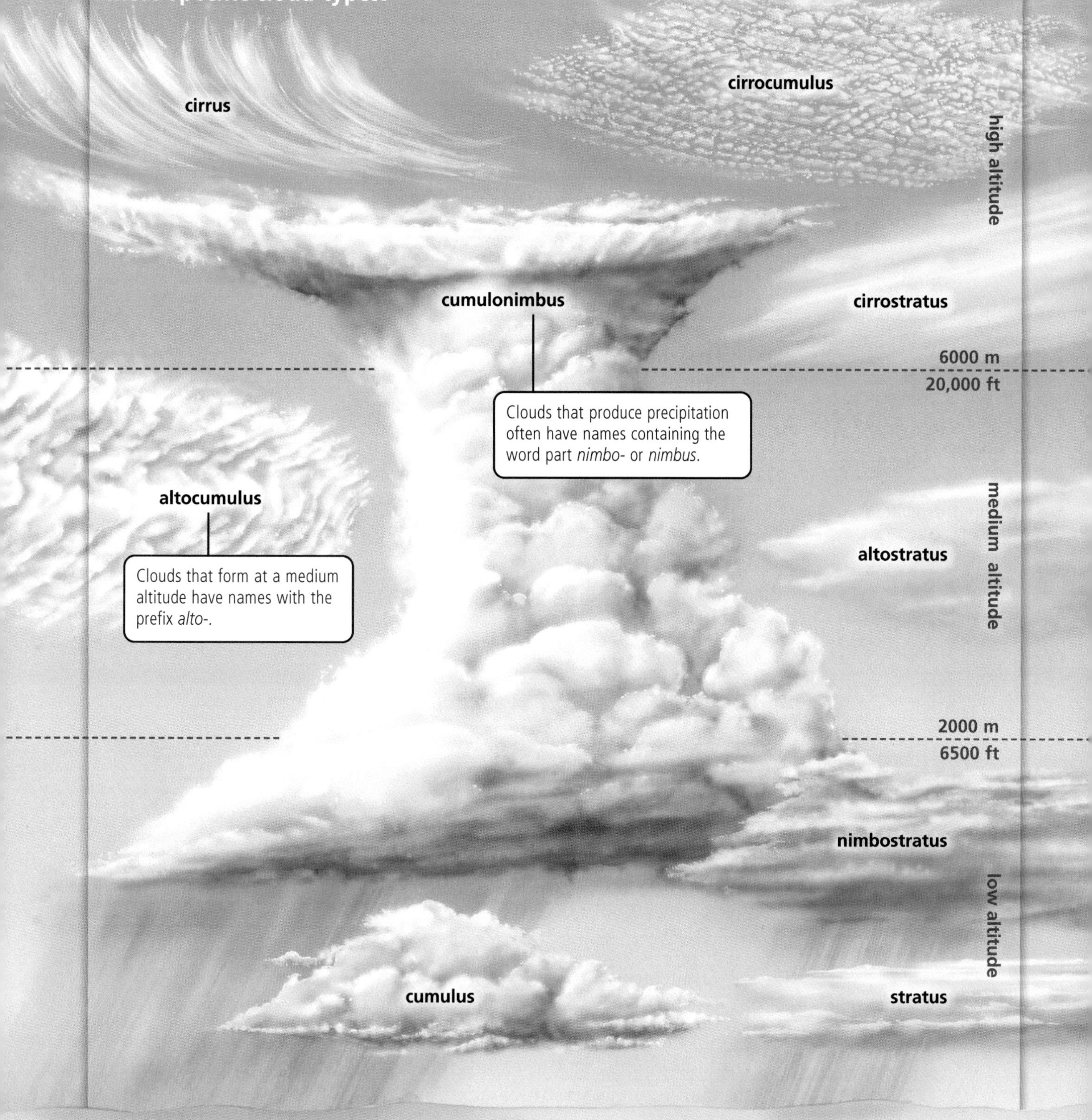


**READING VISUALS** Which cloud names are combinations of names of two main cloud types?

READING TIP

As you read each description of a main cloud type, look back at the visual on page 97. Notice the different clouds that have the main cloud type as part of their names.

## Cumulus Clouds

cumulus clouds

Cumulus clouds are puffy white clouds with darker bases. They look like cotton balls floating in the sky. There are several varieties of cumulus clouds. Usually they appear in the daytime in fair weather, when warm air rises and its water vapor condenses. Cooler air sinks along the sides of the clouds, keeping cumulus clouds separate from one another.

cumulonimbus clouds

If cumulus clouds keep growing taller, they can produce showers. The precipitation usually lasts less than half an hour in an area because the clouds are moving. The tallest clouds are cumulonimbus clouds, or thunderheads. These clouds produce thunderstorms that drop heavy rainfall. A cumulonimbus cloud can tower 18 kilometers (11 mi) above Earth's surface. By comparison, jet planes usually fly at about 10 kilometers (6 mi). Strong high-altitude winds often cause the top of the cloud to jut out sharply.

CHECK YOUR READING How are cumulonimbus clouds different from other cumulus clouds?

## Stratus Clouds

stratus clouds

Have you ever noticed on some days that the whole sky looks gray? You were looking at stratus clouds. They form in layers when air cools over a large area without rising or when the air is gently lifted. Stratus clouds are smooth because they form without strong air movement.

Some low stratus clouds are so dark that they completely block out the Sun. These clouds produce steady, light precipitation—unlike the brief showers that come from cumulus clouds. Stratus clouds that form at high altitudes are much thinner than low stratus clouds. You can see the Sun and the Moon through them. The ice crystals in high stratus clouds can make it seem as if there's a circle of colored light around the Sun or the Moon.

This layer of fog covers most of the Golden Gate Bridge. The fog formed as water vapor condensed in the air above cool ocean water.

## Fog

Fog is a cloud that rests on the ground or a body of water. Like stratus clouds, fog has a smooth appearance. It usually forms when a surface is colder than the air above it. Water vapor in the air condenses as it cools, forming a thick mist. Fog on land tends to be heaviest at dawn, after the ground has cooled overnight. It clears as the ground is heated up by sunlight.

Fog can look beautiful rolling over hills or partly covering structures such as bridges. However, it often makes transportation dangerous by limiting visibility. In the United States close to 700 people die each year in automobile accidents that occur in dense fog.

## 3.3 Review

### KEY CONCEPTS

1. Describe the three forms in which water is present in the atmosphere. (6.4.a)
2. How does altitude affect the composition of clouds? (6.4.e)
3. How are clouds classified? (6.4.e)

### CRITICAL THINKING

4. **Summarize** Describe the main characteristics of cirrus, cumulus, and stratus clouds.
5. **Draw Conclusions** Why might cumulonimbus clouds be more likely to form on sunny days than on days with little sunlight?

### CHALLENGE

6. **Apply** Imagine that the sky has turned very cloudy after a hot morning. You notice that the bread in your sandwich is soggy and the towels on the towel rack won't dry. Explain why these things are happening. Use the following terms in your answer: *condensation, evaporation, relative humidity.*

# CHAPTER INVESTIGATION

## Relative Humidity

**OVERVIEW AND PURPOSE** Finding out the relative humidity can help you predict how comfortable you will feel on a hot day or whether dew will form on the ground. You can use a psychrometer to measure relative humidity. A psychrometer is a device made from two thermometers—one with a wet bulb and the other with a dry bulb. In this activity you will

- make a milk-carton psychrometer
- use it to measure the relative humidity of the air at two locations in your school

### Problem

Write It Up

Which location will have the greater relative humidity?

### Hypothesize

Write It Up

Write a hypothesis in "If . . . , then . . . , because . . ." form to answer the problem.

**MATERIALS**

- 2 thermometers
- cotton or felt cloth
- 3 rubber bands
- plastic bowl
- water at room temperature
- scissors
- pint milk carton
- ruler
- Relative Humidity Chart

6.4.e, 6.7.a, 6.7.b, 6.7.d, 6.7.e

### Procedure

1. Make a table like the one shown on the sample notebook page to record your data.

2. Check the two thermometers that you are using in this experiment to make sure they show the same temperature. Wrap a piece of cotton or felt cloth around the bulb of one thermometer. Hold the cloth in place with a rubber band as shown in the photograph. Dip this wet-bulb thermometer into a bowl of room-temperature water until the cloth is soaked.

step 3

3. Use scissors to cut a small hole in one side of the milk carton, 2 centimeters from the bottom of the carton. Place the wet-bulb thermometer on the same side as the hole that you made in the milk carton, and attach it with a rubber band. Push the tail of the cloth through the hole. Attach the dry-bulb thermometer as shown.

**Content Standard**
6.4.e Students know differences in pressure, heat, air movement, and humidity result in changes of weather.

**Investigation Standard**
6.7.b Select and use appropriate tools and technology (including calculators, computers, balances, spring scales, microscopes, and binoculars) to perform tests, collect data, and display data.

4 Fill the carton with water to just below the hole so that the cloth will remain wet. Empty the bowl and place the completed psychrometer inside it.

5 Write "science room" under the heading "Location 1" in your data table. Take your first readings in the science classroom about 10 minutes after you set up your psychrometer. Read the temperatures on the two thermometers in degrees Celsius. Record the temperature readings for the first location in the first column of your table.

6 Choose a second location in your school, and identify it under the heading "Location 2" in the data table. Take a second set of temperature readings with your psychrometer in this location. Record the readings in the second column of your table.

7 Subtract the wet-bulb reading from the dry-bulb reading for each location. Record this information in the third row of your data table.

8 Use the relative humidity table your teacher provides to find each relative humidity (expressed as a percentage). In the left-hand column, find the dry-bulb reading for location 1 that you recorded in step 5. Then find in the top line the number you recorded in step 7 (the difference between the dry-bulb and wet-bulb readings). Record the relative humidity in the last row of your data table. Repeat these steps for location 2.

## Observe and Analyze

Write It Up

1. **RECORD OBSERVATIONS** Draw the setup of your psychrometer. Be sure your data table is complete.
2. **IDENTIFY** Identify the variables and constants in this experiment. List them in your **Science Notebook.**
3. **COMPARE** How do the wet-bulb readings compare with the dry-bulb readings?
4. **ANALYZE** If the difference between the temperature readings on the two thermometers is large, is the relative humidity high or low? Explain why.

## Conclude

Write It Up

1. **INTERPRET** Answer the question in the problem. Compare your results with your hypothesis.
2. **IDENTIFY LIMITS** Describe any possible errors that you made in following the procedure.
3. **APPLY** How would you account for the differences in relative humidity that you obtained for the two locations in your school?

## INVESTIGATE Further

**CHALLENGE** Use the psychrometer to keep track of the relative humidity in your classroom over a period of one week. Make a new chart to record your data. What do you notice about how the changes in relative humidity relate to the weather conditions outside?

Relative Humidity

**Problem** Which location will have the greater relative humidity?

**Hypothesize**

**Observe and Analyze**

Table 1. Relative Humidity at Two Locations

| | Location 1 | Location 2 |
|---|---|---|
| | | |
| Dry-bulb temperature | | |
| Wet-bulb temperature | | |
| Difference between dry-bulb and wet-bulb readings | | |
| Relative humidity | | |

**Conclude**

KEY CONCEPT

# 3.4 Water falls to Earth's surface as precipitation.

**CALIFORNIA Content Standards**

**6.4.a** Students know the sun is the major source of energy for phenomena on Earth's surface; it powers winds, ocean currents, and the water cycle.

**6.4.e** Students know differences in pressure, heat, air movement, and humidity result in changes of weather.

**BEFORE, you learned**

- Water moves between Earth's surface and the atmosphere
- Water vapor condenses into clouds

**NOW, you will learn**

- How precipitation forms
- How precipitation is measured
- About acid rain

**VOCABULARY**

**freezing rain** p. 104
**sleet** p. 104
**hail** p. 104
**acid rain** p. 106

**THINK ABOUT**

### *Why does steam from a shower form large drops?*

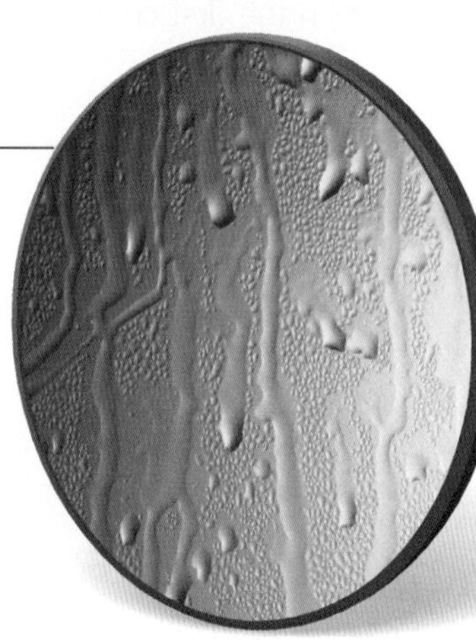

When you run a hot shower, the bathroom fills up with water vapor. The vapor condenses into tiny droplets that make it seem as if you are standing in fog. You may also see larger drops running down cool surfaces, such as a mirror. Why do some drops fall while others remain suspended?

## Precipitation forms from water droplets or ice crystals.

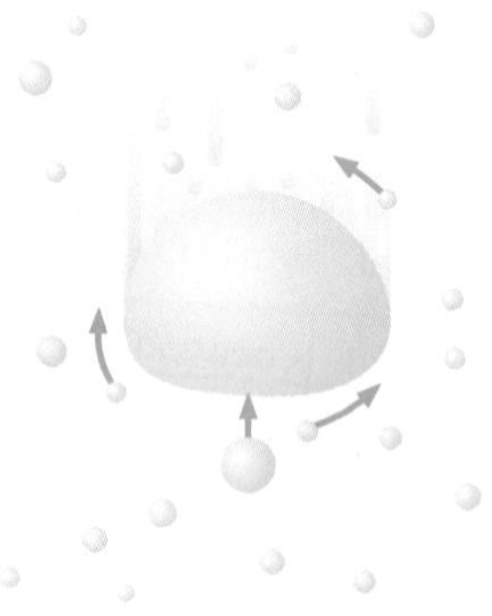

Water droplets combining to form a raindrop

All precipitation comes from clouds. For example, rain occurs when water droplets in a cloud fall to the ground. Then why doesn't every cloud produce precipitation? Cloud droplets are much smaller than a typical raindrop. They weigh so little that it takes only a slight upward movement of air to hold them up. In order for rain to fall from a cloud and reach Earth's surface, the cloud droplets must become larger and heavier.

One way that precipitation can form is through the combining of cloud droplets. The tiny droplets of water move up and down in clouds. Some collide with each other and combine, forming slightly bigger droplets. As the droplets continue to combine, they grow larger and larger. Eventually they become heavy enough to fall. It takes about a million droplets to make a single raindrop.

Another way that precipitation can form is through the growth of ice crystals. When the temperature inside a cloud is below freezing, water vapor changes into tiny ice crystals. The crystals grow by collecting more water vapor or by colliding and merging with one another. When the crystals become heavy enough, they fall from the cloud. Snow isn't the only type of precipitation that forms this way. Most rain in the United States actually starts out as falling ice crystals. Before the crystals reach the ground, they melt in a layer of warm air.

**CHECK YOUR READING** How do cloud droplets become large enough to fall as precipitation?

## Measuring Precipitation

Scientists use a rain gauge to measure rainfall. A funnel or opening at the top of the gauge allows rain to flow into a cylinder. By measuring the water collected, you can find out how much rain fell in a storm or over a period of time.

**READING TIP**
A gauge (gayj) is an instrument used for measuring or testing.

Snow depth can be measured with a long ruler. Because the amount of water in snow varies, scientists use a special gauge to find out how much water the snow contains. A built-in heater melts the snow so that it can be measured just like rain.

## INVESTIGATE Precipitation

### *How do precipitation patterns vary across California?*

**SKILL FOCUS**
Analyzing data (6.4.e)

**MATERIALS**
- Precipitation Datasheet

**TIME**
15 minutes

**PROCEDURE**

1. Study the precipitation map of California. Match the patterns used to show amounts of precipitation to the map key.
2. Find on the map the locations of Crescent City, San Francisco, Los Angeles, and Furnace Creek.
3. Compare the annual precipitation for the four cities.

**WHAT DO YOU THINK?**

- List the cities in order of amount of precipitation received, from lowest to highest.
- Why do you think there is a large difference between the average annual precipitation of Crescent City and Furnace Creek?

**CHALLENGE** Determine the annual precipitation for the city or region of the state in which you live. Give two factors that help determine the amount of precipitation your area receives.

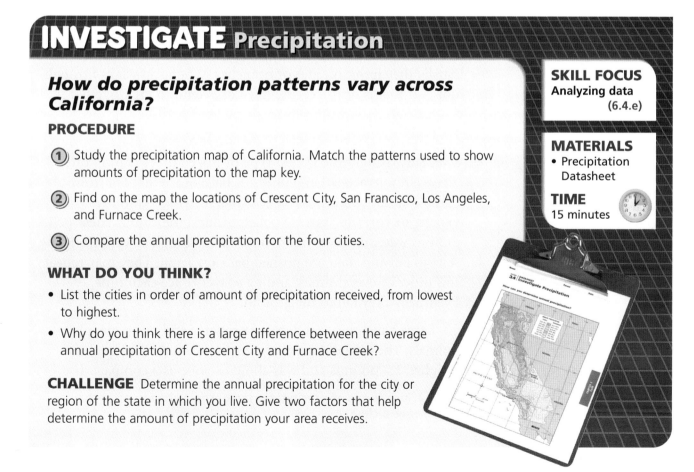

When you watch weather reports on television, you often see storm systems passing across a weather map. Some of these images are made with Doppler radar. The radar shows which areas are getting precipitation and how fast it is falling. Forecasters use this information to estimate the total amount of precipitation an area will receive.

**COMBINATION NOTES**
Record information on precipitation in your combination notes.

## Types of Precipitation

Precipitation reaches Earth's surface in various forms. Some precipitation freezes or melts as it falls through the atmosphere.

1. **Rain and Drizzle** Rain is the most common type of precipitation. Raindrops form from liquid cloud droplets or from ice crystals that melt as they fall. A light rain with very small drops is called drizzle. Drizzle usually comes from stratus clouds, which don't have enough air movement to build up larger raindrops.

2. **Freezing Rain** Raindrops may freeze when they hit the ground or other surfaces in cold weather. **Freezing rain** covers surfaces with a coating of ice. During an ice storm, roads become slippery and dangerous. The weight of ice can also bring down trees and power lines.

3. **Sleet** When rain passes through a layer of cold air, it can freeze before hitting the ground. The small pellets of ice that form are called **sleet.**

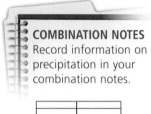

Most snowflakes have six branches or sides.

4. **Snow** As ice crystals grow and merge in clouds, they become snowflakes. Snowflakes come in many different shapes and sizes. Usually they have six sides or branches. When snow falls through moist air that is near freezing, the flakes tend to join together in clumps. When snow falls through colder and drier air, snowflakes don't join together, and the snow is powdery.

5. **Hail** Surprisingly, the largest type of frozen precipitation often arrives in warm weather. Lumps or balls of ice that fall from cumulonimbus clouds are called **hail.** During a thunderstorm, violent air currents hurl ice pellets around the cloud. These pellets grow as water droplets freeze onto them at high elevations. Some start to fall and then are pushed back up again. They may repeat this process several times, adding a layer of ice each time. Eventually they fall to the ground.

   Large hailstones can damage property and injure people and animals. The biggest hailstone ever found in the United States weighed 1.7 pounds and was about as wide as a compact disc.

**CHECK YOUR READING** Which forms of precipitation undergo a change after they leave a cloud?

## How Precipitation Forms

**All precipitation forms from water droplets or ice crystals in clouds. Some precipitation freezes or melts after it falls from the clouds.**

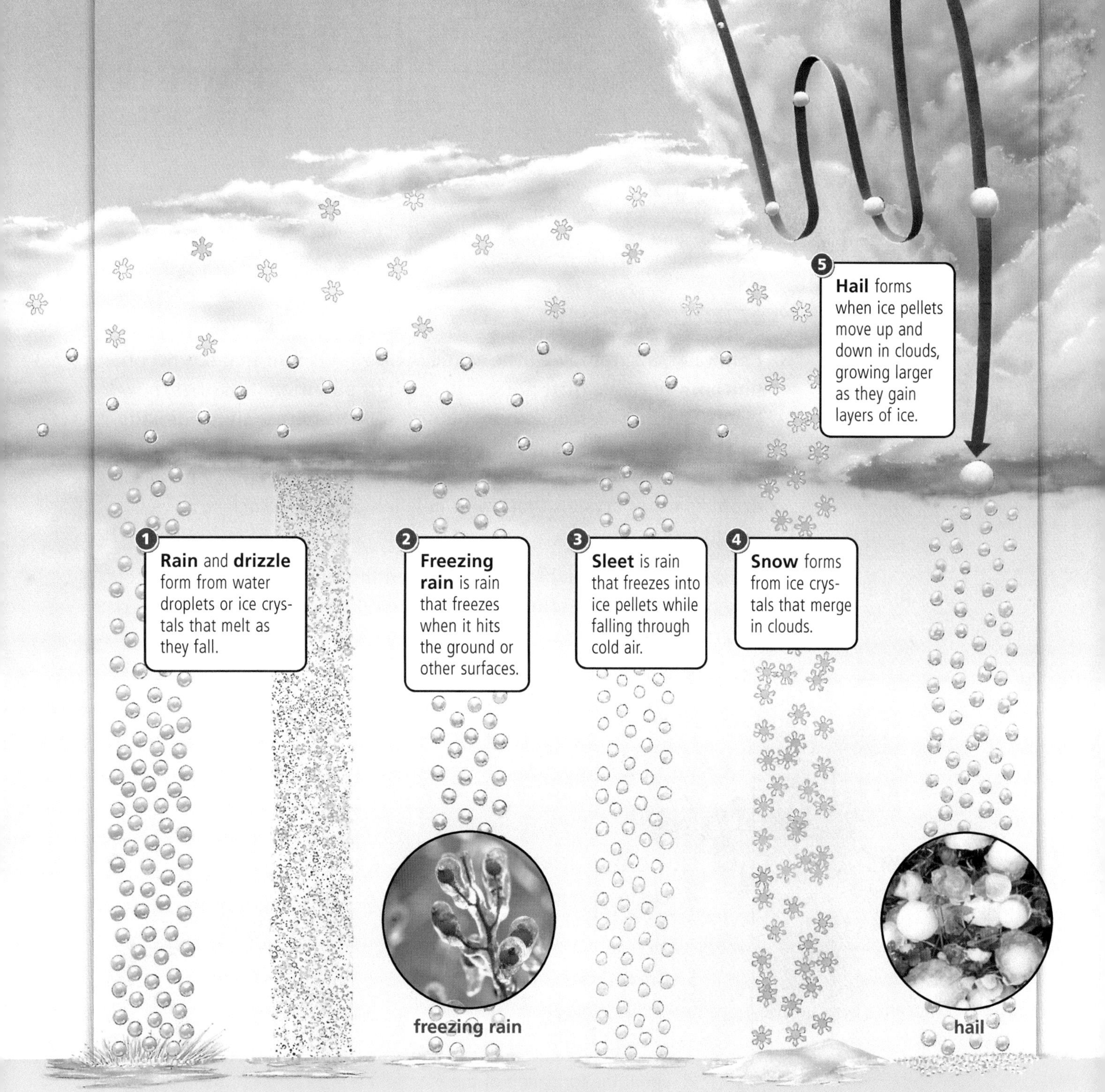

1
**Rain** and **drizzle** form from water droplets or ice crystals that melt as they fall.
2
**Freezing rain** is rain that freezes when it hits the ground or other surfaces.
3
**Sleet** is rain that freezes into ice pellets while falling through cold air.
4
**Snow** forms from ice crystals that merge in clouds.
5
**Hail** forms when ice pellets move up and down in clouds, growing larger as they gain layers of ice.
freezing rain
hail


**READING VISUALS** What forms of precipitation occur most often where you live?

These trees have few needles because acid rain has damaged the trees.

## Precipitation can carry pollution.

**VOCABULARY**
Add a description wheel for *acid rain* to your notebook.

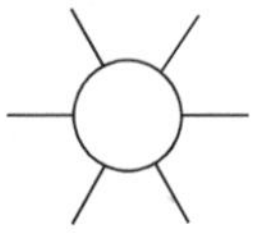

Rainwater is naturally a little acidic. **Acid rain** is rain that has become much more acidic than normal because of pollution. Factories, power plants, automobiles, and some natural sources release sulfur dioxide and nitrogen oxides into the air. These gases can combine with water vapor to form sulfuric acid and nitric acid. The acids mix with cloud droplets or ice crystals that eventually fall to Earth's surface as precipitation.

Because wind can blow air pollution hundreds of kilometers, acid rain may fall far from the source of the pollution. Acid rain harms trees and raises the acidity of lakes, making it difficult for fish to live in them. Acid rain also damages the surfaces of buildings and sculptures.

**CHECK YOUR READING** How does acid rain form? Your answer should mention water vapor.

# 3.4 Review

### KEY CONCEPTS

1. What are the two ways that rain can form? (6.4.a)
2. How are rain and snow measured? (6.4.e)
3. What human activities cause acid rain? (6.4.e)

### CRITICAL THINKING

4. **Compare and Contrast** How are sleet and freezing rain similar? How are they different?
5. **Draw Conclusions** When a large hailstone is cut open, four layers can be seen. What conclusions can you draw about the formation of the hailstone?

### CHALLENGE

6. **Predict** Temperatures in a cloud and on the ground are below freezing. A warmer layer of air lies between the cloud and the ground. What type of precipitation do you predict will occur? Explain.

Lightning flashes to the ground from a thunderhead, or cumulonimbus cloud.



# Caught Inside a Thunderhead

6.4.e Students know differences in pressure, heat, air movement, and humidity result in changes of weather.

In 1959, engine failure forced Lieutenant Colonel William Rankin to eject from his plane at a high altitude. When his parachute opened, he thought he was out of danger. However, he soon realized that he was caught inside a cumulonimbus cloud during a fierce thunderstorm.

As Rankin hung by his parachute, violent convection currents inside the cloud tossed him "up, down, sideways, clockwise." The rain was so heavy that he feared he would drown in midair. Lightning flashed all around him. Rankin finally landed after 40 minutes. He had many injuries, including bruises from hailstones. Fortunately, none of the storm's lightning had struck him.

## Where Lightning Strikes

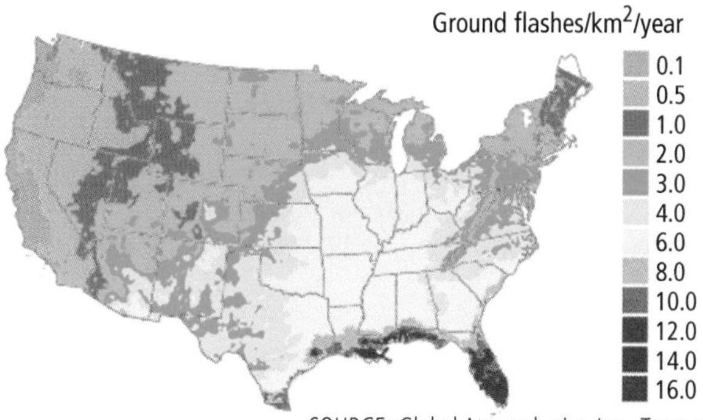


SOURCE: Global Atmospherics, Inc., Tucson, AZ

### Water, Wind, Hail, and Lightning

- A cumulonimbus cloud, or thunderhead, can rise to over 18 kilometers above Earth's surface. Convection currents transfer energy in the form of heat from Earth's surface to the storm.
- A cumulonimbus cloud may contain 500,000 tons of water.
- Thunderstorm clouds cause 8 million lightning flashes each day.

## EXPLORE

1. **ANALYZE** Find where you live on the map. Use the color key to figure out how often lightning strikes each square kilometer in your area.
2. **CHALLENGE** Use information from the Resource Center to propose an explanation for the pattern of lightning frequencies shown on the map.

**RESOURCE CENTER**
CLASSZONE.COM
Learn more about lightning.

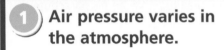

# 3 Chapter Review

## the BIG idea

**Some features of weather have predictable patterns.**

CONTENT REVIEW
CLASSZONE.COM

## KEY CONCEPTS SUMMARY

### 1 Air pressure varies in the atmosphere.

Air pressure is the force of air molecules pushing on an area.
Air pressure decreases as you move higher in the atmosphere. Air pressure can also differ in two locations at the same altitude.

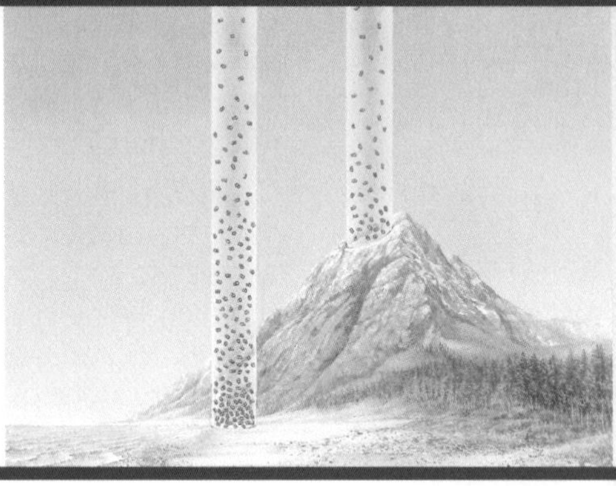

**VOCABULARY**
**air pressure** p. 79
**barometer** p. 82

### 2 The atmosphere has wind patterns.

Wind blows from areas of high pressure toward areas of low pressure. Earth's rotation causes long-distance winds to curve.

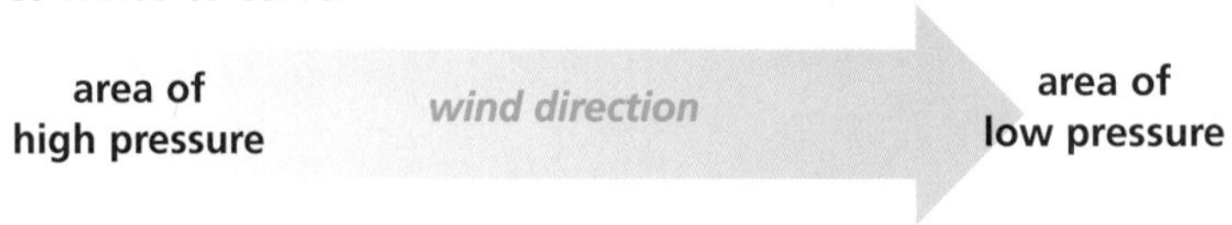


**VOCABULARY**
**wind** p. 83
**global wind** p. 84
**Coriolis effect** p. 85
**jet stream** p. 88
**monsoon** p. 90

### 3 Most clouds form as air rises and cools.

Clouds are made of tiny water droplets or ice crystals that condense from water vapor in rising air.

**VOCABULARY**
**evaporation** p. 92
**condensation** p. 92
**precipitation** p. 93
**humidity** p. 94
**saturation** p. 94
**relative humidity** p. 94
**dew point** p. 94

### 4 Water falls to Earth's surface as precipitation.

Water droplets in clouds merge to form raindrops.

Ice crystals in clouds can form snow, rain, and other types of precipitation.

**VOCABULARY**
**freezing rain** p. 104
**sleet** p. 104
**hail** p. 104
**acid rain** p. 106

## Reviewing Vocabulary

*Write a definition of each term. Use the meaning of the underlined root to help you.*

| Word | Root Meaning | Definition |
|---|---|---|
| EXAMPLE air pressure | to apply force | the force of air molecules pushing on an area |
| 1. barometer | weight | |
| 2. saturation | to fill | |
| 3. global wind | sphere | |
| 4. monsoon | season | |
| 5. evaporation | steam | |
| 6. condensation | thick | |
| 7. humidity | moist | |
| 8. precipitation | thrown down | |

## Reviewing Key Concepts

**Multiple Choice** *Choose the letter of the best answer.*

9. The movement of air molecules causes (6.4.e)
   **a.** air density **c.** humidity
   **b.** air pressure **d.** relative humidity

10. Winds curve as they move across Earth's surface because of (6.4.e)
    **a.** the Coriolis effect **c.** humidity
    **b.** air pressure **d.** relative humidity

11. Jet streams generally flow toward the (6.4.e)
    **a.** north **c.** east
    **b.** south **d.** west

12. Condensation increases with greater (6.4.e)
    **a.** relative humidity **c.** air pressure
    **b.** air temperature **d.** wind speed

13. Any type of liquid or solid water that falls to Earth's surface is called (6.4.a)
    **a.** precipitation **c.** a monsoon
    **b.** dew **d.** humidity

14. What are low-altitude clouds composed of? (6.4.e)
    **a.** snowflakes **c.** water droplets
    **b.** raindrops **d.** water vapor

15. Clouds made of ice crystals form under conditions of (6.4.e)
    **a.** strong winds **c.** low humidity
    **b.** high altitude **d.** high pressure

16. Which type of cloud is most likely to bring thunderstorms? (6.4.e)
    **a.** stratus **c.** cumulonimbus
    **b.** altostratus **d.** cirrus

17. Over short distances wind blows toward areas of (6.4.e)
    **a.** high pressure **c.** low temperature
    **b.** high density **d.** low pressure

18. The doldrums and the horse latitudes are both regions of (6.4.e)
    **a.** high air pressure **c.** heavy rains
    **b.** light winds **d.** low temperatures

19. As altitude increases, air pressure usually (6.4.e)
    **a.** decreases **c.** varies more
    **b.** increases **d.** varies less

**Short Answer** *Write a short answer to each question.*

20. What causes land breezes to flow at night? (6.4.e)

21. Why does hair take longer to dry after a shower on days with high relative humidity? (6.4.e)

22. How does air pressure affect air density? (6.4.e)

23. Why are dust and other particles necessary for precipitation? (6.4.a)

24. How did global wind belts and calm regions affect transportation in the past? (6.4.e)

## Thinking Critically

The soil in this terrarium was soaked with water two weeks ago. Then the box was sealed so that no moisture could escape. Use the diagram to answer the next six questions.

25. **IDENTIFY EFFECTS** How does sunlight affect conditions inside the terrarium? (6.4.a)

26. **ANALYZE** Draw a diagram of the water cycle inside the terrarium. (6.4.a)

27. **INFER** What do the water drops on the glass indicate about the temperatures inside and outside the terrarium? (6.4.a)

28. **PREDICT** Explain how long you think the plants will live without being watered.

29. **PREDICT** What would happen if you placed the terrarium on top of a block of ice? (6.4.a)

30. **HYPOTHESIZE** How would conditions inside the terrarium change if there were a hole in one side of it? (6.4.a)

31. **COMPARE AND CONTRAST** How are sea breezes and monsoon winds alike, and how are they different? (6.4.e)

32. **PREDICT** A cumulus cloud is growing taller. What will happen to the density of the air beneath it? Explain. (6.4.e)

33. **INFER** Imagine that a group of factories and power plants lies 200 kilometers to the west of a forest where trees are dying. Describe three steps in a process that could be causing the trees to die.

**IDENTIFY EFFECTS** Write the type of precipitation that would form under each set of conditions. (6.4.e)

| Conditions | Precipitation |
|---|---|
| **34.** above-freezing air inside a cloud and freezing air beneath it | |
| **35.** above-freezing air beneath a cloud and freezing temperatures on the ground | |
| **36.** below-freezing air inside a cloud and above-freezing temperatures in the air beneath it and on the ground | |
| **37.** below-freezing air inside a cloud and beneath it | |
| **38.** ice pellets hurled around by air currents inside a cloud | |

## the BIG idea

39. **APPLY** Look again at the photograph on pages 76–77. Now that you have finished the chapter, how would you change your response to the question on the photograph? (6.4.e)

40. **WRITE** Write one or more paragraphs explaining how energy from the Sun influences the weather. In your discussion, include at least three of the following topics: (6.4.a)
    - global wind belts
    - high- and low-pressure areas
    - local winds
    - monsoons
    - the water cycle
    - cloud formation

## UNIT PROJECTS

If you need to do an experiment for your unit project, gather the materials. Be sure to allow enough time to observe results before the project is due.

For more practice, go to . . .
TEST PRACTICE
CLASSZONE.COM

## Analyzing a Diagram

6.4.a, 6.4.e

*This diagram shows the water cycle. Use it to answer the questions below.*

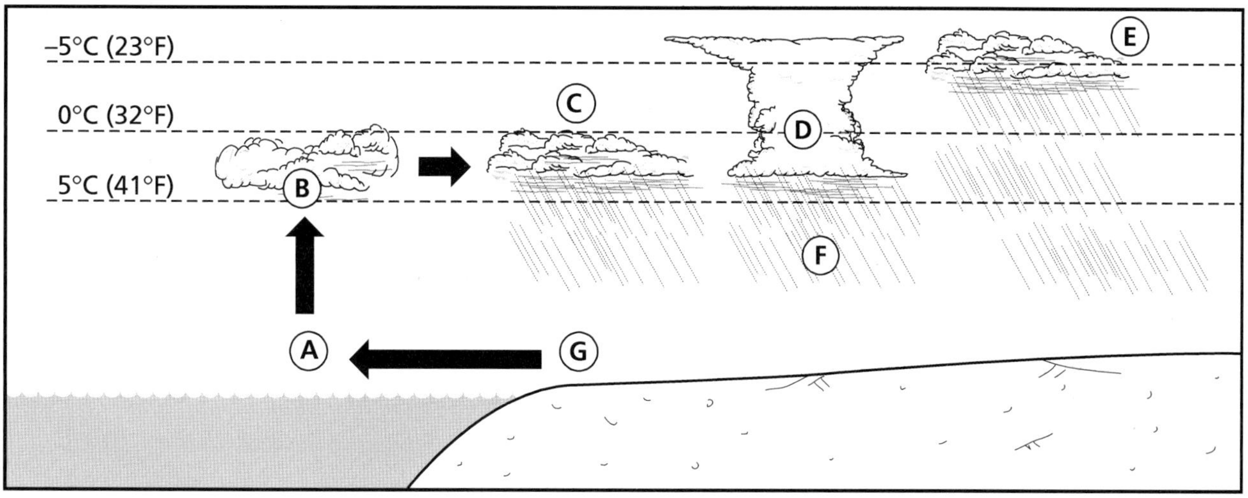


1. Where is evaporation occurring?
   **a.** A **c.** F
   **b.** D **d.** G
2. Where is condensation occurring?
   **a.** A **c.** F
   **b.** B **d.** G
3. Where is precipitation shown?
   **a.** A **c.** E
   **b.** C **d.** F
4. Where is hail most likely to form?
   **a.** C **c.** E
   **b.** D **d.** F
5. From which cloud will precipitation fall as snow and then turn to rain?
   **a.** B **c.** D
   **b.** C **d.** E
6. Which is the best estimate for the temperature in B?
   **a.** 8°C (46°F) **c.** –3°C (27°F)
   **b.** 3°C (37°F) **d.** –8°C (17°F)
7. What does the arrow pointing up between A and B indicate?
   **a.** the movement of moisture
   **b.** the direction of the wind
   **c.** a low pressure area
   **d.** a reflection off the water

## Extended Response

*Answer the two questions below in detail. Include some of the terms shown in the word box. In your answers underline each term you use.*

| | | |
|---|---|---|
| low air pressure | cool air | west |
| high air pressure | warm air | east |
| Coriolis effect | | |

8. Whenever Richard rides in an airplane, he feels a pop inside his ears. Explain what is happening in the air to produce the pop in Richard's ears.

9. Winds tend to blow from west to east across the United States. If Earth spun in the other direction, how might the winds across the United States be different?

CHAPTER 4

# Weather Fronts and Storms

## the BIG idea

The interaction of air masses causes changes in weather.

## Key Concepts

SECTION 1
**Weather changes as air masses move.**
Learn about air masses, fronts, and high- and low-pressure systems.

SECTION 2
**Low-pressure systems can become storms.**
Learn about hurricanes and winter storms.

SECTION 3
**Vertical air motion can cause severe storms.**
Learn about thunderstorms, lightning, and tornadoes.

SECTION 4
**Weather forecasters use advanced technologies.**
Learn about different types of weather data and how forecasters predict weather.

**California ClassZone**

CLASSZONE.COM

Chapter 4 online resources: Content Review, two Visualizations, one Resource Center, Math Tutorial, Test Practice

*What types of weather can move a house?*

# EXPLORE the BIG idea

## How Does Cold Air Move?

6.4.e Students know differences in pressure, heat, air movement, and humidity result in changes of weather.

Hold one hand near the top of a refrigerator door and the other hand near the bottom. Open the refrigerator door just a little bit.

**Observe and Think**
How did each hand feel before and after you opened the door? How did the air move?

## How Does Weather Move?

6.4.e Students know differences in pressure, heat, air movement, and humidity result in changes of weather.

Collect newspaper weather maps for three days in a row. Find the key on the first day's map. Identify the symbols used for weather fronts—lines with triangles or half-circles attached to them. Select one of the fronts on the first day's map. Track the front's movement over three days.

**Observe and Think**
How did the weather change after the front had passed over an area? Why did the front move the way it did?

NSTA scilinks.org SCILINKS
Severe Weather **Code: MDL011**

CHAPTER 4

# Getting Ready to Learn

## CONCEPT REVIEW

- Temperature affects air density.
- Pressure differences make air move.
- Uneven heating of Earth's surface produces winds.
- Clouds form as air rises, expands, and cools.

## VOCABULARY REVIEW

**convection** p. 28
**evaporation** p. 92
**condensation** p. 92
**relative humidity** p. 94

**CONTENT REVIEW**
CLASSZONE.COM
Review concepts and vocabulary.

## TAKING NOTES

### MAIN IDEA WEB

Write each new blue heading—a main idea—in a box. Then put notes with important terms and details into boxes around the main idea.

### CHOOSE YOUR OWN STRATEGY

Take notes about new vocabulary terms using one or more of the strategies from earlier chapters—**Magnet Word, Frame Game,** or **Description Wheel**. Feel free to mix and match the strategies, or use an entirely different vocabulary strategy.

See the Note-Taking Handbook on pages R45–R51.

SCIENCE NOTEBOOK

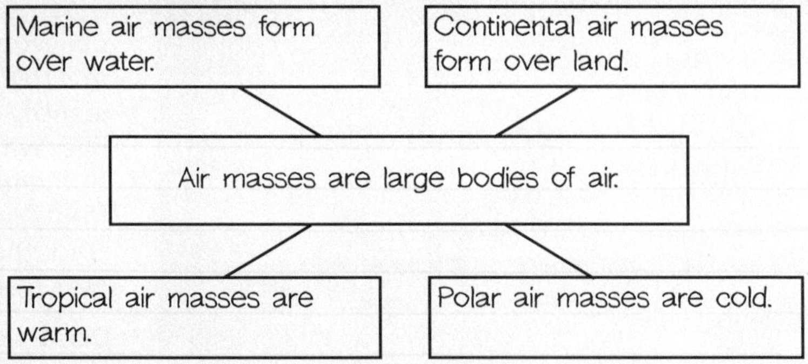
Marine air masses form over water.
Continental air masses form over land.
Air masses are large bodies of air.
Tropical air masses are warm.
Polar air masses are cold.

Description Wheel

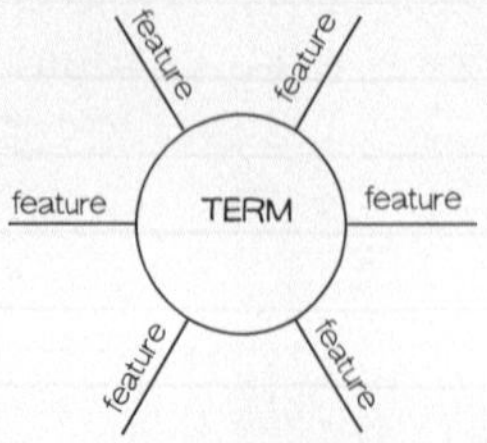
feature
feature
feature
TERM
feature
feature
feature

Magnet Word

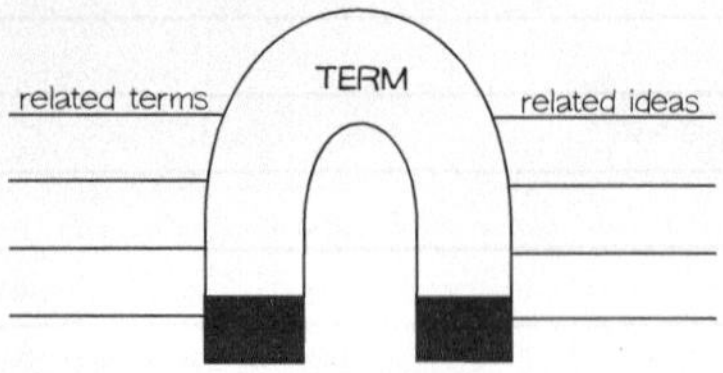
related terms
TERM
related ideas

Frame Game

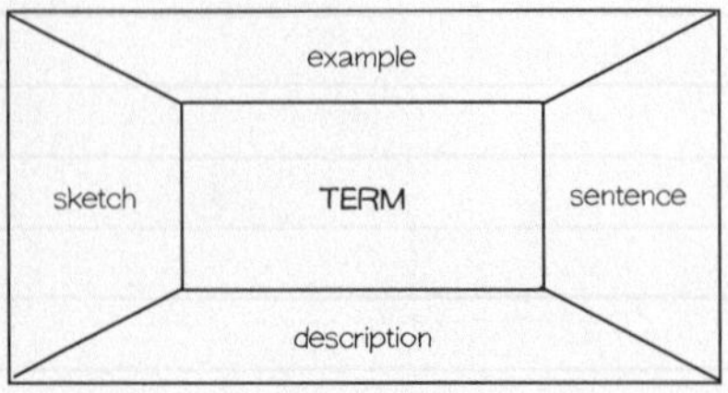
example
sketch
TERM
sentence
description

KEY CONCEPT

# 4.1 Weather changes as air masses move.

**CALIFORNIA Content Standard**

6.4.e Students know differences in pressure, heat, air movement, and humidity result in changes of weather.

**BEFORE, you learned**

- Air pressure changes with location and altitude
- Water vapor in the atmosphere condenses when air rises

**NOW, you will learn**

- What air masses are
- What happens when air masses meet
- How pressure systems affect the weather

**VOCABULARY**

**air mass** p. 115
**front** p. 118
**high-pressure system** p. 120
**low-pressure system** p. 121

**EXPLORE Air Masses** (6.4.e)

### *How does an air mass form?*

**PROCEDURE**

1. Put ice into one bowl and warm water into a second bowl. Leave the third bowl empty.
2. Place each bowl in a different box and cover the box with plastic wrap. Wait a few minutes.
3. Put your hand into each box in turn.

**WHAT DO YOU THINK?**

- How would you describe the air in each box?
- Which box's air feels the most humid? Why?

**MATERIALS**

- 3 bowls
- ice
- warm water
- 3 shoeboxes
- plastic wrap

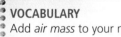

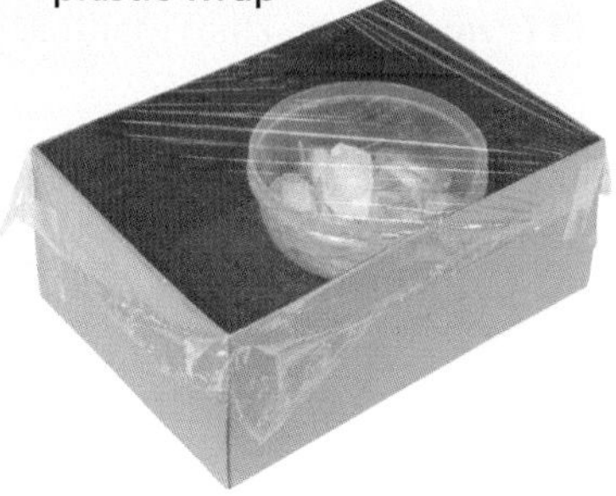

## Air masses are large bodies of air.

**VOCABULARY** Add *air mass* to your notebook, using the vocabulary strategy of your choice.

You have probably experienced the effects of air masses—one day is hot and humid, and the next day is cool and pleasant. The weather changes when a new air mass moves into your area. An **air mass** is a large volume of air in which temperature and humidity are nearly the same in different locations at the same altitude. An air mass can cover many thousands of square kilometers.

An air mass forms when the air over a large region of Earth sits in one place for many days. The air gradually takes on the characteristics of the land or water below it. Where Earth's surface is cold, the air becomes cold. Where Earth's surface is wet, the air becomes moist. As an air mass moves, it brings its temperature and moisture to new locations.

**CHECK YOUR READING** Explain how the weather can change with the arrival of a new air mass. Your answer should include two ways that weather changes.

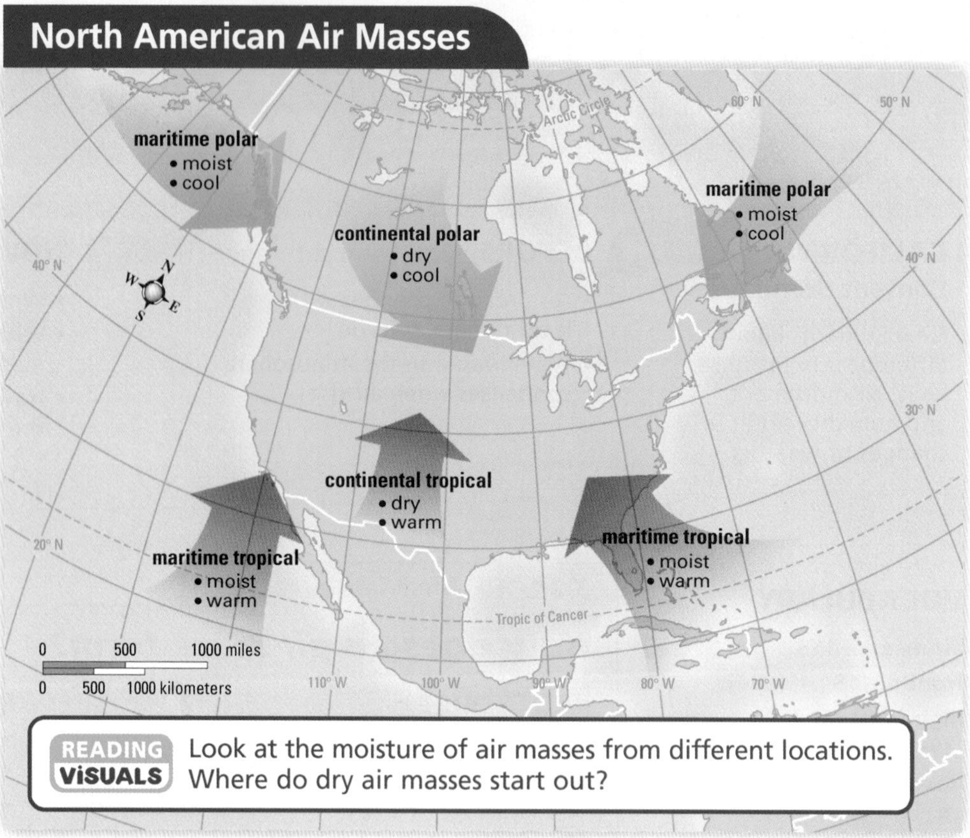


**READING VISUALS** Look at the moisture of air masses from different locations. Where do dry air masses start out?

## Characteristics of an Air Mass

Some regions of Earth's surface, such as those shown in the map above, produce air masses again and again. The characteristics of an air mass depend on the region where it forms. A hot desert produces dry, hot air masses, while cool ocean waters produce moist, cool air masses. Scientists classify air masses into categories according to the characteristics of regions. Each category name is made of two words—one for moisture, one for temperature.

The first word of an air mass's category name tells whether the air mass formed over water or dry land. It describes the moisture of the air mass.

- **Continental** air masses form over land. Air becomes dry as it loses its moisture to the dry land below it.
- **Maritime** (MAR-ih-TYM) air masses form over water. Air becomes moist as it gains water vapor from the water below it.

**READING TIP**

The word *maritime* has the same root as the word *marine*. Both come from the Latin word *mare*, which means "sea."

The second word of a category name tells whether an air mass formed close to the equator. It describes the air mass's temperature.

- **Tropical** air masses form near the equator. Air becomes warm as it gains energy from the warm land or water.
- **Polar** air masses form far from the equator. Air becomes cool as it loses energy to the cold land or water.

The combination of words gives the characteristics of the air mass. A maritime tropical air mass is moist and warm, while a continental polar air mass is dry and cold.

**CHECK YOUR READING** What can you tell from each word of an air mass's name?

## Movement of an Air Mass

Air masses can travel away from the regions where they form. They move with the global pattern of winds. In most of the United States, air masses generally move from west to east. They may move along with the jet stream in more complex and changing patterns.

When an air mass moves to a new region, it carries along its characteristic moisture and temperature. As the air moves over Earth's surface, the characteristics of the surface begin to change the air mass. For example, if a continental polar air mass moves over warm water, the air near the surface will become warmer and gain moisture. These changes begin where the air touches the surface. It may take days or weeks for the changes to spread upward through the entire air mass. An air mass that moves quickly may not change much. If it moves quickly enough, a continental polar air mass can move cold air from northern Canada all the way to the southern United States.

## INVESTIGATE Air Masses

### *What happens when air masses collide?*

**PROCEDURE**

1. Cut the cardboard to create a snug barrier that divides your beaker in half.
2. Mix about 5 mL of salt, 50 mL of water, and a drop of blue food coloring in one cup. This dense mixture represents a cold air mass.
3. Mix 50 mL of water with a drop of red food coloring in the other cup. This less-dense mixture represents a warm air mass.
4. Carefully pour the red water into one side of your divided beaker and the blue saltwater into the other side. As you look through the side of the beaker, quickly remove the barrier.

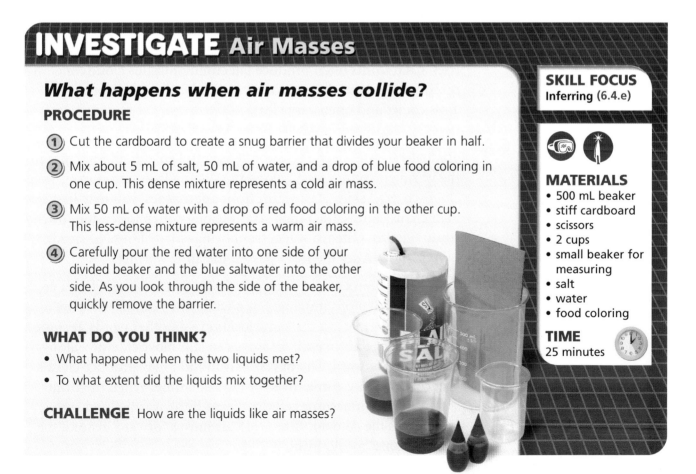

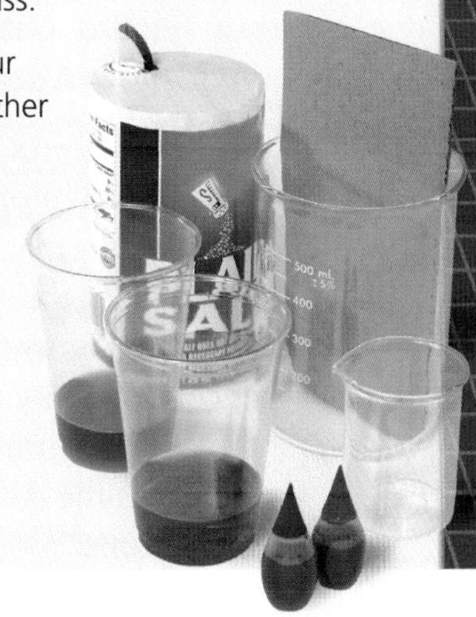

**WHAT DO YOU THINK?**

- What happened when the two liquids met?
- To what extent did the liquids mix together?

**CHALLENGE** How are the liquids like air masses?

**SKILL FOCUS**
Inferring (6.4.e)

**MATERIALS**
- 500 mL beaker
- stiff cardboard
- scissors
- 2 cups
- small beaker for measuring
- salt
- water
- food coloring

**TIME**
25 minutes

## Weather changes where air masses meet.

When a new air mass moves over your area, you can expect the weather to change. Perhaps you have heard a weather forecaster talk about fronts. A **front** is a boundary between air masses. The weather near a front can differ from the weather inside the rest of an air mass. As one air mass pushes another, some of the air at the boundary will be pushed upward. Clouds can form in this rising air. The weather often becomes cloudy or stormy as a front passes. Afterward, you experience the temperature and humidity of the air mass that has moved in.

### Fronts and Weather

**MAIN IDEA WEB**
Organize the notes you take about fronts.

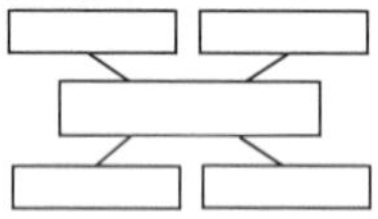

Different types of fronts produce different patterns of weather. When a cold, dense air mass pushes warmer air, it produces a cold front. When a warm air mass pushes colder air, it produces a warm front. These names tell you which way the temperature will change but not how much it will change. A cold front can turn a heat wave into normal summer weather or turn cold winter air into very cold weather.

**CHECK YOUR READING** How would the weather change if a cold front moved into your area today?

1. **Cold fronts** can move into regions quickly. As you can see on page 119, a cold front is steeper than the other types of fronts. As a mass of cold, dense air moves forward, warmer air ahead of it is pushed upward. Water vapor in the warm air condenses as the air rises. Cold fronts often produce tall cumulonimbus clouds and precipitation. Brief, heavy storms are likely. After the storms, the air is cooler and often very clear.

2. **Warm fronts** move more slowly than cold fronts. Warm air moves gradually up and over a mass of denser and colder air. Moisture in the warm air condenses all along the sloping front, producing cloud-covered skies. As a warm front approaches, you may first see high cirrus clouds, then high stratus clouds, then lower and lower stratus clouds. Often, a warm front brings many hours of steady rain or snow. After the front passes, the air is warmer.

**VISUALIZATION**
CLASSZONE.COM
See how the air moves in warm fronts and cold fronts.

3. **Stationary fronts** occur when air masses first meet or when a cold or warm front stops moving. For a while, the boundary between the air masses stays in the same location—in other words, it stays stationary. The air in each air mass can still move sideways along the front or upward. The upward air motion may produce clouds that cover the sky, sometimes for days at a time. When the front starts moving, it becomes a warm front if the warm air advances and pushes the cold air. If the cold air moves forward instead, the front becomes a cold front.

## Fronts and Weather

**As fronts move across Earth's surface, they produce changes in the weather.**

### 1 Cold Front

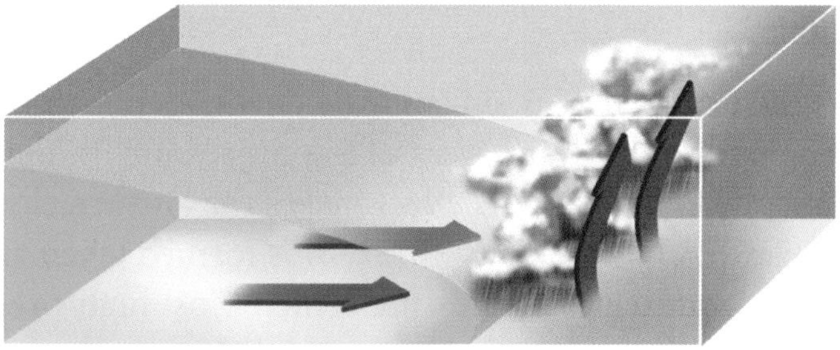

A **cold front** forms when a cold air mass pushes a warm air mass and forces the warm air to rise. As the warm air rises, its moisture condenses and forms tall clouds.

Triangles show the direction that a cold front moves.

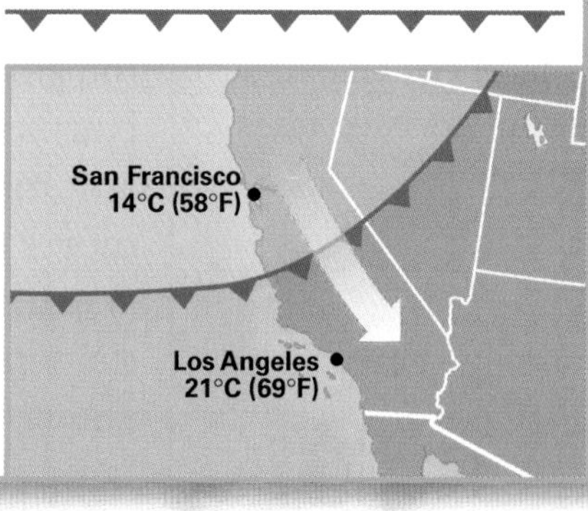


### 2 Warm Front

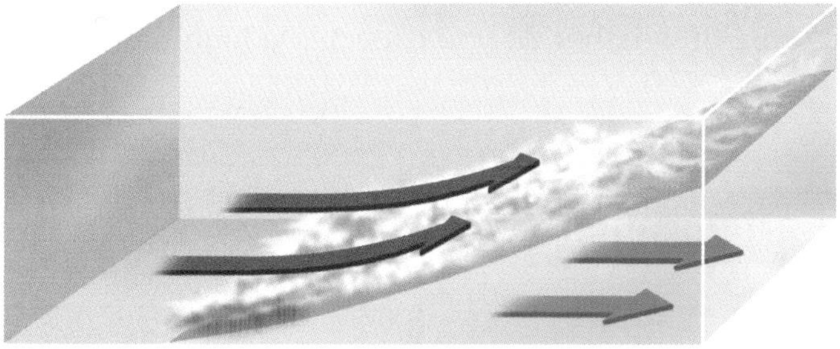

A **warm front** forms when a warm air mass pushes a cold air mass. The warm air rises slowly over the cold air and its moisture condenses into flat clouds.

Semicircles show the direction that a warm front moves.

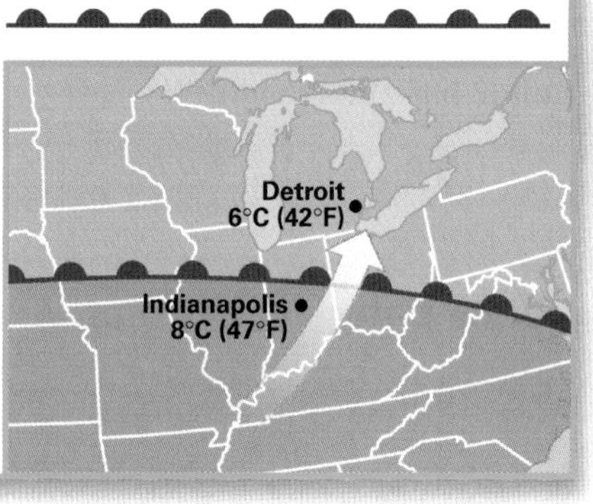


### 3 Stationary Front

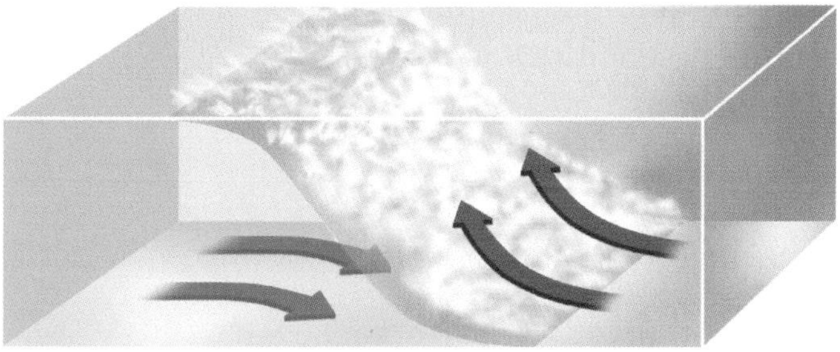

A **stationary front** occurs when two air masses push against each other without moving. A stationary front becomes a warm or cold front when one air mass advances.

Alternating triangles and semicircles show a stationary front.

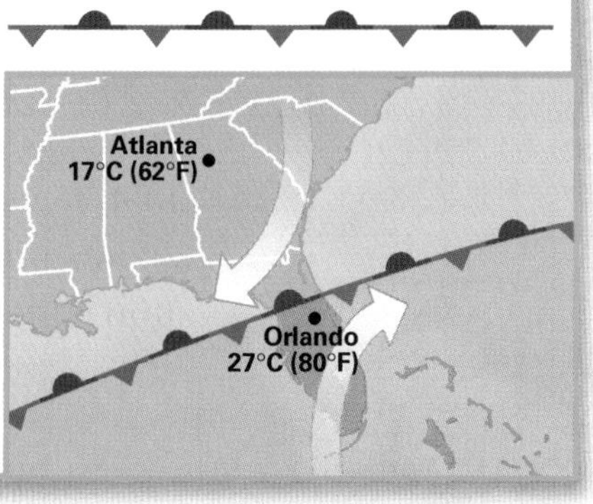


READING VISUALS **PREDICT** Which city will the cold front affect next?

## High-Pressure Systems

You may have seen the letters H and L on a weather map. These letters mark high-pressure centers and low-pressure centers, often simply called highs and lows. Each center is the location of the highest or lowest pressure in a region. The pressure differences cause air to move in ways that may make a high or low become the center of a whole system of weather.

READING TIP
A *system* includes different parts that work together.

At a high-pressure center, air sinks slowly down. As the air nears the ground, it spreads out toward areas of lower pressure. In the Northern Hemisphere, the Coriolis effect makes the air turn clockwise as it moves outward. A **high-pressure system** is formed when air moves all the way around a high-pressure center. Most high-pressure systems are large and change slowly. When a high-pressure system stays in one location for a long time, an air mass may form. The air—and resulting air mass—can be warm or cold, moist or dry.

A high-pressure system generally brings clear skies and calm air or gentle breezes. This is because as air sinks to lower altitudes, it warms up a little bit. Water droplets evaporate, so clouds often disappear.

CHECK YOUR READING What type of weather do you expect in a high-pressure system?

### Weather Systems in the Northern Hemisphere

**High-pressure systems and low-pressure systems produce patterns of weather across Earth's surface.**

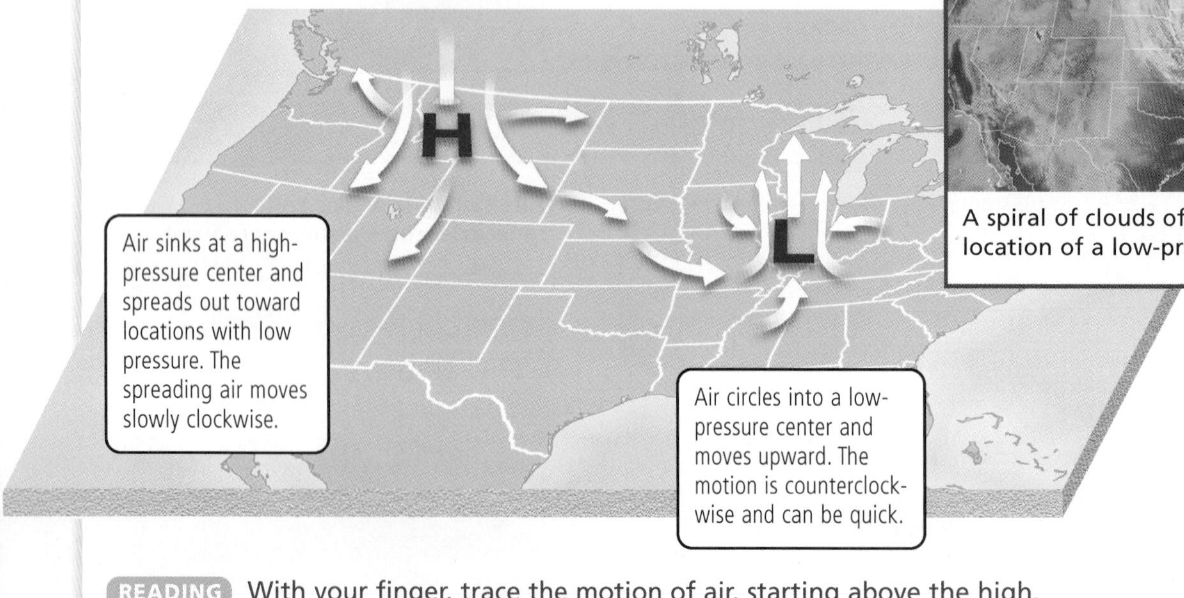

H
L
Air sinks at a high-pressure center and spreads out toward locations with low pressure. The spreading air moves slowly clockwise.
Air circles into a low-pressure center and moves upward. The motion is counterclockwise and can be quick.

A spiral of clouds often shows the location of a low-pressure system.

READING VISUALS With your finger, trace the motion of air, starting above the high. Where have you seen similar patterns in earlier chapters?

## Low-Pressure Systems

A small area of low pressure can also develop into a larger system. A **low-pressure system** is a large weather system that surrounds a center of low pressure. It begins as air moves around and inward toward the lowest pressure and then up to higher altitudes. The upward motion of the air lowers the air pressure further, and so the air moves faster. The pattern of motion strengthens into a low-pressure weather system. The rising air produces stormy weather. In the Northern Hemisphere, the air in a low-pressure system circles in a counterclockwise direction.

A low-pressure system can develop wherever there is a center of low pressure. One place this often happens is along a boundary between a warm air mass and a cold air mass. The diagram shows an example of this process.

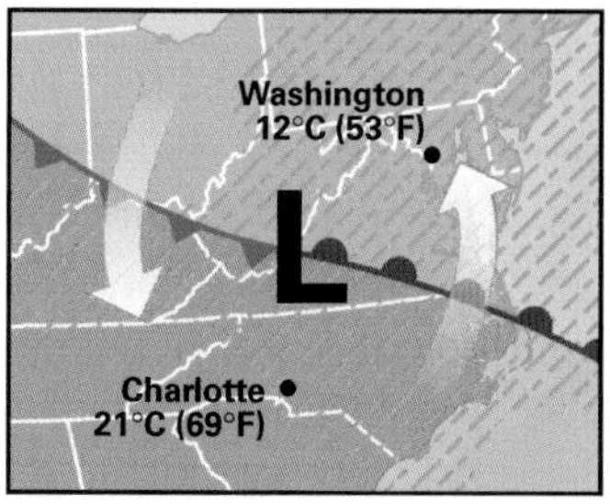


- Part of the boundary between the air masses moves south and becomes a cold front.
- Part of the boundary moves north and becomes a warm front.
- A center of low pressure forms where the ends of the two fronts meet.

The low-pressure center and fronts become parts of a whole system of weather. Rising air at the fronts and at the low can cause very stormy weather.

The diagram on page 120 shows how air moves between pressure centers. Air moves down, out, and around a high-pressure center. Then it swirls around and into a low-pressure center and moves upward. Highs and lows affect each other as they move across the surface. Large weather systems generally move with the pattern of global winds—west to east over most of North America. But, within a weather system, winds can blow in different directions.

# 4.1 Review

### KEY CONCEPTS

1. What are the two characteristics of an air mass that you need to know in order to classify it? (6.4.e)
2. What happens when a warmer air mass pushes a cooler air mass? (6.4.e)
3. What type of weather system brings calm, clear weather? (6.4.e)

### CRITICAL THINKING

4. **Compare and Contrast** Explain how air moves differently in low- and high-pressure systems.
5. **Apply** If the weather becomes stormy for a short time and then becomes colder, which type of front has passed?

### CHALLENGE

6. **Synthesize** You check a barometer and observe that the air pressure has been dropping all day. Is tonight's weather more likely to be calm or stormy?

**MATH in SCIENCE**

**MATH TUTORIAL**
CLASSZONE.COM
Click on Math Tutorial for more help with rates as ratios.

**Math** 6.NS.1.2, 6.AF.2.2
**Science** 6.4.e

## SKILL: DETERMINING RATES

# Movement of a Front

Scientists measure the speeds of weather fronts to forecast weather conditions. The speed at which a front moves is an example of a rate. A rate can be written as a ratio. For example, the rate of a front that moves a distance of 500 kilometers in 1 day can be written as follows:

500 kilometers : 1 day

The map below shows the movement of a cold front over four consecutive days. Use the map scale to determine the distance that the front moves on each day.

**Cold Front Movement**

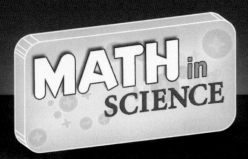

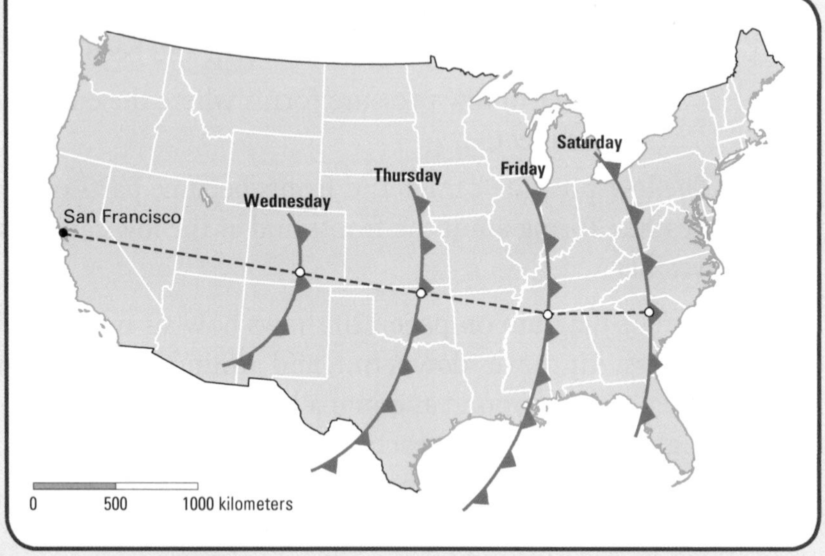


**Answer the following questions.**

1. What was the front's rate of movement between Wednesday and Thursday? Express your answer as a ratio.

   ? : 1 day

2. What was the front's rate of movement between Friday and Saturday? Express your answer as a ratio.

3. What was the mean rate of the front's movement from Wednesday to Saturday? Remember, *mean* means "average." Express your answer as a ratio.

**CHALLENGE** Use the rate from Wednesday to Saturday to estimate the day on which the front must have moved through San Francisco.

KEY CONCEPT

# 4.2 Low-pressure systems can become storms.

**CALIFORNIA Content Standard**

6.4.e Students know differences in pressure, heat, air movement, and humidity result in changes of weather.

**BEFORE, you learned**

- Moving air masses cause changes in weather
- A low-pressure system brings stormy weather

**NOW, you will learn**

- How hurricanes develop
- About the dangers of hurricanes
- About different types of winter storms

**VOCABULARY**

**tropical storm** p. 123
**hurricane** p. 123
**storm surge** p. 125
**blizzard** p. 126

**EXPLORE Hurricanes (6.4.e)**

### *What things make hurricanes lose strength?*

**PROCEDURE**

1. Crumple a piece of paper, then flatten it out. Crumple and flatten it out again.
2. Spin the top on the flattened paper. Count the seconds until it stops spinning.
3. Spin the top on a smooth surface. Count the seconds until it stops spinning.

**MATERIALS**

- sheet of paper
- top

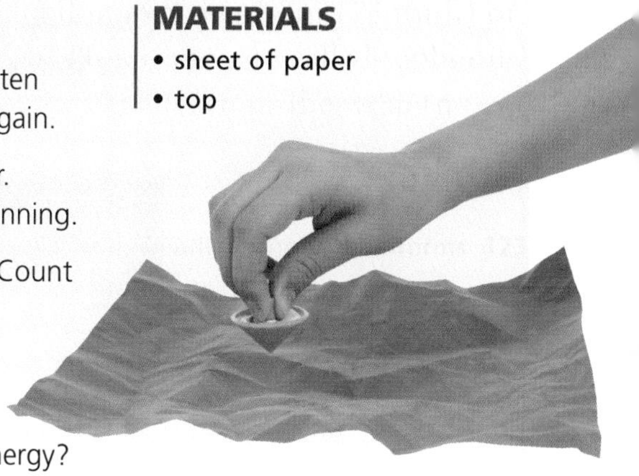

**WHAT DO YOU THINK?**
How does the texture of the surface affect the rate at which the top loses energy?

**MAIN IDEA WEB**
Remember to make notes about hurricanes.

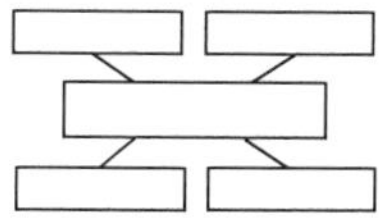

## Hurricanes form over warm ocean water.

Near the equator, warm ocean water provides the energy that can turn a low-pressure center into a violent storm. As water evaporates from the ocean, energy moves from the ocean water into the air. This energy makes warm air rise faster. Tall clouds and strong winds develop. As winds blow across the water from different directions into the low, the Coriolis effect bends their paths into a spiral. The winds blow faster and faster around the low, which becomes the center of a storm system.

A **tropical storm** is a low-pressure system that starts near the equator and has winds that blow at 65 kilometers per hour (40 mi/h) or more. A **hurricane** (HUR-ih-KAYN) is a tropical low-pressure system with winds blowing at speeds of 120 kilometers per hour (74 mi/h) or more—strong enough to uproot trees. Hurricanes are called typhoons or cyclones when they form over the Indian Ocean or the western Pacific Ocean.

## Formation of Hurricanes

**VISUALIZATION**
CLASSZONE.COM
Watch the progress of a hurricane.

In the eastern United States, hurricanes most often strike between August and October. Energy from warm water is necessary for a low-pressure center to build into a tropical storm and then into a hurricane. The ocean water where these storms develop only gets warm enough—26°C (80°F) or more—near the end of summer.

Tropical storms and hurricanes generally move westward with the trade winds. Near land, however, they will often move north, south, or even back eastward. As long as a storm stays above warm water, it can grow bigger and more powerful. As soon as a hurricane moves over land or over cooler water, it loses its source of energy. The winds lose strength and the storm dies out. If a hurricane moves over land, the rough surface of the land reduces the winds even more.

A tropical storm may gain energy and become a hurricane. When the hurricane shown below moved north, the storm lost energy and was called a tropical storm again as its winds slowed.

**CHECK YOUR READING** What is the source of a hurricane's energy?

### Structure of a Hurricane

**Saffir-Simpson Hurricane Scale**

A hurricane does not stay at the same category of strength its entire life. The strength of each hurricane when it first hit land is recorded here.

| Category | Wind Speed | Examples | Typical Damage |
|---|---|---|---|
| 1 | 74–95 mph (119–153 km/h) | Irene 1999<br>Lili 2002<br>Gaston 2004 | Minimal. Trees and unanchored mobile homes damaged. Some coastal flooding. |
| 2 | 96–110 mph (154–177 km/h) | Isabel 2003<br>Frances 2004 | Moderate. Minor damage to buildings. Some trees blown down. |
| 3 | 111–130 mph (178–209 km/h) | Jeanne 2004<br>Ivan 2004<br>Emily 2005<br>Rita 2005 | Extensive. Some structural damage to small buildings. Mobile homes destroyed. |
| 4 | 131–155 mph (210–249 km/h) | Iris 2001<br>Charley 2004<br>Dennis 2005<br>Katrina 2005 | Extreme. Some roofs destroyed. Evacuations as far as 6 miles (10 km) inland. Storm surge 13–18 feet (4–5.5 m) above normal. |
| 5 | 155+ mph (250+ km/h) | Camille 1969<br>Andrew 1992 | Catastrophic. Buildings destroyed. Evacuations as far as 10 miles (16 km) inland. Storm surge over 18 feet (5.5 m) above normal. |

Eye: The small center of a hurricane is clear and calm because air is moving downward.
Bands of thunderstorms give the hurricane a spiral shape.
Eye wall: Just outside the eye, the air swirls upward very quickly. It is like a wall of stormy weather.

At the center of a hurricane is a small area of clear weather, 20–50 kilometers (10–30 mi) in diameter, called the eye. The storm's center is calm because air moves downward there. Just around the eye, the air moves very quickly around and upward, forming a tall ring of cumulonimbus clouds called the eye wall. This ring produces very heavy rains and tremendous winds. Farther from the center, bands of heavy clouds and rain spiral inward toward the eye.

**SAFETY TIPS**

**HURRICANES**

- Before a storm, prepare a plan to leave the area. Gather emergency supplies.
- Listen to weather reports for storm updates.
- Secure loose objects outside, and cover windows.
- If ordered to evacuate, leave immediately.
- During a storm, stay indoors and away from windows.
- After a storm, be aware of power lines, hanging branches, and flooded areas.

## Effects of Hurricanes

A hurricane can pound a coast with huge waves and sweep the land with strong winds and heavy rains. Hurricane winds can lift cars, uproot trees, and tear the roofs off buildings. Hurricanes may also produce tornadoes that cause even more damage. Heavy rains from hurricanes may make rivers overflow their banks and flood nearby areas. When a hurricane moves into a coastal area, it often pushes a huge mass of ocean water known as a **storm surge.** In a storm surge, the sea level rises several meters, backing up rivers and flooding the shore. A storm surge can be destructive and deadly. Large waves add to the destruction. A hurricane may affect an area for a few hours or a few days, but the flooding and damage may take weeks, months, or years to clean up.

**CHECK YOUR READING** What are the effects of hurricanes? Make a list for your answer.

The National Hurricane Center helps people know when to prepare for a hurricane. The center puts out a tropical-storm or hurricane watch when a storm is likely to strike within 36 hours. People are sometimes evacuated, or moved away for safety, from areas where they may be in danger. As the danger gets closer—24 hours or less—the center issues a tropical-storm or hurricane warning. The warning stays in effect until the danger has passed.

This photograph shows New Orleans, Louisiana, after it was hit by Hurricane Katrina in August 2005. The hurricane's storm surge flooded part of the city and also weakened several levees, or earthen dams. Most of the flooding happened after levees broke and allowed water from a nearby lake to pour into the city.

## Winter storms produce snow and ice.

**CALIFORNIA Focus**

Fresh water is scarce in southern California. However, along the northern coast, excess rain and snowmelt cause flooding of rivers during the winter.

Most severe winter storms in the United States are part of low-pressure systems. Unlike hurricanes, the systems that cause winter storms form when two air masses collide. A continental polar air mass that forms over snow-covered ground is especially cold, dry, and dense. It can force moist air to rise very quickly, producing a stormy low-pressure system.

The National Weather Service (NWS) alerts people to dangerous weather. The NWS issues a winter storm watch up to 48 hours before a storm is expected. A winter storm warning means that dangerous conditions are already present or will affect an area shortly.

**VOCABULARY**
Remember to add *blizzard* to your notebook, using the vocabulary strategy of your choice.

**Blizzards** Strong winds can blow so much snow into the air at once that it becomes difficult to see and dangerous to travel. **Blizzards** are blinding snowstorms with winds of at least 56 kilometers per hour (35 mi/h) and low temperatures—usually below –7°C (20°F). Blizzards occur in many parts of the northern and central United States. Wind and snow can knock down trees and power lines. Without heat, buildings can become very cold, and water in pipes may freeze. Schools, hospitals, and businesses may have to close. Deep, heavy snow on top of a building may cause the roof to cave in.

**Lake-Effect Snowstorms** Some of the heaviest snows fall in the areas just east and south of the Great Lakes. Cold air from the northwest gains moisture and warmth as it passes over the Great Lakes. Over cold land, the air cools again and releases the moisture as snow. The lake effect can cover areas downwind of the Great Lakes with clouds and snow even when the rest of the region has clear weather.

## INVESTIGATE Ice

### *Why put salt on icy roads?*

**PROCEDURE**

1. Place one ice cube in each cup.
2. Sprinkle salt onto the top of one of the ice cubes and observe the cubes for several minutes.

**WHAT DO YOU THINK?**

- Which ice cube melted more?
- Why do people put salt on roads in winter?

**CHALLENGE** Why do people put sand or cinders on icy roads? Design an experiment to test your ideas.

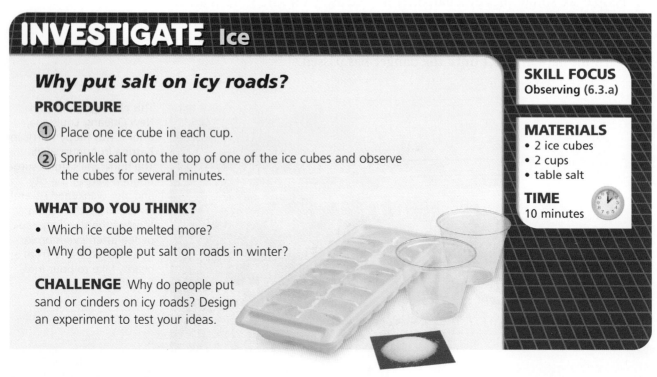

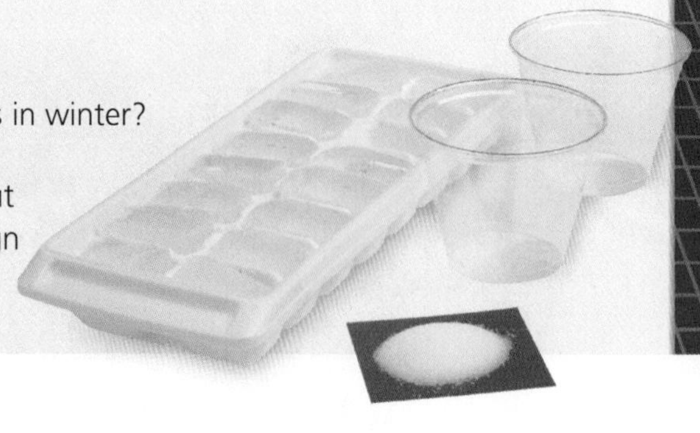

**SKILL FOCUS**
Observing (6.3.a)

**MATERIALS**
- 2 ice cubes
- 2 cups
- table salt

**TIME**
10 minutes

> **SAFETY TIPS**
>
> **WINTER STORMS**
>
> - Before a storm, prepare emergency kits for home and car.
> - Listen to weather reports for updates.
> - If caught in a storm, find or make a shelter and try to stay dry.
> - If you are in a car or truck, make sure the exhaust pipe is clear and open a window a little bit.
> - Use a colored cloth, fire, or light to help rescuers find you.
> - Exercise a little to keep warm and keep blood flowing to your fingers and toes.
> - If at home, stay inside even if there is no heat or power. Wear layers of clothing.

**Ice Storms** When rain falls onto freezing-cold ground, conditions can become dangerous. The cold rain freezes as it touches the ground and other surfaces. This freezing rain covers everything with heavy, smooth ice. The ice-covered roads become slippery and dangerous. Drivers may find it hard to steer and to stop their cars. Branches or even whole trees may break from the weight of ice. Falling branches can block roads, tear down power and telephone lines, and cause other damage. Damage from ice storms can sometimes shut down entire cities.

**CHECK YOUR READING** What type of precipitation occurs in each type of winter storm?

# 4.2 Review

**KEY CONCEPTS**

1. Where and when do hurricanes form? (6.4.e)
2. What are two ways that hurricanes can cause floods? (6.4.e)
3. List three of the possible dangers from winter storms. (6.4.e)

**CRITICAL THINKING**

4. **Compare and Contrast** What are the differences between the eye and the eye wall of a hurricane?
5. **Compare** What do hurricanes and winter storms have in common?

**CHALLENGE**

6. **Apply** If the wind is blowing from the west and the conditions are right for lake-effect snow, will the snow fall to the north, south, east, or west of a lake? Drawing a diagram may help you work out an answer.

KEY CONCEPT

# 4.3 Vertical air motion can cause severe storms.

**CALIFORNIA Content Standards**

**6.4.d** Students know convection currents distribute heat in the atmosphere and oceans.

**6.4.e** Students know differences in pressure, heat, air movement, and humidity result in changes of weather.

**BEFORE, you learned**

- Fronts produce changes in weather
- Rising moist air can produce clouds and precipitation

**NOW, you will learn**

- How thunderstorms develop
- About the effects of thunderstorms
- About tornadoes and their effects

**VOCABULARY**

**thunderstorm** p. 128
**tornado** p. 131

**THINK ABOUT**

***Where do thunderstorms get their energy?***

Thunderstorms form as warm, moist air rises quickly in strong convection currents. As water vapor in the rising air condenses, it releases energy in the form of heat. This energy provides fuel for the thunderstorm. What is the source of energy that causes currents of warm air to rise in the first place?

## Thunderstorms form from rising moist air.

If you have ever shuffled your shoes on a carpet, you may have felt a small shock when you touched a doorknob. Electrical charges collected on your body and then jumped to the doorknob in a spark of electricity.

In a similar way, electrical charges build up near the tops and bottoms of clouds as pellets of ice move up and down through the clouds. Suddenly, a charge sparks from one part of a cloud to another or between a cloud and the ground. The spark of electricity, called lightning, causes a bright flash of light. The air around the lightning is briefly heated to a temperature hotter than the surface of the Sun. This fast heating produces a sharp wave of air that travels away from the lightning. When the wave reaches you, you hear it as a crack of thunder. A **thunderstorm** is a storm with lightning and thunder.

**VOCABULARY**
Add the term *thunderstorm* to your notebook. Use the vocabulary strategy of your choice.

**CHECK YOUR READING** Is thunder a cause or an effect of lightning?

## Formation of Thunderstorms

Thunderstorms get their energy from humid air. When warm, humid air near the ground moves vertically into cooler air above, the rising air, or updraft, can build a thunderstorm quickly.

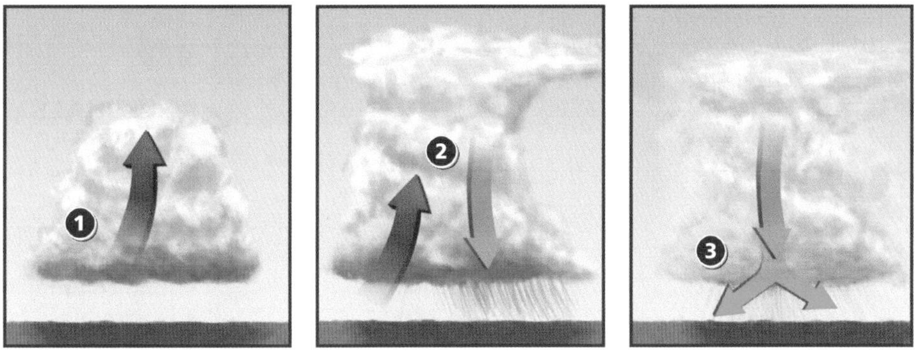


1. Rising humid air forms a cumulus cloud. The water vapor releases energy when it condenses into cloud droplets. This energy increases the air motion. The cloud continues building up into the tall cumulonimbus cloud of a thunderstorm.
2. Ice particles form in the low temperatures near the top of the cloud. As the ice particles grow large, they begin to fall and pull cold air down with them. This strong downdraft brings heavy rain or hail—the most severe stage of a thunderstorm.
3. The downdraft can spread out and block more warm air from moving upward into the cloud. The storm slows down and ends.

Thunderstorms can form at a cold front or within an air mass. At a cold front, air can be forced upward quickly. Within an air mass, uneven heating can produce convection and thunderstorms. In some regions, the conditions that produce thunderstorms occur almost daily during part of the year. In Florida, for example, the wet land and air warm up during a long summer day. Then, as you see in the diagram, cool sea breezes blow in from both coasts of the peninsula at once. The two sea breezes together push the warm, humid air over the land upward quickly. Thunderstorms form in the rising air.

In contrast, the summer air along the coast of California is usually too dry to produce thunderstorms. The air over the land heats up, and a sea breeze forms, but there is not enough moisture in the rising warm air to form clouds and precipitation.

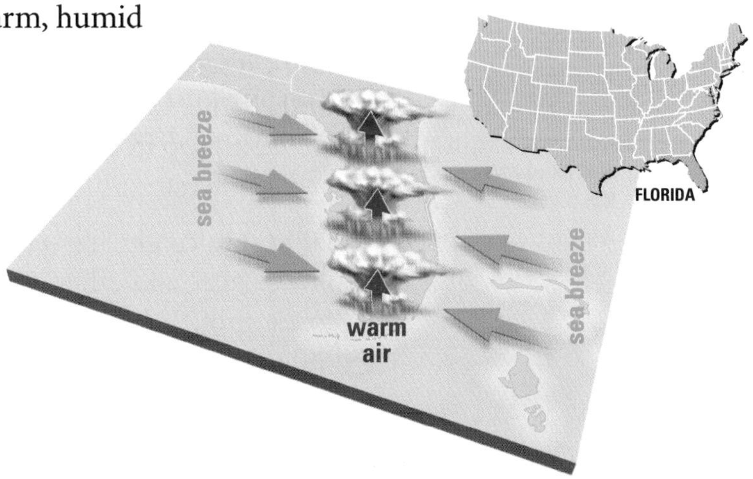

# INVESTIGATE Updrafts

## How do updrafts form?

**SKILL FOCUS**
Inferring (6.4.d)

**PROCEDURE**

1. Set up the cardboard, the cups, the container, and the cool water as shown in the photograph. Wait for the water to become still.
2. Use the eyedropper to place 2–3 drops of coloring at the bottom of the water.
3. Slide a cup of hot water (about 70°C) beneath the food coloring.

**WHAT DO YOU THINK?**

In what ways was the motion of the water like the air in a thunderstorm?

**CHALLENGE** How could you observe updrafts in air?

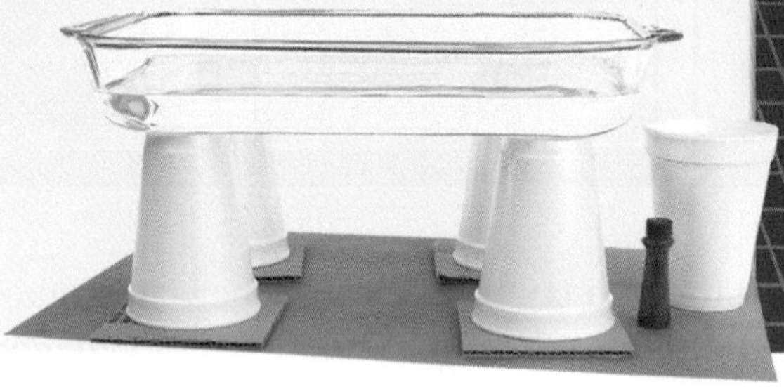

**MATERIALS**
- 4 cardboard squares
- 5 foam cups
- clear container
- cool water
- food coloring
- eyedropper
- hot tap water

**TIME**
20 minutes

## Effects of Thunderstorms

A thunderstorm may provide cool rain at the end of a hot, dry spell. The rain can provide water for crops and restore lakes and streams. However, thunderstorms are often dangerous.

**Flash floods** can be strong enough to wash away people, cars, and even houses. One thunderstorm can produce millions of liters of rain. If a thunderstorm dumps all its rain in one place, or if a series of thunderstorms dump rain onto the same area, the water can cover the ground or make rivers overflow their banks.

**Winds** from a thunderstorm can be very strong. They can blow in bursts that exceed 270 kilometers per hour (170 mi/hr). Thunderstorm winds once knocked down a stretch of forest in Canada that was about 16 kilometers (10 mi) wide and 80 kilometers (50 mi) long. Thunderstorms can also produce sudden, dangerous bursts of air that move downward and spread out.

**Hail** causes nearly $1 billion in damage to property and crops in the United States every year. Hail can wipe out entire fields of a valuable crop in a few minutes. Large hailstones can damage roofs and kill livestock.

**Lightning** can kill or seriously injure any person it hits. It can damage power lines and other equipment. Lightning can also spark dangerous forest fires.

**SAFETY TIPS**

**THUNDERSTORMS**

- Stay alert when storms are predicted or dark, tall clouds are visible.
- If you hear thunder, seek shelter immediately and stay there for 30 minutes after the last thunder ends.
- Avoid bodies of water, lone trees, flagpoles, and metal objects.
- Stay away from the telephone, electrical appliances, and pipes.
- If flash floods are expected, move away from low ground.
- Do not try to cross flowing water, even if it looks shallow.

**CHECK YOUR READING** In what ways are thunderstorms dangerous? Did any surprise you?

## Tornadoes form in severe thunderstorms.

Under some conditions, the up-and-down air motion that produces tall clouds, lightning, and hail may produce a tornado. A **tornado** is a violently rotating column of air stretching from a cloud to the ground. A tornado moves along the ground in a winding path underneath the cloud. The column may even rise off the ground and then come down in a different place.

**READING TIP**

A spinning column of air is not called a tornado unless it touches the ground. If it touches water instead, it is called a waterspout.

You cannot see air moving. A tornado may become visible when water droplets appear below the cloud in the center of the rotating column. A tornado may lift dust and debris from the ground, so the bottom of the column becomes visible, as you see in the photographs below. Water droplets and debris may make a tornado look like an upright column or a twisted rope.

**CHECK YOUR READING** What makes a tornado become visible?

More tornadoes occur in North America than anywhere else in the world. Warm, humid air masses move north from the Gulf of Mexico to the central plains of the United States. There, the warm air masses often meet cold, dense air and form thunderstorms. In the spring, the winds in this region often produce the conditions that form tornadoes. A thunderstorm may form a series of tornadoes or even a group of tornadoes all at once.

### Tornado Formation

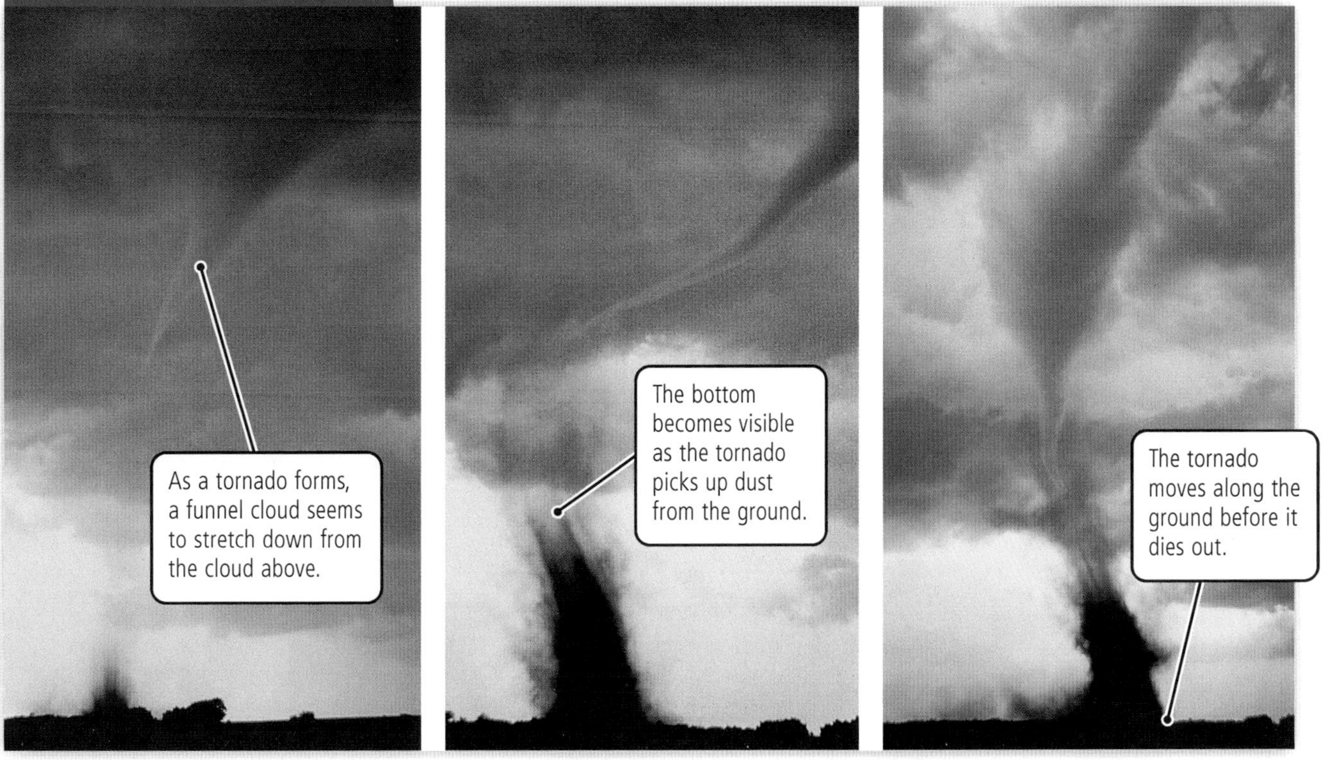

As a tornado forms, a funnel cloud seems to stretch down from the cloud above.
The bottom becomes visible as the tornado picks up dust from the ground.
The tornado moves along the ground before it dies out.

## Effects of Tornadoes

The powerful winds of a tornado can cause damage as the bottom of the tornado moves along the ground. Tornado winds can also pick up and slam dirt and small objects into buildings or anything else in the tornado's path.

The most common tornadoes are small and last only a few minutes. Their winds may be strong enough to break branches off trees, damage chimneys, and tear highway billboards. A typical path along the ground may be 100 meters (300 ft) wide and 1.5 kilometers (1 mi) long.

Larger tornadoes are less common but have stronger winds and last longer. About 20 percent of tornadoes are strong enough to knock over large trees, lift cars off the ground, and tear the roofs off houses. Very few—about 1 percent of all tornadoes—are violent enough to lift or completely demolish sturdy buildings. These huge tornadoes may last more than two hours. You can find more details about tornadoes in the Appendix.

**SAFETY TIPS**

**TORNADOES**

- Listen for tornado warnings when severe weather is predicted.
- If you are in a car or mobile home, get out and go into a sturdy building or a ditch or depression.
- Go to the basement if possible.
- Avoid windows and open areas.
- Protect your head and neck.

## Paths of Tornadoes

A tornado moves along with its thunderstorm. It travels at the same pace and weaves a path that is impossible to predict. A tornado may appear suddenly and then disappear before anyone has time to report it. However, the conditions that form tornadoes may persist, so citizens' reports are still useful. The National Weather Service issues a tornado watch when the weather conditions might produce tornadoes. A tornado warning is issued when a tornado has been detected.

# 4.3 Review

**KEY CONCEPTS**

1. What conditions produce thunderstorms? (6.4.d)
2. How can rain from thunderstorms become dangerous? (6.4.e)
3. How do tornadoes cause damage? (6.4.e)

**CRITICAL THINKING**

4. **Compare** What do hail and tornadoes have in common? Hint: Think about how each forms.
5. **Synthesize** Which type of front is most likely to produce thunderstorms and tornadoes? Explain why.

**CHALLENGE**

6. **Compare and Contrast** If you saw the photograph above in a newspaper, what details would tell you that the damage was due to a tornado and not a hurricane?

Think SCIENCE

SKILL: EVALUATING HYPOTHESES

# What Type of Weather Buried This Truck?

6.7.e Recognize whether evidence is consistent with a proposed explanation.

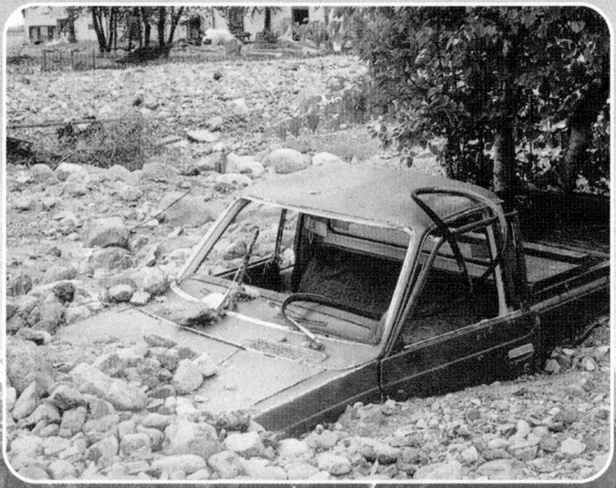

This picture was taken soon after a weather event partly buried this truck in Britannia Beach, British Columbia.

## Observations and Inferences

One observer made this analysis.

a. The truck, the tree, and two fences in the background were partly buried by sand and stones.
b. No stones are visible inside the truck.
c. The rounded stones must have come from an ocean or river.
d. The tree near the truck has green leaves. The wind must have been too weak to tear off the leaves.
e. The area is near the Pacific Ocean. It is far from the equator. There is a very large island between the location and the open ocean.

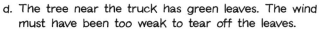

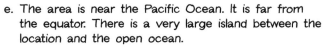

A waterway leads south and west from Britannia Beach to a bay, around an island, to the Pacific Ocean.

## Hypotheses

The observer made the following hypotheses.

a. A storm surge carried sand and stones from the Pacific Ocean. The material covered a large area. The truck floated, so it was not filled with material.
b. A tornado picked up the truck with other material. It dumped everything together, and the material partly buried the truck, fences, and tree.
c. Thunderstorms produced a flash flood that carried sand and stones from a riverbed to this area. The flood receded and left material that covered the area.
d. The truck was parked on a pile of snow during a blizzard. When the snow melted, the area under the truck collapsed and the truck sank into the ground.

## Evaluate Each Hypothesis

Review each hypothesis and think about whether the observations support it. Some facts may rule out some hypotheses. Some facts may neither support nor weaken some hypotheses.

**CHALLENGE** How could you model one or more of the hypotheses with a toy truck, sand, and a basin of water?

KEY CONCEPT

# 4.4 Weather forecasters use advanced technologies.

**CALIFORNIA Content Standard**

6.4.e Students know differences in pressure, heat, air movement, and humidity result in changes of weather.

**BEFORE, you learned**

- Weather changes when air masses move
- High-pressure systems bring fair weather
- Fronts and low-pressure systems bring stormy weather

**NOW, you will learn**

- How weather data are collected
- How weather data are displayed
- How meteorologists forecast the weather

**VOCABULARY**

**meteorologist** p. 134
**isobar** p. 137

**EXPLORE Weather Maps (6.4.e)**

### *What does a weather map show?*

**PROCEDURE**

1. Look at the weather outside. Write down the conditions you observe.
2. Use the map to check the weather conditions for your region.

**WHAT DO YOU THINK?**

- What symbols on the map do you recognize?
- How does the information on the weather map compare with the weather you observed outside?

**MATERIALS**

newspaper weather map

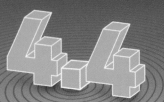

## Weather data come from many sources.

Looking at the weather outside in the morning can help you decide what to wear. Different things give you clues to the current weather. If you see plants swaying from side to side, you might infer that it is windy. If you see a gray sky and wet, shiny streets, you might decide to wear a raincoat.

You might also check a weather report to get more information. A weather report can show conditions in your area and also in the region around you. You can look for weather nearby that might move into your area during the day. More detailed predictions of how the weather will move and change may be included in a weather report by a meteorologist. A **meteorologist** (MEE-tee-uh-RAHL-uh-jihst) is a scientist who studies weather.

**VOCABULARY**
Remember to add *meteorologist* to your notebook, using the vocabulary strategy of your choice.

**CHECK YOUR READING** What information can a weather report show?

In order to predict the weather, meteorologists look at past and current conditions. They use many forms of technology to gather data. The illustration below shows how weather information is gathered. For example, radar stations and satellites use advanced technologies to gather data for large areas at a time.

Instruments within the atmosphere can make measurements of local weather conditions. Newer instruments can make measurements often and automatically and then report the results almost instantly. Instruments are placed in many ground stations on land and weather buoys at sea. Instruments can also be carried by balloons, ships, and planes. These instruments report a series of measurements along a path within the atmosphere.

**RESOURCE CENTER**
CLASSZONE.COM

Learn more about weather forecasting and your local weather.

## Collection of Weather Data

**Instruments that gather weather data use many technologies and can be found in many places.**

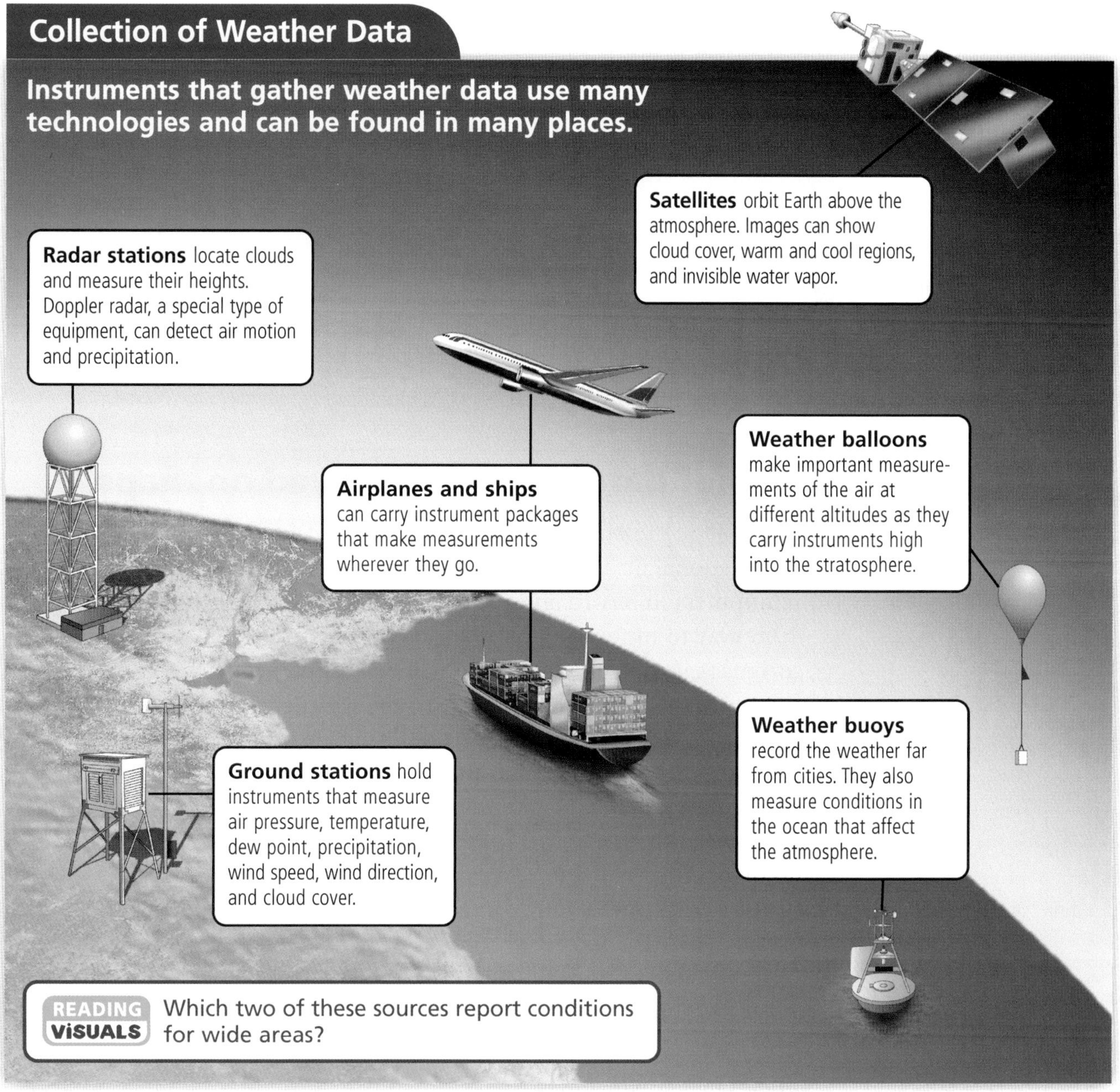

**Satellites** orbit Earth above the atmosphere. Images can show cloud cover, warm and cool regions, and invisible water vapor.
**Radar stations** locate clouds and measure their heights. Doppler radar, a special type of equipment, can detect air motion and precipitation.
**Weather balloons** make important measurements of the air at different altitudes as they carry instruments high into the stratosphere.
**Airplanes and ships** can carry instrument packages that make measurements wherever they go.
**Weather buoys** record the weather far from cities. They also measure conditions in the ocean that affect the atmosphere.
**Ground stations** hold instruments that measure air pressure, temperature, dew point, precipitation, wind speed, wind direction, and cloud cover.


**READING VISUALS** Which two of these sources report conditions for wide areas?

## Information on a Weather Map

**Meteorologists use maps to display a lot of weather information at once.**

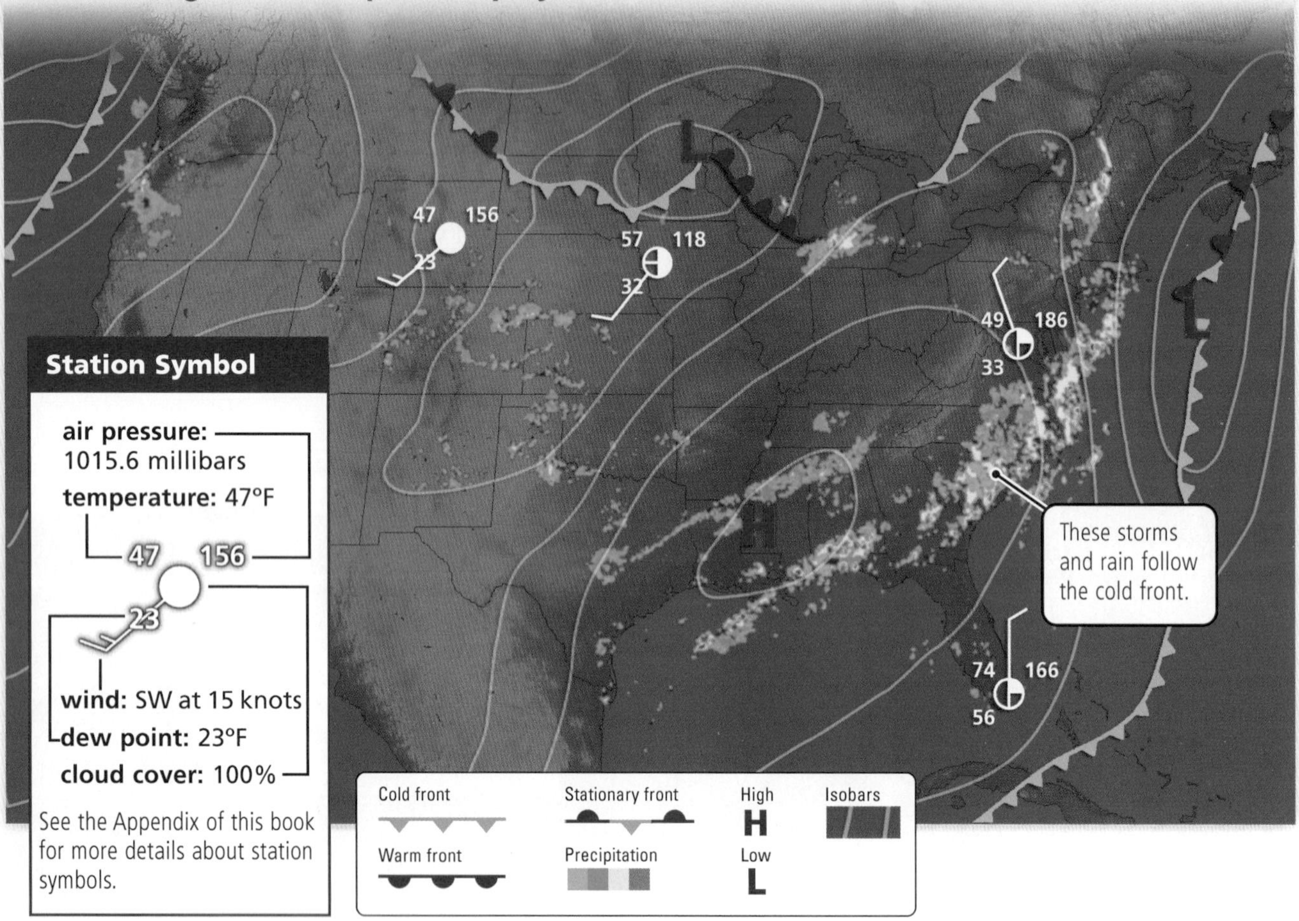


# Weather data can be displayed on maps.

**MAIN IDEA WEB**
Add notes about weather data to your notebook.

Automatic measurements from many sources constantly pour in to the National Oceanic and Atmospheric Administration. Scientists use computers to record and use the enormous amount of data gathered. One way to make the information easier to understand is to show it on maps. A single map can show many different types of data together to give a more complete picture of the weather. The map above combines information from ground stations with Doppler radar measurements of precipitation.

- Precipitation is shown as patches of blue, green, yellow, and red. The colors indicate the amounts of rain or other precipitation.
- Station symbols on the map show data from ground stations. Only a few stations are shown.
- Symbols showing fronts and pressure patterns are added to the map to make the overall weather patterns easier to see.

**CHECK YOUR READING** How is information from Doppler radar shown?

Computer programs are used to combine information from many ground stations. The resulting calculations give the highs, lows, and fronts that are marked on the map. The cold front near the East Coast has triangles to show that the front is moving eastward. This cold front produced the heavy rain that is visible in the Doppler radar data.

## Air Pressure on Weather Maps

The map below shows conditions from the same date as the map on page 136. Thin lines represent air pressure. An **isobar** (EYE-suh-BAHR) is a line that connects places that have the same air pressure. Each isobar represents a different air pressure value. All the isobars together, combined with the symbols for highs and lows, show the patterns of air pressure that produce weather systems.

READING TIP

*Iso-* means "equal," and *bar* means "pressure."

Each isobar is labeled with the air pressure for that whole line in units called millibars (MIHL-uh-BAHRZ). A lower number means a lower air pressure. As you read earlier, differences in pressure cause air to move. Meteorologists use isobars to understand air motion.

Sometimes air-pressure measurements are listed in inches of mercury. This unit comes from an old type of barometer that measures how high the air pressure pushes a column of mercury, a liquid metal. Computer-controlled instruments are used more often today, but the measurements may be converted to inches of mercury.

### Understanding Isobars

**Isobars show pressure patterns, which determine winds.**

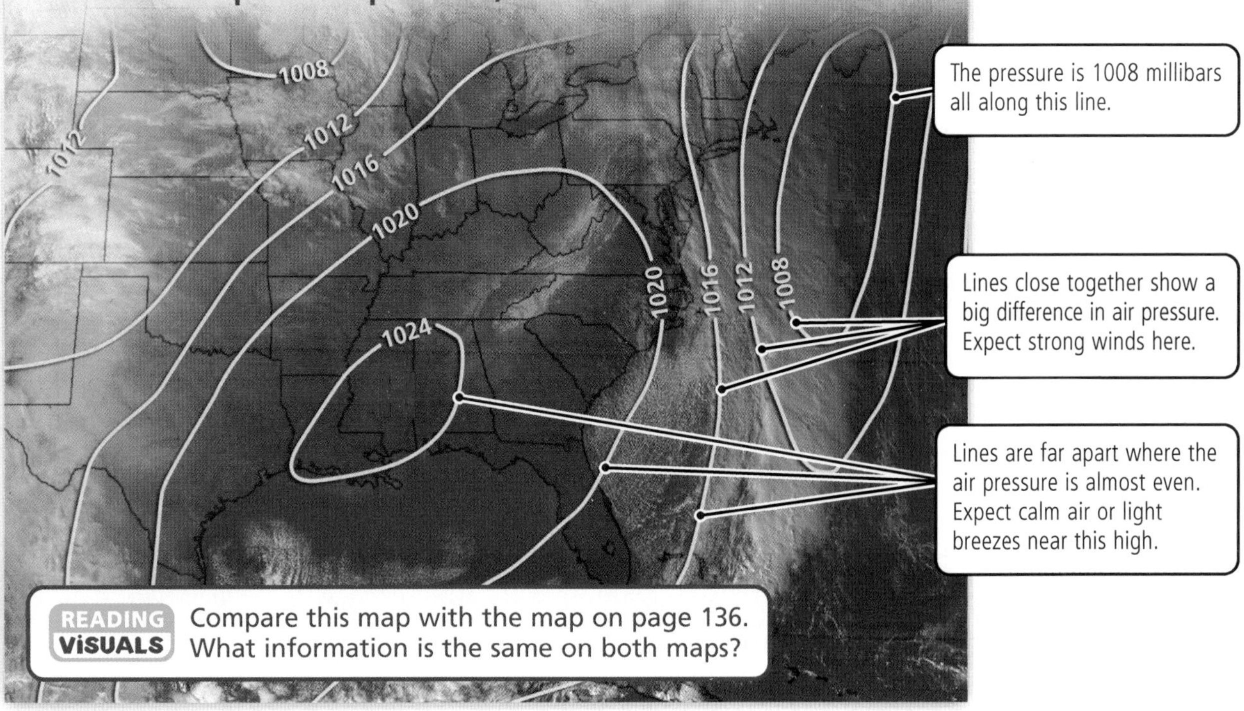

1008
1012
1012
1016
1020
1024
1020
1016
1012
1008
The pressure is 1008 millibars all along this line.
Lines close together show a big difference in air pressure. Expect strong winds here.
Lines are far apart where the air pressure is almost even. Expect calm air or light breezes near this high.

READING VISUALS Compare this map with the map on page 136. What information is the same on both maps?

## Satellite Images

**Visible Light**

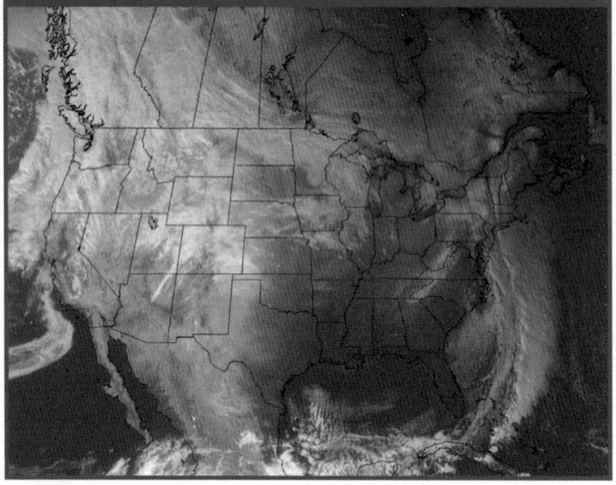

This visible-light satellite image shows clouds from above. The patches of white are clouds.

**Infrared Radiation**

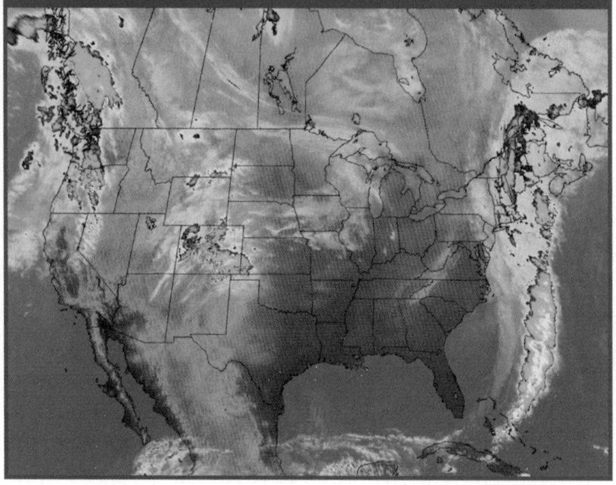

This infrared satellite image also shows clouds, but uses colors to show where there are tall clouds.

**READING VISUALS** Find a location on these maps and the map on page 136. What were the weather conditions?

## Satellite Images and Special Maps

Satellites take different types of images from space. Some images record the visible light that reflects off clouds and Earth's surface. Clouds and snow-covered land look white in sunlight. Unfortunately, visible-light images do not show much at night.

Another type of image shows infrared radiation given off by the warm surface and cooler clouds. These infrared images can show cloud patterns even at night because objects with different temperatures show up differently. Air temperatures change with altitude, so infrared images also show which clouds are low and which are high or tall. You can see in the maps above how visible and infrared satellite images show similar clouds but different details. Outlines of the states have been added to make the images easier to understand.

The colors on this map represent different ranges of temperature (°F).

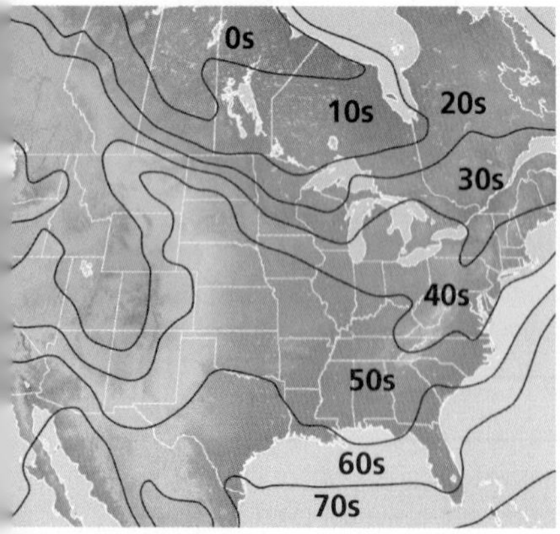


Data from ground stations and other sources can be used to make other types of maps. The map at left shows the pattern of temperatures on the same date as the images above and the map on page 136. Other maps may show winds or amounts of pollution. A map can be made to show any type of measurement or weather prediction. Different types of maps are often used together to give a more complete picture of the current weather.

**CHECK YOUR READING** Why would a weather report show more than one map?

## Forecasters use computer models to predict weather.

Instruments can measure only the current weather conditions. Most people want to know what the weather will be like in the future.

Forecasters use maps and satellite images to communicate weather conditions and predictions.

Forecasters can make some predictions from their own observations. If they see cirrus clouds above and high stratus clouds to the west, they might infer that a warm front is approaching. They would predict weather typical for a warm front—more clouds, then rain, and eventually warmer weather. If they also have information from other places, the forecasters might be able to tell where the warm front is already and how fast it is moving. They might be able to predict how soon it will arrive and even how warm the weather will be after the front passes.

Computers have become an important tool for forecasting weather. When weather stations send in data, computers can create maps right away. Computer models combine many types of data to forecast what might happen next. Different computer models give different types of forecasts. Scientists study the computer forecasts, then apply their knowledge and experience to make weather predictions.

Forecasting the weather is complicated. As a result, some forecasts are more dependable than others. The farther in advance a forecast is made, the more time there is for small differences between the predicted and the actual weather to add up. For this reason, short-range forecasts—up to three days in advance—are the most accurate. Forecasts of fast-changing weather, such as severe storms, are less accurate far in advance. It is best to watch for new predictions close to the time the storm is forecast.

## 4.4 Review

### KEY CONCEPTS

1. List three of the sources of weather data.
2. What does a map with isobars show? (6.4.e)
3. How do meteorologists use computers?

### CRITICAL THINKING

4. **Draw Conclusions** Why do meteorologists not combine all their weather information into one map?
5. **Analyze** How is the information from radar and satellites different from the information from ground stations?

### CHALLENGE

6. **Apply** Suppose you are planning an afternoon picnic a week in advance. Fair weather is forecast for that day, but a storm is expected that night. What will you do? Explain your reasoning.

# CHAPTER INVESTIGATION

## Design a Weather Center

**DESIGN — YOUR OWN —**

**OVERVIEW AND PURPOSE** The accuracy of a weather forecast depends largely on the type and quality of the data that it is based on. In this lab, you will use what you have learned about weather to

- observe and measure weather conditions
- record and analyze the weather-related data

**MATERIALS**
- thermometer
- magnetic compass
- other weather instruments
- graph paper

6.4.e, 6.7.b

### Procedure

1. Survey the possible sources of weather data in and around your classroom. You can use a thermometer to record the outside air temperature. You can observe cloud types and the amount of cloud cover from a window or doorway. You can also observe precipitation and notice if it is heavy or light. If there is a flag in view, use it to find the wind direction and to estimate wind speed.

2. Assemble or make tools for your observations. You may want to make a reference chart with pictures of different cloud types or other information. Decide if you wish to use homemade weather instruments. You may have made a barometer, and a psychrometer already. If not, see the instructions on pages 81 and 100. You may also wish to do research to learn how to make or use other weather instruments, such as a rain gauge.

3. Make an initial set of observations. Write down the date and time in your **Science Notebook.** Record the readings from the thermometer and other instruments.

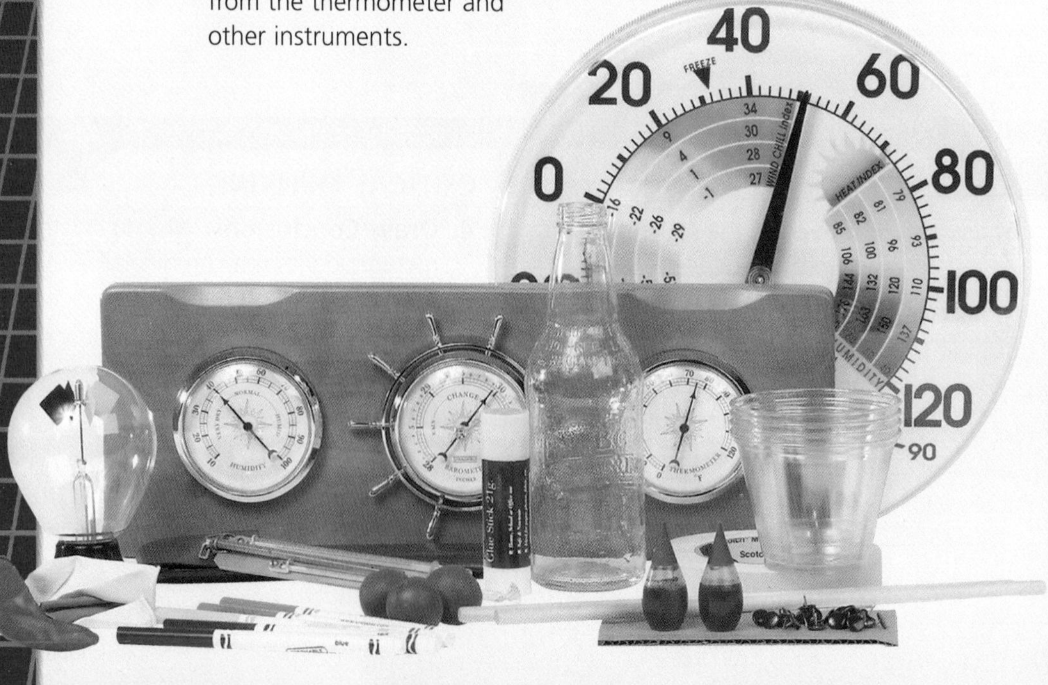

Content Standard
6.4.e Students know differences in pressure, heat, air movement, and humidity result in changes of weather.

Investigation Standard
6.7.b Select and use appropriate tools and technology (including calculators, computers, balances, spring scales, microscopes, and binoculars) to perform tests, collect data, and display data.

4. Decide how to record your observations of the clouds, the wind, and any precipitation. Organize your notes to make it easy for you to record later observations in a consistent way.

5. Create a chart with a row for each type of observation you are making. You might darken fractions of circles to record amounts of cloud cover, as in the station symbols on page 136. Make sure each row has a heading and enough room for numbers, words, or sketches. Include a row for notes that do not belong in the data rows.

6. Record your observations every day at the same time. Try to make the observations exactly the same way each time. If you have to redraw your chart, copy the information carefully.

## Observe and Analyze

Write It Up

1. **GRAPH** Graph the data you collected that represent measurable quantities. Use graphs that are appropriate to your data. Often a simple line graph will work. Choose an appropriate scale and interval based on the range of your data. Make the *x*-axis of each graph the same so that you can compare the different types of data easily.

2. **COMPARE AND CONTRAST** Look at your graphs for patterns in your data. Some aspects of weather change at the same time because they are related to each other. Did one type of change occur before a different type of change? If so, this pattern may help you predict weather.

## Conclude

Write It Up

1. **INTERPRET** Did a front pass through your area during the period you observed? What observations helped you answer this question?

2. **EVALUATE** Why was it necessary to observe at the same time each day?

3. **APPLY** If you predicted that each day's weather would be repeated the next day, how often would you be right?

## INVESTIGATE Further

**CHALLENGE** Locate a newspaper weather page for the period during which you were making your weather observations. How do the weather data reported for your area compare with your measurements? How do you account for any differences you notice in the data?

Design a Weather Center

Table 1. Daily Weather Chart

| | | | |
|---|---|---|---|
| Date/time of observations | | | |
| Temperature (°C) | | | |
| Cloud types | | | |
| Cloud coverage | ○ | ○ | ○ |
| Precipitation (cm) and notes | | | |
| Wind direction | | | |
| Other notes | | | |

# 4 Chapter Review

## the BIG idea

**The interaction of air masses causes changes in weather.**

CONTENT REVIEW
CLASSZONE.COM

### KEY CONCEPTS SUMMARY

### 1 Weather changes as air masses move.

**Air masses** meet and produce **fronts,** which can bring lowered pressure and stormy weather. Fronts can be cold, warm, or stationary.

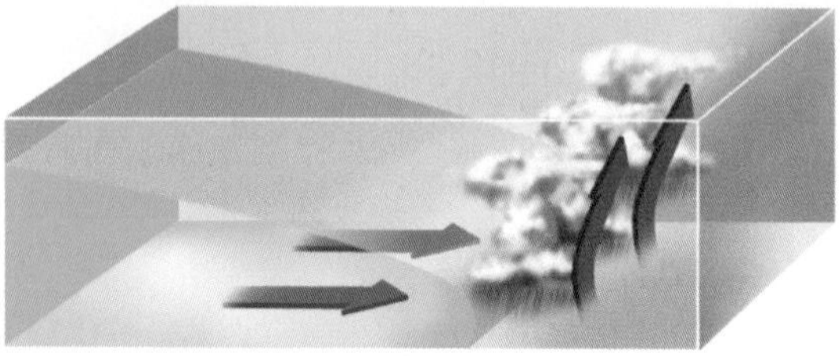

**VOCABULARY**
**air mass** p. 115
**front** p. 118
**high-pressure system** p. 120
**low-pressure system** p. 121

### 2 Low-pressure systems can become storms.

**Hurricanes** and winter storms develop from low-pressure systems.

Hurricanes form over warm ocean water.

**VOCABULARY**
**tropical storm** p. 123
**hurricane** p. 123
**storm surge** p. 125
**blizzard** p. 126

### 3 Vertical air motion can cause severe storms.

Rising moist air can produce **thunderstorms.** The up-and-down motion of air in a thunderstorm can produce a **tornado.**

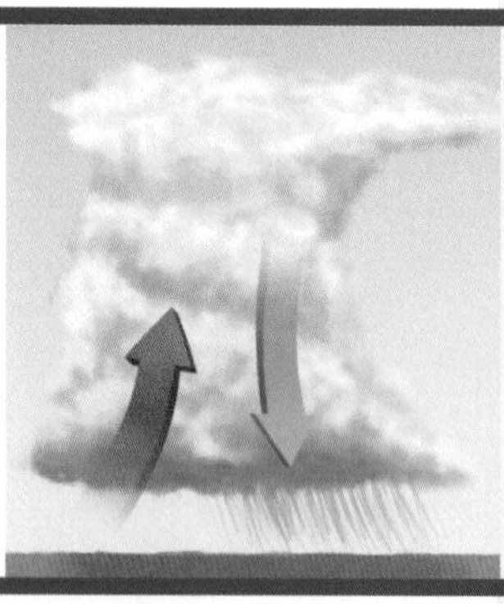

**VOCABULARY**
**thunderstorm** p. 128
**tornado** p. 131

### 4 Weather forecasters use advanced technologies.

Weather information comes from many sources.

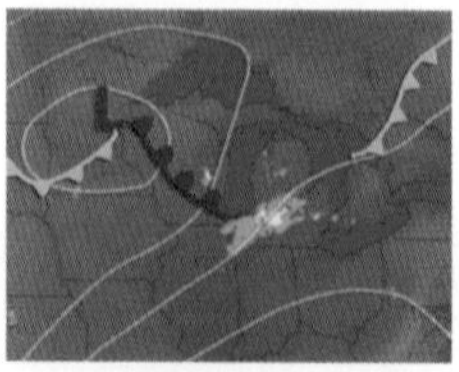

**Meteorologists** use weather data and computer models to forecast weather.

**VOCABULARY**
**meteorologist** p. 134
**isobar** p. 137

## Reviewing Vocabulary

*Describe each term below, using the related term as part of the description.*

| Term | Related Term | Description |
|---|---|---|
| EXAMPLE hurricane | low-pressure system | a low-pressure system in the tropics with winds at least 120 km/h |
| **1.** front | air mass | |
| **2.** low-pressure system | low-pressure center | |
| **3.** storm surge | hurricane | |
| **4.** tropical storm | low-pressure system | |
| **5.** air mass | humidity | |
| **6.** thunderstorm | convection | |
| **7.** tornado | thunderstorm | |
| **8.** blizzard | low-pressure system | |

## Reviewing Key Concepts

**Multiple Choice** *Choose the letter of the best answer.*

**9.** What qualities are nearly the same at different locations in a single air mass? (6.4.e)
- **a.** temperature and pressure
- **b.** temperature and humidity
- **c.** air pressure and wind speed
- **d.** air pressure and humidity

**10.** Which is the name for an air mass that forms over the ocean near the equator? (6.4.e)
- **a.** maritime tropical
- **b.** maritime polar
- **c.** continental tropical
- **d.** continental polar

**11.** A meteorologist is a scientist who
- **a.** predicts meteor showers
- **b.** studies maps
- **c.** studies the weather
- **d.** changes the weather

**12.** An isobar shows locations with the same (6.4.e)
- **a.** temperature
- **b.** rainfall
- **c.** air pressure
- **d.** wind speed

**13.** Which is produced when a warm air mass pushes a colder air mass? (6.4.e)
- **a.** a stationary front
- **b.** a cold front
- **c.** a warm front
- **d.** a thunderstorm

**14.** Which can be measured in inches of mercury?
- **a.** air pressure
- **b.** temperature
- **c.** hail
- **d.** lightning

**15.** Which source provides measurements for just one location?
- **a.** ground station
- **b.** radar station
- **c.** weather balloon
- **d.** satellite

**16.** Compared with warm fronts, cold fronts are (6.4.e)
- **a.** faster moving
- **b.** less dense
- **c.** more cloudy
- **d.** less steep

**17.** Which statement is usually true of high-pressure systems in North America? (6.4.e)
- **a.** They bring fair weather.
- **b.** They change quickly.
- **c.** The air in them is cold and dense.
- **d.** The air in them moves counterclockwise.

**18.** Thunderstorms often begin with the rising of (6.4.d)
- **a.** cool, dry air
- **b.** cool, humid air
- **c.** warm, dry air
- **d.** warm, humid air

**19.** What is the relationship between lightning and thunder? (6.4.e)
- **a.** They have separate causes.
- **b.** They have the same cause.
- **c.** Lightning causes thunder.
- **d.** Thunder causes lightning.

**Short Answer** *Write a short answer to each question.*

**20.** Why are hurricanes in the eastern United States more likely in autumn than in spring? (6.4.e)

**21.** What causes lake-effect snow? (6.4.e)

**22.** In what four ways can thunderstorms be dangerous? (6.2.d)

## Thinking Critically

*Use this weather map to answer the next six questions. The numbers under each city name are the highest and the lowest temperature for the day in degrees Fahrenheit.*

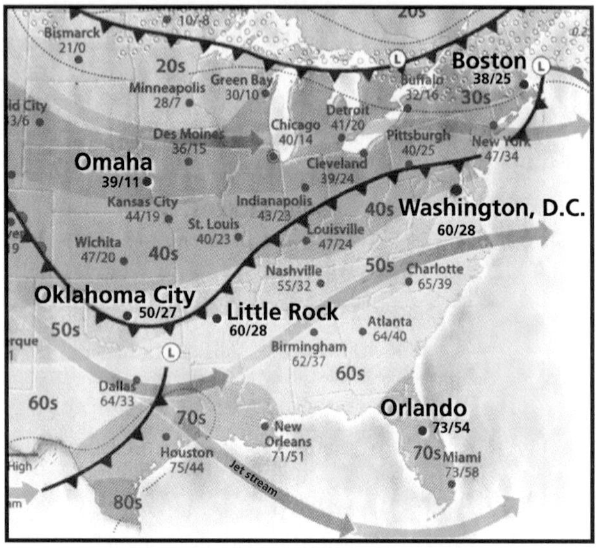


23. **INFER** Name and describe the air mass that has moved south to Omaha from Canada. (6.4.e)

24. **IDENTIFY EFFECTS** How are two low-pressure systems affecting the weather near Boston? (6.4.e)

25. **PREDICT** Explain whether Washington, D.C., or Orlando is more likely to have a big change in weather in the next two days. (6.4.e)

26. **COMPARE AND CONTRAST** Explain the difference in temperature between Oklahoma City and Little Rock. (6.4.e)

27. **PREDICT** How will the weather in Little Rock change in the next day or two? (6.4.e)

28. **APPLY** Does this map indicate that it is hurricane season? Explain your reasoning. (6.4.e)

29. **CONNECT** Describe today's weather and explain what fronts and pressure systems might be influencing it. (6.4.e)

30. **COMPARE AND CONTRAST** Use a Venn diagram to compare images from visible light and infrared radiation. (6.4.e)

**PREDICT** *For each set of conditions listed in the chart, write a weather prediction.* (6.4.e)

| Conditions | Prediction |
|---|---|
| **31.** A cold front is moving into an area that has warm, moist air. | |
| **32.** A warm front is moving into an area that has cold, dense air. | |
| **33.** A cool sea breeze is blowing inland, causing warm, humid air to rise. | |
| **34.** Air pressure is falling and the temperature is rising. | |
| **35.** Air pressure is increasing and the temperature is steady. | |
| **36.** A thunderstorm is developing spinning winds at its center. | |
| **37.** A low-pressure center is over the Atlantic Ocean where the water temperature is above 27°C (81°F). | |
| **38.** Cold air is pushing warm air where the air is 2°C (36°F) and the ground is -3°C (27°F). | |

39. **COMPARE** How is the air motion in the eye of a hurricane similar to the air motion at a high-pressure center? (6.4.e)

40. **EVALUATE** Which type of storm is most dangerous? Explain your reasoning. (6.4.e)

## the BIG idea

41. **APPLY** Look again at the photograph on pages 112–113. Now that you have finished the chapter, how would you change your response to the question on the photograph? (6.4.e)

42. **SEQUENCE** Draw a storyboard with at least four sketches to show how cool, sunny weather might change into warm, rainy weather. (6.4.e)

## UNIT PROJECTS

Evaluate all of the data, results, and information from your project folder. Prepare to present your project to the class. Be ready to answer questions posed by your classmates about your results.

For more practice, go to . . .
TEST PRACTICE
CLASSZONE.COM

## Analyzing a Map

6.4.d, 6.4.e

*Use this weather map to answer the questions below.*

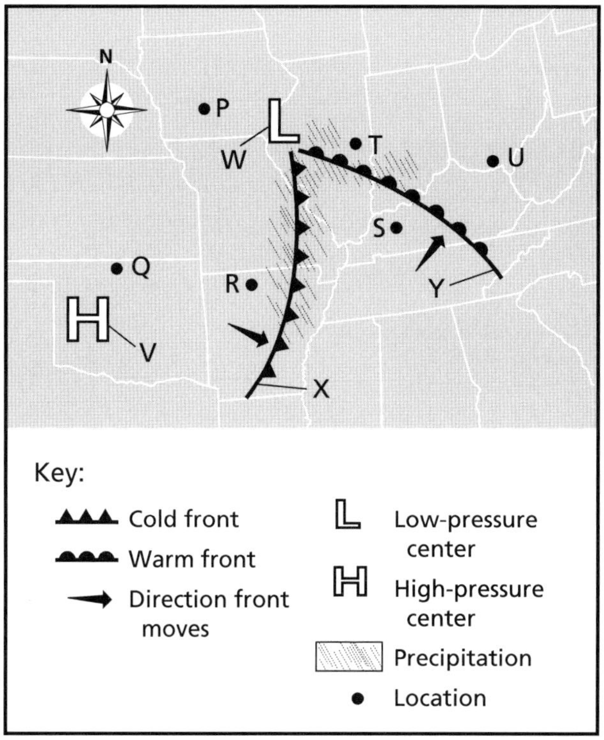


**1.** Which letter labels a cold front?

**a.** Q **b.** U **c.** X **d.** Y

**2.** Which word best describes the general movement of the fronts?

**a.** to the north **b.** to the east **c.** clockwise **d.** counterclockwise

**3.** A warm front occurs where warm air moves into colder air. Which of these locations is probably warmest?

**a.** R **b.** S **c.** T **d.** U

**4.** Temperatures usually change quickly near a front and more slowly away from a front. The temperature at Q is 10°C (50°F). The temperature at S is 20°C (68°F). Which is the best estimate for the temperature at R?

**a.** 6°C (43°F) **b.** 11°C (52°F) **c.** 20°C (68°F) **d.** 24°C (75°F)

**5.** If the fronts continue to move as shown, which location will get warmer soon?

**a.** Q **b.** R **c.** S **d.** T

**6.** Low pressure often brings stormy weather, and high pressure often brings fair weather. Which of these locations is most likely to have clear skies?

**a.** Q **b.** R **c.** S **d.** U

## Extended Response

*Use the map above to answer the two questions below in detail. Include some of the terms shown in the word box. Underline each term you use in your answers.*

| | | |
|---|---|---|
| cold front | humid | west |
| warm front | east | prevailing winds |

**7.** Along which front on the weather map above would you expect to find cumulonimbus clouds? Explain why.

**8.** The weather system shown on the map above is in the continental United States. In which direction do you expect it to move? Explain why.

# UNIT 2

# Earth's Surface

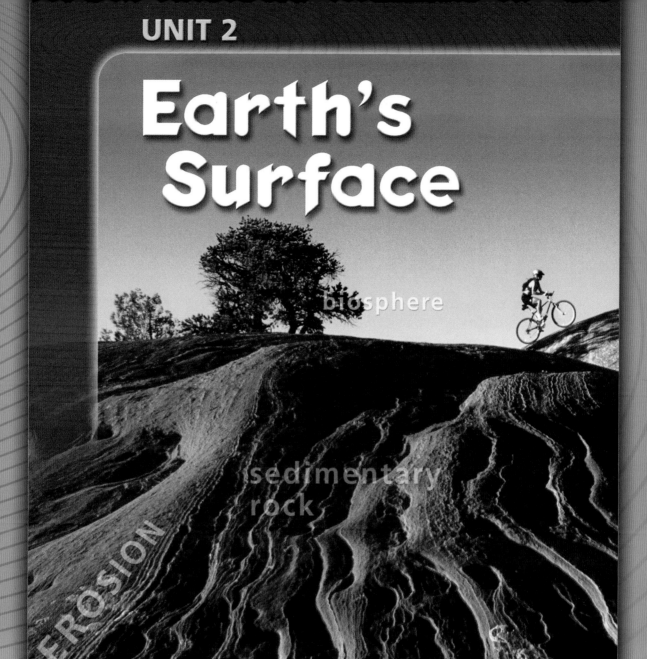

## Contents Overview

# REMOTE SENSING

**Technology high above Earth's surface is giving scientists a whole new look at our planet. This image is of Jasper Ridge, near Palo Alto, California.**

**California Content Standards**

**6.3.d** Students know heat energy is also transferred between objects by radiation (radiation can travel through space).

**6.4.b** Students know solar energy reaches Earth through radiation, mostly in the form of visible light.

**SCIENTIFIC AMERICAN FRONTIERS**

View the video segment "All That Glitters" to learn how explorers use remote sensing and other methods to find valuable materials.

This research jet aircraft carries instruments to study Earth's land surface, ocean, and atmosphere. It flies at high altitudes, allowing it to collect data and images over large areas during a single flight.

## Mapping Earth

You're probably familiar with images of gold prospectors in the Old West. Maybe you've seen them in old movies or read about them in history books. Prospectors wandered through the mountains, looking for signs of ores or gemstones. They went here and there in response to rumors or stories, pitching camp in remote canyons on a hunch. People still prospect for minerals today, but they're more likely to fly in airplanes than to ride mules. And stories of fabled mines are just stories. Today's prospectors rely on scientific evidence from remote sensing.

Remote sensing—the use of instruments to gather data from a distance—has two great advantages. The first is that sensors mounted in satellites and airplanes can collect vast amounts of detailed information over large areas. The second is that the sensors can easily collect information about the same area again and again.

For example, scientists use remote sensing to make better and more detailed maps of Earth and to track changes over time. Thanks to remote sensing, scientists now know that Mount Everest, the highest point on Earth, is actually getting higher by about 1 centimeter (0.4 in.) per year. Remote sensors on satellites are also mapping global ocean temperatures and showing how they change over the course of a year.

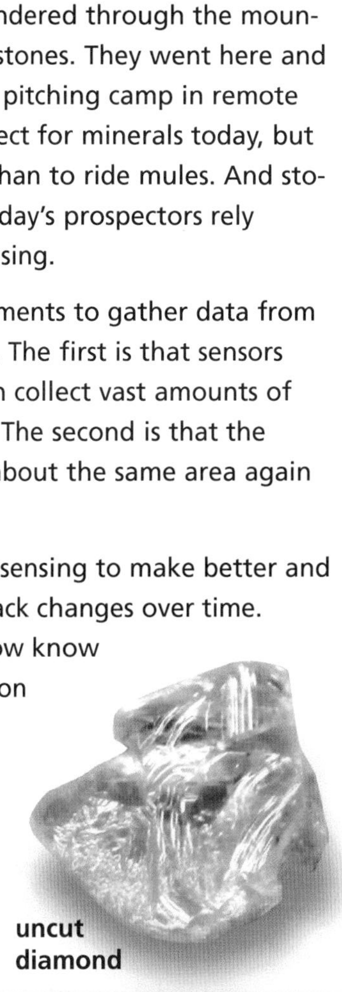

**uncut diamond**

## Detecting Minerals from Above

One of the many uses of remote sensing is to find new sources of valuable minerals, such as diamonds. To detect minerals from airplanes or satellites, remote sensors make use of the energy in sunlight. Sunlight reaches Earth as radiation, which travels in the form of waves. All objects absorb some types of radiation and reflect others. The particular wavelengths absorbed or reflected depend upon the materials that make up the objects. Each kind of material has a unique "fingerprint" of the wavelengths it absorbs and the wavelengths it reflects.

Energy from the Sun reflects at different wavelengths from materials at Earth's surface. Instruments on the jet analyze the reflected energy and map the surface.

When sunlight strikes Earth's surface, some of it is reflected back into the sky. Some of the radiation is absorbed by rocks and other objects and then emitted, or given off, in a different form. Remote sensors in airplanes and satellites collect the reflected and emitted radiation and analyze it to determine which types of rocks and minerals lie on the surface. The remote sensing systems collect so much data that computer processing and analysis are difficult and expensive. Still, the data are usually clear enough to show the types of minerals located in the regions scanned. However, minerals that are buried cannot be detected by remote sensing from aircraft or satellites. The sensors receive only energy from or near the surface.

### SCIENTIFIC AMERICAN FRONTIERS

**View the "All that Glitters" segment of your *Scientific American Frontiers* video to see how finding certain common minerals can indicate the presence of a valuable mineral like diamond.**

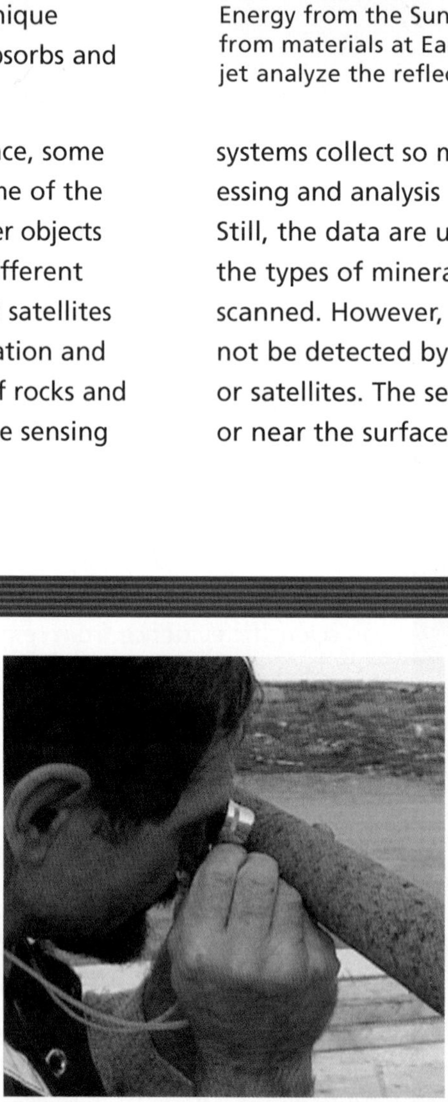

**IN THIS SCENE FROM THE VIDEO** a mineral prospector searches for diamonds in a cylinder of rock drilled from beneath Earth's surface.

**SEARCHING FOR DIAMONDS** People used to think that North America did not have many diamonds. However, northern Canada is geologically similar to the world's major diamond-producing areas: southern Africa, Russia, and Australia. A few diamond prospectors kept searching, using remote sensing and other techniques. The prospectors looked for more common minerals that form under the same conditions as diamonds. They made maps showing where these minerals were most plentiful and used the maps to search for diamond-rich rock. Once the prospectors realized that the glaciers of the last ice age had moved the minerals, they looked for and found diamonds farther northward. Canada is now a big producer of diamonds.

Remote sensing can show the presence of minerals that occur with diamonds, but people must still use older methods to collect samples for further analysis.

## Prospecting for Diamonds

One of the major regions of mineral exploration in which remote sensing is used is in the Northwest Territories of Canada, where the first diamond mine began operating in 1998. The Canada Centre for Remote Sensing has helped develop sensing equipment that can fit easily onto light airplanes and computer equipment to analyze results quickly. The sensing equipment is used to detect certain types of minerals that are often found along with diamonds.

Using remote sensing to locate minerals associated with diamonds or valuable ores is only a beginning. The data cannot show how far the minerals or ores extend underground. Prospectors must still explore the area and take samples. However, remote sensing gives mineral prospectors an excellent idea of where to start looking.

### UNANSWERED Questions

As scientists use remote sensing to study Earth's land surface, ocean, and atmosphere, they work to answer new questions.

- Can remote sensing be used to locate sources of iron, platinum, or gold in areas that are difficult to explore on foot?
- How do changes in water temperature at the ocean surface affect long-range weather patterns and the health of ocean organisms?
- How do different types of clouds affect the amount of sunlight reaching Earth's surface and the average temperature of the surface?

## UNIT PROJECTS

**As you study this unit, work alone or with a group on one of the projects listed below.**

### Hiker's Guide Video (6.7.f)

Like prospectors, wilderness hikers must be able to read maps that show the shape of the land. Prepare a video to teach hikers how to choose hiking and camping areas by reading maps.

- Obtain a topographic map of a wilderness area in a national or state park.
- Write a script outlining what you will teach and how you will videotape it.
- Present your video and display the maps you used.

### Diamond Mine Model (6.1.b)

Diamonds can be carried toward Earth's surface by kimberlite pipes. Show how diamonds are mined from kimberlite.

- Build a model of a diamond-mine tunnel that passes through kimberlite.
- Present your model to your class. Explain the relationship between kimberlite and diamonds.

### Glacier Photo Essay (6.2.a)

Make a photo essay showing how glaciers reshape Earth's surface as they move and melt.

- Find images of areas that are or have been affected by glaciers. Write captions for them.
- Present the images as a photo essay on a poster or in a portfolio.

**CAREER CENTER**
CLASSZONE.COM

Learn more about careers in mineralogy.

CHAPTER 5

# Views of Earth Today

## the BIG idea

**Modern technology has changed the way we view and map Earth.**

## Key Concepts

SECTION 1

**Maps and globes are models of Earth.**
Learn how to locate any place on Earth and how Earth's sphere is portrayed on flat maps.

SECTION 2

**Topographic maps show the shape of the land.**
Learn about representing the features of Earth's surface on flat maps.

SECTION 3

**Technology is used to map Earth.**
Learn how satellites and computers are used to provide more detailed maps of Earth.

**California ClassZone**

CLASSZONE.COM

Chapter 5 online resources: Content Review, Simulation, Visualization, three Resource Centers, Math Tutorial, Test Practice

***What do all these views show about Earth?***

*Swirling clouds over North and South America: NASA Terra satellite data*

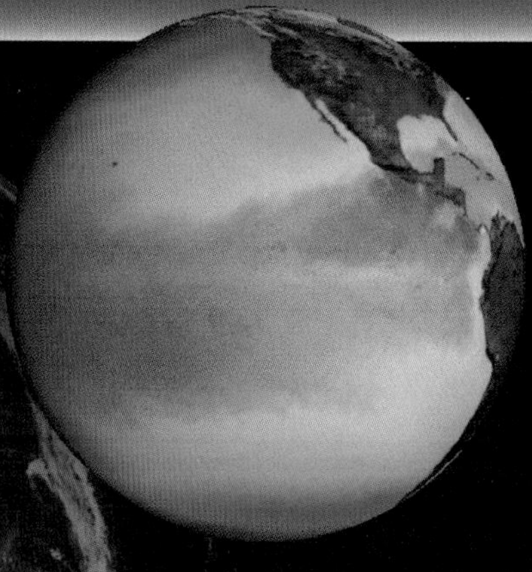

*Warm and cool ocean-surface temperatures: NASA satellite image*

*Chlorophyll levels (green) on land and sea: SeaStar spacecraft image*

*Earth's rocky surface without the oceans: NASA satellite data*

# EXPLORE the BIG idea

## Earth's Changing Surface

6.2.a Students know water running downhill is the dominant process in shaping the landscape, including California's landscape.

Go outside and find evidence of how wind, water, or living things change the surface of Earth. You might look in alleyways, parks, wooded areas, or backyards. For example, you might find a path worn through a grassy area near a parking lot.

**Observe and Think** What changes do you observe? What do you think caused the changes?

## Internet Activity: Mapping

6.1.b Students know Earth is composed of several layers: a cold, brittle lithosphere; a hot, convecting mantle; and a dense, metallic core.

Go to **ClassZone.com** to learn more about mapping Earth from space. Find out about a NASA mission to develop the most accurate map of Earth ever made. Using a radar system, the mission collected elevation data to make a high-resolution digital topographic database of Earth.

**Observe and Think** Why do you think scientists need different maps produced from satellite data?

NSTA scilinks.org SCILINKS

Topographic Maps **Code: MDL071**

CHAPTER 5

# Getting Ready to Learn

## CONCEPT REVIEW

- Many processes shape Earth's surface.
- The crust is Earth's outermost layer.
- Earth consists of many parts that interact with one another.

## VOCABULARY REVIEW

**energy** p. 9

*See Glossary for definitions.*

**matter, planet, satellite**

**CONTENT REVIEW**
CLASSZONE.COM

Review concepts and vocabulary.

## TAKING NOTES

### MAIN IDEA AND DETAIL NOTES

Make a two-column chart. Write the main ideas, such as those in the blue headings, in the column on the left. Write details about each of those main ideas in the column on the right.

### VOCABULARY STRATEGY

Draw a **word triangle** diagram for each new vocabulary term. On the bottom line write and define the term. Above that, write a sentence that uses the term correctly. At the top, draw a picture to show what the term looks like.

See the Note-Taking Handbook on pages R45–R51.

SCIENCE NOTEBOOK

| MAIN IDEAS | DETAIL NOTES |
|---|---|
| 1. Maps show natural and human-made features. | 1. Relief maps show how high or low land features are.<br>1. Road and city maps include a map scale. |

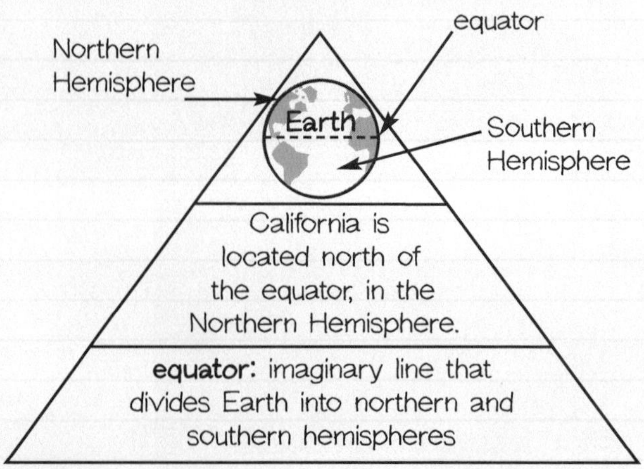

equator
Northern Hemisphere
Earth
Southern Hemisphere
California is located north of the equator, in the Northern Hemisphere.
**equator:** imaginary line that divides Earth into northern and southern hemispheres

KEY CONCEPT

# 5.1 Maps and globes are models of Earth.

**CALIFORNIA Content Standard**

6.7.f Read a topographic map and a geologic map for evidence provided on the maps and construct and interpret a simple scale map.

**BEFORE, you learned**

- The Earth system's parts interact to shape Earth's surface
- Earth's crust has many different features

**NOW, you will learn**

- What information maps can provide about natural and human-made features
- How to find exact locations on Earth
- Why all maps distort Earth's surface

**VOCABULARY**

**relief map** p. 156
**map scale** p. 157
**map legend** p. 157
**equator** p. 158
**latitude** p. 158
**prime meridian** p. 159
**longitude** p. 159
**projection** p. 160

**EXPLORE Mapping** (6.7.f)

## *What makes a good map?*

**PROCEDURE**

1. Draw a map to guide someone from your school to your home or to a point of interest, such as a park, statue, or store, near your school.
2. Trade maps with a classmate. Is his or her map easy to understand? Why or why not?
3. Use feedback from your partner to revise your own map.

**MATERIALS**

- paper
- pencil or pen

**WHAT DO YOU THINK?**
What visual clues make a map easy to understand and use?

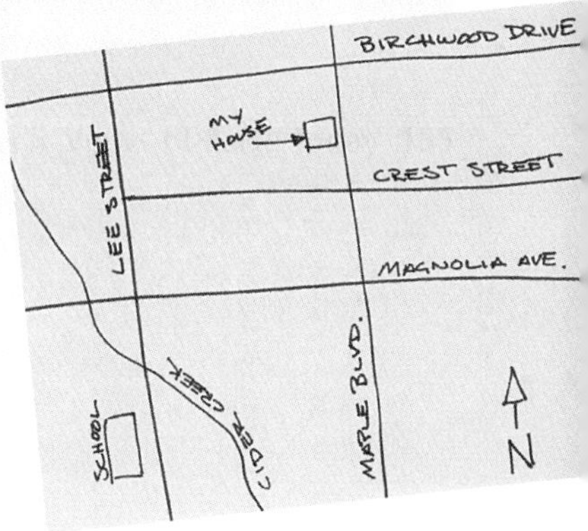


## Maps show natural and human-made features.

Have you ever drawn a map to help someone get to your home? If so, your map is actually a rough model of your neighborhood. It shows important streets and landmarks. Any map you use is a flat model of Earth's surface, showing Earth's features as seen from above.

In contrast, a globe shows Earth in three dimensions. A globe is a sphere that shows the relative sizes and shapes of Earth's land and water features.

In this section you will learn how maps and globes provide different types of information about Earth's surface. They can show everything from city streets to land features to the entire world.

**CHECK YOUR READING** How are maps and globes alike? How are they different?

Relief Map of United States

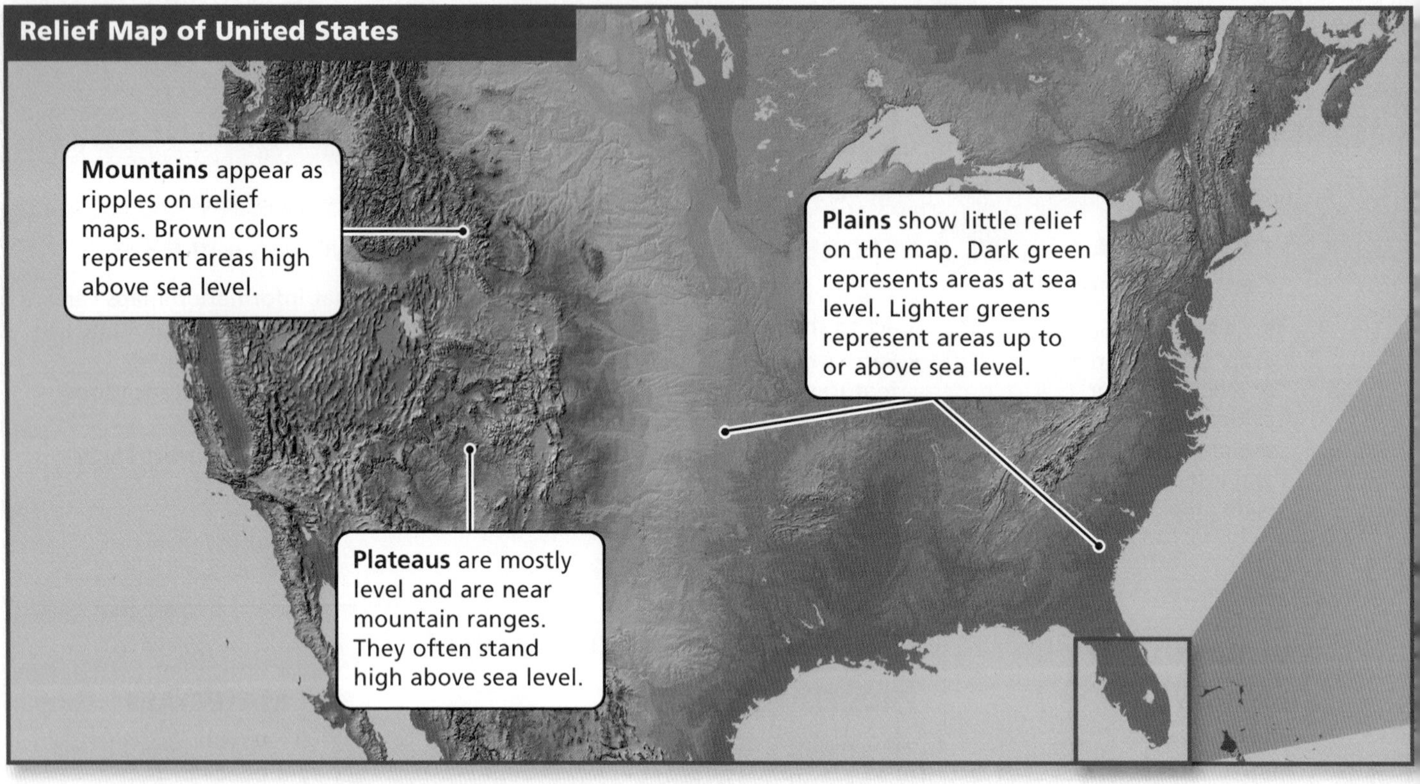

Mountains appear as ripples on relief maps. Brown colors represent areas high above sea level.
Plains show little relief on the map. Dark green represents areas at sea level. Lighter greens represent areas up to or above sea level.
Plateaus are mostly level and are near mountain ranges. They often stand high above sea level.


## Land Features on Maps

**VOCABULARY**
Add a word triangle diagram for *relief map* to your notebook.

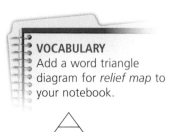

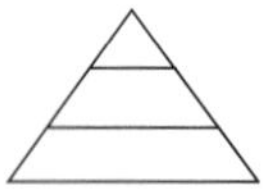

When scientists or travelers want to know about the landscape of an area, they often use a relief map. A **relief map,** such as the one above, shows how high or low each feature is on Earth. A mapmaker uses photographs or satellite images to build a three-dimensional view of Earth's surface. A relief map shows three main types of land features: mountains, plains, and plateaus.

**Mountains** stand higher than the land around them. A mountain's base may cover several square kilometers. A group of mountains is called a mountain range. Mountain ranges connected in a long chain form a mountain belt. The Rocky Mountains in the United States are part of a huge mountain belt. It includes the Canadian Rockies and the Andes Mountains in South America.

**Plateaus** have fairly level surfaces but stand high above sea level. Plateaus are often found near large mountain ranges. In the United States, the Colorado Plateau is about 3350 meters (11,000 ft) above sea level. This plateau includes parts of Arizona, Colorado, New Mexico, and Utah.

**Plains** are gently rolling or flat features. The United States has two types of plains. Coastal plains lie near the eastern and southeastern shores, and interior plains lie in the center of the nation. The interior Great Plains cover the middle third of the United States.

**CHECK YOUR READING** How is a plateau different from either a mountain or a plain?

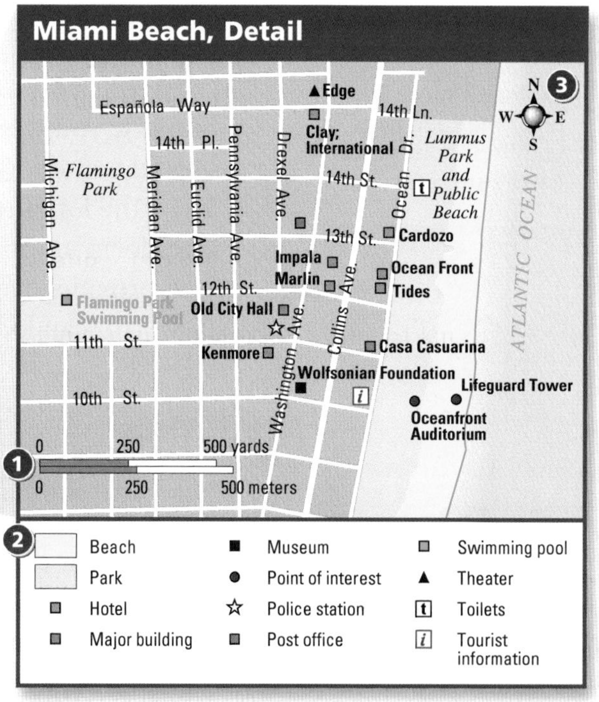


## Scale and Symbols on Maps

The maps most people use are road and city maps like the ones above. These maps provide information about both human-made features and natural features. To use these maps, you need to know how to read a map scale and a map legend, or key.

1. A **map scale** relates distances on a map to actual distances on Earth's surface. Notice that on the map of southern Florida above, the scale is in kilometers and miles. On the Miami Beach map, the scale is in meters and yards. The smaller the area a map shows, the more detail it includes.

The scale can be given as a ratio, a bar, or equivalent units of distance. For example, a ratio of 1:25,000 means that 1 centimeter on the map represents 25,000 centimeters (0.25 kilometer) on Earth.

**Three Types of Map Scale**

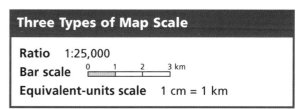

**Ratio** 1:25,000
**Bar scale** 0 1 2 3 km
**Equivalent-units scale** 1 cm = 1 km

2. A **map legend,** also called a key, is a chart that explains the meaning of each symbol used on a map. Symbols can stand for highways, parks, and other features. The legend on the Miami Beach map shows major points of interest for tourists.

3. A map usually includes a compass rose to show which directions are north, south, east, and west. Usually, north on a map points to the top of the page.

**READING TIP**
As used here, *legend* does not refer to a story. It is based on the Latin word *legenda,* which means "to be read."

**CHECK YOUR READING** What information do map scales and map legends provide?

VISUALIZATION CLASSZONE.COM

Explore how latitude and longitude help you find locations on Earth's surface.

## Latitude and longitude show locations on Earth.

Suppose you were lucky enough to find dinosaur bones in the desert. Would you know how to find that exact spot again? You would if you knew the longitude and latitude of the place. Latitude and longitude lines form an imaginary grid over the entire surface of Earth. This grid provides everyone with the same tools. Using latitude and longitude, you can locate any place on the planet.

### Latitude

READING TIP

*Hemi-* is a Greek prefix meaning "half."

Latitude is based on an imaginary line that circles Earth halfway between the north and south poles. This line is called the **equator.** The equator divides Earth into northern and southern hemispheres. A hemisphere is one half of a sphere.

**Latitude** is a distance in degrees north or south of the equator, which is 0°. A degree is 1/360 of the distance around a full circle. If you start at one point on the equator and travel all the way around the world back to that point, you have traveled 360 degrees.

The illustration below shows that latitude lines are parallel to the equator. These lines are evenly spaced between the equator and the poles. Latitude lines show distance north or south of the equator.

**Latitude and Longitude**

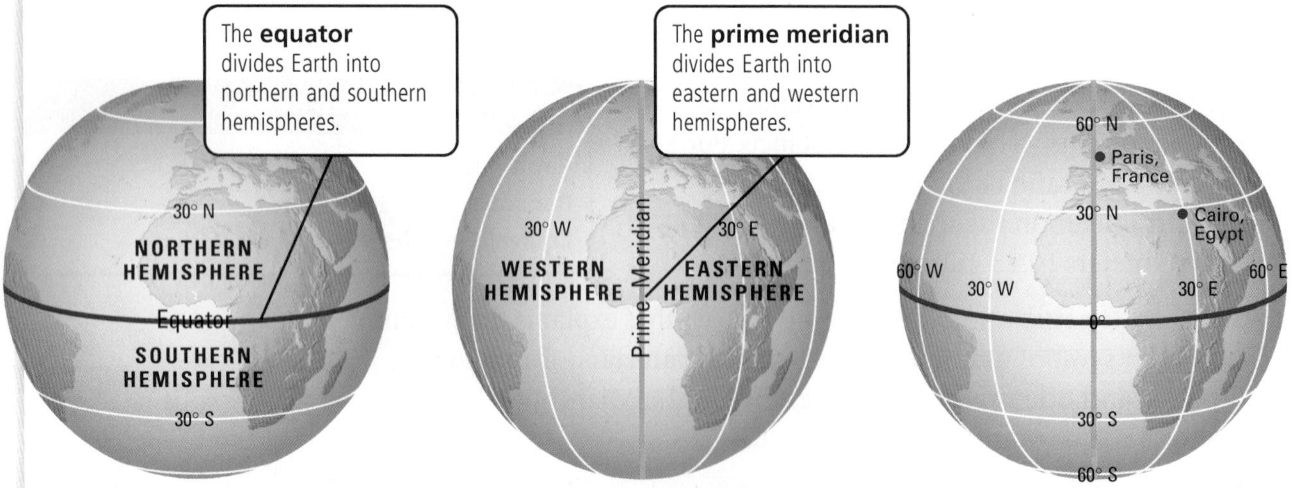


**Latitude** is a distance in degrees north or south of the equator.

**Longitude** is a distance in degrees east or west of the prime meridian.

You can find a location by noting where latitude and longitude lines cross.

READING VISUALS What are the approximate latitudes and longitudes of Cairo, Egypt, and Paris, France?

A label of north or south shows whether a location is in the northern or southern hemisphere. For instance, the North Pole is 90° north, or 90° N, while the South Pole is 90° south, or 90° S. However, latitude is only half of what you need to locate any spot on Earth. You also need to know its longitude.

## Longitude

Longitude is based on an imaginary line that stretches from the North Pole through Greenwich, England, to the South Pole. This line is called the **prime meridian.** Any place up to 180° west of the prime meridian is in the Western Hemisphere. Any place up to 180° east of the prime meridian is in the Eastern Hemisphere.

**Longitude** is a distance in degrees east or west of the prime meridian, which is 0°. Beginning at the prime meridian, longitude lines are numbered 0° to 180° west and 0° to 180° east.

Longitude lines are labeled east or west to indicate whether a location is in the eastern or western hemisphere. For example, the longitude of Santa Cruz, California, is about 122° west, or 122° W. The city of Hamburg, Germany, is about 10° east, or 10° E. If you understand latitude and longitude, you can find any spot on Earth's surface.

**READING TIP**

There is an easy way to remember the difference between latitude and longitude. Think of longitude lines as the "long" lines that go from pole to pole.

## INVESTIGATE California's Natural Resources

### *How can a map show natural resources?*

**PROCEDURE**

1. Examine the map of California's natural resources. Identify the symbols used to represent gold, clay, iron ore, titanium, and sand and gravel. Each symbol on the map identifies a location where a resource is mined.
2. Locate on the map the area where you live. Identify the natural resources shown on the map that are closest to the area where you live.
3. Look at the lines of latitude and longitude shown on the map. Find the intersection of latitude and longitude lines that is closest to the area where you live.

**WHAT DO YOU THINK?**

- What latitude line is closest to the area where you live? What longitude line is closest to the area where you live?
- Which natural resources are mined closest to where you live? Are these resources distributed evenly throughout the state? Explain.

**CHALLENGE** Which materials in your classroom might have been made from the types of natural resources that are mined closest to the area where you live?

**SKILL FOCUS**
Analyzing Data
(6.6.c, 6.7.f)

**MATERIALS**
- California Natural Resources Map

**TIME**
15 minutes

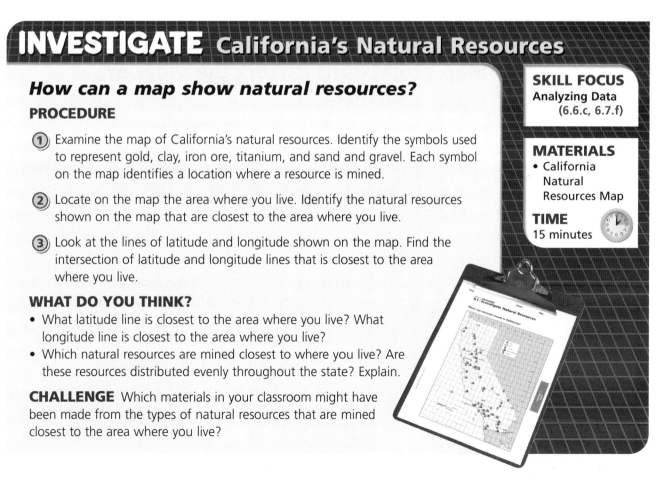

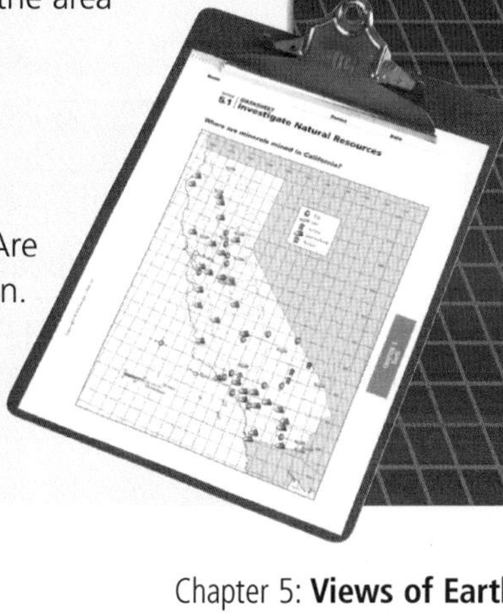

### Global Positioning System

The Global Positioning System (GPS) is a network of satellites. They are used to find the latitude, longitude, and elevation, or height above sea level, of any site. Twenty-four GPS satellites circle Earth and send signals that are picked up by receivers on the surface. At least three satellites need to be above the horizon for GPS to work. A computer inside a receiver uses the satellite signals to calculate the user's exact location—latitude, longitude, and elevation. GPS is an accurate, easy method for finding location.

GPS devices are used by many people, including pilots, sailors, hikers, and mapmakers. Some cars now have GPS receivers and digital road maps stored in their computers. A driver types in an address, and the car's computer finds the best way to get there.

Never be lost again. This hiker turns on his GPS unit to find out his current latitude and longitude. He then locates these data on his map to pinpoint his exact location.

**CHECK YOUR READING** Explain how GPS can help someone find his or her exact location.

## Map projections distort the view of Earth's surface.

The most accurate way to show Earth's surface is on a globe. A globe, however, cannot show much detail. It is also awkward to carry. People use flat maps for their detail and ease of use. A **projection** is a way of showing Earth's curved surface on a flat map. Mapmakers use different types of projections, but all of them distort Earth's surface.

### Cylindrical Projection

**READING TIP**

The Mercator (muhr-KAY-tuhr) map projection was developed by Flemish mapmaker Gerhardus Mercator in 1568.

The Mercator projection shows Earth as if the map were a large cylinder wrapped around the planet. The outlines of the landmasses and seas are then drawn onto the map. As shown in the diagram on page 161, the cylinder is unrolled to form a flat map. Latitude and longitude appear as straight lines, forming a grid of rectangles.

The Mercator projection is useful for navigating at sea or in the air. It shows the entire world, except for areas near the poles, on one map. People can plot a course by drawing straight lines.

The problem with Mercator maps is that areas far away from the equator appear much larger than they really are. On the map below, Greenland looks bigger than South America. In reality, South America is about eight times larger than Greenland.

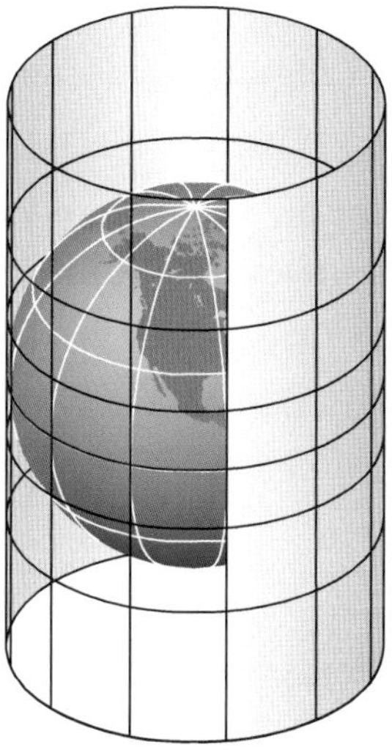

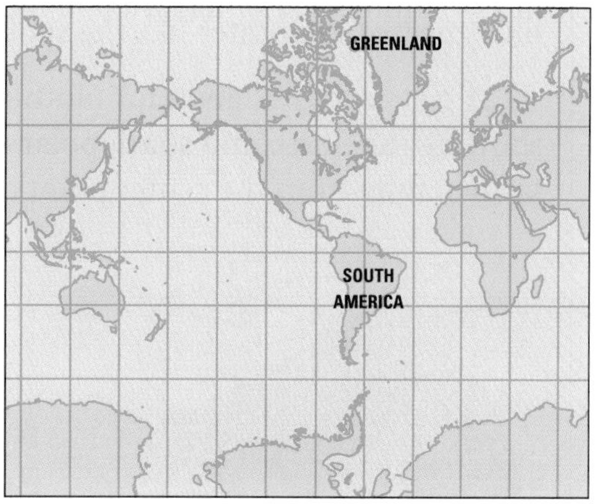


**Mercator projection** Latitude and longitude lines form a grid of rectangles. Areas away from the equator are distorted.

## Conic Projections

Conic projections are based on the shape of a cone. The diagram below shows how a cone of paper might be wrapped around the globe. The paper touches the surface only at the middle latitudes, halfway between the equator and the North Pole.

When the cone is flattened out, the latitude lines are curved slightly. The curved lines represent the curved surface of Earth. This allows the map to show the true sizes and shapes of some landmasses.

Conic projections are most useful for mapping large areas in the middle latitudes, such as the United States. However, landmasses near the equator or near the north or south pole will be distorted.

**CHECK YOUR READING** What are the main uses of Mercator and conic projections?

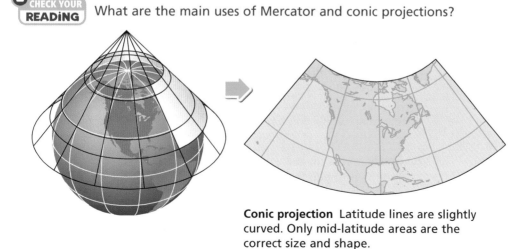

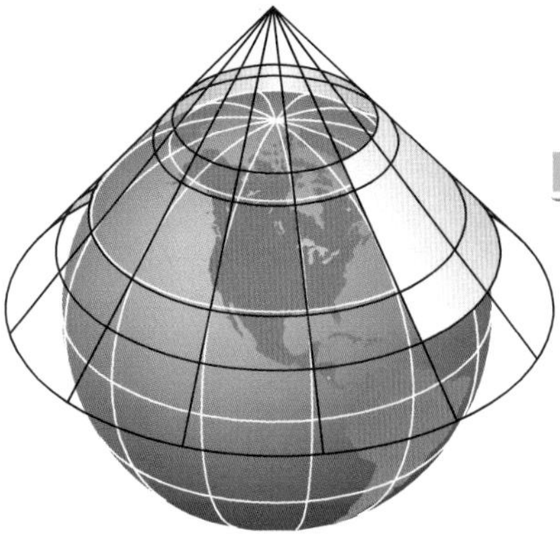

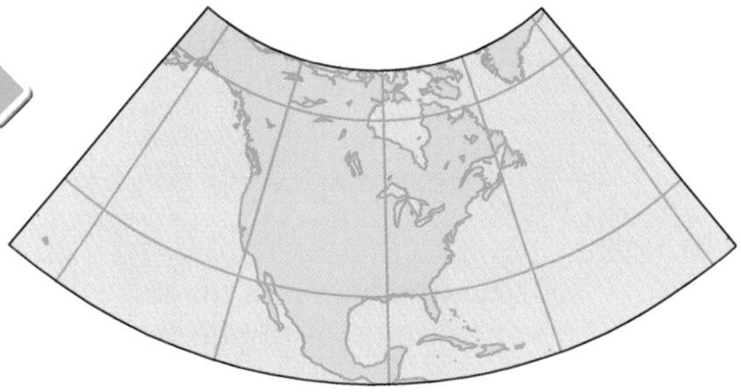

**Conic projection** Latitude lines are slightly curved. Only mid-latitude areas are the correct size and shape.

## Planar Projections

RESOURCE CENTER
CLASSZONE.COM

Find out more about map projections and how they are used.

Planar projections were developed to help people find the shortest distance between two points. They are drawn as if a circle of paper were laid on a point on Earth's surface. As you look at the diagram below, notice how the shape of the sphere is transferred to the flat map. When a planar map represents the polar region, the longitude lines meet at the center like the spokes of a wheel.

A planar map is good for plotting ocean or air voyages and for showing the north and south polar regions. However, landmasses farther away from the center point are greatly distorted.

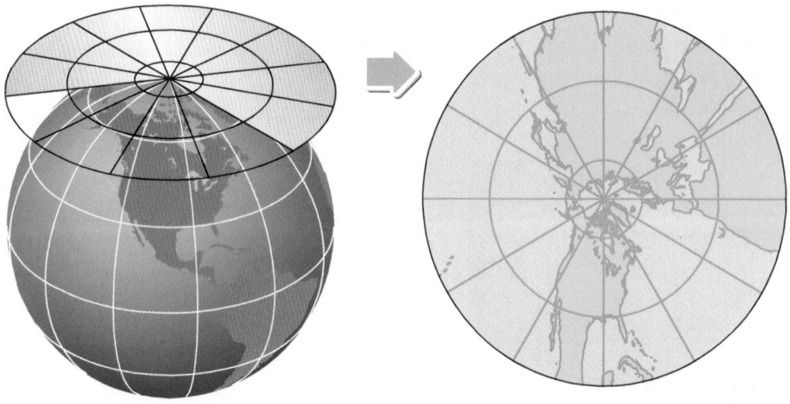

**Planar projection** Only areas near the center point are the correct size and shape.

The Mercator, conic, and planar projections are all attempts to solve the problem of representing a curved surface on a flat map. Each projection can show certain areas of the world accurately but distorts other areas.

**CHECK YOUR READING** What areas does the planar projection show accurately?

# 5.1 Review

### KEY CONCEPTS

1. What natural and human-made features can maps show? Give two examples of each. (6.7.f)
2. Explain how latitude and longitude can help you locate any place on Earth. (6.7.f)
3. Why do all flat maps distort Earth's surface? (6.7.f)

### CRITICAL THINKING

4. **Provide Examples** Imagine that your family is on a long car trip. What symbols on a road map would you pay the most attention to? Explain.
5. **Apply** Use a world map to find the approximate latitudes and longitudes of Moscow, Russia; Tokyo, Japan; Denver, Colorado; and La Paz, Bolivia.

### CHALLENGE

6. **Apply** Working with a partner or with a small group, select the shortest airline route from Chicago to London, using a globe and a Mercator map. **Hint:** Notice that as you go farther north on the globe, the longitude lines become closer together.

MATH in SCIENCE

## SKILL: USING PROPORTIONS

MATH TUTORIAL
CLASSZONE.COM
Click on Math Tutorial for more help with solving proportions.
**Math** 6.NS.1.3
**Science** 6.7.f

# How Far Is It?

A science class is visiting Chicago and is using the map on the left to walk to the lakefront museums. Remember, a map scale shows how distances on the map compare to actual distances on the ground.

Buckingham Fountain

## Example

In this case, the map scale indicates that 1 centimeter on the map represents 300 meters on the ground. The map scale shows this as equivalent units. By using these units to write a proportion, you can use cross products to determine actual distances.

What distance does 3 cm on the map represent? Set up the problem like this:

$$\frac{1 \text{ cm}}{300 \text{ m}} = \frac{3 \text{ cm}}{x}$$

**(1)** $1 \text{ cm} \cdot x = 3 \text{ cm} \cdot 300 \text{ m}$

**(2)** $x = 3 \cdot 300 \text{ m}$

**(3)** $x = 900 \text{ m}$

**ANSWER** 3 centimeters on the map represents 900 meters on the ground.

**Use cross products and a metric ruler to answer the following questions.**

1. The science class divides into two groups. Each group starts at Buckingham Fountain. How far, in meters, will one group walk to get to the Adler Planetarium if they follow the red dotted line?
2. How far, in meters, will the other group walk to get to the end of Navy Pier if they follow the blue dotted line?
3. The group that walked to Adler decides to take a boat to join the other group at Navy Pier. How far, in meters, is their boat ride along the red dotted line?

**CHALLENGE** What is the total distance, in kilometers, that the two groups traveled? Set up the problem as a proportion. **Hint:** There are 1000 meters in a kilometer.

KEY CONCEPT

# 5.2 Topographic maps show the shape of the land.

**CALIFORNIA Content Standard**

6.7.f Read a topographic map and a geologic map for evidence provided on the maps and construct and interpret a simple scale map.

**BEFORE, you learned**

- Different maps provide information about natural and human-made features
- Latitude and longitude are used to find places on Earth
- All flat maps distort Earth's surface

**NOW, you will learn**

- How contour lines show elevation, slope, and relief
- What rules contour lines follow
- What common symbols are used on topographic maps

**VOCABULARY**

**topography** p. 164
**contour line** p. 165
**elevation** p. 165
**slope** p. 165
**relief** p. 165
**contour interval** p. 166

**EXPLORE Topographic Maps (6.7.f)**

***How can you map your knuckles?***

**PROCEDURE**

1. Hold your fist closed, knuckles up, as shown in the photo.
2. Draw circles around the first knuckle. Make sure the circles are the same distance from each other.
3. Flatten out your hand. Observe what happens. Write down your observations.

**MATERIAL**

washable colored pen

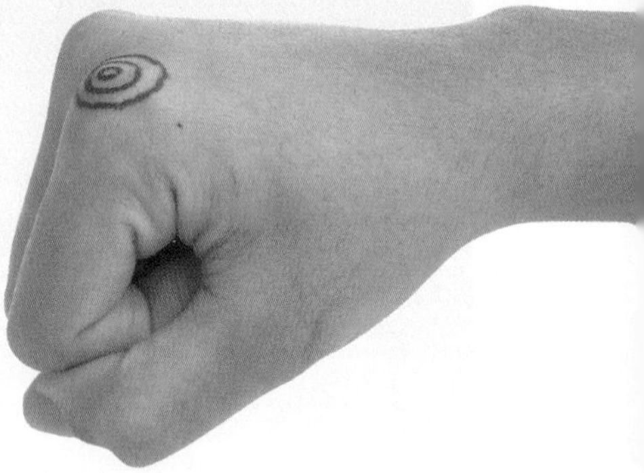

**WHAT DO YOU THINK?**

- How does the height of your knuckles change when you clench your fist, then flatten out your hand?
- What do you think the circles represent?

## Topographic maps use contour lines to show features.

VOCABULARY
Add a word triangle diagram for *topography* to your notebook.

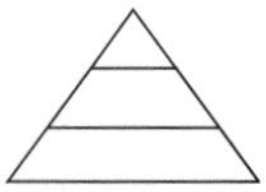

Imagine you are on vacation with your family in a national park. You have a simple trail map that shows you where to hike. But the map does not tell you anything about what the land looks like. Will you have to cross any rivers or valleys? How far uphill or downhill will you have to hike?

To answer these questions, you need to know something about the topography of the area. **Topography** is the shape, or features, of the land. These features can be natural—such as mountains, plateaus, and plains. They can be human-made—such as dams and roads. To show the topography of an area, mapmakers draw a topographic map.

A topographic map is a flat map that uses lines to show Earth's surface features. Distance and elevation are given in feet or meters. Take a look at the topographic map of Mount Hood on this page. The wiggly lines on the map are called **contour lines.** They show an area's elevation, slope, and relief.

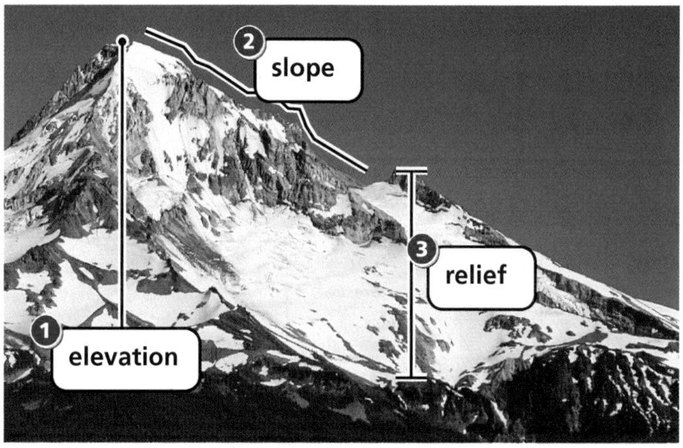

2 slope
3 relief
1 elevation

1. The **elevation** of a place is how high above sea level it is. An area can range from a few meters to several thousand meters above sea level. The numbers on the contour lines show the elevations of different points in the Mount Hood area.
2. The **slope** of a landform or area is how steep it is. The more gradual the slope, the farther apart the contour lines on the map. The steeper the slope, the closer together the contour lines.
3. The **relief** of an area is the difference between its high and low points. For example, subtracting the lowest elevation on the map from the highest gives you a measure of the area's relief.

**CHECK YOUR READING** What is the difference between elevation and slope?

## Mount Hood Topographic Map

**A topographic map shows the land as if you were above the land looking down on it.**

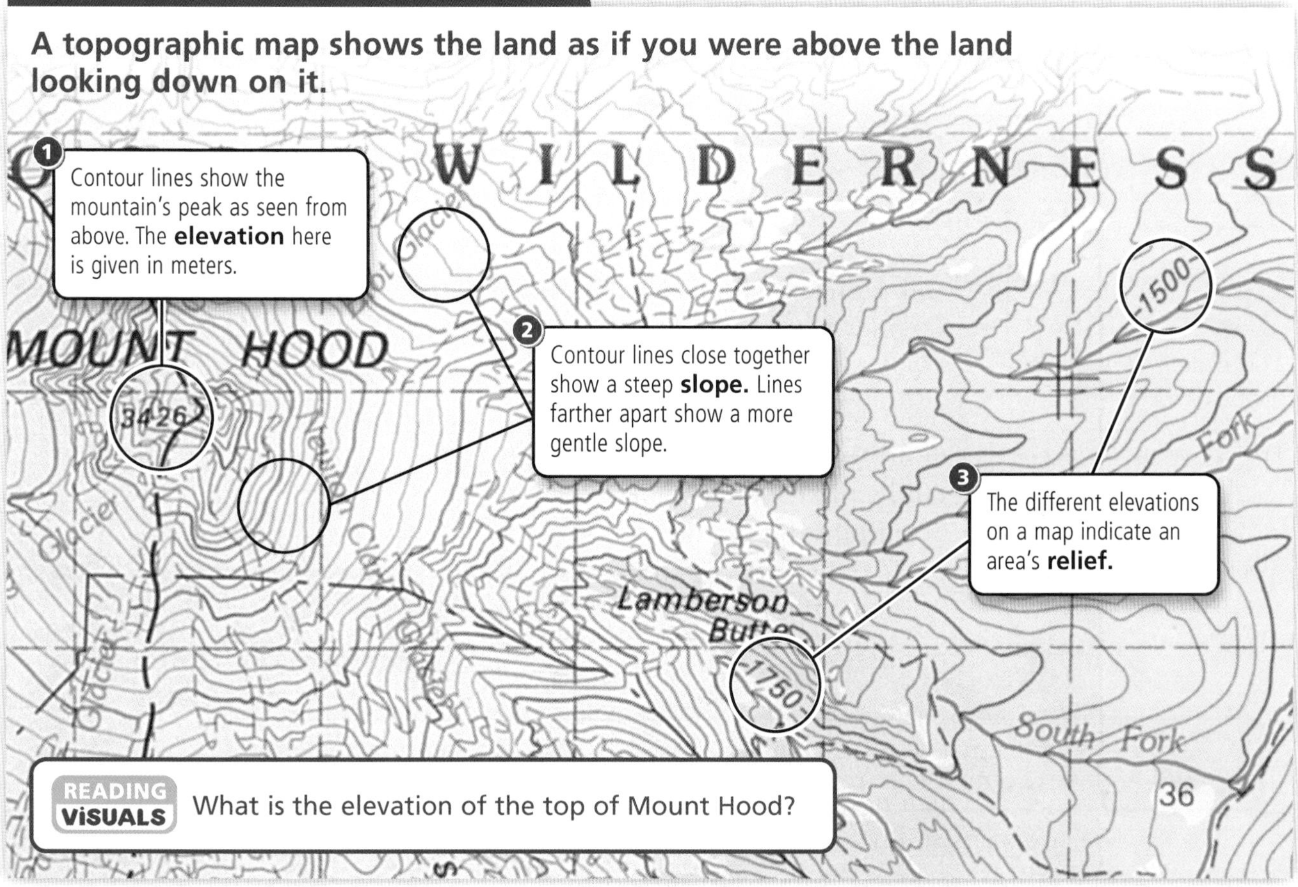

WILDERNESS
MOUNT HOOD
3426
1500
Lamberson Butte
1750
South Fork
Fork
36
1 Contour lines show the mountain's peak as seen from above. The **elevation** here is given in meters.
2 Contour lines close together show a steep **slope.** Lines farther apart show a more gentle slope.
3 The different elevations on a map indicate an area's **relief.**

**READING VISUALS** What is the elevation of the top of Mount Hood?

## Contour lines follow certain rules.

**MAIN IDEA AND DETAILS** Use your main idea and details chart to take notes on the rules for reading a topographic map.

Contour lines on topographic maps can help you picture landforms in your mind. Think of the following statements as rules for reading topographic maps:

- **Lines never cross.** Contour lines never cross, because each line shows an exact elevation.
- **Circles show highest and lowest points.** Contour lines form closed circles around mountaintops and hilltops. They also form circles around depressions, or sunken areas in the ground. Sometimes, the elevation of a mountain or hill is written in meters or feet in the middle of the circle.
- **Contour interval is always the same on a map.** The **contour interval** is the difference in elevation from one contour line to the next. For example, the contour interval on the map below is 10 feet. This means that the change in elevation between contour lines is always 10 feet. The contour interval can differ from map to map, but it is always the same on one map.

### Ely, Minnesota, Topographic Map

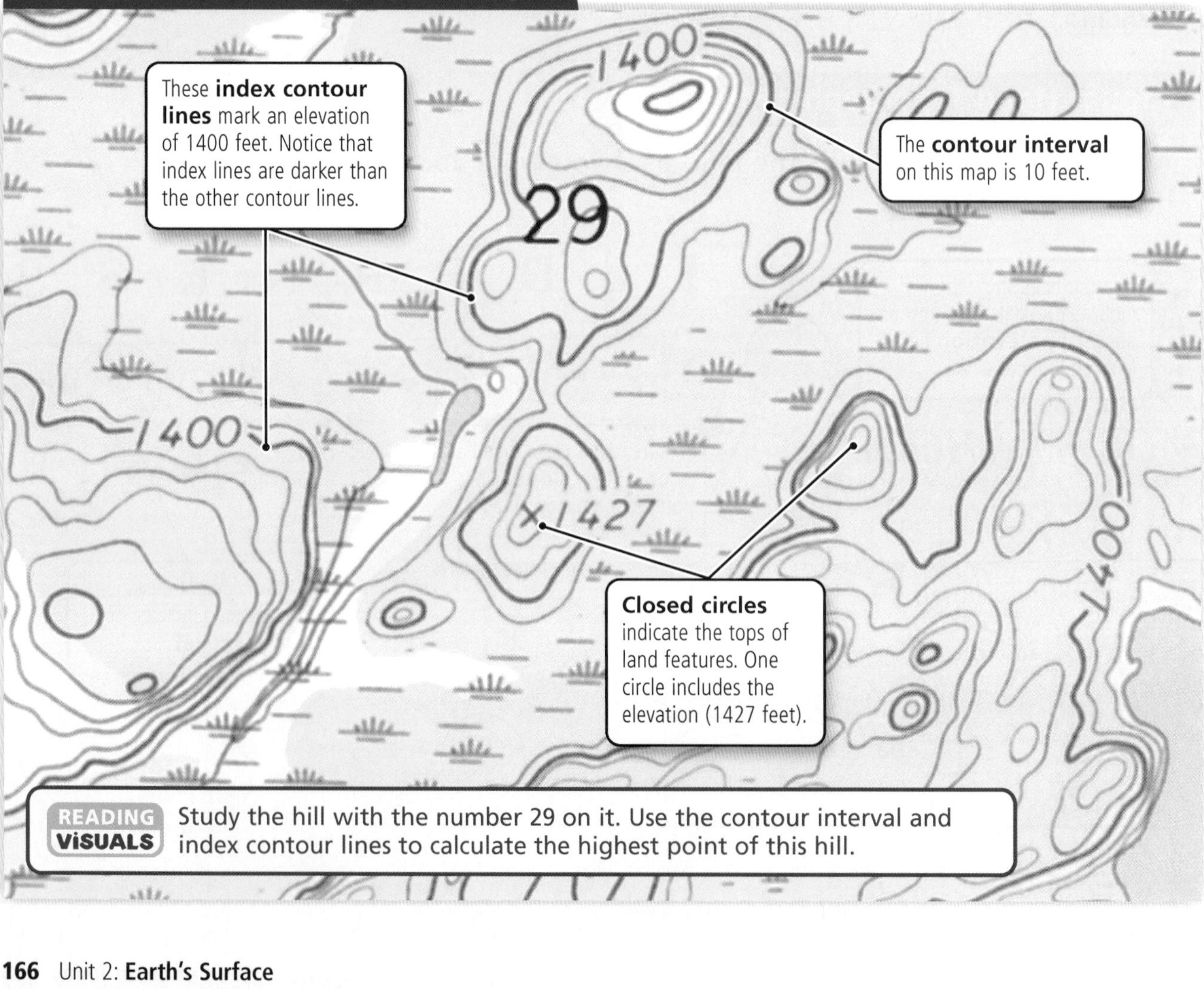
1400
29
1400
1427
1400
These **index contour lines** mark an elevation of 1400 feet. Notice that index lines are darker than the other contour lines.
The **contour interval** on this map is 10 feet.
**Closed circles** indicate the tops of land features. One circle includes the elevation (1427 feet).

**READING VISUALS** Study the hill with the number 29 on it. Use the contour interval and index contour lines to calculate the highest point of this hill.

- **Index contour lines mark elevations.** The darker contour lines on a map are called index contour lines. Numbers that show elevations are often written on these lines. To calculate higher or lower elevations, simply count the number of lines above or below an index line. Then multiply that number by the contour interval. Look at the Ely map, where one index line marks 1400 feet. To find the elevation of a point three lines up from this index line, you would multiply 10 feet (the contour interval) by 3. Add the result, 30, to 1400. The point's elevation is 1430 feet.

**CALIFORNIA Focus**

The highest elevation in California is Mt. Whitney, which rises 4419 meters (14,497 ft) above sea level. The lowest elevation in California is in Death Valley, at a spot that is 86 meters (282 ft) below sea level.

**CHECK YOUR READING** What information do index contour lines provide?

Besides contour lines, topographic maps also contain symbols for natural and human-made features. Below are some common map symbols that the United States Geological Survey (USGS) uses on its topographic maps.

**Topographic Map Symbols**

| | |
|---|---|
| Marsh or swamp | Hiking trail |
| Vegetation | Stream |
| Lake or pond | Railroad tracks |

**SIMULATION** CLASSZONE.COM

Discover the relationship between topographic maps and surface features.

The USGS provides topographic maps for nearly every part of the United States. These maps cover urban, rural, and wilderness areas. Hikers and campers are not the only ones who use topographic maps. Engineers, archaeologists, forest rangers, biologists, and others depend on them as well.

## 5.2 Review

### KEY CONCEPTS

1. How do contour lines show elevation, slope, and relief? (6.7.f)
2. Why do contour lines never cross on a topographic map? (6.7.f)
3. How would you show the top of a hill, an area of vegetation, or a hiking trail on a topographic map? (6.7.f)

### CRITICAL THINKING

4. **Apply** For an area with gently sloping hills and little relief, would you draw contour lines close together or far apart? Explain why.
5. **Compare and Contrast** How would a road map and a topographic map of the same area differ? What information would each provide?

### CHALLENGE

6. **Synthesize** Work with a group to make a topographic map of the area around your school. First decide how big an area you will include. Then choose a contour interval, a map scale, and symbols for buildings, sports fields, and other features. Let other students test the map's accuracy.

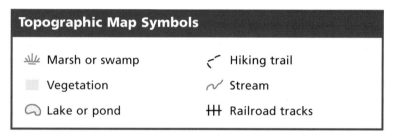

# CHAPTER INVESTIGATION

## Investigate Topographic Maps

**OVERVIEW AND PURPOSE** Topographic maps show the shape of the land. In this lab you will use what you have learned about how Earth's three-dimensional surface is represented on maps to

- make a terrain model out of clay
- produce a topographic map of the model

### Procedure

1. Build a simple landscape about 6–8 cm high from modeling clay. Include a variety of land features. Make sure your model is no taller than the sides of the container.

2. Place your model into the container. Stand a ruler upright inside the container and tape it in place.

3. Lay the clear plastic sheet over the container and tape it on one side like a hinge. Carefully trace the outline of your clay model.

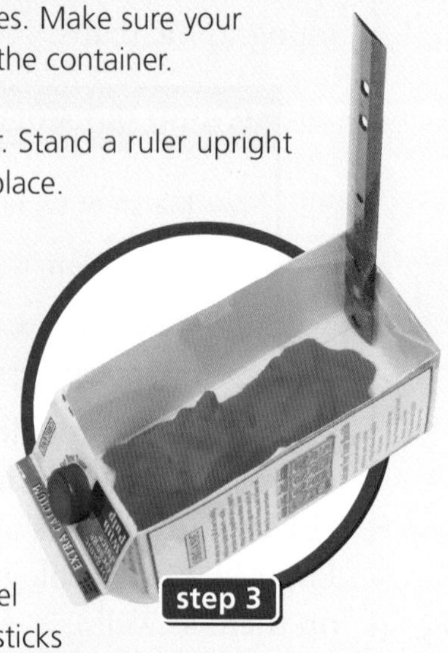

step 3

4. Add 2 cm of colored water to the container.

5. Insert spaghetti sticks into the model all around the waterline. Place the sticks about 3 cm apart. Make sure the sticks are vertical and are no taller than the sides of the container.

6. Lower the plastic sheet back over the container. Looking straight down on the container, make a dot on the sheet wherever you see a spaghetti stick. Connect the dots to trace the contour line accurately onto your map.

7. Continue adding water, 2 cm at a time. Each time you add water, insert the sticks into the model at the waterline and repeat step 6. Continue until the model landscape is underwater. Carefully drain the water when finished.

step 5

**MATERIALS**
- half-gallon cardboard juice container
- scissors
- modeling clay
- clear plastic sheet (transparency or sheet protector)
- cellophane tape
- ruler
- water
- food coloring
- box of spaghetti
- erasable marker pen

6.2.a, 6.7.f

**Content Standard**
6.2.a Students know water running downhill is the dominant process in shaping the landscape, including California's landscape.

**Investigation Standard**
6.7.f Read a topographic map and a geologic map for evidence provided on the maps and construct and interpret a simple scale map.

## Observe and Analyze

Write It Up

1. Compare your topographic map with the three-dimensional model. Remember that contour lines connect points of equal elevation. What do widely spaced or tightly spaced contour lines mean? What does a closed circle mean?
2. Make a permanent record of your map to keep in your **Science Notebook** by carefully tracing the contour lines onto a sheet of white paper. To make reading the map easier, use a different color for an index contour line.
3. What is the contour interval of your model landscape? For example, each 2 centimeters might represent 20 meters in an actual landscape. Record the elevation of the index contour line on your map.

## Conclude

Write It Up

1. **INFER** How would you determine the elevation of a point located halfway between two contour lines?
2. **EVALUATE** Describe any errors that you may have made in your procedure or any places where errors might have occurred.
3. **APPLY** Explain how you would use a topographic map if you were planning a hiking trip or a cross-country bike race.

## INVESTIGATE Further

**CHALLENGE** Choose one feature on a topographic map—such as the map on page 166—to translate into a cross-sectional diagram.

1. Lay a piece of ruled paper across the center of the topographical feature.
2. Mark each of the contour lines on the ruled paper and label each mark with the elevation.
3. Mark the same elevations on the side of the paper, as shown in the example.
4. Use a ruler to draw a straight line down from each mark to the matching elevation on the side of the paper.
5. Connect the points to draw a profile of the landform.
6. Describe how you would expect the profile to change over time as water running downhill shapes the landscape.

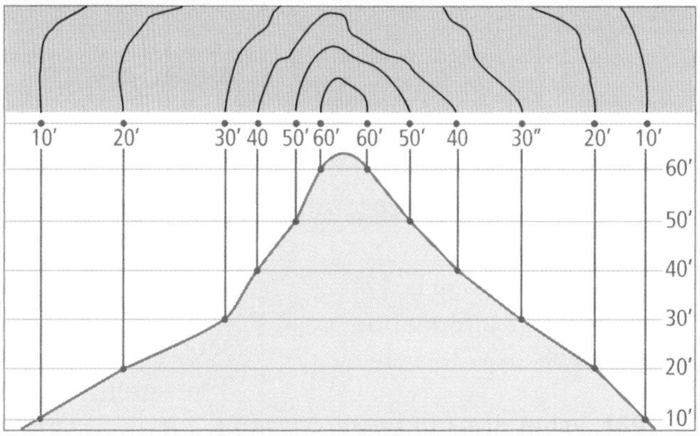


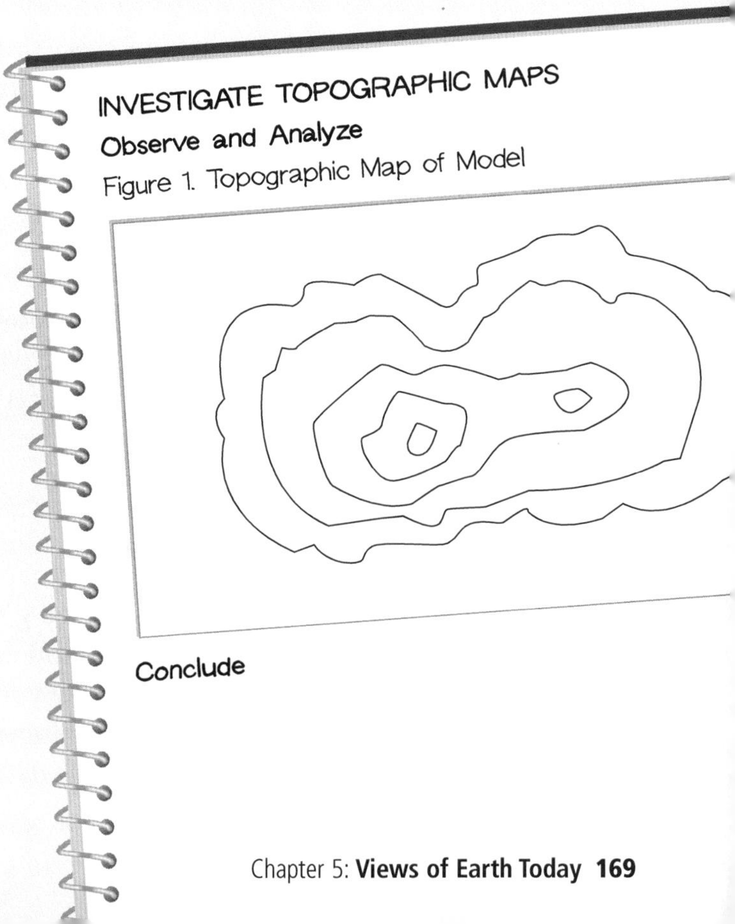

KEY CONCEPT

# 5.3 Technology is used to map Earth.

**CALIFORNIA Content Standard**

6.7.f Read a topographic map and a geologic map for evidence provided on the maps and construct and interpret a simple scale map.

**BEFORE, you learned**

- Contour lines are used on topographic maps to show elevation, slope, and relief
- Contour lines follow certain rules
- Map symbols show many natural and human-made features

**NOW, you will learn**

- How remote-sensing images can provide detailed and accurate information about Earth
- How geographic data can be displayed in layers to build maps

**VOCABULARY**

**remote sensing** p. 170
**sensor** p. 171
**false-color image** p. 171
**geographic information systems** p. 173

**THINK ABOUT**

***What can you see in this image?***

Satellites can record all types of information about Earth's surface. This image shows a section of Washington, D.C. The satellite that collected the data is 680 kilometers (420 mi) above Earth. What familiar items can you see in the picture? How might images like this be useful to scientists, mapmakers, and engineers?

## Remote sensing provides detailed images of Earth.

VOCABULARY
Add a word triangle diagram for *remote sensing* to your notebook.

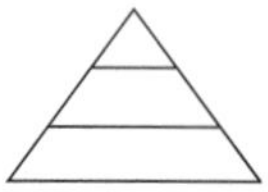

If you have ever looked at an object through a pair of binoculars, you have used remote sensing. **Remote sensing** is the use of scientific equipment to gather information about something from a distance. Remote-sensing technology can be as simple as a camera mounted on an airplane. It can be as complex as a satellite orbiting Earth.

Imagine that you are a mapmaker in the 1840s. You have been asked to draw a map of a state. You have no cameras or satellites to help you. To get a good view of the land, you have to climb to the highest points and carefully draw every hill, valley, river, and landform. It will take you months to map the state. Today, mapmakers use remote-sensing images from airplanes and satellites. With these, they can make highly detailed and accurate maps of Earth's surface.

Airplane cameras use film to record data. Satellites use sensors to build images of Earth. A **sensor** is a mechanical or electrical tool that receives a signal, such as light, and responds to it. Satellite sensors detect far more than your eyes can see. They collect information about the different types of energy coming from Earth's surface. The satellite then sends that information to computers on Earth.

The computers turn the information into images, as shown in the illustration below. Satellite data can be used to build an image of the entire planet. It can show a single continent or a detail of your area. For example, the image on the right shows a close-up of the Jefferson Memorial in Washington, D.C.

One of the ways scientists study changes to Earth's surface is by using false-color images. In a **false-color image,** natural colors are replaced with artificial ones to show special features.

This satellite image includes the Jefferson Memorial, walkways, and roads. See if you can find the memorial in the image on page 170.

## Satellite Imaging

**Objects on Earth reflect or emit different types of energy. Satellite sensors can detect and record these energies.**

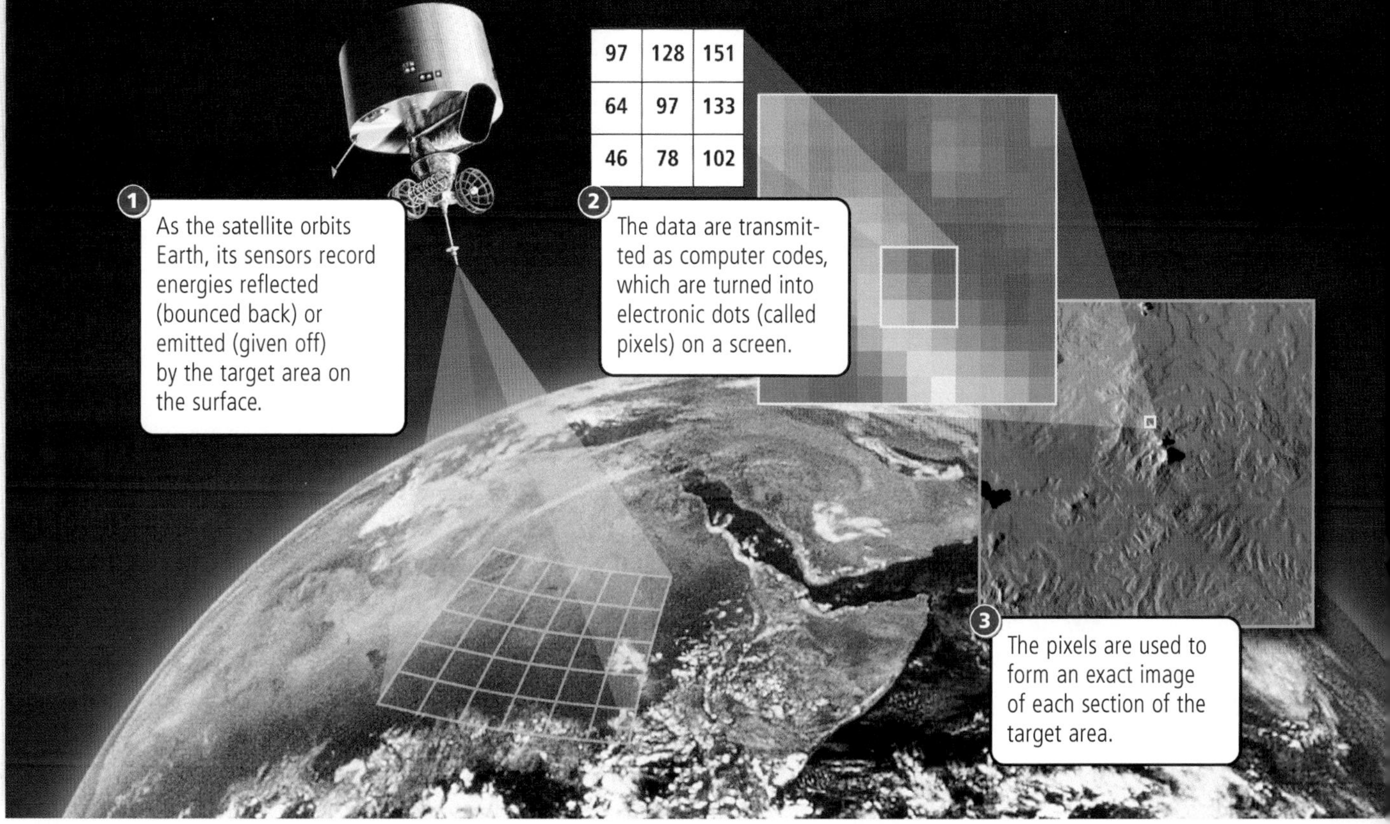

97 128 151
64 97 133
46 78 102
1 As the satellite orbits Earth, its sensors record energies reflected (bounced back) or emitted (given off) by the target area on the surface.
2 The data are transmitted as computer codes, which are turned into electronic dots (called pixels) on a screen.
3 The pixels are used to form an exact image of each section of the target area.

## Satellite Images

**People can compare true-color satellite images and false-color satellite images to see a wider range of detail. These images show the same area of California on March 7, 2004.**

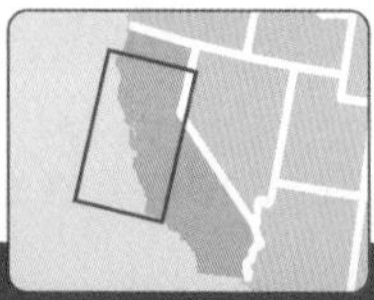

**True Color**

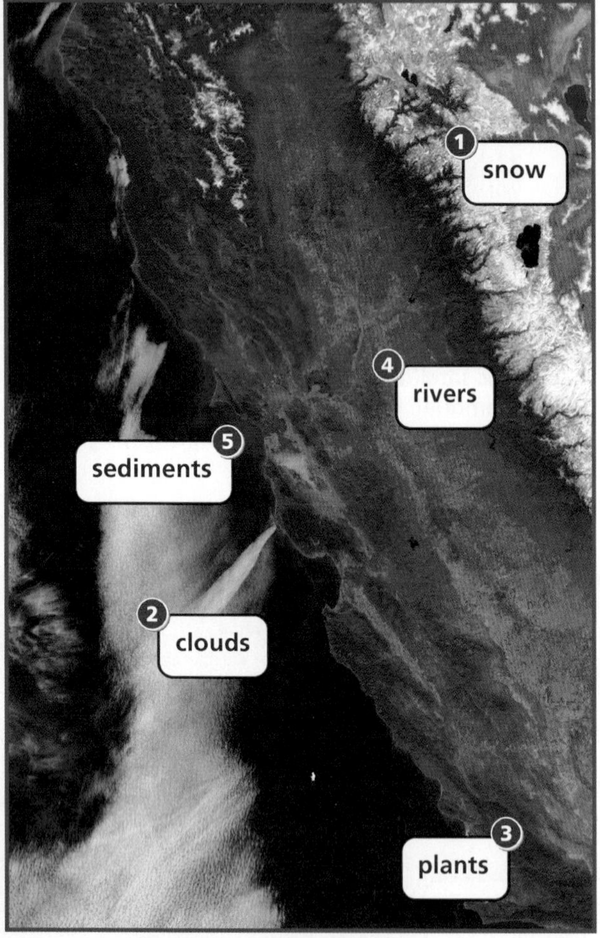


**False Color**

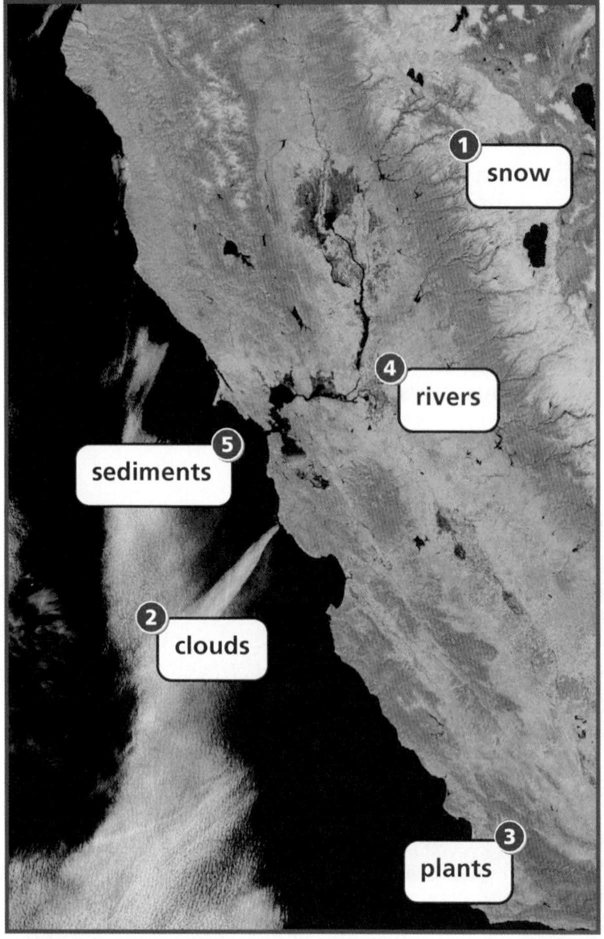


1. **Snow** In the true-color image, snow is white. In the false-color image, snow is bright blue. The amount of snow cover is important because the melting of snow in the spring provides California with much of its fresh water.
2. **Clouds** In the true-color image, clouds are white. They are white to light blue in the false-color image.
3. **Plants** In the false-color image, plants are bright green. This increases the contrast between areas covered by plants and areas of bare ground, which are shown in tan and pink.
4. **Rivers** In the false-color image, water is shown in dark blue and black. This makes the rivers in central California easier to see.
5. **Sediments** Rivers carry sediments to the ocean. Sediments in water can make the location of the coastline more difficult to see in the true-color image.

**READING VISUALS** How can you tell the difference between clouds and snow cover shown in these satellite images? Why might this be useful?

## Geographic information systems display data in layers.

RESOURCE CENTER
CLASSZONE.COM

Find out more about how GIS is used.

Any good city map will show you what is on the surface—buildings, streets, parks, and other features. But suppose you need to know about tunnels under the city. Or maybe you want to know where the most students live. An ordinary map will not tell you what you want to know.

Instead, you would turn to geographic information systems. **Geographic information systems** (GIS) are computer systems that can store and arrange geographic data and show the data in many different types of maps. Scientists, city planners, and engineers all use GIS maps to help them make decisions. For example, suppose your city wants to build a new airport. It must be away from populated areas and near major highways. The illustration below shows how city officials might use GIS to pick the best site.

### Geographic Information Systems

**GIS can be used to produce maps that help people make decisions.**

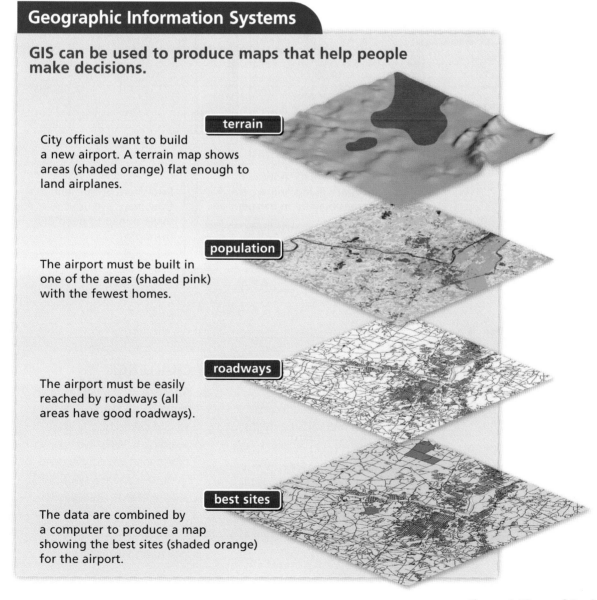

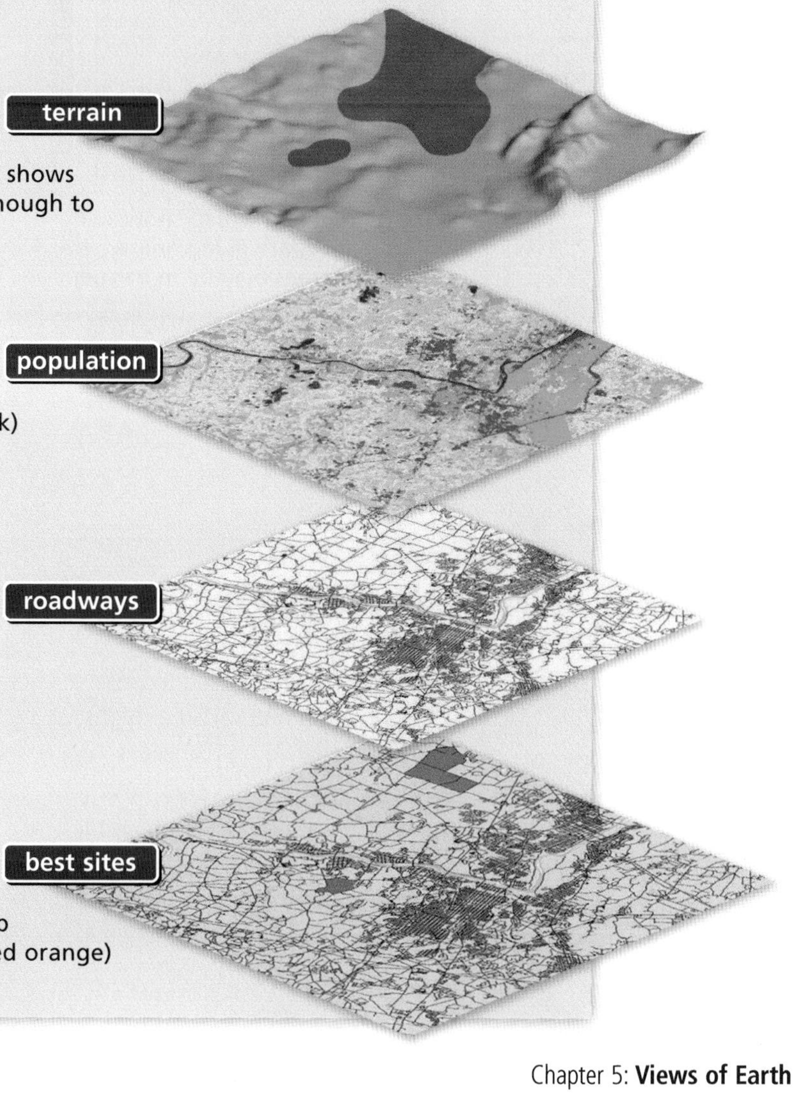


City officials want to build a new airport. A terrain map shows areas (shaded orange) flat enough to land airplanes.

The airport must be built in one of the areas (shaded pink) with the fewest homes.

The airport must be easily reached by roadways (all areas have good roadways).

The data are combined by a computer to produce a map showing the best sites (shaded orange) for the airport.

Any geographic information can be entered into GIS and converted into a map. These systems are especially useful in showing information about changes in the environment.

For example, near Long Valley in California, the volcano known as Mammoth Mountain began giving off carbon dioxide, or $CO_2$. As the gas rose through the soil, it began killing the roots of trees nearby. Scientists measured the flow of $CO_2$ around Horseshoe Lake and other areas. They used computer software to build the maps shown below.

**CHECK YOUR READING** Summarize the ways GIS maps can be helpful to engineers, city planners, and scientists.

## Mammoth Mountain

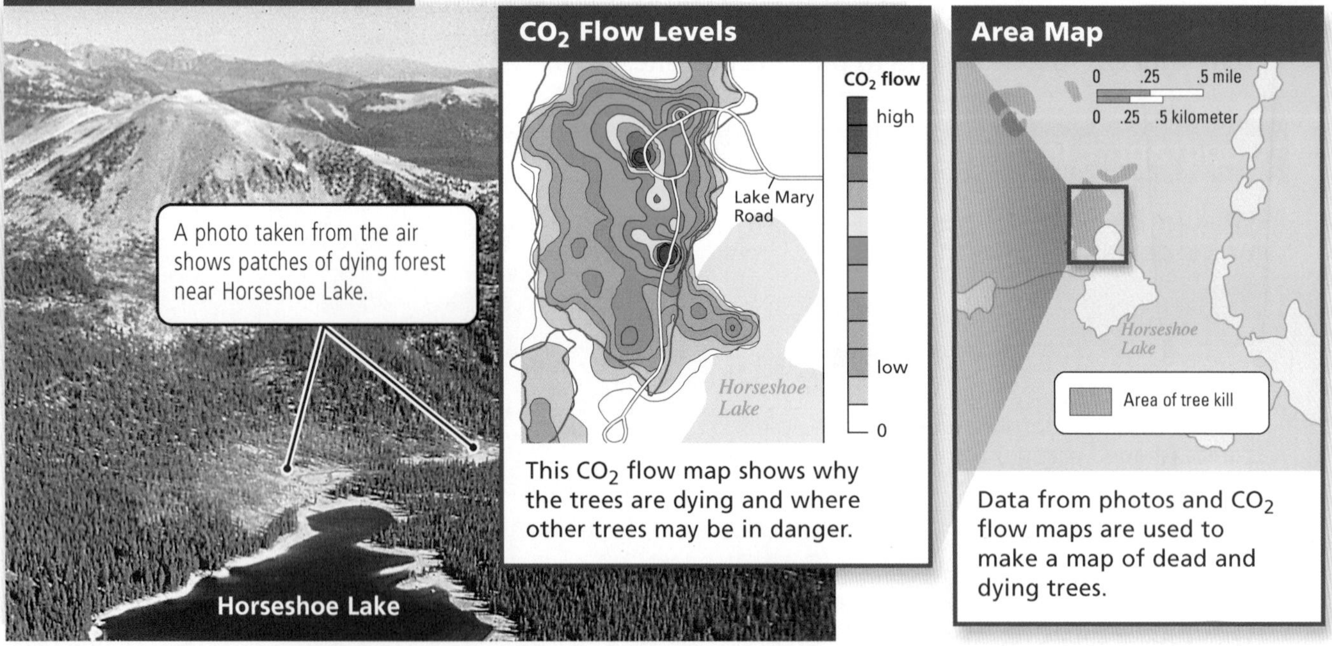


This $CO_2$ flow map shows why the trees are dying and where other trees may be in danger.

Data from photos and $CO_2$ flow maps are used to make a map of dead and dying trees.

# 5.3 Review

### KEY CONCEPTS

1. How are satellites used to make images of Earth from outer space? (6.7.f)
2. What are some of the types of information obtained by remote sensing? (6.7.f)
3. Explain in your own words what a GIS map is. (6.7.f)

### CRITICAL THINKING

4. **Infer** Explain how satellite images might be used to predict what a natural area might look like in 50 or 100 years.
5. **Evaluate** If you wanted to compare a region before and during a flood, how could false-color images help you?

### CHALLENGE

6. **Analyze** Work with a small group. Suppose you wanted to ask the city to build a skateboard park. What types of information would you need in order to propose a good site? Draw a map to display each type of information.

California Close-Up

## MAPPING

# The Big Picture

6.7.f Read a topographic map and a geologic map for evidence provided on the maps and construct and interpret a simple map scale.

In 1602 Spanish explorer Sebastian Vizcaíno sailed along the California coast. A journal from the voyage claimed that California was separated from the mainland by the "Sea of California." As a result, California was shown as an island on maps for over 100 years. In 1747 King Ferdinand VII of Spain declared that California was part of the mainland, and maps were corrected.

Today's mapmakers can do in minutes what used to take months or even years to do. Explorers in Vizcaíno's time probably made their maps by measuring the angles of elevation of stars at certain points and estimating distances from place to place. Remote sensing technology now allows scientists to make an extremely accurate map of most of Earth's surface in a matter of days.

In February 2000 an 11-day mission aboard the space shuttle *Endeavor* collected topographic data from more than 46 million square miles of Earth's surface. This Shuttle Radar Topography Mission (SRTM) was a joint project of NASA and the German and Italian space agencies. It was managed by NASA's Jet Propulsion Laboratory in Pasadena, California.

A specially modified radar system on the shuttle gathered data to make detailed 3-D maps of 80 percent of Earth's surface. These maps will have many applications, such as making better water drainage models and finding better locations for cell phone towers.

This satellite image of the California coast was taken in October 2000.

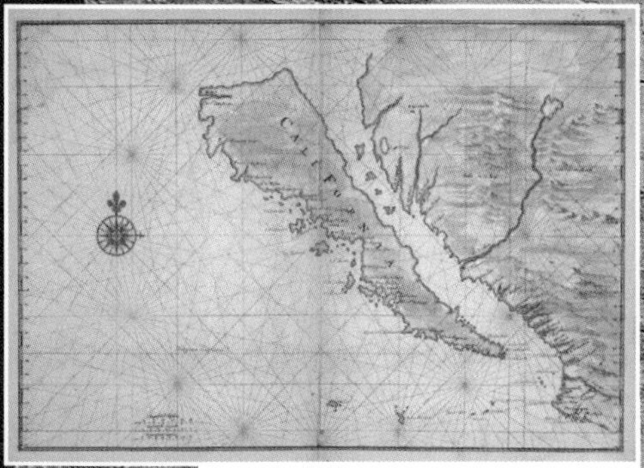

This map from about 1650 shows California as an island.

This view of the Los Angeles area was generated using data from the SRTM and a Landsat 5 satellite.

### WRITING ABOUT SCIENCE

Suppose California really were an island, as shown on the old map. How would transportation technology change from the way it is today? Write a description of the necessary transportation system.

# 5 Chapter Review

## the BIG idea

**Modern technology has changed the way we view and map Earth.**

CONTENT REVIEW
CLASSZONE.COM

### KEY CONCEPTS SUMMARY

#### 1 Maps and globes are models of Earth.

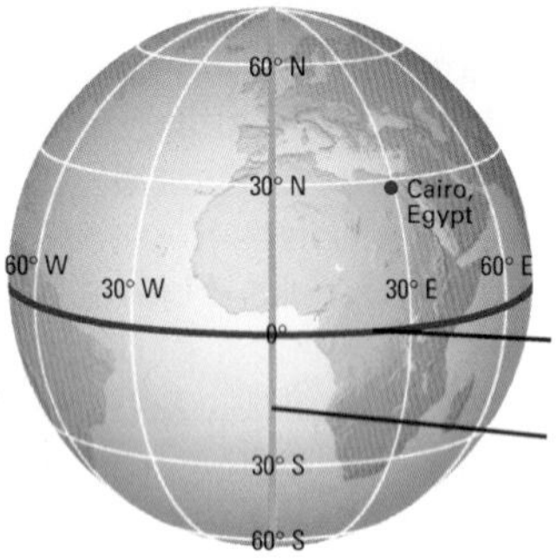


Latitude and longitude are used to locate any point on Earth.

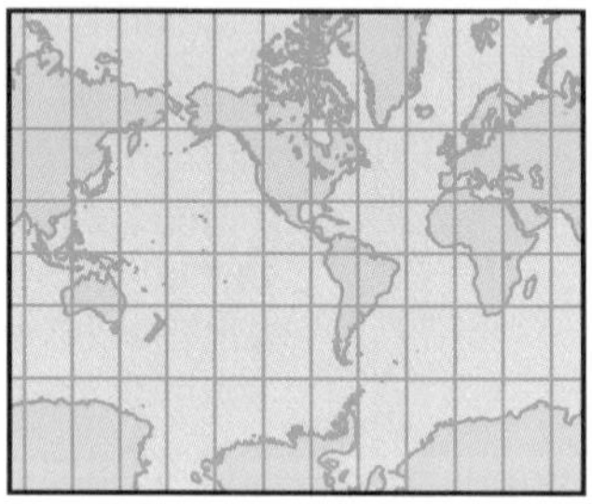

All map projections distort Earth's surface.

**VOCABULARY**
**relief map** p. 156
**map scale** p. 157
**map legend** p. 157
**equator** p. 158
**latitude** p. 158
**prime meridian** p. 159
**longitude** p. 159
**projection** p. 160

#### 2 Topographic maps show the shape of the land.

Contour lines show elevation, slope, and relief.

Contour lines never cross.

Closed circles represent hilltops.

Contour lines show steepness of slope.

Index contour lines show elevation.

**VOCABULARY**
**topography** p. 164
**contour line** p. 165
**elevation** p. 165
**slope** p. 165
**relief** p. 165
**contour interval** p. 166

#### 3 Technology is used to map Earth.

Remote-sensing technology gathers accurate data about Earth.

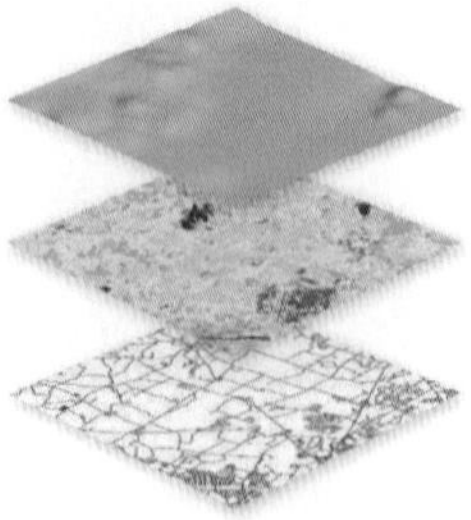

Geographic information systems are computer programs used to merge layers of information.

**VOCABULARY**
**remote sensing** p. 170
**sensor** p. 171
**false-color image** p. 171
**geographic information systems** p. 173

## Reviewing Vocabulary

*Copy and complete the chart below, using vocabulary terms from this chapter.*

| Term | Use | Appearance |
|---|---|---|
| *map legend* | *to explain map symbols* | *chart of symbols* |
| **1.** latitude | to show distance from the equator | |
| **2.** longitude | | lines going from pole to pole |
| **3.** | to show land features | rippled and smooth areas |
| **4.** map scale | to represent distances | |
| **5.** equator | | line at 0° latitude |
| **6.** prime meridian | to separate east and west hemispheres | |
| **7.** | to show height above sea level | line showing elevation |
| **8.** false-color image | to highlight information | |

## Reviewing Key Concepts

**Multiple Choice** *Choose the letter of the best answer.*

**9.** California is located in which of the following two hemispheres? (6.7.f)
- **a.** Southern and Eastern
- **b.** Northern and Eastern
- **c.** Northern and Western
- **d.** Southern and Western

**10.** The darkest contour lines on a topographic map are called (6.7.f)
- **a.** contour intervals
- **b.** topographic symbols
- **c.** hiking trails
- **d.** index contour lines

**11.** How is a steep slope depicted on a topographic map? (6.7.f)
- **a.** contour lines that are close together
- **b.** contour lines that are straight
- **c.** contour lines that are far apart
- **d.** contour lines are jagged

**12.** A flat map shows Earth's curved surface by means of (6.7.f)
- **a.** elevation
- **b.** topography
- **c.** relief
- **d.** projection

**13.** People use latitude and longitude lines mostly to identify (6.7.f)
- **a.** map scales
- **b.** country names
- **c.** exact locations
- **d.** distances

**14.** The most accurate way to show Earth's surface is a (6.7.f)
- **a.** globe
- **b.** conic projection
- **c.** cylindrical projection
- **d.** planar projection

**15.** One example of remote sensing is the use of (6.7.f)
- **a.** contour lines
- **b.** projections
- **c.** GIS
- **d.** binoculars

**Short Answer** *Write a few sentences to answer each question.*

**16.** How does the Global Positioning System work? In your answer use each of the following terms. Underline each term in your answer. (6.7.f)

| | | |
|---|---|---|
| 24 satellites | computer | longitude |
| receiver | latitude | elevation |

**17.** How do Mercator maps distort the view of Earth's surface? (6.7.f)

**18.** How do people use sensors in making maps? (6.7.f)

## Thinking Critically

*Use the topographic map below to answer the next seven questions.*

| | |
|---|---|
| ⚓ marsh | ⟋⟍ road |
| ▪ ▪ buildings | ⌐⌐ : unpaved road |

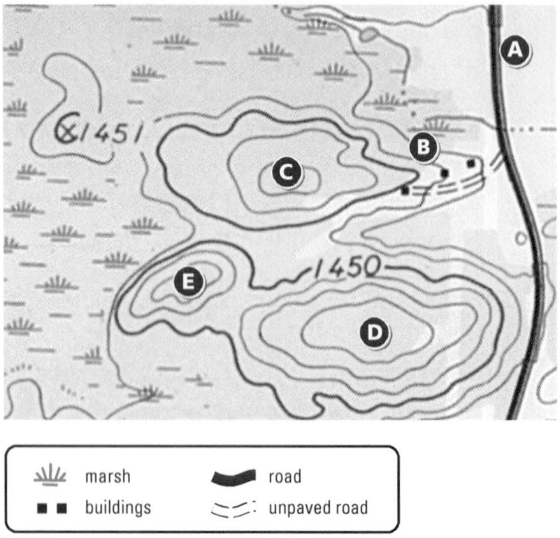

**19. APPLY** Imagine you are hiking through this area. Which hill—*C, D,* or *E*—has the steepest slope? How do you know? (6.7.f)

**20. ANALYZE** What is the topography of the land through which the curved road *A* goes? (6.7.f)

**21. IDENTIFY CAUSE** The squares at *B* represent buildings. Why do you think the buildings were placed here instead of somewhere else in the area? (6.7.f)

**22. APPLY** The contour interval is 10 meters. What is the elevation of the highest point on the map? (6.7.f)

**23. SYNTHESIZE** Sketch the two hills *D* and *E*. What would they look like to someone on the ground? (6.7.f)

**24. INFER** Suppose someone wanted to build a road through the terrain on the far left side of the map. What are the advantages and disadvantages of such a route? (6.7.f)

**25. EVALUATE** Do you think this area would be a good place to ride mountain bikes? Why or why not? (6.7.f)

**CHART INFORMATION** *On a separate sheet of paper, identify which map projection best matches each description.* (6.7.f)

| Description | Projection |
|---|---|
| distorts landmasses farther from center point | planar |
| **26.** curved latitude and longitude lines | |
| **27.** distorts landmasses far from equator | |
| **28.** depicts polar regions accurately | |
| **29.** straight latitude and longitude lines | |
| **30.** distorts landmasses near equator | |

## the BIG idea

**31. APPLY** Look again at the photographs on pages 152–153. Now that you have finished the chapter, reread the question on the main photograph. What would you change in or add to your answer? (6.7.f)

**32. SYNTHESIZE** Describe some of the types of information that new technology has provided about Earth. (6.7.f)

**33. DRAW CONCLUSIONS** What type of technology do you think has done the most to change the way people view and map Earth? Explain your conclusion. (6.7.f)

## UNIT PROJECTS

If you are doing a unit project, make a folder for your project. Include in your folder a list of the resources you will need, the date on which the project is due, and a schedule to track your progress. Begin gathering data.

## Using a Map Scale

6.7.f

*The map shows the Cabrillo National Monument, a national park located on the Point Loma peninsula in San Diego, California. Use it to answer the questions below.*

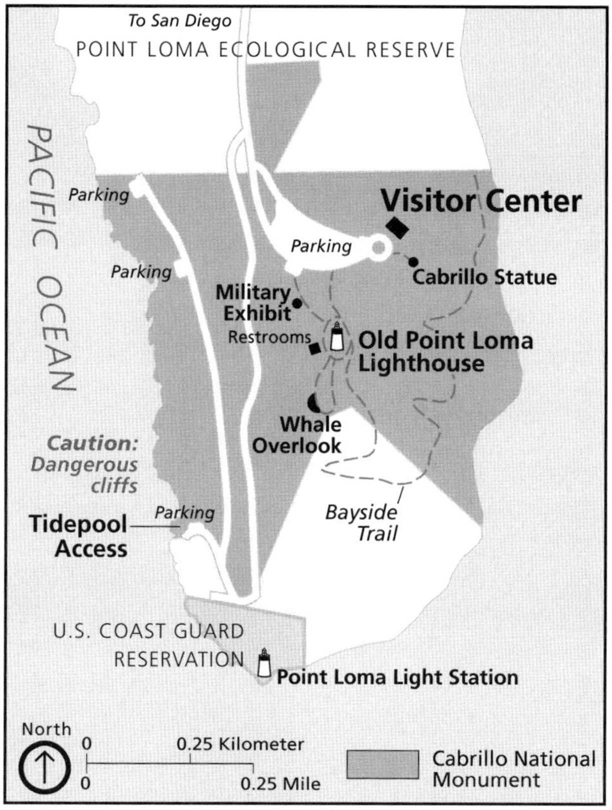


**1.** Which statement about the map is true?

**a.** If it showed a larger area, it could show more detail.

**b.** If it showed a smaller area, it could show more detail.

**c.** If it showed a larger area, it would need a ratio scale.

**d.** If it showed a smaller area, it would need an equivalent-units scale.

**2.** Notice that the map scale is in kilometers and miles. If the map showed only the Visitor Center, what measurements would it likely show?

**a.** millimeters and inches **c.** meters and yards

**b.** centimeters and inches **d.** kilometers and miles

**3.** Which type of scale does this map have?

**a.** ratio

**b.** bar scale

**c.** detail scale

**d.** equivalent-units scale

**4.** What is the distance between the parking lot in the northwest corner of the park and the parking lot that is closest to it?

**a.** 0.25 km **c.** 0.75 km

**b.** 0.50 km **d.** 1.25 km

**5.** Which is a natural feature on the map?

**a.** Visitor Center

**b.** Cabrillo Statue

**c.** Pacific Ocean

**d.** Old Point Loma Lighthouse

**6.** If you were at the Tidepool Access, in what direction would you have to travel to reach the restrooms?

**a.** northwest **c.** southwest

**b.** northeast **d.** southeast

**7.** If you walked in a straight line from the Cabrillo Statue to the Whale Overlook, about how many miles would you walk?

**a.** 0.25 mile **c.** 0.75 mile

**b.** 0.50 mile **d.** 1.25 miles

## Extended Response

*Answer the two questions below in detail.*

**8.** If you were planning to hike the Bayside Trail, what other type of map would be useful to have? Explain why.

**9.** Describe a situation in which knowing how to use a map scale can benefit people.

CHAPTER 6

# Minerals and Rocks

## the BIG idea

**Minerals and rocks are basic building blocks of Earth.**

## Key Concepts

SECTION 1
**Minerals are all around us.**
Learn about the characteristics all minerals share.

SECTION 2
**Rocks form in different ways.**
Learn about the three types of rocks and how they form.

SECTION 3
**Natural processes break down rocks.**
Learn about the mechanical and chemical processes that break down rocks.

SECTION 4
**Geologic maps show Earth's surface features.**
Learn how geologic maps show information about rocks, geologic structures, natural resources, and geologic hazards.

**California ClassZone**

CLASSZONE.COM
Chapter 6 online resources: Content Review, three Visualizations, three Resource Centers, Math Tutorial, Test Practice

***Why might gold be found in this river?***

Visitors to historic Jamestown, California, can pan for gold in Woods Creek.

# EXPLORE the BIG idea

## What Makes Up Rocks?

**6.1.b.** Students know Earth is composed of several layers: a cold, brittle lithosphere; a hot, convecting mantle; and a dense, metallic core.

Find three different rocks near your home or school. Examine them closely with a magnifying glass.

**Observe and Think**
Describe the rocks. How many materials can you see in each rock? How do you think they got there? How are the rocks different from one another?

## Internet Activity: Rocks

**6.1.b.** Students know Earth is composed of several layers: a cold, brittle lithosphere; a hot, convecting mantle; and a dense, metallic core.

Go to **ClassZone.com** to explore how rocks form and change in the lithosphere.

**Observe and Think**
Give an example of a rock from each of the three main types of rock. Then give three examples of the ways in which rocks are continually changing.

NSTA scilinks.org SCILINKS
The Rock Cycle **Code: MDL015**

CHAPTER 6

# Getting Ready to Learn

## CONCEPT REVIEW

- The Earth system has four main parts.
- Matter exists in the forms of gas, liquid, and solid.
- The four parts of the Earth system shape the planet's surface.

## VOCABULARY REVIEW

*See Glossary for definitions.*

**atom**

**crust**

**lithosphere**

**CONTENT REVIEW**
CLASSZONE.COM

Review concepts and vocabulary.

## TAKING NOTES

### SUPPORTING MAIN IDEAS

Make a chart to show each main idea and the information that supports it. Copy each blue heading. Below each heading, add supporting information, such as reasons, explanations, and examples.

### VOCABULARY STRATEGY

For each vocabulary term, make a **magnet word** diagram. Write other terms or ideas related to that term around it.

See the Note-Taking Handbook on pages R45–R51.

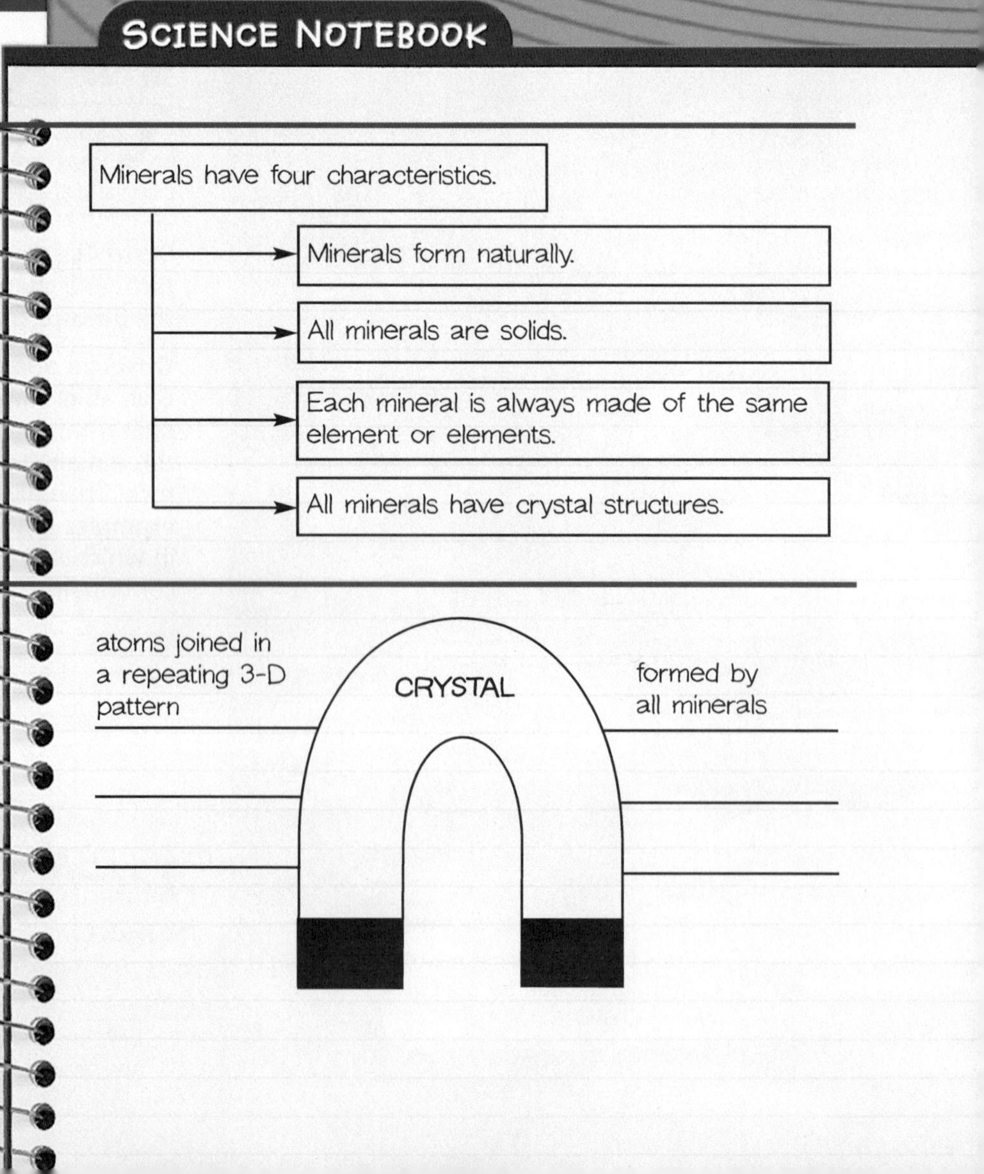
SCIENCE NOTEBOOK
Minerals have four characteristics.
Minerals form naturally.
All minerals are solids.
Each mineral is always made of the same element or elements.
All minerals have crystal structures.
atoms joined in a repeating 3-D pattern
CRYSTAL
formed by all minerals

KEY CONCEPT

# 6.1 Minerals are all around us.

**CALIFORNIA Content Standard**

**Background for 6.1.b.** Students know Earth is composed of several layers: a cold, brittle lithosphere; a hot, convecting mantle; and a dense, metallic core.

**BEFORE, you learned**

- Earth is made of layers
- Earth's outermost rocky layer is the crust

**NOW, you will learn**

- About the characteristics of minerals
- How minerals are classified into groups
- Which mineral group is most common

**VOCABULARY**

**mineral** p. 184
**element** p. 184
**crystal** p. 185
**rock** p. 187

**EXPLORE Minerals (6.1.b)**

***What are some characteristics of a mineral?***

**PROCEDURE**

1. Sprinkle some table salt on a sheet of colored paper. Look at a few grains of the salt through a magnifying glass. Then rub a few grains between your fingers.
2. In your notebook, describe all the qualities of the salt that you observe.
3. Examine the rock salt in the same way and describe its qualities in your notebook. How do the two differ?

**MATERIALS**

- colored paper
- table salt
- rock salt
- magnifying glass

**WHAT DO YOU THINK?**

Salt is a fairly common mineral in Earth's crust. From your observations of salt, what do you think are some characteristics of minerals?

## Minerals and rocks are part of daily life.

SUPPORTING MAIN IDEAS
Enter this blue heading in a chart and record supporting information.

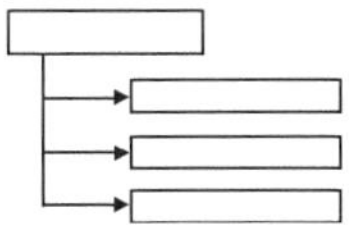

You use minerals all the time. Every time you turn on a microwave oven or a TV, you depend on minerals. The wires that carry electric current are made of copper, which is a mineral. Table salt, or halite (HAL-YT), is another mineral that you use in your everyday life.

Earth's lithosphere is made of rocks. As you will read later in this chapter, almost all rocks are made of minerals. People use rocks in many ways. If you look at large buildings, you might see that parts of their outside walls are made of rocks. Sometimes you can see minerals in the rocks. In a museum, you might see statues and other artworks carved from rocks.

# Minerals have four characteristics.

A mineral can be so small that you need a microscope to see it, or it can be large. No matter what size a mineral is, it has four characteristics. A **mineral** is a substance that

- forms in nature
- is a solid
- has a definite chemical composition
- has a crystal structure

## Forms in Nature

Minerals are formed by natural processes. Every type of mineral can form in nature by processes that do not involve living organisms. A few minerals can also be produced by organisms as part of their shells or bones.

Minerals form in many ways. Halite can form when water evaporates in a shallow part of the ocean, leaving behind the salt it contained. Many types of minerals develop when molten rock cools. Talc, a mineral that can be used to make baby powder, forms inside Earth as high pressure and temperature cause changes in solid rock.

READING TIP

*Molten rock* refers to rock that has become so hot that it has melted.

## Solid

A mineral is a solid—that is, it has a definite volume and a rigid shape. Volume refers to the amount of space an object takes up. For example, a golf ball has a smaller volume than a baseball, and a baseball has a smaller volume than a basketball.

A substance that is a liquid or a gas is not a mineral. However, in some cases its solid form is a mineral. For example, liquid water is not a mineral, but ice is.

## Definite Chemical Composition

Each mineral has a definite chemical makeup: it consists of a specific combination of atoms of certain elements. An **element** is a substance that contains only one type of atom. In turn, an atom is the smallest particle an element can be divided into.

REMINDER

You may remember *compound* from compound words—words formed by joining together smaller words: *note* + *book* = *notebook*. Likewise, a chemical compound has two or more elements joined together.

Look at the illustration on page 185. You can see that some substances, including the minerals gold and copper, consist of just one element. However, most minerals are compounds, substances that consist of several elements in specific proportions. Notice that halite has one atom of sodium for every atom of chlorine.

## Atoms in Minerals

The mineral copper is made up of only copper atoms.

The mineral halite is made up of equal numbers of sodium and chlorine atoms.

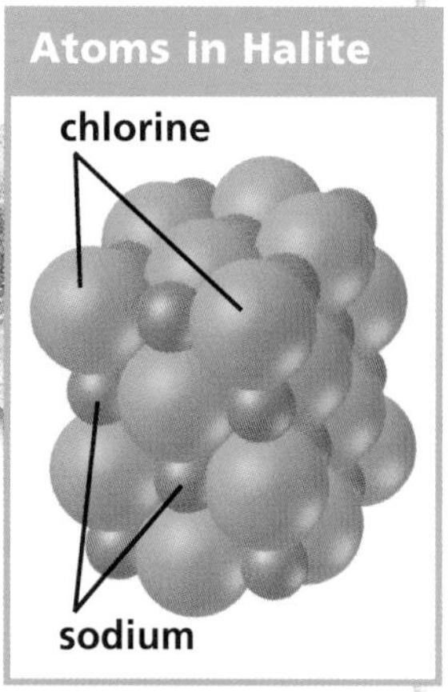


**READING VISUALS** How do the diagrams show that copper consists of only one element and halite is a compound?

## Crystal Structure

If you look closely at the particles of ice that make up frost, you will notice that they have smooth, flat surfaces. These flat surfaces form because of the arrangement of atoms in the ice, which is a mineral. This arrangement is a characteristic of minerals. It is the structure of a **crystal,** a solid in which the atoms are arranged in an orderly, repeating three-dimensional pattern.

Each mineral has its own type of crystal structure. In some cases, two minerals have the same chemical composition but different crystal structures. For example, both diamond and graphite consist of just one element—carbon. But the arrangements of the carbon atoms in these two minerals are not the same. Therefore, they have different crystal structures and very different properties. Diamonds are extremely hard and have a brilliant sparkle. Graphite is soft, gray, and dull.

**CHECK YOUR READING** Why do graphite and diamond have different properties?

In nature, a perfect crystal is rare. One can grow only when a mineral is free to form in an open space. This condition rarely exists within Earth's crust. The amount of space available for growth influences the shapes and sizes of crystals. Most crystals have imperfect shapes because their growth was limited by other crystals that formed next to them. But even though most crystals do not have perfect shapes, their atoms are still arranged in orderly crystal structures.

# INVESTIGATE Crystal Shape

## *How do crystals differ in shape?*

**PROCEDURE**

1. Cut sheets of paper so that they fit inside the pie plates as shown. Place one sheet in each pie plate.
2. Observe the shape of the particles of the table salt then add the salt to 30 mL of water in a cup. Stir the water until the salt has dissolved.
3. Pour enough salt solution into one of the pie plates to completely cover the paper with a small film of liquid. Be careful not to pour into the plate any undissolved salt that may be in the bottom of the cup.
4. Repeat steps 2 and 3 with the Epsom salts. Let the plates dry overnight.

**WHAT DO YOU THINK?**

- What do you see on the paper? Compare and describe the shapes of the crystals.
- Why are the shapes of the crystals the same as or different from the shapes in the materials you started with?

**CHALLENGE** Which layers of Earth contain mineral crystals?

**SKILL FOCUS**
Observing (6.1.b)

**MATERIALS**
- 2 pie plates
- 2 sheets black paper
- scissors
- tablespoon
- 2 cups or jars
- 2 stirring rods
- 1 tbs table salt
- 1 tbs Epsom salts
- 60 mL water

**TIME**
20 minutes for setup

## Minerals are grouped according to composition.

**REMINDER**
You can see a chart of common minerals and their properties on pages R66–R68.

Although there are thousands of different minerals, only about 30 are common in Earth's crust. These 30 minerals make up most of the rocks in the crust. For that reason, they are called rock-forming minerals. Scientists classify minerals into groups based on their compositions. Silicates (SIHL-ih-KAYTS) make up about 90 percent of the rocks in Earth's crust. They are the most common rock-forming minerals. Quartz, feldspar, and mica (MY-kuh) are common silicates. All the minerals in this group contain oxygen and silicon, the two most common elements in Earth's crust, joined together.

**CHECK YOUR READING** Which mineral group do most rock-forming minerals belong to?

The second most common group of rock-forming minerals is the carbonates. These minerals contain carbon and oxygen joined together. Some carbonate minerals are commonly produced by living things.

For example, clams and oysters produce carbonate minerals such as calcite (KAL-SYT) when they form their shells. Carbonate minerals also form by processes that do not involve living things.

There are many other mineral groups. All are important, even though their minerals are not as common as silicates or carbonates. For example, the mineral group known as oxides contains the minerals from which most metals are refined. Examples of metals include tin and chromium. An oxide consists of an element, usually a metal, joined to oxygen. This group includes hematite (HEE-muh-TYT), a source of iron.

**RESOURCE CENTER**
CLASSZONE.COM
Find information on minerals.

**CHECK YOUR READING** Why is the oxide mineral group important?

## Most rocks are made of minerals.

You might think that minerals and rocks are the same things. But a mineral must have the four characteristics listed on page 184. A rock has only two of the four—it is a solid and it forms naturally. A **rock** is a naturally formed solid that is usually made up of one or more types of minerals.

**VOCABULARY**
Add a magnet word diagram for *rock* in your notebook.

### Minerals in Rocks

**Most rocks contain several types of minerals.**

This piece of granite contains the minerals quartz, feldspar, and mica.

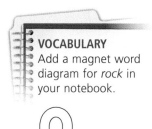

READING TIP

Proportions show relationships between amounts. For example, a quartz crystal always has the same proportion of oxygen atoms to silicon atoms: two oxygen atoms for every silicon atom.

The structure of rocks is different from that of minerals. A mineral is always made of the same elements in the same proportions. All minerals have an orderly crystal structure. However, the proportion of different minerals in a certain type of rock may vary. Also, the minerals in a rock can be all jumbled together.

CHECK YOUR READING How are minerals different from rocks?

Gabbro, like most rocks, is made up of several types of minerals.

Obsidian is an unusual rock because it contains no minerals.

A few types of rocks are made up of one type of mineral. A few contain no minerals at all. Limestone, for example, can be made up entirely of the mineral calcite. Obsidian (ahb-SIHD-ee-uhn) is a rock that contains no minerals. It is made of natural glass, which is not a mineral because it does not have a crystal structure.

Coal is another rock that does not have a crystal structure. It is made up of the remains of ancient plants that were buried and pressed into rock. Coal started forming millions of years ago in swamps. As plants died, their remains fell on the remains of earlier plants. Then other materials buried the plant remains. Over time, the weight of the materials above pressed the plant remains into coal. You will read in Chapter 13 how people use coal as an energy source.

## 6.1 Review

### KEY CONCEPTS

1. What are the four characteristics of a mineral? (6.1.b)
2. How are minerals classified? (6.1.b)
3. What is the most common group of minerals? What percentage of the crust do they make up? (6.1.b)

### CRITICAL THINKING

4. **Classify** Can oil and natural gas be classified as minerals? Why or why not?
5. **Apply** When a piece of quartz is heated to a very high temperature, it melts into a liquid. Is it still a mineral? Why or why not?

### CHALLENGE

6. **Interpret** You can see perfect crystals lining the inside of certain rocks when they are broken open. How do you think the crystals were able to form?

MATH in SCIENCE

**MATH TUTORIAL**
CLASSZONE.COM
Click on Math Tutorial for more help with percents and fractions.

Math 6.NS.2.4

## SKILL: WRITING FRACTIONS AS PERCENTS

# Minerals in Rocks

Like most rocks, granite is a mixture of several minerals. Each mineral makes up a certain proportion, or fraction, of a granite sample. You can compare mineral amounts by expressing each mineral's fraction as a percentage.

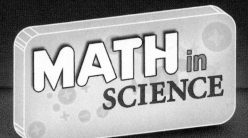

Granite

### Example

To change a fraction to a percentage, you must find an equivalent fraction with 100 as the denominator. Suppose, for example, you want to change the fraction $\frac{1}{5}$ to a percentage. First, divide 100 by the denominator 5, which gives you 20. Then multiply both the numerator and denominator by 20 to find the percentage.

$\frac{1}{5} \cdot \frac{20}{20} = \frac{20}{100}$ or 20%      $\frac{1}{5}$ is 20%

The table below shows the fraction of each mineral in a granite sample.

**Minerals in Granite Sample**

| Mineral | Fraction of Granite Sample | Percentage of Granite |
|---|---|---|
| Quartz | $\frac{1}{4}$ | ? |
| Feldspar | $\frac{13}{20}$ | ? |
| Mica | $\frac{3}{50}$ | ? |
| Dark minerals | $\frac{1}{25}$ | ? |

**Use the table to answer the following questions.**

1. Copy the table. Calculate and fill in the percentage of each mineral in the granite sample.
2. Which minerals make up the greatest and smallest percentages of the granite?
3. In another granite sample, feldspar makes up $\frac{3}{5}$ and mica makes up $\frac{2}{25}$. What is the percentage of each mineral in the rock?

**CHALLENGE The mineral hornblende is often one of the dark minerals in granite. If hornblende makes up $\frac{1}{32}$ of a granite sample, approximately what percentage of the rock is hornblende?**

KEY CONCEPT

# 6.2 Rocks form in different ways.

**CALIFORNIA Content Standards**

**Background for**
**6.1.b** Students know Earth is composed of several layers: a cold, brittle lithosphere; a hot, convecting mantle; and a dense, metallic core.

**6.2** Topography is reshaped by the weathering of rock and soil and by the transportation and deposition of sediment.

**BEFORE, you learned**

- Minerals and rocks are basic components of Earth
- Minerals have four characteristics
- Most rocks are made of minerals

**NOW, you will learn**

- About the three types of rocks
- How one type of rock can change into another
- How common each rock type is in Earth's crust

**VOCABULARY**

**igneous rock** p. 191
**magma** p. 191
**lava** p. 191
**sedimentary rock** p. 192
**metamorphic rock** p. 194
**recrystallization** p. 195
**rock cycle** p. 196

**EXPLORE Rocks (6.1.b)**

***How do rocks differ from one another?***

**PROCEDURE**

1. Closely examine the rock samples. What do you notice about the forms, shapes, colors, and textures of the rocks?
2. In your notebook, make lists of the characteristics of the rocks.

**MATERIALS**

- rock samples
- magnifying glass

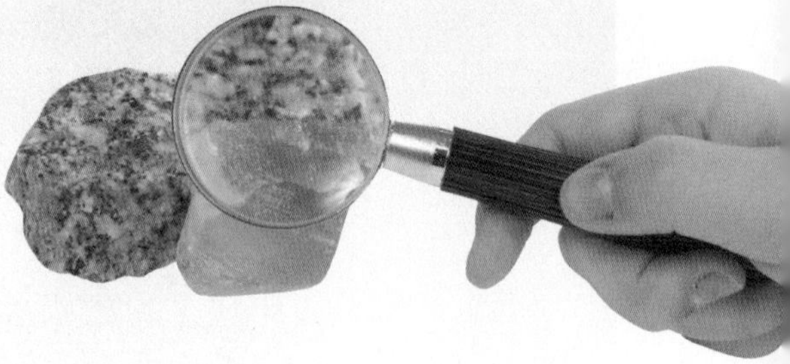

**WHAT DO YOU THINK?**

- What are the similarities and differences between the rocks?
- Which of Earth's layers did the rocks come from? How do you know?

**SUPPORTING MAIN IDEAS**
As you read, write each blue heading in a chart and record supporting information.

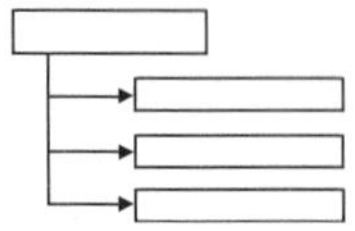

## Our world is built of rocks.

Earth is built almost entirely of rock. When you look at Earth's surface, you can see soil, plants, rivers, and oceans. These surface features, however, form only a very thin covering on the planet. Between this thin layer and Earth's metallic core, Earth is made of solid and molten rock.

Because rocks are so common, it is not surprising that people use them for many different purposes, including using them as

- building materials for houses and skyscrapers
- sources of metals, such as iron, aluminum, and copper
- materials for statues and other works of art
- a base for pavement of roads and highways

People value rocks because rocks are strong and long-lasting, and because some are beautiful. Rock structures and carvings still exist from ancient times and give us a link to our distant past. Many famous monuments and sculptures are made from rocks. Granite blocks form part of the Great Wall of China. Limestone blocks make up the Great Pyramid in Egypt. The faces of four U.S. presidents are carved in the granite of Mount Rushmore.

**CHECK YOUR READING** Why do people use rocks for many different purposes?

This sculptor in Indonesia, like artists throughout the world, shapes rocks into lasting works of art.

## Rocks are classified by how they form.

Earth has three types of rocks that form in distinct ways. As you read about these types of rocks, you will see that rocks do not last forever. Over time—usually thousands to millions of years—rocks change, break down, and re-form. But they still last longer than almost any other building material you can name, including iron.

### Igneous Rock

**Igneous rock** (IHG-nee-uhs) forms when molten rock cools and becomes solid. Molten rock is a mixture of melted rock, solid mineral crystals, and dissolved gases. Igneous rock can form under Earth's surface, or it can form on the surface. Molten rock inside Earth is called **magma.** Molten rock that reaches Earth's surface is called **lava.**

Depending on where they form, igneous rocks are referred to as intrusive (ihn-TROO-sihv) or extrusive (ihk-STROO-sihv). The illustration on page 192 shows that an intrusive igneous rock is one that forms when magma cools inside Earth. An extrusive igneous rock is one that forms when lava cools on Earth's surface.

**READING TIP**

The words *intrusive* and *extrusive* come from the Latin words *intrudere,* "to push in," and *extrudere,* "to push out." The prefix *in-* means "into," or "within." The prefix *ex-* means "outside," or "away from."

An intrusive igneous rock can have the same mineral composition as an extrusive igneous rock. However, the rocks will have different names, because the size of their mineral crystals will be very different. For example, granite is a common intrusive rock. If magma with the same composition reaches the surface, it forms an extrusive rock such as rhyolite.

**CHECK YOUR READING** How are granite and rhyolite similar? How are they different?

## Crystal Size and Cooling Time

**The more slowly molten rock cools, the larger the igneous rocks' mineral crystals will be.**

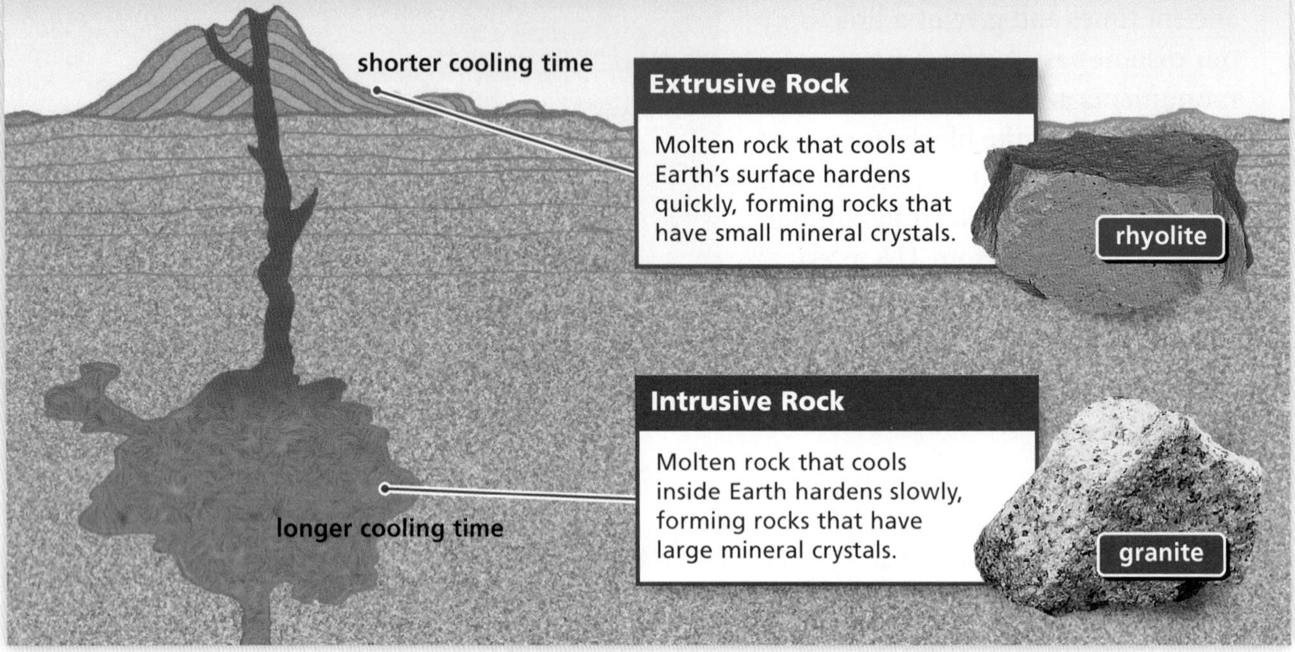

shorter cooling time
Extrusive Rock
Molten rock that cools at Earth's surface hardens quickly, forming rocks that have small mineral crystals.
rhyolite
Intrusive Rock
Molten rock that cools inside Earth hardens slowly, forming rocks that have large mineral crystals.
granite
longer cooling time

**VISUALIZATION**
CLASSZONE.COM

Explore an animation showing how crystals form as molten rock cools.

You can see extrusive igneous rocks at Earth's surface. But intrusive igneous rocks form within Earth. How do they reach the surface? Forces inside Earth can push rocks up, as when mountains form. Also, water and wind break apart and carry away surface rocks. Then deeper rocks are uncovered at the surface.

## Sedimentary Rock

Most **sedimentary rock** (SEHD-uh-MEHN-tuh-ree) forms when pieces of minerals and rocks, plants, and other loose materials get pressed or cemented together. Loose materials that are carried by water or wind and then settle on a surface are called sediments. Sediments build up in layers as they settle from water or wind.

Younger layers of sediments form on top of older layers. The illustration on page 193 shows sediments carried by water. The distance that sediments are carried depends on the size of the sediments and the speed of the water. Large, heavy sediments settle quickly as the speed of the water decreases. Small, light sediments can be carried a long way—even by slowly flowing water.

Lower layers of sediments can get pressed into rock by the weight of layers of sediments above them. Also, new minerals can grow in the spaces between the sediments, cementing them together. Over time, sedimentary rocks can break apart into individual sediments. The sediments can then become part of new sedimentary rocks.

## Sorting Sediments by Size

**The speed of water and the size of sediments determine how far sediments are carried.**

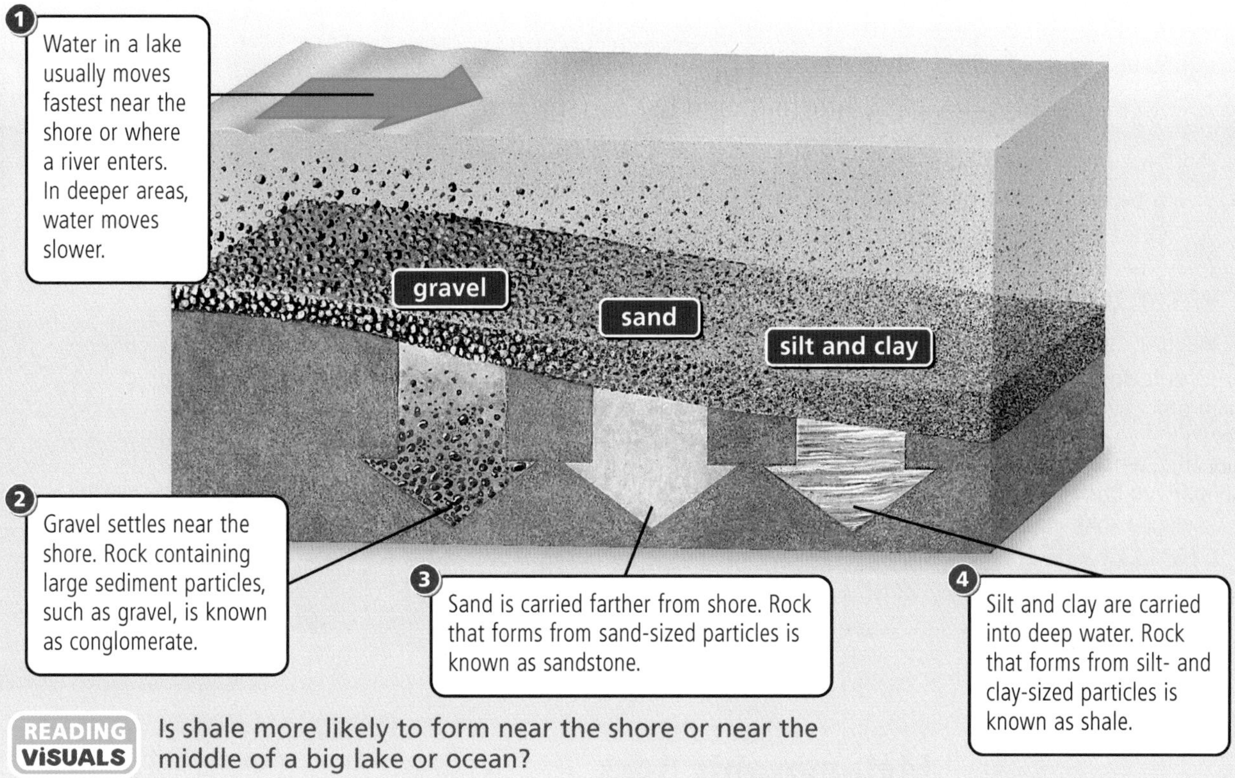

1
Water in a lake usually moves fastest near the shore or where a river enters. In deeper areas, water moves slower.
gravel
sand
silt and clay
2
Gravel settles near the shore. Rock containing large sediment particles, such as gravel, is known as conglomerate.
3
Sand is carried farther from shore. Rock that forms from sand-sized particles is known as sandstone.
4
Silt and clay are carried into deep water. Rock that forms from silt- and clay-sized particles is known as shale.

**READING VISUALS** Is shale more likely to form near the shore or near the middle of a big lake or ocean?

Processes similar to the ones that produce sedimentary rocks from rock particles also produce rocks from fossils. Fossils are the remains or traces of organisms from long ago. Limestone is a rock that is usually made up of the fossils of ocean organisms. When the organisms die, their shells and skeletons settle to the ocean floor as layers of sediment. Over time, the layers become buried, pressed together, and cemented to form limestone. You have read that coal is made up of the remains of ancient plants that have been pressed into rock.

Sedimentary rocks form in ways other than being pressed or cemented together. Consider processes that take place along the edges of lakes and oceans where the climate is dry and water evaporates quickly. As water evaporates, it leaves behind materials that were dissolved in it. Minerals form as the materials combine into crystals. Over time, layers of minerals can build up and form sedimentary rocks, such as rock salt or gypsum. Under the city of Detroit, for example, is a thick layer of rock salt that developed when part of an ancient ocean dried up.

**REMINDER**

When material dissolves in water, it breaks into many tiny parts. When the water evaporates, the parts join together and the material becomes solid again.

**CHECK YOUR READING** What are three processes that can form sedimentary rock?

# INVESTIGATE Sediment Layers

## How do sedimentary layers form?

**PROCEDURE**

1. Pour 2 cups of water into the jar.
2. Add the gravel and sand to the water.
3. Shake the jar for a few seconds and then set it down on a counter. Observe and record what happens to the materials in the water.

**WHAT DO YOU THINK?**

- What determines how the materials settle to the bottom of the jar?
- In a lake, how would a mixture of different-sized rock particles settle to the bottom?

**CHALLENGE** How does the movement of sediment by water running downhill help shape the landscape?

**SKILL FOCUS**
Modeling (6.2.a)

**MATERIALS**
- jar
- measuring cup
- water
- 1/3 cup gravel
- 1/3 cup sand

**TIME**
20 minutes

## Metamorphic Rock

**READING TIP**

Rocks change into other rocks by the process of metamorphism. A similar word, *metamorphosis,* refers to what happens when a caterpillar changes into a butterfly.

**Metamorphic rock** (MEHT-uh-MAWR-fihk) forms when heat or pressure causes older rocks to change into new types of rocks. For example, a rock can get buried deeper in the crust, where pressure and temperature are much greater. These conditions cause the structure of the rock to change so that new minerals grow in place of the original minerals. The rock becomes a metamorphic rock. The process by which this occurs is called metamorphism. Many metamorphic rocks form deep in the crust. They can reach Earth's surface over time as mountains are pushed up or as surface rocks are worn away, uncovering deeper rocks.

**RESOURCE CENTER**
CLASSZONE.COM

Find out more about the three types of rocks.

Most metamorphic changes occur over large areas in which both temperature and pressure are high. An example is a region where large blocks of the lithosphere are pressing together and pushing up mountain ranges. This process can affect an area hundreds of kilometers wide and tens of kilometers deep. When either high pressure or high temperature conditions occur alone, metamorphic changes tend to occur over smaller areas. For example, surface rock can be covered with a lava flow. The lava heats the rock it touches, causing metamorphism to occur. The changes are due to high temperature, not pressure.

During metamorphism, rocks undergo many changes. One type of change occurs when pressure causes a rock's minerals to line up in layers, as shown in the illustration below. Metamorphic changes occur while rocks remain solid. Rocks do not melt when they undergo metamorphism. If the temperature gets high enough to melt the rock, the end result is an igneous rock, not a metamorphic rock.

Heat and pressure can break the bonds that join atoms in minerals. Then the atoms can join together differently as new bonds form. This process is called **recrystallization.** It has two main results. First, individual mineral crystals can grow larger as more atoms join their crystal structures. Second, atoms can combine in different ways, and new minerals can form in place of older ones. For example, shale is a sedimentary rock that is formed from silt and clay. During recrystallization, garnet can form from these materials.

**CALIFORNIA Focus**

The state rock of California is a metamorphic rock known as serpentine. Serpentine is shiny and commonly has a green color. It contains minerals such as chromite, a source of chromium, and magnesite, a source of magnesium.

## Metamorphic Changes

**Because pressure and temperature increase with depth, rocks change when they are buried deeper in the crust.**

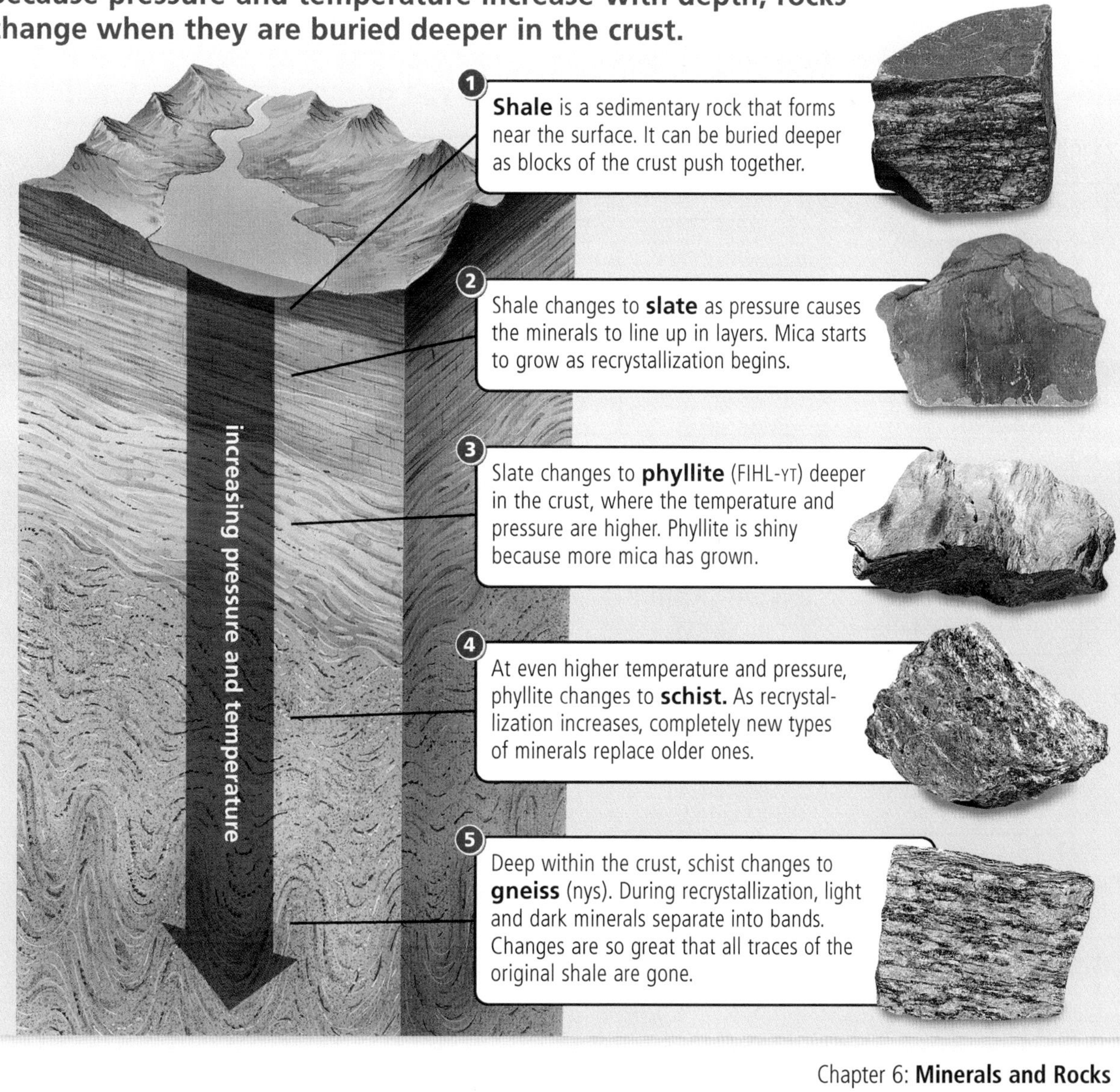

increasing pressure and temperature
1 **Shale** is a sedimentary rock that forms near the surface. It can be buried deeper as blocks of the crust push together.
2 Shale changes to **slate** as pressure causes the minerals to line up in layers. Mica starts to grow as recrystallization begins.
3 Slate changes to **phyllite** (FIHL-YT) deeper in the crust, where the temperature and pressure are higher. Phyllite is shiny because more mica has grown.
4 At even higher temperature and pressure, phyllite changes to **schist.** As recrystallization increases, completely new types of minerals replace older ones.
5 Deep within the crust, schist changes to **gneiss** (nys). During recrystallization, light and dark minerals separate into bands. Changes are so great that all traces of the original shale are gone.

## Rocks can change into other types of rocks.

When rocks are raised to the surface, water and wind can break them down into sediments. Over time, the sediments might become sedimentary rock. When rocks at or near the surface are pushed deeper into the crust, they might become metamorphic rocks. Or they might melt and then cool into igneous rocks. For example, rocks can be raised up or pushed deeper when mountains are forming. You will read more about this topic in Chapter 8.

### The Rock Cycle

**READING TIP**

The word *cycle* comes from the Greek word *kuklos,* which means "circle." A cycle is made up of a set of repeating events.

The **rock cycle** is the set of natural processes by which rocks form, change, break down, and re-form. Rocks do not move through the rock cycle in a particular order. As you can see in the illustration below, a rock at any point in the cycle can change in two or three different ways. The rock cycle has no beginning or end. It goes on continually.

**The Rock Cycle**

**In the rock cycle, natural processes change each type of rock into other types.**

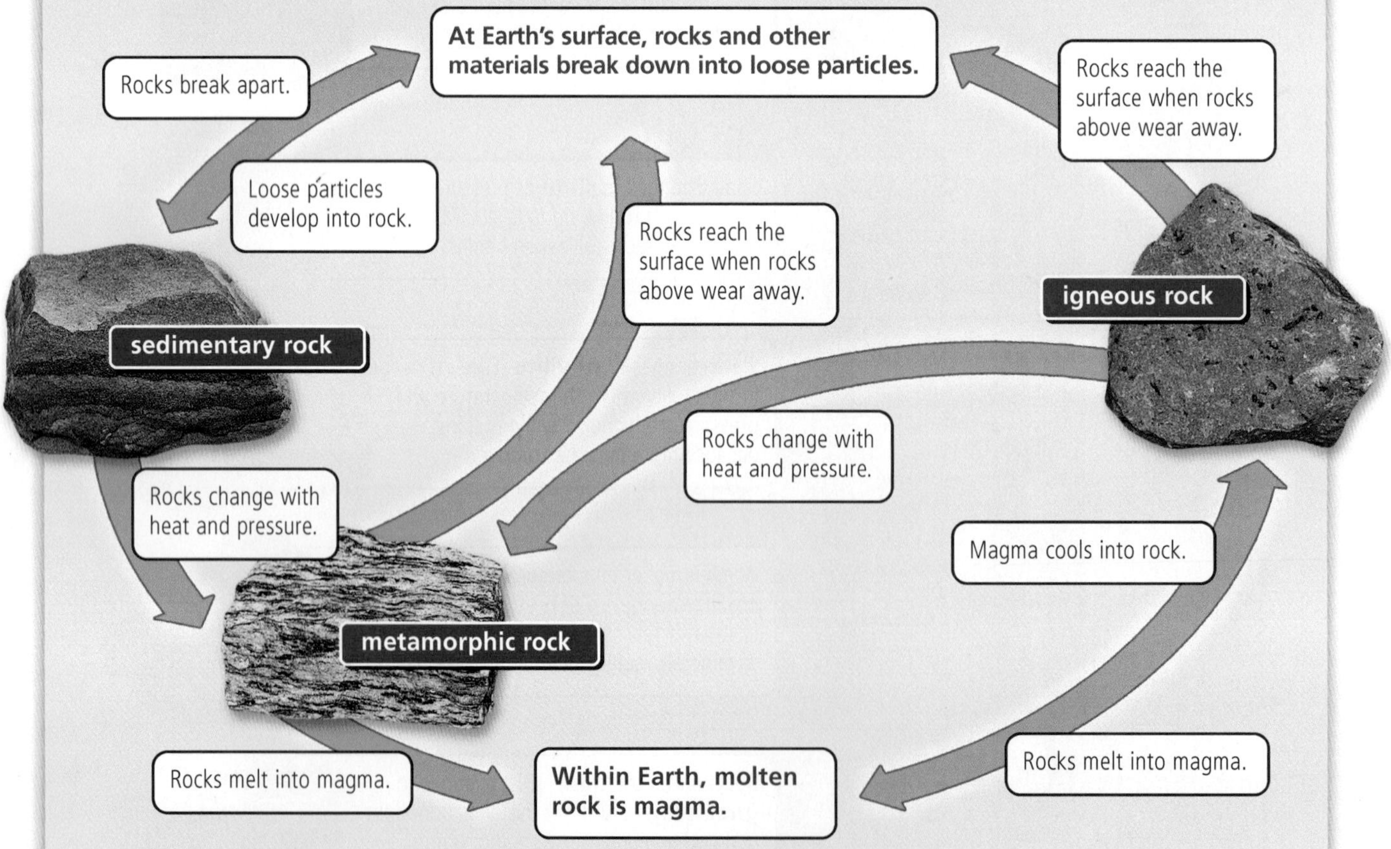

At Earth's surface, rocks and other materials break down into loose particles.
Rocks break apart.
Rocks reach the surface when rocks above wear away.
Loose particles develop into rock.
Rocks reach the surface when rocks above wear away.
igneous rock
sedimentary rock
Rocks change with heat and pressure.
Rocks change with heat and pressure.
Magma cools into rock.
metamorphic rock
Rocks melt into magma.
Within Earth, molten rock is magma.
Rocks melt into magma.

**READING VISUALS** What are two ways a sedimentary rock can change as it moves to another stage of the rock cycle?

## Rocks in the Crust

**Even though sedimentary rock is common at Earth's surface, the crust as a whole consists mainly of igneous and metamorphic rock.**

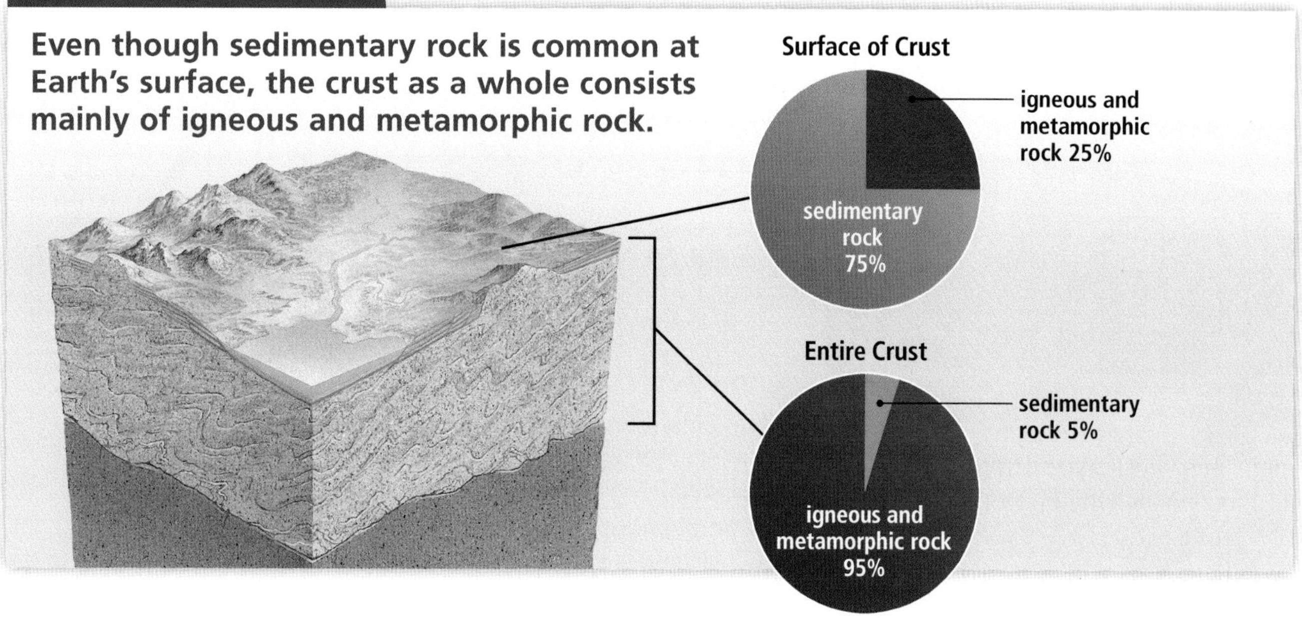


### Rocks in the Crust

Igneous, sedimentary, and metamorphic rocks are all found in Earth's crust. But these rock types are not evenly distributed. Most of Earth's crust—95 percent of it—consists of igneous rock and metamorphic rock. Sedimentary rock, which forms a thin covering on Earth's surface, makes up only 5 percent of the crust.

The distribution of rock types is a reflection of the rock cycle. Sedimentary rocks are most common at the surface because they are formed by processes that occur at the surface. Most igneous rocks and metamorphic rocks are formed by processes that occur deeper within Earth.

**REMINDER**

The crust is the upper layer of the lithosphere. The uppermost mantle makes up the rest of the lithosphere.

**CHECK YOUR READING** Would you expect to find sedimentary rock deep in Earth's crust? Why or why not?

# 6.2 Review

### KEY CONCEPTS

1. What are the three types of rock? (6.1.b)
2. Give an example of how one type of rock can change into another type. (6.1.b)
3. Which rock types are most common within Earth's crust? Which type is most common at Earth's surface? (6.1.b)

### CRITICAL THINKING

4. **Analyze** Why is the set of natural processes by which rocks change into other types of rocks called a cycle?
5. **Infer** Which type of rock would be most likely to form on the bottom of a large, deep lake? Why?

### CHALLENGE

6. **Synthesize** Draw a diagram showing how an igneous rock could change into a metamorphic rock and how the metamorphic rock could change into a sedimentary rock.

CONNECTING SCIENCES

## EARTH SCIENCE AND LIFE SCIENCE

# Coral Polyps Rock!

6.5.b Students know matter is transferred over time from one organism to others in the food web and between organisms and the physical environment.

What is a type of rock that comes from once-living organisms? Limestone! Limestone is made up of carbonate minerals, such as calcite—a major mineral in the shells and skeletons of sea organisms.

## Coral Reefs and Coral Polyps

Coral organisms build their limestone skeletons one on top of another. Over time, countless skeletons of these organisms form coral reefs.

Coral polyps, the creatures that create reefs, are often only a few millimeters long, although some can grow much larger. Those that live in colonies are about 1–3 millimeters in diameter. Corals do not move because their bases are stuck to the reef surface. But their tentacles do move. Corals have stinging threads with tiny barbs on the tip. Those threads are filled with venom that can kill small animals. The tentacles move the food to the coral's mouth. Reef-building corals make their own cup-shaped skeletons out of carbonate minerals. The coral polyp can hide almost totally inside the skeleton. Huge numbers of these skeletons eventually become large formations of limestone. Imagine how many tiny corals it takes to build one huge coral reef!

The skeletons of these tiny coral organisms eventually make huge coral reefs.

## Limestone Towers

Some limestone forms without the help of organisms. As water dries up, materials that had been dissolved in it can crystallize into minerals. Also, water can contain so many dissolved substances that minerals form in it. The towers of limestone in Mono Lake formed around the openings of underwater springs. The springs' water was rich in dissolved substances that formed into carbonate minerals.

These limestone towers in Mono Lake, California, formed underwater. They are now above the surface because the lake level has dropped.

### EXPLORE

1. **COMPARE AND CONTRAST** Compare the pictures of the coral reef and the limestone towers. What similarities do you see? Contrast them with other pictures in the book showing other types of rock.
2. **CHALLENGE** Break up small pieces of coral and limestone. Place the coral and limestone into separate cups. Drop a few drops of vinegar in each cup. What happens? Why?

KEY CONCEPT

# 6.3 Natural processes break down rocks.

**CALIFORNIA Content Standards**

**Background for 6.2.** Topography is reshaped by the weathering of rock and soil and by the transportation and deposition of sediment.

**6.2.a** Students know water running downhill is the dominant process in shaping the landscape, including California's landscape.

**BEFORE, you learned**

- Minerals make up almost all rocks
- Different minerals have different properties
- Rocks are broken down to form sediments

**NOW, you will learn**

- About the relationship between weathering and the geological cycle
- How mechanical weathering breaks down rocks
- How chemical weathering changes rocks
- What factors affect the rate at which weathering occurs

**VOCABULARY**

**geologic cycle** p. 199
**weathering** p. 199
**mechanical weathering** p. 200
**chemical weathering** p. 202

**EXPLORE Weathering (6.2)**

***What can cause a rock to break down?***

**PROCEDURE**

1. Place a piece of chalk in a cup.
2. Pour vinegar over the chalk and observe any changes that occur.

**MATERIALS**

- chalk
- cup
- vinegar

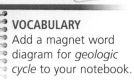

**WHAT DO YOU THINK?**

- What happened to the chalk and why?
- What processes in nature might affect rocks in similar ways?

## Weathering helps change Earth's features over time.

**VOCABULARY**
Add a magnet word diagram for *geologic cycle* to your notebook.

Earth's features change over time. For example, the actions of water, ice, and wind wear mountains down into small pieces of sediment. Eventually, the sediment is changed back into large bodies of rock again, and new mountains are pushed up. All of these changes and more are processes in the geologic cycle. The **geologic cycle** includes all the processes by which Earth's features are worn down and built up. The rock cycle is part of the geologic cycle.

**Weathering** is the set of natural processes that break down rocks. It is part of the geologic cycle too. Rocks must be broken down before sediments can be carried to new places, changing the shape of Earth's surface. One kind of weathering occurs when a rock is physically broken apart. Another kind occurs when a chemical reaction changes the composition of the rock.

## Mechanical weathering produces physical changes in rocks.

RESOURCE CENTER
CLASSZONE.COM
Learn more about weathering.

If you smash a walnut with a hammer, you will break it into a lot of small pieces. But you will not change what it is. Even though the pieces of the walnut are no longer connected, they are still made up of the same materials. **Mechanical weathering**—the breaking up of rocks by physical forces—works in much the same way. In this natural process, physical forces split rocks apart but do not change what they are made of. Ice wedging, pressure release, plant root growth, and abrasion can all cause mechanical weathering.

READING TIP
The word *expand* means "to increase in size or volume."

1. **Ice Wedging** When water freezes, it expands. When water freezes in the cracks and pores of rocks, the force of its expansion is strong enough to split the rocks apart. This process, which is called ice wedging, can break up huge boulders. Ice wedging is common in places where temperatures rise above and fall below the freezing point for water, which is 0°C (32°F).

2. **Pressure Release** Rock deep within Earth is under great pressure from rocks around it. Over time, processes within Earth can push the rock up to the surface. At the same time, the rock above it can wear away. In either case, the pressure inside the rock is still high, but the pressure on the surface of the rock is released. This release of pressure causes the rock to expand. As the rock expands, cracks form in it, leading to exfoliation. Exfoliation (ehks-FOH-lee-AY-shuhn) is a process in which layers or sheets of rock gradually break off. This process is sometimes called onion-skin weathering. The rock surface breaks off in thin layers like the layers of an onion.

3. **Plant Root Growth** Trees, bushes, and other plants may take root in cracks in rocks. As the roots of these plants grow, they wedge open the cracks. The rock—even if it is large—can be split completely apart.

4. **Abrasion** Water can wear down rocks on riverbeds and along shorelines. Abrasion (uh-BRAY-zhuhn) is the process of wearing down by friction, the rubbing of one object or surface against another. The force of moving water alone can wear away particles of rock. Water also causes rocks to tumble downstream. The tumbling rocks wear down as they grind against the riverbed and against each other. Ocean waves beating against a rocky shore also wear down rocks by abrasion.

CHECK YOUR READING How does moving water weather rocks?

## Mechanical Weathering

**Ice wedging, pressure release, plant root growth, and abrasion can all break apart rocks.**

### ① Ice Wedging

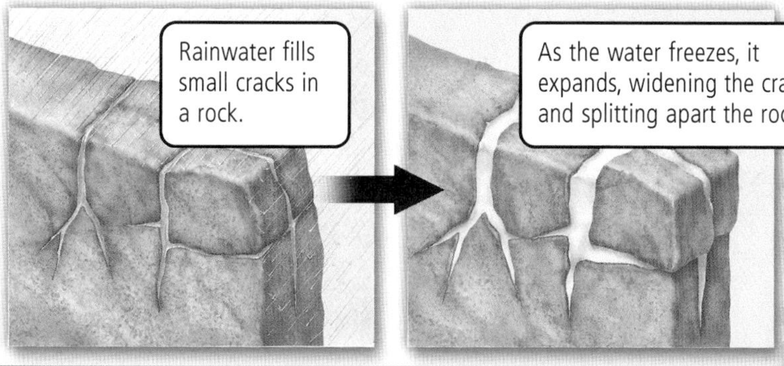

Rainwater fills small cracks in a rock.
As the water freezes, it expands, widening the cracks and splitting apart the rock.

### ② Pressure Release

Earth's forces can push rock that formed deep underground up to the surface.

The release of pressure causes the rock to expand and crack.

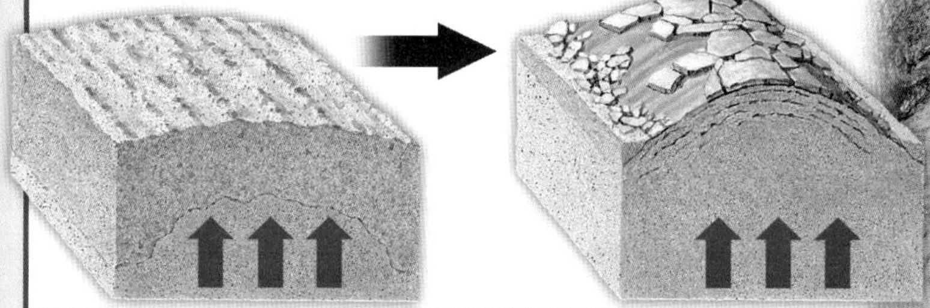

### ③ Plant Root Growth

When plants grow in cracks in a rock, their roots can widen the cracks and force the rock apart.

### ④ Abrasion

Flowing water can move rocks, causing them to rub together and wear down into rounded shapes.

**READING VISUALS** What evidence of mechanical weathering can you see in each photograph above?

## Chemical weathering changes the mineral composition of rocks.

If you have seen a rusty nail, you have seen the result of a chemical reaction. A chemical reaction causes a chemical change. The steel in the nail contains iron. Oxygen in air and water react with the iron to form rust.

Minerals in rocks also undergo chemical changes when they react with water and air. **Chemical weathering** is the breakdown of rocks by chemical reactions that change the rocks' composition. When minerals in rocks come into contact with air and water, some dissolve. Others react and are changed into different minerals.

### Dissolving

Water is the main cause of chemical weathering. Some minerals completely dissolve in ordinary water. Many more minerals dissolve in water that is slightly acidic. In the atmosphere, small amounts of carbon dioxide dissolve in rainwater. The water and carbon dioxide react to form a weak acid. After falling to Earth, the rainwater moves through the soil, picking up more carbon dioxide. The slightly acidic water breaks down minerals in rocks. In the process, the rocks may also break apart into smaller pieces.

The rocks in Oak Creek Canyon are reddish because iron in the rocks reacted with water and air to produce iron oxides.

Air pollution can make rainwater more acidic than it is naturally. Power plants and automobiles produce gases such as sulfur dioxide and nitric oxide. These gases react with water vapor in the atmosphere to form acid rain. Acid rain causes rocks to weather much faster than they would otherwise.

### Rusting

The oxygen in the air is also involved in chemical weathering. Many common minerals contain iron. When these minerals dissolve in water, oxygen in the air and the water combines with the iron to produce iron oxides, or rust. The iron oxides form a coating that colors the weathered rocks. Notice the colors in the photograph of Oak Creek Canyon in Arizona.

**CHECK YOUR READING** How is air involved in chemical weathering?

## Weathering occurs at different rates.

Most weathering processes occur over long periods of time. For example, it can take hundreds or thousands of years for a very hard rock to wear down only a few millimeters—a few times the thickness of your fingernail. But the rate of weathering is not the same for all rocks. Factors such as surface area, rock composition, and climate influence the rate of weathering.

**SUPPORTING MAIN IDEAS**
Enter this blue heading in a chart and record supporting information.

**Surface Area** The more of a rock's surface that is exposed to air and water, the faster the rock will break down. A greater surface area allows chemical weathering to affect more of a rock.

1. Over time, mechanical weathering breaks a rock into smaller pieces.

2. As a result, the rock has more surface area exposed to chemical weathering.

**Rock Composition** Different kinds of rock break down at different rates. Granite, for example, breaks down much more slowly than limestone. Both of these rocks are often used for tombstones and statues.

**Climate** Water is needed for chemical weathering to occur, and heat speeds up chemical weathering. As a result, chemical weathering occurs faster in hot, wet regions than it does in cold, dry regions. However, mechanical weathering caused by freezing and thawing occurs more in cold regions than in hot regions.

## 6.3 Review

### KEY CONCEPTS

1. How is weathering related to the geologic cycle? (6.2)
2. What are four causes of mechanical weathering? (6.2)
3. How do water and air help cause chemical weathering? (6.2.a)
4. Describe three factors that affect the rate at which weathering occurs. (6.2)

### CRITICAL THINKING

5. **Infer** How does mechanical weathering affect the rate of chemical weathering?
6. **Predict** Would weathering affect a marble sculpture inside a museum? Explain your answer.

### CHALLENGE

7. **Infer** The word *weather* is most commonly used to refer to the state of the atmosphere at a certain time. Why do you think the same word is used to refer to the breakdown of rocks?

# CHAPTER INVESTIGATION

## Weathering

**OVERVIEW AND PURPOSE** Mechanical and chemical weathering break down rocks. Different types of rocks react in various ways to different weathering processes. In this investigation you will

- observe conditions that allow rusting, a form of chemical weathering, to occur
- design a procedure to model the effects of mechanical and chemical weathering on different types of rocks

**DESIGN — YOUR OWN — EXPERIMENT**

### MATERIALS

**for Part One:**
- steel wool
- 3 cups
- water
- graduated cylinder

**for Part Two:**
- rock samples
- dilute acids (such as vinegar, cola, lemon juice)
- plastic container and lid
- duct tape
- clear plastic sealable bag
- balance
- graduated cylinder
- water

6.2, 6.7.b, 6.7.c, 6.7.d

### Procedure

**PART ONE**

1. Make a data table like the one shown in the Science Notebook on page 205.
2. Fill a cup almost to the top with water. Place a piece of steel wool in the cup.
3. Put a small amount of water in a second cup. Place a piece of steel wool in the cup.
4. The third cup should have no water. Place a piece of steel wool in the third cup.
5. Allow the three cups to sit overnight. Observe the appearance of the steel wool in each container the next day.

**Content Standard**
6.2 Topography is reshaped by the weathering of rock and soil and by the transportation and deposition of sediment.

**Investigation Standard**
6.7.b Select and use appropriate tools and technology (including calculators, computers, balances, spring scales, microscopes, and binoculars) to perform tests, collect data, and display data.

## PART TWO

1. Design a procedure to model the effects of different weathering processes on several rock samples. You might use some or all of the materials available. Your procedure should enable you to collect data, determine if the rocks changed, and describe how they changed.
2. Record your procedure in your Science Notebook.
3. Create a data table to organize the data you will collect.
4. Measure and record the mass or volume of each rock sample. Record this information in your notebook.
5. Carry out your procedure. Make both qualitative and quantitative observations. Be aware that acids can irritate the skin and eyes. Be sure to wear your safety goggles when using an acid and when modeling mechanical weathering processes.

## Observe and Analyze

Write It Up

1. **RECORD OBSERVATIONS** Complete your data table for Part One.
2. **COMPARE** What happened to the steel wool in each cup?
3. **IDENTIFY VARIABLES** What was the independent variable—the factor you changed—in Part One? What was the dependent variable—the factor you measured?
4. **RECORD OBSERVATIONS** Make sure your data table for Part Two is completed.

## Conclude

Write It Up

1. **ANALYZE** Judging by the appearance of the pieces of steel wool in Part One, what do you think is necessary for rusting to occur?
2. **APPLY** What can you conclude about the best way to protect metal objects, such as bicycles, from rusting?
3. **IDENTIFY** Which processes in Part Two were models of mechanical weathering? chemical weathering?
4. **IDENTIFY LIMITS** What limitations of materials or methods could have affected your results from modeling different weathering processes?
5. **PREDICT** Based on your observations, predict how weathering processes affect common types of rocks near your home or school. How might these weathering processes affect the local topography?

## INVESTIGATE Further

**CHALLENGE** Tear apart the steel wool that rusted the most and compare the appearances of the inside and outside. Why might the inside and outside look different?

CHEMICAL WEATHERING

Observe and Analyze

Table 1. Formation of Rust

| Cup | Amount of Water | Observations |
|---|---|---|
| 1 | full cup | |
| 2 | approximately 30 mL | |
| 3 | no water | |

KEY CONCEPT

# 6.4 Geologic maps show Earth's surface features.

**CALIFORNIA Content Standards**

**6.7.f** Read a topographic map and a geologic map for evidence provided on the maps and construct and interpret a simple scale map.

**6.6** Sources of energy and materials differ in amounts, distribution, usefulness, and the time required for their formation.

**BEFORE, you learned**

- A topographic map shows the shape of the land
- A map key explains the meanings of map symbols
- Rocks are classified by how they formed

**NOW, you will learn**

- What a geologic map shows about Earth's surface
- How a geologic map shows information about resources
- How a geologic map shows information about hazards

**VOCABULARY**

**geologic map** p. 206

**THINK ABOUT**

### *Why do people make geologic maps?*

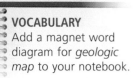

People make many different kinds of maps. City maps include the locations of streets and important landmarks. Topographic maps show the shape of the land. A geologic map shows features of Earth's surface, including rock types. The photograph shows Point Loma, California. What would a geologic map of this area look like? What might the map be used for?

## Geologic maps show information about rocks at and near Earth's surface.

The geologic features of your area make up your landscape. The shape of the land depends in large part on the types of rock at Earth's surface. The types of rock at the surface help determine the types of plants that grow best in an area. Some geologic features, such as faults, can greatly affect people who live nearby. People feel shaking caused by an earthquake when blocks of rock suddenly move past one another along a fault.

**VOCABULARY**
Add a magnet word diagram for *geologic map* to your notebook.

A **geologic map** is a type of map that shows the locations of geologic features at and near Earth's surface. In many areas, plants and soil cover geologic features such as rocks and faults. A geologic map shows what you would see if the plants and soil were removed. It often also includes towns, roads, and topographic contour lines.

## Types and Ages of Rocks

On the right is a geologic map that shows the San Diego area. The map uses colors and symbols to show geologic features. Each color stands for a type of rock of a certain age or age range. For example, the map uses yellow and peach to show sedimentary rocks of different ages. The map's key lists the types of rock shown by each color. A key often includes a short description of the types of rock shown on the map.

The map of the San Diego area uses only color to show different rock types. As you will see later in this section, many geologic maps use special letter codes as well as colors to give information about types of rocks and their ages.

**CHECK YOUR READING** What do different colors show on a geologic map?

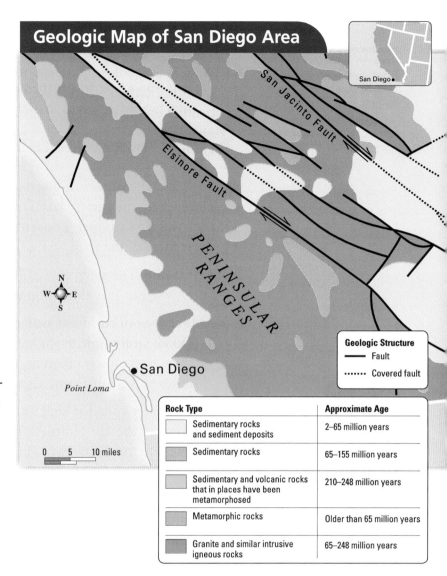

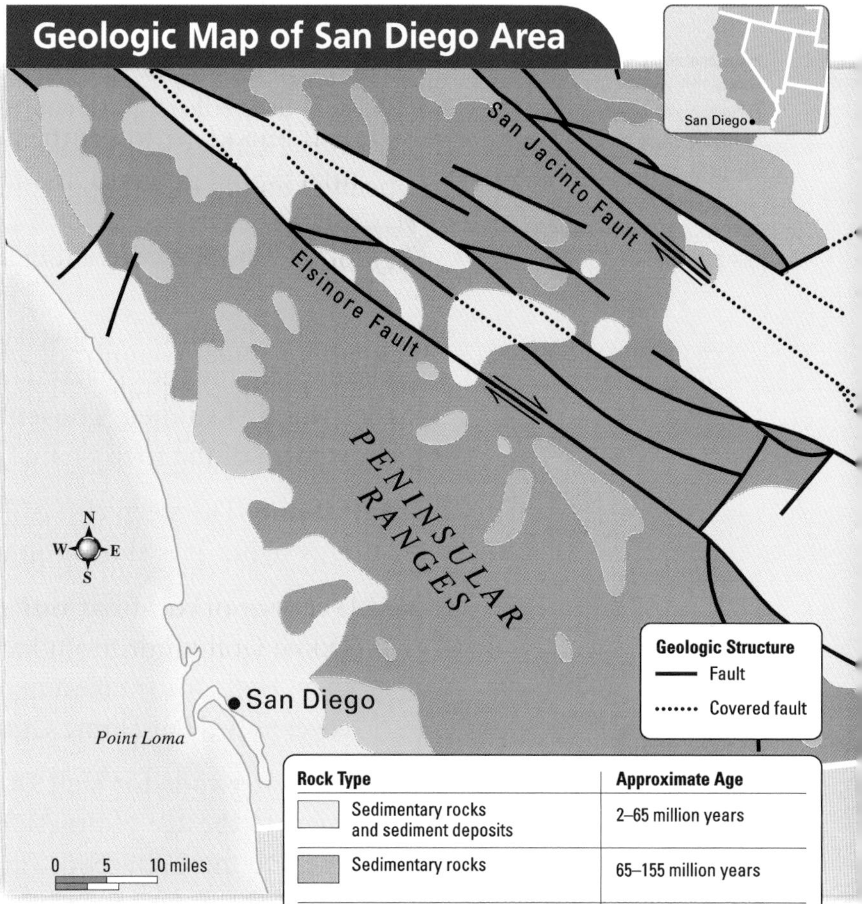


| Rock Type | Approximate Age |
|---|---|
| Sedimentary rocks and sediment deposits | 2–65 million years |
| Sedimentary rocks | 65–155 million years |
| Sedimentary and volcanic rocks that in places have been metamorphosed | 210–248 million years |
| Metamorphic rocks | Older than 65 million years |
| Granite and similar intrusive igneous rocks | 65–248 million years |

## Geologic Structures

The term *geologic structure* refers to features of rocks and the relationships among them. Geologic structures include fracture patterns within a rock layer, the direction and angle at which rock layers are tilted, and faults. Geologic maps use symbols to show these geologic structures.

What symbols are used to show the locations of faults on the map of the San Diego area? Faults are shown by solid lines and by dotted lines. Solid lines show faults that cut through Earth's surface. Dotted lines show faults that are covered by rock layers or sediment layers.

Arrows show the relative direction of movement of rocks on either side of a fault. Find the San Jacinto Fault on the map. The arrows show how rocks on one side of the fault are moving in relation to rocks on the other side of the fault. You will read more about how rocks move along faults in Chapter 9.

## Geologic Map of Yosemite

READING TIP

The geologic time scale is a chart that divides Earth's history into sections. You can see a chart of the geologic time scale on pages R62–R63.

The map on page 209 shows the geology of part of Yosemite National Park. It uses colors, patterns, and letter codes to show the types of rocks at Earth's surface. Like most geologic maps, this map has been printed on top of a topographic map.

CHECK YOUR READING How are different types of rock shown on a geologic map?

Each type of rock is given a name. The name often comes from a place where the rock's characteristics are easiest to see or where the rock was first studied. The letter code for a type of rock includes a short form of the rock's name.

**Half Dome** The steep cliff of Half Dome is one of Yosemite's most famous sights. It is shown on the eastern side of the map.

1. The type of rock that makes up Half Dome is known as Half Dome Granodiorite (GRAN-uh-DY-uh-RYT). As you can see on the map, Half Dome takes up only a very small part of the total area covered by Half Dome Granodiorite.

2. The letter code for Half Dome Granodiorite is Khd. The first letter refers to the age of the rock on the geologic time scale. The "K" refers to the Cretaceous (krih-TAY-shuhs) Period. You may have heard of this period in connection with dinosaurs. At the end of this period, dinosaurs became extinct.

READING TIP

The letter code for the El Capitan Granite is Kec. The first letter refers to the geologic time period in which the rock formed. The next two letters abbreviate the name of the rock.

Cretaceous Half Dome
↓ ↓ ↓
K h d

**Yosemite Valley** The bottom of Yosemite Valley is covered by sediments, which are shown in yellow on the map.

3. The contour lines are far apart at the bottom of the valley. The land there is fairly flat. The contour lines around the valley are close together. The sides of the valley are steep.

4. Most of the sediments in the middle of the valley were deposited by streams. Sediments along the sides of the valley are made up of pieces of rocks that fell from nearby cliffs.

5. Because sediments form at Earth's surface, they lie in a fairly thin layer on top of the rocks underneath. Suppose you could remove the sediments shown in yellow from the eastern side of Yosemite Valley. You would probably find Half Dome Granodiorite lying underneath the sediments.

**El Capitan** The tall cliff of El Capitan is popular with rock climbers. It is shown near the western edge of the map.

6. El Capitan is made up mainly of the rock known as El Capitan Granite. The letter code for this rock type is Kec. This rock type contains granite and granodiorite.

## Yosemite Geologic Map

**A geologic map gives information about the rocks at Earth's surface.**

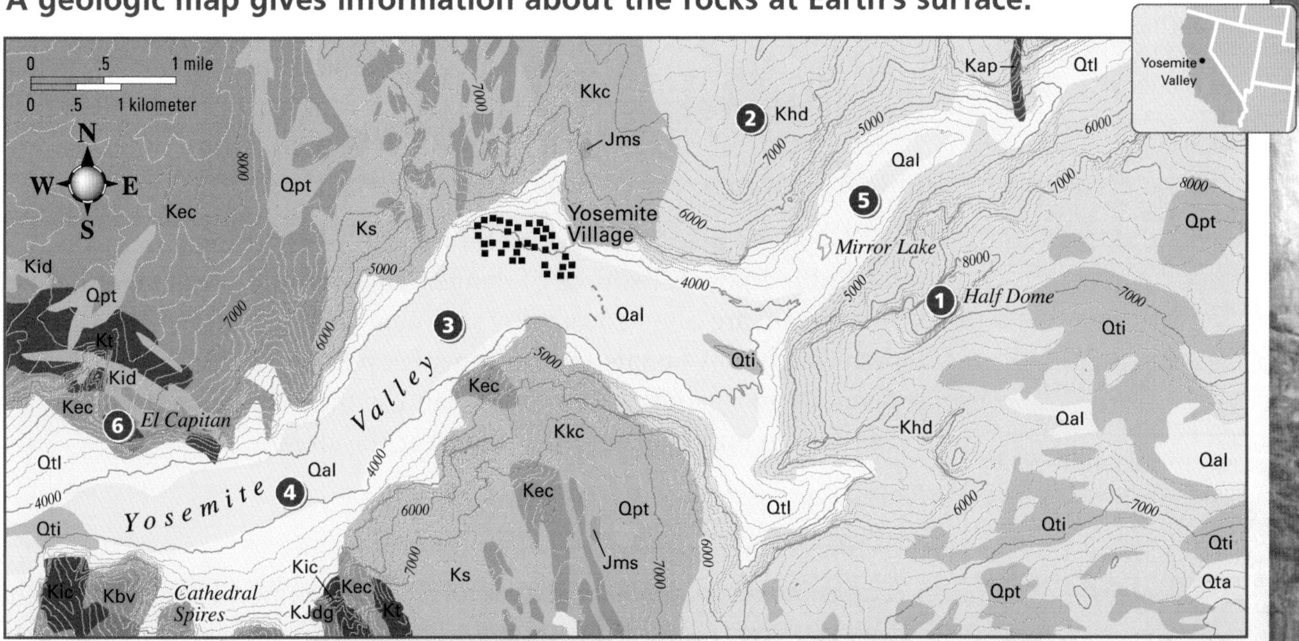

The bottom of **Yosemite Valley** is covered by three types of sediments. The letter code for each type starts with "Q," which stands for the Quaternary Period of geologic time. This period began 1.8 million years ago and extends to the present.

**Half Dome** Granodiorite has the letter code Khd. It formed about 86 to 88 million years ago during the Cretaceous Period.

**El Capitan** Granite, or Kec, is made up of both granite and granodiorite. These rocks formed 102 million years ago during the Cretaceous Period.

## Geologic maps show information about resources and hazards.

**SUPPORTING MAIN IDEAS**
Enter this blue heading in a chart and record supporting information.

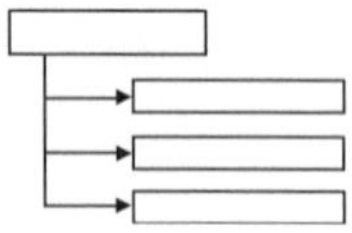

Geologic maps show information about the types and ages of rocks in an area. Therefore, they are useful for locating natural resources such as oil and minerals. Suppose a valuable mineral has been found in a certain type of rock. A geologic map can be used to find other places where that rock is at or near the surface.

Geologic maps are also useful for studying geologic hazards. A hazard is a possible source of danger. For example, areas on either side of a stream are often covered by sediment deposits left by floods. These areas might not be safe for building. People can see the size of these deposits on a geologic map. They can use the map when deciding whether to build houses or a park near the stream.

### Resources

The geologic map below shows some of the mineral resources in the Mojave Desert area of California. This type of map is useful when people want an overview of the geology and resources of a large area. They could also get a more detailed map with information about a location.

### Geologic Map of the Mojave Desert

**This geologic map shows rock types and mineral resources in the Mojave Desert.**

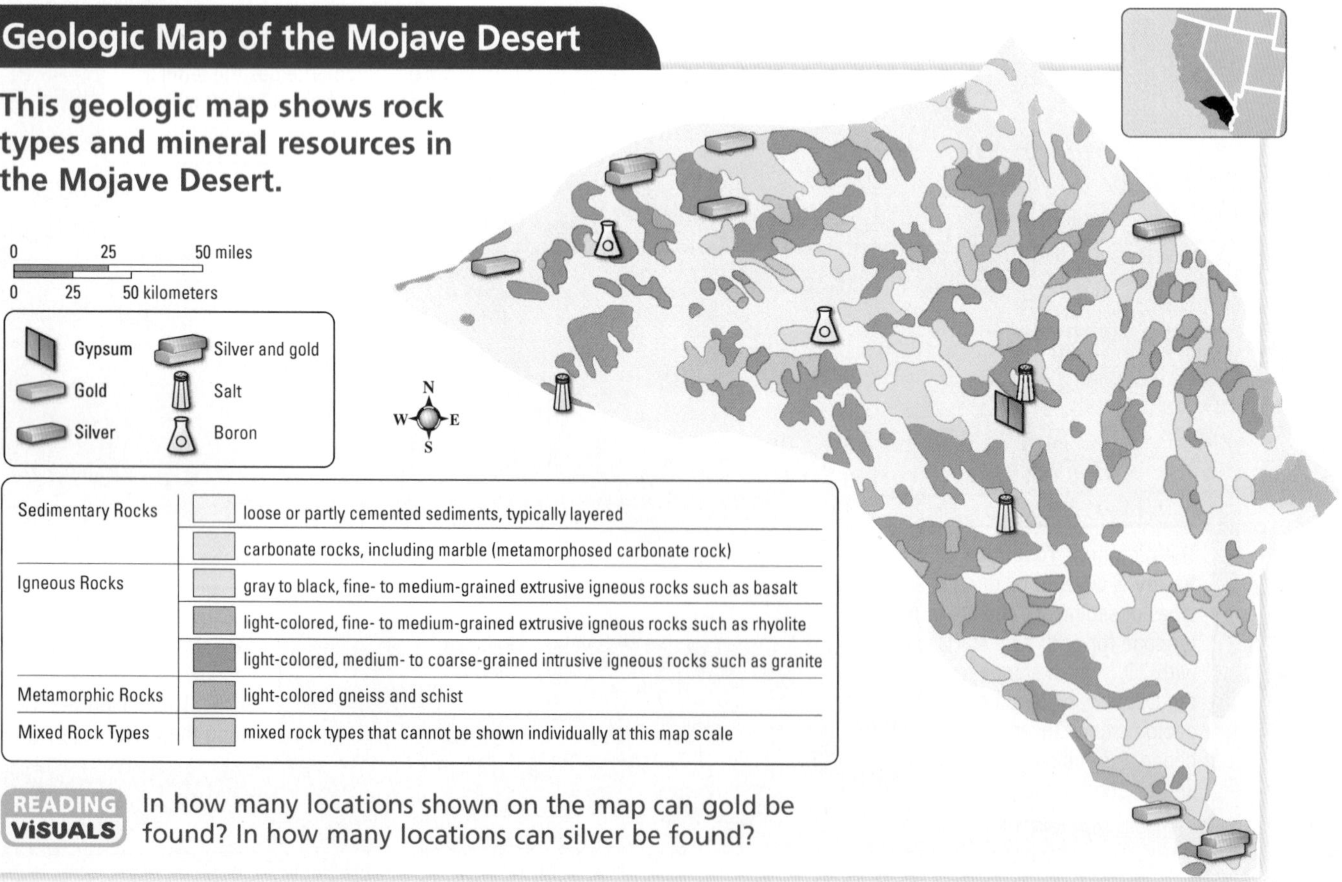


| | | |
|---|---|---|
| Sedimentary Rocks | | loose or partly cemented sediments, typically layered |
| | | carbonate rocks, including marble (metamorphosed carbonate rock) |
| Igneous Rocks | | gray to black, fine- to medium-grained extrusive igneous rocks such as basalt |
| | | light-colored, fine- to medium-grained extrusive igneous rocks such as rhyolite |
| | | light-colored, medium- to coarse-grained intrusive igneous rocks such as granite |
| Metamorphic Rocks | | light-colored gneiss and schist |
| Mixed Rock Types | | mixed rock types that cannot be shown individually at this map scale |

**READING VISUALS** In how many locations shown on the map can gold be found? In how many locations can silver be found?

## Hazards

Geologic maps show many types of hazards. For example, a map of an active volcano would show the locations of lava flows and other hazards related to eruptions. The data shown on the map can tell how powerful the volcano's eruptions tend to be and how often they happen. You will read more about volcanic eruptions and hazards in Chapter 10.

Landslides are another type of hazard shown on a geologic map. Areas where landslides have happened are marked. People can use the maps to get data about the landslides. The maps can show the types of rocks involved, the angle and direction at which the rock layers were tilted, and the slope of the land. People can then use these data to identify areas where new landslides are likely to occur.

**CHECK YOUR READING** Name two types of hazards that might be shown on a geologic map.

## INVESTIGATE Landslide Areas

### *Where are landslides most likely to affect a road?*

**SKILL FOCUS**
Analyzing (6.7.f)

**MATERIALS**
Geologic Map of Highway 101

**TIME**
20 minutes

**PROCEDURE**

1. Look at the geologic map of part of Highway 101. Use the map key to identify the geologic units shown on the map.
2. On the lines provided, write two ways in which the rocks that make up units KJFb and KJFm are similar.
3. On the map, mark the locations where there is a border between different landslide areas. On the line provided, write the number of borders between landslides.
4. Use the map scale to estimate the length of Highway 101 that goes through landslide areas shown on the map. Write your estimate on the line provided.
5. Determine which individual landslide covered the greatest distance. Mark that landslide on the map. On the line provided, write the distance covered by the landslide.

**WHAT DO YOU THINK?**

- Why is it important to show landslide areas on a geologic map?
- Why do some landslide areas share a border? Did the landslides overlap? Explain.

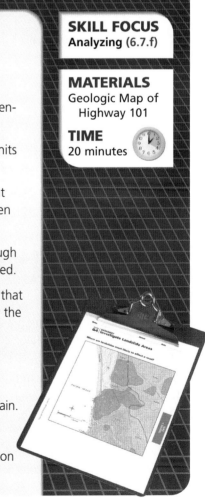

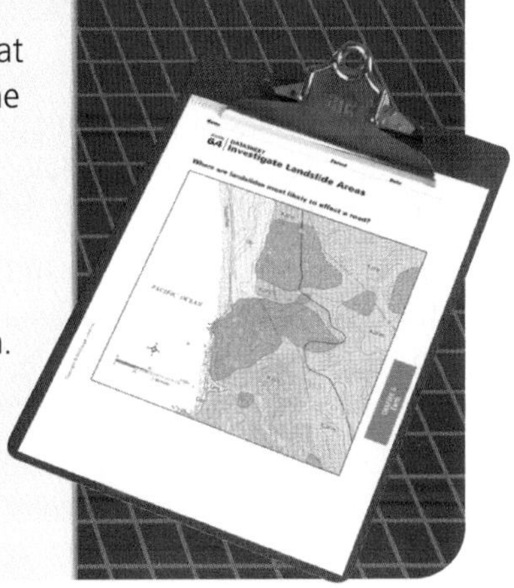

**CHALLENGE** At what elevation did the landslide that covered the greatest distance begin? At what elevation did it stop? How does the change in elevation affect the path of a landslide?

## Earthquake Hazard Map

**This geologic map of an area of central California shows soil types and how they are likely to react during an earthquake.**

| Surface Rock or Soil Type | Predicted Reaction During an Earthquake |
|---|---|
| volcanic rock, sedimentary rock, and sands | may cause an increase in shaking |
| soils, including muds, sands, gravels, and silts | moderate increase in shaking |
| soils, including water-saturated mud and artificial landfill | greatest increase in shaking |

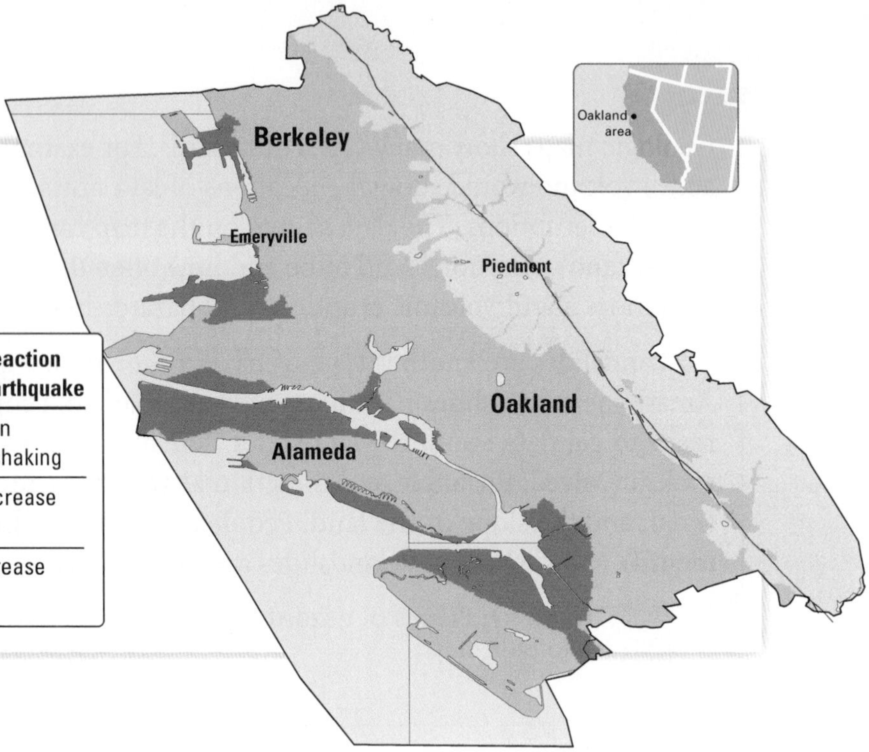


Some geologic maps focus on a specific type of hazard. The map above shows the amount of shaking that is likely to take place during an earthquake. This map gives information about soils rather than just about rock. Some types of soil can cause the ground to shake more during an earthquake.

People can use this type of map to get an idea of the shaking hazard for an area. For detailed information about the hazard at a certain place, people study soil samples. They also check factors not shown on the map, such as soil depth. You will read more about earthquake hazards, as well as how people build structures to resist earthquake damage, in Chapter 9.

## 6.4 Review

### KEY CONCEPTS

1. What sorts of information are usually shown on a geologic map? (6.7.f)
2. How can a geologic map be used to find natural resources? (6.6)
3. How can a geologic map be used to analyze potential hazards such as landslides or floods? (6.7.f)

### CRITICAL THINKING

4. **Analyze** Why do geologic maps usually show features such as towns or topographic contour lines?
5. **Infer** Describe three ways in which letter codes on geologic maps are useful.

### CHALLENGE

6. **Evaluate** What is a geologic hazard in your area? How might it be shown on a map?

# California Close-Up



# Gold Fever!

6.6.c Students know the natural origin of the materials used to make common objects.

It is 1848. A man races through the town, waving a small container of gold. Gold has been discovered near Sutter's Mill. The California gold rush is on!

At that time, gold could be used as money. Soon, gold seekers from the East traveled across the mountains to California or sailed there around the southern tip of South America. In the foothills of the Sierra Nevada, prospectors claimed mines and got to work.

This gold nugget is still partly attached to the rock in which it formed.

Until 1847 San Francisco was called Yerba Buena. About 460 people lived there. Two years later, about 79,000 people lived in the city. The successful prospectors used their gold to buy homes and businesses.

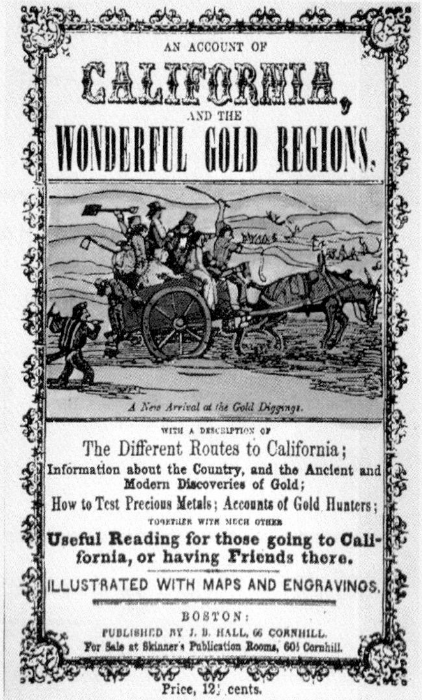

AN ACCOUNT OF

CALIFORNIA,

AND THE

WONDERFUL GOLD REGIONS,

*A New Arrival at the Gold Diggings.*

WITH A DESCRIPTION OF

The Different Routes to California;

Information about the Country, and the Ancient and Modern Discoveries of Gold;

How to Test Precious Metals; Accounts of Gold Hunters;

TOGETHER WITH MUCH OTHER

Useful Reading for those going to California, or having Friends there.

ILLUSTRATED WITH MAPS AND ENGRAVINGS.

BOSTON:

PUBLISHED BY J. B. HALL, 66 CORNHILL.

For Sale at Skinner's Publication Rooms, 60½ Cornhill.

Price, 12½ cents.

The mining region was called the Mother Lode. A lode is a deposit of a valuable mineral within a body of rock. Movement along earthquake faults in the area caused rocks to crack. Over time, gold that was dissolved in water settled into the cracks. These cracks became veins of gold. Some veins were 5 feet wide. One was 40 feet long! The gold formed as lumpy nuggets. Most nuggets were small, but a few were as big as a fist.

The Castle Mountain open-pit gold mine is located in the Mojave Desert near Ivanpah, California.

Much of the gold in the Mother Lode region weathered out of the rock in which it formed. Eventually it was washed into streams and rivers, where it built up in sedimentary deposits. Such deposits in the Mother Lode region are associated with many streams and rivers, include the Feather, American, and Yuba rivers.

Gold is still mined in California today. Gold is commonly used in jewelry, and it also has many other uses that people might not know about. For example, small amounts of gold are used in many common electronic products, including computers, telephones, and cellular phones.

## WRITING ABOUT SCIENCE

Gold is used in electronics, lasers, communications satellites, and medicine. Research one of the uses of gold. Write a description of how and why gold is used in that way.

# 6 Chapter Review

## the BIG idea

**Minerals and rocks are basic building blocks of Earth.**

CONTENT REVIEW
CLASSZONE.COM

## KEY CONCEPTS SUMMARY

### 1 Minerals are all around us.

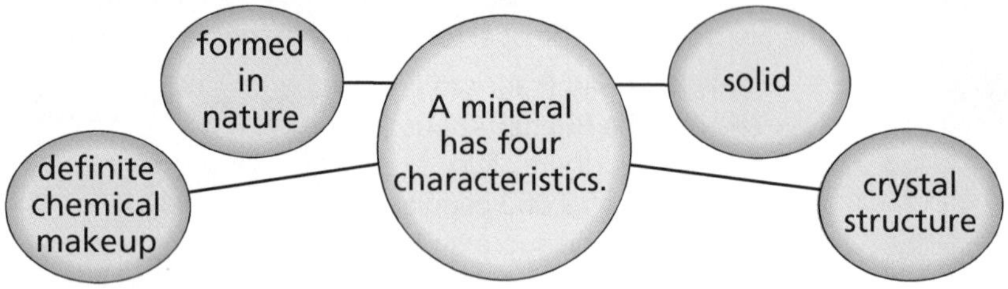


**VOCABULARY**
**mineral** p. 184
**element** p. 184
**crystal** p. 185
**rock** p. 187

### 2 Rocks form in different ways.

There are three types of rocks.

Igneous rocks form from molten rock.

Sedimentary rocks form from earlier rocks.

Metamorphic rocks form as existing rocks change.

**VOCABULARY**
**igneous rock** p. 191
**magma** p. 191
**lava** p. 191
**sedimentary rock** p. 192
**metamorphic rock** p. 194
**rock cycle** p. 196

### 3 Natural processes break down rocks.

Over time, **mechanical weathering** breaks a rock into smaller pieces.

**Chemical weathering** affects exposed rock surfaces.

**VOCABULARY**
**geologic cycle** p. 199
**weathering** p. 199
**mechanical weathering** p. 200
**chemical weathering** p. 202

### 4 Geologic maps show Earth's surface features.

Geologic maps show
- types and ages of rocks
- geologic structures
- resources and hazards

**VOCABULARY**
**geologic map** p. 206

## Reviewing Vocabulary

On a separate sheet of paper, write a sentence or two describing the relationship between the two terms.

1. mineral, crystal
2. magma, lava
3. intrusive, extrusive
4. igneous rock, metamorphic rock
5. geologic cycle, weathering
6. mechanical weathering, chemical weathering
7. geologic map, topographic map

## Reviewing Key Concepts

**Multiple Choice** *Choose the letter of the best answer.*

8. A crystal structure is characteristic of (6.6)
   **a.** an element
   **b.** a rock
   **c.** magma
   **d.** a mineral

9. How is it possible for two different minerals to have the same chemical composition? (6.6)
   **a.** They have different crystal structures.
   **b.** One is formed only by organisms.
   **c.** Only one is a rock-forming mineral.
   **d.** They have different appearances.

10. The rock cycle shows how rocks continually (6.1.b)
   **a.** increase in size
   **b.** increase in number
   **c.** become more complex
   **d.** change over time

11. Which kind of rock forms by recrystallization? (6.1.b)
   **a.** intrusive igneous
   **b.** extrusive igneous
   **c.** sedimentary
   **d.** metamorphic

12. Rock salt is an example of a sedimentary rock that develops from dissolved minerals as (6.1.b)
   **a.** water evaporates
   **b.** magma cools
   **c.** sediments break down
   **d.** sand settles in water

13. The force of expanding water in the cracks and pores of a rock is an example of (6.2.a)
   **a.** chemical weathering
   **b.** mechanical weathering
   **c.** oxidation
   **d.** crystallization

14. The breakdown of rock by acidic water is an example of (6.2.a)
   **a.** chemical weathering
   **b.** mechanical weathering
   **c.** oxidation
   **d.** crystallization

15. Three factors that affect the rate of weathering are (6.2.a)
   **a.** microorganisms, plants, and animals
   **b.** weather, landforms, and rainfall
   **c.** surface area, rock composition, and climate
   **d.** texture, color, and pore space

16. The term *geologic structure* refers to (6.1.b)
   **a.** types and ages of rocks
   **b.** characteristics of minerals
   **c.** patterns of weathering in rocks
   **d.** features of rocks and relationships among rocks

**Short Answer** *Write a short answer for each question.*

17. Why aren't all solids minerals? Include the term *crystal structure* in your answer. (6.6)

18. What is the difference between a rock and a mineral? (6.1.b)

19. Compare the distribution of rock types at Earth's surface with their distribution in the entire crust. How are any differences related to processes that take place in the rock cycle? (6.1.b)

## Thinking Critically

*Use the map and key to answer the next seven questions.* (6.7.f)

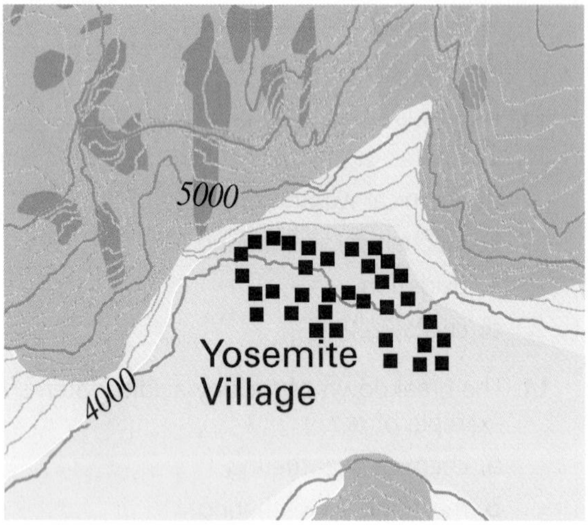


| Sediment or Rock Type | Approximate Age |
|---|---|
| Sediment deposits mainly left by streams | 0–2 million years |
| Sediment deposits made up of rocks fallen from cliffs | 0–10,000 years |
| Igneous rock: granodiorite | 88 million years |
| Igneous rock: granodiorite | 93 million years |
| Igneous rock: granite and granodiorite | 102 million years |
| Metamorphic rock formed from sedimentary rock | 144–206 million years |

20. **APPLY** Which two types of maps have been combined to make this map? (6.7.f)

21. **APPLY** From what type of rock did the metamorphic rock form?

22. **INTERPRET** All of the igneous rocks have large mineral crystals. Did they form from magma or from lava? Explain.

23. **CALCULATE** What is the difference in age between the youngest and oldest types of igneous rock?

24. **SYNTHESIZE** Why are sediments likely to be found at the lowest elevations? (6.2.a)

25. **DRAW CONCLUSIONS** The age of the sediment deposits left by streams is given as a range. What is a likely reason why it is not given as a single age? (6.2.b)

26. **SYNTHESIZE** How might weathering processes help form the sediment deposits made up of rocks fallen from cliffs? (6.2.a)

27. **HYPOTHESIZE** Thick layers of halite are mined near Detroit, Michigan. At one time, seawater covered the area. Write a hypothesis that explains how the halite formed there. (6.7.a)

28. **COMPARE AND CONTRAST** How does mechanical weathering differ from chemical weathering? How are the two processes similar? (6.2.a)

29. **SYNTHESIZE** A cycle is a series of events or actions that repeats regularly. Describe a cycle that involves living things. (6.2.a)

## the BIG idea

30. **ANALYZE** Minerals are basic components of planets such as Earth and Mars. Other planets in our solar system, such as Jupiter and Saturn, are called gas giants because they are made up mainly of the gases hydrogen and helium. They do not have solid surfaces. Do you think that minerals are basic components of gas giants? Why or why not? (6.6)

31. **INFER** Minerals make up much of Earth. People use minerals as sources of many materials, such as metals. Some metals are used to make machine parts or build houses. How would your life be different if minerals that contain metals were rare in Earth's crust? (6.6.c)

32. **SYNTHESIZE** Use your knowledge of the rock cycle and weathering to explain why loose pieces of gold might be found in a river.

## UNIT PROJECTS

If you need to do an experiment for your unit project, gather the materials. Be sure to allow enough time to observe results before the project is due.

## Analyzing a Diagram

6.1.b

*This diagram shows a simple version of the rock cycle. Use it to answer the questions.*

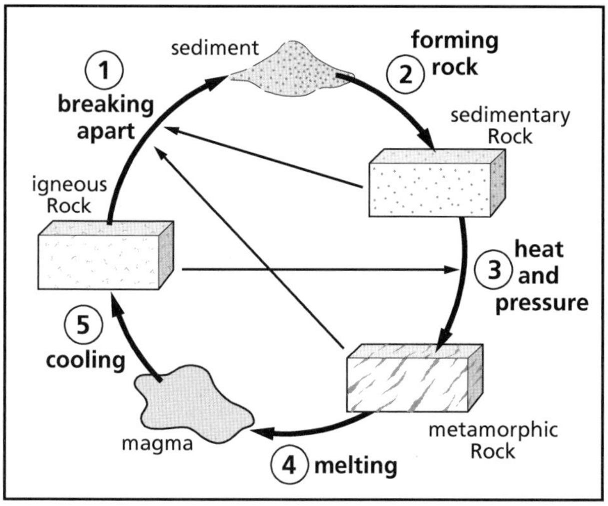


1. Where are loose materials developing into rock?
   - **a.** 1
   - **b.** 2
   - **c.** 4
   - **d.** 5

2. Where are sand and other small particles forming from rock?
   - **a.** 1
   - **b.** 2
   - **c.** 4
   - **d.** 5

3. Where is magma developing into rock?
   - **a.** 1
   - **b.** 3
   - **c.** 4
   - **d.** 5

4. Where is molten rock forming?
   - **a.** 1
   - **b.** 3
   - **c.** 4
   - **d.** 5

5. Where are heat and pressure changing solid rock into another type of rock without melting it?
   - **a.** 1
   - **b.** 3
   - **c.** 4
   - **d.** 5

6. According to the diagram, what can happen to sedimentary rock?
   - **a.** It can become sediment or magma.
   - **b.** It can become igneous rock or magma.
   - **c.** It can become sediment or metamorphic rock.
   - **d.** It can become sediment, metamorphic rock, or magma.

7. How could you change the diagram to show that igneous rock can become magma again?
   - **a.** Add an arrow from igneous rock to metamorphic rock.
   - **b.** Add an arrow from heat and pressure to igneous rock.
   - **c.** Add an arrow from igneous rock to melting.
   - **d.** Add an arrow from melting to igneous rock.

8. What must happen to rock that formed inside Earth before it can become sediment?
   - **a.** It must reach the surface as rock above it wears away.
   - **b.** It must become magma and erupt from a volcano.
   - **c.** Heat and pressure must change it into sediment.
   - **d.** It must become sedimentary rock while inside Earth.

## Extended Response

*Answer the two questions below in detail.*

9. In the water cycle, different forms of water cycle between Earth's surface and the atmosphere. For example, liquid water from oceans and lakes changes into gas and enters the atmosphere. How is this cycle similar to the rock cycle? How is it different?

10. Melba is trying to decide whether an igneous rock formed deep inside Earth or at the surface. What should she look for? Why?

# TIMELINES in Science

6.1.a, 6.1.e

## THE STORY OF FOSSILS

Fossils are an important source of information about the history of life on Earth. The first observer to suggest that fossils provided clues to the past was Xenophanes. He lived in Greece around 500 B.C. Today, knowledge about fossils helps people find deposits of oil and understand changes in weather patterns. Above all, fossils reveal information about plants and animals that lived in the past.

The timeline shows a few events in the history of the study of fossils. Tools that were invented for other purposes, such as radar and CT scanners, have helped scientists learn more about fossils. The boxes below the timeline highlight the role of technology, along with applications of knowledge about fossils.

**1669**

***Scientist Notes Importance of Rock Layers***

Danish-born scientist Nicolaus Steno recognizes that sediments form new layers of rock on top of old layers. Therefore, digging down provides a way to move back in time. Scientists plan to build on Steno's discovery to determine the ages of fossils found in rock layers.

EVENTS

1640 1660 1680 1700

APPLICATIONS AND TECHNOLOGY

This sandstone formation in Utah displays layers of sediment that were laid down one on top of another.

### 1799
#### *Siberian Discovers Frozen Mammoth*

While hunting for ivory tusks in Siberia, a man discovers a 37,000-year-old mammoth frozen in ice. Unfortunately, before scientists can study the five-ton animal, it thaws and wild animals eat most of it. However, the skeleton and bits of hair still provide clues to Earth's past.

### 1785
#### *New Theory Suggests Naturalness of Change*

James Hutton of Scotland revolutionizes geology with his theory of uniformitarianism. He argues that volcanoes, erosion, and other forces shaped Earth's landscape slowly over a very long period and continue to do so. Hutton's ideas challenge the belief that the landscape is the result of sudden changes and one-time events. His theory leads to a better understanding of the vast ages of Earth and fossils.

### 1824
#### *Geologist Identifies Bones from Extinct Animal*

English geologist William Buckland concludes that a fossilized jawbone comes from an enormous reptilelike animal that is extinct. He names the animal *Megalosaurus.* This is the first dinosaur to be given a scientific name.

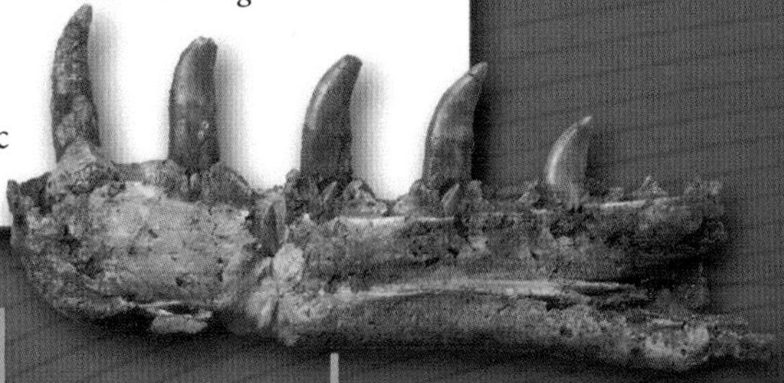

1720 1740 1760 1780 1800 1820 1840

## APPLICATION
### Mapping Earth's Layers

In the late 1700s, the geologist William Smith helped survey land for canals throughout England and Wales. As workers dug deeper into the ground, Smith noticed that fossils always appeared in the same order. He used this information to create the first map showing the locations of rock layers under surface soil. It was published in 1815. As people began to understand the importance of rock layers, they collected more information from projects that required digging. Maps showing this type of information became more detailed and more useful. Today, geologists combine information collected in the field with data from satellite images to create precise maps of rock layers.

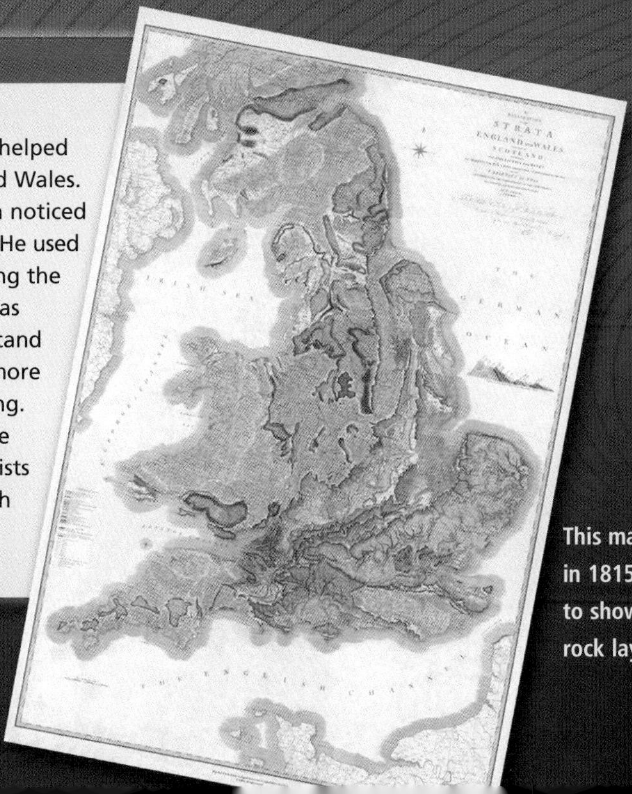

**This map, hand-painted in 1815, was the first to show locations of rock layers.**

## 1861

### *Workers Uncover Bird Fossil*

Laborers digging up limestone rock in southern Germany find a fossil that looks like a lizard with wings. The fossil is about 150 million years old—the oldest known one of a bird.

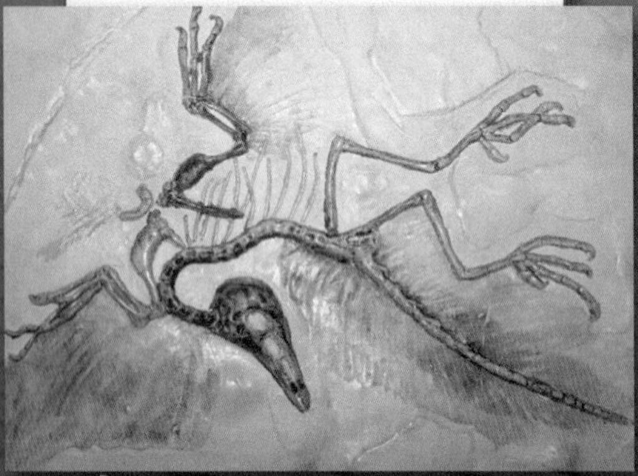

## 1922

### *Fossils Support Hypothesis About Continents*

German scientist Alfred Wegener presents more evidence supporting his hypothesis of continental drift. He points to fossils that are found on continents in the Southern Hemisphere that seem to fit together. This pattern supports the idea that the continents were once a single landmass.

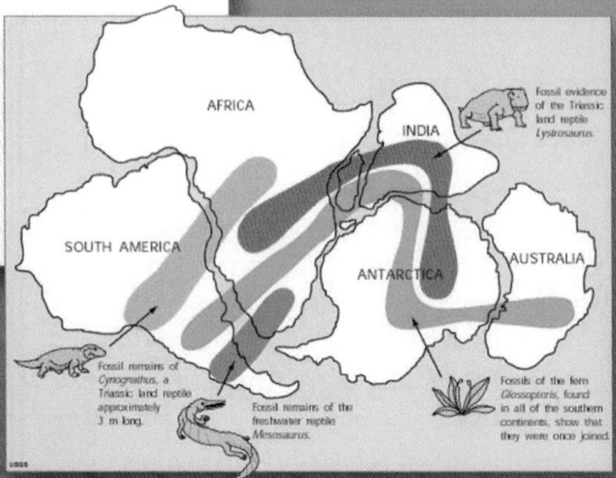


## 1965

### *Microfossils Cause Sensation*

Two new scientific papers focus attention on Earth's earliest life forms. In these papers scientists describe rocks from Canada that contain microfossils of algae and fungi—traces of life vastly older than any others yet found. These findings trigger huge new efforts in scientific research on ancient life.

1860 1880 1900 1920 1940 1960 1980

## TECHNOLOGY

### Chemist Creates New Time Scale

In the 1890s, scientists studying radiation began to understand the idea of half-life. The chemist B. B. Boltwood used half-life data to identify the ages of various rocks and create a new geologic time scale. The ages he calculated were in the hundreds of millions or even billions of years—far greater than the ages many scientists had been using. The time scale continues to be modified as new technologies allow for ever more precise measurements.

The half-life of carbon 14 will be used to calculate the ages of the samples this researcher is preparing.

**2000**

***Dinosaur Heart Surprises Many***

North Carolina scientists use a medical device called a CT scanner to identify the first known fossilized dinosaur heart. The heart surprises those who thought all dinosaurs were cold-blooded. Its structure suggests that the dinosaur was warm-blooded.

**2001**

***Researchers Find Earliest Mammal***

Scientists in China find the oldest known mammal fossil. The 195-million-year-old skull is from an animal that weighed just 2 grams—less than the weight of a penny.

**RESOURCE CENTER**
CLASSZONE.COM
Learn more about fossils.

**2000**

## TECHNOLOGY

### CT Scans Show That *T. Rex* Could Smell

Computerized tomography (CT) scans are commonly used in medicine to search inside human bodies without surgery. A CT scan of the skull of a *Tyrannosaurus rex* known as Sue showed that it had a large area in its brain for smelling. Its sharp sense of smell, combined with its size and strength, made the tyrannosaur an effective hunter and scavenger.

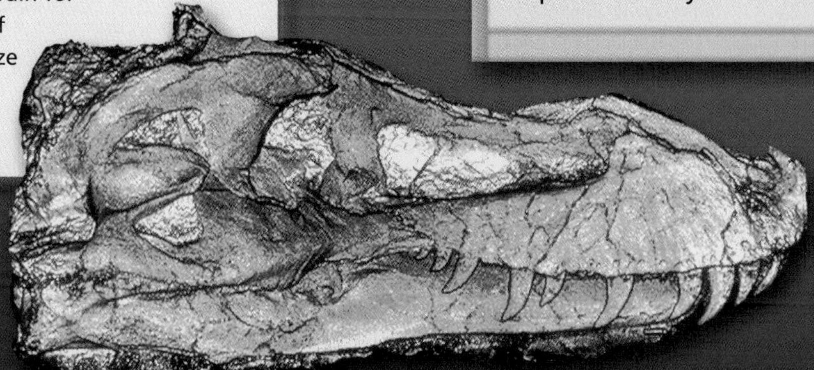

This skull is part of Sue's skeleton—the largest and most complete *T. rex* yet found.

## SPOTLIGHT on PAUL SERENO

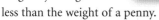

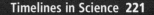

Paleontologist Paul Sereno has discovered new dinosaur species on five continents. In 2000 he also found the fossilized remains of "Super-Croc," a 12-meter-long (40 ft) dinosaur-eating crocodile.

Looking for dinosaur fossils can be physically and mentally demanding. Teams work long hours in temperatures as high as 52°C (125°F), digging carefully in the ground with chisels and picks. Despite the harsh conditions, Sereno says, "In paleontology, I saw an irresistible combination of travel, adventure, art, biology, and geology."

One of Sereno's goals is to understand the role of continental drift in dinosaur evolution. Based on his fossil finds, Sereno thinks there may have been a land bridge linking Europe and Africa for several million years after the continents drifted apart.

## ACTIVITIES

### Reliving History

Get permission to dig a hole outside. Dig down two feet or more. Draw a sketch showing the layers of soil. Add notes to describe any variations that are not clear in the sketch. Try to explain the differences you notice in the layers.

### Writing About Science

Suppose you are an archaeologist who has made one of the fossil discoveries on the timeline. Write a speech to your fellow scientists explaining the importance of your discovery.

CHAPTER 7

# Erosion and Deposition

## the BIG idea

**Water, wind, and ice shape Earth's surface.**

## Key Concepts

SECTION 1
**Processes wear down and build up Earth's surface.**
Learn how natural forces shape and change the land.

SECTION 2
**Moving water shapes land.**
Learn about the effects of water moving over land and underground.

SECTION 3
**Waves and wind shape land.**
Discover how waves and wind affect land.

SECTION 4
**Glaciers carve land and move sediments.**
Learn about the effect of ice moving over land.

**California ClassZone**

CLASSZONE.COM
Chapter 7 online resources: Content Review, one Visualization, three Resource Centers, Math Tutorial, Test Practice

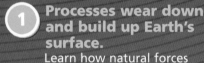

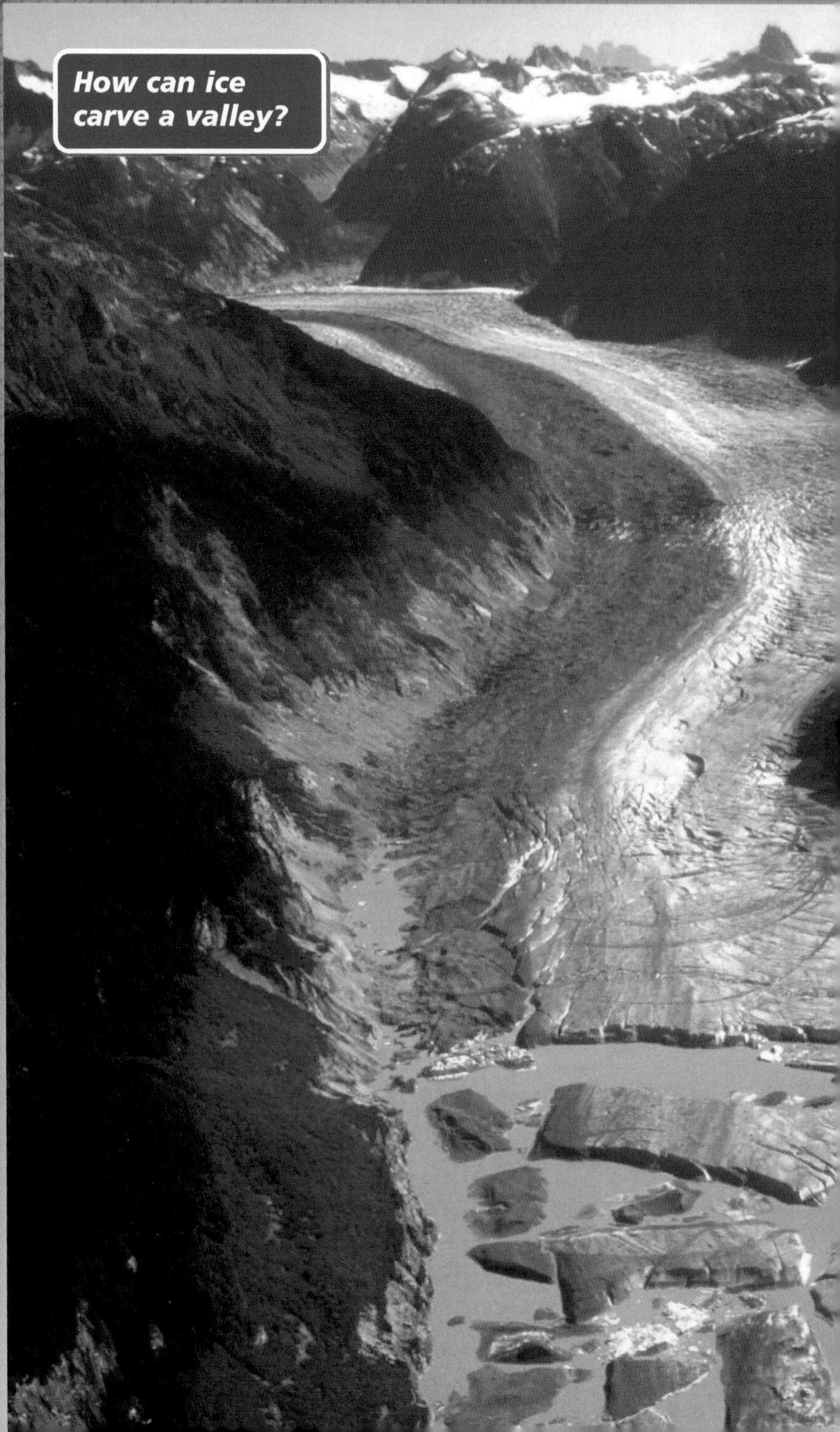

*How can ice carve a valley?*

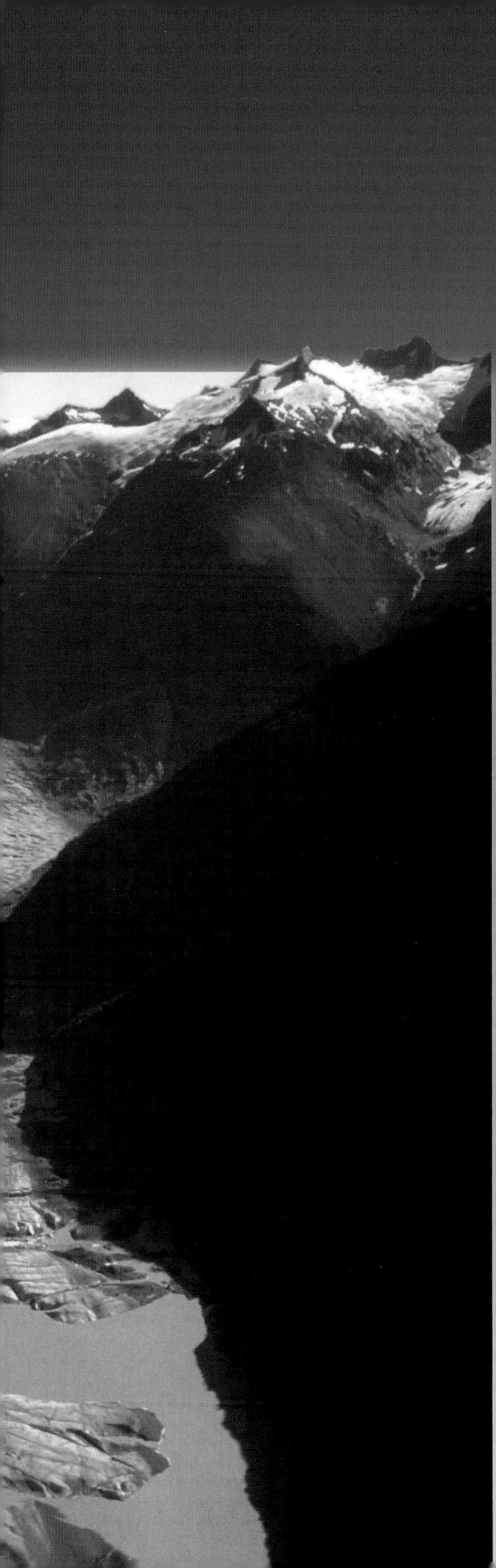

# EXPLORE the BIG idea

## Where Has Water Been?

6.2.a Students know water running downhill is the dominant process in shaping the landscape, including California's landscape.

Think about what water does when it falls and flows on the ground. Go outside your school or home and look at the ground and pavement carefully. Look in dry places for evidence of where water has been.

**Observe and Think** What evidence did you find? How does it show that water was in a place that is now dry?

## How Do Waves Shape Land?

6.2.c Students know beaches are dynamic systems in which the sand is supplied by rivers and moved along the coast by the action of waves.

Pile a mixture of sand and gravel on one side of a pie tin to make a "beach." Slowly add water away from the beach until the tin is about one-third full. Use your hand to make waves in the tin and observe what happens.

**Observe and Think**
What happened to the beach? How did the waves affect the sand and gravel?

NSTA scilinks.org SCILINKS
Wind Erosion **Code: MDL017**

CHAPTER 7

# Getting Ready to Learn

## CONCEPT REVIEW

- Energy can be transferred by the movement of matter.
- Weathering breaks down rocks.
- Water and ice are agents of weathering.

## VOCABULARY REVIEW

**weathering** p. 199

*See Glossary for definitions.*

**gravity, sediment, soil**

**CONTENT REVIEW**
CLASSZONE.COM

Review concepts and vocabulary.

## TAKING NOTES

### CHOOSE YOUR OWN STRATEGY

Take notes using one or more of the strategies from earlier chapters, such as **main idea and detail notes, supporting main ideas,** or **main idea web.** Feel free to mix and match the strategies, or use an entirely different note-taking strategy.

### VOCABULARY STRATEGY

Write each new vocabulary term in the center of a **four square** diagram. Write notes in the squares around each term. Include a definition, some characteristics, and some examples of the term. If possible, write some things that are not examples of the term.

See the Note-Taking Handbook on pages R45–R51.

SCIENCE NOTEBOOK

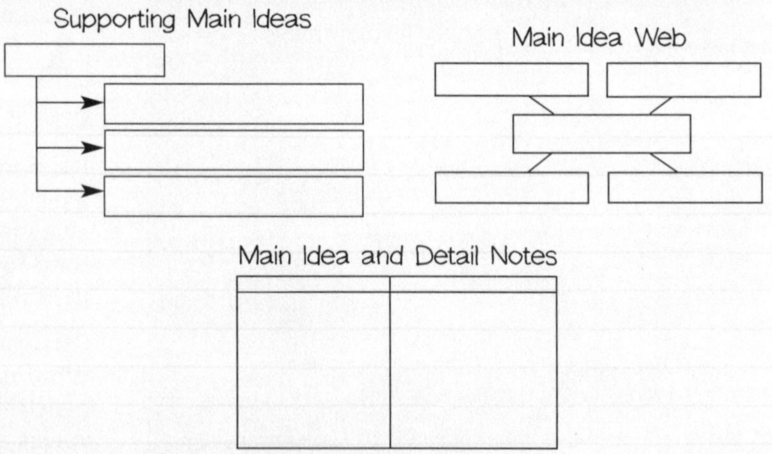


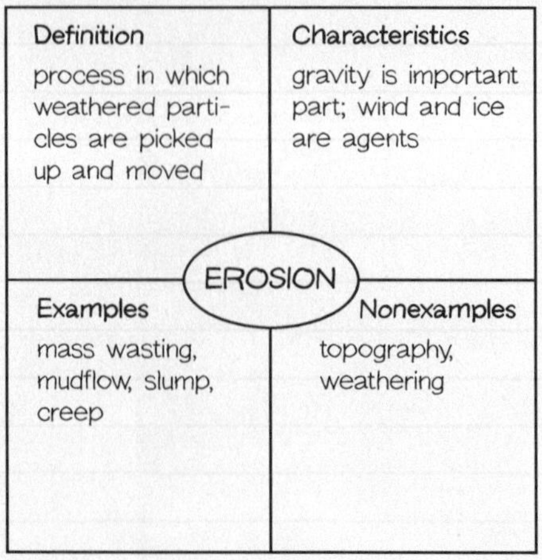

Definition
process in which weathered particles are picked up and moved
Characteristics
gravity is important part; wind and ice are agents
EROSION
Examples
mass wasting, mudflow, slump, creep
Nonexamples
topography, weathering

KEY CONCEPT

# 7.1 Processes wear down and build up Earth's surface.

**CALIFORNIA Content Standards**

**6.2.a** Students know water running downhill is the dominant process in shaping the landscape, including California's landscape.

**6.2.d** Students know earthquakes, volcanic eruptions, landslides, and floods change human and wildlife habitats.

**BEFORE, you learned**

- Weathering breaks rocks apart
- Water can move sediment from one place to another

**NOW, you will learn**

- How erosion moves and deposits rock and soil
- How gravity causes movement of large amounts of rock and soil

**VOCABULARY**

**erosion** p. 225
**deposition** p. 225
**mass wasting** p. 227

**THINK ABOUT**

***How did natural forces shape this landform?***

This valley in Iceland was formed by the action of water. How long might it have taken to form? Where did the material that once filled the valley go?

## Natural forces move and deposit sediments.

The valley in the photograph was formed by the movement of water. The water flowed over the land and carried away weathered rock and soil. This shaped a valley where the water flows. In this section you will learn about the processes that shape landscapes.

The process in which weathered particles are picked up and moved from one place to another is called **erosion** (ih-ROH-zhuhn). Erosion has a constant impact on Earth's surface. Over millions of years, it wears down mountains by removing byproducts of weathering and depositing them elsewhere. The part of the erosion process in which sediment is placed in a new location, or deposited, is called **deposition** (DEHP-uh-ZIHSH-uhn).

VOCABULARY
Use four square diagrams to take notes about the terms *erosion* and *deposition.*

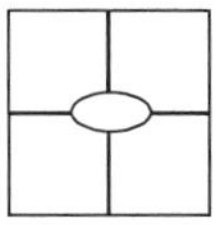

The force of gravity is an important part of erosion and deposition. Gravity causes water to move downward, carrying and depositing sediment as it flows. Gravity can pull huge masses of ice slowly down mountain valleys. And gravity causes dust carried by the wind to fall to Earth.

Erosion of weathered rock by the movement of water, wind, and ice occurs in three major ways:

- **Water** Rainwater and water from melting snow flow down sloping land, carrying rock and soil particles. The water makes its way to a river, which then carries the sediment along. The sediment gets deposited on the river's bottom, banks, or floodplain, or near its mouth. Waves in oceans and lakes also carry sediment and deposit it to form beaches and other features.
- **Wind** Strong winds lift tiny particles of dust and carry them long distances. When the wind dies down, the particles drop to the ground. Wind can also push larger particles of sand along the ground.
- **Ice** As ice moves slowly downhill, it transports rock and soil particles that are contained in it.

**READING TIP**

A floodplain is a flat area of land on either side of a stream that becomes flooded when a river overflows its banks. You will learn more about river and stream features in Section 7.2.

**CHECK YOUR READING** What are the three major ways in which erosion moves sediment?

# INVESTIGATE Erosion

## How does the effect of rainwater on sloping land differ from its effect on flat land?

**DESIGN — YOUR OWN — EXPERIMENT**

Streams cause much of the erosion on Earth. Design an experiment to show the effect that rainwater has on sloping land.

**SKILL FOCUS**
Designing experiments (6.2.a)

**MATERIALS**
- soil
- 2 large trays
- pitcher of water

**TIME**
25 minutes

### PROCEDURE

1. Figure out how to use the soil, water, and trays to test the effects of rainwater on sloping land and on flat land.
2. Write up your procedure.
3. Carry out your experiment.

### WHAT DO YOU THINK?

- What were the results of your experiment? Did it work? Why or why not?
- What were the variables in your experiment?
- What does your experiment demonstrate about erosion and running water?

**CHALLENGE** How would you design an experiment to demonstrate the relationship between floods and erosion?

## Gravity can move large amounts of rock and soil.

Along the California coast many homes are built atop cliffs, backed by mountains and looking out to the sea. These homes are in beautiful areas. However, their location is risky.

The California coast region and other mountainous areas have many landslides. A landslide is one type of **mass wasting**—the downhill movements of masses of rock and soil.

In mass wasting, gravity pulls material downward. A triggering event, such as heavy rain or an earthquake, might loosen the rock and soil. As the material becomes looser, it gives way to the pull of gravity and moves downward.

Mass wasting can occur suddenly or gradually. It can involve tons of rock sliding down a steep mountain slope or moving little by little down a gentle hillside. One way to classify a mass wasting event is by the type of material that is moved and the speed of the movement. A sudden, fast movement of rock and soil is called a landslide. Movements of rock are described as slides or falls. Movement of mud or soil is described as a mudflow or a mudslide.

**VOCABULARY**
Be sure to make a four square diagram for *mass wasting* in your notebook.

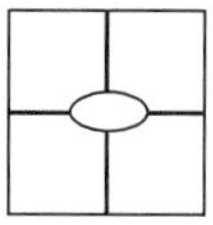

### Mass Wasting of Rock

Mass wasting of rock includes rockfalls and rockslides:

- In a rockfall, individual blocks of rock drop suddenly and fall freely down a cliff or steep mountainside. Weathering can break a block of rock from a cliff or mountainside. The expansion of water that freezes in a crack, for example, can loosen a block of rock.
- In a rockslide, a large mass of rock slides as a unit down a slope. A rockslide can reach a speed of a hundred kilometers per hour. Rockslides can be triggered by earthquakes.

Mass wasting of rock often takes place in high mountains. In some places, rocks can fall or slide onto roads. You might also see evidence of rockfalls and rockslides at the base of steep cliffs, where piles of rock slope outward.

Rockslides, such as this one near Yosemite National Park in California, can drop huge amounts of rock onto highways.

Mudflows in 1999 in Venezuela happened very quickly and took as many as 30,000 lives.

## Mudflow

Sometimes a mountain slope collapses. Then a mixture of rock, soil, and plants—called debris (duh-BREE)—falls or slides down. Like mass wasting of rock, mass movements of debris are common in high mountains with steep slopes.

RESOURCE CENTER
CLASSZONE.COM
Learn more about mudflows.

A major type of mass wasting of debris is a mudflow. A mudflow consists of debris with a large amount of water. Mudflows often happen in mountain canyons and valleys after heavy rains. The soil becomes so heavy with water that the slope can no longer hold it in place. The mixture of soil, water, and debris flows downward, picking up sediment as it rushes down. When it reaches a valley, it spreads in a thin sheet over the land.

Mudflows also occur on active volcanoes. In 1985, a huge mudflow destroyed the town of Armero, Colombia, and killed more than 20,000 people. When a volcano erupted there, the heat melted ice and snow near the top of the volcano. This released a large amount of water that mixed with ash from the volcano. The mixture of ash and water rushed down the volcano and picked up debris. It formed gigantic mudflows that poured into all the surrounding valleys.

Mount St. Helens, a volcanic mountain in the state of Washington, is a place where large mudflows have occurred. During an eruption in 1980, some mudflows from the volcano traveled more than 90 kilometers (56 mi) from the mountain.

CHECK YOUR READING What causes a mudflow to occur?

In this example of slump, at Mesa Verde National Park in Colorado, a huge mass of rock and soil moved downward.

## Slumps and Creep

Slumps and creep are two other main types of mass wasting on hilly land. These forms of mass wasting can be much less dramatic than rockslides or mudflows. But they are the types of mass movement that you are most likely to see evidence of.

A slump is a slide of loose debris that moves as a single unit. Slumps can occur along roads and highways where construction has made slopes unstable. They can cover sections of highway with debris. Like other types of mass movement, slumps can be triggered by heavy rain.

The slowest form of mass movement of soil or debris is creep. The soil or debris moves at a rate of about 1 to 10 millimeters a year—a rate too slow to be seen. But evidence of creep can be seen on hillsides that have old fences or telephone poles. The fences or poles may lean downward, or some may be out of line. They have been moved by the creeping soil. The soil closer to the surface moves faster than the soil farther down, which causes the fences or poles to lean.

Originally, the fence posts stand vertically in the ground.

Over many years, the soil holding the posts slowly shifts downhill, and the posts lean.

Even the slight slope of this land in Alberta, Canada, caused these posts to tilt because of creep.

Creep can affect buildings as well. The weight of a heavy mass of soil moving slowly downhill can be great enough to crack a building's walls. Creep affects all hillsides covered with soil, but its rate varies. The wetter the soil, the faster it will creep downhill.

# 7.1 Review

## KEY CONCEPTS

1. How does erosion change landscapes? (6.2.a)
2. Describe why weathering is important in erosion. (6.2.a)
3. How can gravity move large amounts of rock and soil? (6.2.d)

## CRITICAL THINKING

4. **Compare and Contrast** What is the main difference between erosion and mass wasting?
5. **Infer** What force and what cause can contribute to both erosion and mass wasting?

## CHALLENGE

6. **Rank** Which of the four locations would be the best and worst places to build a house? Rank the four locations and explain your reasoning.

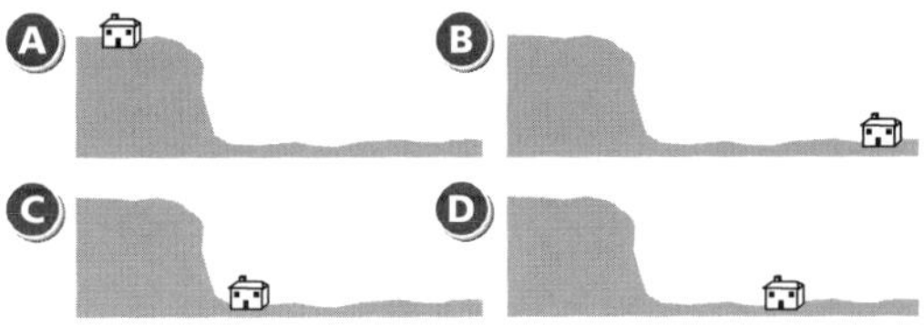

KEY CONCEPT

# 7.2 Moving water shapes land.

**CALIFORNIA Content Standards**

**6.2.a** Students know water running downhill is the dominant process in shaping the landscape, including California's landscape.

**6.2.b** Students know rivers and streams are dynamic systems that erode, transport sediment, change course, and flood their banks in natural and recurring patterns.

**6.2.d** Students know earthquakes, volcanic eruptions, landslides, and floods change human and wildlife habitats.

**BEFORE, you learned**

- Erosion is the movement of rock and soil
- Gravity causes mass movements of rock and soil

**NOW, you will learn**

- How moving water shapes Earth's surface
- How water moving underground forms caves and other features

### EXPLORE Divides (6.2.a)

#### *How do divides work?*

**PROCEDURE**

1. Fold the sheet of paper in thirds and tape it as shown to make a "ridge."
2. Drop the paper clips one at a time directly on top of the ridge from a height of about 30 cm. Observe what happens and record your observations.

**WHAT DO YOU THINK?**

How might the paper clips be similar to water falling on a ridge?

**MATERIALS**

- sheet of paper
- tape
- paper clips

**VOCABULARY**

**drainage basin** p. 231
**divide** p. 231
**floodplain** p. 232
**alluvial fan** p. 233
**delta** p. 233
**sinkhole** p. 235

**NOTE-TAKING STRATEGY**
A main idea and detail notes chart would be a good strategy to use for taking notes about streams and Earth's surface.

## Streams shape Earth's surface.

If you look at a river or stream, you may be able to notice something about the land around it. The land is higher than the river. If a river runs through a steep valley, you can easily see that the river is the low point. But even in very flat places, the land slopes down to the river, which itself runs downhill in a low path through the land.

Running water is the major force shaping the landscape over most of Earth. From the broad, flat land around the lower Mississippi River to the steep mountain valleys of the Himalayas, water running downhill changes the land. Running water shapes a variety of landforms by moving sediment in the processes of erosion and deposition. In this section, you will learn how water on land flows in systems of streams and rivers and how water shapes and changes landscapes. You also will learn that water can even carve out new features underground.

## Drainage Basins and Divides

When water falls or ice melts on a slope, some of the water soaks into the ground and some of it flows down the slope in thin sheets. But within a short distance, this water becomes part of a channel that forms a stream. A stream is any body of water—large or small—that flows down a slope along a channel.

> **READING TIP**
> One meaning of *channel* is "the bed or bottom of a body of water." The word *channel* comes from the Latin word *canālis*, meaning "tube." The word *canal* comes from the same Latin word.

Streams flow into one another to form complex drainage systems, with small streams flowing into larger ones. The area of land in which water drains into a stream system is called a **drainage basin.** In most drainage basins, the water eventually drains into a lake or an ocean. For example, in the Mississippi River drainage basin, water flows into the Mississippi and then drains into the Gulf of Mexico, which is part of the ocean.

Drainage basins are separated by ridges called divides, which are continuous lines of high land. A **divide** is a ridge from which water drains to one side or the other. Divides can run along high mountains. On flatter ground, a divide can simply be the highest line of land and can be hard to see.

Divides are the borders of drainage basins. A basin can be just a few kilometers wide or can drain water from a large portion of a continent. The Continental Divide runs from Alaska to Mexico. Most water that falls west of the Continental Divide ends up draining into the Pacific Ocean. Most water that falls east of it drains into the Gulf of Mexico and the Atlantic Ocean.

### Divides and Drainage Basins

**Divides are ridges that form the borders of drainage basins.**

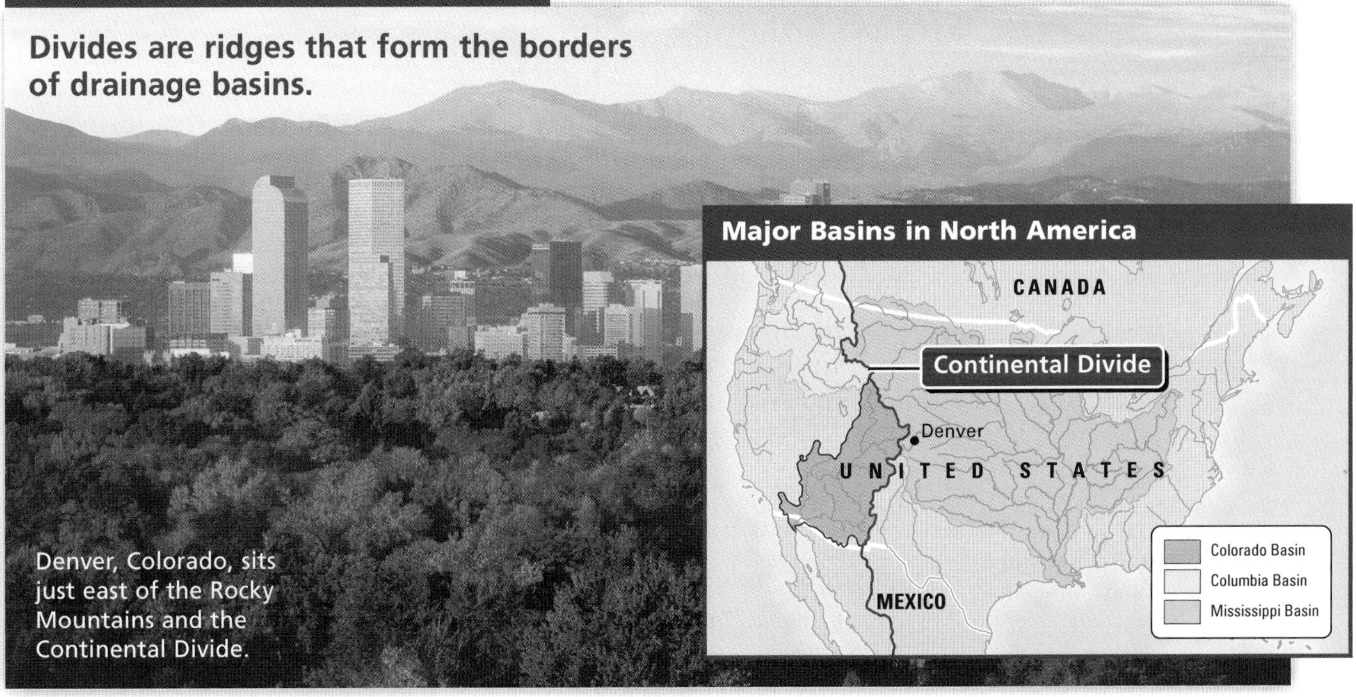


Denver, Colorado, sits just east of the Rocky Mountains and the Continental Divide.

Downtown Davenport, Iowa, sits in the floodplain of the Mississippi River. The city was covered with water when the river flooded in 1993.

## Valleys and Floodplains

As streams flow and carry sediment from the surface of the land, they form valleys. In high mountains, streams often cut V-shaped valleys that are narrow and steep walled. In lower areas, streams may form broad valleys that include floodplains. A **floodplain** is an area of land on either side of a stream that is underwater when the stream floods. The floodplain of a large river may be many kilometers wide.

When a stream floods, it deposits much of the sediment that it carries onto its floodplain. This sediment can make the floodplain very fertile, or able to support a lot of plant growth. In the United States, the floodplains of the Mississippi River are some of the best places for growing crops.

RESOURCE CENTER
CLASSZONE.COM
Find out more about rivers and erosion.

CHECK YOUR READING Why is fertile land often found on flat land around rivers?

## Stream Channels

As a stream flows through a valley, its channel may run straight in some parts and curve in other parts. Curves and bends that form a twisting, looping pattern in a stream channel are called meanders (mee-AN-duhrz). The moving water erodes the outside banks and deposits sediment along the inside banks. Over many years, meanders shift position.

Oxbow lakes and meanders formed as this river deposited sediment and changed course.

During a flood, the stream may cut a new channel that bypasses a meander. The cut-off meander forms a curved lake called an oxbow lake. An oxbow is a U-shaped piece of wood that fits under the neck of an ox. An oxbow lake has a similar shape.

## Alluvial Fans and Deltas

Besides shaping valleys and forming oxbow lakes, streams also create landforms called alluvial fans and deltas. Both of these landforms are formed by the deposition of sediment.

An **alluvial fan** (uh-LOO-vee-uhl) is a fan-shaped deposit of sediment at the base of a mountain. It forms where a stream leaves a steep valley and enters a plain. The stream slows down and spreads out on the flatter ground. As it slows down, it can carry less sediment. The slower-moving water drops some of its sediment, leaving it at the base of the slope.

This alluvial fan was formed by a stream flowing into the Jago River in Alaska.

A **delta** is an area of land formed by the buildup of sediment at the end, or mouth, of a river. When a river enters the ocean, the river's water slows down, and the river drops much of its sediment. This sediment gradually builds up to form a plain. Like alluvial fans, deltas tend to be fan-shaped. Over a very long time, a river may build up its delta far out into the sea. A large river, such as the Mississippi, can build up a huge delta. Like many other large rivers on Earth, the Mississippi has been building up its delta out into the sea for many thousands of years.

### From Divide to Delta

**On their path to the ocean, streams and rivers slow down and flatten out.**

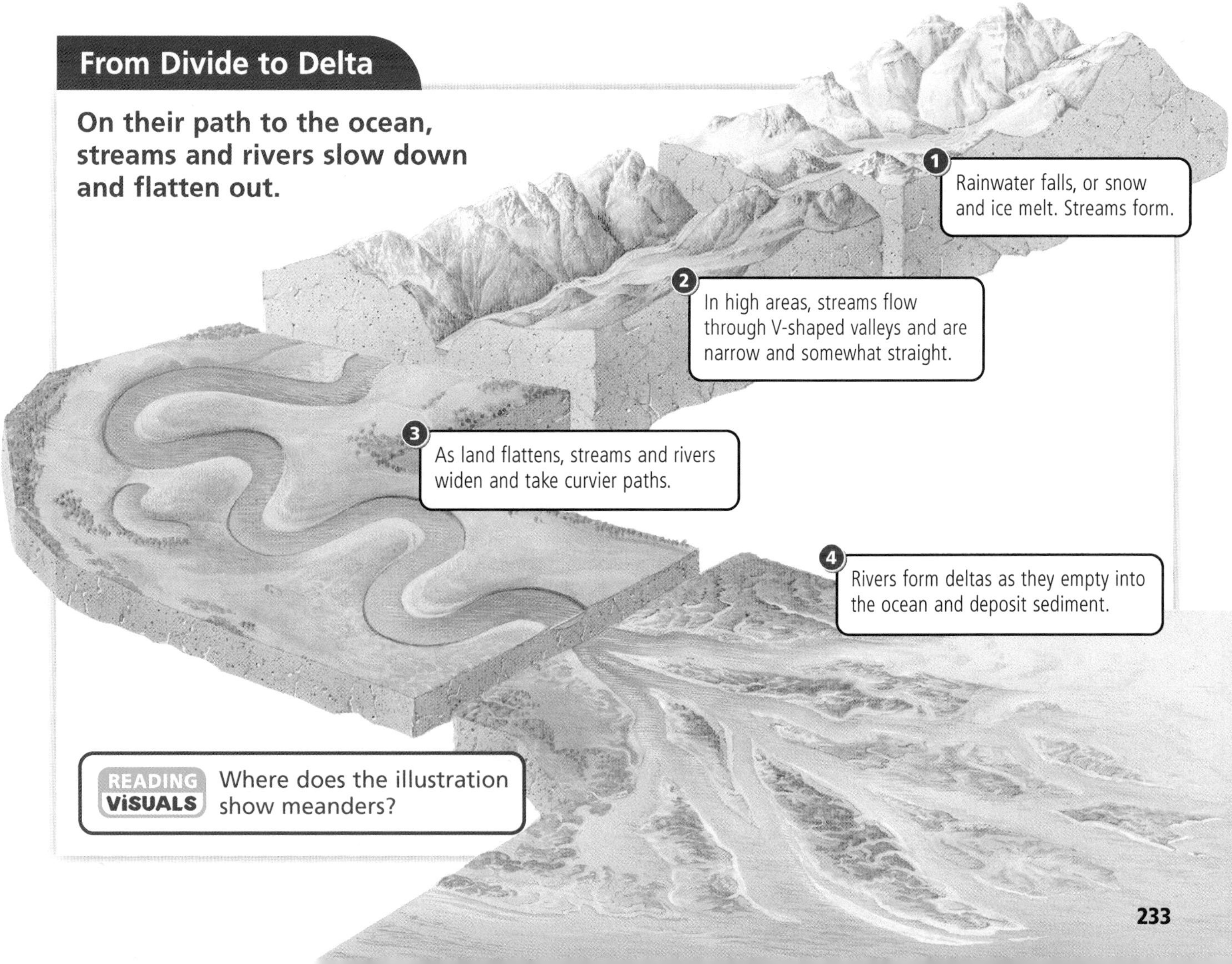

1 Rainwater falls, or snow and ice melt. Streams form.
2 In high areas, streams flow through V-shaped valleys and are narrow and somewhat straight.
3 As land flattens, streams and rivers widen and take curvier paths.
4 Rivers form deltas as they empty into the ocean and deposit sediment.

READING VISUALS Where does the illustration show meanders?

## Water moving underground forms caverns.

Not all rainwater runs off the land and flows into surface streams. Some of it evaporates, some is absorbed by plants, and some soaks into the ground and becomes groundwater. At a certain depth below the surface, the spaces in soil and rock become completely filled with water. The top of this water-filled region is called the water table. The water below the water table is called groundwater.

The water table is at different distances below the surface in different places. Its level can change over time in the same location, depending on changes in rainfall. Below the water table, groundwater flows slowly through underground beds of rock and soil, where it causes erosion to take place.

**VISUALIZATION**
CLASSZONE.COM
Observe the process of cave formation.

You have read that chemicals in water and air can break down rock. As you read in Chapter 6, rainwater is slightly acidic. This acidic water can dissolve certain rocks, such as limestone. In some areas, where the underground rock is limestone, the groundwater can dissolve some of the limestone and carry it away. Over time, this process

### Cavern Formation

**Caves form as water underground dissolves limestone, leaving open spaces.**

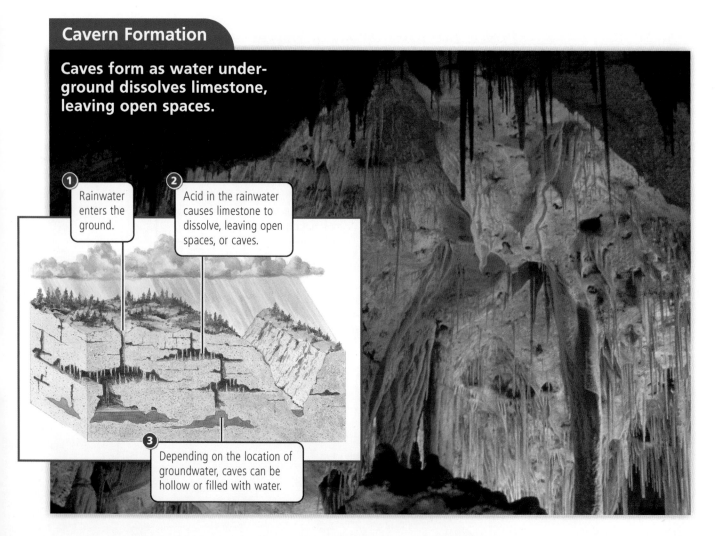

1 Rainwater enters the ground.
2 Acid in the rainwater causes limestone to dissolve, leaving open spaces, or caves.
3 Depending on the location of groundwater, caves can be hollow or filled with water.

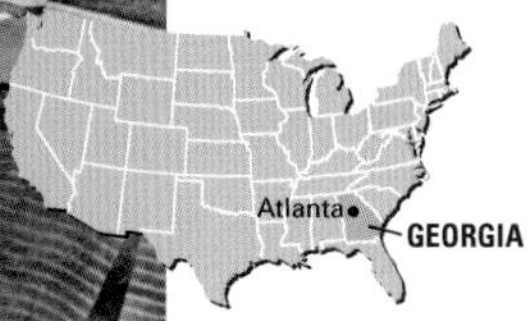


This sinkhole took down a large part of a parking lot in Atlanta, Georgia.

produces open spaces, or caves. Large caves are called caverns. If the water table drops, a cavern may fill with air.

Some caverns have huge networks of rooms and passageways. Mammoth Cave in Kentucky, for example, is part of a cavern system that has more than 560 kilometers (about 350 mi) of explored passageways. Within the cavern are lakes and streams.

A surface feature that often occurs in areas with caverns is a sinkhole. A **sinkhole** is a basin that forms when the roof of a cave becomes so thin that it suddenly falls in. Sometimes it falls in because water that supported the roof has drained away. Landscapes with many sinkholes can be found in southern Indiana, south central Kentucky, and central Tennessee. In Florida, the collapse of shallow underground caverns has produced large sinkholes that have destroyed whole city blocks.

**CHECK YOUR READING** Why do caverns form in areas with limestone?

# 7.2 Review

## KEY CONCEPTS

1. What is the difference between a drainage basin and a divide? (6.2.b)
2. How do streams change as they flow from mountains down to plains? (6.2.b)
3. How do caverns form? (6.2.a)

## CRITICAL THINKING

4. **Sequence** Draw a cartoon with three panels showing how a sinkhole forms.
5. **Compare and Contrast** Make a Venn diagram to compare and contrast alluvial fans and deltas.

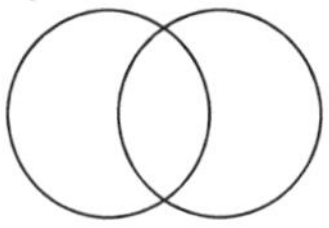

## CHALLENGE

6. **Apply** During a flood, a river drops the largest pieces of its sediment on the floodplain close to its normal channel. Explain why. (**Hint:** Think about the speed of the water.)

# CHAPTER INVESTIGATION

## Creating Stream Features

**OVERVIEW AND PURPOSE** A view from the sky reveals that a large river twists and bends in its channel. But as quiet as it might appear, the river constantly digs up and dumps Earth materials along its way. This erosion and deposition may cause twists and curves called meanders and form a delta at the river's mouth. In this investigation you will

- create a "river" in a stream table to observe the formation of meanders and deltas
- identify the processes of erosion and deposition

### Problem

Write It Up

How does moving water create meanders and deltas?

**MATERIALS**
- stream table, with hose attachment or recirculating pump
- sieve (optional)
- wood blocks
- sand
- ruler
- water
- sink with drain
- pitcher (optional)
- bucket (optional)

6.2.a, 6.2.b, 6.7.b

### Procedure

1. Arrange the stream table on a counter so that it drains into a sink or bucket. If possible, place a sieve beneath the outlet hose to keep sand out of the drain. You can attach the inlet hose to a faucet if you have a proper adapter. Or you can gently pour water in with a pitcher or use a recirculating pump and a bucket.

2. Place wood blocks beneath the inlet end of the stream table so that the table tilts toward the outlet at about a 20-degree angle. Fill the upper two-thirds of the stream table nearly to the top with sand. Pack the sand a bit, and level the surface with the edge of a ruler. The empty bottom third of the stream table represents the lake or bay into which the river flows.

3. Using the end of the ruler, dig a gently curving channel halfway through the thickness of the sand from its upper to its lower end.

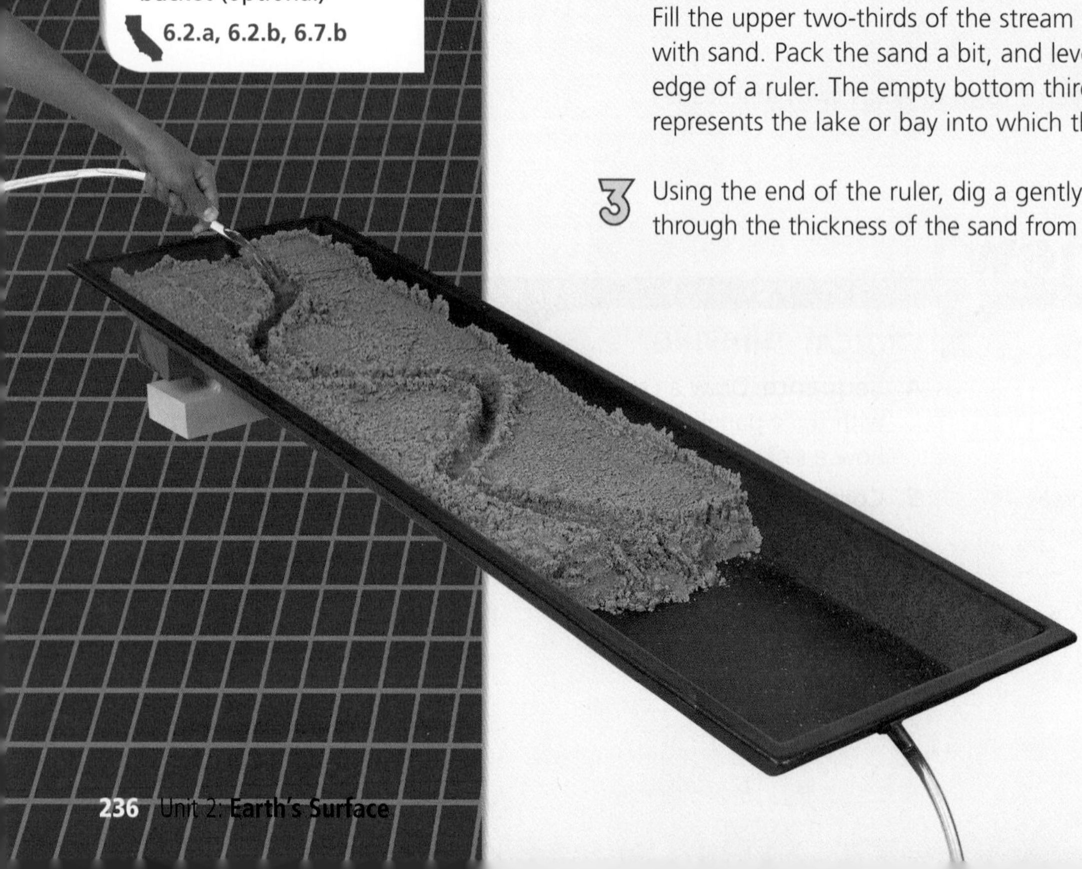

**Content Standard**
**6.2.a** Students know water running downhill is the dominant process in shaping the landscape, including California's landscape.

**Investigation Standard**
**6.7.b** Select and use appropriate tools and technology (including calculators, computers, balances, spring scales, microscopes, and binoculars) to perform tests, collect data, and display data.

4 Direct a gentle flow of tap water into the upper end of the channel. Increase the flow slightly when the water begins to move through the channel. You may have to try this several times before you find the proper rate of flow to soak the sand and fill the stream channel. Avoid adding so much water that it pools at the top before moving into the channel. You can also change the stream table's tilt.

5 Once you are successful in creating a river, observe its shape and any movement of the sand. Continue pouring water until the top part of the sand is completely washed away and your river falls apart. Scrape the sand back into place with the ruler and repeat the procedure until you thoroughly understand the stream and sand movements.

## Observe and Analyze

Write It Up

1. **RECORD** Make a series of drawings showing changes in your river over time. Be sure to label the river's features, as well as areas of erosion and deposition. Be sure to diagram what happens to the sand at the river's mouth.
2. **RECORD** Write a record of the development of your river from start to finish. Include details such as the degree of tilt you used, your method of introducing water into the stream table, and features you observed forming.

## Conclude

Write It Up

1. **EVALUATE** How do you explain the buildup of sand at the mouth of your river? Use the words *speed, erosion,* and *deposition* in your answer. Did the slope of the stream change over time?
2. **INTERPRET** Where in your stream table did you observe erosion occurring? deposition? What features did each process form?
3. **INFER** What might have happened if you had increased the amount of the water flowing into your river? the speed?
4. **IDENTIFY LIMITS** In what ways was your setup a simplified version of what would actually occur on Earth? Describe how an actual stream would be more complex.
5. **APPLY** Based on what you observed in this investigation, write two statements that relate the age of a stream to (1) the number of its meanders and (2) to the size of its delta or alluvial fan.

## INVESTIGATE Further

**CHALLENGE** Revise this activity to test a problem statement about a specific stream feature. You might choose to vary the stream's slope, speed, or volume to test the effects on meanders and deltas. Or you could vary the sediment size and observe the movements of each size. Write a hypothesis and design an experimental procedure. Identify the independent and dependent variables.

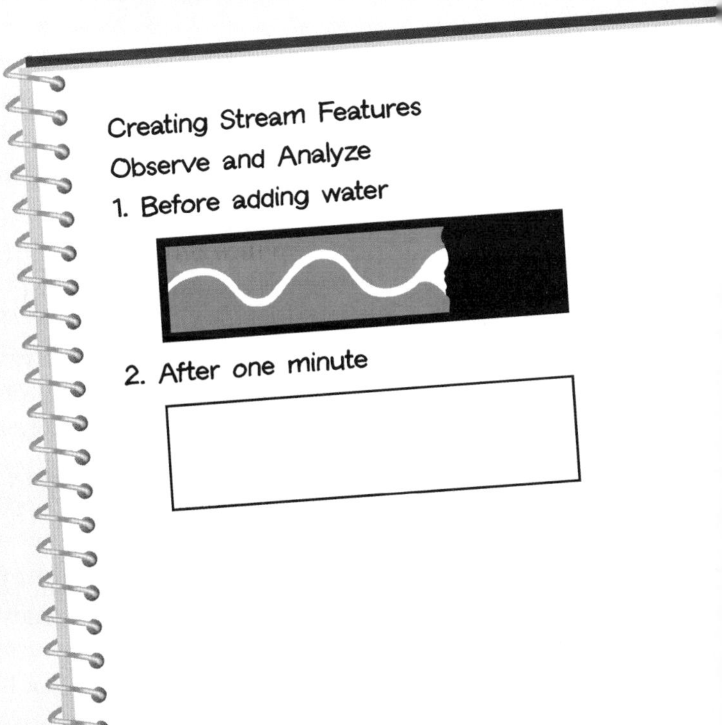

KEY CONCEPT

# 7.3 Waves and wind shape land.

**CALIFORNIA Content Standards**

**6.2.c** Students know beaches are dynamic systems in which the sand is supplied by rivers and moved along the coast by the action of waves.

**6.2.d** Students know earthquakes, volcanic eruptions, landslides, and floods change human and wildlife habitats.

**6.7.h** Identify changes in natural phenomena over time without manipulating the phenomena (e.g., a tree limb, a grove of trees, a stream, a hillslope).

**BEFORE, you learned**

- Stream systems shape Earth's surface
- Groundwater creates caverns and sinkholes

**NOW, you will learn**

- How waves and currents shape shorelines
- How wind shapes land

**VOCABULARY**

**longshore drift** p. 239
**longshore current** p. 239
**sandbar** p. 240
**barrier island** p. 240
**dune** p. 241
**loess** p. 242

**THINK ABOUT**

***How did these pillars of rock form?***

The rock formations in this photograph stand along the shoreline of Garrapata State Park in California. What natural process created these stone pillars? What evidence of this process can you see in the photograph?

**NOTE-TAKING STRATEGY** Remember to organize your notes in a chart or web as you read.

## Waves and currents shape shorelines.

The stone pillars, or sea stacks, in the photograph above add to the scenic beauty of Garrapata State Park, which is located at the northern end of the Big Sur coastline. They were formed by the movement of water. The constant action of waves breaking against the cliffs slowly wore rock away, leaving behind pillarlike formations. Waves continue to wear down the pillars and cliffs. In the years to come, the waves will likely wear away the stone pillars completely.

The force of waves, powered by wind, can wear away rock and move thousands of tons of sand on beaches. The force of wind can change the look of the land. Moving air can pick up sand particles and move them around to build up dunes. Wind can carry huge amounts of fine sediment thousands of kilometers.

In this section, you'll read more about how waves and wind shape shorelines and many other landforms.

## Shorelines

Some shorelines, such as the Big Sur coastline, are steep and rocky. As waves crash against the rock, they wear away the bottom of the cliffs. Eventually, parts of the cliffs above break away and fall into the water, where they are worn down and carried away by the water.

While high, rocky coasts get worn away, low coastlines often get built up. As you read earlier, when a stream flows into an ocean or a lake, it deposits sediment near its mouth. This sediment mixes with the sediment formed by waves beating against the coast. Waves and currents move this sediment along the shore, building up beaches. Beaches are dynamic, or ever-changing, systems. Two terms are used to describe the movement of sediment and water along a shore: *long-shore drift* and *longshore current.*

- **Longshore drift** is the zigzag movement of sand along a beach. Waves formed by wind blowing across the water far from shore may hit a shoreline at an angle. These angled waves carry sand up onto the shore. Then gravity pulls the water and sand straight back into the water. The sand gradually moves down the beach. The illustration below shows longshore drift.
- A **longshore current** is movement of water along a shore as waves strike the shore at an angle. The direction of the longshore current can change from day to day as the direction of the waves striking the shore changes.

Longshore drift moves large amounts of sand along beaches. It can cause a beach to shrink at one location and grow at another.

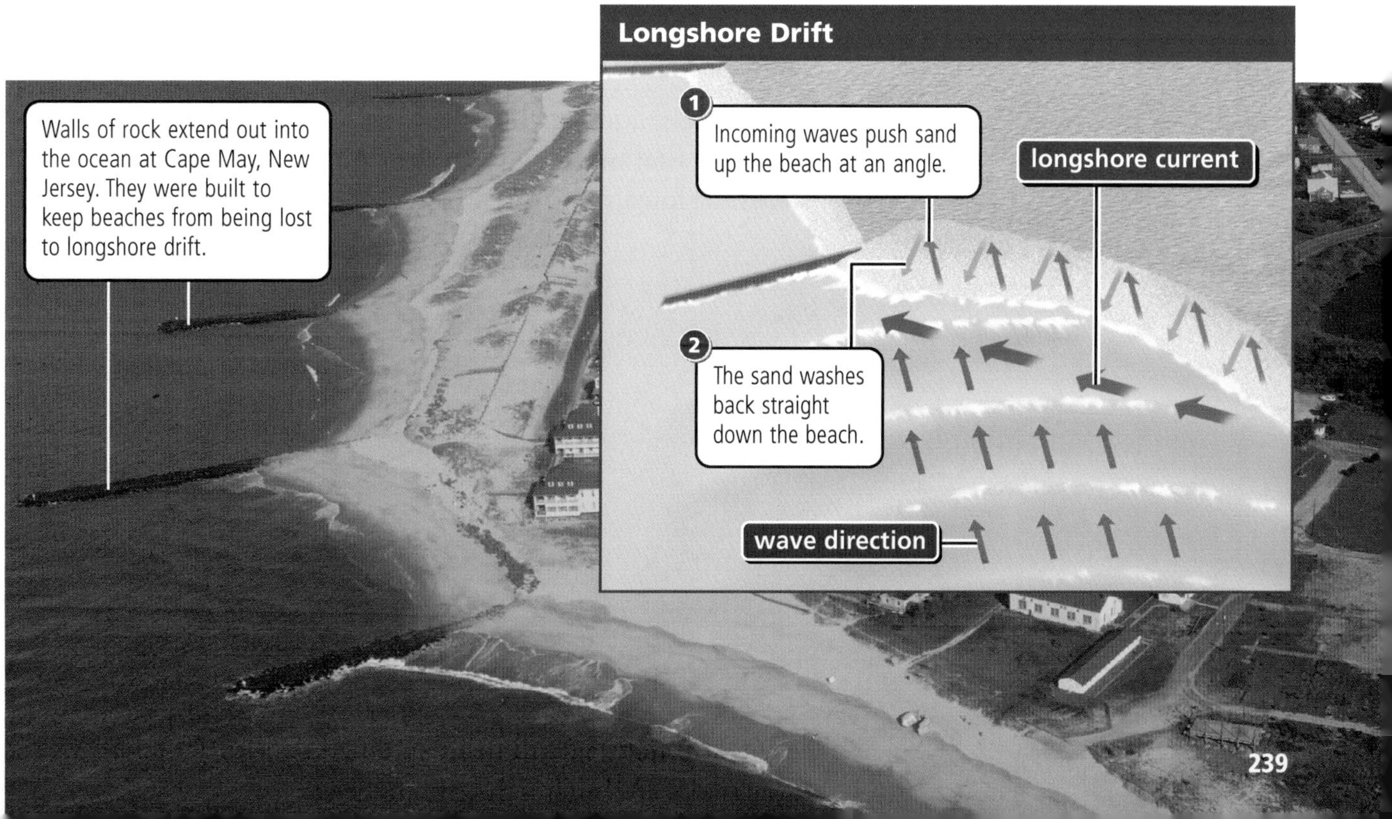

Walls of rock extend out into the ocean at Cape May, New Jersey. They were built to keep beaches from being lost to longshore drift.
Longshore Drift
1 Incoming waves push sand up the beach at an angle.
longshore current
2 The sand washes back straight down the beach.
wave direction

# INVESTIGATE Longshore Drift

## *How does sand move along a beach?*

**SKILL FOCUS**
**Observing (6.2.c)**

**MATERIALS**
- 2 or 3 books
- coin

**TIME**
15 minutes

**PROCEDURE**

1. Prop up a book as shown.
2. Hold a coin with your finger against the bottom right corner of the book.
3. Gently flick the coin up the slope of the book at an angle. The coin should slide back down the book and fall off the bottom. If necessary, change the angle of the book and the strength with which you are flicking the coin.
4. Repeat step 3 several times. Observe the path the coin takes. Record your observations. Include a diagram that shows the path the coin takes as it slides up and down the book.

**WHAT DO YOU THINK?**

- What path did the coin take on its way up? on its way down?
- In this model of longshore drift, what represents the beach? What represents the sand? What represents a wave?

**CHALLENGE** In this model, in which direction will the longshore current move? How could you change the model to change the direction of the current?

## Sandbars and Barrier Islands

As ocean waves and currents transport sand, they shape a variety of coastal landforms. Longshore currents, for example, often deposit sand along shorelines. The sand builds up to form sandbars. A **sandbar** is a ridge of sand built up by the action of waves and currents. A sandbar that has built up above the water's surface and is joined to the land at one end is called a spit. The tip of Cape Cod, Massachusetts, is a spit.

Strong longshore currents that move mostly in one direction may produce sandbars that build up over time into barrier islands. A **barrier island** is a long, narrow island that develops parallel to a coast.

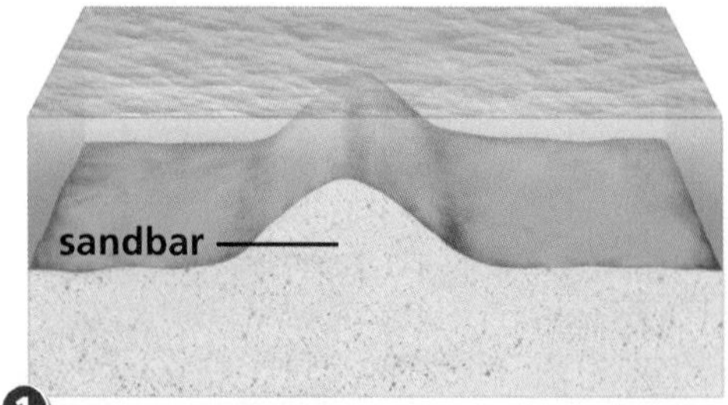


1 Waves and currents move and build up sand deposits to form a sandbar under the water surface.

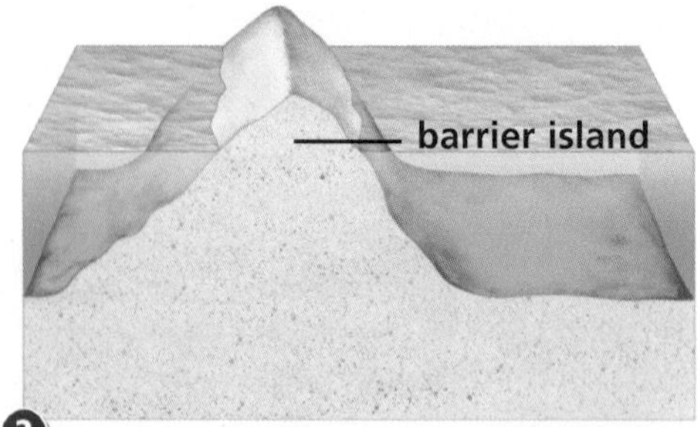


2 As more sand is deposited, the sandbar rises above the surface to become a barrier island.

This lighthouse on a barrier island in North Carolina had to be moved because of beach erosion. The photograph shows the lighthouse before it was moved.

A barrier island gets its name from the fact that it forms a barrier between the ocean waves and the mainland. As a barrier island builds up, grasses, bushes, and trees begin to grow on it.

Barrier islands are common along gently sloping coasts around the world. They occur along the coasts of New Jersey and North Carolina and along the coastline of the Gulf of Mexico. Padre Island in Texas is a barrier island about 180 kilometers (110 mi) in length.

Barrier islands constantly change shape. Hurricanes or other storms can speed up the change. During large storms, waves can surge across the land, carrying away huge amounts of sediment and depositing it elsewhere. Houses on beaches can be destroyed in storms.

**CHECK YOUR READING** How and where do barrier islands form?

## Wind shapes land.

At Indiana Dunes National Lakeshore, not far from the skyscrapers of Chicago, you can tumble or slide down huge sand dunes. First-time visitors to the Indiana dunes find it hard to believe that sand formations like these can be found so far from a desert or an ocean. What created this long stretch of dune land along the southern shore of Lake Michigan? The answer: wind. A **dune** is a mound of sand built up by wind.

Like water, wind has the power to transport and deposit sediment. Although wind is a less powerful force of erosion than moving water, it can still shape landforms. This often happens in dry regions and in areas that have few or no plants to hold soil in place. Wind can build up dunes, deposit layers of dust, or make a land surface as hard as pavement.

Wind makes sand particles build up and tumble down. This can cause a dune to migrate, or move.

These hills of sand are at the Great Sand Dunes National Monument in Colorado.

## Dune Formation

Even a light breeze can carry dust. A moderate wind can roll and slide grains of sand along a beach or desert, creating ripples. Only a strong wind can actually pick up and carry sand particles. When the wind dies down or hits something—such as a cliff or a hill—it drops the sand. Over time, the deposits of sand build up to create dunes.

Some dunes start out as ripples that grow larger. Others form as wind-carried sand settles around a rock, log, or other obstacle. In climates with enough rainfall, plants begin to grow on dunes a short distance from beaches.

Dunes form only where there are strong winds and a constant supply of loose sand. They can be found on the inland side of beaches of oceans and large lakes, on the sandy floodplains of large rivers, and in sandy deserts.

Dunes can form in a variety of sizes and shapes. They can reach heights of up to 300 meters (about 1000 ft). Some dunes are curved; others are long, straight ridges. Still others are mound-shaped hills. A dune usually has a gentle slope on the side that faces the wind and a steeper slope on the side sheltered from the wind.

**CALIFORNIA Focus**

The Imperial Sand Dunes are the largest group of sand dunes in California. The dune system is more than 64 kilometers (40 mi) long. Some dunes are more than 91 meters (300 ft) tall.

## Loess

Besides forming dunes, wind also changes the soil over large regions of Earth by depositing dust. A strong windstorm can move millions of tons of dust. As the wind dies down, the dust drops to the ground. Deposits of fine wind-blown sediment are called **loess** (LOH-uhs).

In some regions, deposits of loess have built up over thousands and even millions of years. Loess is a valuable resource because it forms good soil for growing crops.

This loess deposit in Iowa built up over many thousands of years.

Loess covers about 10 percent of the land surface of Earth. China has especially large deposits of loess, covering hundreds of thousands of square kilometers. Some of the deposits are more than 300 meters (about 1000 ft) thick. Such thick deposits take a long time to develop. Some of the loess deposits in China are 2 million years old. Winds blowing over the deserts and dry regions of central Asia carried the dust that formed these deposits.

Parts of east central Europe and the Mississippi Valley in the United States also contain large loess deposits. In the central United States, loess deposits are between 8 and 30 meters (25 and 100 ft) thick.

## Desert Pavement

Wind does not only shape land surfaces by depositing dust. It also shapes land surfaces by removing dust. When wind blows away all the smallest particles from a mixture of sand, silt, and gravel, it leaves behind a layer of stones and gravel. This stony surface is called desert pavement because it looks like a cobblestone street. The coarse gravel and rocks are too large to be picked up by wind.

**CHECK YOUR READING** How are both loess and desert pavement formed by wind?

Desert pavement is made up of particles too large to be picked up by wind.

# 7.3 Review

### KEY CONCEPTS

1. What kinds of landforms do longshore drift and longshore currents produce? (6.2.c)
2. How do dunes form? (6.7.h)
3. How does loess form, and why is it important? (6.7.h)

### CRITICAL THINKING

4. **Identify Cause and Effect** Is longshore drift the cause or the effect of a longshore current? Explain.
5. **Predict** What effect would a barrier island have on the shoreline of the mainland?

### CHALLENGE

6. **Hypothesize** The southern and eastern shores of Lake Michigan have large areas of sand dunes, but the northern and western shores do not. Write a hypothesis that explains why. You might want to use a map and draw the shape of Lake Michigan to explain.

California Close-Up

EROSION

# The Changing Shoreline

6.2.c Students know beaches are dynamic systems in which the sand is supplied by rivers and moved along the coast by the action of waves.

A natural cycle of erosion and deposition shapes beaches and cliffs along the California coast. Rivers carry sand and silt down to the ocean. Ocean currents move sand along the shoreline. In the winter, storms can move sand offshore. The large storm waves also cause cliff erosion.

## Where's the Beach?

Cliffs erode as waves crash against the cliff and break up the rocks. Different parts of a cliff can erode at different rates. In 1998, after an unusual number of winter storms, scientists measured the changes in a cliff near Pacifica. Part of the cliff suffered from erosion equal to 50 years of normal erosion. Meanwhile, a nearby part of the cliff had almost no erosion at all. Even normal erosion takes place at different rates along a cliff. Scientists have studied the cliff erosion rates in Isla Vista over many years. Some parts of the cliff erode as quickly as 38 centimeters (15 in.) a year. Other areas erode less than 5 centimeters (2 in.) in a year.

This photograph of a house in Isla Vista was taken in January 2005. In January 2002, the cliff edge was about where the pillars are.

## Measuring Ups and Downs

To study the patterns of erosion and deposition, scientists measure the change in height along the shoreline. LIDAR, which stands for LIght Detection And Ranging, is an instrument that helps scientists measure the change in a shoreline. LIDAR is like radar except it uses laser light instead of radio waves. An airplane flies over a beach, and the LIDAR on the plane bounces light off the ground and measures how long it takes for the light to bounce back and reach the plane. This time measurement can be converted to a distance. With LIDAR, scientists can accurately measure shoreline changes.

## WRITING ABOUT SCIENCE

Sometimes people build seawalls to protect cliffs from erosion. Waves break against the seawall instead of against the cliff. How might a seawall affect ocean and shore life? Write a few paragraphs that discuss the effects a seawall might have on the coastal ecosystem.

KEY CONCEPT

# 7.4 Glaciers carve land and move sediments.

**CALIFORNIA Content Standard**

6.2.a Students know water running downhill is the dominant process in shaping the landscape, including California's landscape.

**BEFORE, you learned**

- Running water shapes landscapes
- Wind changes landforms

**NOW, you will learn**

- How moving ice erodes land
- How moving ice deposits sediment and changes landforms

**VOCABULARY**

**glacier** p. 245
**till** p. 248
**moraine** p. 248
**kettle lake** p. 249

**EXPLORE Glaciers** (6.2.a)

### *How do glaciers affect land?*

**PROCEDURE**

1. Flatten the clay on top of a paper towel.
2. Drag the ice cube across the clay as shown. Record your observations.
3. Leave the ice cube to melt on top of the clay.

**MATERIALS**

- modeling clay
- paper towel
- ice cube containing sand and gravel

**WHAT DO YOU THINK?**

- What happened when you dragged the ice cube across the clay?
- What happened to the sand and gravel in the ice cube as it melted?

## Glaciers are moving bodies of ice.

**VOCABULARY**
Remember to add a four square diagram for *glacier* to your notebook.

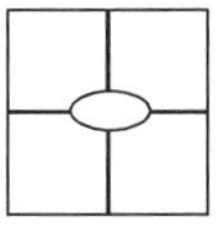

You might not think of ice as something that moves. But think about what happens to an ice cube on a table. The cube begins to melt, makes a small puddle, and may slide a little. The water under the cube makes the table surface slippery, which allows the ice cube to slide.

A similar process happens on a much larger scale with glaciers. A **glacier** is a large mass of ice that moves over land. A glacier forms in a cold region when more snow falls than melts each year. As the snow builds up, its weight presses the snow on the bottom into ice. On a mountain, the weight of a heavy mass of ice causes it to flow downward, usually slowly. On flatter land, the ice spreads out as a sheet. As glaciers form, move, and melt away, they shape landscapes.

## Extent of Glaciers

Glaciers can exist only in places where it is cold enough for water to stay frozen year-round. Glaciers are found in mountain ranges all over the world and in land regions near the north and south poles.

**Ice Age in North America**

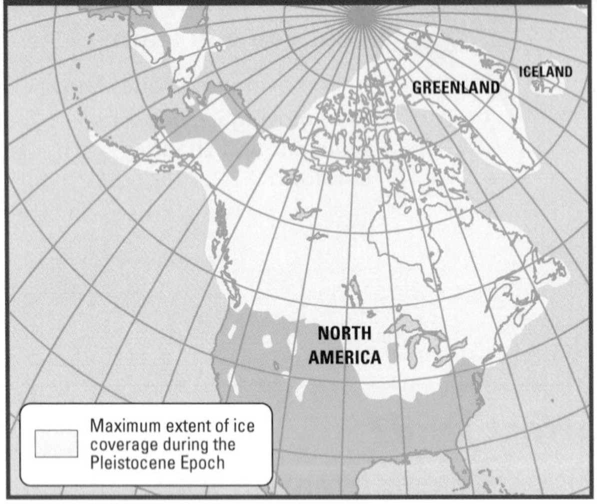


Today, glaciers cover about 10 percent of Earth's land surface. However, the amount of land surface covered by glaciers has varied greatly over Earth's history. Glaciers have expanded during long cold periods called ice ages and have disappeared during long warm periods. About 30,000 years ago—during the last major ice age—glaciers extended across the northern parts of North America, Europe, and Asia. They covered nearly 30 percent of the present land surface of Earth.

There are two major types of glaciers: alpine glaciers and continental glaciers.

**RESOURCE CENTER**
CLASSZONE.COM
Learn more about the movement and effects of glaciers.

## Alpine Glaciers

Alpine glaciers are also called valley glaciers. They form in mountains and flow down through valleys. As these glaciers move, they cause erosion by breaking up rock and carrying away the resulting sediment. Over time, an alpine glacier can change a V-shaped mountain valley into a U-shaped valley with a wider, flatter bottom.

Some glaciers extend all the way down into the lower land at the bases of mountains. At an alpine glacier's lower end, where temperatures are warmer, melting can occur. The melting glacier drops sediment, and streams flowing from the glacier carry some of the sediment away. If an alpine glacier flows into the ocean, big blocks may break off and become icebergs.

## Continental Glaciers

Continental glaciers are also called ice sheets. They are much larger than alpine glaciers. They can cover entire continents, including all but the highest mountain peaks. An ice sheet covered most of Canada and the northern United States during the last ice age. This ice sheet melted and shrank about 10,000 years ago.

Today, ice sheets cover most of Greenland and Antarctica. Each of these glaciers is shaped like a wide dome over the land. The ice covering Antarctica is as much as 4500 meters (15,000 ft) thick.

**CHECK YOUR READING** What are the two major types of glaciers and where do they form?

## Types of Glaciers and Movement

**A glacier is a large mass of ice that moves over land.**

### Alpine Glaciers

A glacier, such as this one in Alaska, changes the landscape as it moves down a mountain valley.

### Continental Glaciers

Huge sheets of ice cover the continent of Antarctica and other land regions.

### Glacier Movement

Gravity causes the ice in a glacier to move downhill. Two different processes cause glaciers to move: flowing and sliding.

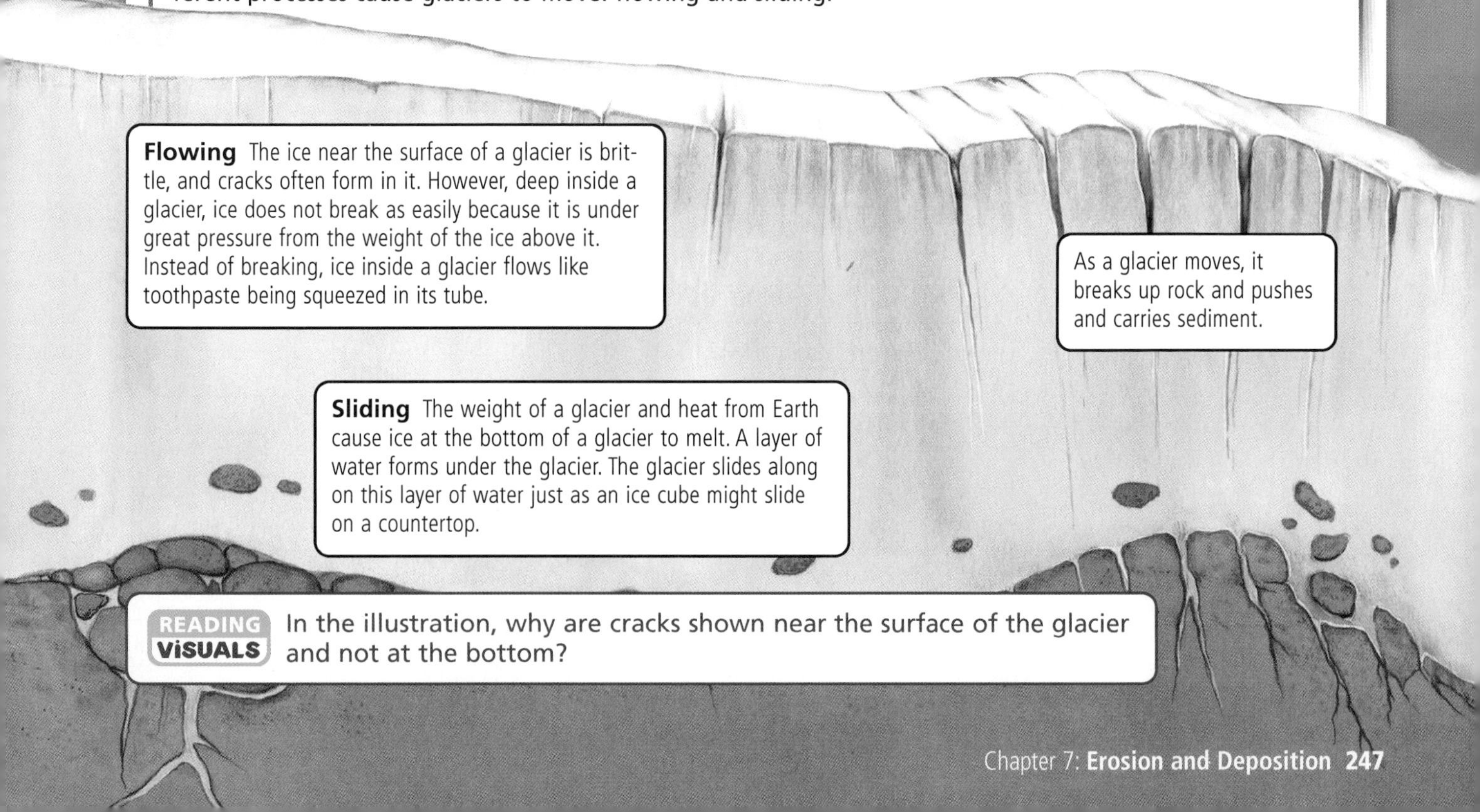

**Flowing** The ice near the surface of a glacier is brittle, and cracks often form in it. However, deep inside a glacier, ice does not break as easily because it is under great pressure from the weight of the ice above it. Instead of breaking, ice inside a glacier flows like toothpaste being squeezed in its tube.

As a glacier moves, it breaks up rock and pushes and carries sediment.

**Sliding** The weight of a glacier and heat from Earth cause ice at the bottom of a glacier to melt. A layer of water forms under the glacier. The glacier slides along on this layer of water just as an ice cube might slide on a countertop.

**READING VISUALS** In the illustration, why are cracks shown near the surface of the glacier and not at the bottom?

A moving glacier left abrasion lines on this rock.

## Glaciers deposit large amounts of sediment.

As glaciers have melted, they have shaped the landscapes of many places on Earth. As a glacier moves or expands, it transports a vast amount of sediment—a mix of boulders, small rocks, sand, and clay. It acts like a plow, pushing rock and soil and plucking out big blocks of rock. As a glacier moves over rock, it scratches and scrapes the rock in a process called abrasion. Abrasion leaves grooves on rock surfaces.

### Moraines

When glaciers expand and advance and then melt and retreat, they affect both the land underneath them and the land around them. A glacier pushes huge amounts of sediment to its sides and front. When the glacier retreats, the deposits of sediment remain as visible evidence that ice once moved through. The sediment left directly on the ground surface by a retreating glacier is called **till.**

A deposit of till left behind by a retreating glacier is called a **moraine** (muh-RAYN). The ridges of till deposited at the sides of a glacier are called lateral moraines. The till that shows how far a glacier advanced forms a deposit called an end moraine. Moraines formed by continental glaciers, such as those in North America during the last ice age, can be huge.

The blanket of till that a glacier deposits along its bottom is called a ground moraine. Rock deposits from glaciers can often be identified as till because the till rocks are different from the rock that was present before the glacier formed.

**CHECK YOUR READING** Draw a sketch of a glacier and label where lateral, end, and ground moraines would form.

A glacier scooped out this valley in the Sierra Nevada and left behind lateral moraines.

## Lakes

Besides ridges, hills, and blankets of till, melting glaciers also leave behind holes, or depressions, of various sizes that can become lakes. Landscapes shaped by glaciers are often dotted with small kettle lakes as well as larger lakes. A **kettle lake** is a bowl-shaped depression that was formed by a block of ice from a glacier and then became filled with water.

The last ice sheet in North America formed many kettle lakes in some regions. Kettle lakes are common in Michigan, Wisconsin, and Minnesota.

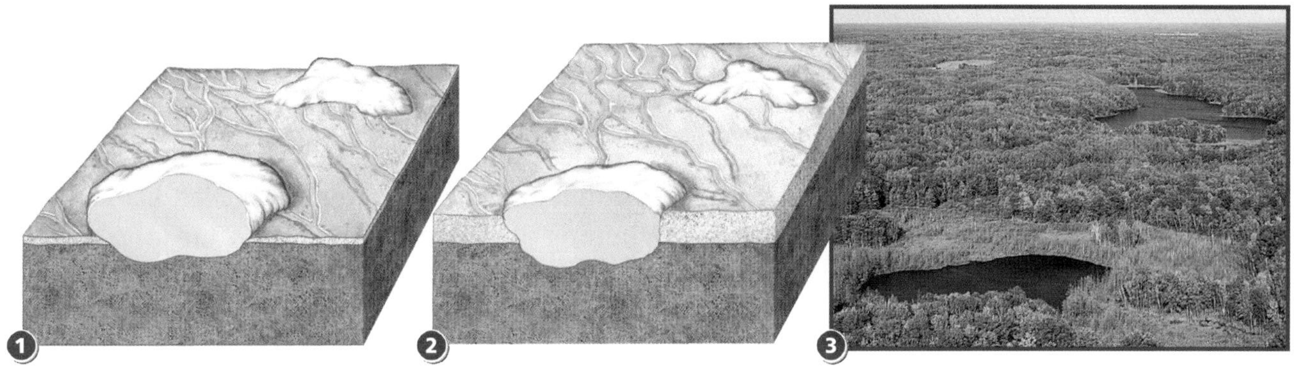


1. As a glacier moves away, it leaves huge blocks of ice.
2. Over time, sediment builds up around the ice.
3. The ice melts, leaving behind holes that become kettle lakes. These lakes are in Wisconsin.

# INVESTIGATE Kettle Lake Formation

### *How do kettle lakes form?*

DESIGN — YOUR OWN —

Kettle lakes form when sediment builds up around blocks of ice left behind by a retreating glacier. Use what you know about kettle lake formation to design a model of the process.

**SKILL FOCUS**
Designing models (6.2.a)

**MATERIALS**
- shallow tray
- ice cubes
- modeling clay
- sand
- gravel
- water

**TIME**
30 minutes

#### PROCEDURE

1. Use the tray, the ice cubes, and the other materials to model how sediment builds up around ice blocks.
2. Write a description of the process you used to make your model.

#### WHAT DO YOU THINK?

- Describe how your model worked. What did you do first? What happened next?
- Did your model accurately represent the formation of kettle lakes? Did it work? Why or why not?
- What were the limitations of your model? Are there any aspects of kettle lake formation that are not represented? If so, what are they?

## Great Lakes Formation

**1 14,000 Years Ago**

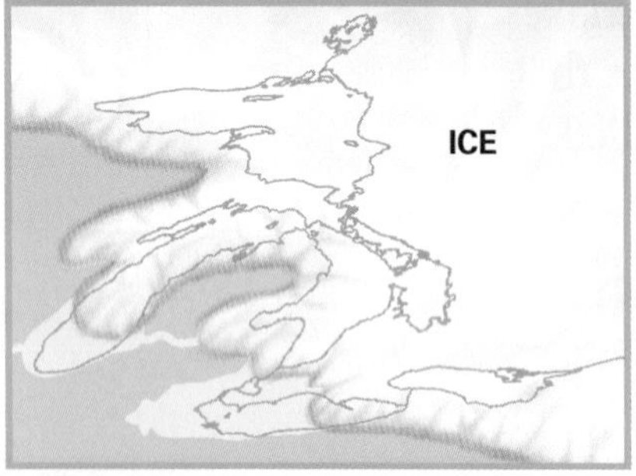


The ice sheet covering a land of river valleys began to retreat.

**2 7000 Years Ago**

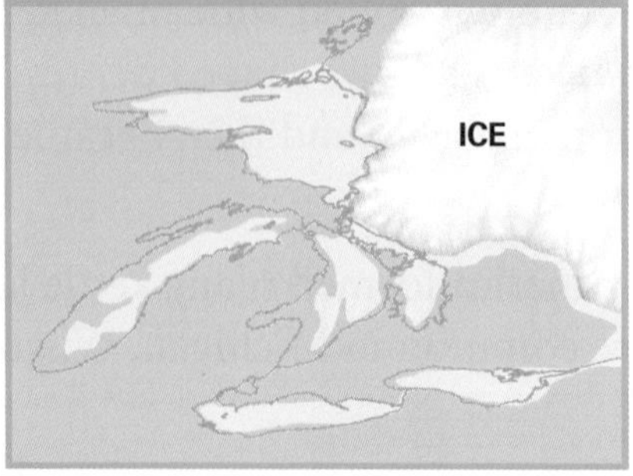


Water filled the holes carved out by the ice.

**3 Today**

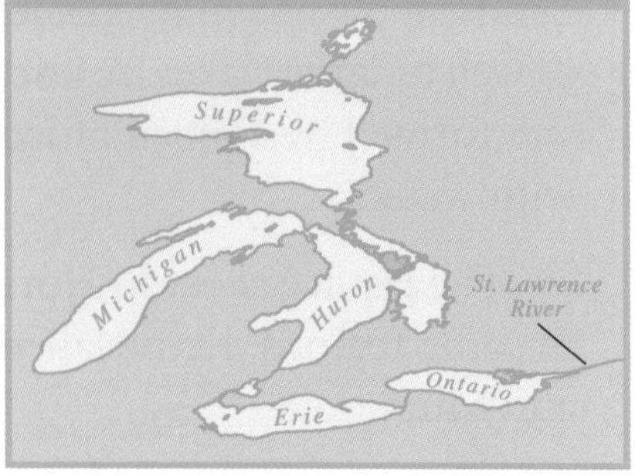


The Great Lakes contain 20 percent of the world's fresh lake water.

Many large lakes are the result of ice ages. In some places, lakes formed after glaciers in valleys melted. Moraines were left behind that blocked water from draining out. Many of these lakes are long and narrow, like the Finger Lakes in New York, which are named for their slender shape.

The Great Lakes were formed thousands of years ago as an ice sheet moved over the land and then melted. A million years ago, the region of the Great Lakes had many river valleys. The ice sheet dug out large depressions in the land and left piles of rock and debris that blocked water from draining out. In some areas, the enormous weight of the glacier actually caused the land to sink as much as one kilometer.

The ice sheet started to melt about 14,000 years ago. By about 7000 years ago, it had melted past what would become Lake Erie and Lake Ontario, the lakes farthest to the east.

**CHECK YOUR READING** What are two ways an ice sheet formed the Great Lakes?

# 7.4 Review

### KEY CONCEPTS

1. Describe the two processes that cause glaciers to move. (6.2.a)
2. What are the two major types of glaciers, and where are they found? (6.2.a)
3. Describe the land features left behind by glaciers that have melted and shrunk. (6.7.h)

### CRITICAL THINKING

4. **Compare and Contrast** Identify two ways in which the erosion effects of glaciers differ from those of rivers.
5. **Predict** How would glaciers be affected by changes in climate, such as global warming and global cooling?

### CHALLENGE

6. **Infer** Regions near the equator are generally the warmest on Earth. However, in one small area of Africa, there are glaciers close to the equator. Form a hypothesis to explain why these glaciers exist.

MATH in SCIENCE

**MATH TUTORIAL**
CLASSZONE.COM
Click on Math Tutorial for more help with making line graphs.

**Math** 6.MR.2.4
**Science** 6.2.a

## SKILL: CREATING A LINE GRAPH

# Snow Line Elevation and Latitude

Glaciers form above the snow line, the lowest elevation at which there is permanent snow in the summer. The snow line elevation depends on temperature and precipitation. In the hot tropics the snow line is high in the mountains, while at the poles it is near sea level. The table shows the snow line elevations at different locations on Earth. The latitude of each location indicates how far the location is from the equator. The latitude of the equator is 0 degrees, and the latitude of the North Pole is 90 degrees.

| Location | Latitude (degrees north) | Snow Line Elevation (meters) |
|---|---|---|
| North Pole | 90 | 0 |
| Juneau, Alaska | 58 | 1050 |
| Glacier National Park | 49 | 2600 |
| Sierra Nevada | 37 | 3725 |
| Himalayas (East Nepal) | 28 | 5103 |
| Ecuador | 0 | 4788 |

**Follow the steps below to make a line graph of the data.**

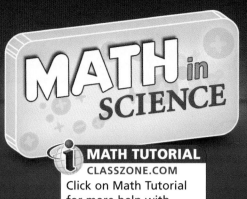

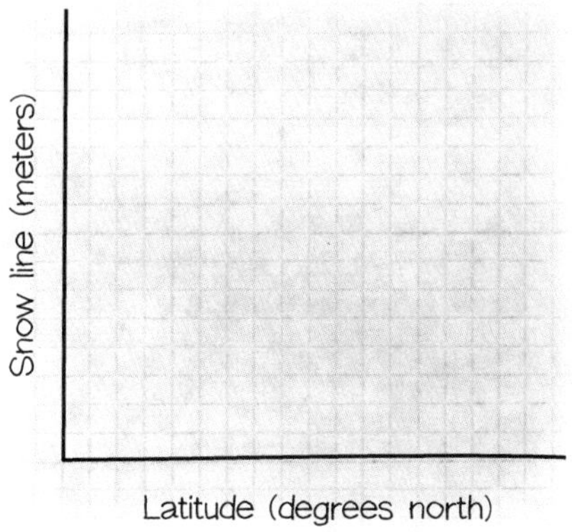


**(1)** On a sheet of graph paper, draw and label axes. Show latitude on the horizontal axis and snow line elevation on the vertical axis.

**(2)** Choose and mark a scale for each axis.

**(3)** Graph each point.

**(4)** Draw line segments to connect the points.

**Use your graph to answer the following questions.**

1. Mount Kenya is very close to the equator. Estimate the snow line elevation on Mount Kenya.
2. Mount Rainier is at 47 degrees north latitude and is 4389 meters tall. Can there be glaciers on Mount Rainier? If so, estimate the elevation above which the glaciers form.
3. Mount Washington in New Hampshire is at 45 degrees north latitude and is 1917 meters tall. Can there be glaciers on Mount Washington? If so, estimate their lowest elevation.

**CHALLENGE** Temperatures are hotter at the equator than at 28 degrees north latitude. Why is the snow line lower at the equator in Ecuador? (**Hint:** The answer involves precipitation.)

# Chapter Review

## the BIG idea

**Water, wind, and ice shape Earth's surface.**

CONTENT REVIEW
CLASSZONE.COM

## KEY CONCEPTS SUMMARY

### 1 Processes wear down and build up Earth's surface.

Water, wind, and ice move sediment in the process called **erosion**. The placement of sediment in a new location is **deposition**, part of the erosion process.

**VOCABULARY**
**erosion** p. 225
**deposition** p. 225
**mass wasting** p. 227

### 2 Moving water shapes land.

Water drains from land in **drainage basins,** which are separated by **divides.** As water flows over land and underground, it moves sediment and changes land features.

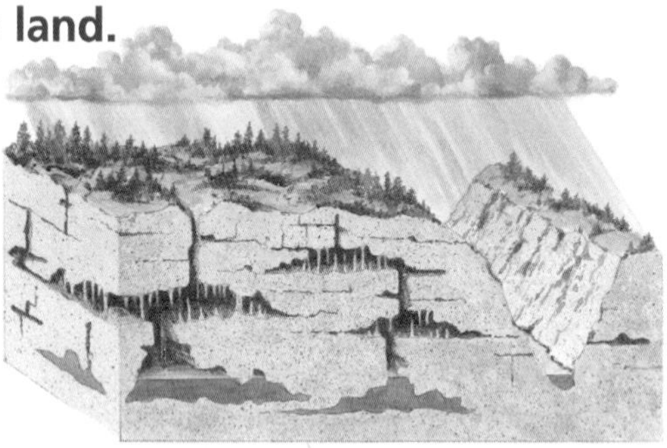

**VOCABULARY**
**drainage basin** p. 231
**divide** p. 231
**floodplain** p. 232
**alluvial fan** p. 233
**delta** p. 233
**sinkhole** p. 235

### 3 Waves and wind shape land.

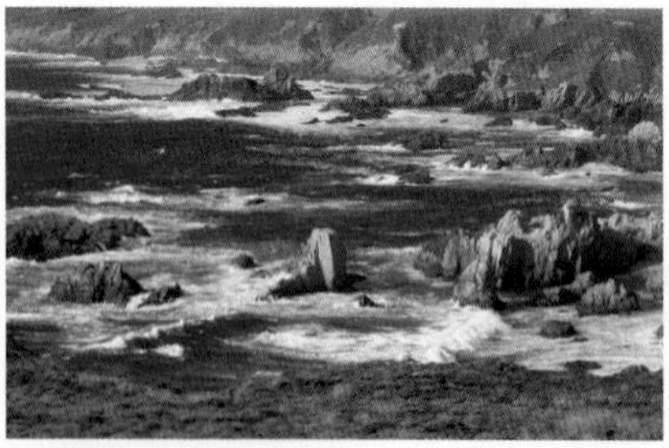

The action of water moves sand and builds up new landforms, such as **sandbars** and **barrier islands.** Wind forms **dunes.**

**VOCABULARY**
**longshore drift** p. 239
**longshore current** p. 239
**sandbar** p. 240
**barrier island** p. 240
**dune** p. 241
**loess** p. 242

### 4 Glaciers carve land and move sediments.

**Glaciers** are large bodies of ice that change landscapes as they move.

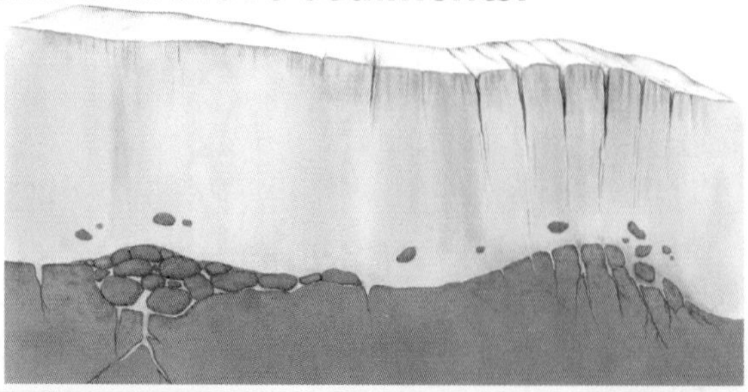

**VOCABULARY**
**glacier** p. 245
**till** p. 248
**moraine** p. 248
**kettle lake** p. 249

## Reviewing Vocabulary

*Copy and complete the chart below. Explain how each landscape feature is formed.*

| Feature | How It Forms |
|---|---|
| EXAMPLE delta | A river deposits sediment as it enters the ocean. |
| 1. alluvial fan | |
| 2. sinkhole | |
| 3. sandbar | |
| 4. barrier island | |
| 5. dune | |
| 6. loess | |
| 7. moraine | |
| 8. kettle lake | |

## Reviewing Key Concepts

**Multiple Choice** *Choose the letter of the best answer.*

**9.** The first stage in the erosion process is (6.2.a)
- **a.** deposition
- **b.** mass wasting
- **c.** drainage
- **d.** weathering

**10.** The main natural force responsible for mass movements of rocks and debris is (6.2.d)
- **a.** rainwater
- **b.** wind
- **c.** gravity
- **d.** fire

**11.** A sinkhole is formed by the collapse of (6.2.a)
- **a.** an alluvial fan
- **b.** a cavern
- **c.** a moraine
- **d.** a kettle lake

**12.** Rivers transport sediment to (6.2.b)
- **a.** drainage basins
- **b.** oceans and lakes
- **c.** the water table
- **d.** moraines

**13.** Drainage basins are separated by a (6.2.b)
- **a.** moraine
- **b.** divide
- **c.** tributary
- **d.** barrier island

**14.** In high mountains, a valley carved by a stream has the shape of a (6.2.b)
- **a.** U
- **b.** crescent
- **c.** plate
- **d.** V

**15.** An oxbow lake is formed by the cutting off of a (6.2.b)
- **a.** meander
- **b.** drainage basin
- **c.** sinkhole
- **d.** glacier

**16.** Sandbars, spits, and barrier islands can all be built up by (6.2.c)
- **a.** glaciers
- **b.** ocean waves
- **c.** wind
- **d.** mass wasting

**17.** A dune is a sand mound built up primarily by (6.7.h)
- **a.** gravity
- **b.** running water
- **c.** glaciers
- **d.** wind

**18.** Strong winds can transport large quantities of (6.7.h)
- **a.** gravel
- **b.** wet sand
- **c.** dry sand
- **d.** clay

**19.** A mountain valley carved by a glacier has the shape of a (6.7.h)
- **a.** U
- **b.** crescent
- **c.** bowl
- **d.** V

**Short Answer** *Answer each of the following questions in a sentence or two.*

**20.** How is deposition part of the erosion process? (6.2.a)

**21.** How can rainwater in the Rocky Mountains end up in the ocean? (6.2.a)

**22.** What is the effect of a longshore current on a beach? (6.2.c)

**23.** Why is a mass movement of mud called a flow? (6.2.d)

**24.** What visual evidence is a sign of creep? (6.2.d)

**25.** What is the connection between icebergs and glaciers? (6.7.h)

## Thinking Critically

*This photograph shows two glaciers joining to form one (A). Make a sketch of the glaciers to answer the next three questions.*

26. **APPLY** Place an arrow to show in which direction the main glacier (A) is moving. (6.7.h)

27. **ANALYZE** Mark the places where you think till would be found. (6.7.h)

28. **APPLY** Mark the location of a lateral moraine. (6.7.h)

29. **ANALYZE** Why does the main glacier not have an end moraine? (6.7.h)

30. **COMPARE AND CONTRAST** Compare the main glacier valley in the photograph with the valley at the far right (B). How are the valleys different? Explain why they might be different. (6.7.h)

31. **APPLY** In exploring an area of land, what clues would you look for to determine whether glaciers were once there? (6.7.h)

32. **COMPARE AND CONTRAST** How is a deposit of till from a glacier similar to a river delta? How is it different? (6.2.b)

33. **EVALUATE** If you were growing crops on a field near a slow-moving, curvy river, what would an advantage of the field's location be? What might be a disadvantage? (6.2.b)

34. **COMPARE AND CONTRAST** How are mudflows and mass wasting of rock similar? How are they different? Include references to speed and types of material in your answer. (6.2.d)

35. **INFER** If the wind usually blows from west to east over a large area of land, and the wind usually slows down over the eastern half of the area, where would you be likely to find loess in the area? Explain your answer. (6.7.h)

36. **APPLY** If you were considering a location for a house and were concerned about creep, what two factors about the land would you consider? (6.2.d)

37. **SYNTHESIZE** Describe how the processes of erosion and deposition are involved in the formation of kettle lakes. (6.2.b)

## the BIG idea

38. **SYNTHESIZE** Describe how snow falling onto the Continental Divide in the Rocky Mountains can be part of the process of erosion and deposition. Include the words *divide, glacier, stream,* and *ocean* in your answer. (6.2.a)

39. **PROVIDE EXAMPLES** Choose three examples of erosion processes—one each from Sections 7.2, 7.3, and 7.4. Explain how gravity is involved in each of these processes. (6.2.d)

## UNIT PROJECTS

Evaluate all the data, results, and information in your project folder. Prepare to present your project. Be ready to answer questions posed by your classmates about your results.

For more practice, go to . . .
TEST PRACTICE
CLASSZONE.COM

## Analyzing a Diagram

6.2.a, 6.2.b, 6.2.c, 6.2.d

*Use the diagram to answer the questions below.*

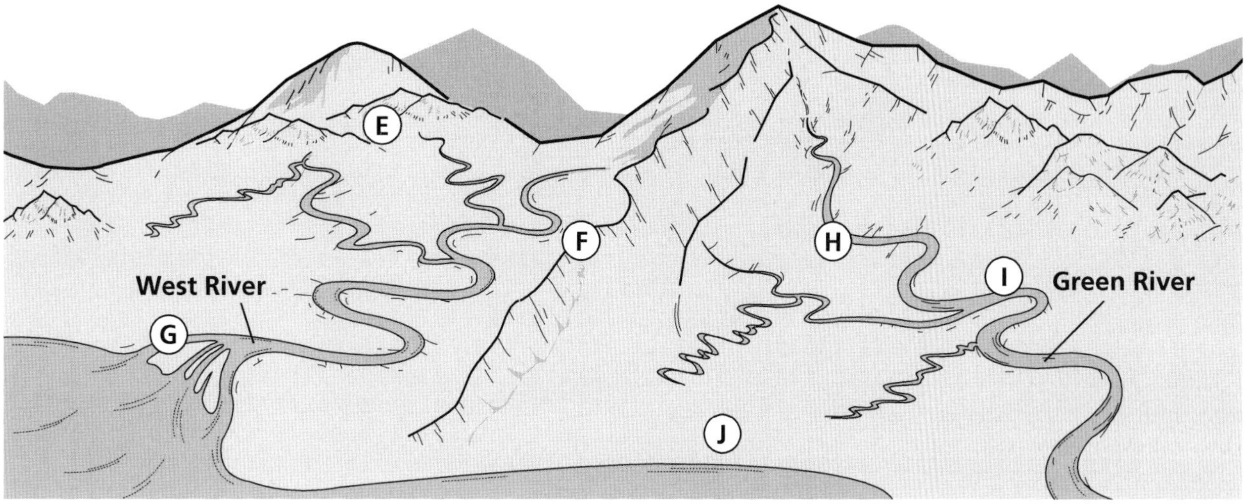

**1.** Where would a glacier be most likely to form?

**a.** E  **c.** G
**b.** F  **d.** H

**2.** Where is a divide?

**a.** E  **c.** H
**b.** F  **d.** I

**3.** Where is a delta?

**a.** E  **c.** G
**b.** F  **d.** J

**4.** Which process could move sediment from point E to point G?

**a.** weathering  **c.** deposition
**b.** erosion  **d.** drifting

**5.** Which word best describes the building up of sediment at point G?

**a.** weathering  **c.** deposition
**b.** erosion  **d.** drifting

**6.** Why might the water in the Green River move faster at point H than at point I?

**a.** The river at point H is warmer.
**b.** The river at point H is smaller.
**c.** The slope at point H is steeper.
**d.** More rain falls at point H.

## Extended Response

*Answer the two questions below in detail. Include some of the terms shown in the word box. In your answers, underline each term you use.*

| | | |
|---|---|---|
| ocean waves | currents | barrier island |
| grass | glaciers | kettle lakes |

**7.** Each year, Clark and his family visit the ocean. Clark notices that a sandbar near the coast is slightly larger each year. Predict what will happen if this trend continues.

**8.** Annika often goes fishing at one of several small, round lakes that are within 20 miles of her house in Minnesota. How might these lakes have formed?

# UNIT 3

# The Changing Earth

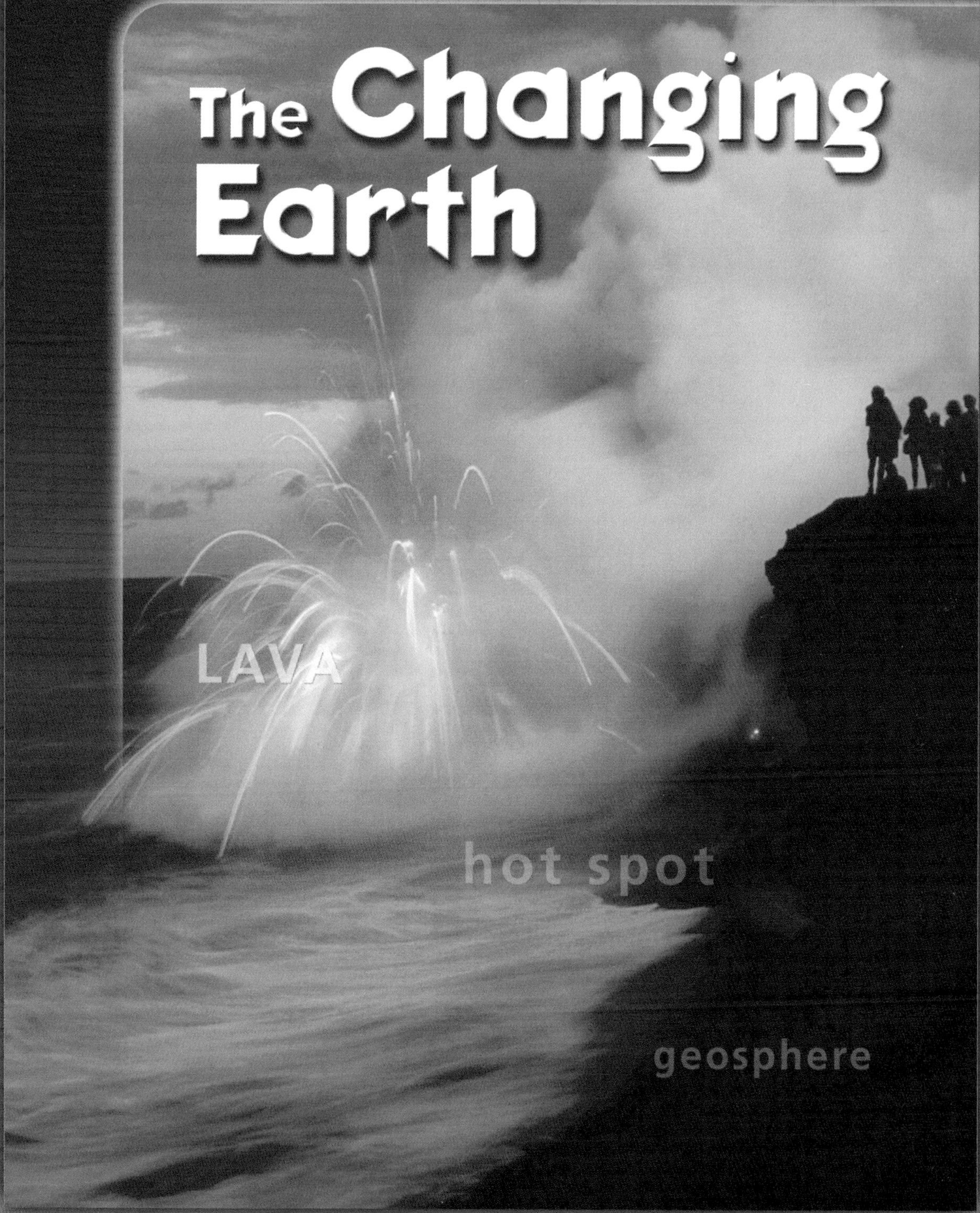


## Contents Overview

## FRONTIERS in Science

# Studying VOLCANOES with Satellites

**New ways of viewing Earth are giving scientists powerful tools for learning about and predicting volcanic eruptions.**

**California Content Standards**

**6.1.d** Students know that earthquakes are sudden motions along breaks in the crust called faults and that **volcanoes and fissures are locations where magma reaches the surface.**

**6.2.d** Students know earthquakes, **volcanic eruptions,** landslides, and floods change human and wildlife habitats.

**SCIENTIFIC AMERICAN FRONTIERS**

View the video segment "Paradise Postponed" to learn how scientists study volcanoes and predict eruptions.

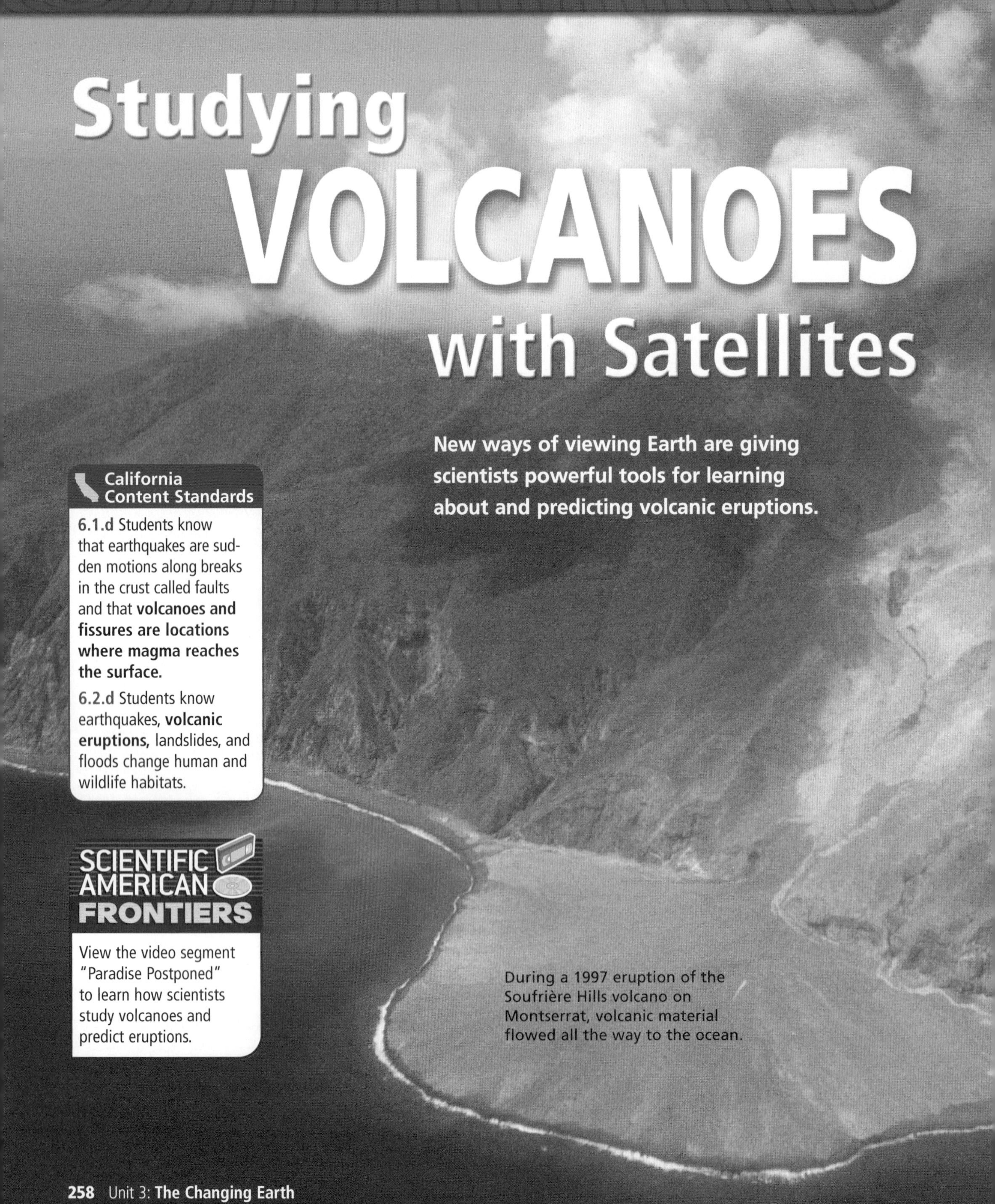

During a 1997 eruption of the Soufrière Hills volcano on Montserrat, volcanic material flowed all the way to the ocean.

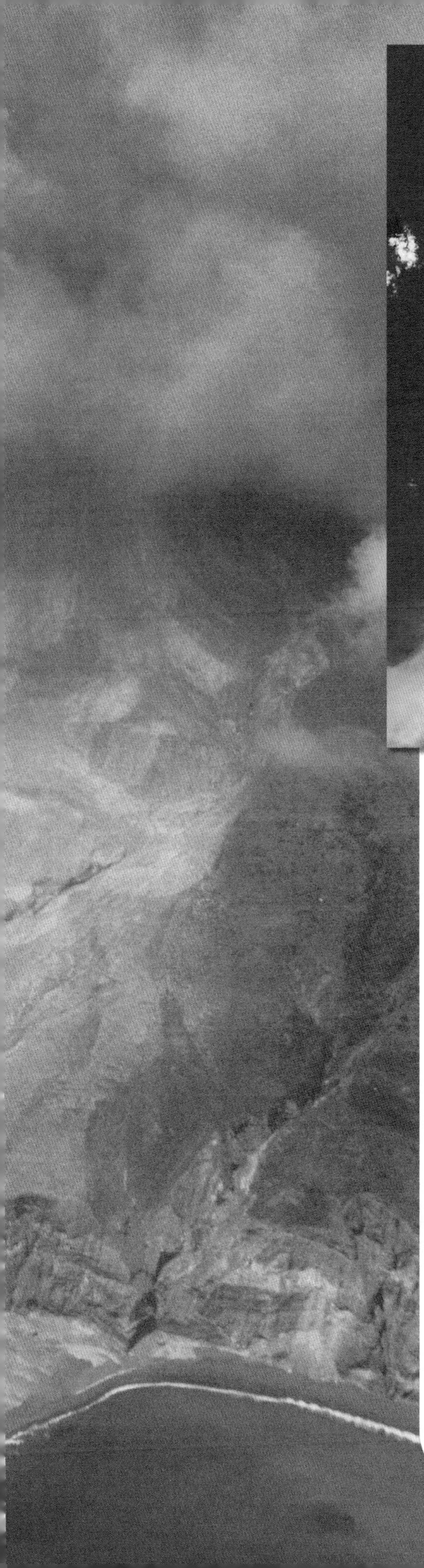

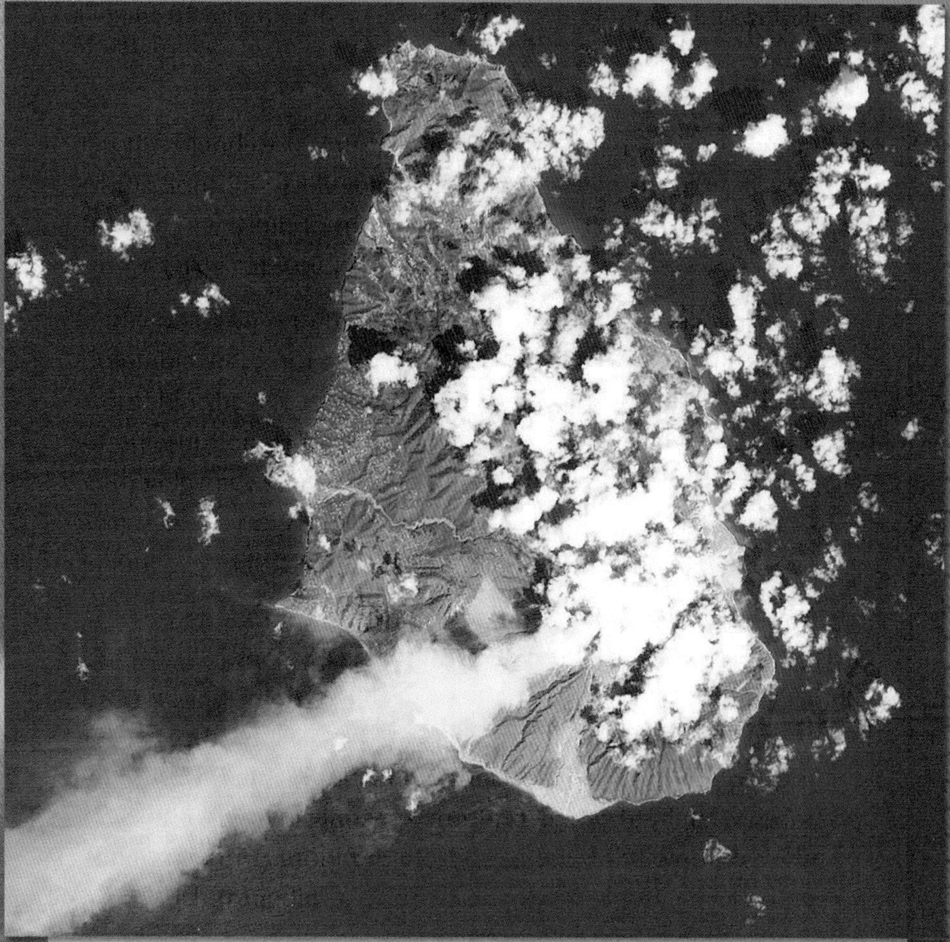

This photograph was taken from a satellite on October 29, 2002. It shows a plume of volcanic ash and gases rising from Soufrière Hills volcano in Montserrat.

## Deadly Eruptions

On the island of Montserrat in the Caribbean Sea, small eruptions of the Soufrière Hills volcano began in 1995. These early warnings gave people time to move away several months before the first of the large explosions.

People living in the towns near Nevado del Ruiz volcano in Colombia were not so lucky. On a night in November 1985, a storm hid the snow-covered volcano. No one could see the start of an eruption. Huge amounts of snow and ice melted and mixed with volcanic ash to form mudflows that killed 25,000 people. The flow that buried much of the town of Armero traveled 74 kilometers in just two and one-half hours.

Throughout history volcanic eruptions have caused some of the world's worst disasters. Warnings might have saved hundreds of thousands of lives. But in most cases people had no idea that falling rocks, toxic gases, or other deadly effects of an erupting volcano would soon surround their area. By the time people realized that a volcano was erupting, it was too late to get away. Today, scientists monitor volcanoes around the world to help avoid such tragedies.

A 1996 eruption of Alaska's Pavlof volcano was the first to be predicted by using data from space. The satellite image recorded during the eruption shows a hot area on the volcano in red.

## Predicting Volcanic Eruptions

Scientists who study volcanoes paid close attention when an instrument on a weather satellite unexpectedly "saw" hot ground in 1996. The instrument's usual function is to measure cloud temperatures. But in this case it detected an area of increased heat on Alaska's Pavlof volcano. The scientists predicted that the volcano would soon erupt. Three days later, it did. This eruption was the first to be predicted by using information from space. Now computers check satellite data as they receive the data. Any unusually hot areas trigger an automatic e-mail alert to scientists.

In 1999 NASA launched the *Terra* satellite as part of a program to study Earth's surface and atmosphere. Among *Terra*'s instruments is one that detects heat given off by Earth's surface. When scientists observe an unusual increase in surface temperature, they find out whether magma, or melted rock, is rising underground. In some cases unusual heat has been the first sign that a volcano may soon erupt.

## After an Eruption

Satellites are also used to monitor eruptions as they happen. Lava flows show up clearly, as you can see in the *Terra* image on page 261. In addition, satellites are used to track the locations of volcanic ash and gas clouds. Airplanes flying into this material can be severely damaged, so pilots need to know where it is. Volcanic material in

### SCIENTIFIC AMERICAN FRONTIERS

**View the "Paradise Postponed" segment of your *Scientific American Frontiers* video to learn how scientists monitor volcanic eruptions.**

**IN THIS SCENE FROM THE VIDEO** **Scientist Barry Voigt looks at the effects of a powerful eruption that happened a few days earlier.**

**STUDYING VOLCANOES** Until 1995 the Caribbean island of Montserrat was a peaceful vacation spot. Then the island's volcano began to erupt. Over the next two years, the volcano erupted dozens of times. Hot ash, rocks, and gases came pouring out. These eruptions destroyed most of the island's towns and drove away many of the people who lived there.

Scientists from around the world have gone to Montserrat to find out how well they can predict eruptions. Seismic stations buried near the volcano detect earthquakes. An earthquake can be a sign that the volcano is about to erupt. Scientists can also predict an eruption by studying changes in the lava that has built up on top of the volcano. When an eruption does occur, scientists visit the site to collect rocks and measure the volcanic ash flow.

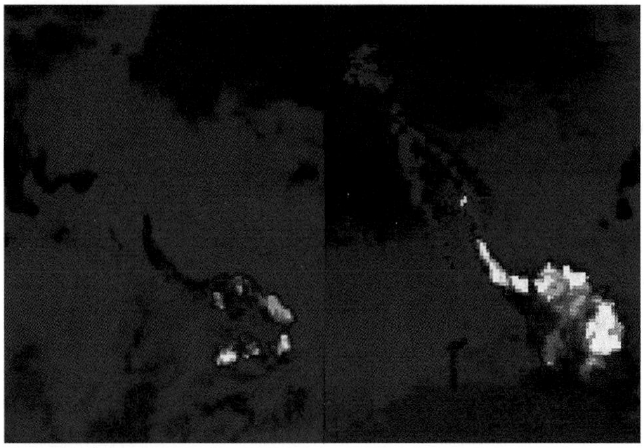

Data collected by the *Terra* satellite show how a Hawaiian lava flow moved. It entered the ocean on May 13, 2000 (left). It is shown again on August 1, 2000 (right).

the air can be hard to see or to tell from normal clouds, especially at night. Satellites are very helpful in identifying and tracking eruptions in areas where there are few or no people.

## Explosive Neighbors

Scientists use satellites such as *Terra* to monitor restless volcanoes near cities. Mount Rainier, a volcano in Washington, is located near the cities of Seattle and Tacoma. In the past, heat from eruptions has melted large amounts of the ice and snow at the top of the volcano. This created mudflows that destroyed everything in their paths. Another extremely dangerous volcano is Mount Vesuvius in Italy. Warnings before eruptions of such volcanoes can allow the millions of people who live near them to get to a safe place.

### UNANSWERED Questions

Even when scientists predict that a volcano will erupt soon, many questions still cannot be answered.

- How powerful will the next eruption be?
- On what day (or even during what week) will the volcano erupt?
- How much magma is rising under the volcano? How fast is it rising? Will it stop?

## UNIT PROJECTS

**As you study this unit, work alone or with a group on one of the projects listed below.**

### Review Movie Science (6.7.d, 6.7.e)

Review a movie that includes a volcanic eruption. Evaluate how accurate the movie's depiction of a volcano is.

- Visit the U.S. Geological Survey Web site for a list of movies about volcanoes, such as *Dante's Peak.*
- Evaluate one movie and prepare a radio or TV report.

### Earthquake Report (6.7.b, 6.7.d)

Make a map of the volcanic eruptions and earthquakes that occur around the world while you are studying this unit.

- Write a news script and create a chart to show the events' locations and intensities.
- Present your findings as a special TV report for an evening news program.

### Ash-Fall Fossil Exhibit (6.7.b, 6.7.f)

Prepare an exhibit showing how volcanic ash can preserve fossils of the organisms it buries. You could begin by researching Ashfall Fossil Beds State Historical Park in Nebraska.

- Create a poster that shows the major steps in the formation of fossils of organisms in volcanic ash.
- Make models or tracings of some ash-fall fossils.
- Display the poster and models as a classroom or Web-site exhibit.

**CAREER CENTER**
CLASSZONE.COM

Learn more about careers in volcanology.

CHAPTER

# 8 Plate Tectonics

## the BIG idea

**The movement of tectonic plates causes geologic changes on Earth.**

## Key Concepts

SECTION
**1 Earth has several layers.**
Learn about Earth's interior and its rigid surface plates.

SECTION
**2 Continents change position over time.**
Learn how continental drift and plate tectonics changed the way people view Earth.

SECTION
**3 Plates move apart.**
Learn about the three types of plate boundaries and what happens when plates move apart.

SECTION
**4 Plates converge or scrape past each other.**
Learn what geologic events occur at these plate boundaries.

**California ClassZone**

CLASSZONE.COM

Chapter 8 online resources: Content Review, two Visualizations, two Resource Centers, Math Tutorial, Test Practice

***What might have made this huge crack in Earth's surface?***

# EXPLORE the BIG idea

## Convection in Action

6.3.c Students know heat flows in solids by conduction (which involves no flow of matter) and in fluids by conduction and by convection (which involves flow of matter).

Put a medium-sized pot of water on to boil. Place a small wet sponge on the water. Watch the water and sponge as the water heats.

**Observe and Think**
What happened to the water as it heated? What happened to the sponge as the water became hotter? How do the movements of the water and the sponge relate to convection?

## Internet Activity: Interior of Earth

6.1.b Students know Earth is composed of several layers: a cold, brittle lithosphere; a hot, convecting mantle; and a dense, metallic core.

Go to **ClassZone.com** to explore Earth's layers. Find out how scientists learned what the interior, or inside, of Earth is like.

**Observe and Think**
Science fiction books and movies show people traveling to the center of Earth. Do you think this can happen any time soon? Give an explanation of your answer using what you've found out about the properties of Earth's interior.

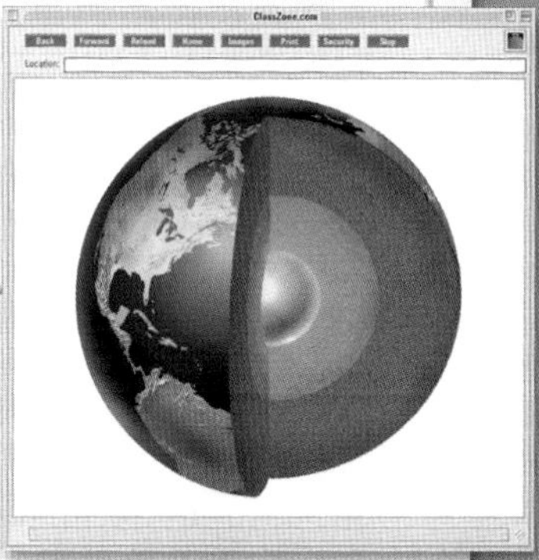

NSTA scilinks.org SCiLINKS
Plates **Code: MDL052**

CHAPTER 8

# Getting Ready to Learn

## CONCEPT REVIEW

- Most rocks are made of minerals.
- Different types of rocks are formed under different temperatures and pressures.
- Earth's surface has changed over millions of years.

## VOCABULARY REVIEW

**density** p. 28
**mineral** p. 184
**rock** p. 187
**magma** p. 191

**CONTENT REVIEW**
CLASSZONE.COM
Review concepts and vocabulary.

## TAKING NOTES

### SUPPORTING MAIN IDEAS

Make a chart to show main ideas and the information that supports them. Copy each blue heading. Below each heading, add supporting information, such as reasons, explanations, and examples.

### VOCABULARY STRATEGY

Place each vocabulary term at the center of a **description wheel** diagram. Write some words describing it on the spokes.

See the Note-Taking Handbook on pages R45–R51.

SCIENCE NOTEBOOK

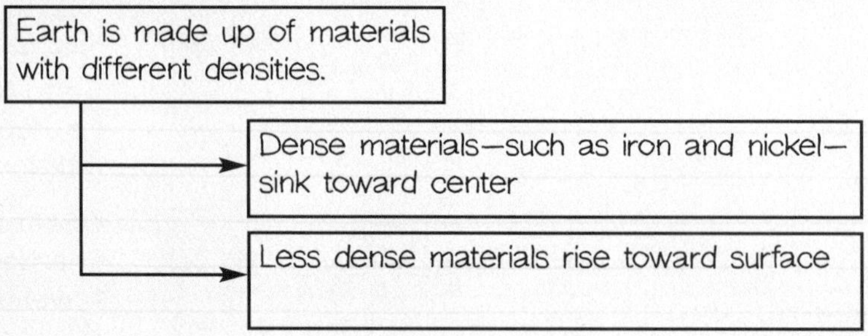
Earth is made up of materials with different densities.
Dense materials—such as iron and nickel—sink toward center
Less dense materials rise toward surface

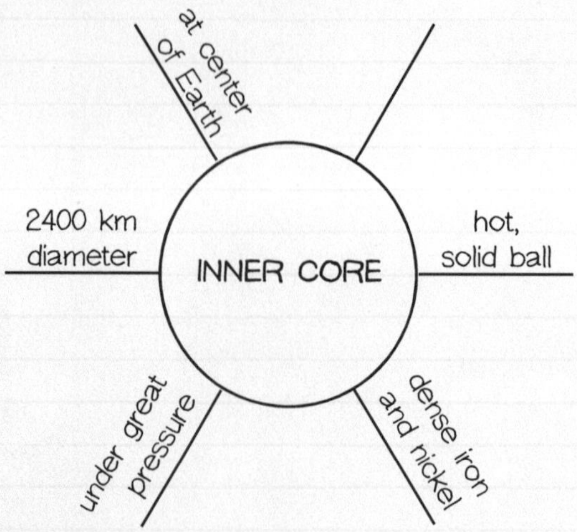
INNER CORE
at center of Earth
2400 km diameter
hot, solid ball
under great pressure
dense iron and nickel

KEY CONCEPT

# 8.1 Earth has several layers.

**CALIFORNIA Content Standards**

6.1.a Students know evidence of plate tectonics is derived from the fit of the continents; the location of earthquakes, volcanoes, and midocean ridges; and the distribution of fossils, rock types, and ancient climatic zones.

6.1.b Students know Earth is composed of several layers: a cold, brittle lithosphere; a hot, convecting mantle; and a dense, metallic core.

**BEFORE, you learned**

- Minerals and rocks are the building blocks of Earth
- Different types of rocks make up Earth's surface

**NOW, you will learn**

- About the different properties of Earth's layers
- About the plates that make up Earth's outermost layers

**VOCABULARY**

**inner core** p. 266
**outer core** p. 266
**mantle** p. 267
**crust** p. 267
**lithosphere** p. 267
**asthenosphere** p. 267
**tectonic plate** p. 268

**EXPLORE Density** (6.1.b)

### *Will a denser material sink or float?*

**PROCEDURE**

1. Add equal amounts of water to the cups. Add 3 spoonfuls of salt to one of the cups. Stir until the salt is dissolved.
2. Add 10 drops of food coloring to the cup with the salt water.
3. Gently pour about one-third of the colored salt water into the cup of fresh water. Observe what happens.

**WHAT DO YOU THINK?**

- What did you observe when the two types of water were mixed?
- What does this activity tell you about materials with different densities in Earth's layers?

**MATERIALS**

- 2 clear plastic cups
- tap water
- table salt
- plastic spoon
- food coloring

## Earth is made up of materials with different densities.

**SUPPORTING MAIN IDEAS** Support the main ideas about Earth's layers with details and examples.

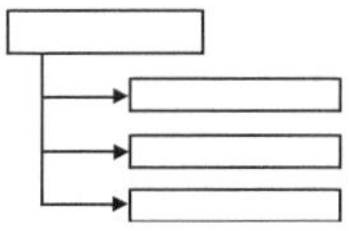

Scientists think that Earth formed about 4.6 billion years ago. Bits of material ran into each other and stuck together. The planet grew larger as more and more material was added. Intense heat was produced by these impacts, radioactive decay, and Earth's gravity. The young planet became a glowing ball of melted rock.

In time, denser materials, such as iron and nickel, sank toward the center of Earth. Less dense materials moved toward the surface. Other materials settled between the planet's center and its surface. Slowly, Earth's main layers formed—the core, the mantle, and the crust.

## Earth's layers have different properties.

**VOCABULARY**
Draw a description wheel diagram in your notebook for each term.

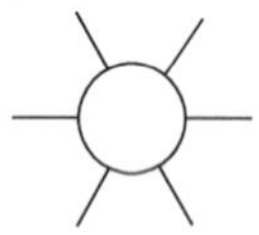

How do scientists know what Earth's deep interior is like? After all, no one has seen it. To explore the interior, scientists study the energy from earthquakes. The energy travels through Earth in the same way that ripples move through a pond. The energy moves slower through less dense materials or liquids. It moves faster through denser materials or solids. In this way, scientists can figure out what each layer is made of and how thick the layers are.

### Core, Mantle, Crust

The core is Earth's densest region and is made up of two parts. The **inner core** is a ball of hot, solid metals. There is great pressure at the center of Earth. This squeezes the atoms of the metals so closely together that the core remains solid despite the intense heat.

The **outer core** is a layer of liquid metals around the inner core. The temperature and pressure in the outer core are lower than in the inner core. The lower pressure allows the metals to remain liquid.

**Earth's Layers**

**Earth's layers formed as denser materials sank toward the center and less dense materials rose toward the surface.**

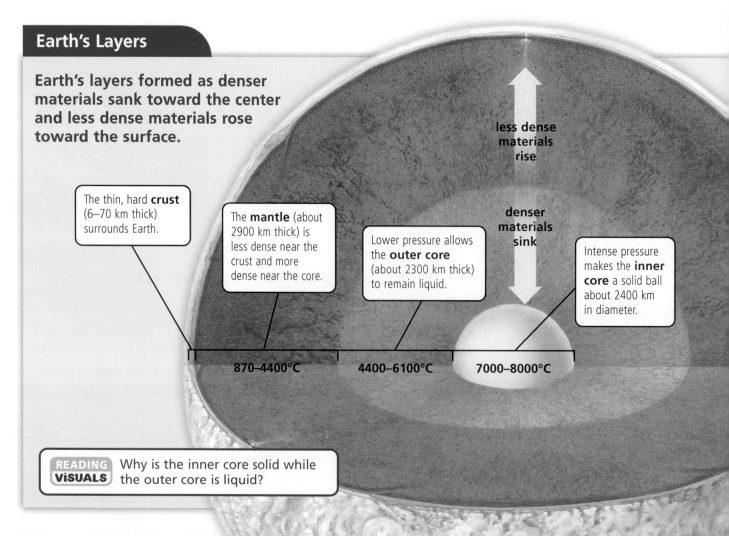

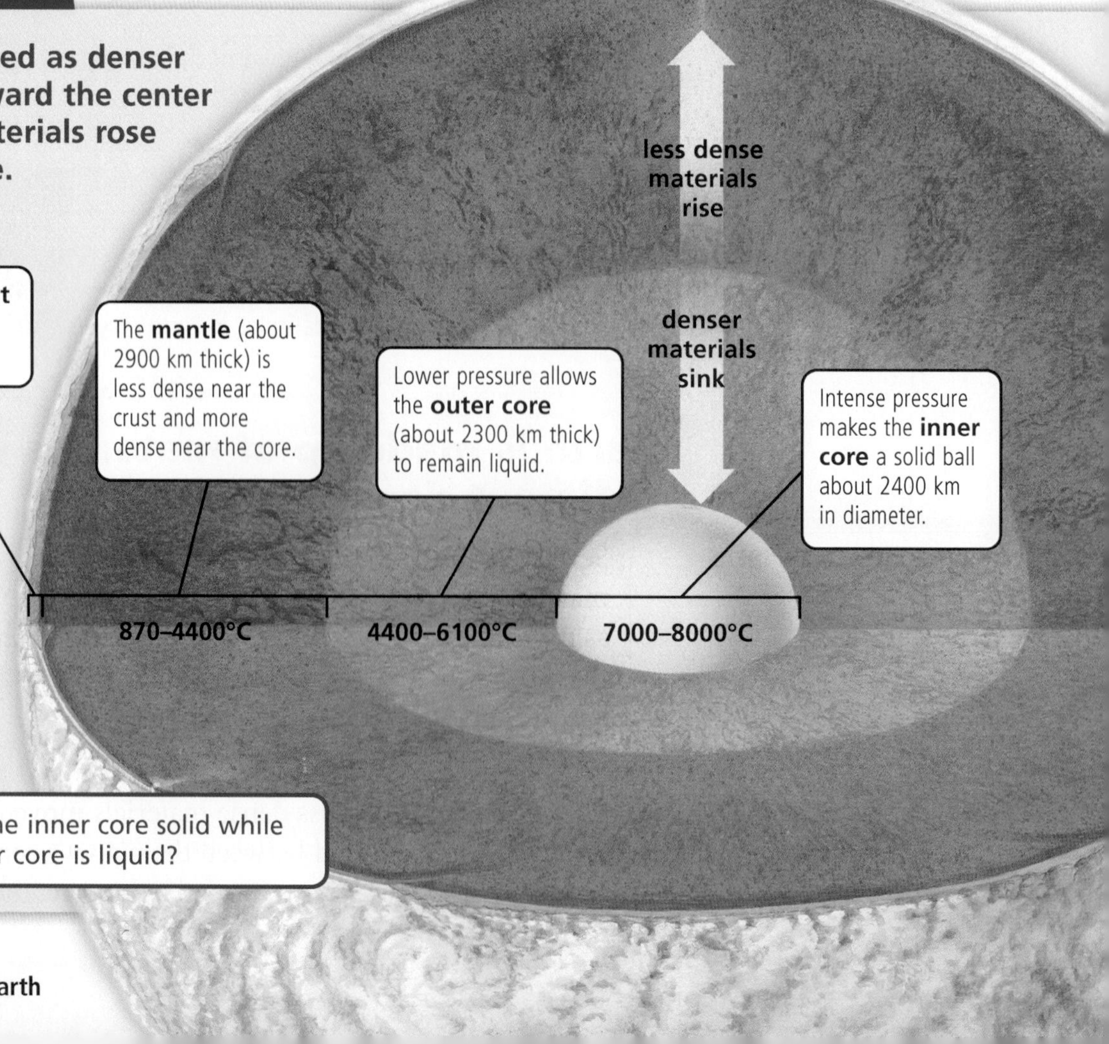

less dense materials rise
denser materials sink
The thin, hard crust (6–70 km thick) surrounds Earth.
The mantle (about 2900 km thick) is less dense near the crust and more dense near the core.
Lower pressure allows the outer core (about 2300 km thick) to remain liquid.
Intense pressure makes the inner core a solid ball about 2400 km in diameter.
870–4400°C
4400–6100°C
7000–8000°C

**READING VISUALS** Why is the inner core solid while the outer core is liquid?

The **mantle** is Earth's thickest layer. It is nearly 2900 kilometers (1700 mi) thick. The mantle is made of hot rock and is less dense than the thick core, which is made of metals. The very top part of the mantle is cool and hard. Just below that, the rock is hot and soft enough to move like a thick paste.

The **crust** is a thin layer of cool rock. It surrounds Earth like a shell surrounds an egg. There are two basic types of crust. Continental crust includes all continents and some major islands. Oceanic crust makes up the ocean floor. Look at the diagram below. You can see that Earth's crust is thinnest under the ocean and thickest under continental mountain ranges. The crust is home to life on Earth.

## Lithosphere and Asthenosphere

The **lithosphere** (LIHTH-uh-SFEER) is made up of Earth's crust and the very top of the mantle. This layer is cold and brittle. The lithosphere sits on top of the **asthenosphere** (as-THEHN-uh-SFEER). This is a layer of hotter, softer rock in the upper mantle. The asthenosphere is soft enough to flow slowly like hot tar. You can imagine the lithosphere as solid pieces of pavement resting on hot tar.

**READING TiP**

The Greek prefix *litho-* means "stone" or "rock." The Greek word *asthenēs* means "weak."

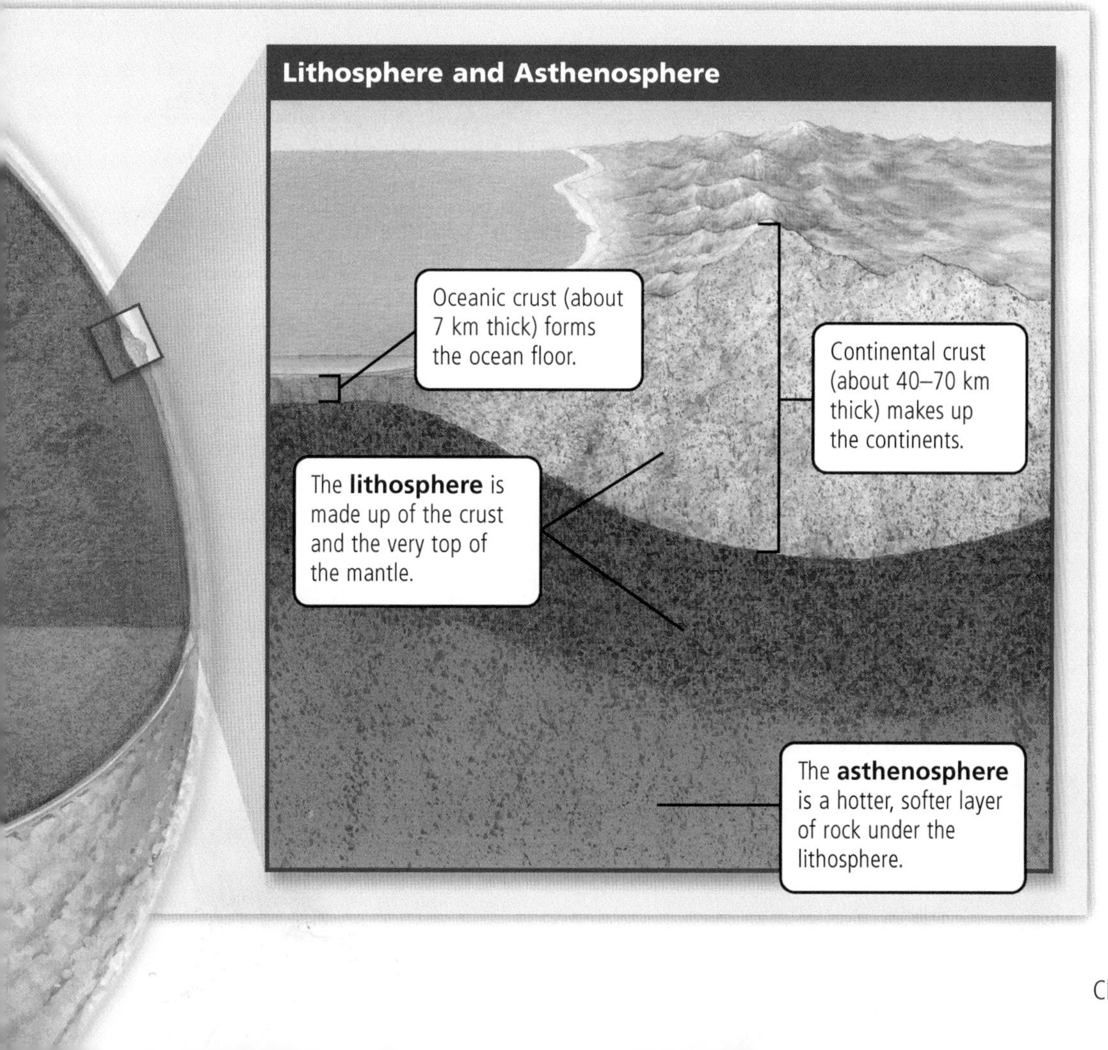

Lithosphere and Asthenosphere
Oceanic crust (about 7 km thick) forms the ocean floor.
Continental crust (about 40–70 km thick) makes up the continents.
The lithosphere is made up of the crust and the very top of the mantle.
The asthenosphere is a hotter, softer layer of rock under the lithosphere.

# INVESTIGATE Earth's Different Layers

## How can you model Earth's layers?

**SKILL FOCUS**
Modeling (6.1.b)

**MATERIALS**
- clear plastic cup
- small colored wooden beads
- gravel
- stirring stick
- tap water

**TIME**
15 minutes

### PROCEDURE

1. Put a layer of wooden beads about 1 centimeter thick at the bottom of a clear plastic cup or small jar.
2. Put a layer of gravel about 2 centimeters thick on top of the wooden beads. Stir the beads and gravel until they are well mixed.
3. Put another layer of gravel about 1 centimeter thick on top of the mix. Do NOT mix this layer of gravel.
4. SLOWLY fill the cup about two-thirds full of water. Be sure not to disturb the layers in the cup.
5. Stir the beads and gravel with the stick. Observe what happens.

### WHAT DO YOU THINK?

- What happened to the materials when you stirred them?
- How do you think this model represents the layers of Earth?

**CHALLENGE** What could you add to the model to represent Earth's solid core?

## The lithosphere is made up of many plates.

**READING TIP**
The word *tectonic* comes from the Greek word *tecktōn,* which means "builder." Tectonic plates are constantly building and changing landforms and oceans on Earth.

As scientists studied Earth's surface, they discovered that the lithosphere does not form a continuous shell around Earth. Instead, they found that the lithosphere is broken into many large slabs of rock called **tectonic plates** (tehk-TAHN-ihk). Scientists think that these giant plates formed early in Earth's history.

Tectonic plates fit together like a jigsaw puzzle. You could compare the lithosphere to the cracked shell of a hard-boiled egg. The shell may be broken into many pieces, but it still forms a "crust" around the egg itself.

Most large tectonic plates include both continental crust and oceanic crust, as shown in the diagram on page 269. Most of the continental crust rises above the ocean. The rest of the plate is thin oceanic crust, or sea floor, and is underwater. The next time you look at the continents on a world map, remember you are seeing only the part of Earth's crust that rises above the ocean.

**CHECK YOUR READING** Why do you see only part of Earth's crust on a typical world map?

## African Plate

**Most tectonic plates have both continental and oceanic crust.**

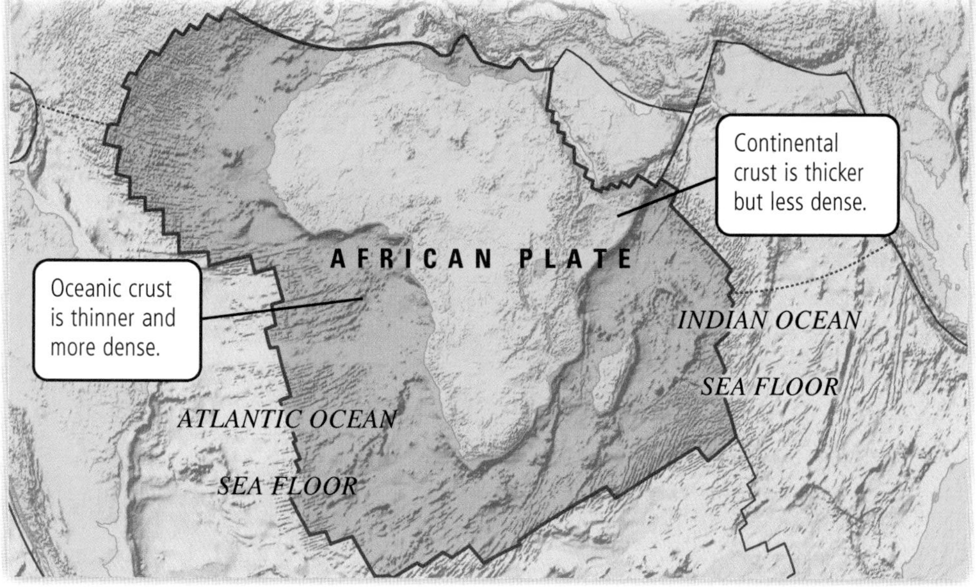

Continental crust is thicker but less dense.
AFRICAN PLATE
Oceanic crust is thinner and more dense.
INDIAN OCEAN
SEA FLOOR
ATLANTIC OCEAN
SEA FLOOR

In the diagram above, much of the African Plate is shaded dark blue. This part lies underwater. The continent of Africa, which looks large on a world map, is actually about half the size of the entire plate. The plate's oceanic crust forms part of the sea floor of the Atlantic and Indian oceans and of the Mediterranean Sea. The ocean crusts of other plates make up the rest of the sea floors.

Earth's layers and tectonic plates are two of the most important discoveries in geology. They helped solve a mystery that had puzzled people for nearly 400 years. The mystery involved two questions. Have the continents always been where they are today? If not, how did they move to their present positions? In Section 8.2, you will find out how scientists are answering these questions.

# 8.1 Review

### KEY CONCEPTS

1. Briefly describe the inner and outer cores, the mantle, and the crust. (6.1.b)
2. In what ways is the lithosphere different from the asthenosphere? (6.1.b)
3. Describe the structure of most tectonic plates. (6.1.b)

### CRITICAL THINKING

4. **Draw Conclusions** Suppose you are looking at a scene that has mountains near an ocean. Where do you think the crust would be the thickest? Why?
5. **Hypothesize** What would Earth look like if most of its crust was above sea level?

### CHALLENGE

6. **Predict** You have learned that Earth's lithosphere is made up of many plates. How do you think this fact might help scientists solve the mystery of the moving continents?

KEY CONCEPT

# 8.2 Continents change position over time.

**CALIFORNIA Content Standards**

**6.1.a** Students know evidence of plate tectonics is derived from the fit of the continents; the location of earthquakes, volcanoes, and midocean ridges; and the distribution of fossils, rock types, and ancient climatic zones.

**6.3.c** Students know heat flows in solids by conduction (which involves no flow of matter) and in fluids by conduction and by convection (which involves flow of matter).

**BEFORE, you learned**

- Earth's main layers are the core, the mantle, and the crust
- The lithosphere and asthenosphere are the topmost layers of Earth
- The lithosphere is made up of tectonic plates

**NOW, you will learn**

- How the continental drift hypothesis was developed
- About evidence for plate movement from the sea floor
- How scientists developed the theory of plate tectonics

**VOCABULARY**

**continental drift** p. 270
**Pangaea** p. 272
**mid-ocean ridge** p. 272
**convection** p. 273
**convection current** p. 273
**theory of plate tectonics** p. 274

**EXPLORE Movements of Continents** (6.1.a)

### *How do you put together a giant continent?*

**PROCEDURE**

1. Work with a small group. Draw the outline of a large landmass. Fill in mountains, rivers, lakes, and any other features you like.
2. Cut out your landmass. Then tear the drawing into several pieces and mix the pieces up. Ask another group to put the puzzle together.

**WHAT DO YOU THINK?**

- What clues helped you fit the pieces together?
- Do any lands on a world map seem to fit together?

**MATERIALS**

- sheet of paper
- colored marking pens
- scissors

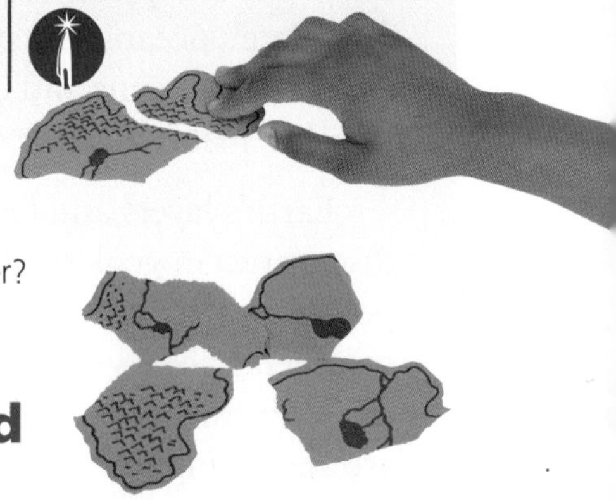

## Continents join together and split apart.

The idea that Earth's surface might be moving is not new. As far back as the 1500s, when mapmakers started including North and South America on their world maps, they noticed something odd. The western coast of Africa and the eastern coast of South America seemed to fit together like pieces of a puzzle. Were these continents joined at one time?

In the late 1800s, German scientist Alfred Wegener (VAY-guh-nuhr) began studying this question. In 1912 he proposed a hypothesis known as **continental drift.** According to Wegener's hypothesis, Earth's continents were once joined in a single landmass. They gradually moved, or drifted, apart. For many years, people did not accept Wegener's ideas. In the mid-1900s scientists found new evidence that made them take continental drift more seriously.

**VOCABULARY**
Draw a description wheel diagram in your notebook for *continental drift*.

## Evidence for Continental Drift

Wegener gathered evidence for his hypothesis from fossils, from studies of ancient climate, and from the geology of continents.

**Fossils** Wegener learned that the fossils of an ancient reptile, *Mesosaurus* (MEHZ-uh-SAWR-uhs), had been discovered in South America and western Africa. This small reptile lived about 270 million years ago. Its fossils were not found anywhere else in the world. Wegener said this fact could easily be explained if South America and Africa were once joined. See the map below.

**Climate** Evidence of climate change also supported Wegener's hypothesis. For example, Greenland today lies near the Arctic Circle and is mostly covered in ice. Yet fossils of tropical plants can be found on its shores. In contrast, South Africa today has a warm climate. Yet its rocks were deeply scratched by ice sheets that once covered the area.

Wegener suggested that these continents had moved, carrying their fossils and rocks with them. For example, Greenland had once been near the equator and had slowly moved to the Arctic Circle. South Africa, once closer to the South Pole, had moved slowly north to a warmer region.

**Geology** Wegener's best evidence for continental drift came from the kinds of rocks that make up the continents. He showed that the rock found in Brazil matched the rock found in western Africa. Also, limestone layers in the Appalachian Mountains of North America were exactly like the limestone in Scotland's Highlands.

**READING TIP**

*Climate* refers to a pattern of wind, temperature, and rain or snow that occurs in a region over time. Earth's climates have changed many times in the planet's long history.

**CHECK YOUR READING** Which evidence for continental drift do you think is the most convincing? Explain your answer.

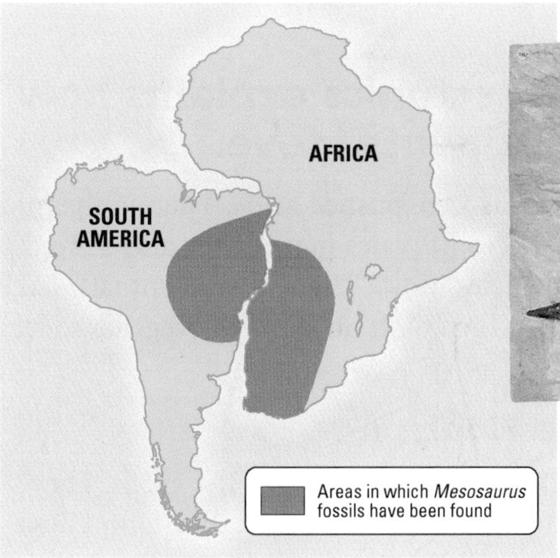

The reptile *Mesosaurus* was about 45 cm (18 in.) long. This fossil was found in Brazil, South America.

## Pangaea and Continental Drift

VISUALIZATION
CLASSZONE.COM

Examine continental movement over the past 150 million years.

For Wegener, all the evidence pointed to a single conclusion. The continents had once been joined in a huge supercontinent he called **Pangaea** (pan-JEE-uh). *Pangaea* comes from the Greek word meaning "all lands." This giant continent reached from pole to pole and was centered over the area where Africa lies today.

Pangaea began to split apart some 200 million years ago. In time, the continents moved to where they are today. Yet Wegener could not explain *how* the continents moved. Because of this, his critics called continental drift "a fairy tale" and rejected his hypothesis.

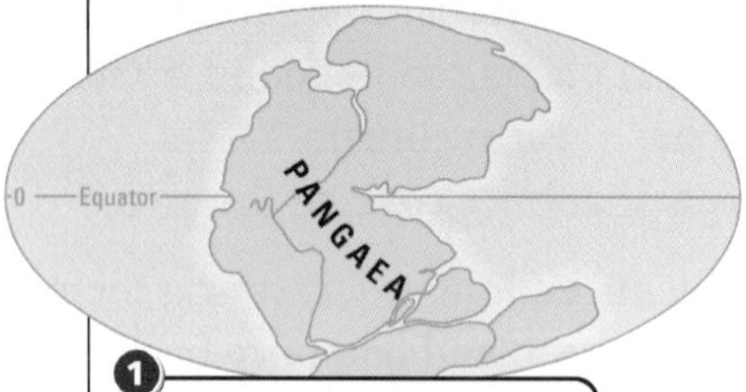


1 200 million years ago—Pangaea stretches from pole to pole.

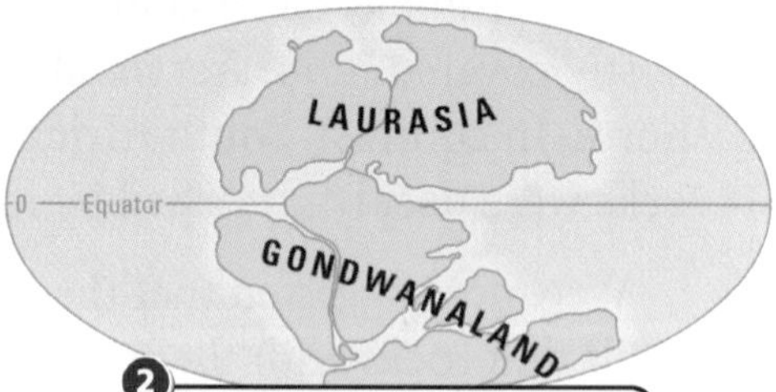


2 180 million years ago—Pangaea splits into Gondwanaland and Laurasia.

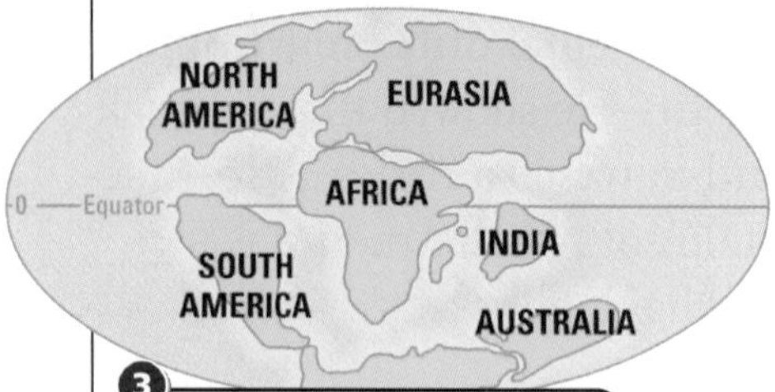


3 65 million years ago—Most of the major continents have moved apart.

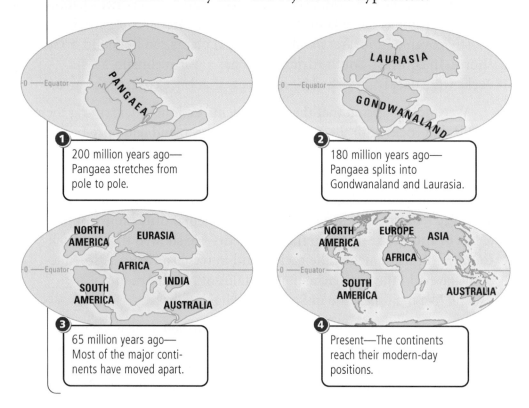

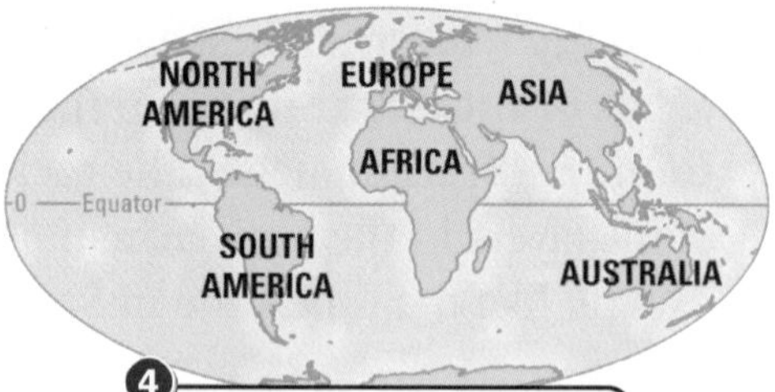


4 Present—The continents reach their modern-day positions.

## The theory of plate tectonics explains how plates and their continents move.

For many years, Wegener's ideas were pushed aside. Then in the mid-1900s, scientists proved that tectonic plates move. They also offered explanations about how the plates move. Their work eventually led to the theory of plate tectonics, which built on some of Wegener's ideas.

### Evidence from the Sea Floor

Scientists began mapping the sea floor in detail in the 1950s. They expected the floor to be smooth and level. Instead, they found huge underwater mountain ranges, called **mid-ocean ridges.** These ridges appeared in every ocean, circling Earth like seams in a baseball.

**Sea-Floor Spreading** Scientists learned that the ridges form along cracks in the crust. Molten rock rises through these cracks. Then it cools and forms new oceanic crust. The old crust is pulled away, making room for new material. In this way, the sea floor slowly spreads apart. Scientists call these areas spreading centers. You will read more about spreading centers in Section 8.3.

**Age of the Sea Floor** Further evidence that the sea floor is spreading apart came from the age of the rocks in the crust. Scientists drilled into the sea floor from a specially equipped ship called the *Glomar Challenger.* The rock samples revealed that the youngest rock is closest to the ridge. The oldest rock is farthest away.

The samples also showed that even the oldest ocean floor is young—only 160 to 180 million years old. Continental crust is much older—up to 4 billion years old. These data confirmed that the ocean floor is constantly forming and moving away from the mid-ocean ridges like a conveyor belt. As the sea floor moves, the tectonic plates and their continents also move.

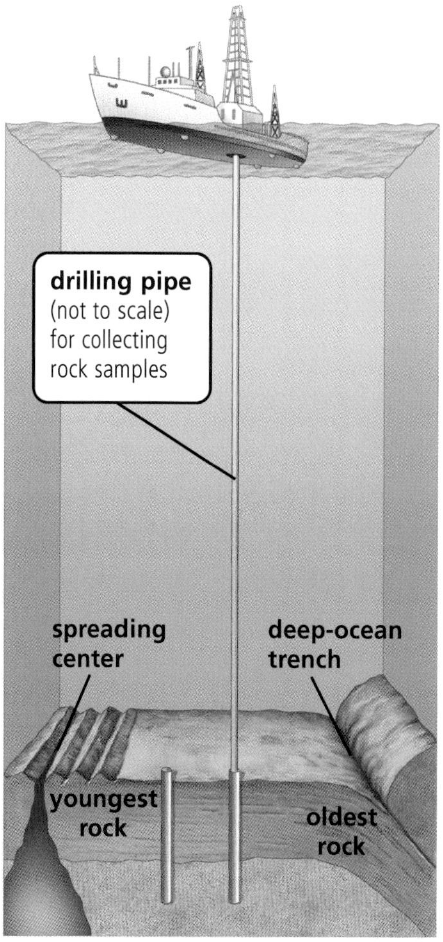


Scientists drill into the sea floor to obtain rock samples. The different ages of the rocks prove that plates move.

**Ocean Trenches** If the sea floor has been spreading for millions of years, why isn't Earth getting larger? Scientists discovered the answer at huge trenches in the sea floor. At these sites, dense oceanic crust is sinking into the asthenosphere. Old crust is being destroyed at the same rate that new crust is forming. As a result, Earth remains the same size.

Scientists now had evidence that tectonic plates move. But the same question remained. *How* could the plates move thousands of kilometers around the planet? The asthenosphere provided a possible answer.

**CHECK YOUR READING** How does the age of the sea floor show that plates move?

## Causes of Plate Movement

Tectonic plates rest on the asthenosphere, a layer of soft, hot rock. Rock in this layer and in the mantle just below it moves by convection. **Convection** is the transfer of energy by the movement of a material. You have seen convection if you have ever boiled a pot of water. The water at the bottom of the pot heats up, becomes less dense, and rises. At the surface, it cools, becomes denser, and sinks. Then the water is heated and rises again.

The rock in the asthenosphere acts in a similar way. The hot, soft rock rises, cools, and sinks. Then it is heated and rises again. If this sinking and rising continues, it is called a **convection current**—a motion that transfers heat energy in a material.

Convection currents in the mantle are much slower than those in boiling water. The rock creeps only a few centimeters a year. The diagram below shows convection currents circulating. The tectonic plates in the lithosphere are carried on the asthenosphere like long, heavy boxes moved on huge rollers. Over millions of years, convection currents carry the plates thousands of kilometers.

Scientists suspect that two other motions help move these huge plates. The motions are called slab pull and ridge push. Slab pull takes place where gravity pulls the edge of a cool, dense plate into the asthenosphere. Because plates are hard, the entire plate is dragged along. Ridge push occurs when material from a mid-ocean ridge slides downhill from the ridge. The material pushes the rest of the plate.

## Putting the Theory Together

Geologists combined their knowledge of Earth's plates, the sea floor, and the asthenosphere to develop the **theory of plate tectonics.** The theory states that Earth's lithosphere is made up of huge plates that move over the surface of Earth.

**REMINDER**
A scientific theory is a well-tested explanation that is consistent with all available evidence.

The map on page 275 shows Earth's major tectonic plates and the directions in which they move. They are the African, Antarctic, Australian, Indian, Eurasian, Nazca, North and South American, and Pacific plates.

### Causes of Plate Movement

**Convection currents, slab pull, and ridge push move Earth's huge tectonic plates.**

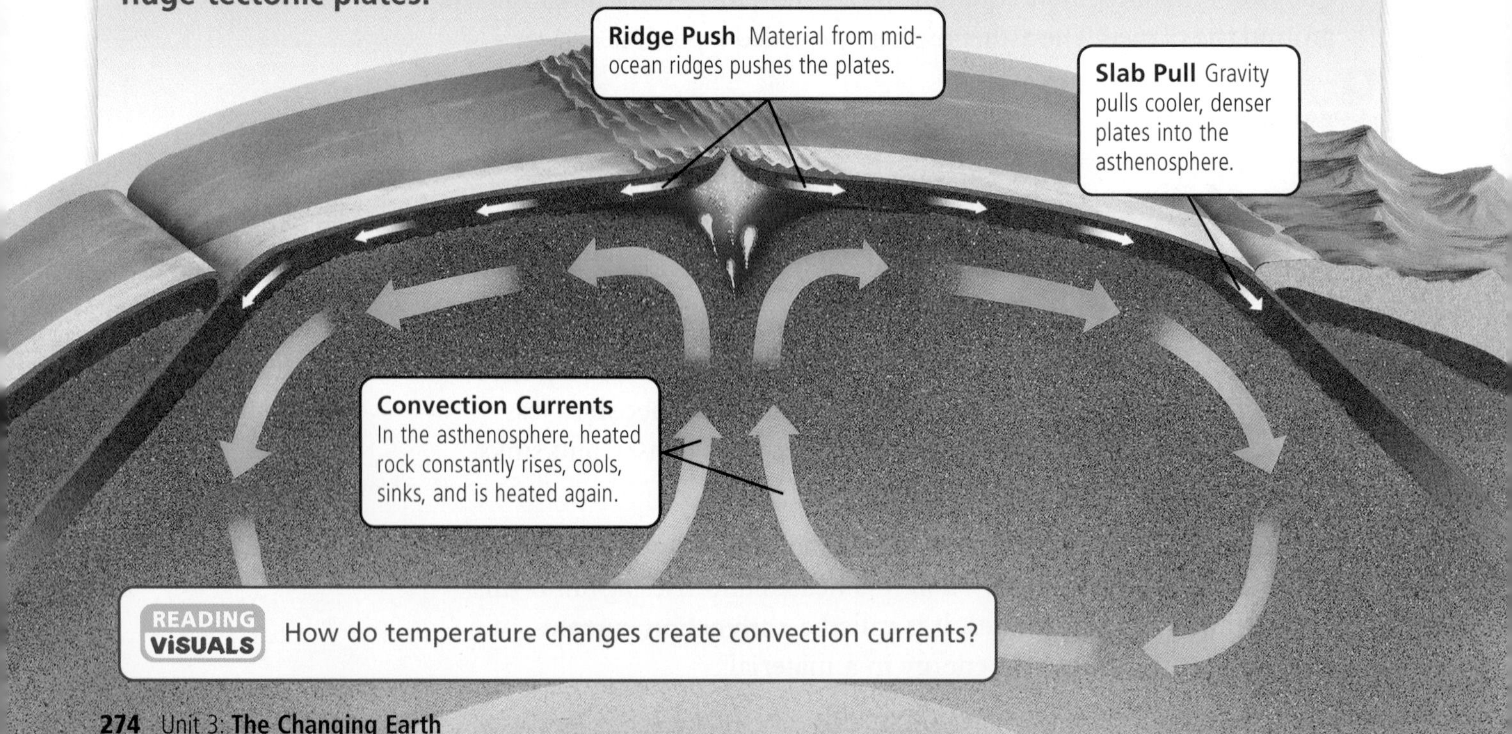
**Ridge Push** Material from mid-ocean ridges pushes the plates.
**Slab Pull** Gravity pulls cooler, denser plates into the asthenosphere.
**Convection Currents** In the asthenosphere, heated rock constantly rises, cools, sinks, and is heated again.

**READING VISUALS** How do temperature changes create convection currents?

## Tectonic Plates

**Earth's lithosphere is made up of moving plates.**

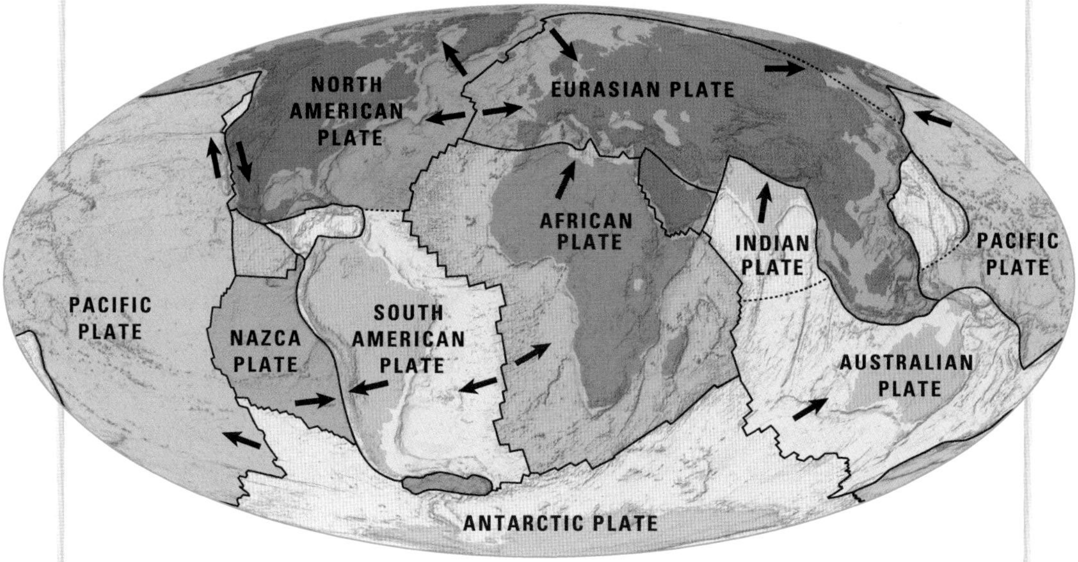


**READING VISUALS** Where on the map are two plates moving apart? pushing together? scraping past each other?

As scientists studied the plates, they realized that one plate could not shift without affecting the others nearby. They found that plates can move apart, push together, or scrape past each other. The arrows on the map above show each type of plate motion.

Plate movements cause great changes in Earth's crust. Most major earthquakes, volcanoes, and mountain ranges appear where tectonic plates meet. You will learn why as you read more about plate movements.

**CALIFORNIA Focus**

Most of California is on the North American Plate, but the part west of the San Andreas Fault is on the Pacific Plate. The plates are moving past each other in opposite directions at an average rate of about 5 cm per year.

## 8.2 Review

### KEY CONCEPTS

1. What evidence did Wegener gather to support his continental drift hypothesis? (6.1.a)
2. Give three types of evidence from the sea floor that prove Earth's tectonic plates move. (6.1.a)
3. Explain how motions in the asthenosphere can move tectonic plates around Earth. (6.1.c)

### CRITICAL THINKING

4. **Apply** A friend tells you he read on a Web site that Earth is getting smaller. What can you tell him that shows Earth's size is not changing?
5. **Evaluate** What other types of scientists, besides geologists, would find the theory of plate tectonics useful in their work?

### CHALLENGE

6. **Infer** Use the arrows on the map above and your knowledge of sea-floor spreading and ocean trenches to answer these questions: What is happening to the size of the Atlantic Ocean? What can you infer is happening to the size of the Pacific Ocean? Explain your answers.

# CHAPTER INVESTIGATION

## Convection Currents and Plate Movement

**OVERVIEW AND PURPOSE** South America and Africa are drifting slowly apart. What powerful force could be moving these two plates? In this investigation you will

- observe the movement of convection currents
- determine how convection currents in Earth's mantle could move tectonic plates

### Problem

Write It Up

How do convection currents in a fluid affect floating objects on the surface?

### Hypothesize

Write It Up

Write a hypothesis to explain how convection currents affect floating objects. Your hypothesis should take the form of an "If . . . , then . . . , because . . ." statement.

### Procedure

1 Use two overturned oblong pans or two bricks to raise and support the rectangular baking dish. Fill the dish with water to a depth of 4 cm.

2 Hold the food coloring over the middle of the dish. Squeeze several drops into the water. Be careful not to touch or disturb the water with the plastic tip or your hands. Write down your observations.

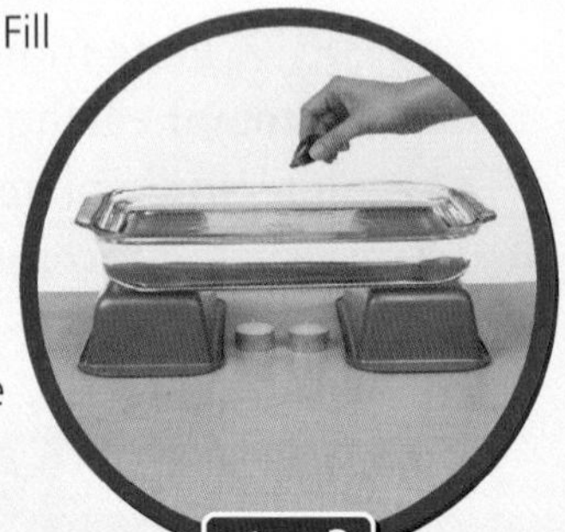

step 3

3 Light the two candles and place them beneath the center of the dish. Then squeeze several more drops of food coloring into the middle of the dish.

4 Observe what happens for a few minutes, and then write down your observations. After you have finished, blow out the candles and wait until the water cools.

5 Moisten the two sponges. Cut one into the shape of South America and the other into the shape of Africa. Insert the pushpins as shown in the photo.

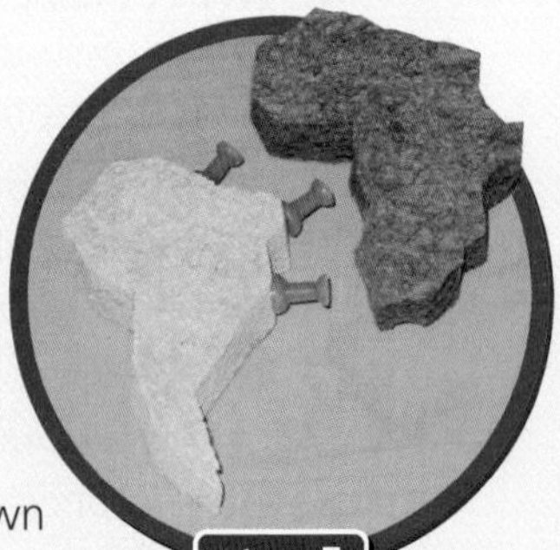

step 5

**MATERIALS**

- rectangular glass baking dish
- 2 oblong pans or 2 bricks
- ruler
- water
- liquid food coloring
- 2 small candles
- matches
- 2 sponges
- scissors
- 3–4 pushpins

6.1.c, 6.3.c, 6.7.a, 6.7.c, 6.7.d

**Content Standard**
6.3.c Students know heat flows in solids by conduction (which involves no flow of matter) and in fluids by conduction and by convection (which involves flow of matter).

**Investigation Standard**
6.7.a Develop a hypothesis.

6 Place the sponges on top of the water in the center of the dish. Fit the two sponges together along their coastlines.

7 Gently hold the sponges together until the water is still. Then let go. Observe them for a few minutes and record what you saw.

8 Light the candles again. Place them under the dish and directly beneath the two sponges.

9 Gently hold the sponges together again until the water heats up. Then carefully let go of the sponges, trying not to disturb the water.

10 Observe the sponges for a few minutes. Then record your observations.

## Observe and Analyze

Write It Up

1. **RECORD** Draw diagrams to show how the food coloring and the sponges moved in cold water and in heated water. Use arrows to indicate any motion.
2. **ANALYZE** Did the food coloring and the sponges move more with or without the candles? Use what you have learned about convection to explain the role of the candles.

## Conclude

Write It Up

1. **EVALUATE** Water is a fluid, but the asthenosphere is not. What properties of the asthenosphere allow it to move like a fluid and form convection currents?
2. **COMPARE AND CONTRAST** How is your setup like Earth's asthenosphere and lithosphere? How is your setup different?
3. **ANALYZE** Compare your results with your hypothesis. Do your observations support your hypothesis? Why or why not?
4. **INTERPRET** Write an answer to your problem statement.
5. **IDENTIFY CONTROLS** Did your experiment include controls? If so, what purpose did they serve?
6. **APPLY** In your own words, explain how the African continent and the South American continent are drifting apart.
7. **APPLY** Suppose you own an aquarium. You want to make sure your fish are warm whether they swim near the top or near the bottom of the aquarium. The pet store sells two types of heaters. One heater extends 5 cm below the water's surface. The other heater rests on the bottom of the aquarium. Based on what you learned in this activity, which heater would you choose? Why?

## INVESTIGATE Further

**CHALLENGE** Design a new version of this experiment that you think would be a better model of the movements in Earth's asthenosphere and lithosphere. What materials will you need? What changes would you make to the procedure? Sketch your experiment, and explain what makes it better.

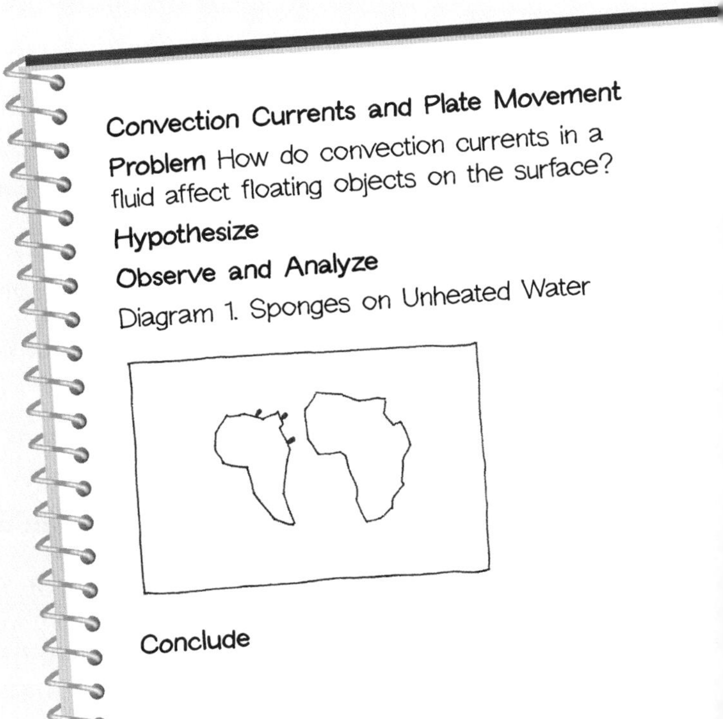
Convection Currents and Plate Movement
Problem How do convection currents in a fluid affect floating objects on the surface?
Hypothesize
Observe and Analyze
Diagram 1. Sponges on Unheated Water
Conclude

KEY CONCEPT

# 8.3 Plates move apart.

**CALIFORNIA Content Standards**

**6.1.c** Students know lithospheric plates the size of continents and oceans move at rates of centimeters per year in response to movements in the mantle.

**6.1.e** Students know major geologic events, such as earthquakes, volcanic eruptions, and mountain building, result from plate motions.

**BEFORE, you learned**

- The continents join and break apart
- The sea floor provides evidence that tectonic plates move
- The theory of plate tectonics helps explain how the plates move

**NOW, you will learn**

- About different plate boundaries
- What happens when plates move apart
- How the direction and speed of plates can be measured

**VOCABULARY**

**divergent boundary** p. 278
**convergent boundary** p. 278
**transform boundary** p. 278
**rift valley** p. 279
**magnetic reversal** p. 280
**hot spot** p. 283

**EXPLORE Divergent Boundaries (6.1.c)**

## *What happens when plates move apart?*

**PROCEDURE**

1. Cut the piece of striped paper into two symmetrical pieces slightly less wide than the slit in the oatmeal box.
2. Match up the lines of the two pieces and tape the pieces together at one edge. Push the taped edge into the box until only a few centimeters of the free edges show at the top.
3. Grasp each piece of paper, one in each hand. Slowly pull the two pieces horizontally out of the cylinder, pulling them in opposite directions.

**WHAT DO YOU THINK?**

How is your model similar to the process of sea-floor spreading?

**MATERIALS**

- scissors
- piece of striped paper
- tape
- small oatmeal box with slit cut in side

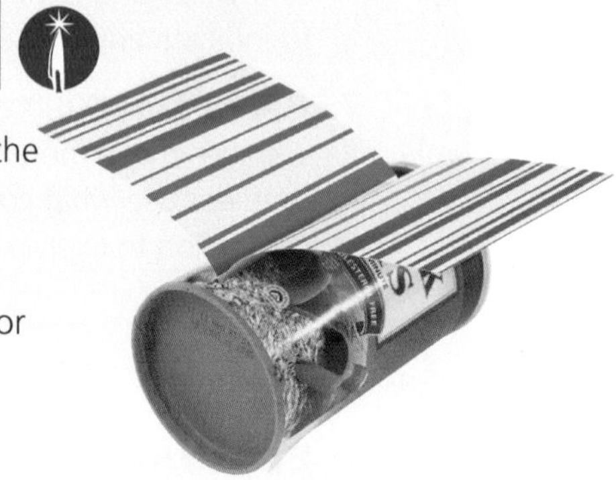

## Tectonic plates have different boundaries.

A plate boundary is where the edges of two plates meet. After studying the way plates move, geologists identified three types of boundaries.

- A **divergent boundary** (dih-VUR-juhnt) occurs where plates move apart. Most divergent boundaries are found in the ocean.
- A **convergent boundary** (kuhn-VUR-juhnt) occurs where plates push together.
- A **transform boundary** occurs where plates scrape past each other.

In this section, you will discover what happens at divergent boundaries in the ocean and on land. You will read more about convergent and transform boundaries in Section 8.4.

**READING TIP**

Use word meanings to help remember science terms.

*diverge* = to go in different directions

*converge* = to come together from different directions

*transform* = to change

## The sea floor spreads apart at divergent boundaries.

In the ocean, divergent boundaries are also called spreading centers. Mid-ocean ridges mark these sites where the ocean floor is spreading apart. As the ridges continue to widen, a gap called a **rift valley** forms. Here, hot material rises to build new crust.

### Mid-Ocean Ridges and Rift Valleys

Mid-ocean ridges are the longest chain of mountains on Earth. Most of these ridges contain a rift valley along their center. See the rift valley in the diagram below. When hot material rises from the asthenosphere, cold ocean water cools the rock until it becomes solid. As the plates move apart, new cracks open in the solid rock. More hot material rises and hardens. The growing ridge stands high above the sea floor.

The world's longest ridge is the Mid-Atlantic Ridge. This ridge runs the length of the Atlantic Ocean. Here, the North and South American plates are moving away from the Eurasian and African plates. The ridge extends nearly 11,000 kilometers (6214 mi) from Iceland to near Antarctica. The rift valley is 24 kilometers (15 mi) wide and 9 kilometers (6 mi) deep. That is about 7 kilometers (4 mi) deeper than the Grand Canyon!

#### Divergent Boundary in the Ocean

**Mid-ocean ridges, rift valleys, and new crust mark where the sea floor spreads apart.**

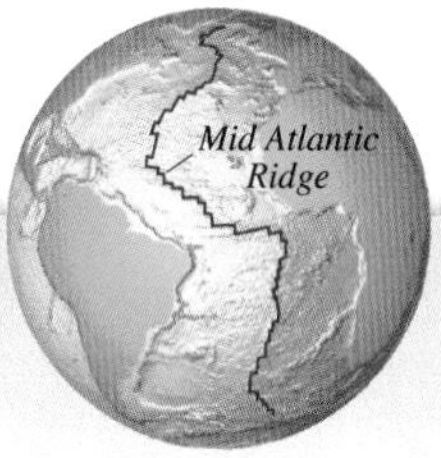


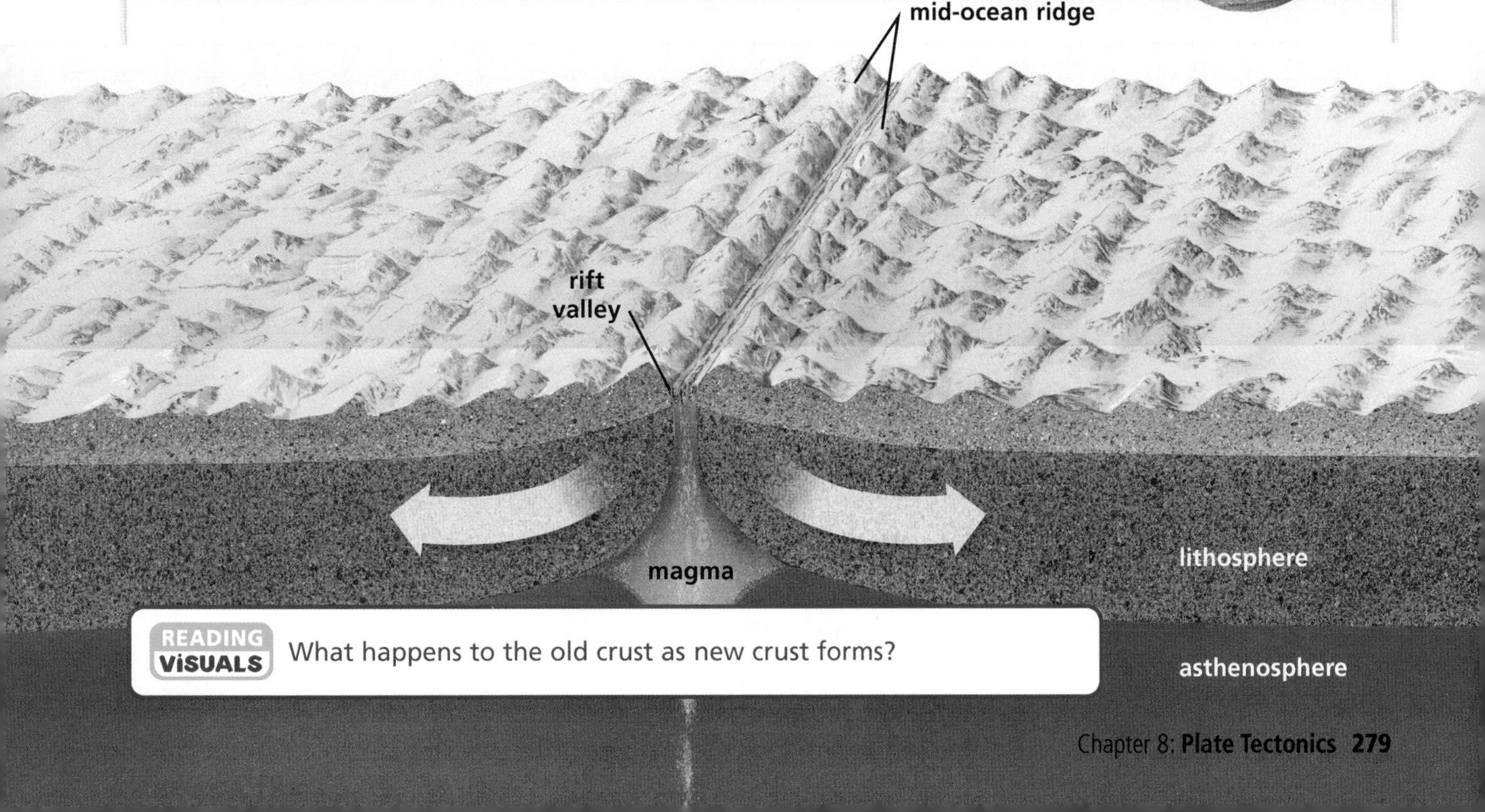


**READING VISUALS** What happens to the old crust as new crust forms?

## Sea-Floor Rock and Magnetic Reversals

You read earlier that the sea floor is younger near a mid-ocean ridge and older farther away. As scientists continued to study the sea-floor rock, they made a surprising discovery about Earth's magnetic field.

To understand Earth's magnetic field, you can compare the planet to a bar magnet. Like a magnet, it has a north pole and a south pole. Earth's magnetic field affects the entire planet. Notice in the diagram below that Earth's geographic and magnetic poles are not in the same place.

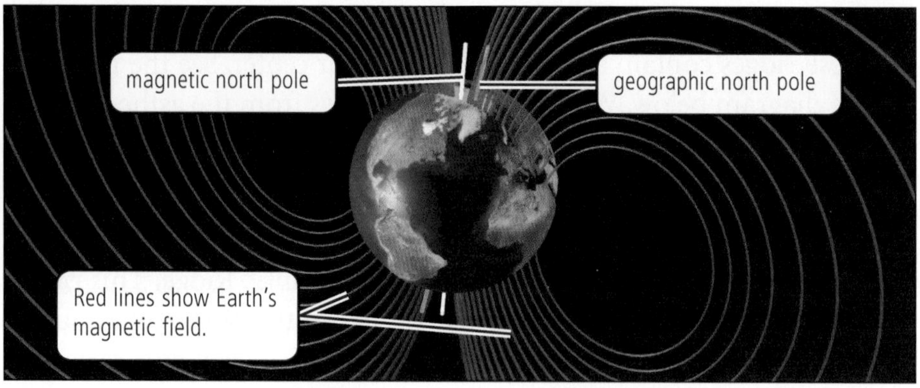


Unlike a bar magnet, Earth's magnetic poles sometimes switch places. The north pole becomes the south pole, and the south pole becomes the north pole. This switch in direction is called a **magnetic reversal.** Such reversals are caused by changes in Earth's magnetic field. No one knows why these changes happen. In contrast, Earth's geographic poles never change places.

### Magnetic Reversals

**Rocks moving away from a mid-ocean ridge carry records of magnetic reversals.**

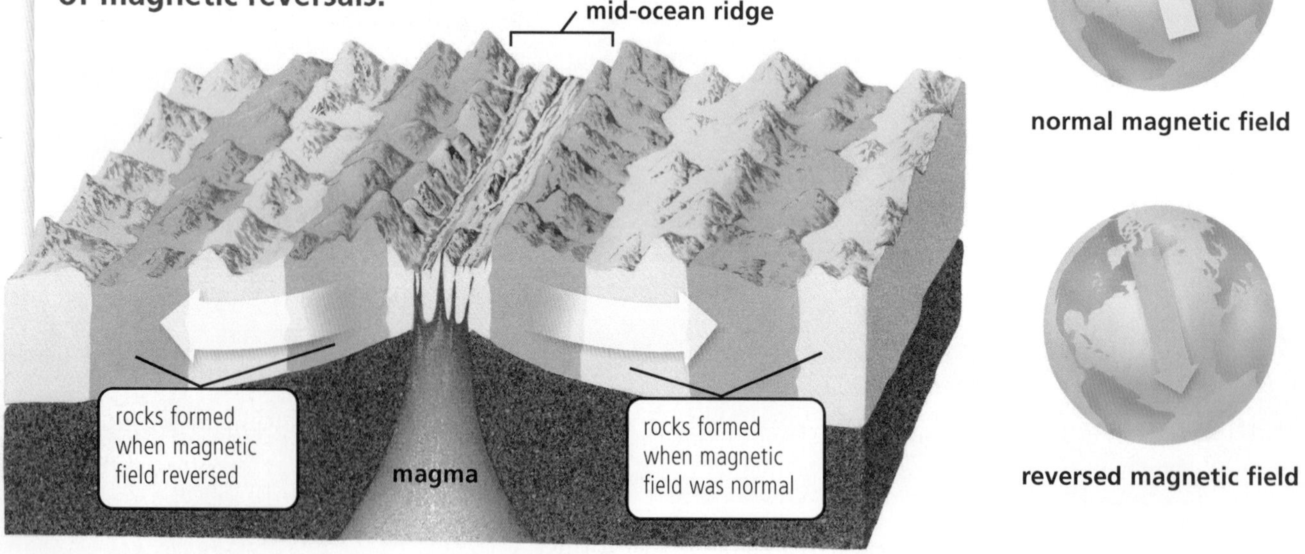

Scientists found that each magnetic reversal is recorded in the sea-floor rock. These records are especially clear at some mid-ocean ridges. As the hot material rises and cools, some magnetic minerals line up with Earth's magnetic field. When the material hardens, these minerals stay in place like tiny compass needles pointing north and south. Whenever the magnetic field reverses, the cooling minerals record the change.

As shown in the diagram on page 280, the records of magnetic reversals line up like stripes in the rock. As the two plates move away from a mid-ocean ridge, each plate carries a record of magnetic reversals with it. The records are the same on either side of the ridge.

As scientists continued to map the ocean floor, they found more records of magnetic reversals. By finding the age of the rock, scientists had more evidence of plate movement. The youngest rock records the most recent reversal, which happened only about 760,000 years ago. The oldest rock records reversals that happened more than 150 million years ago.

**CHECK YOUR READING** Explain how records of magnetic reversals show that plates move apart.

## INVESTIGATE Magnetic Reversals

### *How can you map magnetic reversals?*

**PROCEDURE**

1. Wrap one end of the string around the middle of the bar magnet. Tape the string in place as shown.
2. Place a small piece of tape on one end of the magnet. Label the tape "N" to represent north.
3. Hold the bar magnet over one end of the sea-floor model as shown. Move the magnet SLOWLY toward the other end of the sea-floor model. Record your observations.

**WHAT DO YOU THINK?**

- What did the magnet reveal about the sea-floor model? Draw a diagram showing any pattern that you might have observed.
- Which part of the model represents the youngest sea floor? Which part represents the oldest sea floor?

**CHALLENGE** If Earth's magnetic field had never reversed in the past, how would the sea-floor model be different?

**SKILL FOCUS**
Modeling (6.1.a)

**MATERIALS**
- string
- bar magnet
- masking tape
- marking pen
- sea-floor model

**TIME**
20 minutes

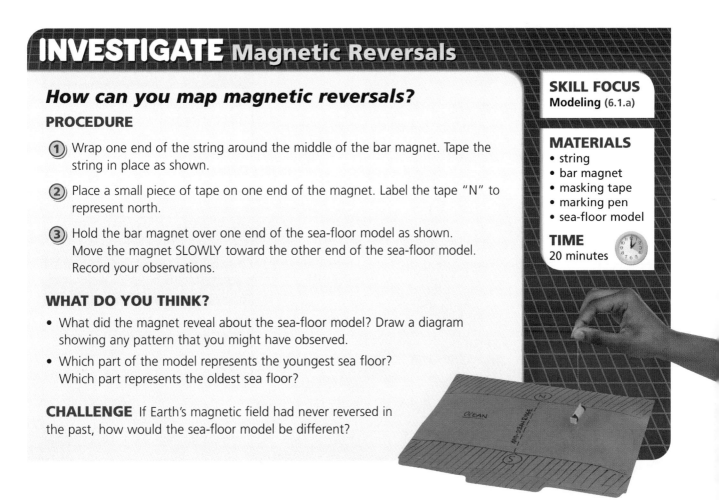

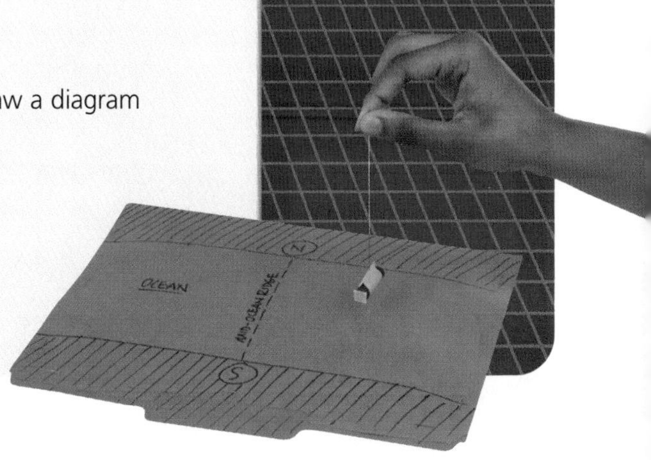

## Continents split apart at divergent boundaries.

**SUPPORTING MAIN IDEAS**
Use this diagram to help you take notes on how continents split apart.

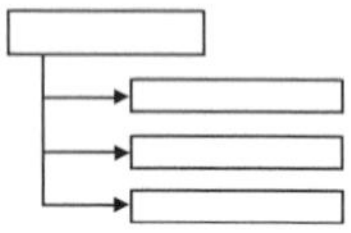

Like the sea floor, continents spread apart at a divergent boundary. The boundary begins to form when hot material rises from deep in the mantle. This heat causes the crust to bulge upward. The crust cracks as it is stretched, and a rift valley forms. This is shown in the diagram below. Magma rises through the cracked, thinned crust and forms volcanoes. As the rift valley grows wider, the continent begins to split apart.

If the rift valley continues to widen, the thinned valley floor sinks lower and lower until it is below sea level. Water from nearby oceans or rivers may fill the valley and form a sea or a lake. In the Middle East, the Arabian Plate and African Plate have been moving apart for several million years. Over time, the waters of the Indian Ocean gradually filled the rift valley, forming the Red Sea. This sea is slowly getting wider as the plates continue to move apart.

**CHECK YOUR READING** What happens when the floor of a rift valley sinks below sea level?

### Divergent Boundary on Land

**As rift valleys widen, continents begin to split apart.**

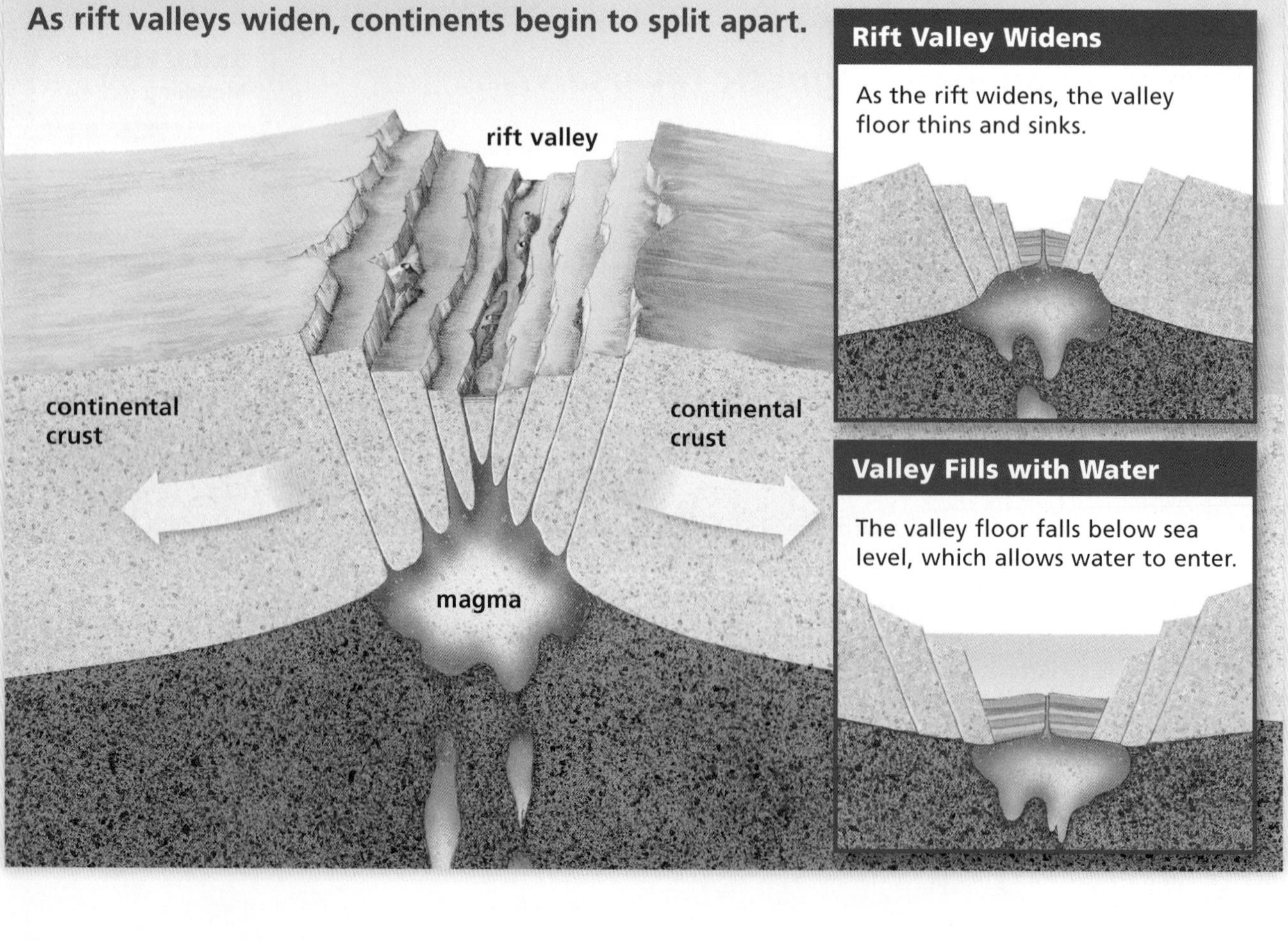
rift valley
continental crust
continental crust
magma
Rift Valley Widens
As the rift widens, the valley floor thins and sinks.
Valley Fills with Water
The valley floor falls below sea level, which allows water to enter.

The Great Rift Valley in eastern Africa is a good example of a continental rift valley. It is getting wider as the African Plate splits apart. This huge valley is thousands of kilometers long and as much as 1800 meters (5900 ft) deep.

**PREDICT** Rift valleys, like the Great Rift Valley in Africa, occur where plates are moving apart. What will happen to the Rift Valley when it gets deep enough?

## Hot spots can be used to track plate movements.

**Hot spots** are places where heated rock rises from the mantle in plumes, or thin columns. Volcanoes often develop above the plume. Although most hot spots occur far from plate boundaries, they offer a way to measure plate movement. This is because a hot spot generally stays in one place while the tectonic plate above it keeps moving.

At a hot spot, the heat from the plume partly melts some of the rock in the tectonic plate above it. Magma formed in this way can rise all the way through the plate. If the plate stays over the hot spot long enough, the rock above it will melt and a volcano will form at the surface of the plate.

After repeated eruptions, a hot-spot volcano that forms on the ocean floor may become high enough to rise above the sea as an island. For example, the Hawaiian Islands are being built as the Pacific Plate moves slowly over a hot spot.

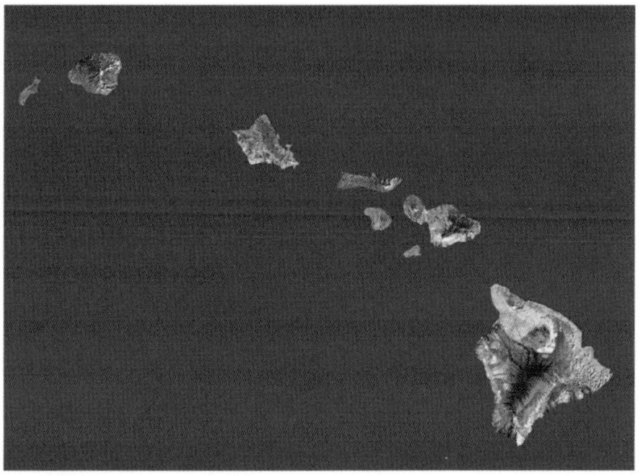

The Hawaiian islands are located in the middle of the Pacific Plate. The largest island, Hawaii, is still over the hot spot.

## Hot Spots

**Tectonic plates move over hot spots in the mantle.**

### Oceanic Hot Spot

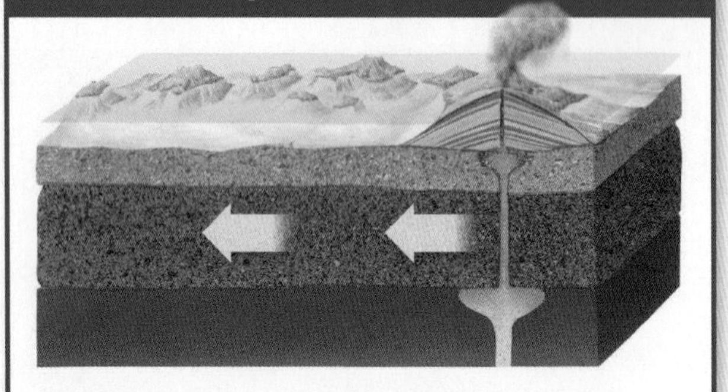

The Pacific Plate carries each Hawaiian island away from the hot spot. Eventually, a new volcano forms over the plume.

### Continental Hot Spot

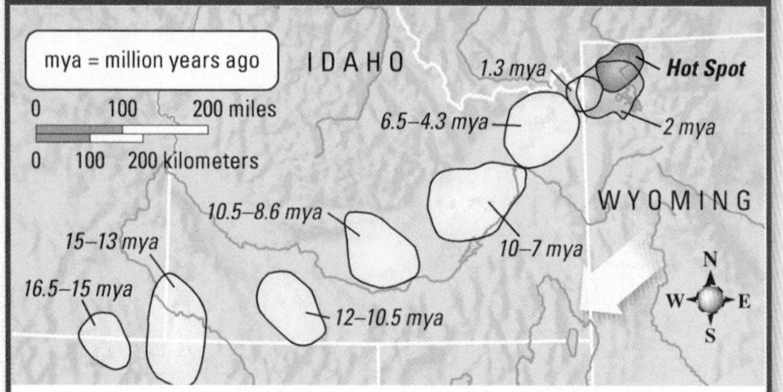


The North American Plate moves southwest, carrying each inactive volcano away from the Yellowstone hot spot.

**READING VISUALS** Which island or landform in each diagram was formed first? How do you know?

When the plate moves on, it carries the first volcano away from the hot spot. Heat from the plume will then melt the rock at a new site, forming a new volcano. The diagram on the left shows this process.

Many hot spots have a fixed point that scientists can use to measure the speed and direction of plate movements. For example, the Yellowstone hot spot under the North American Plate has formed a chain of inactive volcanoes. These are shown in the diagram on the right. Scientists estimate that the North American Plate is moving southwest at about 2.3 cm (1 in.) per year.

**CHECK YOUR READING** How does a hot-spot volcano form?

# 8.3 Review

### KEY CONCEPTS

1. Name and describe the three types of plate movements. (6.1.b)
2. Create a two-column chart with these headings: Divergent Boundary, Features. Fill in the chart for divergent boundaries at sea and on land. (6.1.a)
3. How are hot spots used to track plate motion? (6.1.e)

### CRITICAL THINKING

4. **Predict** Suppose a magnetic reversal occurred today. How would new rocks at mid-ocean ridges differ from rocks that formed last year?
5. **Infer** A huge crack runs through Iceland, an island that lies above the Mid-Atlantic Ridge. What do you think is happening to this country?

### CHALLENGE

6. **Hypothesize** Look carefully at the diagram above and the Hawaiian Islands picture on page 283. Notice that some hot-spot islands or landforms are larger than other islands or landforms in the same chain. Develop a hypothesis, based on plate movement, that might explain this fact.

MATH in SCIENCE

## SKILL: CALCULATING EQUIVALENT RATES

# Tracking Tectonic Plates

**MATH TUTORIAL**
CLASSZONE.COM
Click on Math Tutorial for more help with rates.

**Math** 6.AF.2.3
**Science** 6.1.c

This satellite photograph shows where the Arabian Plate and the African Plate are moving apart. As a result, the Red Sea is slowly growing wider.

Scientists use lasers to track the movements of tectonic plates. They bounce laser light off satellites and measure the distance from each satellite to the ground. As the plates move, the distance changes. With this tracking system, scientists know exactly how far tectonic plates move each year.

**This 0.61-meter-wide satellite is covered with mirrors to reflect laser light back to Earth.**

You can use equivalent rates to predict how far two divergent plates will move over a given time. A rate is a ratio of two measures expressed in different units, such as

$$\frac{10 \text{ cm}}{4 \text{ yr}}$$

### Example

If Boston, Massachusetts, and Lisbon, Portugal, are moving apart at an average rate of 10 cm every 4 years, how much farther apart will they move in 20 years?

**Solution**

Write an equivalent rate.

$$\frac{10 \text{ cm}}{4 \text{ yr}} = \frac{?}{20 \text{ yr}}$$

Divide 20 yr by 4 yr to get 5, then multiply 10 cm by 5.

$$20 \div 4 = 5$$

$$10 \times 5 = 50$$

$$\frac{10 \text{ cm}}{4 \text{ yr}} = \frac{50 \text{ cm}}{20 \text{ yr}}$$

**ANSWER** Boston and Lisbon will move 50 centimeters farther apart in 10 years.

**Answer the following questions.**

1. If New York, New York, and London, England, are moving apart at an average rate of 5 cm every 2 years, how much farther apart will they move in 8 years?
2. If Miami, Florida, and Casablanca, Morocco, are moving apart at an average rate of 25 cm every 10 years, how much farther apart will they move in 30 years?
3. If Portland, Maine, and Dublin, Ireland, are moving apart at an average rate of 50 cm every 20 years, how much farther apart will they move in 10 years?

**CHALLENGE** **If Halifax, Nova Scotia, and Birmingham, England, are moving apart at an average rate of 5 cm every 2 years, how long will it take them to move 35 cm farther apart?**

KEY CONCEPT

# 8.4 Plates converge or scrape past each other.

**CALIFORNIA Content Standards**

**6.1.a** Students know evidence of plate tectonics is derived from the fit of the continents; the location of earthquakes, volcanoes, and midocean ridges; and the distribution of fossils, rock types, and ancient climatic zones.

**6.1.e** Students know major geologic events, such as earthquakes, volcanic eruptions, and mountain building, result from plate motions.

**6.1.f** Students know how to explain major features of California geology (including mountains, faults, volcanoes) in terms of plate tectonics.

**BEFORE, you learned**

- Plates move apart at divergent boundaries
- In the oceans, divergent boundaries mark where the sea floor spreads apart
- On land, continents split apart at divergent boundaries

**NOW, you will learn**

- What happens when two continental plates converge
- What happens when an oceanic plate converges with another plate
- What happens when one plate scrapes past another plate

**EXPLORE Tectonic Plates (6.1.e)**

### *What happens when tectonic plates collide?*

**PROCEDURE**

1. Arrange six square napkins in two rows.
2. Slowly push the two rows of napkins together. Observe what happens.

**MATERIALS**

6 square napkins

**WHAT DO YOU THINK?**

- In what ways did the napkin edges move?
- How might your observations relate to the movement of tectonic plates?

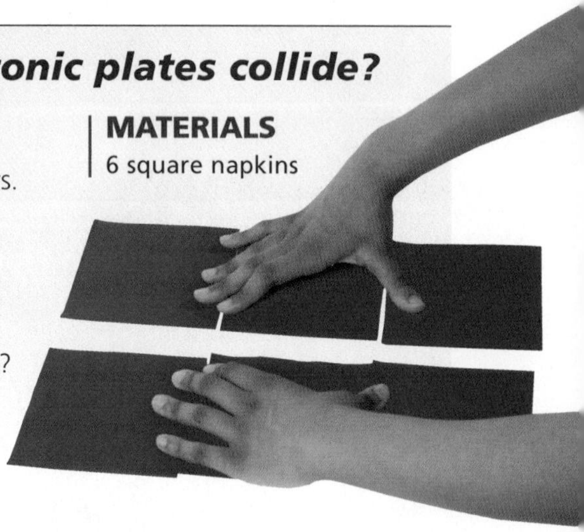

**VOCABULARY**

**subduction** p. 286
**continental-continental collision** p. 287
**oceanic-oceanic subduction** p. 288
**oceanic-continental subduction** p. 289

VOCABULARY
Remember to make a description wheel diagram for the terms in this section.

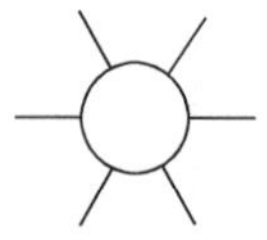

## Tectonic plates push together at convergent boundaries.

You read earlier that new crust forms at divergent boundaries where plates move apart. At convergent boundaries, plates push together. Here, crust is either folded or destroyed.

When two plates with continental crust collide, they crumple and fold the rock between them. A plate with older, denser oceanic crust will sink beneath another plate. The crust melts in the asthenosphere and is destroyed. When one plate sinks beneath another, it is called **subduction.** The word is based on the Latin prefix *sub-*, meaning "under," and the Latin *ducere,* meaning "to lead." Therefore, subduction is a process in which one plate is "led under" another.

There are three types of convergent boundaries: where two continental plates meet, where two oceanic plates meet, or where an oceanic plate and a continental plate meet. Major geologic events occur at all three types of boundaries.

## Continental-Continental Collision

A **continental-continental collision** occurs where two plates carrying continental crust push together. Because both crusts are the same density, neither plate can sink beneath the other. If the plates keep moving, their edges crumple and fold. See the diagram below.

You can see the same effect if you put two blocks of clay on a table and push them together. If you push hard enough, one or both of the blocks will buckle. One cannot sink under the other, so the clay folds under the pressure.

In some cases, the folded crust can be pushed up high enough to form mountains. Some of the world's largest mountains appear along continent-continent boundaries. The European Alps, shown in the photograph at right, are found where the African and Eurasian plates are colliding. The tallest mountains in the world are the Himalayas. They first formed when the Indian Plate began colliding with the Eurasian Plate.

The Himalayas and the Alps are still forming today. As long as the plates keep moving, these mountains will keep rising higher.

The European Alps began rising nearly 40 million years ago as a section of the African Plate collided with the Eurasian Plate.

**CHECK YOUR READING** Explain how colliding plates form mountain ranges.

### Convergent Boundary—Collision

**Rocks crumple and fold to form mountains.**

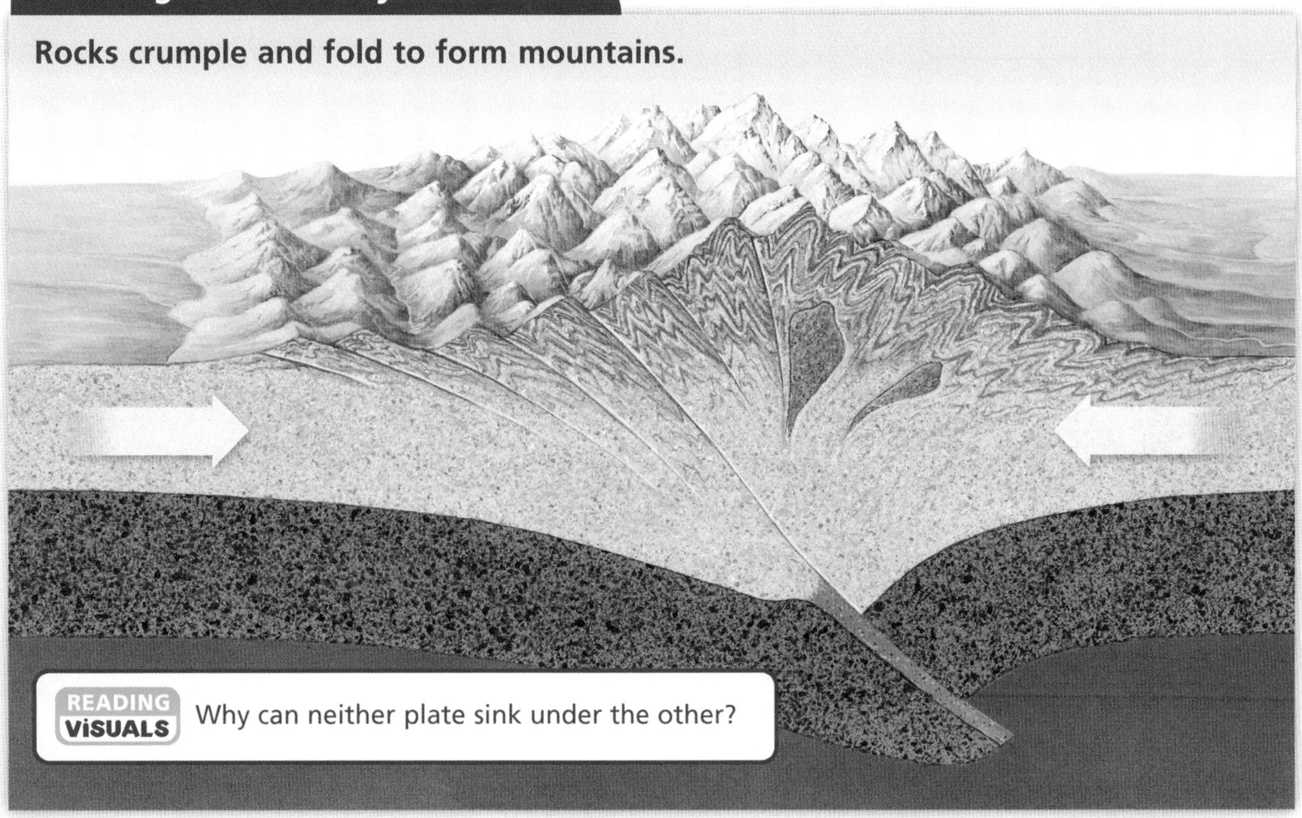

**READING VISUALS** Why can neither plate sink under the other?

### Oceanic-Oceanic Subduction

An **oceanic-oceanic subduction** occurs where one plate with oceanic crust sinks under another plate with oceanic crust. The older plate sinks because it is colder and denser than the younger plate. When the older crust reaches the asthenosphere, it melts in the intense heat. Two main features form at oceanic-oceanic subductions: deep-ocean trenches and island arcs.

**Deep-Ocean Trenches** These trenches are like deep canyons that form in the ocean floor as a plate sinks. Most deep-ocean trenches are found in the Pacific Ocean. One example is the Mariana Trench. There, the Pacific Plate is sinking under the Philippine Plate. This trench is the deepest place in the world's oceans. It extends nearly 11,000 meters (36,000 ft) into the sea floor.

**Island Arcs** Chains of volcanic islands form on the top plate, parallel to a deep-ocean trench. As oceanic crust of the sinking plate melts, magma rises through the top plate. Over time, the flows build up a series of islands. Island arcs include the Philippine Islands, the Aleutian Islands of Alaska, and the islands of Japan.

## Convergent Boundaries—Subduction

**Sinking plates form deep-ocean trenches, island arcs, and coastal mountains.**

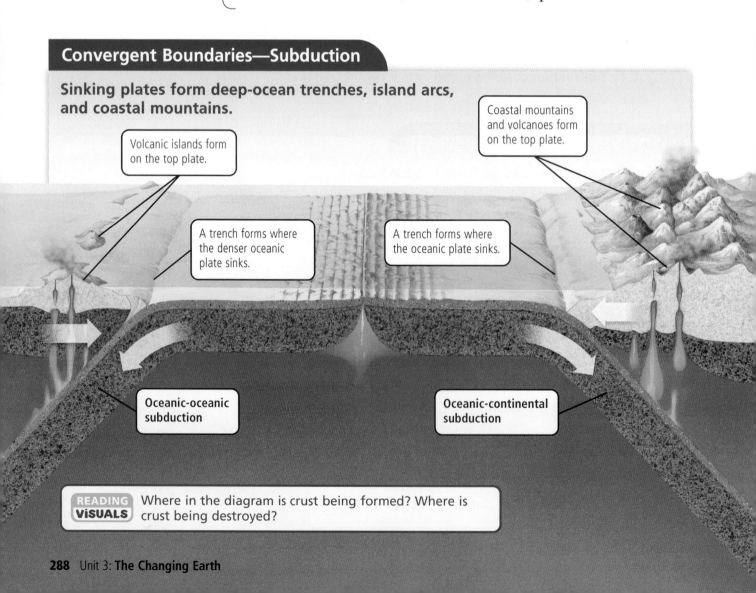

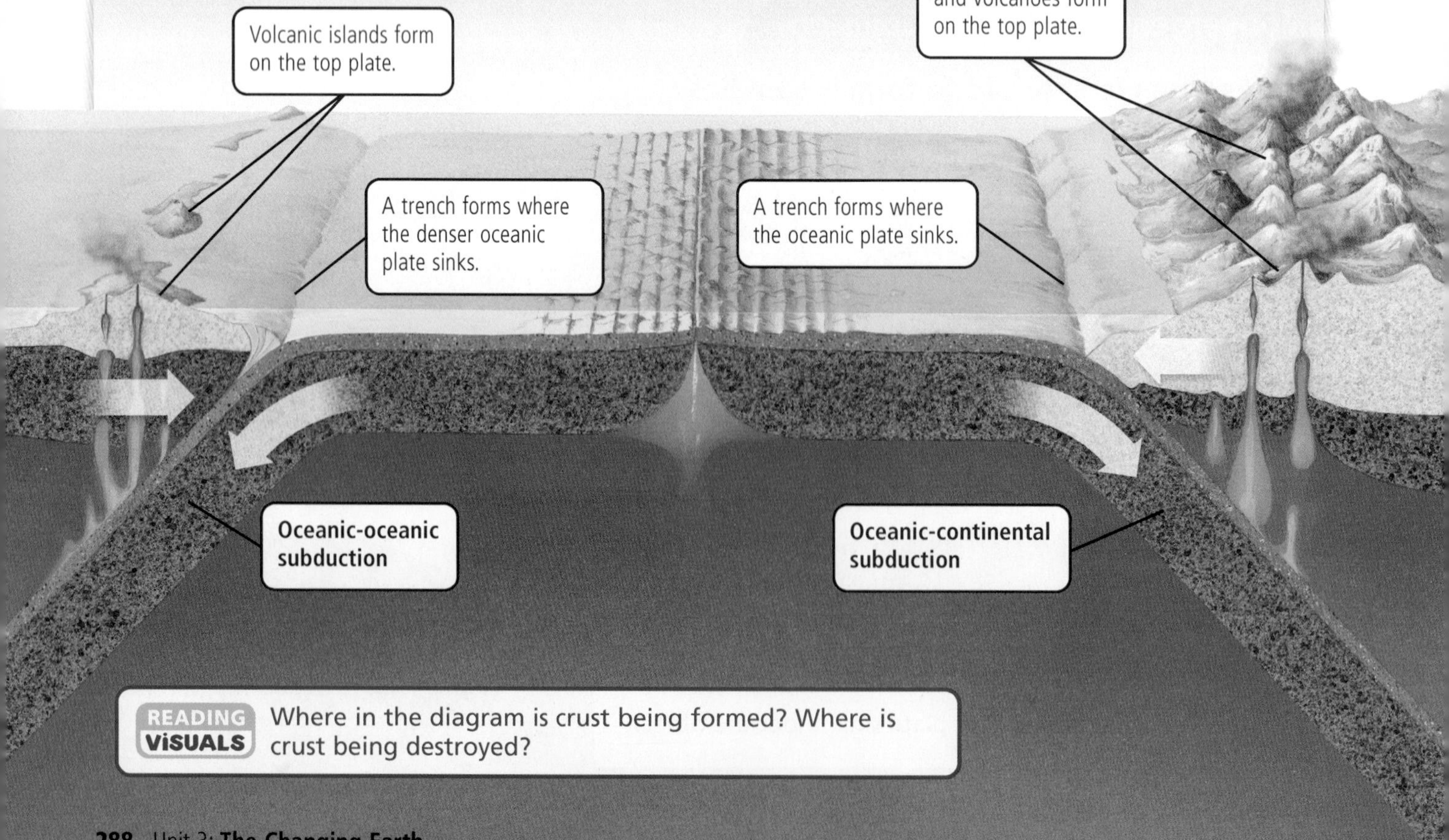

Volcanic islands form on the top plate.
Coastal mountains and volcanoes form on the top plate.
A trench forms where the denser oceanic plate sinks.
A trench forms where the oceanic plate sinks.
Oceanic-oceanic subduction
Oceanic-continental subduction

**READING VISUALS** Where in the diagram is crust being formed? Where is crust being destroyed?

## Oceanic-Continental Subduction

An **oceanic-continental subduction** occurs when ocean crust sinks under continental crust, as shown in the diagram on page 288. The oceanic crust sinks because it is colder and denser than the continental crust. At these sites, deep-ocean trenches and coastal mountains form.

**Deep-Ocean Trenches** Some of the world's youngest trenches are in the eastern Pacific Ocean. Here, the Pacific Plate is sinking under the North American Plate. As the oceanic crust moves, it often causes underwater earthquakes.

**Coastal Mountains** As oceanic crust sinks under a continent, the continental crust buckles to form a range of mountains. Like island arcs, these mountains are parallel to a deep-ocean trench. Some of these mountains are volcanoes, which form as melted oceanic crust rises through the top plate.

The Cascade Mountains in California, Oregon, and Washington are coastal mountains. They formed as the Juan de Fuca Plate began sinking under the North American Plate. Some of these peaks, such as Mount St. Helens in Washington, are active volcanoes.

**CHECK YOUR READING** Why do deep-ocean trenches form at both types of subduction?

**VISUALIZATION** CLASSZONE.COM

Explore what happens along plate boundaries.

# INVESTIGATE Convergent Boundaries

### *How can you model converging plates?*

Tectonic plates move so slowly and are so large that it is hard to see exactly how they move. Use what you know to design models showing subduction.

**DESIGN YOUR OWN**

#### PROCEDURE

1. Design your models using the materials listed. You can use the diagrams on pages 287–288 as a guide.
2. Add more clay to your models if you need it.

#### WHAT DO YOU THINK?

- Describe how your models worked. You can draw a picture of each model to go along with your description.
- How well did your models represent each type of zone? Did each model work? Why or why not?
- How would you modify your designs now that you have seen the results?

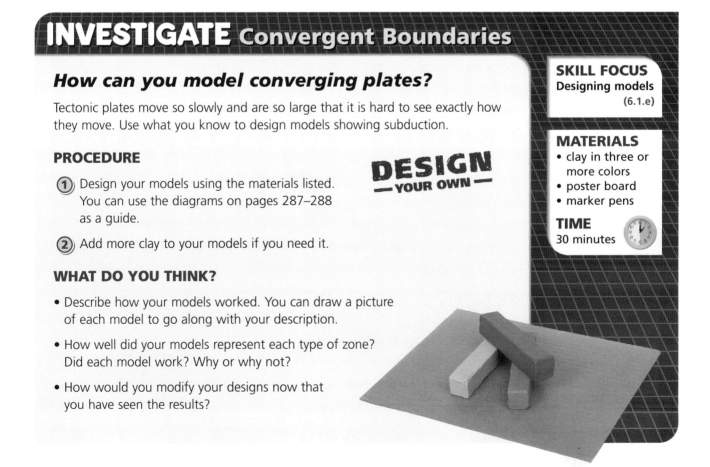

**SKILL FOCUS**
Designing models (6.1.e)

**MATERIALS**
- clay in three or more colors
- poster board
- marker pens

**TIME**
30 minutes

## Tectonic plates scrape past each other at transform boundaries.

You learned that crust is formed at a divergent boundary. It is folded or destroyed at a convergent boundary. At a transform boundary, crust is neither formed nor destroyed. Here, two plates move past each other in opposite directions, as shown in the diagram below. As the plates move, their edges scrape and grind against each other.

This long crack in the earth shows the transform boundary known as the San Andreas Fault.

Transform boundaries occur mostly on the sea floor near mid-ocean ridges. They also occur on land, where some are clearly visible as long cracks in Earth's surface. The San Andreas Fault in California is a transform boundary that runs from the Gulf of California through the San Francisco area. It marks where the Pacific Plate and part of the North American Plate are moving in opposite directions. If the plates keep moving at their present rate, Los Angeles will be a neighbor of San Francisco in about 10 million years.

**CHECK YOUR READING** What makes the San Andreas Fault a transform boundary?

### Transform Boundary

**Plate edges grind and scrape past each other. Crust is neither formed nor destroyed.**

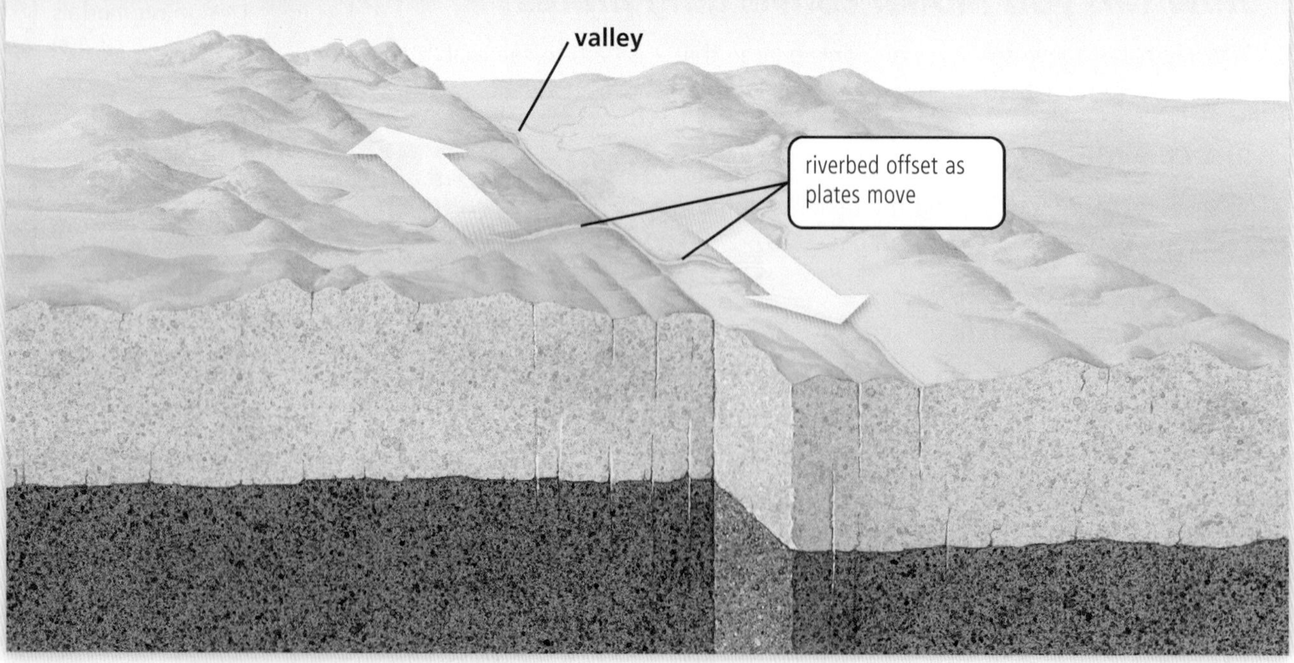

## Tectonic Plate Boundaries

**There are three types of plate boundaries: transform, divergent, and convergent. Major geologic events occur at all three types.**

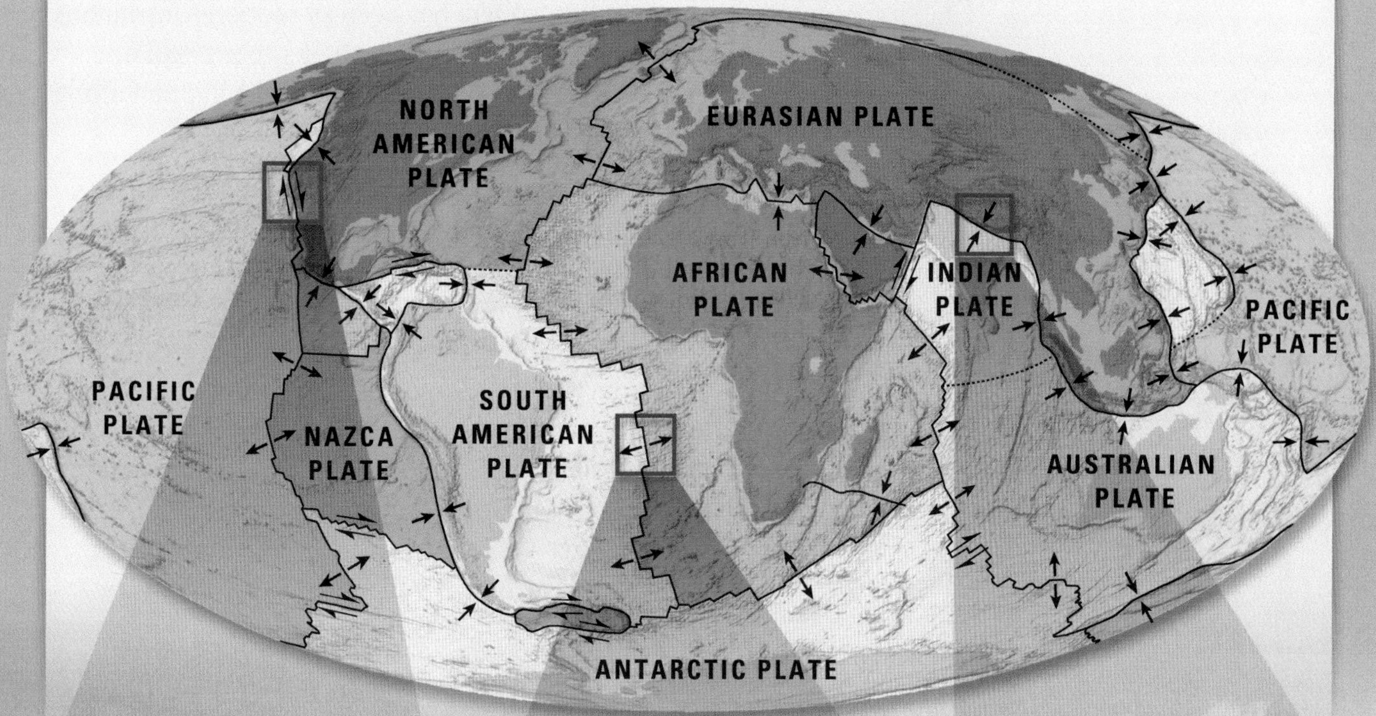


### Transform Boundaries

Plates scrape horizontally past each other. Crust is neither formed nor destroyed.

### Divergent Boundaries

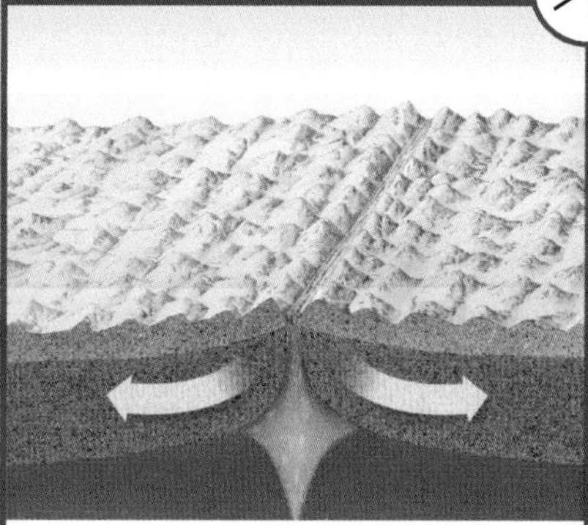

As plates move apart, new crust is built, forming mid-ocean ridges and rift valleys.

### Convergent Boundaries

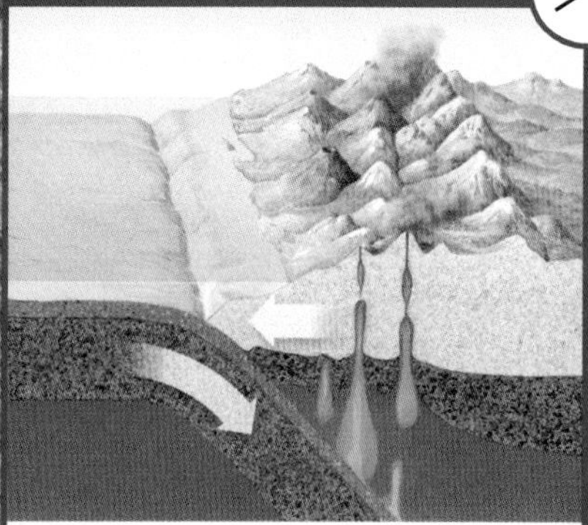

Crust is destroyed where plates subduct. It is folded where plates collide.

**READING VISUALS** Where else on the map above can you find a transform, divergent, and convergent boundary?

**Current U. S. Eastern Coastline**

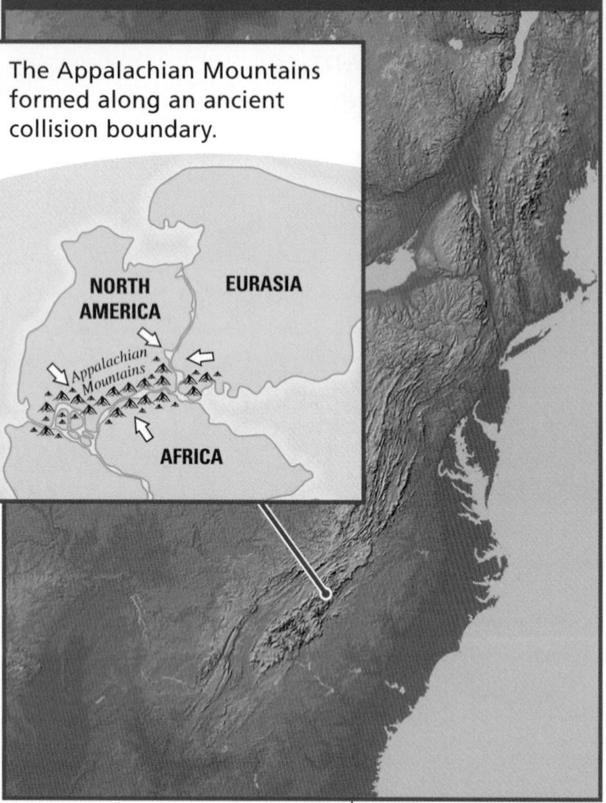
The Appalachian Mountains formed along an ancient collision boundary.
NORTH AMERICA
EURASIA
Appalachian Mountains
AFRICA

## The theory of plate tectonics helps geologists today.

The theory of plate tectonics changed the way that scientists view Earth. They learned that the planet's lithosphere has been in motion for millions of years. Today, the theory helps them explain Earth's past and predict what might happen along plate boundaries in the future.

By studying rock layers and using the theory, geologists can uncover the history of any region on Earth. In the eastern United States, the deformed and folded rocks in the Appalachian Mountains show there was once a convergent boundary there. Geologists discovered that these rocks are the same type and age as rocks in northwest Africa. These facts reveal that the mountains formed when North America collided with Africa and Eurasia as part of Pangaea. Where the plates pulled apart, the rift valleys formed part of the current U.S. eastern coastline.

The theory of plate tectonics also gives scientists a way to study and predict geologic events. For example, scientists can predict that there are likely to be more earthquakes where plates slide past each other. They can look for volcanic activity where plates are sinking beneath other plates. And they can predict that mountains will continue to rise where plates push together.

**CHECK YOUR READING** What future events can scientists predict using the theory of plate tectonics? Give two examples.

# 8.4 Review

### KEY CONCEPTS

1. What are the three types of convergent boundaries? (6.1.e)
2. Describe what happens at a transform boundary. (6.1.e)
3. Why is the theory of plate tectonics so important to geologists? (6.1.a)

### CRITICAL THINKING

4. **Compare and Contrast** Use a Venn diagram to compare and contrast oceanic-oceanic and oceanic-continental subduction boundaries.
5. **Interpreting Visuals** Look again at the map on page 291. Identify the plates and type of boundary that formed the Andes Mountains on the west coast of South America.

### CHALLENGE

6. **Synthesize** Sketch a diagram of the following landscape and label all the features. A plate with oceanic crust is sinking beneath a plate with continental crust. Farther inland on the continent, a transform boundary can be seen in Earth's crust.

Think SCIENCE

SKILL: EVALUATING CONCLUSIONS

# What on Earth Is Happening Here?

6.7.e Recognize whether evidence is consistent with a proposed explanation.

When tectonic plates move, they cause major changes in Earth's surface. The ground shakes, magma erupts on the surface, crust is built or destroyed, and mountains or islands form. Read the observations about plate movements below. Then evaluate the conclusions given.

## Observations

Scientists made these observations about a region where two major tectonic plates move.

a. The region is on the coast of a landmass.
b. Along the coast is a deep-ocean trench.
c. The mountains on the coast are volcanic.
d. A line connecting these mountains is fairly straight.
e. The mountains are getting higher.
f. Far out at sea, a mid-ocean ridge is forming.

## Conclusions

Here are three possible conclusions about the movement of tectonic plates in the region.

- One plate is pulling away from the other.
- One plate is sinking under the other.
- One plate is scraping past the other.

## Evaluate Each Conclusion

**On Your Own** Decide how well the observations support each conclusion. Note any observations that don't support a conclusion.

**As a Group** Decide which conclusion is most reasonable. Discuss your ideas in a small group, and see if the group can agree.

**CHALLENGE** What further observations would support or weaken each conclusion? How could you make these observations? What other geologic events might this conclusion help explain?

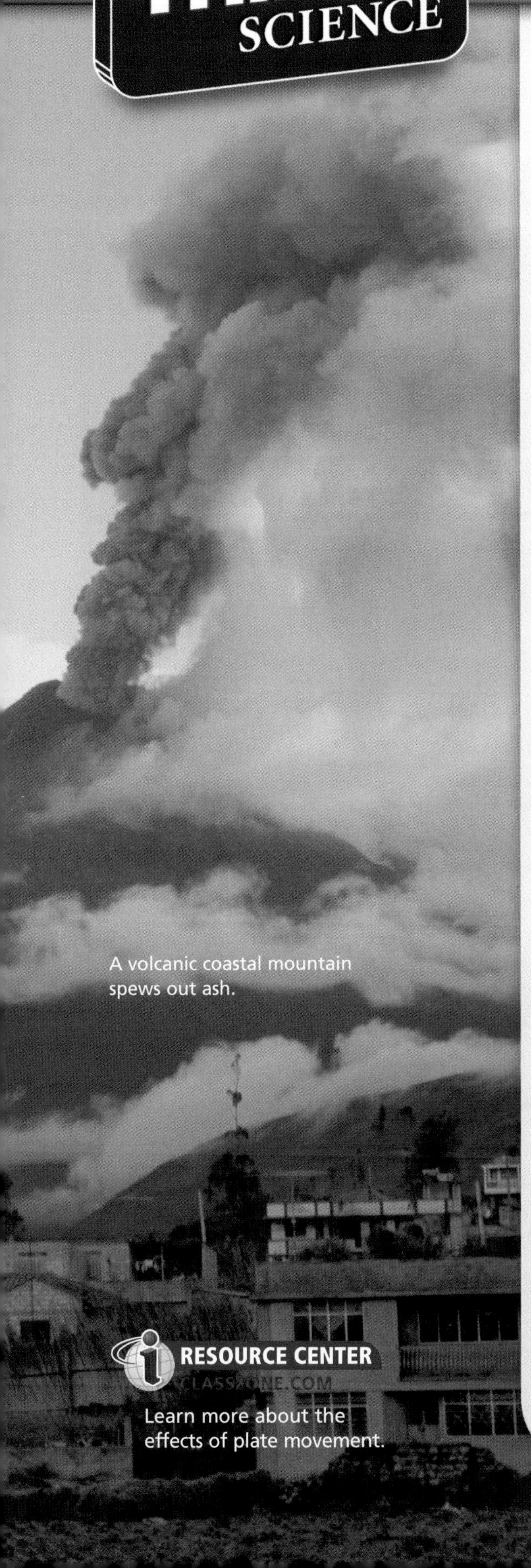

A volcanic coastal mountain spews out ash.

RESOURCE CENTER
CLASSZONE.COM
Learn more about the effects of plate movement.

# 8 Chapter Review

## the BIG idea

**The movement of tectonic plates causes geologic changes on Earth.**

CONTENT REVIEW
CLASSZONE.COM

### KEY CONCEPTS SUMMARY

#### 1 Earth has several layers.

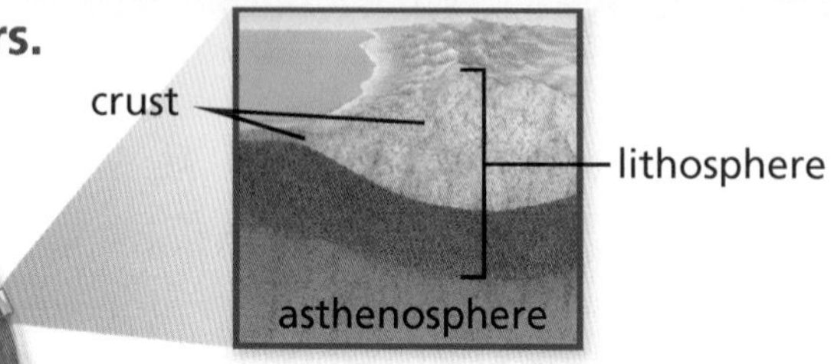


The lithosphere is made up of tectonic plates, which rest on the asthenosphere.

**VOCABULARY**
**inner core** p. 266
**outer core** p. 266
**mantle** p. 267
**crust** p. 267
**lithosphere** p. 267
**asthenosphere** p. 267
**tectonic plate** p. 268

#### 2 Continents change position over time.

Gravity and motions in the asthenosphere move tectonic plates over Earth's surface.

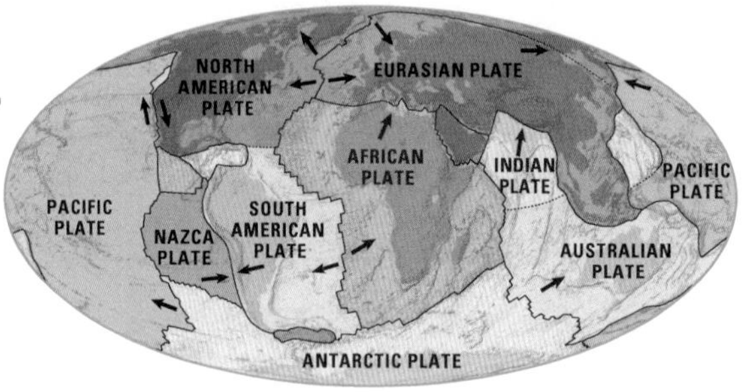


**VOCABULARY**
**continental drift** p. 270
**Pangaea** p. 272
**mid-ocean ridge** p. 272
**convection** p. 273
**convection current** p. 273
**theory of plate tectonics** p. 274

#### 3 Plates move apart.

New crust is formed at divergent boundaries. Features include:
- mid-ocean ridges
- records of magnetic reversals
- rift valleys

**VOCABULARY**
**divergent boundary** p. 278
**convergent boundary** p. 278
**transform boundary** p. 278
**rift valley** p. 279
**magnetic reversal** p. 280
**hot spot** p. 283

#### 4 Plates converge or scrape past each other.

Crust is destroyed or folded at convergent boundaries.
- Subduction boundaries form island arcs, deep-ocean trenches, and coastal mountains.
- Collision boundaries can form mountains.

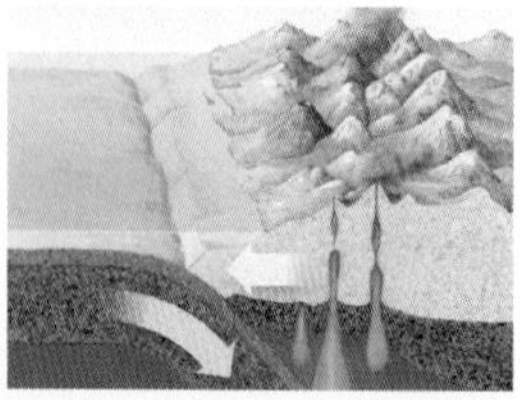

Crust is neither formed nor destroyed at transform boundaries.

**VOCABULARY**
**subduction** p. 286
**continental-continental collision** p. 287
**oceanic-oceanic subduction** p. 288
**oceanic-continental subduction** p. 289

## Reviewing Vocabulary

***Make a magnet word diagram for each of the vocabulary terms listed below. Write the term in the magnet. Write other terms or ideas related to it on the lines around the magnet.***

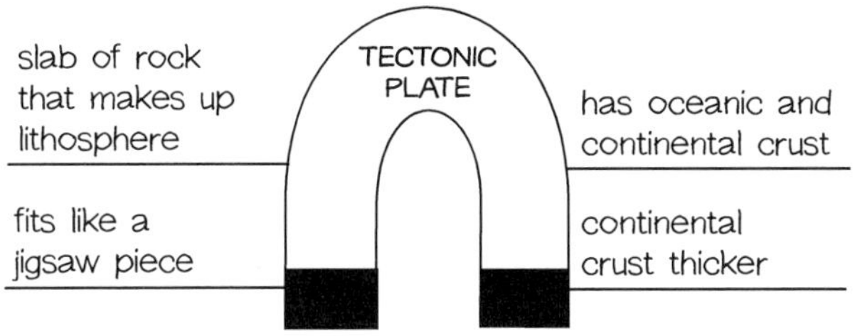


**1.** mantle
**2.** lithosphere
**3.** mid-ocean ridge
**4.** convection current
**5.** divergent boundary
**6.** convergent boundary

## Reviewing Key Concepts

**Multiple Choice** *Choose the letter of the best answer.*

**7.** Which of the following best describes Earth's mantle? (6.1.a)
- **a.** the densest of Earth's layers
- **b.** the home of all life on Earth
- **c.** the thickest layer of hot rock
- **d.** the thinnest and hottest layer

**8.** Tectonic plates make up Earth's (6.1.a)
- **a.** lower mantle
- **b.** lithosphere
- **c.** asthenosphere
- **d.** inner core

**9.** Why did many scientists reject Wegener's continental drift hypothesis? (6.1.a)
- **a.** He could not explain how the continents moved.
- **b.** The geology of continents did not support his hypothesis.
- **c.** Fossil evidence showed that the continents were never joined.
- **d.** The climates of the continents have remained the same.

**10.** What evidence from the sea floor shows that tectonic plates move? (6.1.a)
- **a.** The sea floor is much older than any of the continents.
- **b.** The sea floor is youngest near a mid-ocean ridge and older farther away.
- **c.** Mid-ocean ridges circle Earth like seams in a baseball.
- **d.** The sea floor is thinner than continental crust.

**11.** A mid-ocean ridge forms where plates (6.1.a)
- **a.** move apart
- **b.** push together
- **c.** scrape past each other
- **d.** subduct

**12.** Plate motion is caused partly by (6.1.c)
- **a.** magnetic reversals
- **b.** convection currents
- **c.** continental drift
- **d.** volcanic hot spots

**13.** Which of the following is formed at a collision zone? (6.1.e)
- **a.** mountain range
- **b.** volcanic island chain
- **c.** deep-ocean trench
- **d.** continental rift valley

**14.** What happens when two oceanic plates meet? (6.1.e)
- **a.** Both plates sink into the asthenosphere.
- **b.** The colder, denser plate sinks.
- **c.** Both plates fold the rock between them.
- **d.** One plate slides past the other.

**15.** Where is crust neither formed nor destroyed? (6.1.e)
- **a.** mid-ocean ridge
- **b.** continental rift valley
- **c.** transform boundary
- **d.** subduction zone

**Short Answer** *Write a short answer to each question.*

**16.** How does the theory of plate tectonics help geologists predict future geologic events? (6.1.e)

**17.** How do rocks record changes in Earth's magnetic field? (6.1.a)

**18.** Explain what happens when a continental plate splits apart. (6.1.c)

## Thinking Critically

*Use the diagram to answer the next six questions.*

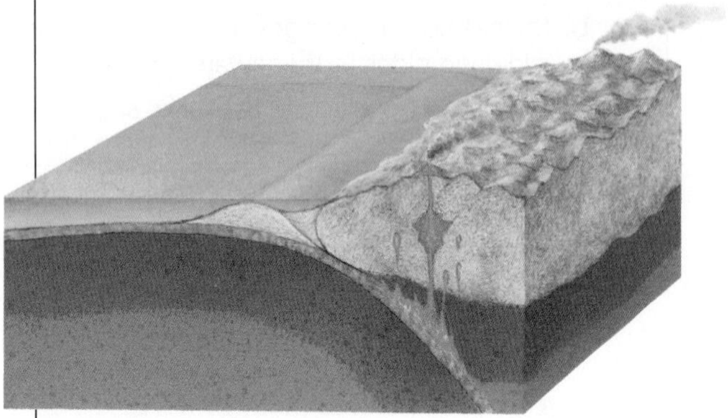

19. **ANALYZE** Write your own explanation of how the coastal mountains formed. (6.1.e)

20. **PREDICT** Would you expect the volcanoes on this coastline to continue to be active? Why or why not? (6.1.d)

21. **APPLY** Looking at the diagram above, why do you think the coastal mountains are in a fairly straight line? (6.1.e)

22. **APPLY** On the diagram above, where would you expect to find a deep ocean trench? Why? (6.1.e)

23. **APPLY** A friend looks at the diagram and tells you that there should be an island arc forming off the coast. Use your own knowledge and the map above to support or reject your friend's statement. (6.1.e)

24. **SYNTHESIZE** On a separate piece of paper, extend the diagram to the left. Draw the type of plate boundary that someone might find far out at sea. (6.1.e)

25. **PREDICT** Will the Andes Mountains on the west coast of South America become taller or shorter in the future? Use the theory of plate tectonics to explain your answer. (6.1.e)

**APPLY** Copy the chart below. Fill in the type of boundary—divergent, convergent, or transform—where each formation is likely to appear. (6.1.f)

| Formation | Type of Boundary |
|---|---|
| **26.** Mid-ocean ridge | |
| **27.** Volcanic island arc | |
| **28.** Rift valley on land | |
| **29.** Mountains | |
| **30.** Deep-ocean trench | |
| **31.** Hot-spot volcano | |

## the BIG idea

32. **IDENTIFY CAUSE AND EFFECT** Look again at the photograph on pages 262–263. Now that you have finished the chapter, explain what may be forming this crack in Earth's surface. (6.1.e)

33. **PREDICT** Use the map on page 275, which shows Earth's tectonic plates and the directions in which they are moving. Based on the plate movements, where do you think the continents might be in a few million years? Draw a map that illustrates your prediction. You might want to give your landmasses names. (6.1.c)

## UNIT PROJECTS

If you are doing a unit project, make a folder for your project. Include in your folder a list of the resources you will need, the date on which the project is due, and a schedule to keep track of your progress. Begin gathering data.

## Analyzing a Diagram

6.1.e, 6.7.h

*The diagram shows several tectonic plates. The arrows indicate the direction each plate is moving. Study the diagram and answer the questions below.*

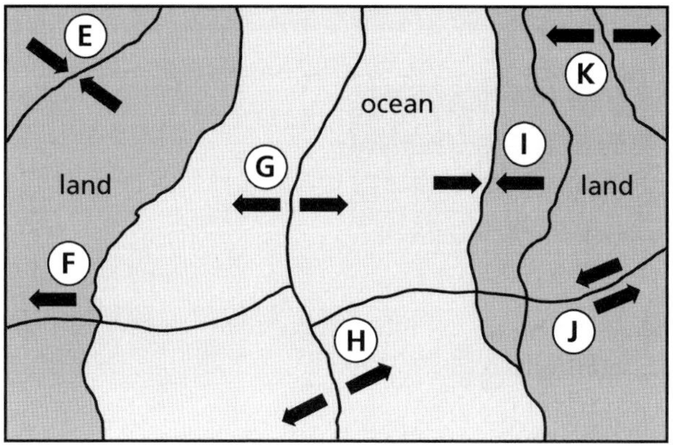


**1.** Where is an ocean trench most likely to form?
- **a.** F
- **b.** G
- **c.** H
- **d.** I

**2.** Where is a continental rift valley most likely to form?
- **a.** E
- **b.** F
- **c.** J
- **d.** K

**3.** Where would you find a convergent boundary?
- **a.** E
- **b.** F
- **c.** H
- **d.** K

**4.** Where is a mid-ocean ridge most likely to form?
- **a.** G
- **b.** J
- **c.** I
- **d.** F

**5.** What is a good example of a transform boundary?
- **a.** E
- **b.** I
- **c.** J
- **d.** K

**6.** Which is most likely to happen at I?
- **a.** Island arcs will form parallel to a trench.
- **b.** A spreading center will create a rift valley.
- **c.** Continental crust will be destroyed.
- **d.** Subduction will cause oceanic crust to melt.

**7.** Why are earthquakes likely to occur at J?
- **a.** Two plates are spreading away from each other.
- **b.** Two plates are colliding with each other.
- **c.** Two plates are scraping past each other.
- **d.** One plate is sliding under another plate.

**8.** Why are mountains likely to form at E?
- **a.** A rift valley is forming.
- **b.** Two plates are colliding.
- **c.** Magma is flowing upward.
- **d.** One plate is sinking.

**9.** Which is most likely to happen at G?
- **a.** Rising magma will create new crust.
- **b.** Subduction will cause a deep trench.
- **c.** Colliding plates will cause rocks to crumple.
- **d.** Moving plates will create island arcs.

## Extended Response

*Answer the two questions below in detail. Include some of the terms shown in the word box. In your answer, underline each term you use.*

| | | | |
|---|---|---|---|
| tectonic plates | subduction | magma | crust |
| continental drift | hot spot | mantle | |

**10.** Two island chains are separated by a deep ocean trench. Although they are close to each other, the islands have very different fossils and types of rock. Explain why these island chains have such different geologic features.

**11.** Andrea lives near a chain of mountains located far from plate boundaries. The closest mountain is an active volcano. The other mountains used to be volcanoes. The farther away a mountain is in the chain, the older it is. Explain these facts.

CHAPTER 9

# Earthquakes

## the BIG idea

**Earthquakes release stress that has built up in rocks.**

### Key Concepts

SECTION 1
**Earthquakes occur along faults.**
Learn how rocks move along different kinds of faults.

SECTION 2
**Earthquakes release energy.**
Learn how energy from an earthquake is used to determine its location and size.

SECTION 3
**Earthquake damage can be reduced.**
Learn how structures are built to better withstand earthquakes.

**California ClassZone**

CLASSZONE.COM
Chapter 9 online resources: Content Review, two Visualizations, three Resource Centers, Math Tutorial, Test Practice

*What caused the damage to these buildings in San Francisco?*

# EXPLORE the BIG idea

## Can You Bend Energy?

> 6.1.b Students know Earth is composed of several layers: a cold, brittle lithosphere; a hot, convecting mantle; and a dense, metallic core.

Put a clear glass filled with water on a table. Holding a flashlight at an angle to the glass, shine light through the water so that an oval of light forms on the table.

**Observe and Think** Did the light, which is a form of energy, travel in a straight line through the layers of air and water? Do you think other forms of energy travel in straight lines through layers inside Earth?

## Internet Activity: Earthquakes

> 6.1.d Students know that earthquakes are sudden motions along breaks in the crust called faults and that volcanoes and fissures are locations where magma reaches the surface.

Go to **ClassZone.com** to see maps of recent earthquakes around the world, in the United States, and in your own area.

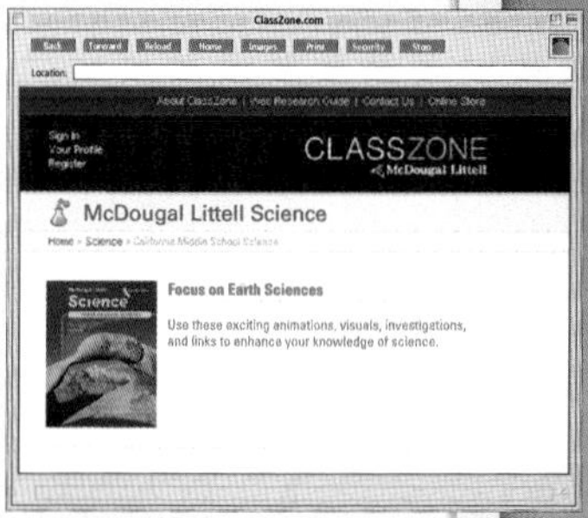


**Observe and Think** Where and when did the largest earthquakes occur? Summarize California's recent earthquake activity. Compare it with Alaska's for the same time period. What conclusions can you draw?

NSTA scilinks.org SCILINKS
Earthquakes **Code: MDL053**

CHAPTER 9

# Getting Ready to Learn

## CONCEPT REVIEW

- Earth's lithosphere is broken into tectonic plates.
- Tectonic plates pull apart, push together, and scrape past one another.
- Major geologic events occur along tectonic plate boundaries.

## VOCABULARY REVIEW

**lithosphere** p. 267
**tectonic plate** p. 268
**mid-ocean ridge** p. 272
**subduction** p. 286

**CONTENT REVIEW**
CLASSZONE.COM

Review concepts and vocabulary.

## TAKING NOTES

### MAIN IDEA AND DETAIL NOTES

Make a two-column chart. Write the main ideas, such as those in the blue headings, in the column on the left. Write details about each of those main ideas in the column on the right.

### VOCABULARY STRATEGY

For each vocabulary term, make a **magnet word** diagram. Write other terms or ideas related to that term around it.

See the Note-Taking Handbook on pages R45–R51.

SCIENCE NOTEBOOK

| MAIN IDEAS | DETAIL NOTES |
|---|---|
| 1. Rocks move along faults. | 1. Blocks of rock can move past one another slowly and constantly.<br>1. Blocks of rock can get stuck and then break free, causing earthquakes. |
| 2. Most faults are located along tectonic plate boundaries. | 2.<br>2.<br>2. |

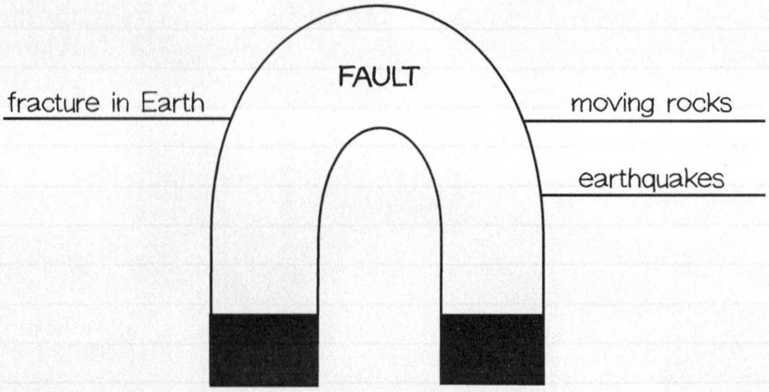

KEY CONCEPT

9.1

# Earthquakes occur along faults.

**CALIFORNIA Content Standards**

**6.1.b** Students know Earth is composed of several layers: a cold, brittle lithosphere; a hot, convecting mantle; and a dense, metallic core.

**6.1.d** Students know that earthquakes are sudden motions along breaks in the crust called faults and that volcanoes and fissures are locations where magma reaches the surface.

**6.1.e** Students know major geologic events, such as earthquakes, volcanic eruptions, and mountain building, result from plate motions.

**BEFORE, you learned**

- The crust and uppermost mantle make up the lithosphere
- The lithosphere is cold and rigid
- Tectonic plates move over hotter, weaker rock in the asthenosphere

**NOW, you will learn**

- Why earthquakes occur
- Where most earthquakes occur
- How rocks move during earthquakes

**EXPLORE Pressure (6.1.d)**

### *How does pressure affect a solid material?*

**PROCEDURE**

1. Hold a wooden craft stick at each end.
2. Bend the stick very slowly. Continue to put pressure on the stick until it breaks.

**WHAT DO YOU THINK?**

- How did the stick change before it broke?
- How might rocks react to pressure?

**MATERIALS**

wooden craft stick

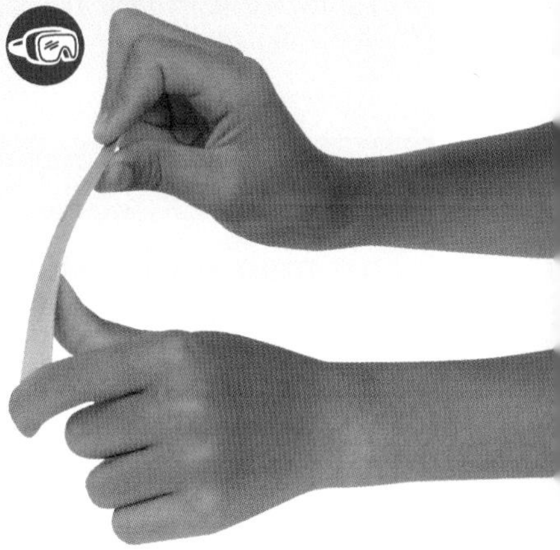

**VOCABULARY**

**fault** p. 301
**stress** p. 301
**earthquake** p. 301

**VOCABULARY**
Add magnet word diagrams for *fault, stress,* and *earthquake* to your notebook.

## Rocks move along faults.

Sometimes when you pull on a drawer, it opens smoothly. At other times, the drawer sticks shut. If you pull hard enough, the drawer suddenly flies open. Rocks along faults behave in a similar way. A **fault** is a fracture, or break, in Earth's lithosphere. Blocks of rock move past each other along a fault.

Along some parts of a fault, the rocks on either side may slide along slowly and constantly. Along other parts of the fault, the rocks may stick, or lock together. The rocks bend as stress is put on them. **Stress** is the force exerted when an object presses on, pulls on, or pushes against another object. As stress increases, the rocks break free. A sudden release of stress in the lithosphere causes an earthquake. An **earthquake** is a shaking of the ground caused by the sudden movement of large blocks of rock along a fault.

Most faults are located along tectonic plate boundaries, so most earthquakes occur in these areas. However, the blocks of rock that move during an earthquake are much smaller than a tectonic plate. A plate boundary can be many thousands of kilometers long. During even a very powerful earthquake, blocks of rock might move only a few meters past each other along a distance of several hundred kilometers. The strength of an earthquake depends in part on

- how much stress builds up before the rocks move
- the distance the rocks move along the fault

About 80 percent of all earthquakes occur in a belt around the edges of the Pacific Ocean. In the United States, the best-known fault in this belt is the San Andreas (san an-DRAY-uhs) Fault in California. It forms part of the boundary between the North American Plate and the Pacific Plate. Unlike many other faults, parts of the San Andreas Fault can be seen on the surface of the ground.

A small percentage of earthquakes occurs along faults within plates. As you read in Chapter 8, a tectonic plate is hard, or rigid. Therefore, stress along a plate's boundary can cause rocks to break and move along weak areas toward the middle of the plate.

**CALIFORNIA Focus**

The San Andreas Fault is not one long fault. Instead, it is a zone consisting of three main segments: southern, central, and northern. The San Andreas Fault zone is more than 1288 kilometers (800 mi) long. Notable earthquakes occurred along the fault in 1857, 1906, and 1989.

## Where Earthquakes Occur

**This map shows the locations of moderate to intense earthquakes for a ten-year period.**

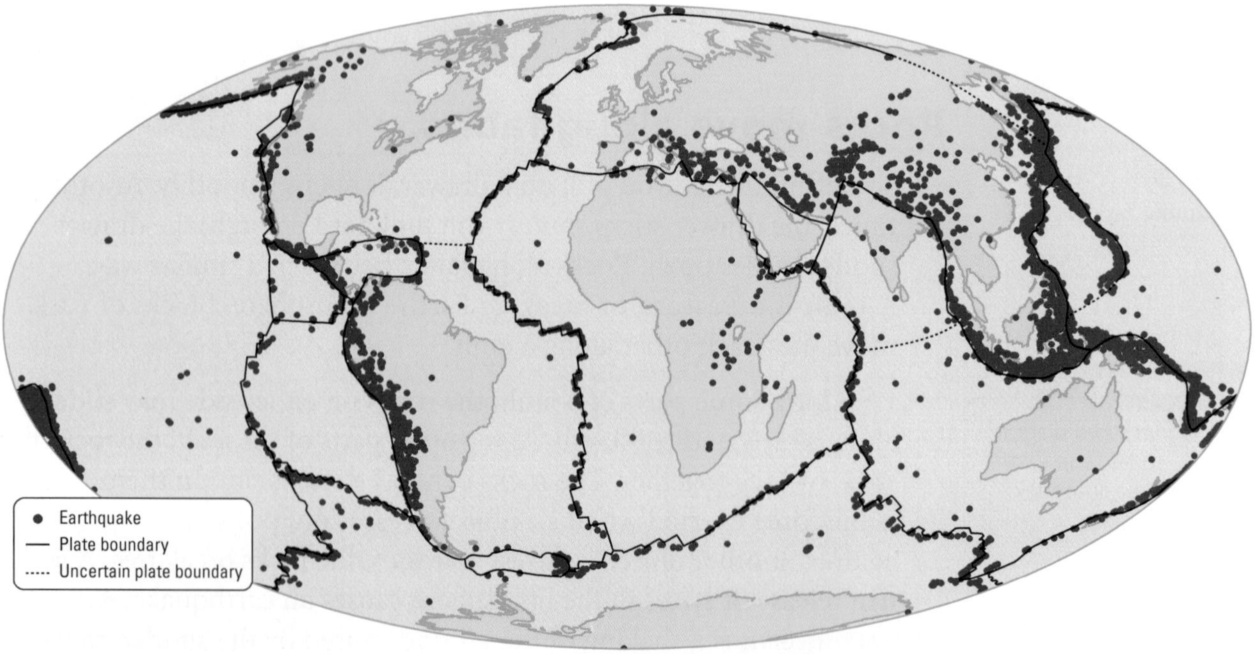


**READING VISUALS** Why do most earthquakes in North America and South America occur near the continents' western coasts?

All earthquakes occur in the lithosphere. To understand why, you might compare a tectonic plate to a piece of cold, hard caramel. Like cold caramel, the plate is rigid and brittle. The rocks can break and move suddenly, causing an earthquake. Now compare the asthenosphere below the plate to warm, soft caramel. In the asthenosphere, hot rock bends and flows rather than breaks. A few earthquakes occur far below the normal depth of the lithosphere only because tectonic plates sinking in subduction zones are still cold enough to break.

**CHECK YOUR READING** Why don't earthquakes occur in the asthenosphere?

## Faults are classified by how rocks move.

The blocks of rock along different types of faults move in different directions, depending on the kinds of stress they are under. Scientists classify a fault according to the way the rocks on one side move in relation to the rocks on the other side.

**MAIN IDEA AND DETAILS** Record information about each type of fault in your notebook.

The three main types of faults are normal faults, reverse faults, and strike-slip faults. More than one type of fault may be present along the same plate boundary. However, the type of fault that is most common along a boundary depends on whether plates are pulling apart, pushing together, or scraping past one another at that boundary.

# INVESTIGATE Faults

### *How can rocks move along faults?*

**SKILL FOCUS**
Modeling (6.1.e)

**MATERIALS**
- 2 triangular blocks of wood
- masking tape
- marker

**TIME**
15 minutes

**PROCEDURE**

1. Place one block of wood against the other to form a rectangle.
2. Put two pieces of masking tape across both blocks. Draw a different pattern on each piece of tape. Break the tape where it crosses the blocks.
3. Keep the blocks in contact and slide one block along the other.
4. Repeat step 3 until you find three different ways the blocks can move relative to each other. Draw diagrams showing how the blocks moved. Include the tape patterns.

**WHAT DO YOU THINK?**

- How can you use the tape patterns to find the relative directions in which the blocks were moved?
- In each case, what sort of stress (such as pulling) did you put on the blocks?

**CHALLENGE** Compare the ways you moved the blocks with the ways tectonic plates move at their boundaries.

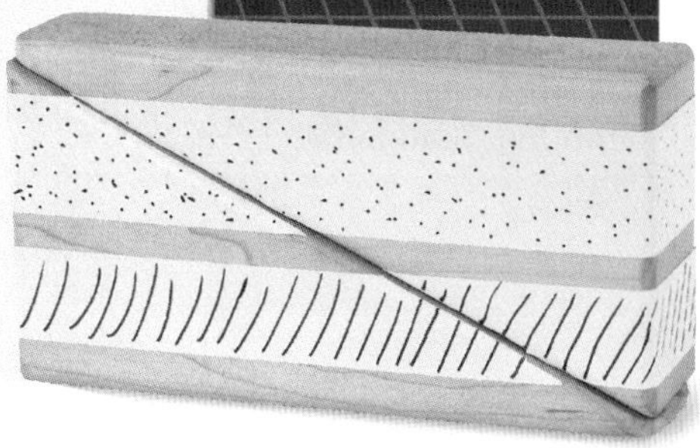

READING TIP

The word *plane* comes from the Latin word *planum,* which means "flat surface."

The illustrations on this page and page 305 show that a fault forms a flat surface, or plane, that extends both horizontally and vertically. Blocks of rock move along the fault plane during an earthquake. Along a normal or reverse fault, the blocks move up or down. Along a strike-slip fault, the blocks move sideways.

## Normal Faults

Along a normal fault, the block of rock above the fault plane slides down in relation to the other block. Stress that pulls rocks apart causes normal faults. Earthquakes along normal faults are common near boundaries where tectonic plates are moving apart, such as in the Great Rift Valley of Africa.

READING TIP

Compare the directions of the arrows in the diagrams with the directions of the arrows on the photographs.

As rocks are pulled apart (white arrows), normal faults form. The block on the right has moved down in relation to the block on the left.

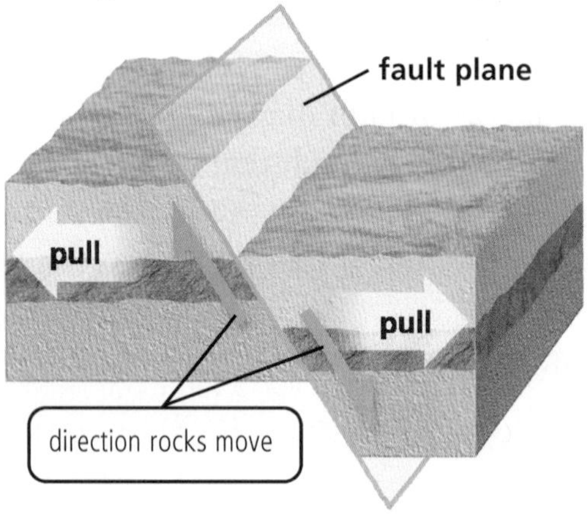

## Reverse Faults

Along a reverse fault, the block of rock above the fault plane moves up in relation to the other block. Stress that presses rocks together causes reverse faults. These faults can occur near collision-zone boundaries.

As rocks are pushed together (white arrows), reverse faults form. The block on the right has moved up in relation to the block on the left.

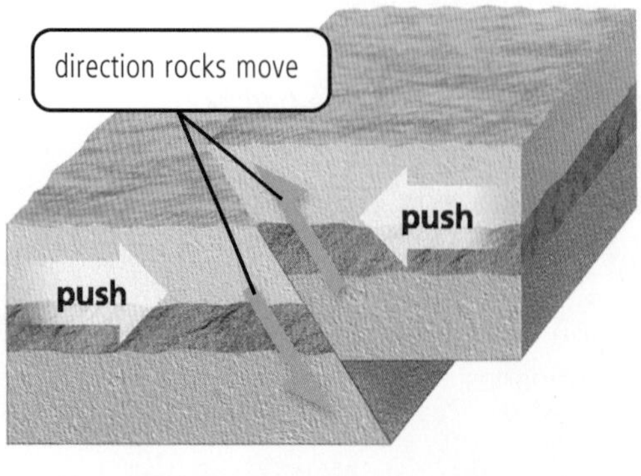

For example, the Himalaya Mountains rise in the area where the Indian Plate is pushing into the Eurasian Plate. The Himalayas have many earthquakes along reverse faults.

**CHECK YOUR READING** What type of stress produces reverse faults?

## Strike-Slip Faults

Along a strike-slip fault, blocks of rock move sideways on either side of the fault plane. Stresses that push blocks of rock horizontally cause earthquakes along strike-slip faults. These faults can occur where plates scrape past each other. The San Andreas Fault is a strike-slip fault.

**VISUALIZATION** CLASSZONE.COM
Explore animations showing fault motion.

As rocks are pushed horizontally in opposite directions, strike-slip faults form. The block on the right has moved to the right with respect to the block on the left.

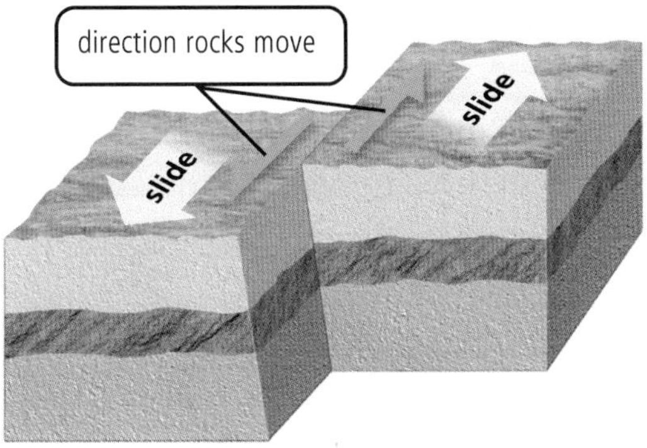

Over time, movement of rocks along normal and reverse faults can push up mountains and form deep valleys. As rocks move along strike-slip faults, rocks that were once in continuous layers can become separated by hundreds of kilometers.

# 9.1 Review

### KEY CONCEPTS

1. What causes earthquakes? (6.1.e)
2. Why do most earthquakes occur along tectonic plate boundaries? (6.1.d)
3. What is the main direction of stress on blocks of rock at normal faults, reverse faults, and strike-slip faults? (6.1.d)

### CRITICAL THINKING

4. **Compare and Contrast** Make a chart showing the similarities and differences between normal and reverse faults.
5. **Connect** Japan is near a subduction zone. What type of faults would you expect to be responsible for many of the earthquakes there? Explain.

### CHALLENGE

6. **Analyze** What evidence from rock layers could show a scientist that earthquakes had occurred in an area before written records were kept?

# Earth Shakes

6.1.e Students know major geologic events, such as earthquakes, volcanic eruptions, and mountain building, result from plate motions.

The most powerful earthquake ever recorded in the United States struck Prince William Sound in Alaska on March 27, 1964. Plates that had been moving a few centimeters per year lurched 9 meters (30 ft), causing the ground to shake for more than three minutes. Energy from the earthquake reached Louisiana, more than 5000 kilometers (3000 mi) away. There, it caused waves high enough to sink fishing boats in a harbor.

The 1964 Alaskan earthquake caused buildings to crumble and collapse. It also produced tsunamis—water waves caused by a sudden movement of the ground during an earthquake, landslide, or volcanic eruption. In Alaska's Valdez Inlet, a landslide triggered by the earthquake produced a tsunami 67 meters (220 ft) high—taller than a 20-story building.

A landslide caused by the 1964 Alaskan earthquake tore this school in Anchorage apart. Fortunately, school was not in session.

In Anchorage, almost 120 km from the center of the earthquake, the ground shook for about three minutes, causing severe damage.

## Missouri Earthquakes Ring Massachusetts Bells

Earthquakes were recorded near New Madrid, Missouri, in 1811 and 1812. The energy from the quakes caused church bells to ring in Boston, Massachusetts—nearly 1600 kilometers (1000 mi) away.

**Five Largest Earthquakes Since 1900**

| Location | Date | Moment Magnitude |
|---|---|---|
| Off the coast of Chile | 1960 | 9.5 |
| Prince William Sound, Alaska | 1964 | 9.2 |
| Andreanof Islands, Alaska | 1957 | 9.1 |
| Kamchatka Peninsula, Russia | 1952 | 9.0 |
| Off the coast of Sumatra | 2004 | 9.0 |

## Largest Earthquake Ever

The most powerful earthquake ever recorded hit Chile in 1960. This earthquake released almost 10 times as much energy as the 1964 earthquake in Alaska. This was about 600 times the energy of the earthquake that destroyed much of San Francisco in 1906.

### EXPLORE

1. **EXPLAIN** How were the 1964 Alaskan earthquake and the 1960 Chilean earthquake related to movements along tectonic plate boundaries?
2. **CHALLENGE** An inlet is a narrow body of water connected to a lake or ocean. Why might a tsunami be higher in an inlet than along the coastline around it?

KEY CONCEPT

# 9.2 Earthquakes release energy.

## CALIFORNIA Content Standards

**6.1.g** Students know how to determine the epicenter of an earthquake and know that the effects of an earthquake on any region vary, depending on the size of the earthquake, the distance of the region from the epicenter, the local geology, and the type of construction in the region.

**6.3.a** Students know energy can be carried from one place to another by heat flow or by waves, including water, light and sound waves, or by moving objects.

## VOCABULARY

**seismic wave** p. 307
**focus** p. 308
**epicenter** p. 308
**seismograph** p. 312

## BEFORE, you learned

- Most earthquakes occur along tectonic plate boundaries
- Different directions of stress cause normal, reverse, and strike-slip faults

## NOW, you will learn

- How energy from an earthquake travels through Earth
- How an earthquake's location is determined

## EXPLORE Movement of Energy (6.3.a)

### *How does energy travel?*

**PROCEDURE**

1. On a flat surface, hold one end of a spring toy while a partner holds the other end. Stretch the spring, then squeeze some coils together and release them.
2. Again, hold one end of the spring while your partner holds the other end. Shake your end of the spring back and forth.

**MATERIALS**

spring toy

**WHAT DO YOU THINK?**

- How did energy travel along the spring when you gathered and released some coils?
- How did energy travel along the spring when you shook one end back and forth?

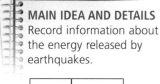

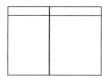

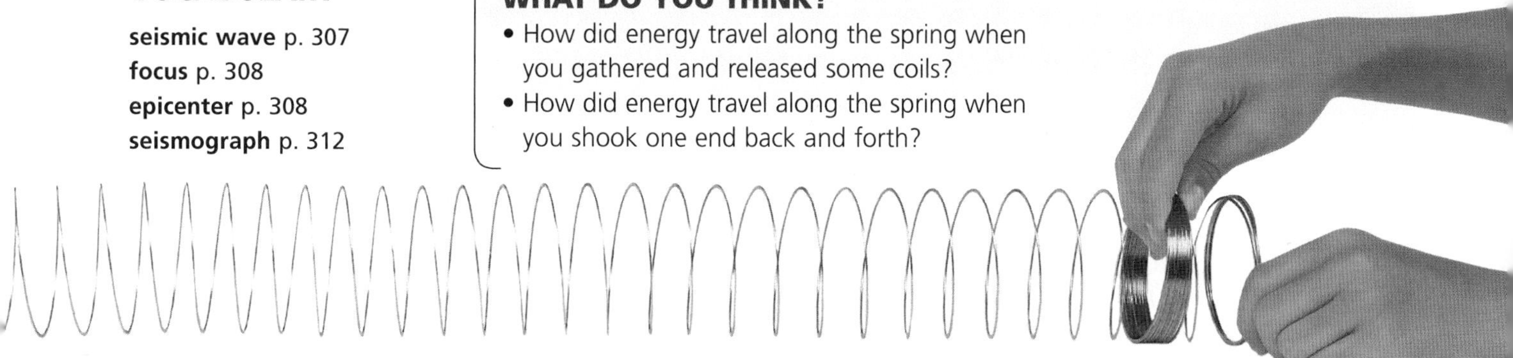

## Energy from earthquakes travels through Earth.

**MAIN IDEA AND DETAILS** Record information about the energy released by earthquakes.

When you throw a rock into a pond, waves ripple outward from the spot where the rock hits the water. The energy released by an earthquake travels in a similar way through Earth. Unlike the pond ripples, though, earthquake energy travels outward in all directions—up, down, and to the sides. The energy travels as **seismic waves** (SYZ-mihk), which are vibrations caused by earthquakes. Seismic waves from even small earthquakes can be recorded by sensitive instruments around the world.

All earthquakes start beneath Earth's surface. The **focus** of an earthquake is the point underground where rocks first begin to move. Seismic waves travel outward from the earthquake's focus. The **epicenter** (EHP-ih-SEHN-tuhr) is the point on Earth's surface directly above the focus. Scientists often name an earthquake after the city that is closest to its epicenter.

READING TIP

The prefix *epi-* comes from a Greek word meaning "on top of." An earthquake's epicenter is directly over its focus.

If two earthquakes of equal strength have the same epicenter, the one with the shallower focus usually causes more damage. Seismic waves from a deep-focus earthquake lose more of their energy as they travel farther up to Earth's surface.

The depths of earthquakes along tectonic plate boundaries are related to the directions in which the plates move. For example, an earthquake along a mid-ocean spreading center has a shallow focus. There, the plates are pulling apart, and the new crust that forms is thin. Subduction zones have a wide range of earthquake depths, from shallow to very deep. Earthquakes can occur anywhere along the sinking plates.

## Focus and Epicenter

**Seismic waves spread out from the focus of an earthquake.**

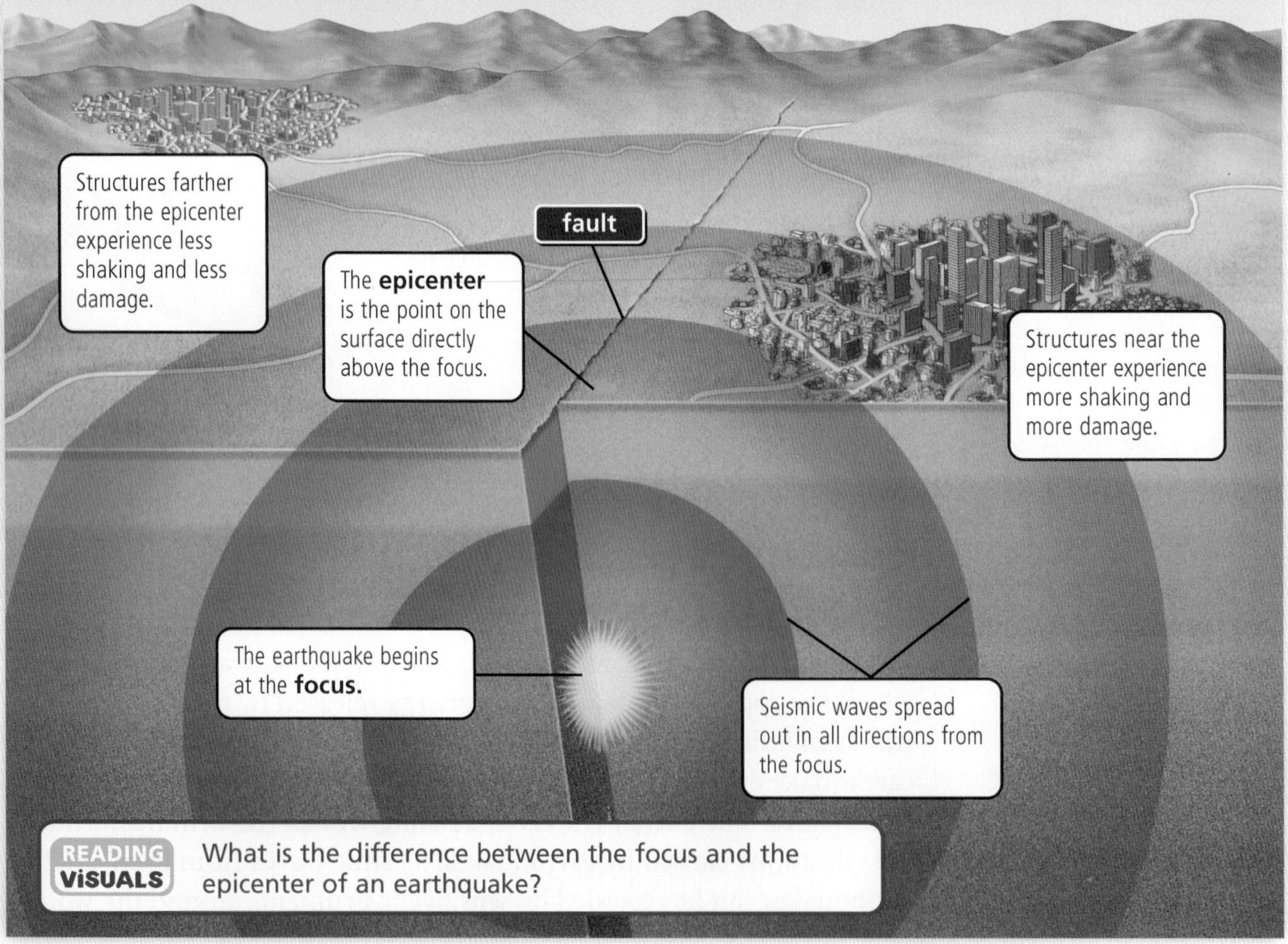
Structures farther from the epicenter experience less shaking and less damage.
fault
The **epicenter** is the point on the surface directly above the focus.
Structures near the epicenter experience more shaking and more damage.
The earthquake begins at the **focus.**
Seismic waves spread out in all directions from the focus.

READING VISUALS What is the difference between the focus and the epicenter of an earthquake?

# INVESTIGATE Subduction-Zone Earthquakes

**SKILL FOCUS**
Analyzing (6.1.a)

**MATERIALS**
- 3 different colors of string
- ruler
- scissors
- Earthquake Map
- tape

**TIME**
20 minutes

## *Why are some earthquakes deeper than others?*

**PROCEDURE**

1. Cut the first string into 4 pieces that are 4 cm long. Cut the second string into 3 pieces that are 8 cm long. Cut the third string into 4 pieces that are 15 cm long.
2. Use the key on the Earthquake Map to match string lengths with earthquake depths.
3. Tape one end of the pieces of string to the map at the earthquake locations, as shown. Always cover the same amount of string with tape.
4. Hold the map upside down, with the strings hanging down. Observe the patterns of earthquake locations and depths.

**WHAT DO YOU THINK?**

- What patterns among the strings do you observe? How do you explain them?
- How might the earthquake depths relate to the sinking of a tectonic plate in a subduction zone?

**CHALLENGE** Draw a line on the map, showing where the subduction zone might be at Earth's surface. How might the depths of the earthquakes be different if the subduction zone were on the other side of the island?

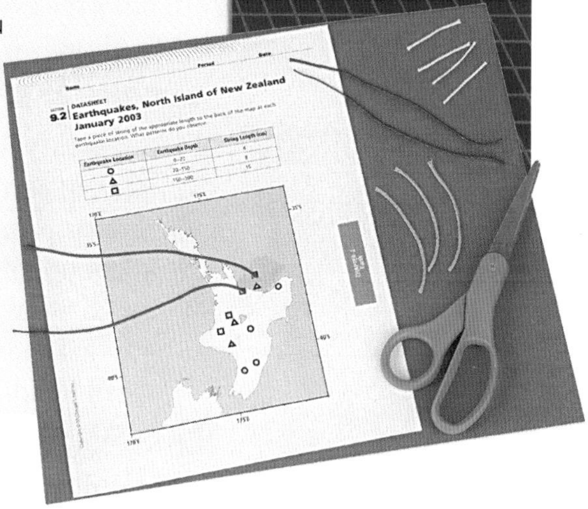


## Waves and Energy

Waves are part of your everyday life. For example, music reaches your ears as sound waves. All waves, including seismic waves, carry energy from place to place. As a wave moves through a material, particles of the material move out of position for a short time. This causes the particles next to them to move. After each particle moves, it returns to its original position. In this way, energy moves through the material, but matter does not.

On October 17, 1989, an earthquake stopped baseball's World Series at Candlestick Park in San Francisco. As the seismic waves arrived, fans heard a low rumble. Then for about 15 seconds, the stadium shook from side to side and up and down. About 20 minutes after the earthquake was felt at the stadium, the seismic waves had traveled to the other side of Earth. There, the waves did not shake the ground hard enough for people to notice. The waves could be detected only by scientific instruments.

Earthquakes produce three types of seismic waves: primary waves, secondary waves, and surface waves. Each type moves through materials differently. The waves can reflect, or bounce, off boundaries between different layers. The waves can also bend as they pass from one layer into another. Scientists learn about Earth's layers by studying the paths and speeds of seismic waves traveling through Earth.

## Primary Waves

READING TIP

One meaning of *primary* is "first." Primary waves arrive before secondary waves.

The fastest seismic waves are called primary waves, or P waves. These waves are the first to reach any location after an earthquake occurs. Primary waves travel through Earth's crust at an average speed of about 5 kilometers per second (3 mi/s). Primary waves can travel through solids, liquids, and gases. As they pass through a material, the particles of the material are slightly pushed together and pulled apart. Buildings also experience this push and pull as primary waves pass through the ground they are built on.

## Secondary Waves

VISUALIZATION
CLASSZONE.COM

Explore primary-wave and secondary-wave motion.

Secondary waves are the second seismic waves to arrive at any location after an earthquake. This is true even though they start at the same time as primary waves. Secondary waves travel through Earth's interior at about half the speed of primary waves. Secondary waves are also called S waves. As they pass through a material, the material's particles are shaken up and down or from side to side. Secondary waves rock small buildings back and forth as they pass.

Secondary waves can travel through rock, but they cannot travel through liquids or gases. Look at the illustrations on page 311. As a primary wave passes through a material, the volume and density of the material change slightly. But as a secondary wave passes, the material changes slightly in shape. Liquids and gases do not have definite shapes. These materials flow—that is, particles in them do not return to their original positions after being moved. When scientists learned that secondary waves cannot pass through Earth's outer core, they realized that the outer core is not solid.

CHECK YOUR READING Why can't secondary waves travel through liquids or gases?

## Surface Waves

Surface waves are seismic waves that move along Earth's surface, not through its interior. They make the ground roll up and down or shake from side to side. Surface waves cause the largest ground movements and the most damage. Surface waves travel more slowly than the other types of seismic waves.

## Seismic Waves

**Earthquakes produce three types of seismic waves.**

### Primary Waves

The particles of materials are slightly pushed together and pulled apart in the direction of the waves' travel.

### Secondary Waves

The particles of materials move at a right angle to the direction of the waves' travel.

### Surface Waves

Surface waves are seismic waves trapped near Earth's surface. Farther below the surface, motion due to surface waves decreases, then stops.

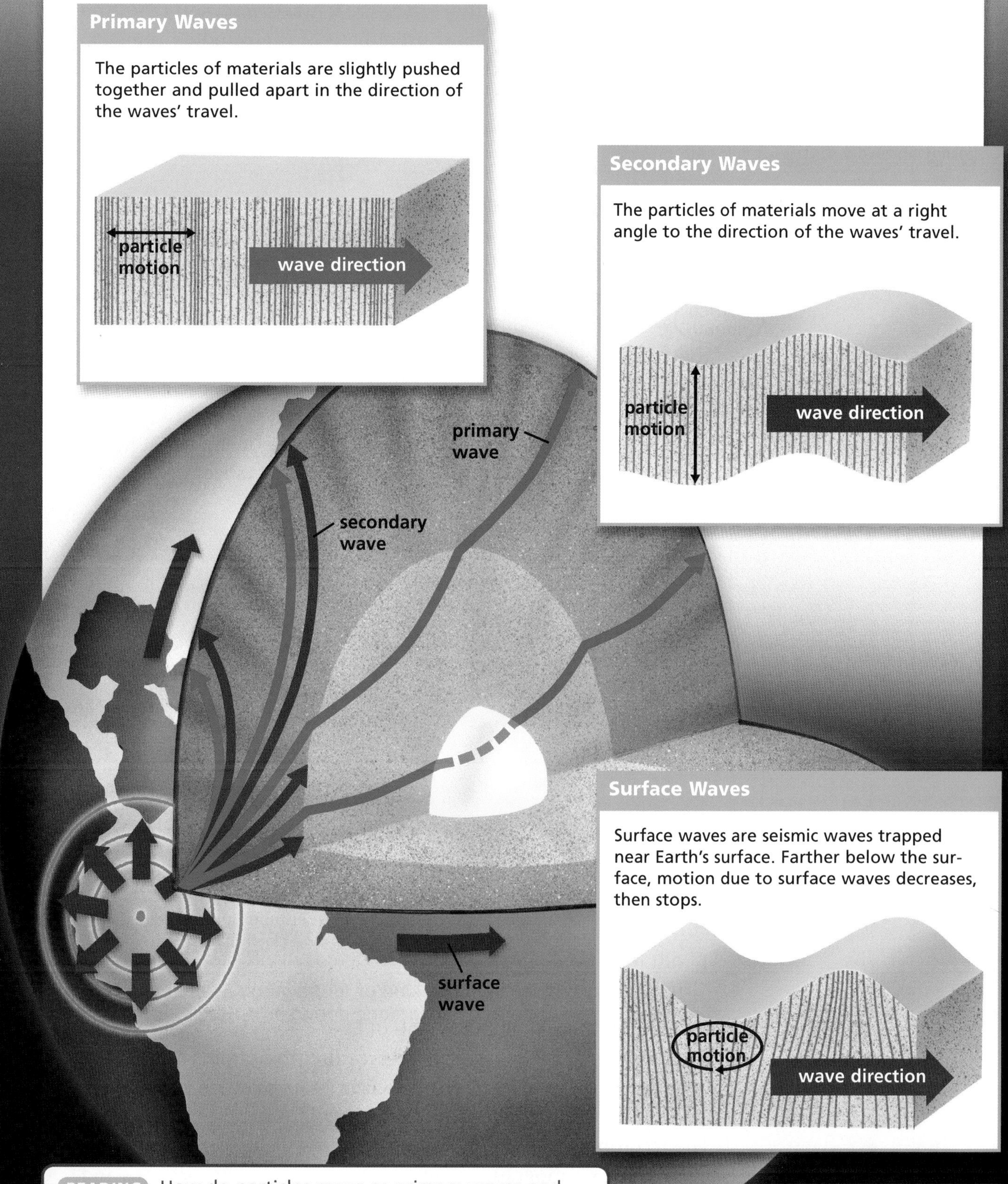


**READING VISUALS** How do particles move as primary waves and secondary waves pass through materials?

## Seismic waves can be measured.

Without listening to the news, scientists at seismic stations all over the world know when an earthquake occurs. Seismic stations are places where ground movements are measured. A **seismograph** (SYZ-muh-GRAF) is an instrument that constantly records ground movements. The recording of an earthquake looks like a group of wiggles in a line. The height of the wiggles indicates the amount of ground movement produced by seismic waves at the seismograph's location.

VOCABULARY
Add a magnet word diagram for *seismograph* to your notebook.

### Using Seismographs

Separate seismographs are needed to record side-to-side movements and up-and-down movements. A seismograph that measures side-to-side movements has a heavy weight hanging from a wire. The weight remains almost still as the ground moves back and forth beneath it. A pen attached to the weight records the movements. A seismograph that records up-and-down movements has a heavy weight hanging from a spring. As the ground moves, the weight stays almost still as the spring absorbs the movement by getting longer or shorter. A pen attached to the weight records the changes in distance between the ground and the weight.

RESOURCE CENTER
CLASSZONE.COM
Learn more about seismology.

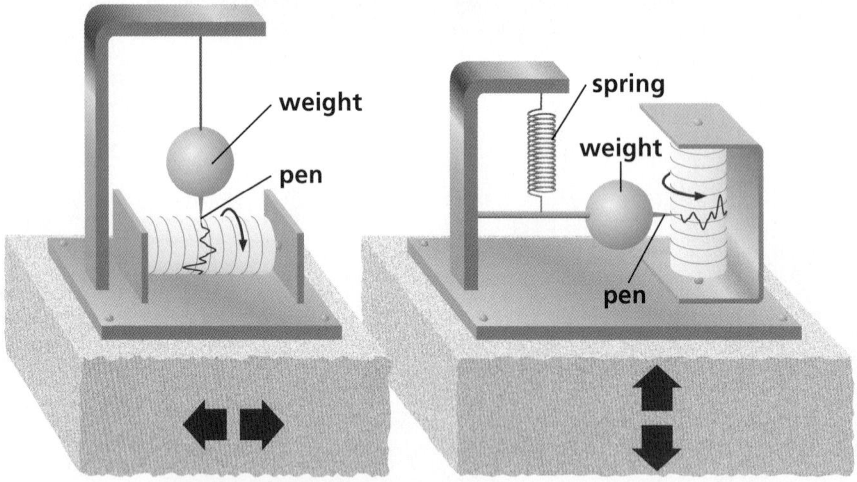


This seismograph records side-to-side movements.

This seismograph records up-and-down movements.

CHECK YOUR READING Why is more than one kind of seismograph needed to record all the movements of the ground during an earthquake?

Scientists use seismographs to measure thousands of earthquakes, large and small, every year. Some seismographs can detect ground movements as small as one hundred-millionth of a centimeter. The recording produced by a seismograph is called a seismogram. By studying seismograms, scientists can determine the locations and strengths of earthquakes.

## Locating an Earthquake

To locate the epicenter of an earthquake, scientists must have seismograms from at least three seismic stations. The procedure for locating an epicenter has three steps:

1. Scientists find the difference between the arrival times of the primary and the secondary waves at each of the three stations.
2. The time difference is used to determine the distance of the epicenter from each station. The greater the difference in time, the farther away the epicenter is.
3. A circle is drawn around each station. Each circle has a radius corresponding to the epicenter's distance from that station. The point where the three circles meet is the epicenter.

### Finding an Epicenter

**Seismograms provide data used to find an earthquake's epicenter.**

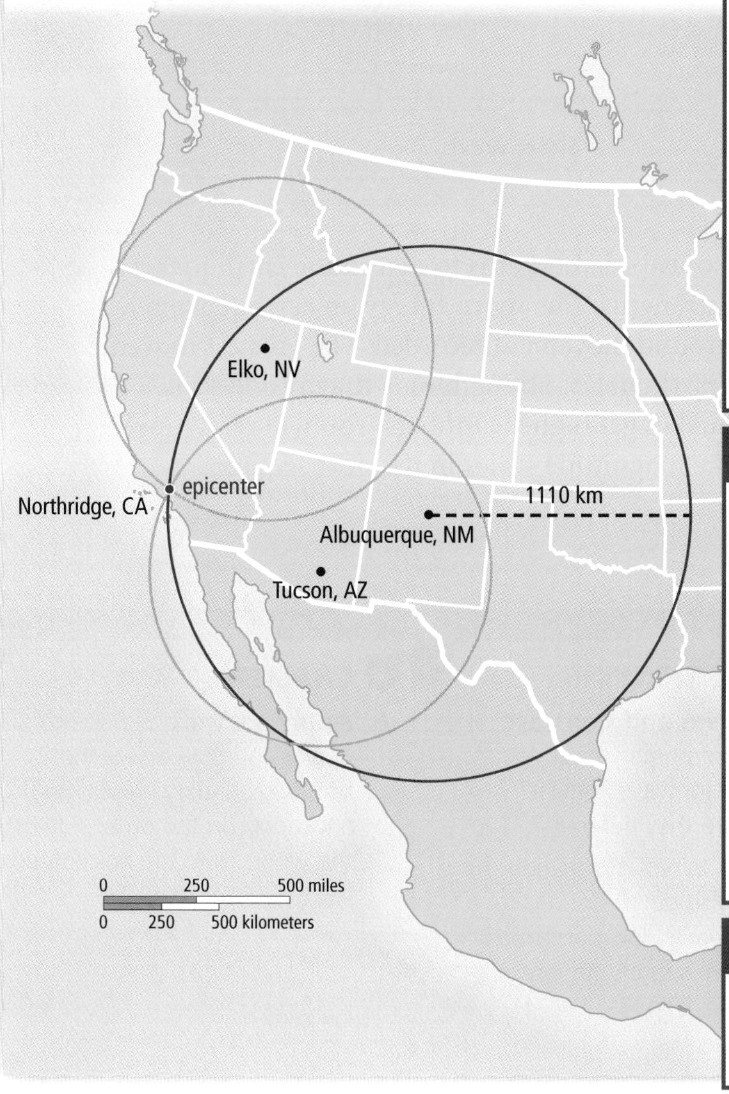


#### ① Determining Arrival Times

The time difference between the arrival of primary and secondary waves is recorded on a seismogram at each location.

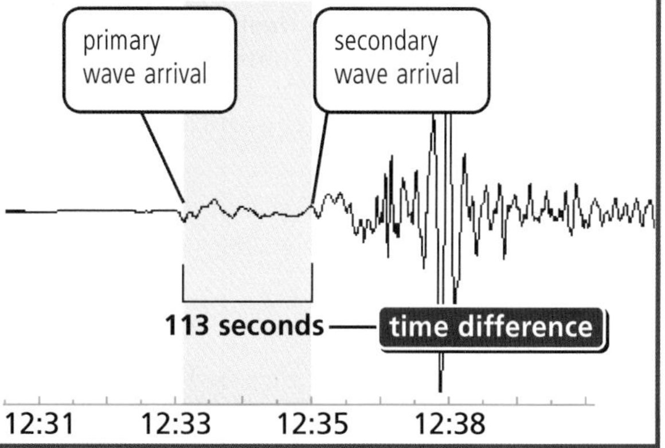


#### ② Calculating Distance

The arrival-time difference is used to determine the distance of the epicenter from the station.

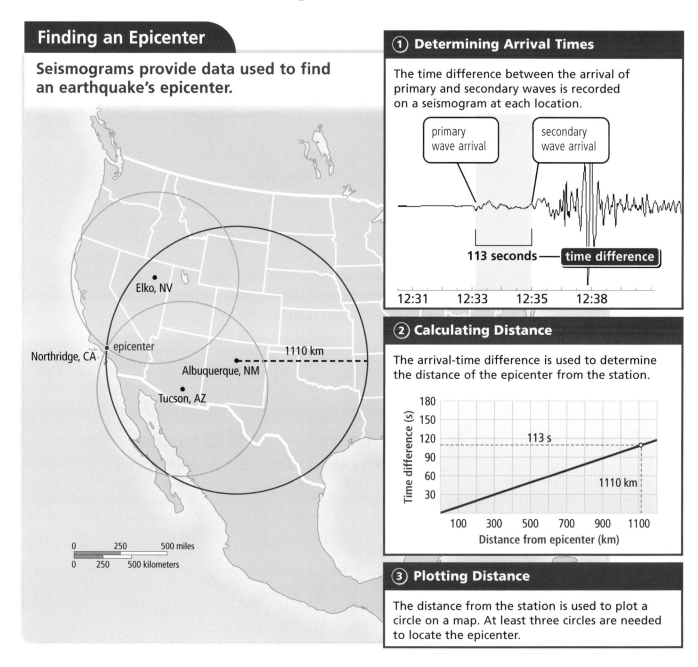

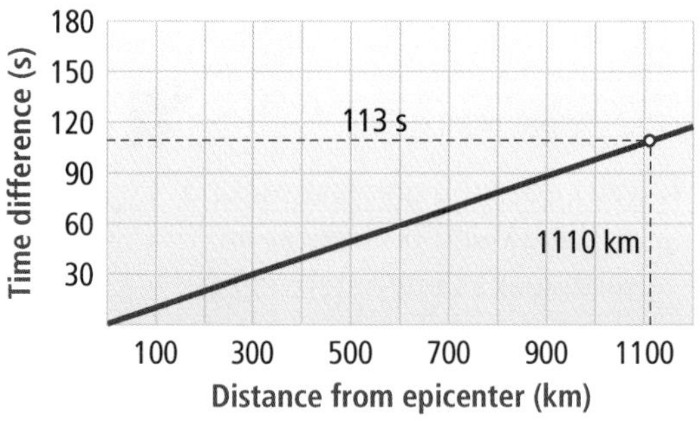


#### ③ Plotting Distance

The distance from the station is used to plot a circle on a map. At least three circles are needed to locate the epicenter.

Scientists can also use seismograph data to locate the focus of an earthquake. They study seismograms to identify waves that have reflected off boundaries inside Earth. Some of these waves help the scientists to determine the earthquake's depth.

A seismogram records the time when the first primary wave arrives. This wave travels by a direct path. The data also show when the first reflected primary wave arrives. After leaving the focus, this wave reflects from Earth's surface and then travels to the seismic station. The reflected wave takes a longer path, so it arrives slightly later. The difference in arrival times indicates the depth of the focus. Scientists usually use computers to calculate the location of an earthquake's epicenter and focus.

An earthquake's depth is determined from the difference in arrival times of direct and reflected seismic waves.

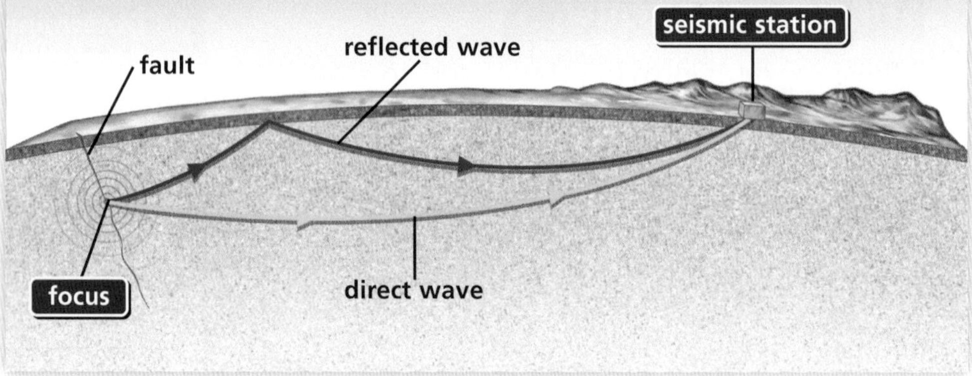


**READING TIP**

The word *magnitude* comes from the Latin word *magnitudo,* meaning "greatness."

Scientists also use seismograms to determine earthquakes' magnitudes, or strengths. The more energy an earthquake releases, the greater the ground movement recorded. The greatest movement determines the earthquake's strength on a magnitude scale. Stronger earthquakes get higher numbers. You will read more about earthquake magnitude scales in the next section.

# 9.2 Review

## KEY CONCEPTS

1. Why does the greatest shaking of the ground occur near an earthquake's epicenter? (6.1.g)
2. What information do you need to completely describe where an earthquake started? (6.1.e)
3. What types of information can a scientist get by studying seismograms? (6.3.a)

## CRITICAL THINKING

4. **Compare and Contrast** How are primary and secondary waves similar? How are they different?
5. **Apply** What information could you get about an earthquake's location from only two seismic stations' data? Explain.

## CHALLENGE

6. **Apply** Why might an earthquake's primary waves, but not its secondary waves, reach a location on the other side of the world from the epicenter?

MATH in SCIENCE

## SKILL: MULTIPLICATION

**MATH TUTORIAL**
CLASSZONE.COM
Click on Math Tutorial for more help with multiplication.

**Math** 6.NS.2.3, 6.MR.2.6
**Science** 6.1.a, 6.1.c

# Earthquake Energy

Seismologists use the moment magnitude scale to describe the energies of earthquakes. Because earthquakes vary from quite weak to very strong, the scale is designed to cover a wide range of energies. Each whole number increase in magnitude represents the release of about 32 times as much energy. For example, a magnitude 5 earthquake releases about 32 times as much energy as a magnitude 4 earthquake.

| Magnitude | 1 | 2 | 3 | 4 | 5 | 6 | 7 | 8 | 9 | 10 |
|---|---|---|---|---|---|---|---|---|---|---|
| Energy | | ×32 | ×32 | ×32 | ×32 | ×32 | ×32 | ×32 | ×32 | ×32 |

Similarly, a magnitude 6 earthquake releases about 32 times as much energy as a magnitude 5 earthquake, and a magnitude 7 earthquake releases about 32 times as much energy as a magnitude 6 earthquake. You can use multiplication to compare the energies of earthquakes.

### Example

Compare the energy of a magnitude 4 earthquake to the energy of a magnitude 7 earthquake. Give your answer to the nearest 1000.

**SOLUTION**

| **Magnitude** | **1** | **2** | **3** | **4** | **5** | **6** | **7** | **8** | **9** | **10** |
|---|---|---|---|---|---|---|---|---|---|---|
| **Energy** | | **×32** | **×32** | **×32** | ×32 | ×32 | ×32 | **×32** | **×32** | **×32** |

**(1)** Multiply: **32 × 32 × 32 =** **32,768**

**(2)** Round your answer to the nearest 1000: **33,000**

**ANSWER** A magnitude 7 earthquake releases about 33,000 times as much energy as a magnitude 4 earthquake.

**Compare the energies of two earthquakes:**

**1.** Magnitude 4 and magnitude 6; give your answer to the nearest 100

**2.** Magnitude 5 and magnitude 9; give your answer to the nearest 100,000

**3.** Magnitude 3.3 and magnitude 4.3

**CHALLENGE** What is the magnitude of an earthquake that releases about 1000 times the energy of a magnitude 2 earthquake?

KEY CONCEPT

# 9.3 Earthquake damage can be reduced.

**CALIFORNIA Content Standards**

**6.1.g** Students know how to determine the epicenter of an earthquake and know that the effects of an earthquake on any region vary, depending on the size of the earthquake, the distance of the region from the epicenter, the local geology, and the type of construction in the region.

**6.2.d** Students know earthquakes, volcanic eruptions, landslides, and floods change human and wildlife habitats.

**BEFORE, you learned**

- Seismic waves travel through Earth
- An earthquake's location and magnitude can be determined

**NOW, you will learn**

- How an earthquake's magnitude is related to the damage it causes
- How structures are built to withstand most earthquakes
- How scientists estimate the earthquake risk in an area

**VOCABULARY**

**aftershock** p. 318
**liquefaction** p. 318
**tsunami** p. 318

**EXPLORE Shaking (6.1.g)**

## *What happens as materials are shaken?*

**PROCEDURE**

1. Pour a pile of sand on a newspaper. Place a metal washer on top of the sand. Shake the paper and observe what happens to the sand and the washer.
2. Now place the washer on top of a flat rock. Shake the rock and observe what happens.

**MATERIALS**

- sand
- newspaper
- flat rock
- washer

**WHAT DO YOU THINK?**

- How did the washer, the sand, and the rock react differently to shaking?
- How might the washer, the sand, and the rock model what happens to buildings and land during earthquakes?

## Earthquakes can cause severe damage and loss of life.

**MAIN IDEA AND DETAILS** Record information about the effects of earthquakes in your notebook.

Every year, on average, an extremely powerful earthquake—one with a magnitude of 8 or higher—strikes somewhere on Earth. Such an earthquake can destroy almost all the buildings near its epicenter and cause great loss of life.

Earthquakes are most dangerous when they occur near areas where many people live. Most injuries and deaths due to earthquakes are not directly caused by the movement of the ground. They are caused by collapsing buildings and other structures and by fires. After an earthquake, fires may start due to broken natural-gas lines, broken electrical power lines, or overturned stoves.

## Earthquake Magnitude

A very powerful earthquake can release more energy than 1 million weak earthquakes combined. Earthquake magnitude scales give scientists and engineers a simple way to describe this huge range in energy.

The first scale of earthquake magnitude was developed in California during the 1930s by the scientists Charles Richter (RIHK-tuhr) and Beno Gutenberg. This scale is called the Richter scale. An earthquake's magnitude is based on how fast the ground moves at a seismic station. However, most scientists today prefer to use a newer, more accurate scale: the moment magnitude scale. This scale is based on the total amounts of energy released by earthquakes. The moment magnitude scale is used for all earthquake magnitudes given in this chapter.

Both the Richter scale and the moment magnitude scale are often shown with a top value of 10. However, neither actually has a maximum value. On each scale, an increase of one whole number indicates an increase of 32 times more energy. For example, a magnitude 5 earthquake releases 32 times as much energy as a magnitude 4 earthquake and about 1000 times as much energy as a magnitude 3 earthquake.

### Magnitude and Effects Near Epicenter

**More powerful earthquakes have higher magnitude values.**

| Magnitude | Effects Near Epicenter |
|---|---|
| **0–3.9** Very Minor to Minor | rarely noticed |
| **4.0–4.9** Light | slight damage |
| **5.0–5.9** Moderate | some structures damaged |
| **6.0–6.9** Strong | major damage to structures |
| **7.0–7.9** Major | some well-built structures destroyed |
| **8.0 and above** Great | major to total destruction |

**Damage from Powerful Earthquake**

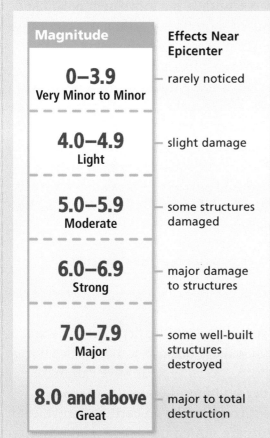

This road collapsed during a magnitude 6.9 earthquake in California on October 17, 1989. About 140 earthquakes with magnitudes of 6 or higher occur each year around the world.

**VOCABULARY**
Add magnet word diagrams for *aftershock* and *liquefaction* to your notebook.

The moment magnitude scale is more accurate for larger earthquakes than the Richter scale. Another advantage of the moment magnitude scale is that it can be used for earthquakes that occurred before seismographs were invented. Geologists can measure the strength of the rocks and the length they moved along a fault to calculate a past earthquake's magnitude. This information is important for geologists to know when they determine an area's earthquake risk.

**CHECK YOUR READING** What are two advantages of the moment magnitude scale over the Richter scale?

## Damage from Earthquakes

Movement of the blocks of rock on either side of a fault can crack roads, buildings, dams, and any other structures on the fault. As blocks of rock move, they can also raise, lower, or tilt the ground surface. Sometimes structures weakened by an earthquake collapse during shaking caused by aftershocks. An **aftershock** is a smaller earthquake that follows a more powerful earthquake in the same area. Also, fires that break out can cause great damage if broken water pipes keep firefighters from getting water. In the 1906 San Francisco earthquake, fires caused more than 90 percent of the building damage.

Earthquakes can cause major damage by affecting the soil and other loose materials. For example, landslides often occur as a result of earthquakes. A landslide is a movement of soil and rocks down a hill or mountain. Earthquakes can cause soil **liquefaction,** a process in which shaking of the ground causes soil to act like a liquid. For a short time the soil becomes like a thick soup. Liquefaction occurs only in areas where the soil is made up of loose sand and silt and contains a large amount of water. As the shaking temporarily changes the wet soil, structures either sink down into the soil or flow away with it. Shaking of the ground also affects areas that have mixtures of soils. Some soil types pack together more than others when shaken.

This building in Venezuela tilted and sank as the ground beneath it collapsed during an earthquake in 1967.

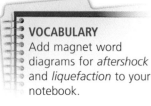

**CHECK YOUR READING** List five ways in which earthquakes can cause damage.

## Damage from Tsunamis

If you sit on an ocean beach, you can watch the depth of the water change as waves come in. If you watch longer, you may notice bigger changes as the tide rises or falls. A special type of wave can make water rise higher than a 20-story building. This wave, a **tsunami** (tsu-NAH-mee), is a water wave triggered by an earthquake, volcanic eruption, or landslide. Tsunamis are sometimes called tidal waves.

However, they are not caused by the forces that produce tides. A tsunami may not be a single wave but several waves that can have different heights and can arrive hours apart.

RESOURCE CENTER
CLASSZONE.COM
Explore tsunamis.

Tsunamis move quickly and can travel thousands of kilometers without weakening. In deep water, they can reach speeds of about 700 kilometers per hour (430 mi/h). A tsunami in the deep water of the open ocean may be less than one meter (3 ft) in height at the surface. As a tsunami reaches shallow water around an island or continent, it slows down and its height greatly increases.

A 1946 earthquake on Alaska's coast caused a tsunami that swept across the entire Pacific Ocean. In less than five hours, the tsunami reached Hawaii as a series of waves. Because people did not know of the danger, no one had evacuated, and 159 people were killed. A 2004 earthquake off the coast of Sumatra caused a tsunami in the Indian Ocean. The earthquake and tsunami killed more than 280,000 people.

In 2004 a tsunami devastated many coastal areas, including this beach in Madras, India.

Many earthquakes occur around the edges of the Pacific Ocean. Therefore, Hawaii and other areas in and around this ocean are likely to be hit by tsunamis. The Pacific Tsunami Warning Center in Hawaii was established in 1949. The center monitors earthquakes and issues warnings to areas that could be struck by tsunamis. A tsunami warning system is being developed for the Indian Ocean.

### Tsunami Travel Time, 2004 Sumatra Earthquake

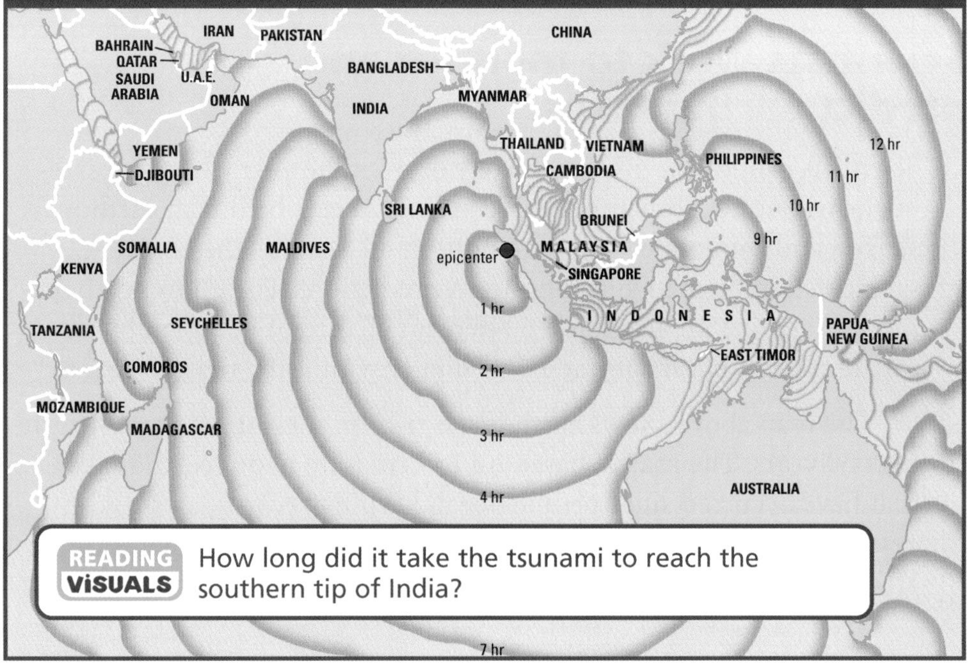


READING VISUALS How long did it take the tsunami to reach the southern tip of India?

## Earthquake Risk in the United States

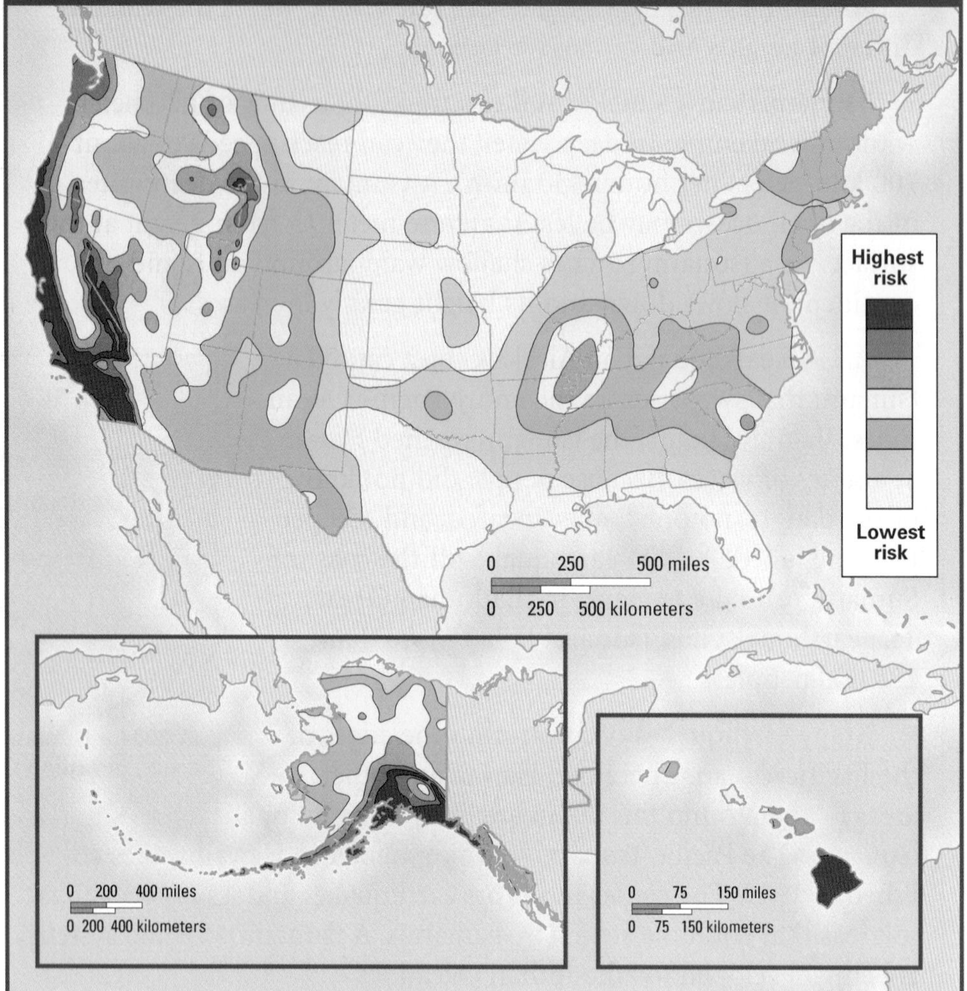


READING VISUALS How does the earthquake risk where you live compare with the risk in southern Alaska?

## Scientists work to monitor and predict earthquakes.

**READING TIP**

A prediction is a statement about an event before it occurs. Scientists use their knowledge to make predictions about when earthquakes might occur.

Scientists cannot yet predict the day or even the year when an earthquake will occur. Sometimes there are signs years before an earthquake strikes, and sometimes there are none at all. Usually the best that scientists can do is to give long-term predictions. For example, they might state that an area has a 60 percent chance of being hit by an earthquake with a magnitude 7 or higher within the next 25 years.

The map above shows earthquake risks in the United States for the next 50 years. The map is based on information about earthquakes that have occurred since people began keeping records, along with evidence of earlier earthquakes preserved in rocks. Note that most areas with the highest earthquake risks are near the Pacific Ocean.

Scientists all over the world study seismic activity along faults to learn more about earthquakes and find ways of predicting them. They monitor whether stress is building up in the rocks along faults. Such signs include

- tilts or changes in the elevation of the ground
- slow movements or stretching in rock
- the development of small cracks in the ground

An increase in small earthquakes can be a sign that stress is building up along a fault and that a large earthquake is likely to occur. But an increase in small earthquakes can also be a sign that a fault is releasing stress bit by bit. This decreases the likelihood of a major earthquake.

Scientists also look for areas where earthquakes have not occurred along an otherwise active fault. They make diagrams in which they plot the locations where earthquakes have started, as shown below. Sometimes such a diagram shows an area of few or no earthquakes that is surrounded by many earthquakes. This area is called a seismic gap. A seismic gap can indicate a location where a fault is stuck. Movement along other parts of the fault can increase stress along the stuck part. This stress could be released by a major earthquake.

**CHECK YOUR READING** Why can a lack of earthquakes in an area near an active fault cause concern?

## Seismic Gaps

**A seismic gap is a section of a fault with few earthquakes compared with sections of the fault on either side of the gap.**

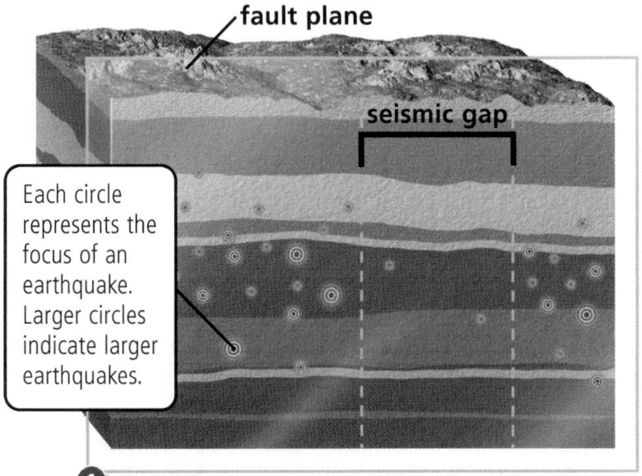
fault plane
seismic gap
Each circle represents the focus of an earthquake. Larger circles indicate larger earthquakes.

1 Over several years many earthquakes have occurred along this fault. However, one section of the fault has had little earthquake activity. Stress is building up along this section.

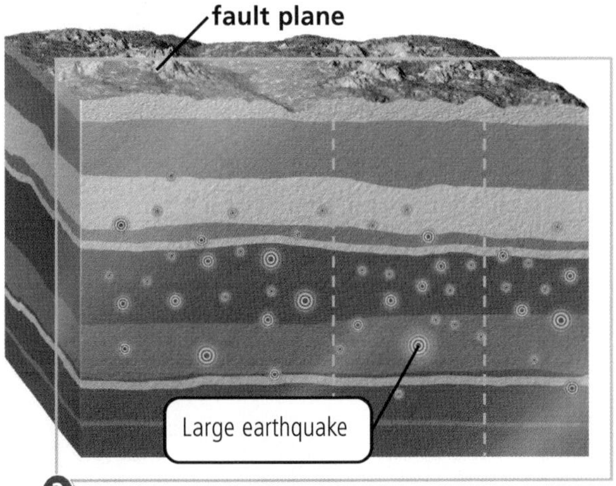
fault plane
Large earthquake

2 A large earthquake and its aftershocks have occurred, releasing built-up stress. Over just a few weeks the seismic gap has been filled in.

## Structures can be designed to resist earthquake damage.

READING TIP

Here, the term *structure* refers to office buildings, homes, bridges, dams, factories—all the things that people build.

It might be best to be outdoors during an earthquake. The safest place would be far from any buildings. But there is no way to tell just when or where an earthquake will occur. For this reason, the best way to reduce deaths, injuries, and damage from earthquakes is to build structures able to withstand strong ground shaking. The first step is to understand what the risks from earthquakes are in an area. The second step is to build structures that are appropriate for the area.

Scientists make maps of areas to show the locations of fault zones, past earthquakes, and areas likely to experience flooding, landslides, or liquefaction. In California, Japan, and other areas that have many earthquakes, planners use these maps to develop rules for building new structures and strengthening older ones. The maps are also used to select building locations that are stable—unlikely to experience landslides or liquefaction.

Earthquake damage to small buildings, such as most houses, often occurs when the buildings are shaken off their foundations. Small buildings are better protected when they are firmly fastened to their foundations. Also, their walls need to be strong. Some houses were built before modern safety rules were in place. The walls of these houses can be made stronger by adding supports. Supports are especially important in brick walls, which can easily collapse in an earthquake. A special type of steel is commonly used for the supports that can bend and then return to its original shape.

### SAFETY TIPS

**Earthquakes**

**Before**

- Fasten heavy objects, such as bookcases, to floors or walls to keep them from falling.
- Put latches on cabinets to keep dishes from falling out.
- Identify safe spots in every room, such as the space under a strong table.
- Keep an emergency supply of bottled water.

**During and After**

- If you are inside a building, stay inside until the shaking stops. Objects falling from buildings cause many injuries.
- If you are outdoors, move away from buildings, poles, and trees.
- Make a family plan for contacting a person who lives in another town. As people call to say they are safe, this person can pass on the information.

Many of the methods used to make larger buildings and other structures safer help reduce the amount they shake during an earthquake. One method is to use devices called base isolators, as shown in the illustration. Base isolators are placed between a building and its foundation. The isolators are made of flexible materials that are stacked in layers like pancakes. When an earthquake occurs, the isolators absorb much of the ground motion. Any shaking that does reach the building is slower and smoother.

**Earthquake-Resistant Building**

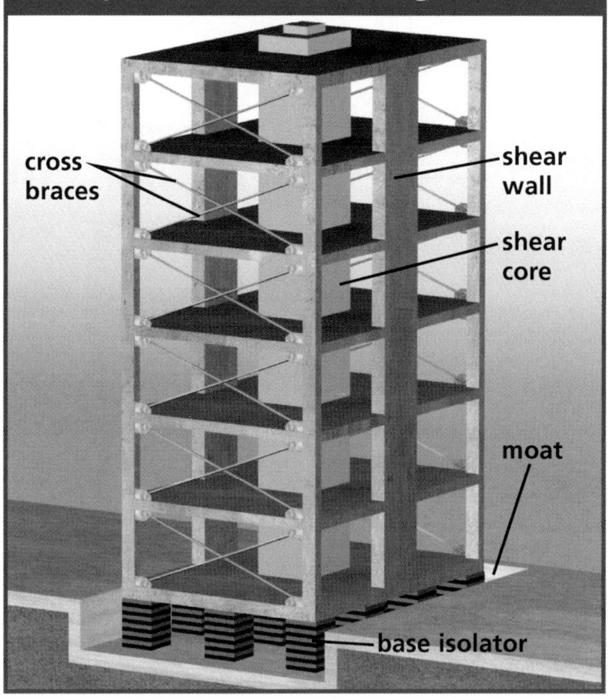


A building may also have an open space, or moat, around it. The moat may be covered at the surface with sidewalks and landscaping. It lets the building shake more gently than the ground during an earthquake.

Special walls, called shear walls, add strength to a structure. These walls contain steel supports. Shear walls in the center of a building are often built around a stairwell or an elevator shaft. These walls make up a part of the building known as the shear core.

Walls can also be made stronger by adding braces. Pairs of braces that form an X shape are called cross braces. They help a structure keep its shape while it is being shaken.

**CHECK YOUR READING** Describe two methods used to make buildings stronger.

# 9.3 Review

## KEY CONCEPTS

1. How is an earthquake magnitude scale related to the amounts of energy released by earthquakes? (6.1.d)
2. What are the major dangers to people from an earthquake? (6.2.d)
3. Name three methods of improving a building's safety before an earthquake. (6.1.g)

## CRITICAL THINKING

4. **Apply** What might people living next to the ocean do to protect themselves if they were given a two-hour warning of an approaching tsunami?
5. **Connect** If you lived in an area where earthquakes were common, what could you do to make your home safer?

## CHALLENGE

6. **Analyze** Earthquakes release stress that has built up in rocks. Why do you think aftershocks occur?

# CHAPTER INVESTIGATION

## How Structures React in Earthquakes

**DESIGN — YOUR OWN —**

### OVERVIEW AND PURPOSE

In 1989 a magnitude 6.9 earthquake struck the San Francisco Bay area, killing 62 people and leaving 12,000 homeless. In 1988 a magnitude 6.9 earthquake occurred near Spitak, Armenia. There, nearly 25,000 people died and 514,000 lost their homes. The difference in the effects of these two earthquakes was largely due to differences in construction methods. In this investigation you will

- build a structure and measure how long it can withstand shaking on a shake table provided by your teacher
- explore methods of building earthquake-resistant structures

### Problem

Write It Up

How can structures be built to withstand most earthquakes?

### Hypothesize

Write It Up

Write a hypothesis to explain how structures can be built to withstand shaking. Your hypothesis should take the form of an "If . . . , then . . . , because . . ." statement.

### Procedure

1. Make a data table like the one shown on the next page.

2. Use stirrers joined with clay to build a structure at least 20 cm tall on top of the cardboard. Cut the stirrers if necessary.

3. Make a diagram of your structure.

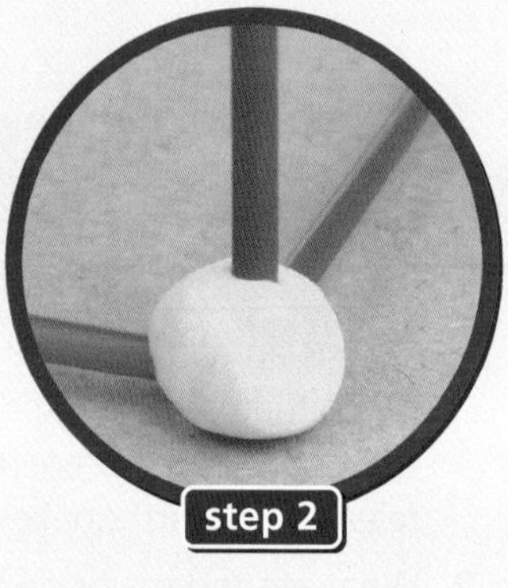
step 2

**MATERIALS**
- modeling clay
- stirrer straws
- piece of thin cardboard 15 cm on each side
- scissors
- ruler
- shake table

6.1.d, 6.2.d, 6.3.a, 6.7.a

Content Standard
6.2.d Students know earthquakes, volcanic eruptions, landslides, and floods change human and wildlife habitats.

Investigation Standard
6.7.a Develop a hypothesis.

4 Lift your structure by its cardboard base and place it on the shake-table platform. Pull the platform 2 centimeters to one side and release it.

step 4

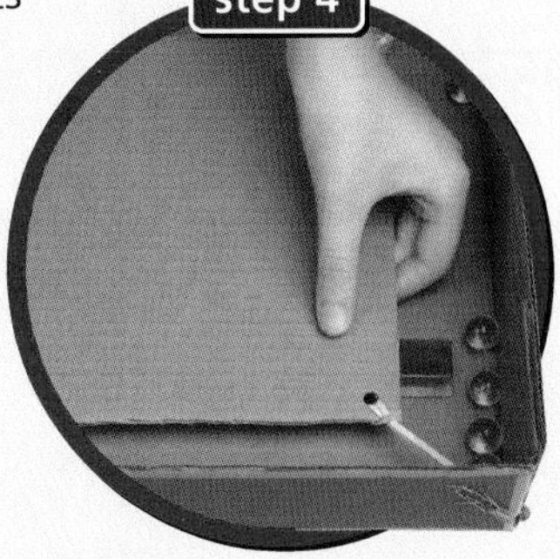

5 Repeat step 4 until the structure begins to collapse.

## Observe and Analyze

Write It Up

1. **RECORD** Complete your data table and make notes about the collapse. Include areas of possible weakness in your structure.
2. **INFER** Use your observations to design a structure that will better withstand shaking.

## Conclude

Write It Up

1. **INTERPRET** Compare your results with your hypothesis. Do your observations support your hypothesis?
2. **INFER** How would you use the shake table to model earthquakes of different magnitudes?
3. **IDENTIFY VARIABLES** How might your results differ if you always pulled the platform to the same side? if you pulled it to different sides?
4. **IDENTIFY LIMITS** In what ways might a building's behavior during an earthquake differ from the behavior of your structure on the shake table?
5. **COMPARE** Examine the diagrams of the three structures that lasted longest in your class. What characteristics, if any, did they have in common?
6. **APPLY** Based on your results, write a list of recommendations for building earthquake-resistant structures.

## INVESTIGATE Further

**CHALLENGE** Have a contest to see who can build the most earthquake-resistant structure. Design your structure as if you were an earthquake engineer. Make a model of your structure at least 30 centimeters tall, using the types of materials you used in this investigation. Test the structure on the shake table. What design features helped the winning structure to resist shaking the longest?

How Structures React in Earthquakes

Problem How can structures be built to withstand most earthquakes?

Hypothesize

Observe and Analyze

Table 1. Number of Trials Until Collapse of Structure

| Trial | Distance Platform Pulled to Side (cm) | Notes |
|---|---|---|
| 1 | 2 | |
| 2 | 2 | |
| 3 | 2 | |
| 4 | 2 | |

Conclude

# 9 Chapter Review

## the BIG idea

**Earthquakes release stress that has built up in rocks.**

CONTENT REVIEW
CLASSZONE.COM

### KEY CONCEPTS SUMMARY

#### 1 Earthquakes occur along faults.

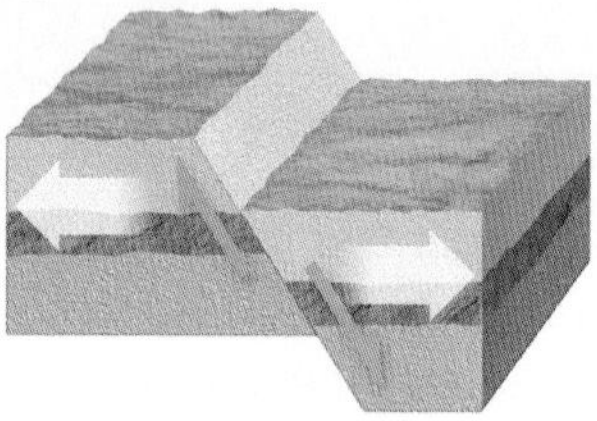

Normal faults form as rocks are pulled apart.

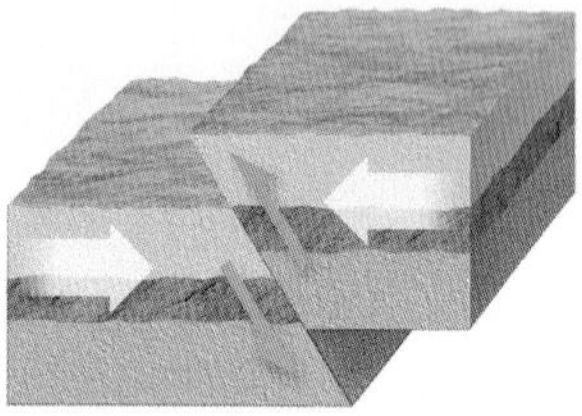

Reverse faults form as rocks are pushed together.

Strike-slip faults form as rocks are pushed horizontally in opposite directions.

**VOCABULARY**
**fault** p. 301
**stress** p. 301
**earthquake** p. 301

#### 2 Earthquakes release energy.

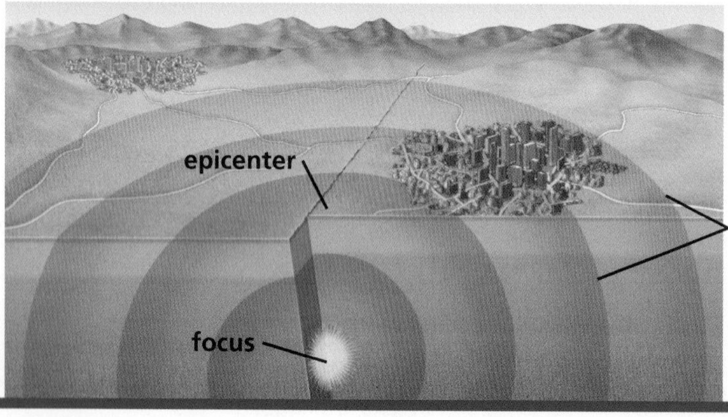

epicenter
focus
Seismic waves move out from the focus in all directions.

**VOCABULARY**
**seismic wave** p. 307
**focus** p. 308
**epicenter** p. 308
**seismograph** p. 312

#### 3 Earthquake damage can be reduced.

A powerful earthquake releases more energy and causes more shaking of the ground than does a weak earthquake.

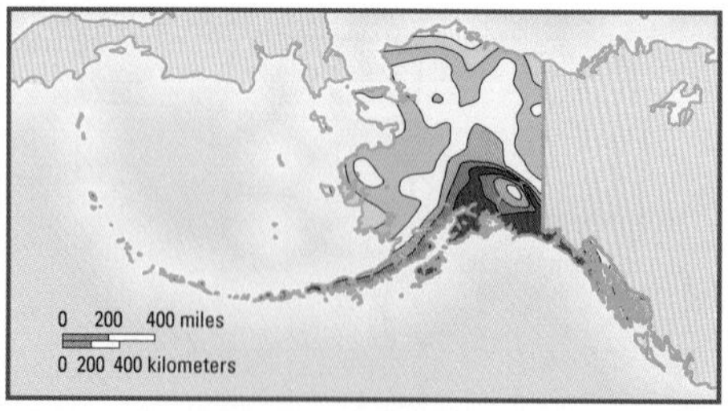


An area's risk of earthquakes can be predicted.

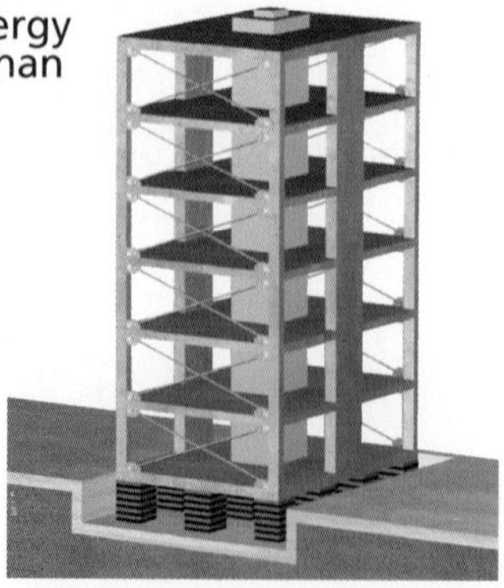

Structures can be designed for greater safety in an earthquake.

**VOCABULARY**
**aftershock** p. 318
**liquefaction** p. 318
**tsunami** p. 318

## Reviewing Vocabulary

***On a separate sheet of paper, draw a diagram to show the relationships among each set of words. One set has been done as an example.***

seismograph, seismic waves, seismogram

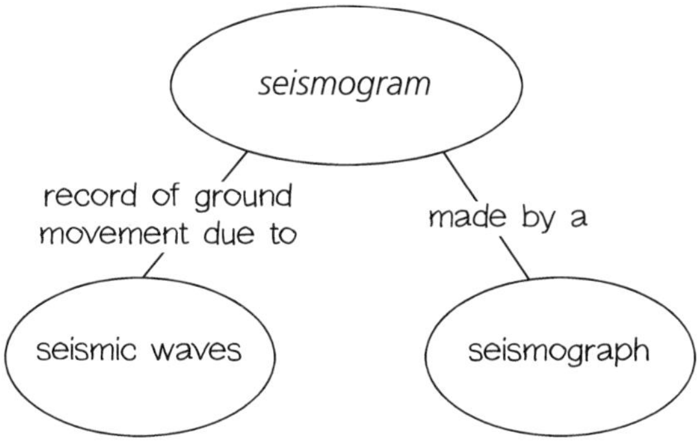


1. earthquake, epicenter, focus
2. earthquake, tsunami, liquefaction
3. fault, stress, earthquake, aftershock
4. tsunami, epicenter, seismogram

## Reviewing Key Concepts

**Multiple Choice** *Choose the letter of the best answer.*

5. What causes an earthquake? (6.1.e)
   - **a.** a rise of magma in the mantle
   - **b.** a sudden movement of blocks of rock
   - **c.** a buildup of seismic waves
   - **d.** a change in Earth's magnetic poles
6. Earthquakes release energy in the form of (6.3.a)
   - **a.** seismic waves
   - **b.** faults
   - **c.** stress lines
   - **d.** seismograms
7. Most damage from an earthquake usually occurs (6.1.g)
   - **a.** below the focus
   - **b.** far from the epicenter
   - **c.** at the focus
   - **d.** near the epicenter
8. To locate the epicenter of an earthquake, scientists need seismograms from at least _____ seismic stations. (6.1.g)
   - **a.** two
   - **b.** three
   - **c.** four
   - **d.** five
9. The seismic waves that usually cause the most damage are (6.3.a)
   - **a.** surface waves
   - **b.** tsunami waves
   - **c.** primary waves
   - **d.** secondary waves
10. Earthquakes release _____ that has built up in rocks. (6.3.a)
    - **a.** water
    - **b.** magnetism
    - **c.** stress
    - **d.** electricity
11. About 80 percent of all earthquakes occur in a belt around the (6.1.a)
    - **a.** Pacific Ocean
    - **b.** San Andreas Fault
    - **c.** North American Plate
    - **d.** African Rift Valley
12. In a strike-slip fault, blocks of rock move _____ along the fault plane. (6.1.d)
    - **a.** up
    - **b.** down
    - **c.** sideways
    - **d.** up and down
13. One method of making a building earthquake resistant is to (6.2.d)
    - **a.** add sand under the foundation
    - **b.** reduce the use of steel
    - **c.** make the walls of brick
    - **d.** use cross braces

**Short Answer** *Write a short answer to each question.*

14. Why do most earthquakes occur at or near tectonic plate boundaries? (6.1.a)
15. How do data from seismic waves indicate that Earth's outer core is liquid? (6.1.b)
16. What causes most of the injuries and deaths due to earthquakes? (6.2.d)

## Thinking Critically

*Study the illustration below, showing the epicenter and focus of an earthquake, then answer the following six questions.*

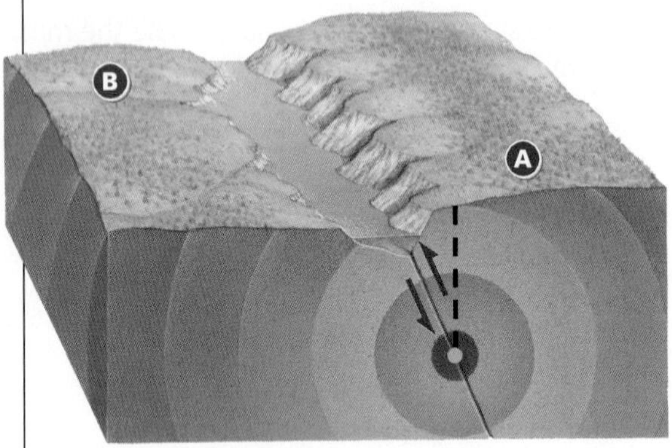


17. **APPLY** What type of fault is shown in the illustration? How do you know? (6.1.d)

18. **APPLY** Where on the surface is the greatest shaking likely to occur? (6.1.g)

19. **INFER** What does the set of circles around the focus represent? (6.3.a)

20. **EXPLAIN** In what ways would the times of arrival of primary and secondary waves be different at points *A* and *B*? (6.3.a)

21. **IDENTIFY EFFECTS** The land surface to the left of the fault is lower than the land surface to the right. How might this be related to movements along the fault? (6.1.d)

22. **ANALYZE** What are the main directions of stress on the blocks of rock on either side of the fault? (6.1.d)

23. **APPLY** A builder is planning to construct a new house near a fault along which earthquakes are common. Write a list of guidelines that the builder might use to decide where and how to build the house. (6.1.g)

24. **ANALYZE** Identify two areas of the United States where earthquakes are most likely to occur. Explain your choices in terms of plate tectonics. (6.1.a)

25. **IDENTIFY EFFECTS** A town has been struck by an earthquake with a magnitude of 5.8. The epicenter was 10 kilometers (6 mi) away, and the focus was shallow. What sort of damage would you expect to find in the town? (6.1.g)

26. **ANALYZE** What role do earthquakes play in shaping Earth's surface? (6.1.f)

27. **CALCULATE** If primary waves travel at a speed of about 5 kilometers per second, how long would it take them to arrive at a seismic station located 695 kilometers from an earthquake's focus? (6.3.a)

## the BIG idea

28. **CONNECT** Look again at the photograph of earthquake damage on pages 298–299. Explain how energy released by an earthquake can travel through rock and cause damage at Earth's surface. (6.3.a)

29. **SYNTHESIZE** The illustration below shows convection in Earth's mantle. What are the relationships among the heat inside Earth, the movements of tectonic plates, and the occurrences of earthquakes? (6.1.b)

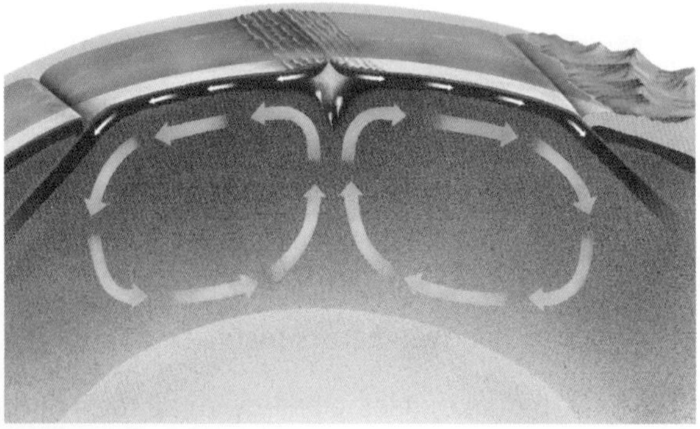

## UNIT PROJECTS

If you need to do an experiment for your unit project, gather the materials. Be sure to allow enough time to observe results before the project is due.

# Standards-Based Assessment

## Analyzing Data

6.1.a, 6.1.d, 6.3.a

*The following tables show magnitudes and average numbers of earthquakes in the world per year, and states in which two or more major earthquakes have been recorded. Use the information in the tables to answer the questions below.*

Earthquakes in the World per Year

| Classification | Magnitude | Average Number per Year |
|---|---|---|
| Great | 8.0 and higher | 1 |
| Major | 7.0–7.9 | 18 |
| Strong | 6.0–6.9 | 120 |
| Moderate | 5.0–5.9 | 800 |
| Light | 4.0–4.9 | 6200 |
| Minor | 3.0–3.9 | 49,000 |

States That Have Recorded Two or More Major Earthquakes

| State | Number of Major Earthquakes |
|---|---|
| Alaska | 74 |
| Arkansas | 2 |
| California | 16 |
| Hawaii | 4 |
| Missouri | 2 |
| Nevada | 3 |

**1.** A major earthquake can have a magnitude of
**a.** 6.0–6.9 **c.** 7.4
**b.** 6.0 and higher **d.** 8.2

**2.** The most major earthquakes have been recorded in which state?
**a.** Arkansas **c.** Missouri
**b.** Hawaii **d.** Nevada

**3.** A magnitude 3.2 earthquake is classified as
**a.** major **c.** moderate
**b.** strong **d.** minor

**4.** The world's most powerful earthquakes occur along reverse faults. In which state are reverse faults most likely to be common?
**a.** Alaska **c.** Hawaii
**b.** California **d.** Nevada

**5.** In which state is a tectonic plate boundary most likely to be located?
**a.** Arkansas **c.** Hawaii
**b.** California **d.** Nevada

**6.** Compared to the number of major earthquakes each year, the number of moderate earthquakes is
**a.** about 40 times greater **c.** about equal
**b.** about 4 times greater **d.** smaller

**7.** Alaska has recorded a total of 82 earthquakes with magnitudes of 7.0 and higher. How many of these earthquakes are classified as "great"?
**a.** 0 **c.** 56
**b.** 8 **d.** 74

**8.** An earthquake of which classification releases the most energy?
**a.** great **c.** strong
**b.** major **d.** minor

## Extended Response

*Answer the two questions below in detail. Include some of the terms shown in the word box. In your answers underline each term you use.*

| | | | |
|---|---|---|---|
| seismic waves | primary | secondary | surface |
| stress | fault | plate boundary | |

**9.** During an earthquake, Dustin felt a small amount of shaking. About 15 seconds later, he felt some more shaking. Then about 45 seconds later he felt the strongest shaking. Explain what happened.

**10.** The island of Sumatra is located in an area where the Pacific Plate sinks under the Eurasian Plate. Explain why Sumatra has many earthquakes.

# TIMELINES in Science

6.1.a, 6.4.a, 6.5.e, 6.6.a

## HISTORY OF THE EARTH SYSTEM

Systems of air, water, rocks, and living organisms have developed on Earth during the planet's 4.6 billion years of history. More and more scientists have become curious about how these parts of Earth work together. Today, scientists think of these individual systems as part of one large Earth system.

The timeline shows a few events in the history of the Earth system. Scientists have developed special tools and procedures to study this history. The boxes below the timeline show how technology has led to new knowledge about the Earth system and how that knowledge has been applied.

**4.6 BYA**

***Earth Forms in New Solar System***

The Sun and planets form out of a cloud of gas and dust. Earth forms and grows larger as particles collide with it. While Earth is still young, a slightly smaller object smashes into it and sends huge amounts of material flying into space. Some of this material forms a new object—the Moon.

**EVENTS**

**5 BYA**

**Billion Years Ago**

**APPLICATIONS AND TECHNOLOGY**

**TECHNOLOGY**

**Measuring Age of Solar System**

In 1956, Clair C. Patterson published his estimate that the solar system was 4.55 billion years old. Previously, scientists had learned how to use radioactive elements present in rocks to measure their ages. Patterson used this technology to determine the ages of meteorites that were formed along with the solar system and later fell to Earth. Since 1956 scientists have studied more samples and used new technologies. These studies have generally confirmed Patterson's estimate.

This iron meteorite fell in Siberia in 1947. Data from such meteorites are clues to how and when the solar system formed.

**4.4 BYA**

### *Earth Gains Atmosphere, Ocean*

Earth's atmosphere forms as volcanoes release gases, including water vapor. Though some gases escape into space, Earth's gravity holds most of them close to the planet. The atmosphere contains no free oxygen. As Earth starts to cool, the water vapor becomes water droplets and falls as rain. Oceans begin to form.

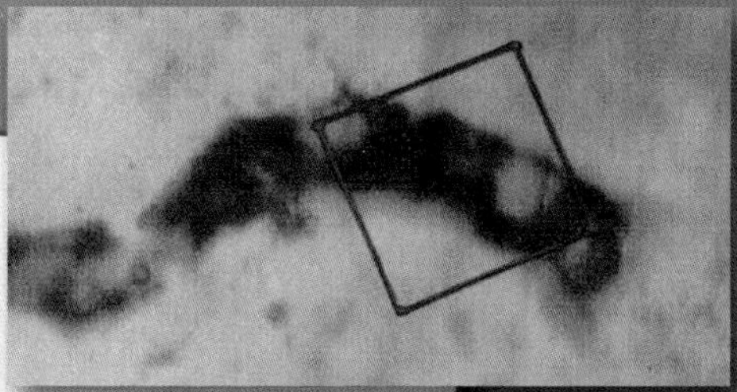

**3.5 BYA**

### *Organisms Affect Earth System*

Tiny organisms use energy from sunlight to make their food, giving off oxygen as a waste product. The oxygen combines with other gases and with minerals. It may be another billion years before free oxygen starts to build up in the atmosphere.

**1.8 BYA**

### *First Supercontinent Forms*

All of Earth's continents come together to form one huge supercontinent. The continents and ocean basins are still moving and changing. This supercontinent will break apart in the future. New supercontinents will form and break apart as time goes on.

4 BYA | 3 BYA | 2 BYA | 1 BYA

## APPLICATION

### Measuring Ozone Levels

In 1924 scientists developed the first instrument to measure ozone, the Dobson spectrophotometer. Ozone is a molecule that consists of three oxygen atoms. In the 1970s scientists realized that levels of ozone in the upper atmosphere were falling. Countries have taken action to preserve the ozone layer, which protects organisms—including humans—from dangerous ultraviolet radiation. Today, computers process ozone data as they are collected and make them available quickly to researchers around the world.

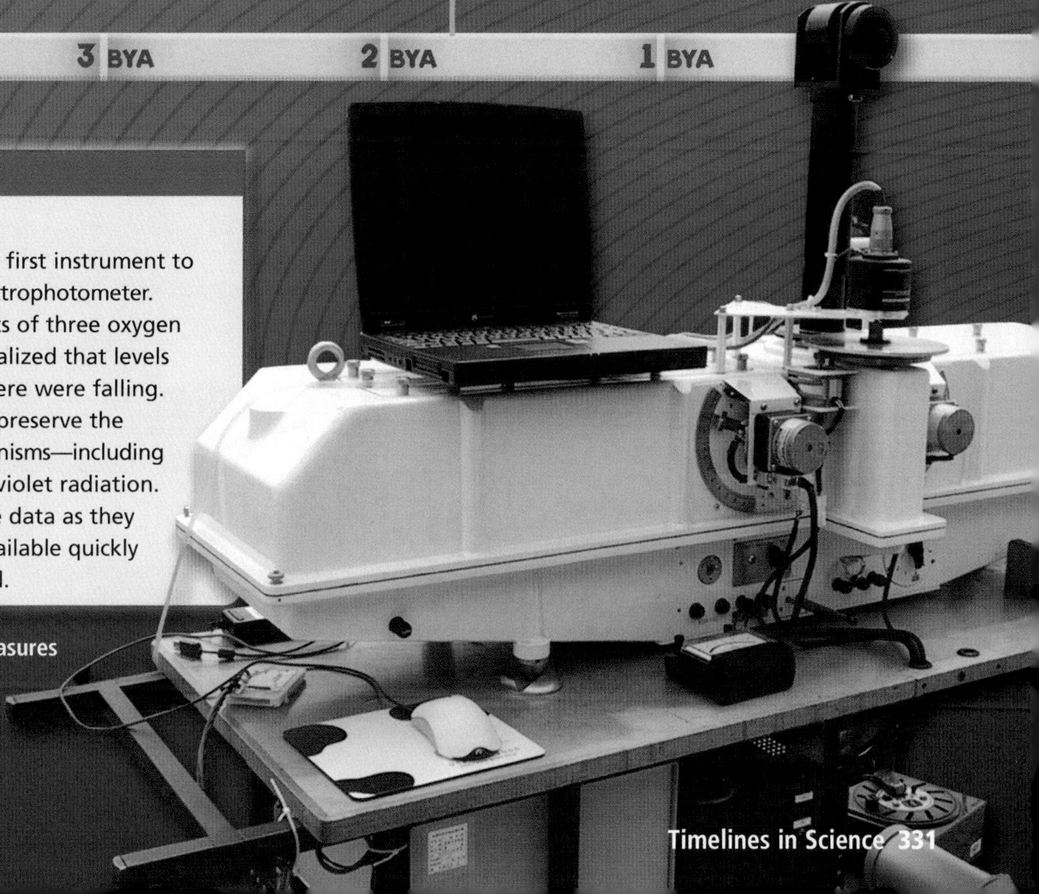

A Dobson spectrophotometer measures the total amount of ozone in the atmosphere above it.

**480 MYA**

### *Plants Appear on Land*

The earliest plants appear. These plants, perhaps similar to mosses, join the lichens that already live on land. Through photosynthesis, plants and lichens decrease the amount of carbon dioxide in the air and increase the amount of oxygen. These changes may lead to the eventual development of large, complex animals.

**600 MYA**

### *New Animals Appear*

The first multicelled animals appear in the ocean. Some types of these animals are fastened to the sea floor and get food from particles in water flowing past them. Worms are the most complex type of animals to appear so far.

**200 MYA**

### *Atlantic Ocean Forms*

Earth's continents, which have been combined into the supercontinent Pangaea, start to separate. The Atlantic Ocean forms as what are now the continents of North America and Africa spread apart.

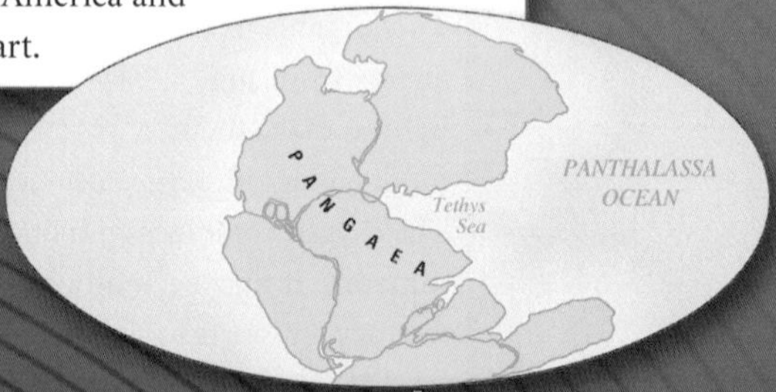


**800 MYA** **600 MYA** **400 MYA** **200 MYA**

**Million Years Ago**

## TECHNOLOGY

### Ocean-Floor Core Samples

In the 1960s scientists began drilling holes into the sea floor to collect long cores, or columns, of sediment and rock. The cores give clues about Earth's climate, geology, and forms of life for millions of years.

The research ship *JOIDES Resolution* has a drilling rig built into it. Equipment attached to the rig is lowered to the sea floor to collect core samples.

**12,000 years ago**

***Earth Emerges from Ice—Again***

Earth's temperature warms slightly. Kilometers-thick ice sheets that formed during the latest of Earth's many ice ages start to melt. Forests and grasslands expand. Sea level rises about 100 meters (330 ft), and the ocean floods the edges of the continents.

**1972**

***New View of Earth***

Harrison "Jack" Schmitt, an astronaut traveling 24,000 kilometers (15,000 mi) above Earth, takes a photograph. It is the first to show Earth fully lit by the Sun, and the image is sometimes called the Blue Marble. It helps people see the planet as one system.

**RESOURCE CENTER**
CLASSZONE.COM
Learn more about the Earth system.

**100 MYA** **Today**

## APPLICATION

### International Space Station

The International Space Station has laboratories in which scientists study Earth, the solar system, and the universe. Also, scientists are doing research to better understand the effects of very low gravity on people. This work is part of an effort to develop the life-support systems needed for people to remain in space a long time. Eventually it might aid in the further exploration of space by humans.

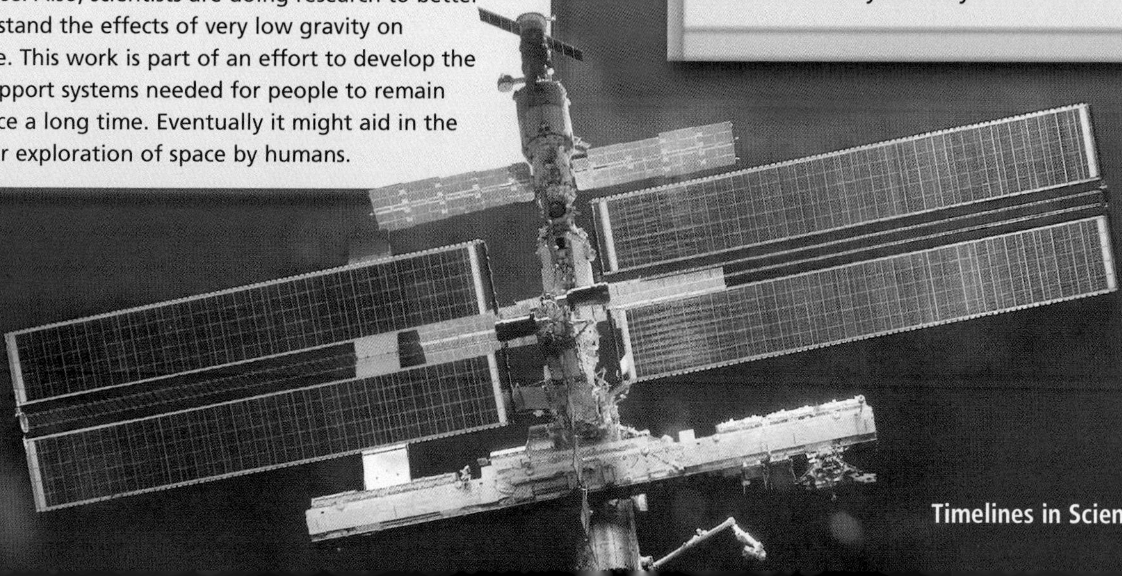

## SPOTLIGHT on MARIO MOLINA

In 1995 Mario Molina won the Nobel Prize in Chemistry for his role in showing how chlorofluorocarbon gases (CFCs) can harm Earth's ozone layer. Molina and others studied the chemistry of atmospheric ozone. They concluded that the ozone layer is sensitive to certain compounds. Their work convinced many countries around the world to ban ozone-depleting chemical compounds.

Molina's recent research focuses on the chemistry of air pollution in the lower atmosphere, which affects rapidly growing cities around the world.

## ACTIVITIES

### Taking a Core Sample

Add layers of damp sand of different colors to a paper cup. Switch cups with a partner. Press a clear straw through the sand, put your finger over the top of the straw, and pull the straw out. Determine the order in which your partner added the sand layers. How would you know if there was a layer of sand that did not go across the entire cup?

### Writing About Science

Imagine you are living in microgravity like the astronauts on the International Space Station. Write a detailed description of two hours of your day.

CHAPTER

# 10 Mountains and Volcanoes

## the BIG idea

**Mountains and volcanoes form as tectonic plates move.**

## Key Concepts

SECTION 1
**Movement of rock builds mountains.**
Learn how different types of mountains form.

SECTION 2
**Volcanoes form as molten rock erupts.**
Learn why there are different types of volcanoes and volcanic eruptions.

SECTION 3
**Volcanoes affect Earth's land, air, and water.**
Learn how volcanic eruptions affect land, air, and water.

**California ClassZone**

CLASSZONE.COM

Chapter 10 online resources: Content Review, Simulation, Visualization, two Resource Centers, Math Tutorial, Test Practice

***How does new land form from molten rock?***

# EXPLORE the BIG idea

## Making Mountains

**6.1.e** Students know major geologic events, such as earthquakes, volcanic eruptions, and mountain building, result from plate motions.

Line up and hold a row of about ten checkers or coins on a table. Tilt the row, and then let it go.

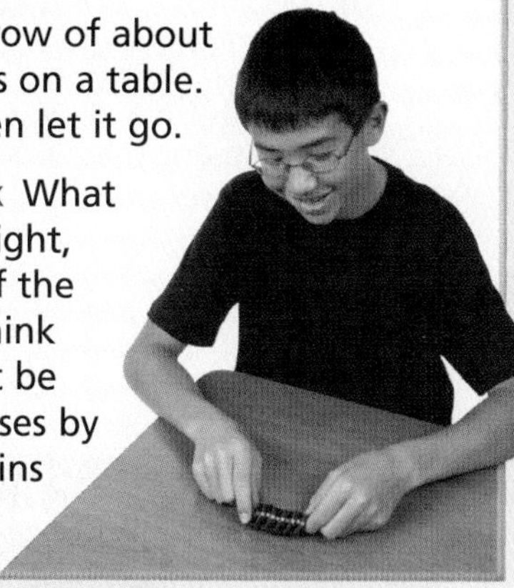

**Observe and Think** What happened to the height, length, and shape of the row? How do you think these changes might be similar to the processes by which some mountains and valleys form?

## Internet Activity: Volcanoes

**6.1.d** Students know that earthquakes are sudden motions along breaks in the crust called faults and that volcanoes and fissures are locations where magma reaches the surface.

Go to **ClassZone.com** to make a volcano erupt. As you watch the simulations, notice how different types of volcanoes form based on silica content and pressure.

**Observe and Think** Why are some volcanic eruptions much more violent than others?

NSTA scilinks.org SCILINKS

Explore Volcanoes **Code: MDL054**

CHAPTER 10

# Getting Ready to Learn

## CONCEPT REVIEW

- Earthquakes occur as blocks of rock move along faults.
- Tectonic plates pull apart, push together, or scrape past one another along their boundaries.

## VOCABULARY REVIEW

**magma** p. 191
**convergent boundary** p. 278
**subduction** p. 286
**fault** p. 301
**earthquake** p. 301

**CONTENT REVIEW**
CLASSZONE.COM

Review concepts and vocabulary.

## TAKING NOTES

### CONTENT FRAME

Organize your notes into a **content frame** for mountains. Make categories at the top that describe their types, features, and how they form. Then fill in the boxes for each type of mountain. Later in the chapter you will make content frames for other topics.

### CHOOSE YOUR OWN STRATEGY

Take notes about new vocabulary terms using one or more of the strategies from earlier chapters, such as **description wheel** and **magnet word.** Feel free to mix and match the strategies or use a different strategy.

See the Note-Taking Handbook on pages R45–R51.

SCIENCE NOTEBOOK

| TYPE OF MOUNTAINS | CHARACTERISTIC | WHERE THEY FORM | EXAMPLES |
|---|---|---|---|
| folded | rocks bent and folded | at convergent plate boundaries | Appalachians Himalayas |
| fault-block | | | |

Description Wheel

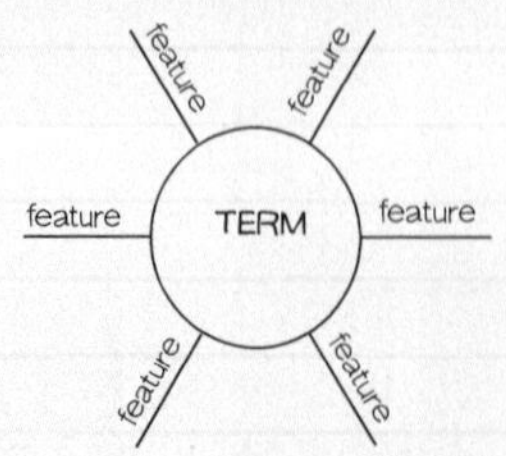


Magnet Word

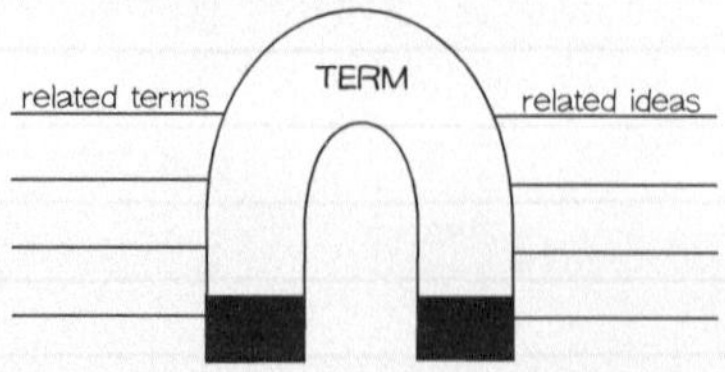

KEY CONCEPT

# 10.1 Movement of rock builds mountains.

**CALIFORNIA Content Standards**

**6.1.b** Students know Earth is composed of several layers: a cold, brittle lithosphere; a hot, convecting mantle; and a dense, metallic core.

**6.1.e** Students know major geologic events, such as earthquakes, volcanic eruptions, and mountain building, result from plate motions.

**6.1.f** Students know how to explain major features of California geology (including mountains, faults, volcanoes) in terms of plate tectonics.

**BEFORE, you learned**

- Major geologic events occur at tectonic plate boundaries
- Most faults are located along plate boundaries

**NOW, you will learn**

- How the folding of rock can form mountains
- How movement along faults can form mountains

**VOCABULARY**

**folded mountain** p. 340
**fault-block mountain** p. 342

**EXPLORE Folding** (6.1.e)

### *How does rock fold?*

**PROCEDURE**

1. Make three flat layers of clay on top of a sheet of newspaper. Put a block at either end of the clay.
2. Hold one block still. Push on the other block slowly to bring the blocks closer together.

**WHAT DO YOU THINK?**

- What happened to the clay when you pushed on the block?
- What shape did the middle layer of clay form?
- If a large block of rock reacted to pressure in a similar way, what kind of landform would result?

**MATERIALS**

- 2 or 3 colors of modeling clay
- newspaper
- 2 blocks

## Most mountains form along plate boundaries.

A shallow sea once covered the area that is now Mount Everest, Earth's tallest mountain. If you were to climb Mount Everest, you would be standing on rocks containing the remains of ocean animals. Mount Everest also contains rocks that formed far away at a spreading center on the sea floor. How can rocks from the sea floor be on top of a mountain on a continent? Plate tectonics provides the answer.

Recall that an oceanic plate sinks when it collides with a continental plate. Some sea-floor material scrapes off the sinking plate and onto the continent. As continental mountains form, material once at the bottom of an ocean can be pushed many kilometers high.

## Mountain Ranges and Belts

A mountain is an area of land that rises steeply from the land around it. A single mountain is rare. Most mountains belong to ranges—long lines of mountains that were formed at about the same time and by the same processes. Ranges that are close together make up mountain belts. For example, the Rocky Mountain belt in western North America contains about 100 ranges.

1 Mountains rise high above the land around them.

2 Most mountains are in groups called mountain ranges.

3 Closely spaced mountain ranges make up mountain belts.

Most of the world's major mountain belts are located along tectonic plate boundaries. But mountain belts like the Appalachians (AP-uh-LAY-chee-uhnz) in eastern North America are in the interior of plates. Mountains such as these were formed by ancient plate collisions that assembled the present-day continents.

### Major Mountain Belts

**Major mountain belts mark the locations of present or past plate boundaries.**

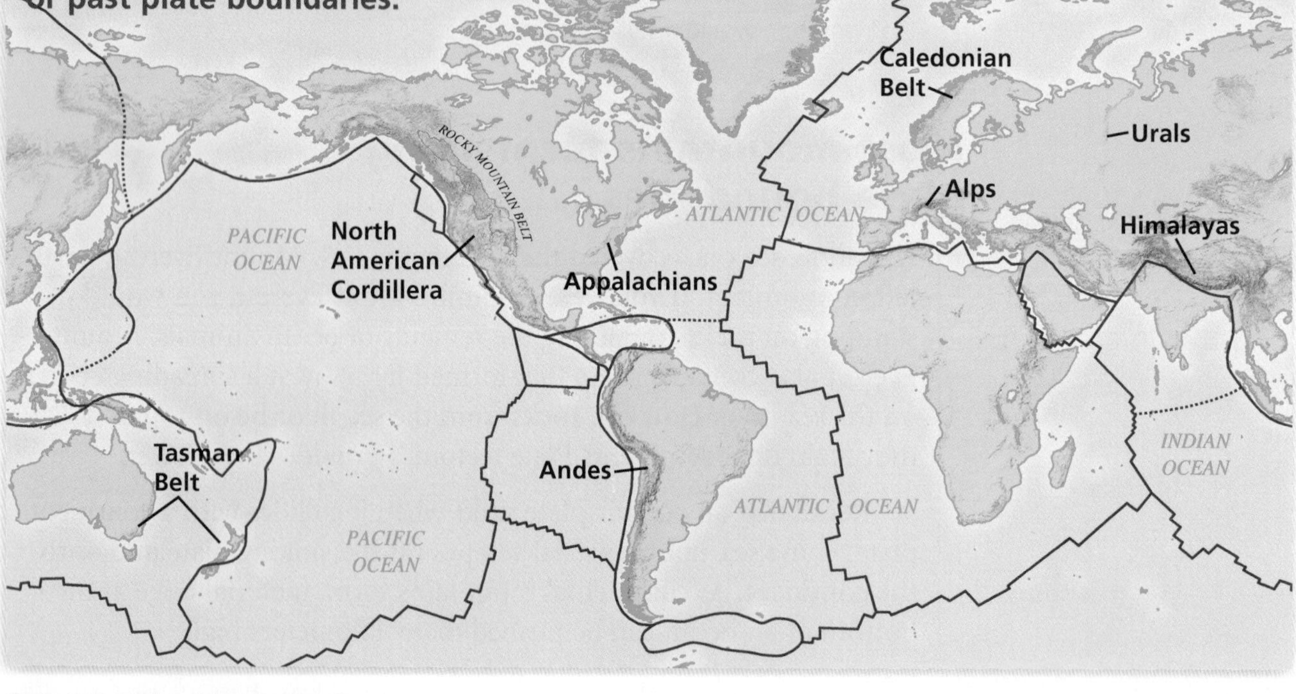

## Mountains, Rocks, and Sediment

At the same time that some processes push mountains up, other processes wear them down. At Earth's surface, water and wind break rocks apart and move the pieces away. As long as mountains are pushed up faster than they wear down, they grow taller. For this reason, young mountains tend to be tall and steep. But eventually mountain-building processes slow, then end. Water and wind take over. Given enough time, all mountains become rounded hills, and then they are gone. Countless mountains have formed and worn away throughout Earth's long history.

Rocks break down into loose pieces that can be carried by water or wind. These pieces are called sediments. For example, sand on a beach is sediment. Thick layers of sediments can build up in low-lying areas, such as valleys, lakes, or the ocean. Pieces of sediments form sedimentary rock as they are pressed together or joined by natural cement.

The land becomes flatter as mountains wear down and valleys fill with sediments. If tectonic plates were to stop moving, eventually the surfaces of all the continents would be completely flat.

### Mountains Wear Down

**Mountains wear down as water and wind break their rocks into sediments and carry them away.**

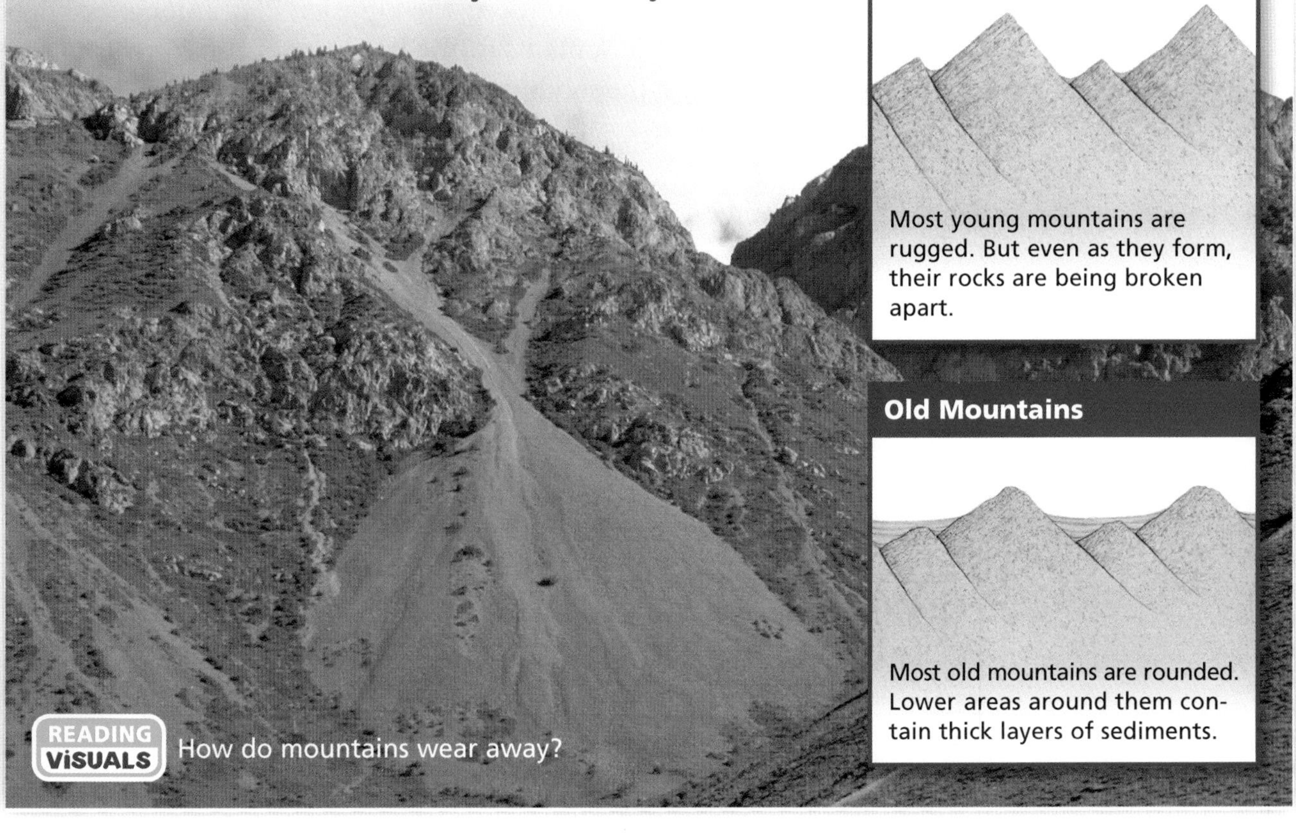

**Young Mountains**

Most young mountains are rugged. But even as they form, their rocks are being broken apart.

**Old Mountains**

Most old mountains are rounded. Lower areas around them contain thick layers of sediments.

**READING VISUALS** How do mountains wear away?

## Mountains can form as rocks fold.

Though people usually do not think of rocks as being able to bend and fold, they can. Think of a wax candle. If you bend a candle quickly, it will break. If you leave a candle propped up at an angle, over many days it will bend. If the candle is in a warm area, it will bend more quickly. Rocks can bend when stress is applied slowly. Rocks deep in the crust are at high temperatures and pressures. They are likely to bend rather than break.

**CHECK YOUR READING** Under what conditions are rocks likely to bend and fold?

**VOCABULARY**
Remember to add *folded mountain* to your notebook, using the vocabulary strategy of your choice.

Remember that tectonic plates move only a few centimeters each year. Stress is applied to the edge of a continent as another plate pushes against it over a long period of time. Some of the continent's rocks break, and others fold. As folding continues, mountains are pushed up. A **folded mountain** is a mountain that forms as continental crust crumples and bends into folds.

Folded mountains form as an oceanic plate sinks under the edge of a continent or as continents collide. One example is the Himalaya (HIHM-uh-LAY-uh) belt, which was formed by a collision between India and Eurasia. Its formation is illustrated on page 341.

**READING TIP**
Eurasia is the landmass consisting of Europe and Asia.

1. **Convergent Boundary Develops** At one time an ocean separated India and Eurasia. As India moved northward, oceanic lithosphere sank in a subduction zone along the Eurasian Plate. Along the edge of Eurasia, folded mountains formed. Volcanoes also formed as magma rose from the subduction zone to the surface.

2. **Continental Collision Begins** Eventually the sea floor was completely destroyed, and India and Eurasia collided. Subduction ended. The volcanoes stopped erupting because they were no longer supplied with magma. Sea-floor material that had been added to the edge of Eurasia became part of the mountains pushed up by the collision.

3. **Collision Continues** India and Eurasia continue to push together. Their collision has formed the Himalayas, the world's tallest mountains. They grow even higher as rock is folded and pushed up for hundreds of kilometers on either side of the boundary.

Earthquakes can also be important to the upward growth of folded mountains. A great deal of rock in the Himalaya belt has been pushed up along reverse faults, which are common at convergent boundaries.

# Formation of Himalayas

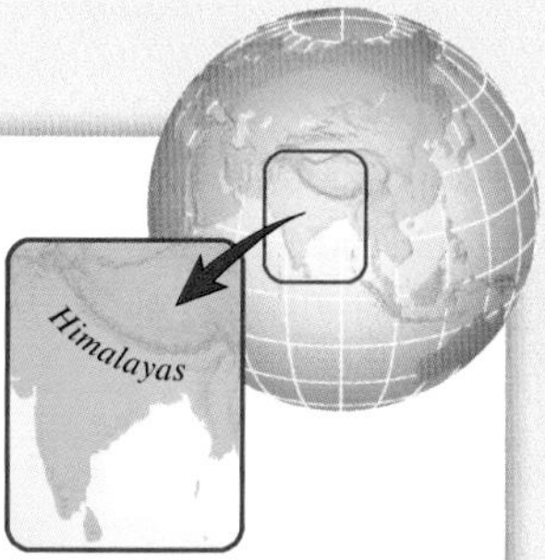


**The Himalayas are being pushed higher by an ongoing continental collision.**

## 1 Convergent Boundary Develops

India began moving toward Eurasia 200 million years ago. A convergent boundary developed along the edge of Eurasia. The oceanic lithosphere between the two continents sank into a subduction zone.

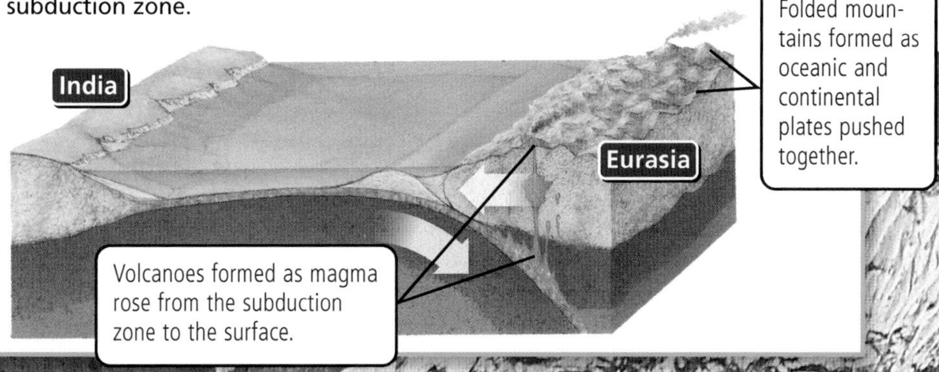


## 2 Continental Collision Begins

The sea floor was completely destroyed about 50 million years ago, and India and Eurasia collided.

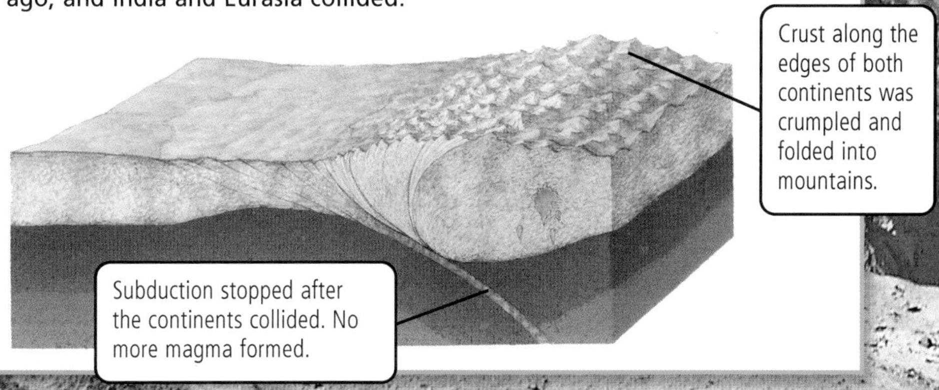

Crust along the edges of both continents was crumpled and folded into mountains.
Subduction stopped after the continents collided. No more magma formed.

## 3 Collision Continues

Currently, the Himalayas are growing more than one centimeter higher each year.

Himalayas
As the collision continues, the crust keeps folding. Earthquakes are common.
A small area of sea-floor crust remains deep under the mountains.

**READING VISUALS** In each illustration, where is the boundary between India and Eurasia?

## Mountains can form as rocks move along faults.

**CONTENT FRAME**
Add information about fault-block mountains to your content frame.

In the southwestern United States and northwestern Mexico, hundreds of mountain ranges line up in rows. The ranges and the valleys between them formed along nearly parallel normal faults. Mountains that form as blocks of rock move up or down along normal faults are called **fault-block mountains.**

**CHECK YOUR READING** How can the movement of rocks along faults lead to the formation of mountains?

Fault-block mountains form as the lithosphere is stretched and pulled apart by forces within Earth. The rocks of the crust are cool and hard. As the lithosphere begins to stretch, the crust breaks into large blocks. As stretching continues, the blocks of rock move along the faults that separate them. The illustrations on page 343 show how this process forms fault-block mountains.

# INVESTIGATE Fault-Block Mountains

### How do fault-block mountains form?

Fault-block mountains form along normal faults as blocks of continental crust are pulled apart. In this activity, you will use wooden blocks to demonstrate the processes that form fault-block mountains.

**SKILL FOCUS**
**Modeling** (6.1.e)

**MATERIALS**
- 3 triangular blocks
- 3 rectangular blocks

**TIME**
15 minutes

#### PROCEDURE

1. Use the triangular blocks to demonstrate how movements along normal faults form two mountains separated by a valley. Start with the blocks arranged as shown. Move the outer blocks apart to form two mountains separated by a valley. Draw a diagram of your results.

2. Use the rectangular blocks to demonstrate how a row of tilted fault-block mountains forms along normal faults. (**Hint:** You can tilt the blocks as they move.) Draw a diagram of your results.

#### WHAT DO YOU THINK?

- How do your diagrams show that fault-block mountains form as the crust is being stretched?
- Along which type of plate boundary would fault-block mountains be most likely to form—divergent, convergent, or transform? Explain.

**CHALLENGE** Why don't fault-block mountains form at strike-slip faults?

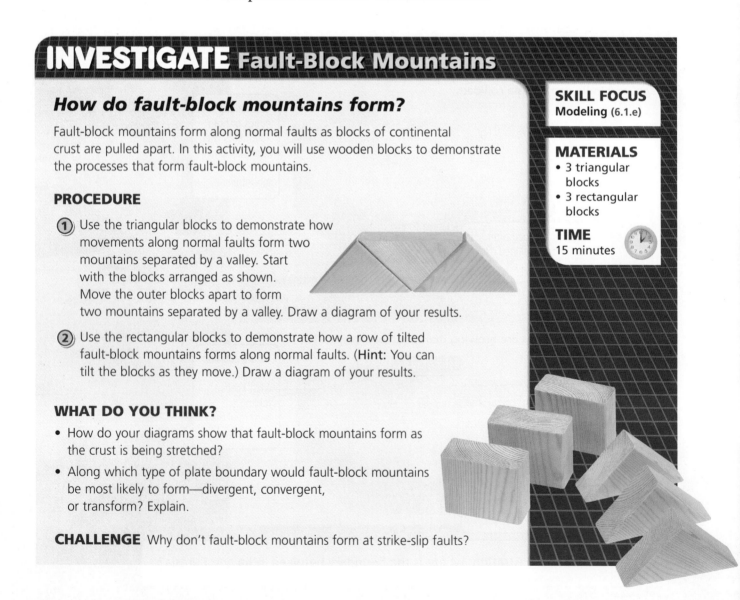

1. An area of the lithosphere can arch upward. For example, it might be heated by material rising in the mantle beneath it. As the crust stretches, it breaks into many blocks separated by faults.
2. As the lithosphere is pulled apart, some blocks tilt. The edges of the blocks that tilt upward form mountains, and the edges that tilt downward form valleys. Other blocks drop down between faults, forming valleys. The edges of the blocks next to blocks that drop down are left standing high above the valleys as mountains.

Fault-block mountains form as stress repeatedly builds up in the crust and then is released during earthquakes. Even the most powerful earthquakes can move blocks of rock only a few meters up or down at one time. Fault-block mountains can be kilometers high. Millions of years and many earthquakes are needed for them to form.

**CHECK YOUR READING** Describe two ways that blocks of rock can move along faults and form mountains.

## Fault-Block Mountains

**Fault-block mountains form as the crust stretches and breaks into blocks that move along faults.**

This block has dropped down.
This block has tilted.

**1 Stretching Begins**

The crust breaks into blocks as it is stretched.

**2 Blocks Tilt or Drop Down**

As the crust is stretched more, the blocks move along the normal faults between them.

The Sierra Nevada moved up along one side of the fault.
Approximate location of fault
The land on the other side of the fault dropped down.

The Sierra Nevada in California is a fault-block mountain range. The range moved up along a normal fault along its eastern edge. The block on the other side of the fault dropped down. This combination of upward and downward movement formed the steep eastern side of the Sierra Nevada. The western side of the range tilts down gently toward California's Central Valley.

In summary, both folded mountains and fault-block mountains form over millions of years. Folded mountains are pushed up by slow, continual stress that causes rock to bend gradually. Fault-block mountains form, earthquake by earthquake, as stress built up in the crust is released by the movement of rock. Folded mountains form where continental crust is being compressed. Fault-block mountains form where it is being stretched.

# 10.1 Review

## KEY CONCEPTS

1. How is the formation of mountain belts related to tectonic plate boundaries? (6.1.f)
2. How do folded mountains form? (6.1.e)
3. How do fault-block mountains form? (6.1.e)

## CRITICAL THINKING

4. **Analyze** The Ural Mountain belt is no longer along the edge of a tectonic plate. Would you expect the Urals to be tall and steep or low and rounded? Why?
5. **Synthesize** How could it be possible for a mountain range to be continually pushed up but not get any higher?

## CHALLENGE

6. **Analyze** This graph shows how the heights of two mountains changed as they formed. Which line shows the formation of a folded mountain? a fault-block mountain? Explain.

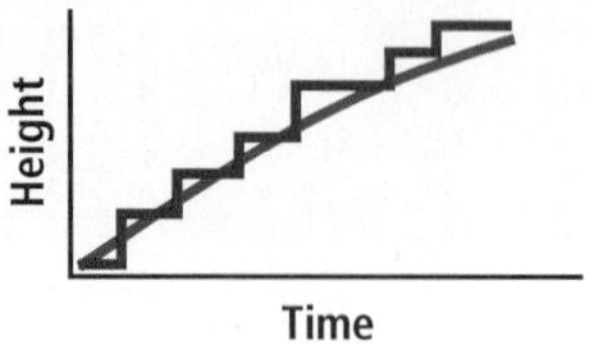
Height
Time

MATH in SCIENCE

## SKILL: CALCULATING THE MEAN OF A DATA SET

# Comparing Mountain Heights

**MATH TUTORIAL**
CLASSZONE.COM
Click on Math Tutorial for more help finding the mean.

**Math** 6.SD.1.1, 6.SD.1.4
**Science** 6.1.e

How do the tallest mountains in the United States compare with the tallest mountains in the world? The table shows the heights of the five tallest mountains in the world. All five are in Asia.

| Mountain | Height (meters) |
|---|---|
| Everest | 8850 |
| K2 | 8611 |
| Kanchenjunga | 8586 |
| Lhotse | 8516 |
| Makalu | 8463 |

To describe data, you can find their average, or mean. The **mean** of a data set is the sum of the values divided by the number of values.

### Example

To find the mean height of the five tallest mountains in the world, first add the heights.

$$\begin{array}{r} 8{,}850 \\ 8{,}611 \\ 8{,}586 \\ 8{,}516 \\ +8{,}463 \\ \hline 43{,}026 \end{array}$$

Then divide by 5, the number of mountains.

$$\frac{43{,}026}{5} = 8605.2$$

Round your result to a whole number.

**ANSWER** The mean height of the five tallest mountains is 8605 meters.

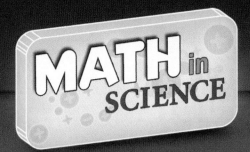

| Mountain | Height (meters) |
|---|---|
| McKinley | 6194 |
| St. Elias | 5489 |
| Foraker | 5304 |
| Bona | 5029 |
| Blackburn | 4996 |

Mount McKinley, Alaska, is the tallest mountain in North America.

**Answer the following questions.**

1. The table to the left shows the heights of the five tallest mountains in the United States. All five are in Alaska. Find the mean of the data.
2. What is the difference between the mean height of the three tallest mountains in the world and the mean height of the three tallest mountains in the United States?
3. Suppose Mount Everest were in the United States. What would the mean of the three tallest mountains in the United States then be?

**CHALLENGE The mean height of all the land in the United States is 763 meters. Does knowing the mean height help you describe the shape of the land in the United States? Explain why or why not.**

KEY CONCEPT

# 10.2 Volcanoes form as molten rock erupts.

**CALIFORNIA Content Standards**

**6.1.b** Students know Earth is composed of several layers: a cold, brittle lithosphere; a hot, convecting mantle; and a dense, metallic core.

**6.1.d** Students know that earthquakes are sudden motions along breaks in the crust called faults and that volcanoes and fissures are locations where magma reaches the surface.

**6.1.e** Students know major geologic events, such as earthquakes, volcanic eruptions, and mountain building, result from plate motions.

**BEFORE, you learned**

- Magma is molten rock inside Earth
- Magma forms as a plate sinking in a subduction zone starts to melt
- Volcanoes can form over hot spots far from plate boundaries

**NOW, you will learn**

- Where most volcanoes are located
- How volcanoes erupt
- What types of volcanoes there are

**VOCABULARY**

**volcano** p. 346
**lava** p. 347
**pyroclastic flow** p. 348

**EXPLORE Eruptions (6.1.d)**

***What happens when a volcano erupts?***

**PROCEDURE**

1. Add water to the film canister until it is three-fourths full.
2. Drop the antacid tablet in the water and put the lid on the canister. Observe what happens.

**WHAT DO YOU THINK?**

- What happened to the water and to the canister lid?
- What caused the changes you observed?
- How might the events you observed be similar to the eruption of a volcano?

**MATERIALS**

- empty film canister
- effervescent antacid tablet
- water

## Volcanoes erupt many types of material.

**VOCABULARY**
Remember to add *volcano* to your notebook, using the vocabulary strategy of your choice.

Earth's thin outer layer is made of cool rock, but most of Earth is made of extremely hot rock and molten metal. Some of the heat inside Earth escapes to the surface through volcanoes. A **volcano** is an opening in Earth's crust through which molten rock, rock fragments, and hot gases erupt. A mountain built up from erupted material is also called a volcano.

A volcano may erupt violently or gently. A violent eruption can cause tremendous destruction even if not much molten rock reaches the surface. For example, a volcano might throw out huge amounts of rock fragments that start fires where they land. Or the fragments might fall in thick layers on roofs, causing them to collapse. A volcano can erupt gently yet pour out rivers of molten rock that flow long distances. The violence of an eruption depends mainly on the type of magma feeding the volcano.

## Magma

A major portion of all magma is silica, which is a compound of silicon and oxygen. Magma also contains gases, which expand as the magma rises. Magma that is high in silica resists flowing, so expanding gases are trapped in it. Pressure builds up until the gases blast out in a violent, dangerous explosion. Magma that has less silica flows easily, so gas bubbles move up through it and escape fairly gently. An eruption of silica-poor magma can throw lava high into the air, but visitors can usually watch safely nearby.

Magma rises toward Earth's surface as long as it is less dense than the surrounding rock. Once magma stops rising, it can collect in areas called magma chambers. Sometimes magma remains in a chamber until it cools, forming igneous rock. At other times, it erupts. Volcanic eruptions can occur when a chamber is not large enough to hold additional magma that pushes in. When magma erupts, it is called lava. **Lava** is magma that has reached Earth's surface.

**CONTENT FRAME**
Make a content frame for volcanic materials. Add categories across the top for what they are made of and how they are erupted.

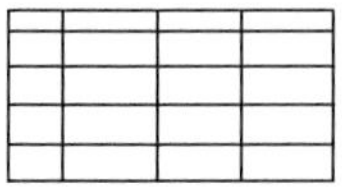

### Structure of a Volcano

**Magma collects in a magma chamber before erupting through a volcano.**

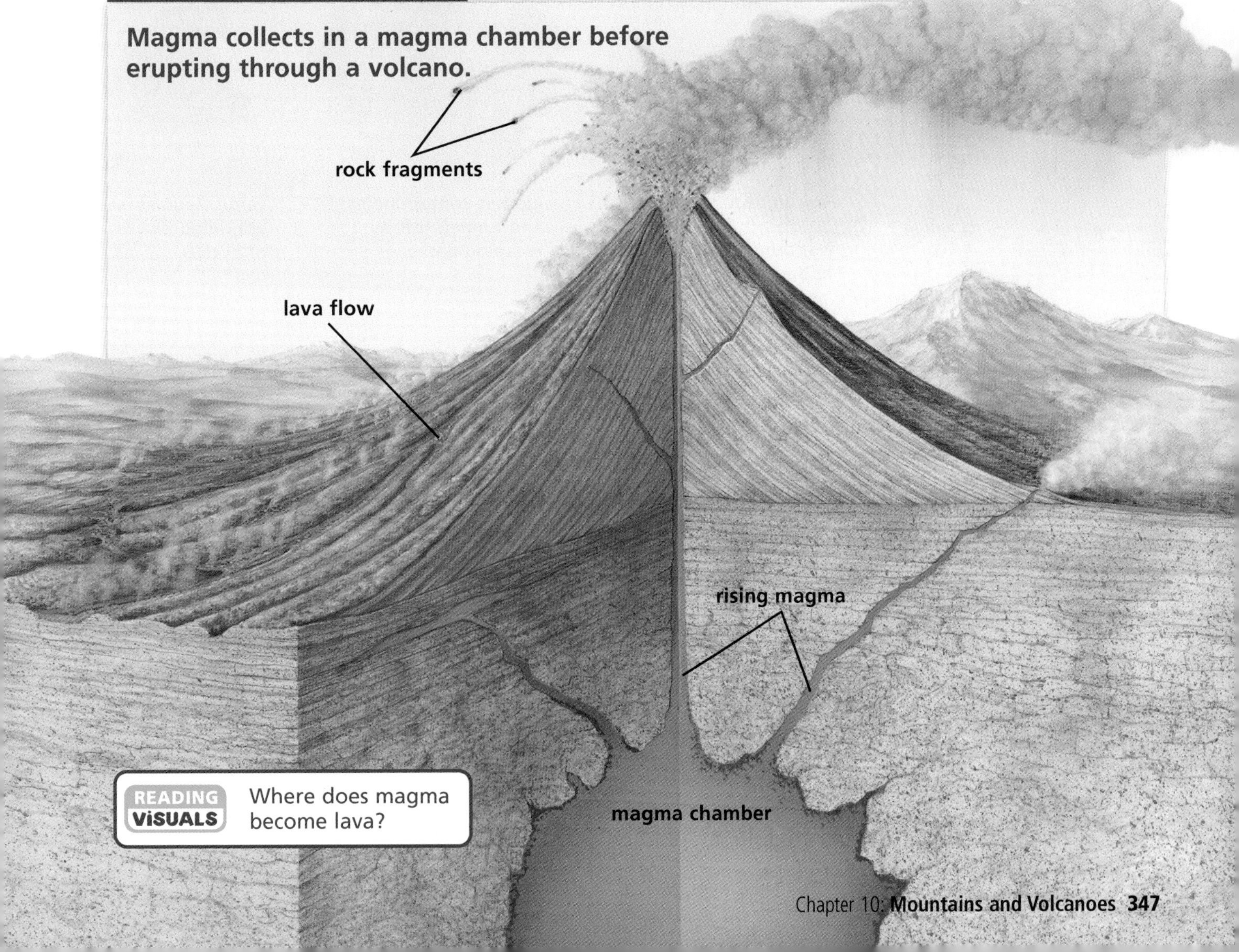


**READING VISUALS** Where does magma become lava?

## Rock Fragments

VISUALIZATION
CLASSZONE.COM
Watch clips of erupted volcanic material.

A great deal of material erupts from volcanoes as rock fragments. The fragments form as

- escaping gas bubbles pop, tearing magma apart
- larger pieces of lava are thrown into the air, cooling and hardening during their flight
- rocks of all sizes rip loose from volcanoes' walls during eruptions

Tiny rock fragments form volcanic ash. Ash consists of particles ranging from the size of dust to about the size of rice grains. Volcanic cinders are somewhat larger. The largest fragments are volcanic bombs and blocks. Bombs are molten when they are thrown out and often have streamlined shapes. Blocks can be the size of houses and erupt as solid pieces of rock. Large rock fragments fall quickly, but ash can be carried long distances by winds—even all the way around Earth.

Volcanic ash is made up of rock fragments less than 2 millimeters in diameter.

Cinders contain holes and tunnels left by escaping gases.

Large fragments are called blocks or bombs.

## Volcanic Gases

What looks like smoke rising from a volcano is actually a mixture of ash and gases. The main gases in magma are water vapor and carbon dioxide. Some volcanic gases combine with water in the air to form acids. You will read about these in the next section.

READING TIP
The prefix *pyro-* means "heat," and *clastic* means "made up of rock fragments."

During an eruption, volcanic gases can mix with rock fragments and stay near the ground. The mixture forms a **pyroclastic flow** (PY-roh-KLAS-tihk), which is a dense cloud of superhot gases and rock fragments that races downhill. Such a flow can be as hot as 800°C (1500°F). It can travel faster than 160 kilometers per hour (100 mi/h). Pyroclastic flows are the most dangerous type of volcanic eruption.

CHECK YOUR READING What are two reasons why pyroclastic flows are dangerous?

## Most volcanoes form along plate boundaries.

Volcanoes are common along tectonic plate boundaries where oceanic plates sink beneath other plates. As a plate sinks deep into a subduction zone, it heats and begins to melt, forming magma. If the magma reaches the surface, it can build tall volcanic mountains.

Volcanoes are also common along tectonic boundaries where plates pull apart. This allows magma to rise from the mantle. Some of these volcanoes are in Africa's Great Rift Valley. However, much of Earth's volcanic activity takes place underwater. Magma erupts along spreading centers in the ocean and cools to form new lithosphere.

Less often, a volcano forms over a hot spot far from a plate boundary. Heat carried by material rising from deep in the mantle melts some of the rock in the lithosphere above it. Eruptions over a hot spot built the Hawaiian Islands.

More than 400 volcanoes are along subduction zones in the Pacific Ocean. This is about 80 percent of all active volcanoes above sea level. An active volcano is one that is erupting or has erupted in recorded history. The volcanoes around the Pacific Ocean form a belt called the Ring of Fire. Some of these volcanoes are in the western United States.

### Ring of Fire

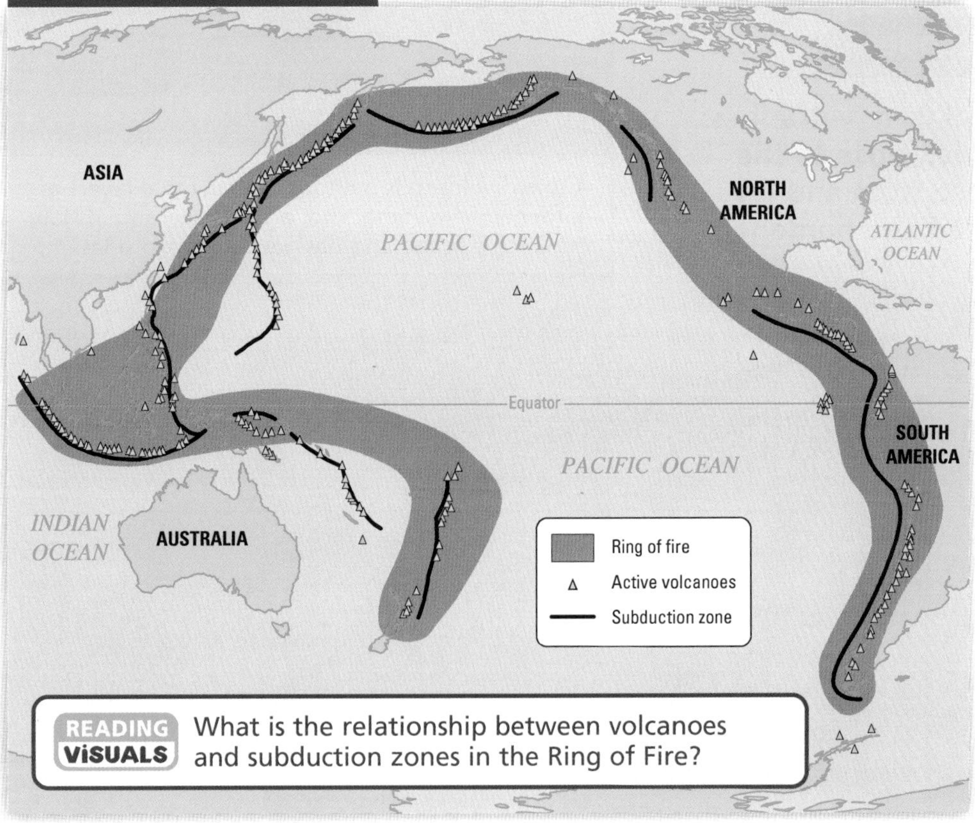


**READING VISUALS** What is the relationship between volcanoes and subduction zones in the Ring of Fire?

## Volcanoes can have many shapes and sizes.

**CONTENT FRAME**
Make a content frame for types of volcanoes. Add categories for shape, size, makeup, and examples.

Mount St. Helens is a cone-shaped volcano in Washington. Its eruption in 1980 killed 57 people. One side of the volcano exploded, blasting out a mixture of hot rock, ash, and gases that destroyed trees tens of kilometers away. Since 1980, this volcano has had many smaller eruptions.

Volcanoes can have many shapes, including steep cones and nearly flat land. Most volcanoes erupt from openings in bowl-shaped pits called craters. Some volcanoes erupt from long cracks in the ground. The type of magma feeding a volcano determines its shape.

**RESOURCE CENTER**
CLASSZONE.COM
Learn more about historic and current volcanic eruptions.

1. **Shield Volcano** A shield volcano is shaped like a broad, flat dome. It is built up by many eruptions of lava that is low in silica and therefore flows easily and spreads out in thin layers. The largest volcano on Earth, Mauna Loa (MOW-nuh LOH-uh), is a shield volcano. It makes up much of the island of Hawaii. The total height of this volcano is about 17 kilometers (10.5 mi), but only about 4 kilometers (2.5 mi) are above sea level. At the top of Mauna Loa is a crater that is 5 kilometers (3 mi) across at its widest point. Mauna Loa is one of Earth's most active volcanoes.

2. **Cinder Cone** A cinder cone is a steep hill formed by the eruption of cinders and other rock fragments that pile up around a crater.

### Three Types of Volcanoes

**Two types of material form volcanoes: rock fragments that fall close to the openings they erupted from and lava flows that have cooled and hardened.**

**① Shield Volcano**

A shield volcano is built up of many thin layers of hardened lava. Rangitoto, a shield volcano in New Zealand, is broad and has gently sloping sides.

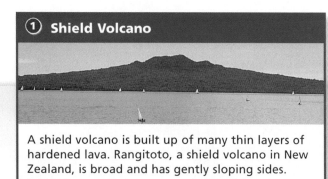

Cinders form as gas-rich magma erupts. Escaping gases throw small chunks of lava into the air, where they harden before landing. Cinder cones are tens to hundreds of meters tall. Many of them form on the sides of other types of volcanoes.

**3 Composite Volcano** A composite volcano is a cone-shaped volcano built up of layers of lava and layers of rock fragments. Its magma is high in silica, and therefore is pasty. A composite volcano is steep near the top and flattens out toward the bottom. Hardened lava flows add strength to the structure of a composite volcano. As a result, it can grow much larger than a cinder cone.

**READING TIP**

The word *composite* comes from a Latin word meaning "put together." Something that is composite is made of distinct parts.

Composite volcanoes have violent eruptions for two reasons. First, expanding gases trapped in rising magma tend to cause explosions. Second, hardened lava from earlier eruptions often plugs openings in these volcanoes. This rock must be blown out of the way before any more magma can escape. Mount St. Helens is a composite volcano. Although its 1980 eruption was devastating, many composite volcanoes have exploded with much greater power.

**CHECK YOUR READING** List the three main types of volcanoes. What questions do you have about how they form?

### ② Cinder Cone

A cinder cone, like this one in Arizona, has steep sides and is a loose pile of volcanic rock fragments.

### ③ Composite Volcano

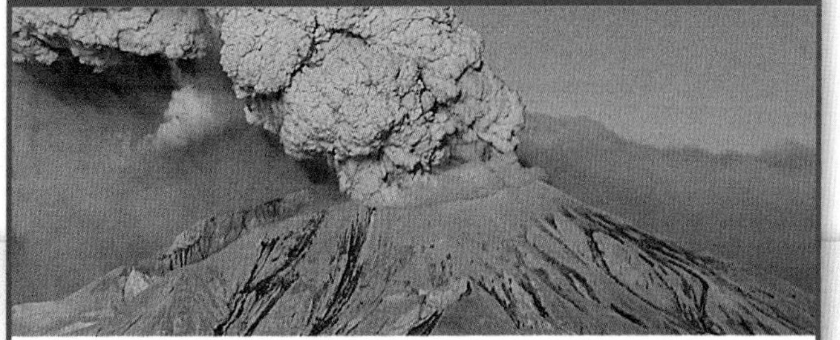

A composite volcano is usually cone-shaped and is built up of layers of hardened lava and of rock fragments. Mount St. Helens is a typical composite volcano.

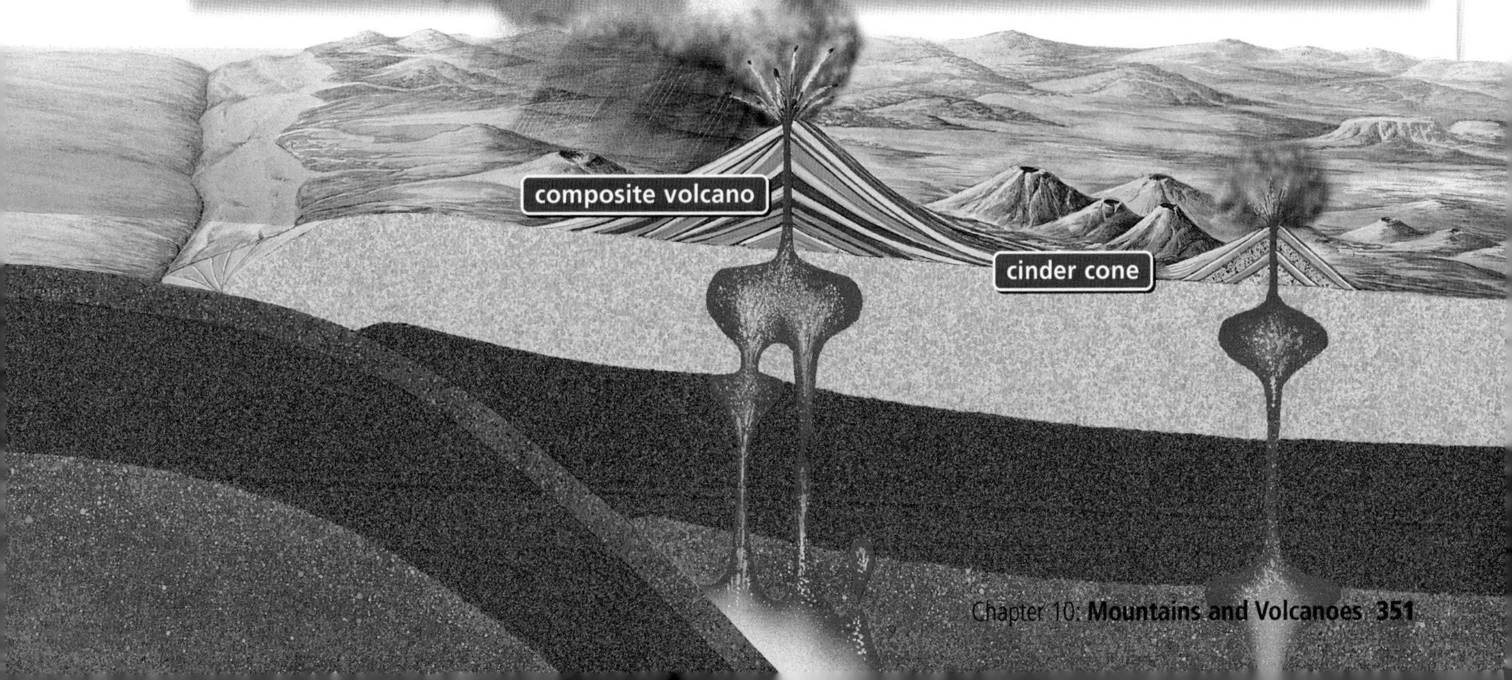

## Formation of Crater Lake

**Crater Lake fills the caldera of a composite volcano.**

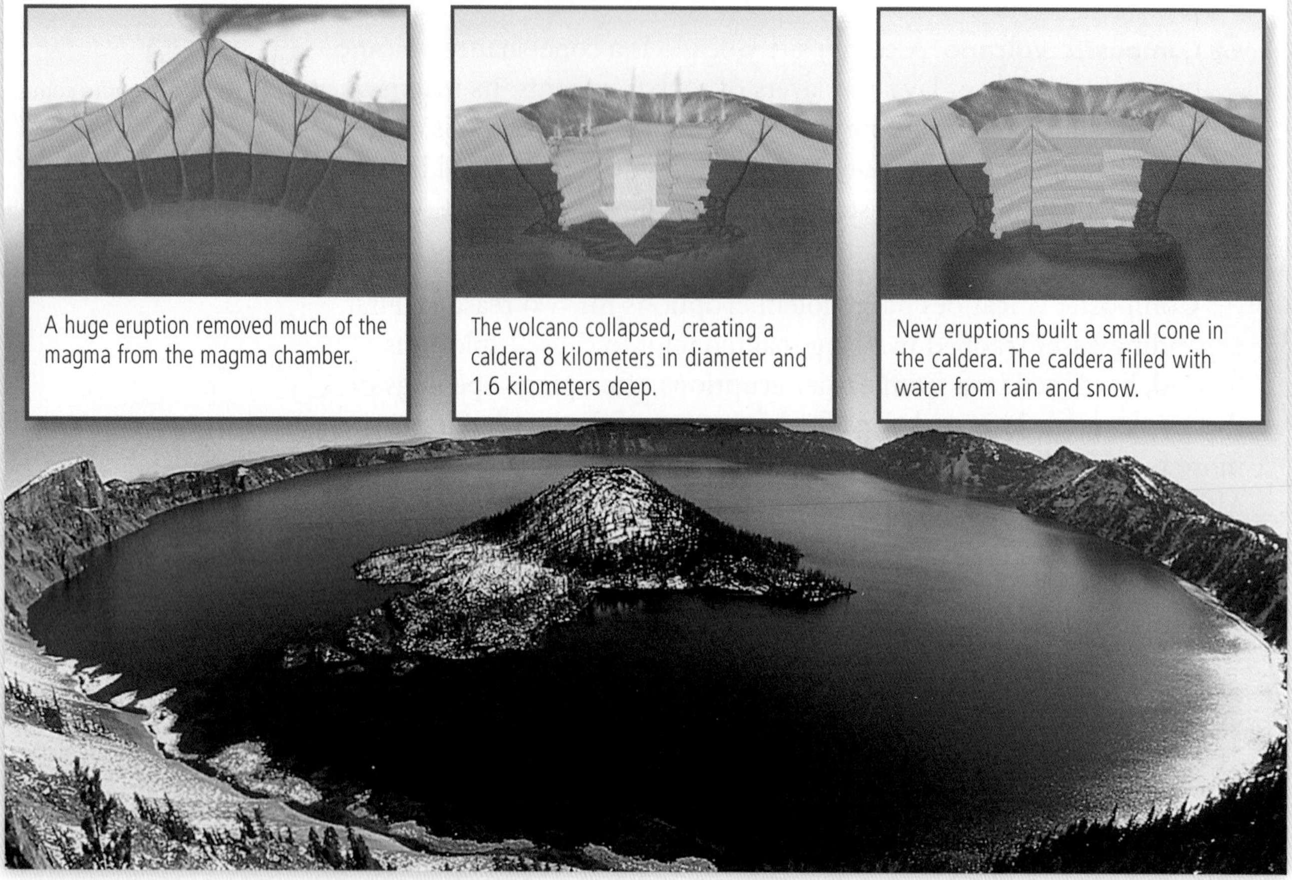

A huge eruption removed much of the magma from the magma chamber.

The volcano collapsed, creating a caldera 8 kilometers in diameter and 1.6 kilometers deep.

New eruptions built a small cone in the caldera. The caldera filled with water from rain and snow.

Both shield volcanoes and composite volcanoes can form features called calderas (kal-DAIR-uhz). A caldera is a huge crater formed by the collapse of a volcano when magma rapidly erupts from underneath it. The crater at the top of Mauna Loa in Hawaii is a caldera. Crater Lake in Oregon fills a caldera formed by a composite volcano about 7700 years ago. A violent eruption emptied much of its magma chamber, and the top of the volcano collapsed into it. The caldera now holds the deepest lake in the United States.

## Scientists monitor volcanoes.

**CONTENT FRAME**
Make a content frame for types of data used to predict eruptions. Include categories for current activity and history.

Mount Pinatubo (PIHN-uh-TOO-boh) in the Philippines erupted in 1991. Before that time, most people living in the area did not realize that it was a composite volcano. It had not erupted in about 500 years, and erosion had changed its shape. Fortunately, scientists in the Philippines knew that the volcano was becoming active months before it exploded. They were able to warn the government and ask people to leave the area. Their efforts probably saved tens of thousands of lives.

As the 1991 eruption of Mount Pinatubo shows, volcanoes can go hundreds of years between eruptions. Before Pinatubo's eruption, scientists noticed warning signs. The signs included many small earthquakes followed by explosions of steam near the volcano's top. Researchers brought in equipment to monitor the volcano's activity. Although they could not stop the eruption, they were able to tell when people should leave.

Scientists monitor, or keep an eye on, volcanoes around the world for signs of eruptions. Earthquake activity and changes in the tilt of the ground are signs that magma is moving underneath a volcano. Scientists monitor the temperatures at openings, springs, and lakes on volcanoes. They also note the amounts and types of gases given off by the volcanoes. Rising temperatures and changes in volcanic gases can indicate that fresh magma has moved into a shallow magma chamber.

Scientists study the ages and types of volcanic rocks around a volcano to understand the volcano's history. They can learn how much time has passed between eruptions and how violent the eruptions have been. This information gives clues about possible future eruptions.

The robot Dante II is about to enter the crater of Mt. Spurr, Alaska, where it will collect video data as well as water and gas samples.

Even with close monitoring, most property damage from volcanic eruptions cannot be prevented. But warning people to move away from a volcano that is about to erupt can save lives. Many of the active volcanoes that are closely monitored are located near major cities. One is Mount Rainier (ruh-NEER), which is near Seattle, Washington. Another is Mount Vesuvius (vih-SOO-vee-uhs), which is near Naples, Italy.

**CHECK YOUR READING** What is the purpose of monitoring volcanoes?

# 10.2 Review

## KEY CONCEPTS

1. Where are most volcanoes located, and why are they located there? (6.1.e)
2. How does the type of material that erupts from a volcano determine the shape of the volcano? (6.1.d)
3. What conditions do scientists examine when they study volcanoes? (6.1.d)

## CRITICAL THINKING

4. **Compare and Contrast** How do the three main types of volcanoes differ?
5. **Infer** Volcanic ash can be deposited in areas many kilometers away from the volcano that produced it. What are two ways in which the ash can reach these areas?

## CHALLENGE

6. **Analyze** Draw diagrams showing how a composite volcano might change in shape by getting larger or smaller with repeated eruptions.

# CHAPTER INVESTIGATION

## Make Your Own Volcanoes

**OVERVIEW AND PURPOSE** Scientists who have never been to a particular volcano can estimate how steep a climb it would be to its top. All they need to know is what type of volcano it is. Volcanoes vary not only in size but also in slope, or the steepness of their sides. The three main types of volcanoes—cinder cones, shield volcanoes, and composite volcanoes—are very different in size and shape. In this activity you will

- make models of volcanoes and measure their slopes
- determine how the types of materials that form a volcano affect how steep it can get

### Problem

Write It Up

What does a volcano's slope reveal about the materials that formed it?

### Hypothesize

Write It Up

Write a hypothesis to explain how a volcano's slope is related to the materials it is made of. Your hypothesis should take the form of an "If . . . , then . . . , because . . ." statement.

### Procedure

1. Make a data table like the one shown in the sample notebook on page 355.

2. Mix 125 mL of plaster of Paris with 60 mL of water in a paper cup. Stir the mixture well. Work quickly because the mixture will harden quickly.

3. Pour the mixture onto a piece of cardboard from a height of 2–3 cm. Write "cone A" on the cardboard and set it aside.

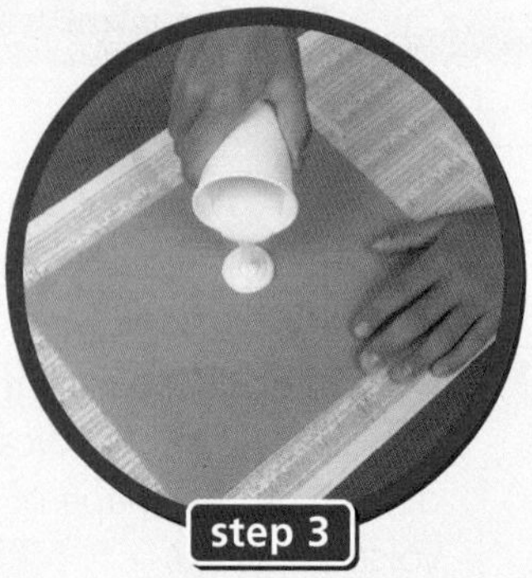

step 3

4. Fill another paper cup with gravel. Slowly pour the gravel onto a second piece of cardboard from a height of about 10 cm. Label this model "cone B" and set it aside.

**MATERIALS**

- 375 mL plaster of Paris
- 180 mL water
- 500 mL gravel
- 3 cardboard pieces
- two 250 mL paper cups
- stirrer
- ruler
- protractor

6.1.d, 6.7.a

**Content Standard**
6.1.d Students know that earthquakes are sudden motions along breaks in the crust called faults and that volcanoes and fissures are locations where magma reaches the surface.

**Investigation Standard**
6.7.a Develop a hypothesis.

**5** In a cup, mix the rest of the plaster of Paris with the rest of the water. Fill the other paper cup with gravel. Pour a small amount of the plaster mixture onto the third piece of cardboard. Then pour some gravel on top. Repeat until all the plaster mixture and gravel have been used. Label this model "cone C" and set it aside until the plaster in both cone A and cone C has hardened (about 20 min).

## Observe and Analyze

Write It Up

1. **MEASURE** Use the protractor to measure the approximate slope of each cone.
2. **RECORD** Complete your data table.
3. **OBSERVE** Compare the appearances of the cones. Record your observations in your **Science Notebook.**
4. **COMPARE** How different are the slopes of the cones?

## Conclude

Write It Up

1. **CONNECT** Which volcanic materials do the plaster mixture and the gravel represent?
2. **IDENTIFY VARIABLES** What is the relationship between the cones' slopes and the materials they are made of?
3. **ANALYZE** Compare your results with your hypothesis. Do your data support your hypothesis?
4. **INTERPRET** Which type of volcano does each model represent?
5. **DRAW CONCLUSIONS** Which of your models represents a volcano that cannot grow as large as the others? Explain.
6. **APPLY** What factors might cause the slopes of real volcanoes to be different from those of your models?
7. **APPLY** If you were a scientist, what might you need to know besides slope in order to determine a volcano's type?
8. **APPLY** How could the method you used to make a model of a cinder cone be used to show how the slope of a hill or mountain contributes to a landslide?

## INVESTIGATE Further

**CHALLENGE** Calculate the slopes of your models using the formula $y = mx + b$. In this formula, $y$ and $x$ are graph coordinates of a point on a straight line. The slope of the line is $m$. The intersection of the line with the $y$-axis of the graph is $b$. For example, if the height of a model is 1.6 cm, and the distance from its edge to its center is 4 cm, then the equation is $1.6 = m4 + 0$.

The slope is $\frac{1.6}{4}$, or 0.4.

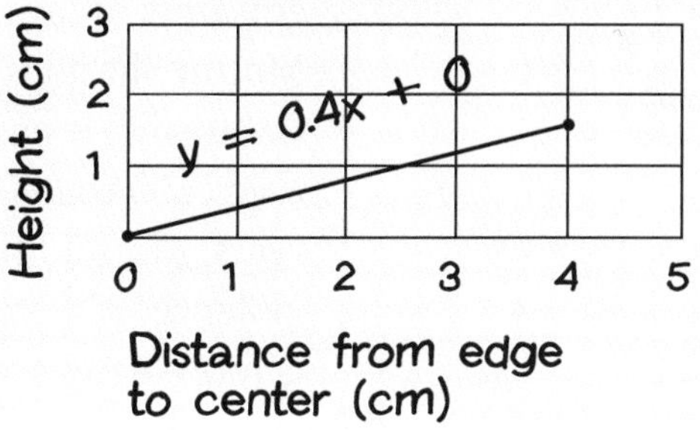


Make Your Own Volcanoes

Table 1. Volcano Model and Slope

| Cone | Drawing of Cone | Slope (degrees) |
|---|---|---|
| A. | | |
| B. | | |
| C. | | |

KEY CONCEPT

# 10.3 Volcanoes affect Earth's land, air, and water.

**CALIFORNIA Content Standards**

**6.2.d** Students know earthquakes, volcanic eruptions, landslides, and floods change human and wildlife habitats.

**6.6.a** Students know the utility of energy sources is determined by factors that are involved in converting these sources to useful forms and the consequences of the conversion process.

**BEFORE, you learned**

- Rock fragments, lava, and gases erupt from volcanoes
- Some volcanoes have explosive eruptions

**NOW, you will learn**

- How volcanic eruptions affect Earth's surface
- How volcanic gases affect the atmosphere
- How volcanic activity affects water

**VOCABULARY**

**acid rain** p. 360
**geyser** p. 361

**THINK ABOUT**

***Which volcano is more dangerous?***

Mauna Loa is a shield volcano that forms a large part of the island of Hawaii. It is one of the most active volcanoes on Earth, frequently producing large amounts of lava that flow long distances. Mount Shasta is a composite volcano in California. It has erupted at least once every 600 to 800 years for the past 10,000 years. Mount Shasta can erupt with great violence. Which volcano do you think it is more dangerous to live near? Why?

**CONTENT FRAME**
Add a content frame for how eruptions affect Earth's land and air. Include categories for what dangers are caused and how long the dangers last.

## Volcanic eruptions affect the land.

A volcanic eruption can knock down forests and clog rivers with volcanic ash. Damage can occur far from the volcano. But volcanoes build as well as destroy. Material erupted from volcanoes can form new land. Over time, lava flows can form new, rich soil.

Many towns and cities are located close to volcanoes. The people of Goma in the Democratic Republic of the Congo experienced an eruption of a nearby volcano in 2002. A lava flow cut the city in half and destroyed the homes of tens of thousands of people, either by flowing into the homes or by starting fires. Hilo (HEE-loh), the largest city on the island of Hawaii, is built in part on young lava flows. The city is at high risk from future volcanic activity.

## Immediate Effects

The effects of a volcanic eruption largely depend on how much material and what types of material the volcano ejects. Near a volcano, lava flows can cover the land with new rock. A much larger area can be affected by events such as ash falls, landslides, mudflows, pyroclastic flows, and steam explosions.

**Lava Flows** Most lava moves slowly enough that people can move away and not be hurt. But even a slow-moving lava flow will knock down, cover, or burn nearly everything in its path.

**Volcanic Ash** Near a volcanic eruption, the weight of fallen volcanic ash can cause the roofs of buildings to collapse. Volcanic ash is heavy because it is made of tiny pieces of rock. Ash makes roads slippery, and it clogs up machinery, including cars and airplanes. Large amounts of falling ash can suffocate plants, animals, and people.

**Mudflows** Mudflows are landslides that occur when loose rocks and soil are mixed with water. Heat from an eruption melts any ice and snow on the volcano very quickly. Mudflows form as the water mixes with volcanic ash and other loose particles. Mudflows also form as ash mixes into rivers flowing from a volcano. Fast-moving mudflows have buried entire towns many kilometers from an eruption.

**Pyroclastic Flows** As a pyroclastic flow rushes downhill, it can knock down or burn everything in its way. Pyroclastic flows tend to follow valleys. However, a fast-moving flow can sweep up and over hills, then race down a neighboring valley. As a flow passes, it can leave a thick layer of volcanic rock fragments. Pyroclastic flows are extremely dangerous. In 1902 a pyroclastic flow from an eruption in the West Indies completely destroyed the city of Saint Pierre. Almost 30,000 people were killed within a few minutes.

**Landslides** Part of a volcano can collapse and start a landslide—a rapid downhill movement of rock and soil. The collapse may be caused by magma moving underground, an eruption, an earthquake, or even heavy rainfall. A landslide can cause a tsunami if a large amount of material falls into the ocean.

**Lava Flow**

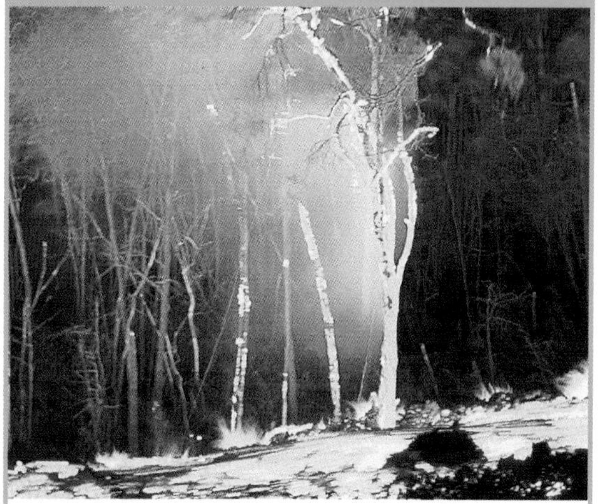

Trees catch fire as a lava flow moves through a forest in Hawaii in 1999.

**Volcanic Ash**

Large piles of volcanic ash from the 1991 eruption of Mount Pinatubo line a street in Olongapo, Philippines.

**REMINDER**

A tsunami is a water wave caused by an earthquake, a volcanic eruption, or a landslide.

RESOURCE CENTER
CLASSZONE.COM

Find out more about the effects of volcanic eruptions.

**Steam Explosions** Steam explosions are rare but can be very destructive. They occur when magma comes near water. A steam explosion may have caused the destruction of a volcanic island in Indonesia. The entire island of Krakatau (KRACK-uh-TOW) exploded in 1883. The explosion caused a tsunami that destroyed hundreds of towns and killed more than 36,000 people.

CHECK YOUR READING What are two ways a volcanic eruption can result in damage to areas hundreds of kilometers away?

## Long-Term Effects

Volcanic eruptions can be very destructive. But even after an eruption ends, a volcano can remain dangerous for many years.

The explosive eruption of Mount Pinatubo in 1991 threw out huge amounts of volcanic ash and rock fragments. The area the volcano is in gets heavy rains each year. Mudflows have formed as large amounts of rainwater mixed with ash and other loose material on the sides of the volcano. Since the eruption, mudflows have destroyed the homes of more than 100,000 people.

This school bus was partly buried by a mudflow from Mount St. Helens. No one was in the bus when the mudflow hit.

Another possible source of water for these mudflows was a lake that began filling the volcano's crater. The upper part of Mount Pinatubo crater is weak, and the lake's level was rising. A collapse of the crater could have emptied the lake of much of its water. In 2001 people dug a channel to lower the level of the lake, greatly decreasing the chance of a collapse.

CHECK YOUR READING Why can volcanic ash be dangerous for years after an eruption?

Even though volcanoes are dangerous, over time they can have positive effects. When a lava flow cools, it forms a layer of hard rock on which no plants can grow. However, over many years, this rock can break down to form rich soil. Volcanic ash can smother plants, but the tiny pieces of rock break down quickly and make soil richer. Highly productive farmland surrounds some active volcanoes.

Over time, repeated volcanic eruptions can build a magnificent landscape of mountains and valleys. People may choose to live in a volcanic area in part for its natural beauty. Many other people may visit the area, supporting a tourist industry.

**CALIFORNIA Focus**

Lava Beds National Monument in northern California features a rugged volcanic landscape formed by eruptions of the giant Medicine Lake shield volcano. Cinder cones, lava flows, and lava tube caves are common. Tourists can explore these caves, which were formed when lava rivers flowing downhill cooled more rapidly on the outside than they did on the inside.

# INVESTIGATE Mudflows

## *How does the shape of the land affect mudflows?*

**SKILL FOCUS**
Analyzing (6.2.d)

**MATERIAL**
Map of Mount Rainier Mudflows

**TIME**
25 minutes

**PROCEDURE**

1. Look at the map of Mount Rainier mudflows. Observe the relationship between the paths of rivers and the paths of the mudflows.
2. Write the number of towns shown within the boundaries of mudflow areas.
3. Write the differences in elevation between the following locations: the top of Mount Rainier and the point where the West Fork joins the White River, the point where the rivers join and the town of Buckley, and the towns of Buckley and Auburn. Where is the land steepest?
4. On the back of the paper, explain why in some areas mudflows have followed rivers and in other areas mudflows have spread out.

**WHAT DO YOU THINK?**

- What three factors are most important in causing mudflows to start near the top of Mount Rainier and flow long distances?
- How likely are future mudflows to follow the same paths as earlier mudflows?

**CHALLENGE** The largest mudflow starting on Mount Rainier moved at about 22 kilometers per hour (14 mi/h). It covered the land to an average depth of 6 meters (20 ft). Describe the steps you would take to protect people from a similar mudflow in the same area.

## Volcanic gases and ash affect the air.

If you visit a volcano, you might notice some unpleasant odors. These odors come from gases released into the air from magma. Some of these gases contain the element sulfur. Hydrogen sulfide gas smells like rotten eggs. Sulfur dioxide gas is what you smell when you strike a match. The volcano might also be releasing carbon dioxide, a gas you would not notice because it has no color or odor. Volcanoes release gases before, during, and after eruptions.

**REMINDER**
An element is a substance that contains only one type of atom.

Many gases from volcanoes are dangerous. They can make breathing difficult and damage the lungs of people and animals. Carbon dioxide can be fatal. In West Africa, a sudden release of carbon dioxide killed 1700 people in 1986. The gas came from a volcano at the bottom of a lake. Carbon dioxide built up in the water until a large amount escaped at once. Pipes are now being used to release carbon dioxide from the bottom of the lake so that the gas will not build up again.

A cloud of hot gases and ash rises high into the atmosphere during an eruption of Mount Etna in Italy.

**VOCABULARY**
Remember to add *acid rain* to your notebook, using the vocabulary strategy of your choice.

Some gases, such as sulfur dioxide, form acids when they mix with water in the air. These acids fall to Earth's surface in rain, snow, or sleet. Rain that contains large amounts of acid is called **acid rain.** Volcanoes are sources of acid-forming gases, but a bigger source is human activity. For example, the burning of coal in electrical power plants adds acid-forming gases to the air. In some areas, acid rain has damaged forests and killed fish in lakes.

Large amounts of volcanic gases in the atmosphere can change weather worldwide. The 1991 eruption of Mount Pinatubo released enough sulfur dioxide to form a haze high in the atmosphere around the entire planet. The haze decreased the amount of sunlight reaching Earth's surface. It lowered average world temperatures in 1992 and 1993.

Volcanic gases can lift ash high above an erupting volcano. Winds can then carry the ash far away. During the May 1980 eruption of Mount St. Helens, ash fell 400 kilometers (250 mi) away in Spokane, Washington. The ash blocked so much sunlight that Spokane's streetlights were turned on during the day. The smallest ash particles can remain in the air for years, circling Earth many times. These particles also reflect sunlight and can lower Earth's temperature.

**CHECK YOUR READING** Describe two ways sulfur dioxide can affect the atmosphere.

## Volcanic activity affects water.

Yellowstone National Park in the western United States is famous for its hot springs. These are places where heated water flows to Earth's surface. Yellowstone is a volcanic region, and its hot springs sit in a huge caldera. The springs' heat comes from a hot spot under the North American Plate.

## Geysers

**Rainwater can sink through cracks in rock. If it is heated within Earth, it can rise to form hot springs and geysers.**

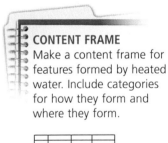

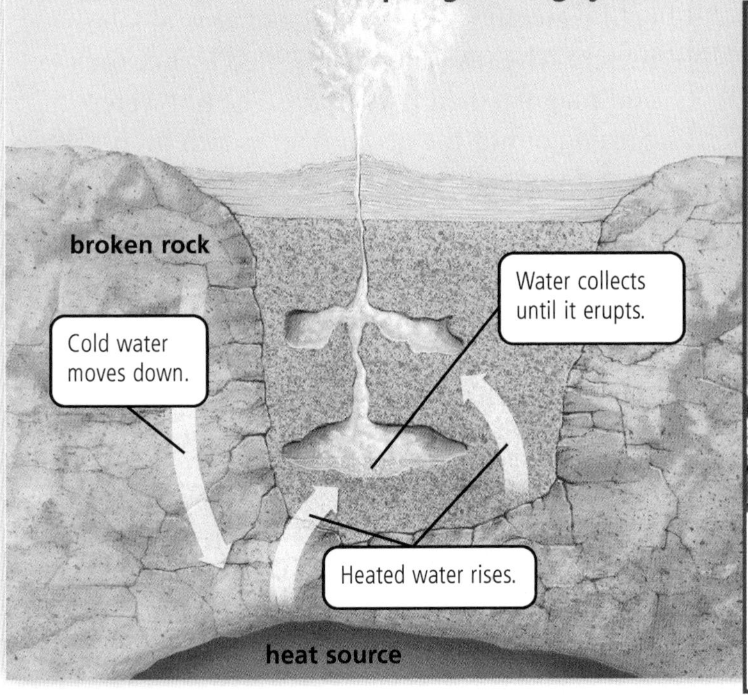
broken rock
Water collects until it erupts.
Cold water moves down.
Heated water rises.
heat source

Old Faithful geyser in Yellowstone National Park erupts more often than any other large geyser. Heated water is forced up into the air through a narrow channel.

## Hot Springs, Geysers, and Fumaroles

Most hot springs are in areas where magma or hot rock is near Earth's surface. Water moves down through the ground, gets heated, and rises at a hot spring. At most hot springs, the water flows out into a calm pool. But at a type of hot spring called a **geyser,** water shoots into the air. A geyser forms where water collects in an underground chamber, then erupts through a narrow channel. Old Faithful is a geyser in Yellowstone National Park. It erupts every 35 minutes to 2 hours. Most geysers erupt less regularly.

Countries with many hot springs and geysers include the United States, New Zealand, and Iceland. Iceland sits on an ocean spreading center. Magma rises underneath the country as plates pull apart. People in Iceland use hot underground water as an energy source.

A fumarole (FYOO-muh-ROHL) is similar to a hot spring. Instead of liquid water, a fumarole releases steam and other gases. Changes in hot springs and fumaroles located on the sides of a volcano can show that the volcano is becoming more active. As magma moves close to the surface, water temperatures get higher. As a result, fumaroles can release more or different gases.

**CONTENT FRAME**
Make a content frame for features formed by heated water. Include categories for how they form and where they form.

**CHECK YOUR READING** Why might fumaroles and hot springs be monitored?

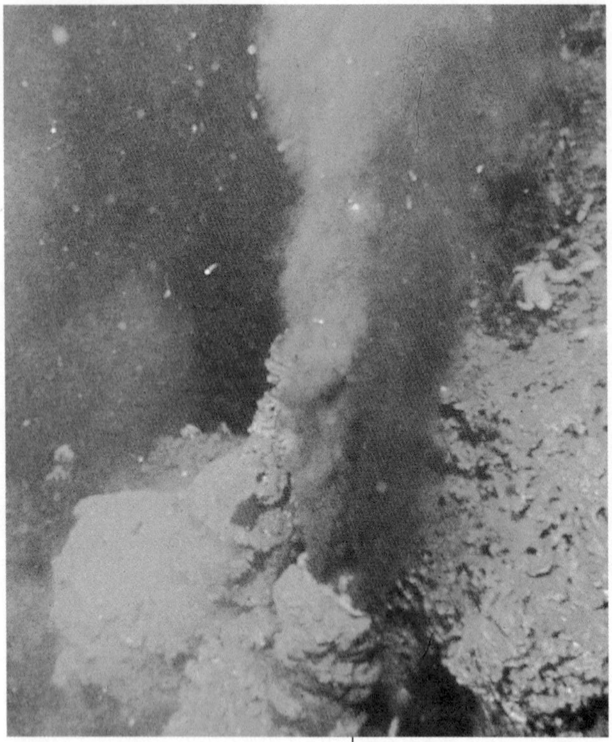

This deep-sea vent is more than 3 kilometers (2 mi) below the surface of the Atlantic Ocean. A black cloud of mineral-rich water rises from the vent.

## Deep-Sea Vents

Deep-sea vents are hot springs that form at spreading centers in the ocean. In these places, the ocean floor has many cracks through which cold seawater sinks to depths of several kilometers. The sea water gets heated by hot rock and magma, then rises again. The hot water coming out of the ocean floor is rich in dissolved minerals and gases from the rock and magma.

At some deep-sea vents, warm water flows gently from cracks in the ocean floor. At others, water that can be hotter than 350°C (660°F) shoots out of chimney-like vents. The water looks black because it contains large amounts of dissolved minerals. As the hot water mixes with cold water, dissolved minerals form into solid minerals again. This process builds up the vent chimneys.

Deep-sea vents support unusual life forms such as blind crabs and tubeworms that measure up to 3 meters (10 ft) long. These animals feed on one-celled organisms that get their energy from chemicals in the vent water. Unlike other one-celled organisms, these organisms do not need sunlight to make their food.

**CHECK YOUR READING** Why do chimneys form around some deep-sea vents?

# 10.3 Review

### KEY CONCEPTS

1. Describe how a heavy ash fall from a volcanic eruption can affect Earth's surface. (6.2.d)
2. Describe how large amounts of volcanic gases can affect weather around Earth. (6.2.d)
3. Why do hot springs occur in volcanic areas? (6.2.d)

### CRITICAL THINKING

4. **Compare and Contrast** What do geysers and deep-sea vents that form chimneys have in common? How are they different?
5. **Evaluate** Which is more dangerous, a pyroclastic flow or a mudflow? Explain.

### CHALLENGE

6. **Analyze** Ice in Greenland and Antarctica contains layers of ash from eruptions that occurred many thousands of years ago. How do you think the ash reached the ice, and why is it preserved?

California Close-Up

GEOTHERMAL FEATURES

# In Hot Water!

6.4.c Students know heat from Earth's interior reaches the surface primarily through convection.

Roaring fumaroles. Steaming hot springs. Thumping mud pots. No, these are not names of California theme-park rides. They are descriptions of geothermal features at Lassen Volcanic National Park in northeastern California. And they are all clues that Lassen Peak is likely to erupt again.

Lassen Volcanic National Park is located at the foot of the Cascade Mountains. Its hydrothermal system heats and recycles groundwater. *Hydro-* refers to "water," and *thermal* refers to "heat," so the word *hydrothermal* means "of or relating to hot water."

Lassen Peak last erupted in 1917. Even without a volcanic eruption, Lassen Park is an active place. Steam and gas escape through fumaroles, or vents in the ground. Since the steam and hot water have only a small opening through which to escape, they shoot up into the air. In some places, you can see the chemicals that were once dissolved in the boiling water. Hot water bubbles up, and when it evaporates, colorful metals are left behind on the rocks. What about thumping mud pots? Well, just imagine the sound made by thick mud when boiling water rises under it.

Lassen Peak hasn't erupted since 1917, but the hydrothermal system at Lassen Volcanic National Park shows there is a heat source under the volcano. The heat causes convection currents that reach the surface at hydrothermal features.

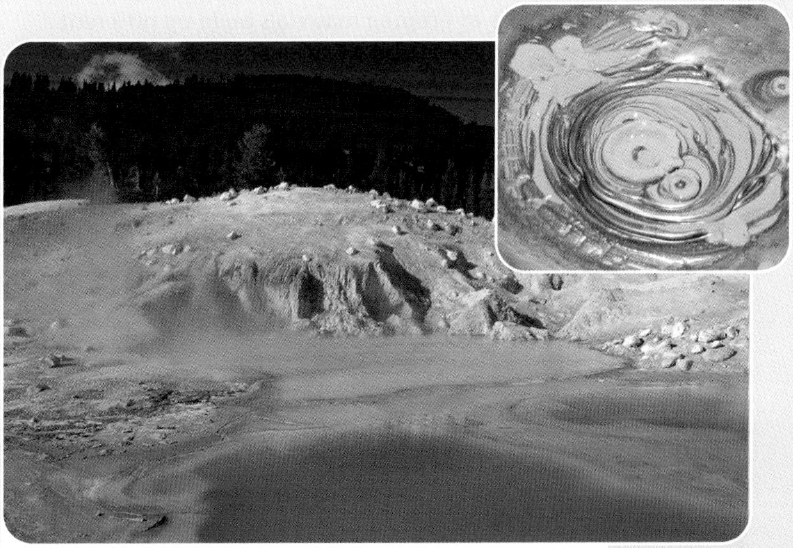

Steam rises from a hot pool in Lassen Park. Mud pots (inset) form where steam and water bubble up through mud at the surface.

## WRITING ABOUT SCIENCE

Make an information pamphlet for Lassen Volcanic National Park. Include a diagram of your favorite geothermal feature. Use the Internet to find more information and photos.

# 10 Chapter Review

## the BIG idea

**Mountains and volcanoes form as tectonic plates move.**

CONTENT REVIEW
CLASSZONE.COM

## KEY CONCEPTS SUMMARY

### 1 Movement of rock builds mountains.

Folded mountains form as plates push together.

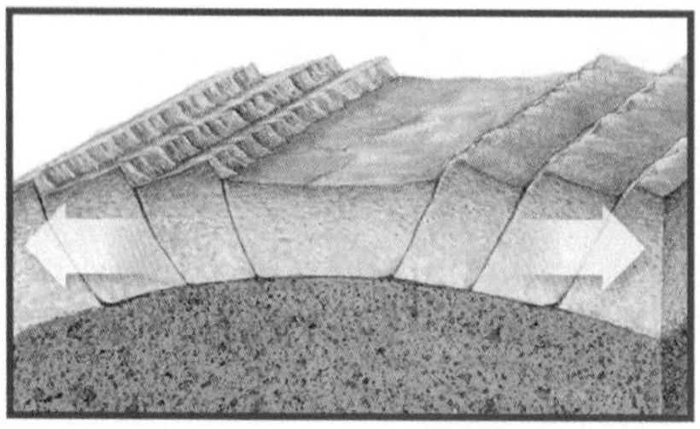

Fault-block mountains form as the lithosphere is stretched.

**VOCABULARY**
**folded mountain** p. 340
**fault-block mountain** p. 342

### 2 Volcanoes form as molten rock erupts.

Volcanoes erupt molten rock, rock fragments, and gases. Different types of erupted materials build up different types of volcanoes.

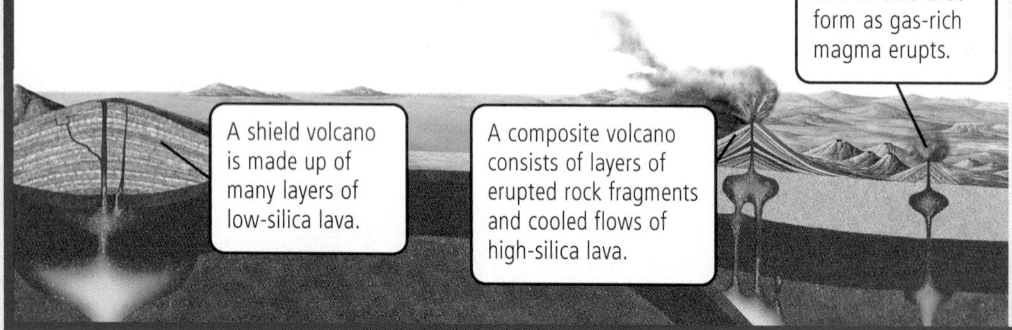

A cinder cone is made up of loose rock fragments and cinders that form as gas-rich magma erupts.
A shield volcano is made up of many layers of low-silica lava.
A composite volcano consists of layers of erupted rock fragments and cooled flows of high-silica lava.

**VOCABULARY**
**volcano** p. 346
**lava** p. 347
**pyroclastic flow** p. 348

### 3 Volcanoes affect Earth's land, air, and water.

Materials erupted from volcanoes, as well as heat from molten rock underground, affect Earth's surface.

**Land**

- lava
- volcanic ash
- landslides
- mudflows
- pyroclastic flows

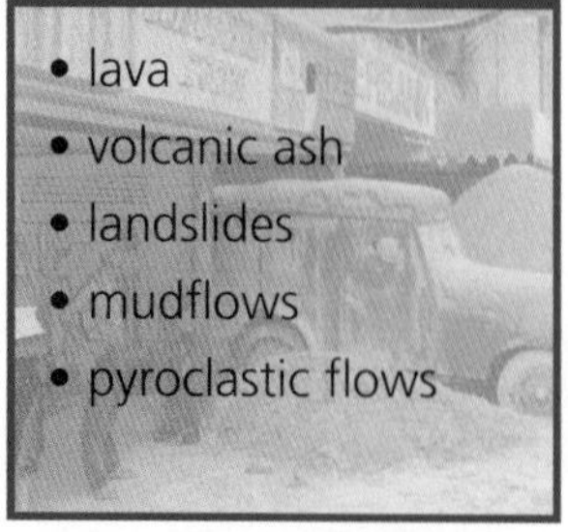

**Air**

- poisonous gases
- acid rain
- haze
- lower temperatures

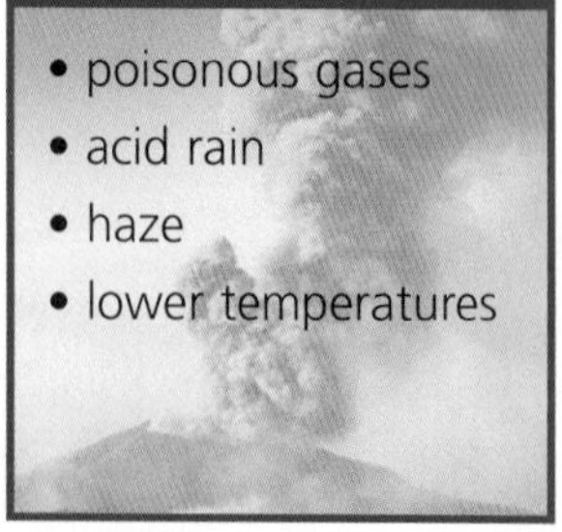

**Water**

- hot springs
- geysers
- fumaroles
- deep-sea vents

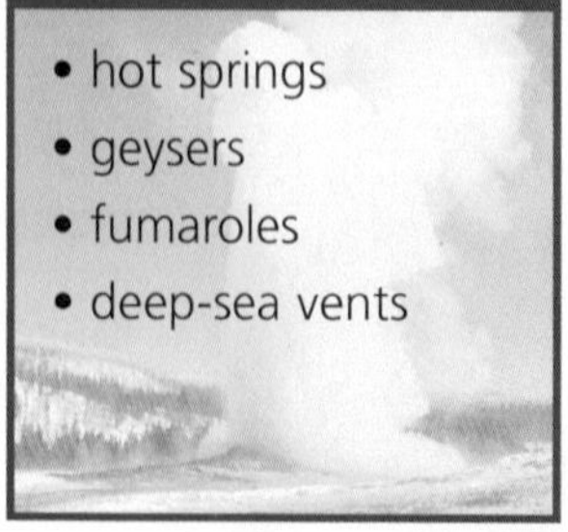

**VOCABULARY**
**acid rain** p. 360
**geyser** p. 361

## Reviewing Vocabulary

*Draw a Venn diagram to compare and contrast each pair of features. Example:*

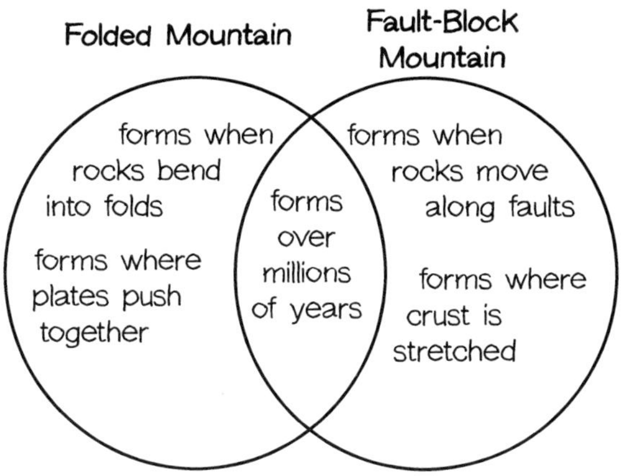


1. folded mountain, volcano
2. lava, pyroclastic flow
3. volcano, geyser

## Reviewing Key Concepts

**Multiple Choice** *Choose the letter of the best answer.*

4. In areas where the lithosphere is being pulled apart, the crust (6.1.b)
   **a.** folds and crumples into mountains
   **b.** breaks into blocks separated by faults
   **c.** slides down into the mantle
   **d.** develops a subduction zone

5. When two plates carrying continental crust collide, the rock of the continents (6.1.e)
   **a.** folds **c.** expands
   **b.** melts **d.** stretches

6. The movement of huge blocks of rock along a fault can produce (6.1.e)
   **a.** lava plugs
   **b.** volcanoes
   **c.** fault-block mountains
   **d.** folded mountains

7. Volcanoes in the Ring of Fire are supplied with magma rising from (6.1.d)
   **a.** spreading centers **c.** rift valleys
   **b.** hot spots **d.** subduction zones

8. Before magma erupts it collects under a volcano in a (6.1.d)
   **a.** chamber **c.** crater
   **b.** caldera **d.** vent

9. The explosiveness of a volcanic eruption depends mostly on what quality of the magma? (6.1.d)
   **a.** gas content **c.** amount
   **b.** silica content **d.** temperature

10. The type of magma erupting from a volcano determines the volcano's (6.1.d)
    **a.** size **c.** shape
    **b.** age **d.** location

11. Volcanic ash can be carried thousands of kilometers from an eruption by (6.2.d)
    **a.** lava flows **c.** landslides
    **b.** pyroclastic flows **d.** winds

12. What happens at a geyser? (6.1.d)
    **a.** Water erupts through a narrow channel.
    **b.** Warm water flows into a calm pool.
    **c.** Lava erupts out of a volcano.
    **d.** Lava flows gently down the side of a volcano.

**Short Answer** *Write a short answer to each question.*

13. Describe how an old mountain belt located in the center of a continent most likely formed. (6.1.e)
14. How are the locations of volcanoes related to tectonic plate boundaries? (6.1.f)
15. What causes a shield volcano to be shaped like a broad dome? (6.1.d)
16. By what processes can a volcanic eruption affect temperatures around the world? (6.2.d)

## Thinking Critically

*This photograph shows a volcanic eruption. The volcano produces rivers of lava that flow long distances. Use the photograph to answer the next six questions.*

17. **INFER** What kind of volcano is shown in the photograph? How do you know? (6.1.d)

18. **APPLY** Is this eruption likely to produce large amounts of ash that could lead to dangerous mudflows for many years afterward? Why or why not? (6.2.d)

19. **IDENTIFY EFFECTS** How might volcanic gases affect the health of people and animals living near the volcano? (6.2.d)

20. **ANALYZE** What would be likely to happen if a large amount of water reached the volcano's magma chamber? (6.1.d)

21. **COMPARE AND CONTRAST** How could this volcano affect nearby farmland during the eruption? many years after the eruption? (6.2.d)

22. **SYNTHESIZE** What types of changes would let scientists monitoring the volcano know that an eruption was likely to occur? (6.1.e)

23. **COMPARE AND CONTRAST** How does the stress on continental crust in areas where folded mountains form differ from that in areas where fault-block mountains form? (6.1.e)

24. **APPLY** Draw a diagram showing how one magma chamber can supply magma to a shield volcano and to a cinder cone on the side of the shield volcano. (6.1.d)

25. **INFER** Many of the volcanoes in the Ring of Fire erupt explosively. Would you expect these volcanoes to be cinder cones, shield volcanoes, or composite volcanoes? Explain your answer (6.1.d).

26. **PREDICT** How might an area with many hot springs and geysers be affected as magma and hot rock near the surface cooled? (6.1.d)

27. **ANALYZE** Why do volcanoes form along boundaries where oceanic plates are pushing into other plates but not along boundaries where continents are pushing together? (6.1.e)

28. **APPLY** Explain why shield volcanoes, composite volcanoes, and cinder cones have different sizes and shapes. (6.1.d)

## the BIG idea

29. **INFER** How would you expect tectonic plates to be moving at a plate boundary where folded mountains are being pushed up and volcanoes are erupting? (6.1.e)

30. **PREDICT** If tectonic plates continue to move as they are moving today, the continents of Australia and Antarctica will collide in the far future. What will happen after the sea floor that is now between the continents is destroyed? (6.1.e)

## UNIT PROJECTS

Evaluate all of the data, results, and information from your project folder. Prepare to present your project to the class. Be ready to answer questions posed by your classmates about your results.

For more practice, go to . . . TEST PRACTICE CLASSZONE.COM

## Analyzing Data

6.1.d, 6.1.e, 6.2.d

*The graph below shows the amounts of lava, rock, and other materials released in four large volcanic eruptions. Study the graph, then answer the questions below.*

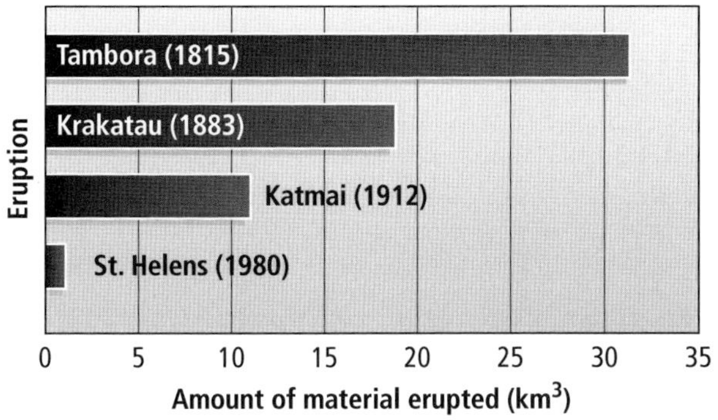


**1.** About how much material did the eruption of Katmai release in 1912?
**a.** 12 $km^3$
**b.** 17 $km^3$
**c.** 29 $km^3$
**d.** 41 $km^3$

**2.** After 1850, which of these eruptions released the greatest amount of material?
**a.** Krakatau
**b.** Tambora
**c.** Katmai
**d.** St. Helens

**3.** About how much more material erupted from Krakatau in 1883 than from Katmai in 1912?
**a.** 28 $km^3$
**b.** 12 $km^3$
**c.** 6 $km^3$
**d.** 2 $km^3$

**4.** Katmai, a large mountain built of layers of hardened lava flows and of rock fragments, is a
**a.** cinder cone
**b.** shield volcano
**c.** pyroclastic cone
**d.** composite volcano

**5.** How much material did the 1815 eruption of Tambora produce compared with the 1883 eruption of Krakatau?
**a.** less than one-half the amount
**b.** a nearly equal amount
**c.** almost two times the amount
**d.** almost four times the amount

**6.** All of the eruptions shown in the graph created calderas—craters formed by the collapse of volcanoes—because the eruptions were large enough to
**a.** mostly empty the volcanoes' magma chambers
**b.** produce lava that flowed long distances
**c.** produce lava that had a low silica content
**d.** form dangerous pyroclastic flows and mudflows

**7.** The average temperature of Earth can decrease for several years when a huge volcanic eruption adds to the atmosphere large amounts of
**a.** acid rain
**b.** energy
**c.** volcanic cinders
**d.** volcanic gases

**8.** A thick layer of volcanic ash can be heavy enough to collapse the roofs of buildings because ash
**a.** is produced as rocks burn
**b.** is made up of tiny pieces of rock
**c.** becomes heavier as it cools
**d.** can hold large amounts of water

## Extended Response

*Answer the two questions below in detail. Include some of the terms shown in the word box. In your answers, underline each term you use.*

| | | |
|---|---|---|
| boundaries | hot spots | rising |
| subduction | magma | heat |
| spreading centers | | |

**9.** Petra is marking the locations of active volcanoes on a map of the world. Explain how the locations of the volcanoes are related to the locations of tectonic plates.

**10.** Scientists regularly check the temperature of a lake on a volcano. Explain how this information might help them learn whether the volcano is becoming more active.

## Contents Overview

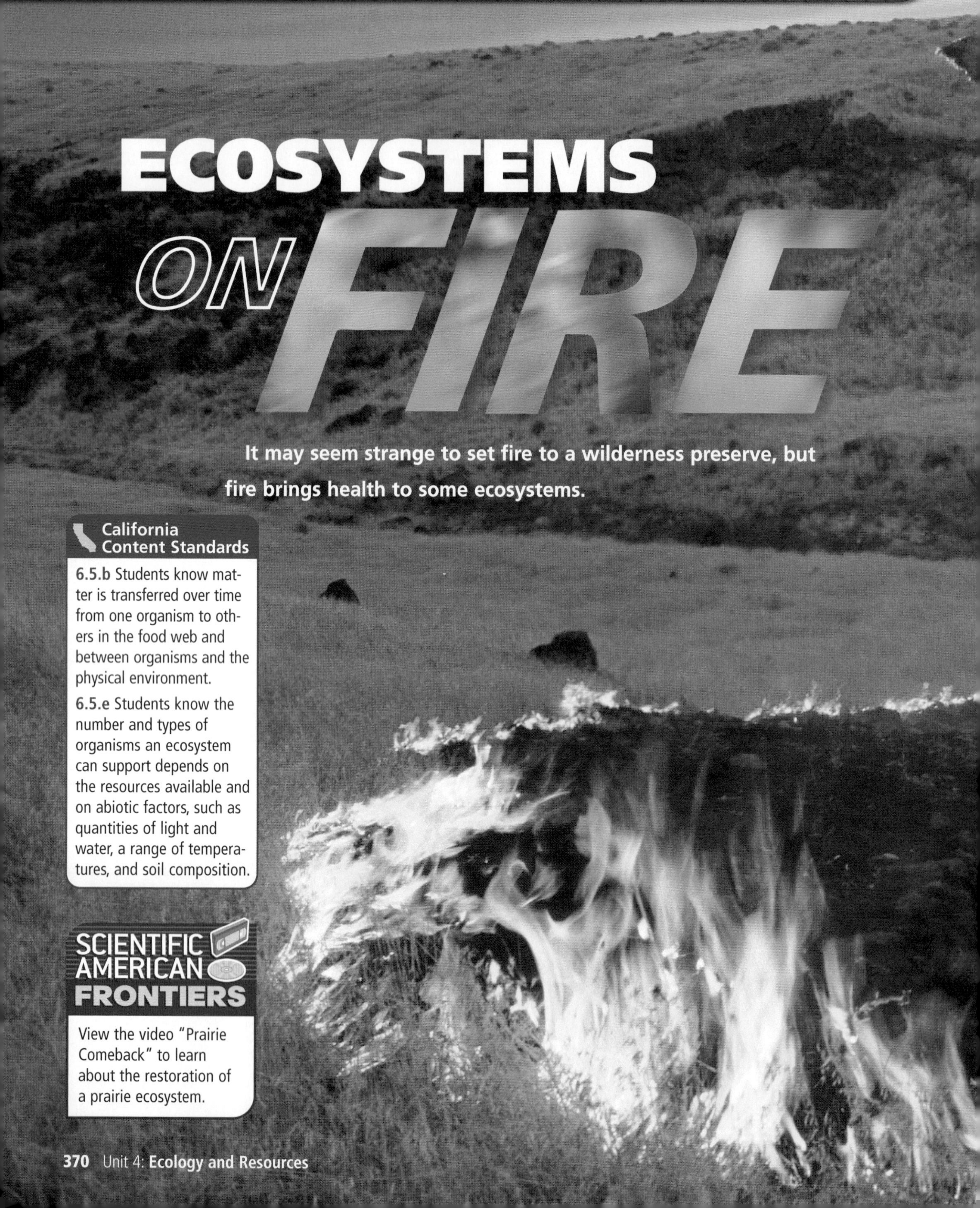

# ECOSYSTEMS ON FIRE

**It may seem strange to set fire to a wilderness preserve, but fire brings health to some ecosystems.**

**California Content Standards**

**6.5.b** Students know matter is transferred over time from one organism to others in the food web and between organisms and the physical environment.

**6.5.e** Students know the number and types of organisms an ecosystem can support depends on the resources available and on abiotic factors, such as quantities of light and water, a range of temperatures, and soil composition.

**SCIENTIFIC AMERICAN FRONTIERS**

View the video "Prairie Comeback" to learn about the restoration of a prairie ecosystem.

An astonishing variety of plants blooms in this prairie in Missouri.

## Fire and Life

Intense heat, smoke, the crackling of burning grasses, the crashing of flaming trees—all these characteristics of fire seem threatening. In recent years, forest fires have burned huge areas of forest and have endangered people and property. But even though fire can be destructive, it can also bring forth life. In fact, scientists are actively using fire to manage ecosystems. Ecosystems are areas that contain specific groups of living and nonliving things. Prairies, forests, and woodlands are examples of ecosystems.

The fear of fire has led people to limit fires that are a natural part of some ecosystems. Preventing or putting out smaller fires in a forest ecosystem can mean trouble. Occasional small fires burn small amounts of material and cause only limited damage. Without these smaller fires, burnable materials may build up and lead to the outbreak of a terrible fire.

Species of living things in some ecosystems have adaptations that allow them to thrive after a fire. In western forests in North America, trees such as lodgepole pine and jack pine depend upon heat from a fire to release seeds from their cones. Cape lilies on the forest floor bloom almost immediately after a forest fire. On prairies, flowers such as the prairie fringed orchid in Illinois benefit from prairie fires.

Seven months after a controlled burn, light shines on a new patch of wild hyacinth growing at the base of an oak tree.

## Observing Patterns

Ecosystems include living things, such as plants and animals. They also include nonliving things, such as water and soil. Fires affect both the living and the nonliving. The photographs above show part of an oak woodland ecosystem. The photograph on the left shows a burn—a fire set on purpose by humans. The photograph on the right shows the same area seven months later.

Ashes left from fires add nutrients to the soil. Fire also opens space on the forest floor. Areas that were shaded by small trees, shrubs, and dead branches receive light. Over time, wild hyacinth and other new plants grow around the oak, and new insects and animals move into the area.

**SCIENTIFIC AMERICAN FRONTIERS**

**View the "Prairie Comeback" segment of your Scientific American Frontiers video to see how understanding ecosystems can help bring a prairie into bloom.**

**IN THIS SCENE FROM THE VIDEO** **a bison grazes on new growth that appears after the prairie is burned.**

**BRINGING BACK THE PRAIRIE** At one time natural events and human activity caused regular patterns of fire on the prairie. Bison grazed on tender young plants that grew up after fires, and the plants that weren't eaten by the bison had room to grow. In 1989 an organization called The Nature Conservancy turned the Chapman-Barnard Cattle Ranch in Northeast Oklahoma into the Tall Grass Prairie Restoration Preserve.

Scientists at the preserve are using controlled fire and reintroducing bison to the area. Today, there are more than 750 species of plants and animals growing in the preserve.

In tall-grass prairie ecosystems, fire provides similar benefits. Fire burns away overgrown plants, enriches the soil, and clears the way for the growth of new plants. Bison prefer to graze on these new plants that appear after a fire.

## A New Understanding

Some of the benefits provided by ecosystems can't be measured. But researchers are starting to measure the financial contributions of ecosystems. Ecosystems help clean our water, balance gases in the atmosphere, and maintain temperature ranges.

Researchers today are studying these benefits. A new frontier in ecology, called ecosystem services, is emerging. This new study is gaining the attention of both scientists and economists.

Given our growing awareness of the importance of ecosystems, should humans deliberately set fire to areas in forests or prairies? The answer to this question requires an understanding of interactions among living and nonliving parts of ecosystems. Forest and prairie fires can be dangerous. However, if properly managed, they can provide important benefits to society as well as to the natural world.

### UNANSWERED Questions

Understanding the connections within ecosystems raises more questions. In the coming years, people will need to analyze the costs and benefits of ecosystem restoration.

- How will humans balance the need to feed the human population with the cost of destroying ecosystems such as the prairie?
- How can scientists and wildlife managers protect people and property near forests while maintaining forest ecosystems?
- How do ecosystems protect natural resources, such as soil and water?

## UNIT PROJECTS

**As you study this unit, work alone or with a group on one of the projects listed below. Use the bulleted steps to guide your project.**

### Build an Ecosystem (6.5.e)

Use an aquarium or other container to build an ecosystem.

- Set up your ecosystem. Observe it daily, and record your observations.
- Bring your ecosystem into your classroom, or take photographs and make diagrams of it. Present the record of your observations along with the visual displays.

### Conservation Campaign (6.6.b)

Find out how much water, paper, and energy are used in a month at your school.

- Describe a plan for conserving resources.
- Present your plan. You might make posters, write announcements, or perform a short skit.

### Design a Park (6.7.d, 6.7.h)

You are part of a group that is planning a park near your school. Your group wants the park to include plants that lived in the area twenty-five years ago.

- Collect information from local museums, park districts, or botanic gardens. You can also visit Web sites sponsored by those organizations.
- Prepare a report and drawing of your park design.

**CAREER CENTER**
CLASSZONE.COM

Learn more about careers in ecology.

CHAPTER

# 11 Ecosystems and Biomes

## the BIG idea

Matter and energy together support life within an environment.

## Key Concepts

SECTION 1
**Ecosystems support life.**
Learn about different factors that make up an ecosystem.

SECTION 2
**Matter cycles through ecosystems.**
Learn about the water, carbon, and nitrogen cycles.

SECTION 3
**Energy flows through ecosystems.**
Learn how energy moves through living things.

SECTION 4
**Biomes contain many ecosystems.**
Learn about different land and water biomes.

**California ClassZone**

CLASSZONE.COM

Chapter 11 online resources: Content Review, Visualization, four Resource Centers, Math Tutorial, Test Practice

***How many living and nonliving things can you identify in this photograph of Lake Tahoe?***

# EXPLORE the BIG idea

## How Do Plants React to Sunlight?

6.5.a Students know energy entering ecosystems as sunlight is transferred by producers into chemical energy through photosynthesis and then from organism to organism through food webs.

Move a potted plant so that sunlight shines on it from a different direction. Observe the plant each day for a week.

**Observe and Think** What change do you observe in the plant? What do plants get from the Sun?

## Internet Activity: A Prairie Ecosystem

6.5.a Students know energy entering ecosystems as sunlight is transferred by producers into chemical energy through photosynthesis and then from organism to organism through food webs.

Go to **ClassZone.com** to discover the types of plants and animals best adapted for tall-grass and short-grass prairies. Learn more about how to keep a prairie growing.

**Observe and Think** What do all prairie plants have in common? How do prairie plants differ?

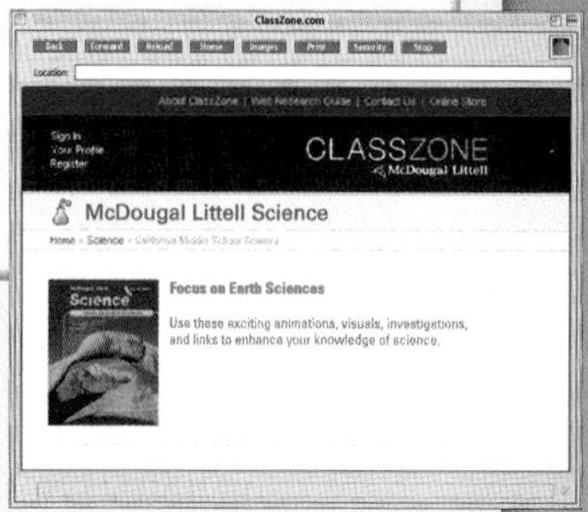

NSTA scilinks.org SCILINKS

Food Chains and Food Webs **Code: MDL001**

CHAPTER 11

# Getting Ready to Learn

## CONCEPT REVIEW

- The natural world that surrounds all living things is called the environment.
- Most living things need water, air, food, and living space.
- All living things need a source of energy to stay alive and grow.

## VOCABULARY REVIEW

**system** p. 41

*See Glossary for definitions.*

**environment**
**nutrient**
**photosynthesis**
**respiration**

**CONTENT REVIEW**
CLASSZONE.COM

Review concepts and vocabulary.

## TAKING NOTES

### COMBINATION NOTES

To take notes about a new concept, first make an informal outline of the information. Then make a sketch of the concept and label it so you can study it later.

### VOCABULARY STRATEGY

Write each new vocabulary term in the center of a **frame game** diagram. Decide what information to frame the term with. Use examples, descriptions, sentences that use the term in context, or pictures. You can change the frame to fit each item.

See the Note-Taking Handbook on pages R45–R51.

**SCIENCE NOTEBOOK**

NOTES

Parts of an ecosystem:
- Animals
- Plants
- Soil
- Water
- Light
- Microorganisms

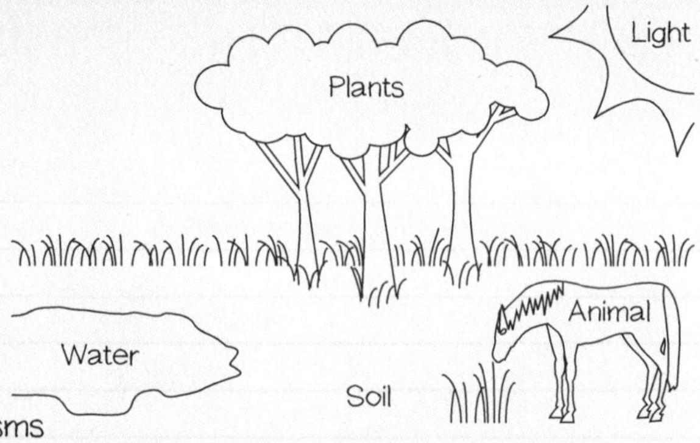


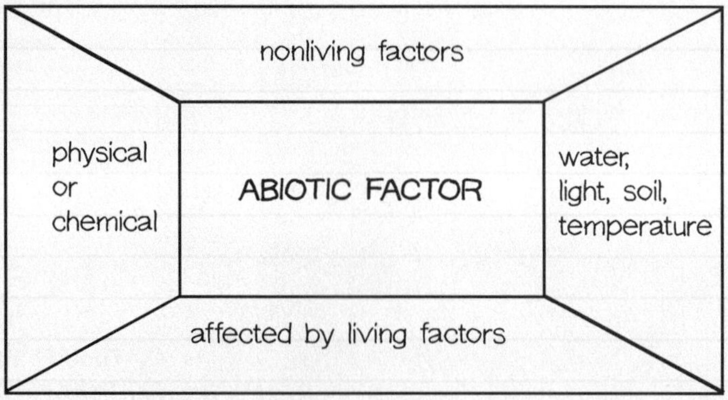

KEY CONCEPT

# 11.1 Ecosystems support life.

**CALIFORNIA Content Standards**

**6.5.a** Students know energy entering ecosystems as sunlight is transferred by producers into chemical energy through photosynthesis and then from organism to organism through food webs.

**6.5.e** Students know the number and types of organisms an ecosystem can support depends on the resources available and on abiotic factors, such as quantities of light and water, a range of temperatures, and soil composition.

**BEFORE, you learned**

- Living things need to obtain matter and energy from the environment
- The Sun provides Earth with light and heat

**NOW, you will learn**

- What factors define an ecosystem
- About living factors in an ecosystem
- About nonliving factors in an ecosystem

**VOCABULARY**

**ecology** p. 377
**ecosystem** p. 377
**biotic factor** p. 378
**abiotic factor** p. 378

### EXPLORE Your Environment (6.5.e)

***How much can temperature vary in one place?***

**PROCEDURE**

1. Choose three locations inside your classroom where you can measure temperature.
2. Place a thermometer at each location. Wait for at least two minutes. Record the temperatures in your notebook.
3. Compare the data you and your classmates have collected.

**MATERIALS**

- thermometer
- stopwatch

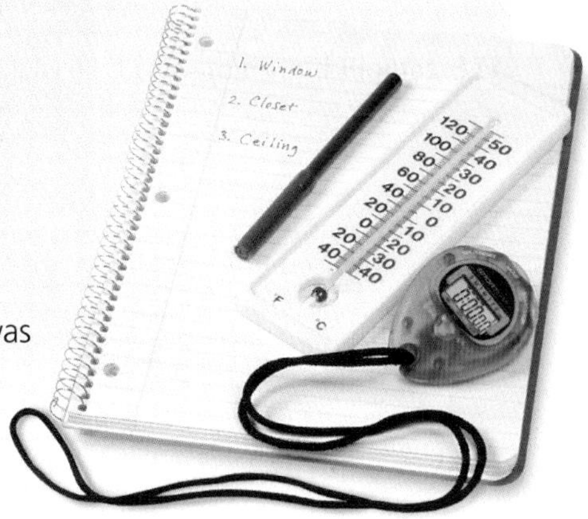


**WHAT DO YOU THINK?**

- Which location was the warmest? Which was the coldest?
- Describe what factors may have affected the temperature at each location.

**VOCABULARY**
Add frame game diagrams for *ecology* and *ecosystem* to your notebook.

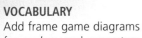

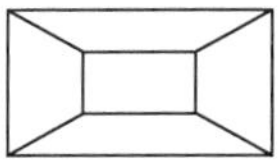

## Living things depend on the environment.

You wouldn't find a kangaroo in the Arctic or a polar bear in Australia. Each animal is suited to a certain environment. The kangaroo and the polar bear are able to survive despite the harsh conditions of their surroundings. **Ecology** is the scientific study of how organisms interact with their environment and all the other organisms that live in that environment.

Scientists use the word **ecosystem** to describe a particular environment and all the living things that are supported by it. An ecosystem can be as small as a rotting log or as large as a desert. What is important in an ecosystem is how the living parts of the ecosystem relate to the nonliving parts.

READING TIP

A microorganism is an organism that is so tiny it can be seen only through a microscope.

READING TIP

The word *biotic* means "living." The prefix *a-* in *abiotic* means "not," so *abiotic* means "not living."

Think about a pond. A pond ecosystem is more than just water and fish. Plants grow in and around the water, and animals feed on these plants. Microorganisms in the water are food for fish and for each other. These are just a few of the living parts, or **biotic factors** (by-AHT-ihk), of a pond ecosystem. The nonliving parts, or **abiotic factors** (AY-by-AHT-ihk), include the air that supplies oxygen and carbon dioxide, the soil that provides nutrients, the water in the pond, and the sunlight that plants need to grow.

**CLASSIFY** Name three living and three nonliving factors that are part of this pond ecosystem.

## Biotic factors interact with an ecosystem.

Living things depend upon an ecosystem for food, air, and water, as well as other things they need for survival. In turn, living things affect the ecosystem in which they live. Plants are biotic factors in land ecosystems. They affect other biotic and abiotic parts of ecosystems. For example, plants are an important source of food. As a result, the types of plants found in an ecosystem determine the types of animals that can live there. Plants can affect temperature by blocking sunlight. Plant roots hold soil in place. Even the atmosphere is affected by plants as they take in carbon dioxide and release oxygen.

Animals are also biotic factors that affect an ecosystem. A beaver that builds a dam changes the flow of a river and so affects the surrounding landscape. Large herds of cattle can overgraze a grassland ecosystem and cause the soil to erode. In an ocean ecosystem, corals form giant reefs that provide food and shelter for marine organisms.

## Many abiotic factors affect ecosystems.

Abiotic factors include both the physical and chemical parts of an ecosystem. Physical factors are factors that you can see or feel, such as the temperature, water, and sunlight. Chemical factors include the minerals and compounds found in the soil and whether the ecosystem's water is fresh or salty. The combination of different abiotic factors determines the types of organisms that an ecosystem can support.

REMINDER
Compounds were discussed in Chapter 6.

CHECK YOUR READING List four different abiotic factors that can affect an ecosystem.

### Temperature

Temperature is an important abiotic factor in any ecosystem. In a land ecosystem, temperature affects the types of plants that grow well there. The types of plants available for food and shelter determine the types of animals that can live there. For example, a tropical rain forest has a lot of rain and consistently warm temperatures. The wide variety of plants in a tropical rain forest supports a wide variety of monkeys, birds, and other organisms.

Animals are as sensitive to temperature as plants are. Musk oxen have a thick coat of fur, so they can survive in very cold environments. Water buffalo have a light coat, so they are better suited to warm temperatures. Wild water buffalo live in tropical climates.

RESOURCE CENTER
CLASSZONE.COM
Learn more about ecosystems.

This musk ox's thick fur keeps it warm in the cold temperatures of northern Canada.

A water buffalo cools itself in a shallow stream during a hot day in India.

READING VISUALS **COMPARE AND CONTRAST** How are these animals alike? How are they different?

## Light

**COMBINATION NOTES**
Remember to make notes and diagrams to show how abiotic factors affect biotic factors in an ecosystem.

You can understand how abiotic factors work together when you think about sunlight and temperature. Sunlight warms Earth's surface and atmosphere. In addition, energy from sunlight supports all life on Earth. The Sun provides the energy that plants capture and use to produce food in a process called photosynthesis. The food produced by plants and other photosynthetic organisms feeds almost all the other living things found on Earth.

The strength of sunlight and the amount of sunlight available in a land ecosystem determine the types of plants in that ecosystem. A desert ecosystem has plants such as cacti, which can survive where sunlight is very strong. In a forest, much of the sunlight is blocked by trees. Mosses and ferns grow well on the shaded ground.

Light is a factor in ocean ecosystems as well. The deeper the water is, the less light there is available. In shallow water near the shore, photosynthetic organisms can survive at the surface and on the ocean floor. In the deep ocean, light is available for photosynthetic organisms only in the first hundred meters below the surface.

## Soil

**READING TIP**
Soil is a mixture of mineral and rock particles, organic matter, water, and air.

Soil is an important abiotic factor in land ecosystems. Organisms in the soil break down the remains of dead plants and animals. These decaying remains become part of the soil. This process of decay provides important raw materials to the living plants and animals of an ecosystem.

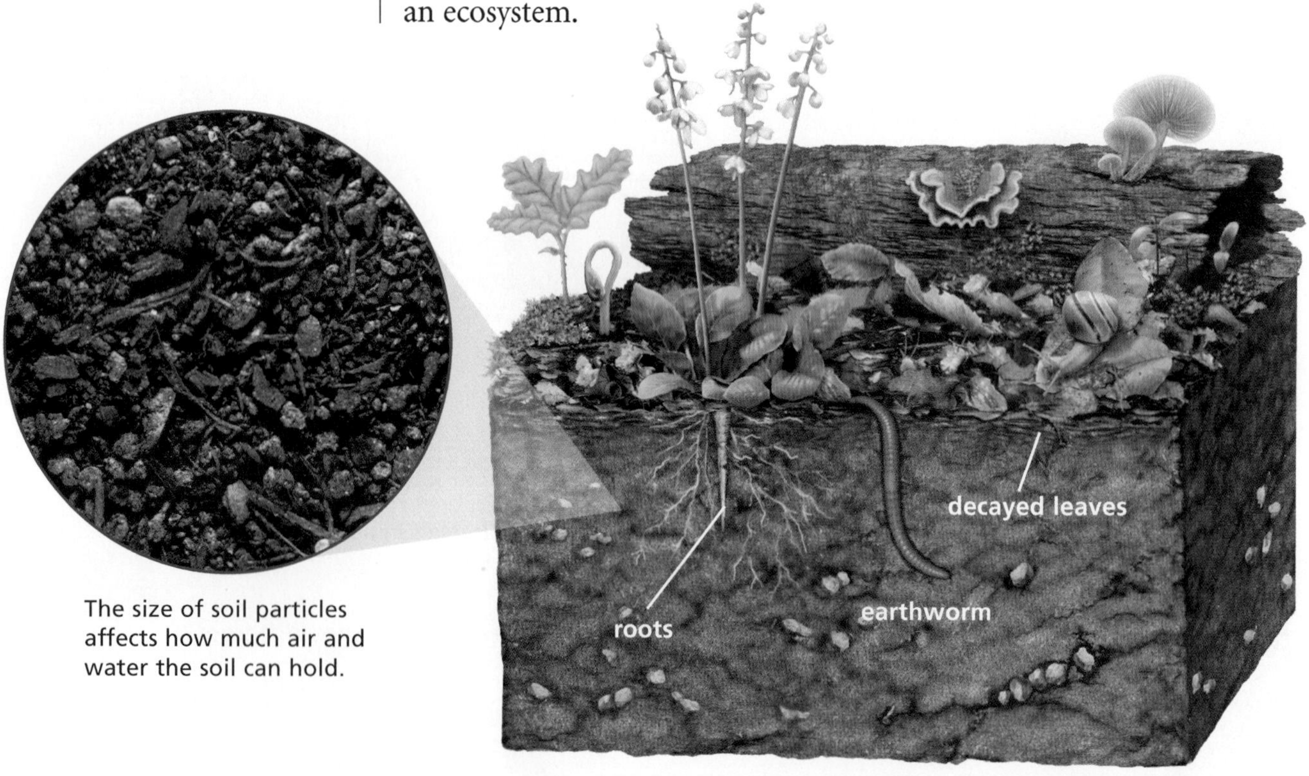


The size of soil particles affects how much air and water the soil can hold.

Different ecosystems have different types of soil. The characteristics of the soil in an ecosystem affect plant growth. Soils that have a lot of organic matter hold water well and allow air to reach the plant roots. Sandy soils usually do not hold water well because the water flows through too easily. Clay soil, which has small, tightly packed particles, does not allow water to move through easily. Minerals in the soil also affect plant growth.

**READING TIP**

Organic matter is made up of carbon compounds from living or once-living organisms.

**CHECK YOUR READING** Explain how soil can affect plant life in an ecosystem.

## Water

Another important abiotic factor in land ecosystems is the amount of water available to support life. All living things need water to carry out life processes. Plants need water as well as sunlight for photosynthesis. Animals need water to digest food and release the energy stored in the food. Look at the photograph to see the effect that an underground water source has on an otherwise dry, desert ecosystem. Trees could not survive there without a plentiful supply of water.

Ecosystems that have a lot of water can support a large number of different types of plants. These plants can then support a large number of different types of animals. Tropical rain forests are the wettest of all ecosystems on land and have the most types of plants and animals. Desert ecosystems are the driest land ecosystems and have far fewer types of plants and animals. The types and number of living things in a land ecosystem are always related to the amount of fresh water available for its inhabitants.

**INFER** An oasis forms in the desert when underground water comes to the surface. How can you identify the boundary of this oasis?

# 11.1 Review

### KEY CONCEPTS

1. Draw a diagram of an ecosystem near where you live. Label the factors "biotic" or "abiotic." (6.5.e)
2. Give two examples of how plants and animals affect their environment. (6.5.e)
3. Describe how temperature, light, and soil affect an ecosystem. (6.5.e)

### CRITICAL THINKING

4. **Predict** Think of a forest ecosystem. Now imagine that a large volcanic eruption throws large amounts of dust and ash into the air, blocking out sunlight. How might the forest ecosystem be affected if the sunlight is blocked for a day? for a year?

### CHALLENGE

5. **Apply** Think of how you fit into your local environment. List ways in which you interact with biotic and abiotic factors in your ecosystem.

# CHAPTER INVESTIGATION

## Testing Soil

**OVERVIEW AND PURPOSE** Soil is necessary for life. Whether a soil is suitable for farming or construction, and whether it absorbs water when it rains, depends on the properties of that soil. In this investigation you will

- test a soil sample to measure several soil properties
- identify the properties of your soil sample

### MATERIALS

- dried soil sample
- 250 mL graduated cylinder
- 1 qt jar with lid
- water
- 2 L plastic bottle
- scissors
- window screening
- rubber band
- pH test strips
- clock with second hand
- *for Challenge:* Texture Flow Chart

6.5.e, 6.7.b

## Procedure

### PORE-SPACE TEST

1. Measure 200 mL of the dried soil sample in the graduated cylinder. Pour it into the jar.

2. Rinse the graduated cylinder, then fill it with 200 mL of water. Slowly pour the water into the jar until the soil is so soaked that any additional water would pool on top.

3. Record the amount of water remaining in the graduated cylinder. Then determine by subtraction the amount you added to the soil sample. Make a soil properties chart in your **Science Notebook** and record this number in it.

4. Discard the wet soil according to your teacher's instructions, and rinse the jar.

### pH TEST AND DRAINAGE TEST

5. Cut off the top of a plastic bottle and use a rubber band to attach a piece of window screening over its mouth. Place the bottle top, mouth down, into the jar.

6. Use the graduated cylinder to measure 200 mL of soil. Pour the soil into the inverted bottle top.

7. Rinse the graduated cylinder, and fill it with 100 mL of water. Use a pH test strip to test the water's pH. Record the result in the "before" space in your soil properties chart.

8. Pour the water into the soil. Measure the amount of time it takes for the first drips to fall into the jar. Record the result in your chart.

**Content Standard**
6.5.e Students know the number and types of organisms an ecosystem can support depends on the resources available and on abiotic factors, such as quantities of light and water, a range of temperatures, and soil composition.

**Investigation Standard**
6.7.b Select and use appropriate tools and technology (including calculators, computers, balances, spring scales, microscopes, and binoculars) to perform tests, collect data, and display data.

9 When the water stops dripping, remove the bottle top. Use a new pH strip to measure the pH of the water in the jar. Record this measurement in the "after" space in your chart. Note any differences in the appearance of the water before and after it was filtered through the soil.

10 Discard the wet soil according to your teacher's instructions, and rinse the jar.

### PARTICLE-TYPE TEST

11 Add water to the jar until it is two-thirds full. Pour in soil until the water level rises to the top of the jar, then replace the lid. Shake the jar, and set it to rest on a countertop overnight.

12 The next day, observe the different soil layers. The sample should have separated into sand (on the bottom), silt (in the middle), and clay (on the top). Measure the height of each layer and the total height of the three layers. Record your measurements in your chart.

13 Use the following formula to calculate the percentage of each kind of particle in the sample:

$$\frac{\text{height of layer}}{\text{total height of all layers}} \times 100$$

Record your results and all calculations in your chart.

## Observe and Analyze

Write It Up

1. **RECORD** Complete your soil properties chart.
2. **IDENTIFY** How did steps 1–3 test your soil sample's pore space?
3. **IDENTIFY** How did steps 5–9 test your soil sample's drainage rate?

## Conclude

Write It Up

1. **EVALUATE** In step 3 you measured the amount of space between the soil particles in your sample. In step 8 you measured how quickly water passed through your sample. Are these two properties related? Explain your answer.
2. **EVALUATE** Would packing down or loosening up your soil sample change any of the properties you tested? Explain your answer.
3. **INTERPRET** What happened to the pH of the water that passed through the soil? Why do you think that happened?
4. **ANALYZE** Look at the percentages of sand, silt, and clay in your sample. How do the percentages help explain the properties you observed and measured?

## INVESTIGATE Further

**CHALLENGE** Soil texture depends on the size of the weathered rock particles the soil contains. Use the Texture Flow Chart to determine the texture of your soil sample.

Testing Soil

Observe and Analyze

Table 1. Soil Properties Chart

| Property | Result | Notes and Calculations |
|---|---|---|
| Pore space | _ mL water added | |
| pH | before: pH = _<br>after: pH = _ | |
| Drainage | _ seconds | |
| Particle type | height of sand = _ cm<br>height of silt = _ cm<br>height of clay = _ cm<br>total height = _ cm | |

Conclude

KEY CONCEPT

# 11.2 Matter cycles through ecosystems.

**CALIFORNIA Content Standard**

6.5.b Students know matter is transferred over time from one organism to others in the food web and between organisms and the physical environment.

**BEFORE, you learned**

- Ecosystems support life
- Living and nonliving factors interact in an ecosystem
- Temperature, light, soil, and water are important nonliving factors in ecosystems

**NOW, you will learn**

- How matter is exchanged between organisms and their environment
- About the water, carbon, and nitrogen cycles

### VOCABULARY

**cycle** p. 384
**carbon cycle** p. 386
**nitrogen cycle** p. 387

**EXPLORE The Water Cycle (6.5.b)**

### *Do plants release water?*

**PROCEDURE**

1. Cover a branch of the plant with a plastic bag. Tape the bag firmly around the stem.
2. Water the plant and place it in a sunny window or under a lamp. Wash your hands.
3. Check the plant after ten minutes, at the end of class, and again the next day.

**WHAT DO YOU THINK?**

- What did you see inside the plastic bag?
- What purpose did the plastic bag serve?

**MATERIALS**

- 1 small potted plant
- 1 clear plastic bag
- tape
- water

## All ecosystems need certain materials.

**RESOURCE CENTER**
CLASSZONE.COM
Explore cycles in nature.

Living things depend on their environment to meet their needs. You can think of those needs in terms of the material, or matter, required by all living things. For example, all organisms take in water and food in order to survive. All of the materials an organism takes in are returned to the ecosystem during the organism's life or after it dies.

The movement of matter through the living and nonliving parts of an ecosystem is a cycle. A **cycle** is a series of events that happens over and over again. Matter in an ecosystem may change form, but it never leaves the ecosystem. Therefore, the matter is said to cycle through the ecosystem. Three of the most important cycles in ecosystems involve water, carbon, and nitrogen.

## Water Cycle

**Different processes combine to move water through the environment.**

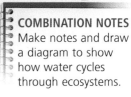

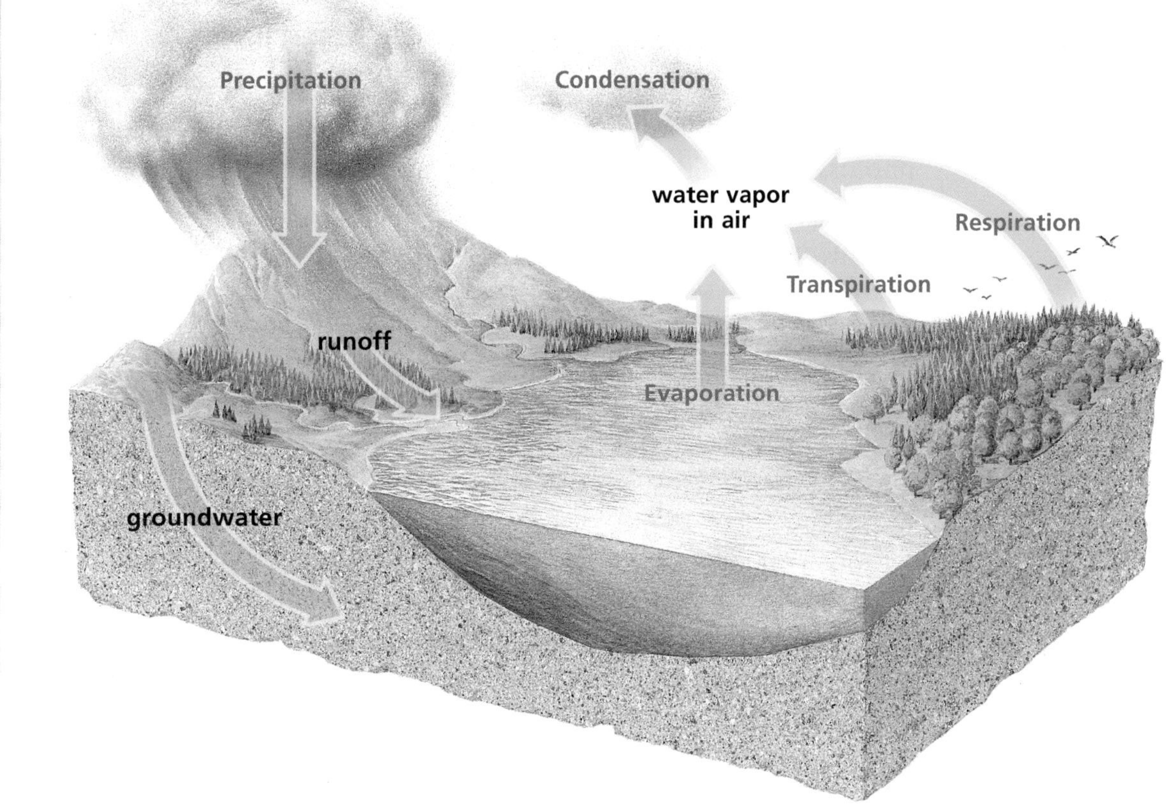


# Water cycles through ecosystems.

Water is stored on Earth's surface in lakes, rivers, and oceans. Water is found underground, filling the spaces between soil particles and cracks in rocks. Large amounts of water are stored in glaciers and polar ice sheets. Water is also part of the bodies of living things. But water is not just stored. It is also constantly moving. As you read in Chapter 1, the movement of water through the environment is called the water cycle.

**COMBINATION NOTES**
Make notes and draw a diagram to show how water cycles through ecosystems.

As water moves through an ecosystem, it changes in physical form. Water moves back and forth between gas, liquid, and solid forms. Water in the atmosphere is usually in the form of a gas—water vapor. Water that falls to Earth's surface is precipitation. For precipitation to occur, water vapor must cool and condense—it must change into a liquid or solid. This water can fall as rain, snow, sleet, mist, or hail.

**CHECK YOUR READING** What are the three physical forms of water in the water cycle?

Water returns to the atmosphere by changing back into vapor when heated. As you learned, this process is called evaporation. Living things also release water vapor. Animals release water vapor when they breathe. Plants release water vapor through a process called transpiration.

## Carbon cycles through ecosystems.

Carbon is an element found in all living things. Carbon moves through Earth's ecosystems in a cycle referred to as the **carbon cycle.** It is through carbon dioxide gas found in Earth's atmosphere that carbon enters the living parts of an ecosystem.

READING TIP

Note that photosynthesis is a process that brings carbon into living matter. Respiration is a process that releases carbon.

Plants use carbon dioxide to produce sugars in a process called photosynthesis. Sugars are carbon compounds that are important building blocks in food and all living matter. Food supplies the energy and materials living things need to live and grow. To release the energy in food, organisms break down the carbon compounds in a process called respiration. Carbon is released and cycled back into the atmosphere as carbon dioxide. When living things die and decay, the rest of the carbon that makes up living matter is released.

CHECK YOUR READING Name three ways that living things are part of the carbon cycle.

Earth's oceans contain far more carbon than the air does. In water ecosystems—lakes, rivers, and oceans—carbon dioxide is dissolved in water. Algae and certain types of bacteria are the photosynthetic organisms that produce food in these ecosystems. Marine organisms also release carbon dioxide during respiration. Carbon is deposited on the ocean floor when organisms die.

### Carbon Cycle

**Different processes combine to move carbon through the environment.**

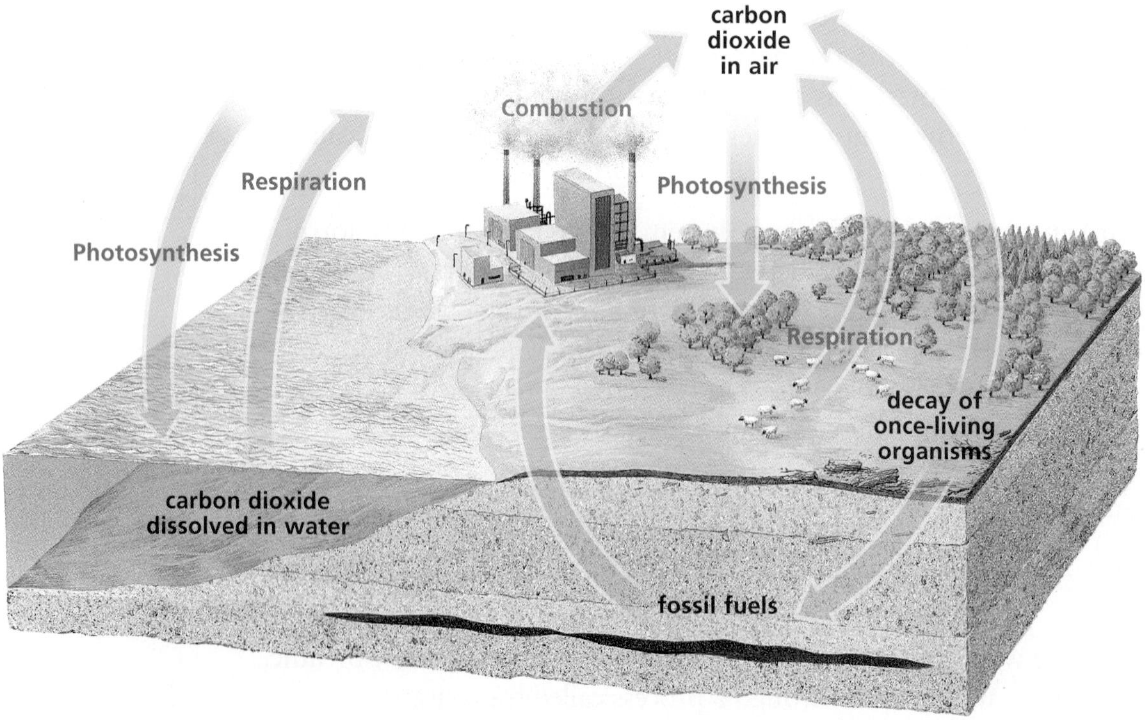

## INVESTIGATE Carbon

### *What is one form in which carbon is stored on the ocean floor?*

**PROCEDURE**

1. Use the mortar and pestle to crush the seashell into a powder.
2. Pour the powder into the beaker.
3. Add enough white vinegar to cover the powder.

**WHAT DO YOU THINK?**

- What happened when white vinegar was added to the crushed shell?
- What material was produced in the reaction? Where did it come from originally?

**CHALLENGE** What type of reaction did you observe?

**SKILL FOCUS**
Observing (6.5.b)

**MATERIALS**
- mortar and pestle
- whole seashell or pieces
- small beaker
- white vinegar

**TIME**
15 minutes

Large amounts of carbon are stored underground. The remains of plants and animals buried for millions of years decay slowly and change into fossil fuels, such as coal and oil. As humans burn fossil fuels to release energy, dust particles and gases containing carbon are released into the environment.

## Nitrogen cycles through ecosystems.

**VISUALIZATION**
CLASSZONE.COM
Watch the nitrogen cycle in action.

Nitrogen is another element that is important to life. Nitrogen cycles through Earth's ecosystems in the **nitrogen cycle.** Almost four-fifths of the air you breathe is clear, colorless nitrogen gas. But you cannot get the nitrogen you need to live from air. All animals must get nitrogen from plants.

Plants cannot use pure nitrogen gas either. Instead, plants can absorb certain compounds of nitrogen. Plants take in these nitrogen compounds through their roots, along with water and other nutrients. So how does the nitrogen from the atmosphere get into the soil? One source is lightning. Every lightning strike fixes pure nitrogen, or changes it into a form that plants can use. This form of nitrogen falls to the ground in rain.

## Nitrogen Cycle

**Different processes combine to move nitrogen through the environment.**

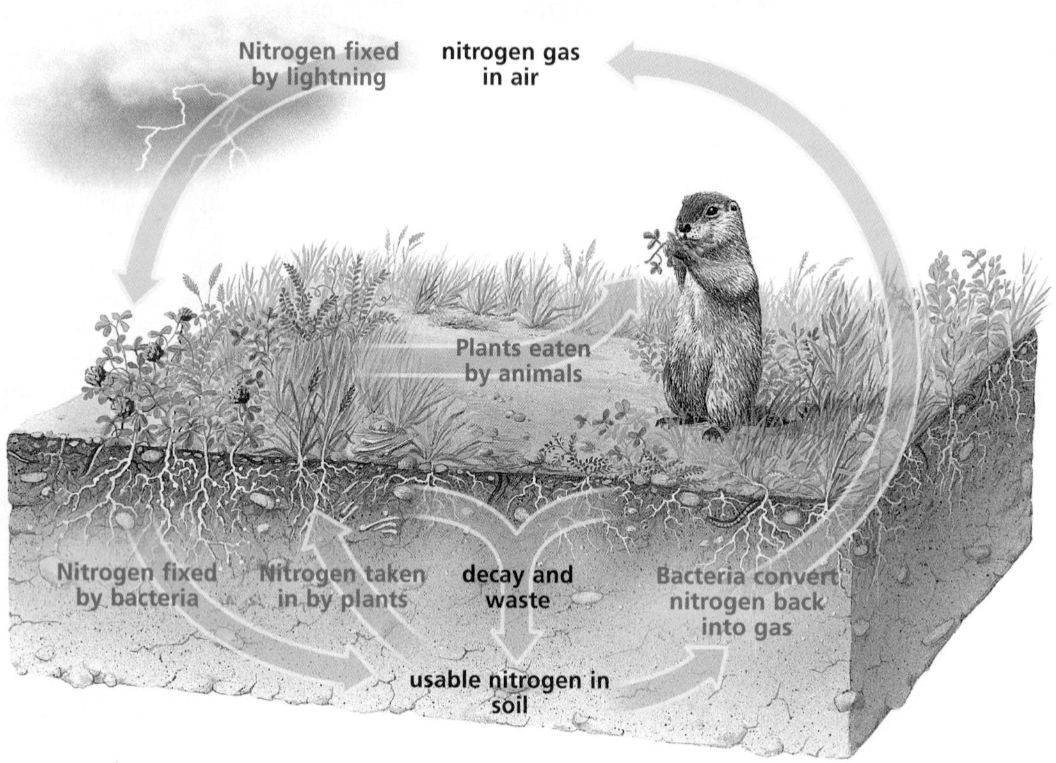


READING TIP

Bacteria are microscopic single-celled organisms.

A far greater source of nitrogen is nitrogen-fixing bacteria. These bacteria live in oceans as well as in soil. Some attach themselves to the roots of plants such as alfalfa and soybeans. When organisms die, decomposers in the ocean or soil break them down. Nitrogen in the soil or water is used again by living things. A small amount is returned to the atmosphere by bacteria that can break down nitrogen compounds into nitrogen gas.

# 11.2 Review

### KEY CONCEPTS

1. Draw a diagram of the water cycle. Show three ways in which water moves through the cycle. (6.5.b)
2. Summarize the main parts of the carbon cycle. (6.5.b)
3. Explain two ways that nitrogen gas in the atmosphere is changed into nitrogen compounds that plants can use. (6.5.b)

### CRITICAL THINKING

4. **Predict** When people burn fossil fuels, carbon dioxide gas is added to the atmosphere. How might increased carbon dioxide affect plant growth?
5. **Compare and Contrast** Review the nitrogen and carbon cycles. How are these two cycles similar and different?

### CHALLENGE

6. **Apply** Draw a cycle diagram that shows how water is used in your household. Include activities that use water, sources of water, and ways that water leaves your house.

MATH in SCIENCE

## SKILL: ADDING INTEGERS

# Temperature and the Water Cycle

**MATH TUTORIAL**
CLASSZONE.COM
Click on Math Tutorial for more help with adding integers.

**Math** 6.NS.2.3
**Science** 6.2.a, 6.3.c

This iceberg is made up of fresh water, which freezes at 0°C. The surrounding ocean is salt water, which doesn't freeze at 0°C.

Changes in temperature help water move through the environment. At freezing temperatures—below 32°F or 0°C for sea-level environments—water can begin to become solid ice. Ice starts to melt when the temperature rises above freezing, causing the water to become liquid again. Temperature change also causes water to become vapor, or gas, within the air.

### Example

Suppose you are waiting for winter to come so you can skate on a small pond near your house. The weather turns cold. One day the temperature is 5°C. The next day the air temperature drops by 8°C. What temperature is the air? If the air stays below 0°C, some of the water will begin to freeze.

**(1)** Write a verbal model:
5 degrees + an 8-degree drop = what temperature?

**(2)** Write an equation. Use negative and positive integers:
$5 + (-8) = ?$

**(3)** Solve the equation:
$5 - 8 = -3$

**ANSWER** −3°C.

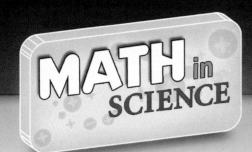

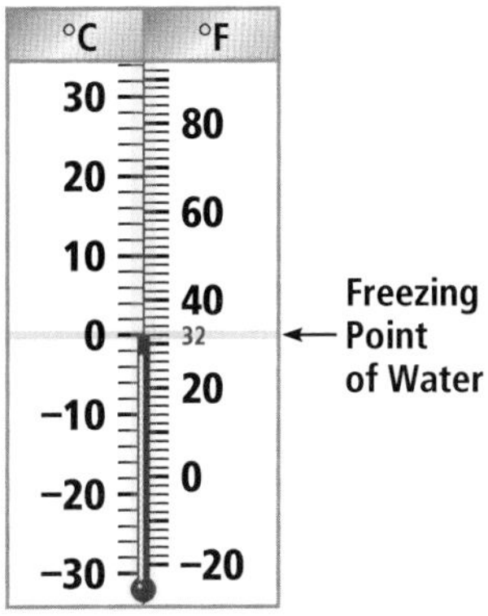


**Answer the following questions.**

1. A container of water is left out overnight, when the temperature is −18°C. In the morning, the air temperature rises by 8°C. What temperature is the air? What will happen to the water?

2. An ice block sits in a field where the air is 0°C. The air temperature rises by 16°C. Then it drops by 8°C. What temperature is the air in the field now? What will happen to the ice?

3. What happens to a block of ice after the temperature in the air follows this pattern: −6°C + 4°C + 3°C + 1°C + (−5°C)? What temperature has the air reached?

**CHALLENGE** Use a thermometer to measure the temperature of the air outside and indoors in degrees Celsius. Write two addition equations that show the temperature change between the two locations. One equation should show a rise, and one should show a drop.

KEY CONCEPT

# 11.3 Energy flows through ecosystems.

**CALIFORNIA Content Standards**

**6.5.a** Students know energy entering ecosystems as sunlight is transferred by producers into chemical energy through photosynthesis and then from organism to organism through food webs.

**6.5.b** Students know matter is transferred over time from one organism to others in the food web and between organisms and the physical environment.

**BEFORE, you learned**

- Matter cycles continuously through an ecosystem
- Living things are part of the water, carbon, and nitrogen cycles

**NOW, you will learn**

- How living things move energy through an ecosystem
- How feeding relationships are important in ecosystems
- How the amount of energy changes as it flows through an ecosystem

**VOCABULARY**

**producer** p. 391
**consumer** p. 392
**decomposer** p. 393
**food chain** p. 394
**food web** p. 394
**energy pyramid** p. 396

**EXPLORE Energy** (6.5.a)

## *How can you demonstrate energy?*

**PROCEDURE**

1. Fill the bowl halfway with sand and place it on the floor. Be sure the sand is level.
2. Place the pebble and rock near the edge of a table above the bowl of sand.
3. Gently push the pebble off the table into the sand. Record your observations.
4. Remove the pebble and make sure the sand is level. Gently push the rock off the table into the sand. Record your observations.

**MATERIALS**

- large plastic bowl
- sand
- pebble
- rock

**WHAT DO YOU THINK?**

- What happened to the sand when you dropped the pebble? when you dropped the rock?
- How can you explain any differences you observed?

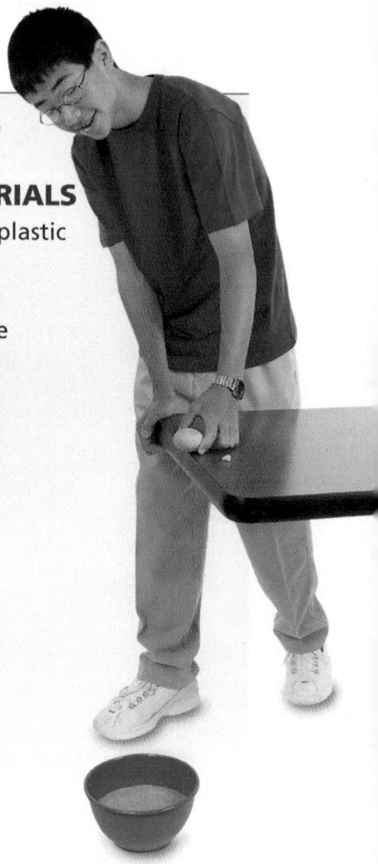

## Living things capture and release energy.

Everything you do—such as running, reading, and working—requires energy. The energy you use is chemical energy, which comes from the food you eat. When you run, you use up energy. As you sweat, some of that energy is released to the environment as heat. Eventually, you will need to replace the energy you've used.

Energy is important to all living things. Most of that energy comes directly or indirectly from sunlight. To use the energy, living things must first capture it and store it in a form they can use. Because energy is continuously used by the activities of living things, it must be continuously replaced in the ecosystem.

## Producers

**All of these producers capture energy from sunlight.**

### Plants

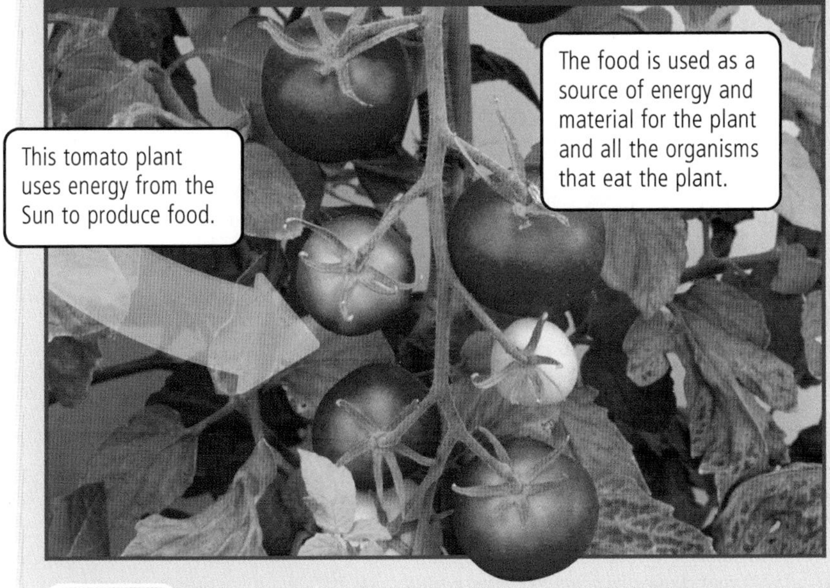

This tomato plant uses energy from the Sun to produce food.
The food is used as a source of energy and material for the plant and all the organisms that eat the plant.

READING VISUALS What process do all of these producers have in common?

### Seaweed

Seaweed is a producer found in Earth's oceans and coastal zones.

### Phytoplankton

The most numerous producers are tiny organisms that live in water called phytoplankton.

## Producers

A **producer** is an organism that takes in energy and stores it in food as chemical energy. The producers in an ecosystem make energy available to all the other living parts of the ecosystem. Most energy enters ecosystems through photosynthesis. Plants and other photosynthetic organisms take water and carbon dioxide from their environment and use energy from sunlight to produce sugars. The chemical energy stored in sugars can be released when sugars are broken down.

**VOCABULARY**
Remember to add a frame game diagram for *producers* to your notebook.

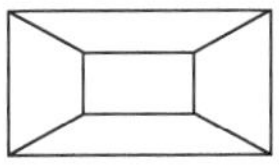

CHECK YOUR READING How does energy enter into the living parts of an ecosystem?

Plants are the most common producers found in land ecosystems. In water ecosystems, most food is produced by photosynthetic bacteria and algae. Examples of producers that use photosynthesis are shown in the photographs above.

**READING TIP**
Algae are photosynthetic, plantlike organisms that live in water.

Sunlight provides most of the energy that is stored in food. One exception is a type of bacteria that lives in the deep ocean, where there is no sunlight. These bacteria produce food using chemicals released from underwater vents. You read about deep-sea vents in Chapter 10.

## Consumers

**A consumer is an organism that gets energy by eating producers or other consumers.**

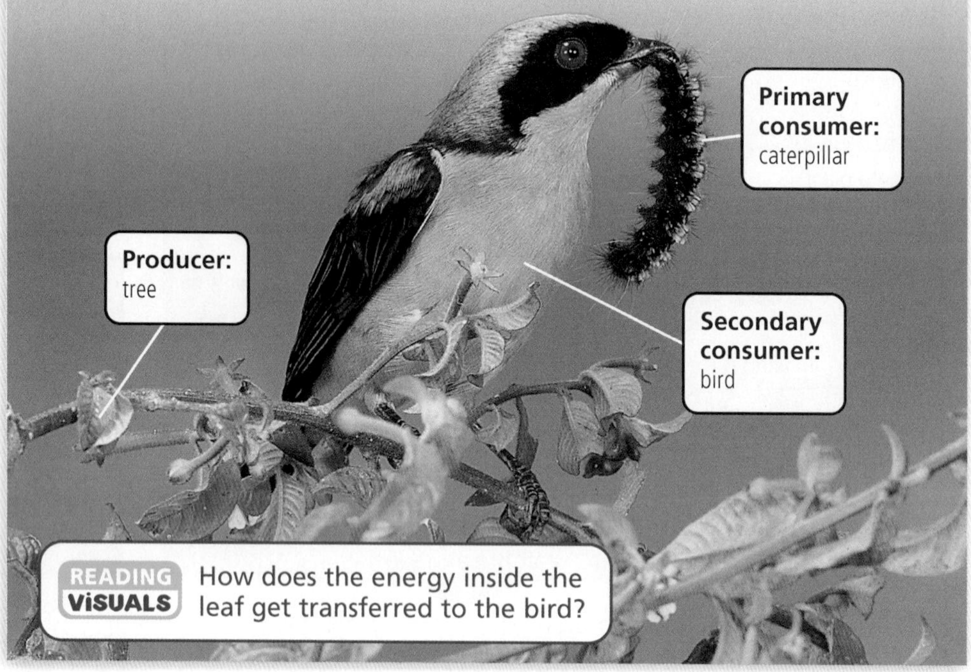


READING VISUALS How does the energy inside the leaf get transferred to the bird?

## Consumers

Organisms that cannot produce their own food must get their food from other sources. **Consumers** are organisms that get their energy by eating, or consuming, other organisms. To understand how energy flows through an ecosystem, you have to study feeding relationships. A feeding relationship starts with a producer, followed by one and often many more consumers.

CHECK YOUR READING Describe the producer-consumer relationship in terms of energy.

READING TIP

*Primary* means "first in order." *Secondary* means "second in order." *Tertiary* means "third in order."

Consumers are classified by their position in a feeding relationship. In a meadow ecosystem, animals such as antelopes and grasshoppers feed on grasses. They are primary consumers because they are the first link between the producers and the rest of the consumers in the ecosystem. The wolves that eat the antelopes are secondary consumers. So are the meadowlarks that eat the grasshoppers. The prairie falcon that eats the meadowlark is a tertiary consumer. Ecosystems also have special consumers called scavengers. A vulture is a scavenger because it feeds on dead animals.

In the photograph above, energy enters the ecosystem through the tree, which is the producer. The caterpillar that gets its energy by feeding on the tree's leaves is the primary consumer. The bird that gets its energy by feeding on the caterpillar is a secondary consumer.

## Decomposers

If you've hiked through a forest or walked through a park, you have seen the interaction of producers and consumers. Tall trees and leafy shrubs are home to many insects and the birds that eat them. Also important to an ecosystem are decomposers, a group of organisms that often go unseen. **Decomposers** are organisms that break down dead plant and animal matter into simpler compounds.

Fungi, such as these mushrooms, are decomposers.

You can think of decomposers as the cleanup crew of an ecosystem. In a forest, consumers such as deer and insects do not eat all of the leaves on trees and shrubs. Many leaves are left on the forest floor, along with dead roots and branches. These materials are eventually digested by fungi and bacteria living in the soil. Decomposers also break down animal remains, including waste materials. A pinch of soil may contain almost half a million fungi and millions of bacteria.

The energy within an ecosystem is used up as it flows from organism to organism. Decomposers are the organisms that release the last bit of energy from once-living matter. Decomposers also return matter to soil or water, where it may be used again and again.

**READING TIP**

Fungi are organisms that are similar to plants, but they have no leaves or flowers. The singular form of *fungi* is *fungus*.

# INVESTIGATE Decomposers

### *Where do decomposers come from?*

**SKILL FOCUS**
**Observing (6.5.b)**

**PROCEDURE**

1. Carefully use scissors to cut an opening across the middle of the bottle.
2. Place a handful of stones in the bottom of the bottle for drainage, and add enough soil to make a layer 10 cm deep.
3. Place some leaves and fruit slices on top of the soil.
4. Seal the cut you made with tape. Mark the date on the tape.
5. Add water through the top of the bottle to moisten the soil, and then put the cap on the bottle. Wash your hands.
6. Observe the fruit slices each day for two weeks. Record your observations. Keep the soil moist.

**WHAT DO YOU THINK?**

- What did you observe happening to the fruit slices?
- Where did the decomposers in your bottle come from?

**CHALLENGE** Predict what would happen if you used potting soil instead of soil from outdoors.

**MATERIALS**
- clear plastic bottle with cap
- scissors
- stones
- garden soil
- leaves
- slices of fruit
- masking tape
- marker
- water

**TIME**
30 minutes

# Models help explain feeding relationships.

**COMBINATION NOTES**
Remember to take notes and draw diagrams for *food chain* and *food web*.

You have learned how energy is captured by producers and moved through ecosystems by consumers and decomposers. Scientists use two different models to show the feeding relationships that transfer energy from organism to organism. These models are food chains and food webs.

## Food Chain

A chain is made of links that are connected one by one. Scientists use the idea of links in a chain to show simple feeding relationships. A **food chain** describes the feeding relationship between a producer and a single chain of consumers in an ecosystem.

The illustration in the white box on page 395 shows a wetland food chain. The first link in the chain is a cattail, a producer that captures energy from sunlight and stores it. The second link is a caterpillar, a primary consumer of the cattail. A frog is a secondary consumer that eats the caterpillar. The final link is a heron, a tertiary consumer that eats the frog. Energy is taken in and released at each link in the chain. The arrows represent the flow of energy from organism to organism. You can see that some of the energy captured by the cattail makes its way through a whole chain of other organisms in the ecosystem.

## Food Web

A **food web** is a model of the feeding relationships among many different consumers and producers in an ecosystem. A food web is like a spider web, with many overlapping and interconnected food chains. It is a better model for the complex feeding relationships in an ecosystem.

**READING TIP**
Notice that the food chain described above is also a part of the food web described here. Follow the blue arrows in the diagram on page 395.

The illustration on page 395 shows a wetland food web. You can see that the feeding relationships can go in several directions. For example, the food web shows that ducks eat bulrushes, which are producers. That makes ducks primary consumers. Ducks are also secondary consumers because they eat snails. A food web shows how one organism can play several roles in an ecosystem.

**CHECK YOUR READING** What is the difference between a food chain and a food web?

Both food chains and food webs show how different organisms receive their energy. They also show how different organisms depend on one another. If one organism is removed from the food web or food chain, it may affect many other organisms in the ecosystem.

## Energy Flows Through Ecosystems

**Energy is transferred from one organism to the next as organisms eat or are eaten.**

### A Wetland Food Chain

**Flow of Energy**
Energy flow starts at the bottom. Arrows represent energy moving from an organism that is eaten to the organism that eats it.

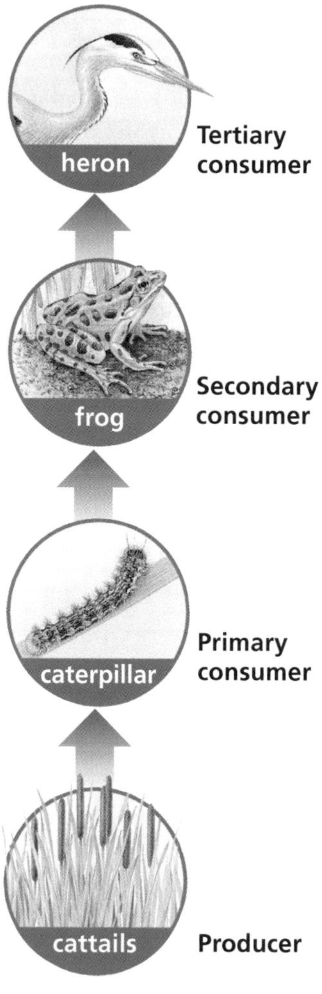


**Decomposers**
These tiny organisms recycle dead and decayed material.

### A Wetland Food Web

## Available energy decreases as it moves through an ecosystem.

Another way to picture the flow of energy in an ecosystem is to use an energy pyramid. An **energy pyramid** shows the amount of energy available at each feeding level of an ecosystem. The first level includes the producers, the second level the primary consumers, and so on. Because usable energy decreases as it moves from producers to consumers, the bottom level is the largest. The available energy gets smaller and smaller the farther up the pyramid you go.

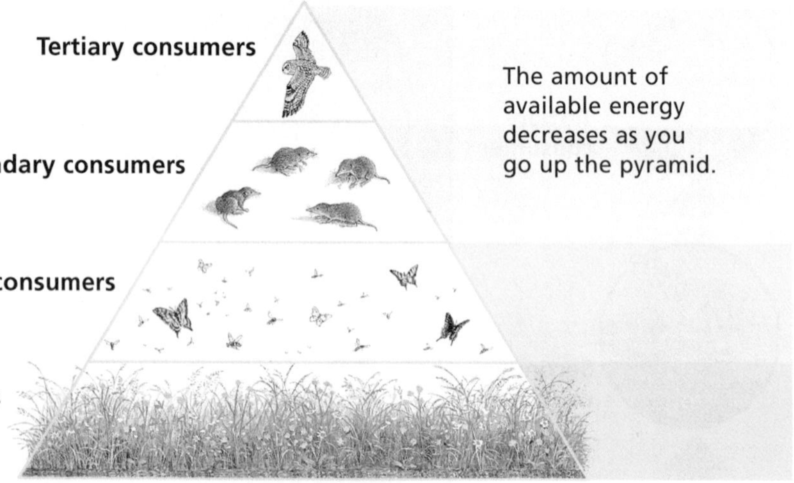


**READING TIP**

Refer to the diagram above as you read the text. The diagram takes the shape of a pyramid because available energy decreases at each level.

In the pyramid shown here, plants are the producers. They capture energy from sunlight, use some of it, then store the rest as food. The plants are eaten by insects, which also use some of the energy before being eaten by small mammals called shrews. The shrews use energy before being eaten by the owl. You can see that it takes a lot of sunlight to support the producers and consumers in a food web that feeds an owl.

# 11.3 Review

### KEY CONCEPTS

1. Describe the role of producers, consumers, and decomposers in an ecosystem. (6.5.b)
2. Explain why a food web provides a better model of an ecosystem than a food chain does. (6.5.a)
3. Explain how the amount of available energy changes as energy moves up a food chain. (6.5.a)

### CRITICAL THINKING

4. **Apply** Draw a food chain and a food web for an ecosystem near your home.
5. **Predict** Imagine that muskrats are removed from a wetland ecosystem. Predict what would happen to producers and secondary consumers.

### CHALLENGE

6. **Synthesize** Explain how the carbon cycle is related to a food web. Describe how energy and matter move through the food web and the carbon cycle.

CONNECTING SCIENCES

## LIFE SCIENCE AND PHYSICAL SCIENCE

# Biomagnification

> 6.5.b Students know matter is transferred over time from one organism to others in the food web and between organisms and the physical environment.

Matter moves through living things in an ecosystem. Some of it is used, and some of it is stored. Sometimes, a poisonous material enters a food chain and is stored. Biomagnification is the process by which matter becomes concentrated in living things.

## Moving up the Food Chain

DDT provides an example of the effects of biomagnification in an ecosystem. DDT is a chemical that was widely used to kill plant-eating insects. Some chemicals break down over time, but DDT does so very slowly. DDT collected in water and soil, was absorbed by living things, and moved up the food chain. The diagram shows how DDT became magnified in a wetland ecosystem.

1. DDT entered the food chain through tiny organisms called zooplankton, which absorbed DDT from the water. The concentration of DDT in zooplankton was about 800 times greater than in the environment.
2. Minnows fed on zooplankton. DDT was magnified 31 times, so the concentration of DDT in minnows was 24,800 times greater than in the environment: 800 x 31 = 24,800.
3. Trout ate minnows. DDT was magnified 1.7 times, so the concentration of DDT in trout was 42,160 times greater than in the environment.
4. Gulls ate trout. DDT was magnified 4.8 times, so the concentration of DDT in gulls was over 200,000 times greater than in the environment.

DDT is especially harmful to large birds, such as osprey and eagles. The chemical made the shells of the eggs of these large birds so thin that the eggs did not survive long enough to hatch.

### Moving up the Food Chain

This diagram shows how DDT moved up a food chain in Long Island Sound. The color in each circle below represents a certain level of DDT.

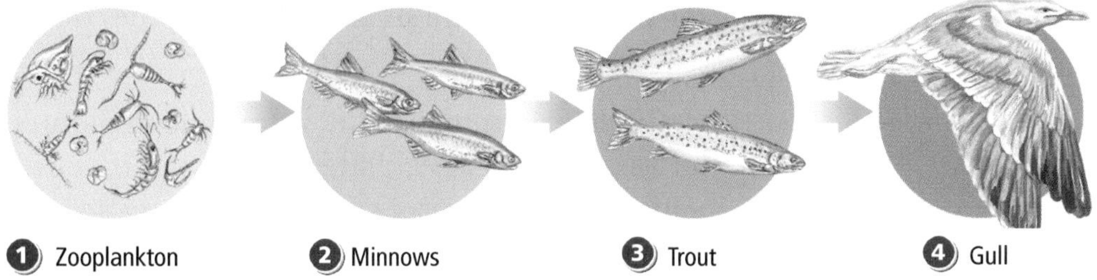


**CHALLENGE** Even though DDT was effective, some insects were not harmed by DDT. Predict what might happen to the numbers of those insects as a result of DDT use.

KEY CONCEPT

# 11.4 Biomes contain many ecosystems.

**CALIFORNIA Content Standard**

6.5.d Students know different kinds of organisms may play similar ecological roles in similar biomes.

**BEFORE, you learned**

- Feeding relationships describe how energy flows through ecosystems
- The amount of available energy decreases as it flows through ecosystems

**NOW, you will learn**

- How biomes vary by region and by the plant life they support
- How different ecosystems make up a biome
- About the different land and water biomes on Earth

**VOCABULARY**

**biome** p. 398
**coniferous** p. 400
**deciduous** p. 401
**estuary** p. 404

**THINK ABOUT**

***What do this plant's characteristics suggest about its environment?***

A plant's overall shape and form help it survive in its environment. Look closely at the plant in the photograph. Describe its shape. Does it have leaves? a stem? flowers? Look at the surrounding area. What do your observations suggest about the environment in general?

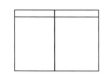

## Regions of Earth are classified into biomes.

COMBINATION NOTES
Remember to take notes and draw a diagram for each of the six land biomes described in the text.

If you could travel on land a long distance, either north or south of the equator, you'd probably notice an interesting pattern. You would move from deserts to grasslands to forests. Across Earth, there are large geographic regions that have similar climates and similar types of plants and animals. Each of these regions is called a **biome** (BY-OHM). There are six major land biomes on Earth, as shown on the map on page 399.

Climate is an important factor in land biomes. Climate describes the long-term weather patterns of a region, such as average yearly rainfall and temperature ranges. Climate also affects soil type. You know that available water, temperature, and soil are important abiotic factors in ecosystems. The abiotic factors of a particular biome are similar, which is why the ecosystems found in that biome are similar. Biomes represent very large areas, so there are many ecosystems within a biome.

## Land Biomes

**Each land biome is characterized by a particular climate, the quality of the soil, and the plant life found there.**

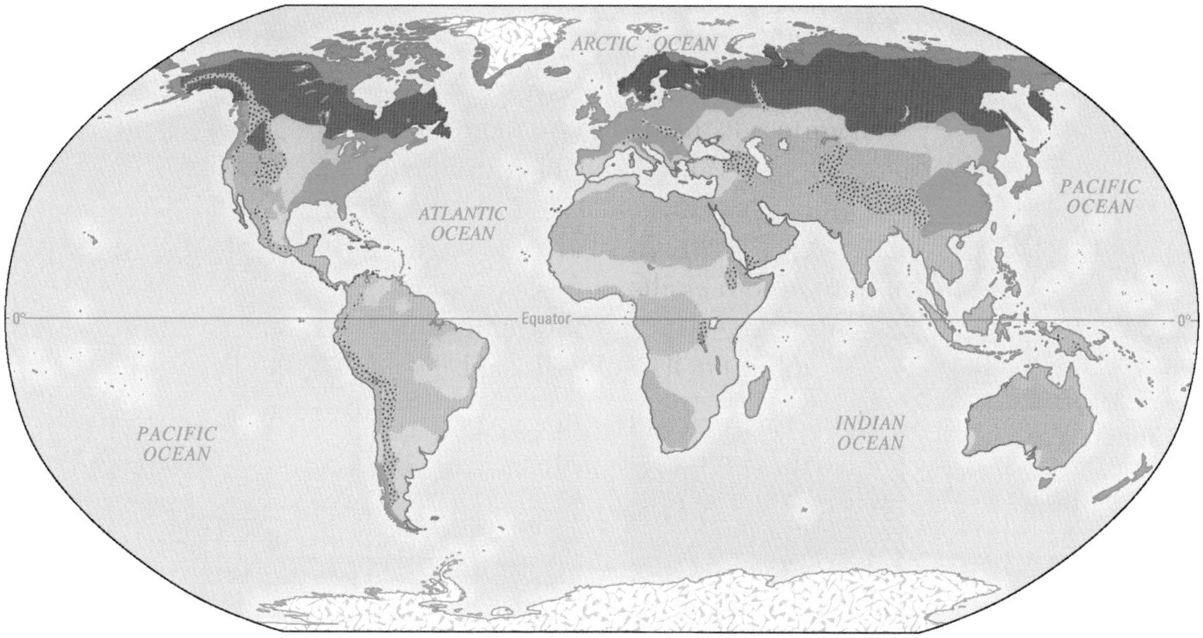


**Biomes**

- Tundra
- Taiga
- Desert
- Grassland
- Temperate Forest
- Tropical Forest

**Other zones**

- Mountain Zones
- Polar Ice

## Taiga and Tundra

If you go to the most northern regions of Earth, you will find two biomes, tundra and taiga. Both are characterized by long, cold winters and short, cool summers. In the Arctic tundra, temperatures can be as low as –45°C, with a high of about 16°C.

Tundra doesn't get much precipitation—less than 25 centimeters each year. Yet the area is wet because cold temperatures keep the water from evaporating. One of the important characteristics of tundra is permafrost, a deep layer of permanently frozen soil that lies just below the surface soil. Permafrost prevents trees from taking root in tundra regions. Tundra plants are small and include mosses, grasses, and woody shrubs. Organisms called lichens also do well in tundra.

The producers of tundra ecosystems support rodents, caribou, and musk oxen. Grizzly bears, Arctic foxes, and snowy owls are predators found there. Migrating birds come to nest in tundra, feeding on insects that mature in summer.

snowy owl

**Tundra** Only small plants and lichens grow in tundra regions, because the soil below the surface is frozen.

**Taiga** Evergreen trees grow in taiga regions, where the ground is cold but not frozen.

Even though the temperatures of taiga (TY-guh) regions are similar to those of tundra regions, taiga has more precipitation—40 to 100 centimeters a year. As a result, there is more snow on the ground. This insulates the soil below, keeping it from freezing permanently.

In taiga ecosystems, you will find evergreen trees called **coniferous** (koh-NIHF-uhr-uhs) trees. These trees have needlelike leaves that produce food all year long. This is an advantage in taiga ecosystems. Decomposers work slowly in the cold, so the soil is low in nutrients. Insects eat the wood and leaves of these trees, and birds and squirrels eat their seeds. Taiga ecosystems support deer, elk, snowshoe hares, and beavers. Predators include lynx, owls, bears, and wolves.

## Desert and Grassland

collared lizard

Deserts and grasslands are biomes found near or in the middle latitudes. You can see from the map on page 399 that a desert biome often leads into a grassland biome. Deserts and some grasslands do not get enough precipitation to support trees.

Some deserts are cold and some deserts are hot, but all deserts have dry soil. Less than 25 centimeters of rain falls each year in a desert. Desert plants and animals can get by on very little water. Small burrowing animals, such as kangaroo rats and ground squirrels, are part of desert ecosystems. Desert predators include snakes, owls, and foxes.

Grassland ecosystems develop in areas of moderate rainfall, generally from 50 to 90 centimeters each year. There is enough rain to support grasses, but too little rain to support forests. Regular wildfires and droughts keep smaller shrubs and tree seedlings from growing. Summers in grassland ecosystems can be hot—more than 30°C—but winters are cold.

Grasses do well in large open areas. The more rain a grassland ecosystem gets, the higher the grasses grow. These ecosystems support seed-eating rodents that make their burrows in the grassland soil. There are also large grazing animals, such as bison, wild horses, gazelles, and zebras. Predators include wolves, tigers, and lions.

**Desert** Desert plants are adapted to survive in dry soil. Many must also survive high daytime temperatures.

**Grassland** Grasslands receive enough rain to support grasses. Wildfires keep shrubs and trees from growing.

## Temperate Forest and Tropical Forest

Trees need more water than smaller plants, shrubs, and grasses. Therefore, forest biomes are usually located in regions where more water is available. The taiga is a forest biome. There, coniferous trees survive on smaller amounts of precipitation because the cold weather limits evaporation. Across the middle latitudes, temperate forests grow where winters are moderate and 75 to 150 centimeters of precipitation fall each year. Near the equator, there are no winters. There, tropical forests grow where more than 200 centimeters of rain fall each year.

Most temperate forests are made up of deciduous trees, sometimes referred to as broadleaf trees. **Deciduous** (dih-SIHJ-oo-uhs) trees drop their leaves as winter approaches and then grow new leaves in the spring.

**Temperate Forest**
Temperate forests contain many trees with leaves that change color and fall as winter approaches.

**Tropical Forest**
Tropical forests are warm enough that trees stay green all year long.

The most common broadleaf trees in North American deciduous forests are oak, birch, beech, and maple. Temperate forests support a wide variety of animals. Animals such as mice, chipmunks, squirrels, raccoons, and deer live off seeds, fruit, and insects. Predators include wolves, bobcats, foxes, and mountain lions.

**CALIFORNIA Focus**

California is home to some of the world's oldest and tallest trees, the giant sequoias. They thrive along the western Sierra Nevada range. Although these trees were once logged for many uses, they are now protected. Trees over 3000 years old can be found in Sequoia and Kings Canyon National Parks in central California.

Most temperate forests in North America are deciduous. However, the wet winters and drier summers in the Pacific Northwest support forests made up mostly of coniferous trees. These include redwood, spruce, and fir trees. These forests are also called temperate rain forests. The largest trees in the United States are found in these temperate rain forests.

Tropical forests are located near the equator where the weather is warm all year—around 25°C. The tropical forest is the wettest land biome, with a rainfall of 200 to 400 centimeters each year. Therefore, it is also called the tropical rain forest. Most trees have leaves year round. This is an advantage because the soil has few nutrients. High temperatures cause materials to break down quickly, but there are so many plants the nutrients are used up quickly.

More types of animals, plants, and other organisms live in tropical rain forests than anywhere else on Earth. The trees grow close together and support many tree-dwelling animals, such as monkeys, birds, insects, and snakes. Some plants, such as orchids and vines, grow in the tops of the trees.

**CHECK YOUR READING** How does the variety of plants in a biome affect the variety of animals in that biome?

## INVESTIGATE Climate

### How can you graph climate data for your area?

**PROCEDURE**

1. Find data about the average monthly precipitation and average monthly temperature for a 12-month period in your area.
2. On graph paper, mark off 12 months along the *x*-axis. Make a *y*-axis for each side of the graph. Label one "Temperature (°C)" and the other "Precipitation (mm)."
3. Make a bar graph that shows the average precipitation for each month.
4. Use a different color to make another bar graph that shows the average temperature for each month.

**WHAT DO YOU THINK?**

- How much precipitation did your area receive overall?
- What was the temperature range for the area?

**CHALLENGE** Find data for the same location from a different year. Graph the data. Compare your graphs. How different are the data for the two years? How might changes in climate affect the plant and animal life in your area?

**SKILL FOCUS**
Graphing data
(6.5.e)

**MATERIALS**
- graph paper
- 2 colored pencils

**TIME**
20 minutes

## Water covers most of Earth's surface.

Almost three-fourths of Earth's surface is covered by water. Water biomes are also called aquatic biomes. They can be divided into two broad categories: freshwater biomes and salt-water biomes. Plants have a role as producers in water biomes that are closely surrounded by land—in ponds and streams and wetlands, and in coastal areas. The food webs of deep-water ecosystems depend on tiny photosynthetic microorganisms called phytoplankton.

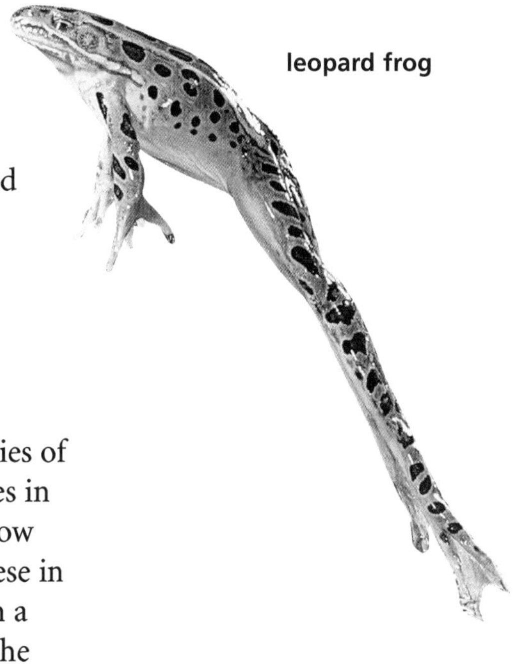
leopard frog

### Freshwater Biomes

The ecosystems of freshwater biomes are affected by the qualities of the landscape in which they are found. For example, differences in elevation affect how water flows in streams and rivers. In shallow rivers, algae and plants provide food for insects and snails. These in turn are eaten by fish, salamanders, turtles, and frogs. Plants in a freshwater biome may take root in the soil under the water if the water is not too deep or moving too fast. Phytoplankton are not part of river ecosystems because of the flowing water.

## Aquatic Biomes

**Freshwater biomes** include the still water of lakes, the running water of rivers, and estuaries where fresh water and salt water mix.

Ponds and lakes have still water. Ponds are shallow and support many plants as producers. Organisms in deeper lakes depend much more on phytoplankton for food. Ponds and lakes support many different insects, shellfish, snakes, fish, and the land animals that eat them.

**CHECK YOUR READING** Name two types of freshwater biomes.

Estuaries are water ecosystems that mark a transition between freshwater and saltwater biomes. An **estuary** is a shoreline area where fresh water from a river mixes with salt water from the ocean. Estuaries are sometimes referred to as the nurseries of the sea because so many marine animals travel into the calm waters to reproduce. Seaweed, marsh grasses, shellfish, and birds all thrive in estuaries.

### Marine Biomes

Marine biomes are saltwater biomes. The three main types of marine biomes are the coastal ocean, the surface zone of the open ocean, and the deep ocean. Beaches are part of the coastal ocean biome. Tidal pools form along the coast as the tide comes in and goes out and the conditions constantly change. Organisms such as crabs and clams thrive in the ever-changing conditions in coastal areas.

The open ocean has two main parts—the surface zone and the deep zone. The surface zone is, on average, about 100 meters deep.

RESOURCE CENTER
CLASSZONE.COM
Find out more about land and aquatic biomes.

**Coastal Ocean**

**Marine biomes** include rocky and sandy shores as well as the surface zone of the open ocean and the deep waters below, where no light can reach.

**Open Ocean**

**Deep Ocean**

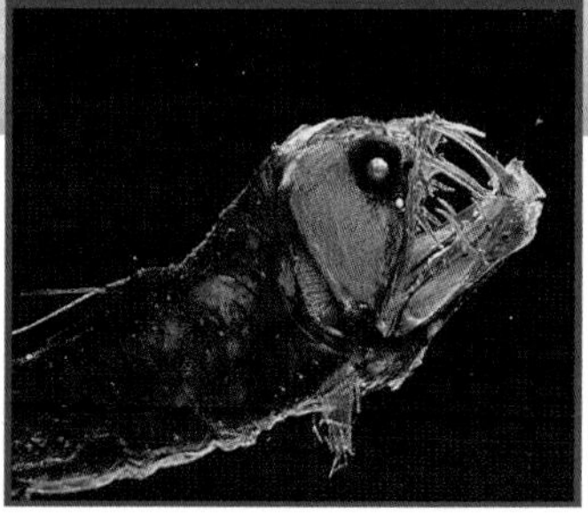

Phytoplankton use the sunlight to make food. They are the main producers in the ocean food web. Many types of fish, other marine animals, and floating seaweed live in the upper ocean.

The dark and cold deep zone of the open ocean lies under the surface zone. Because sunlight does not reach the deep zone, no phytoplankton can live there. Therefore, deep-sea animals must either eat other animals or eat food that drifts down from the surface zone.

# 11.4 Review

## KEY CONCEPTS

1. In biomes located on land, abiotic factors are used to classify the different biome types. What are these abiotic factors? (6.5.d)
2. Name a type of plant found in each of the six land biomes. (6.5.d)
3. Name six different aquatic biomes. (6.5.d)

## CRITICAL THINKING

4. **Predict** If an ecosystem in the grassland biome started to receive less and less rainfall every year, what new biome would be established?
5. **Infer** Name some abiotic factors that affect aquatic biomes and ecosystems.

## CHALLENGE

6. **Apply** Use the map on page 399 to list the following four biomes in the order you would find them moving from the equator to the poles.
   - desert
   - taiga
   - tropical forest
   - tundra

# Chapter Review

## the BIG idea

**Matter and energy together support life within an environment.**

CONTENT REVIEW
CLASSZONE.COM

## KEY CONCEPTS SUMMARY

### 1 Ecosystems support life.

Ecosystems are made up of living things (biotic) and nonliving things (abiotic).

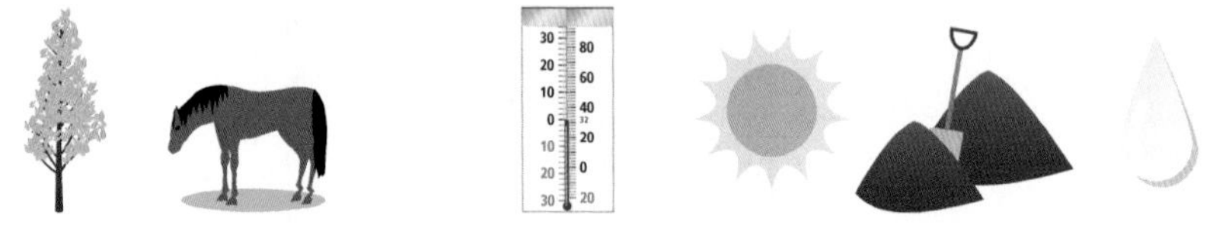

plants animals temperature Sun soil water

**Biotic Factors** **Abiotic Factors**

**VOCABULARY**
**ecology** p. 377
**ecosystem** p. 377
**biotic factor** p. 378
**abiotic factor** p. 378

### 2 Matter cycles through ecosystems.

Water, carbon, and nitrogen are materials that are necessary for life. They move through ecosystems in continuous cycles.

**VOCABULARY**
**cycle** p. 384
**carbon cycle** p. 386
**nitrogen cycle** p. 387

### 3 Energy flows through ecosystems.

Producers are the basis of feeding relationships in ecosystems.

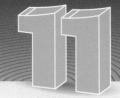

**Producer** **Primary consumer** **Secondary consumer**

Food chains and food webs help show how energy moves through living things.

**VOCABULARY**
**producer** p. 391
**consumer** p. 392
**decomposer** p. 393
**food chain** p. 394
**food web** p. 394
**energy pyramid** p. 396

### 4 Biomes contain many ecosystems.

Ecosystems of land biomes
- are affected by climate
- are affected by conditions of the soil
- are characterized by types of plants

Ecosystems of water biomes
- can be freshwater or saltwater
- are affected by landscape if freshwater
- are affected by ocean depth

**VOCABULARY**
**biome** p. 398
**coniferous** p. 400
**deciduous** p. 401
**estuary** p. 404

## Reviewing Vocabulary

*Write a statement describing how the terms in each pair are similar and different.*

1. biotic, abiotic
2. producer, consumer
3. food chain, food web

*The table shows the meanings of word roots that are used in many science terms.*

| Root | Meaning |
|---|---|
| bio- | life |
| oikos (eco) | house |
| -logy | study of |

*Use the information in the table to write definitions for the following terms.*

4. ecology
5. biome
6. ecosystem

## Reviewing Key Concepts

**Multiple Choice** *Choose the letter of the best answer.*

7. Which best describes the parts of an ecosystem? (6.5.e)
   - **a.** light, water, soil, and temperature
   - **b.** plants and animals
   - **c.** biotic factors and abiotic factors
   - **d.** producers, consumers, and decomposers

8. What is the main source of energy for most ecosystems? (6.5.a)
   - **a.** water
   - **b.** nitrogen
   - **c.** soil
   - **d.** sunlight

9. What is the process by which the water in rivers, lakes, and oceans becomes a gas and moves into the atmosphere? (6.5.b)
   - **a.** precipitation
   - **b.** evaporation
   - **c.** condensation
   - **d.** transpiration

10. The process called nitrogen fixation is essential for life on Earth. Which of the following is an example of nitrogen fixation? (6.5.b)
    - **a.** Plants take in nitrogen gas from the atmosphere.
    - **b.** Animals take in nitrogen gas from the atmosphere.
    - **c.** Water absorbs nitrogen.
    - **d.** Bacteria convert nitrogen gas into a form that plants can use.

11. Which organism is a decomposer? (6.5.d)
    - **a.** vulture
    - **b.** sunflower
    - **c.** musk ox
    - **d.** fungus

12. How are decomposers important in an ecosystem? (6.5.d)
    - **a.** They make atmospheric nitrogen available to plants in a usable form.
    - **b.** They convert organic matter into more complex compounds.
    - **c.** They are an important source of food for scavengers.
    - **d.** They break down organic matter into simpler compounds.

13. What factor is least important in determining the plant life in a biome? (6.5.e)
    - **a.** average annual rainfall
    - **b.** average annual temperature
    - **c.** the type of soil
    - **d.** the type of animals living there

**Short Answer** *Write a short answer to each question.*

14. Write a paragraph to describe how carbon dioxide gas in the atmosphere can become part of the carbon compounds found inside animals. (6.5.b)
15. Write a paragraph to explain how the amount of available energy changes as you move from producers to consumers in a food web. (6.5.a)
16. Write a paragraph to describe one important way in which the flow of energy through ecosystems is different from the cycling of matter. (6.5.a)

## Thinking Critically

*Use the diagram to answer the next four questions.*

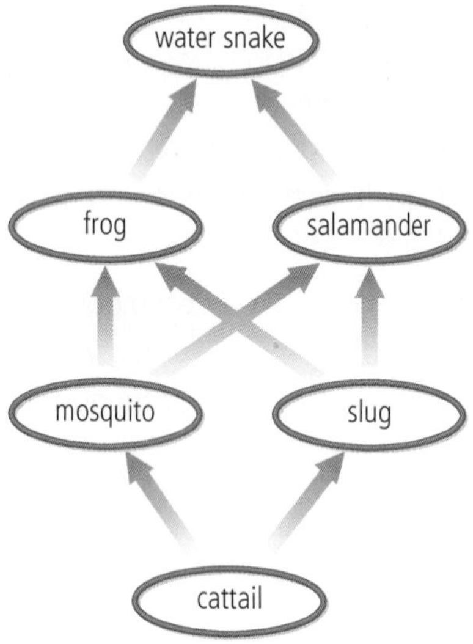


17. **CONNECT** What does the diagram above represent and how does it relate to energy in an ecosystem? (6.5.a)

18. **CLASSIFY** Identify each of the animals in the diagram above as a producer, primary consumer, secondary consumer, or tertiary consumer. (6.5.d)

19. **APPLY** An animal that is found in many wetland ecosystems is the shrew. The shrew eats salamanders and slugs and is eaten by water snakes. Copy the diagram above and show how you would add the shrew to the diagram. (6.5.d)

20. **CONNECT** Use the diagram above to make an energy pyramid. If only one-tenth of the energy available at each level is passed on to the next higher level, how much of the energy in a cattail is transferred to a salamander? (6.5.a)

21. **SYNTHESIZE** Why would it be difficult to show a decomposer as part of an energy pyramid? (6.5.d)

22. **RANK** Arrange the following list of biomes according to the relative amounts of precipitation in each, going from the least amount to the most: grassland, desert, deciduous forest, taiga, tropical rain forest. (6.5.e)

23. **SYNTHESIZE** Why are plants but not animals considered important factors in classifying a land biome? (6.5.d)

24. **SUMMARIZE** Draw a diagram that illustrates aquatic biomes. On your diagram label the following: freshwater river, freshwater lake, estuary, coastal zone, open ocean zone. How do abiotic factors differ among these biomes? (6.5.e)

25. **COMPARE AND CONTRAST** In what ways is your home like an ecosystem? In what ways is it different? (6.5.e)

26. **APPLY** Describe a change in an abiotic factor that affected living factors in an ecosystem near you. (6.5.e)

## the BIG idea

27. **CLASSIFY** Look again at the photograph on pages 374–375. Now that you have finished the chapter, how would you change or add details to your answer to the question on the photograph? (6.5.e)

28. **SYNTHESIZE** Write one or more paragraphs describing how matter and energy together support life in an ecosystem. You may use examples from one specific ecosystem if you wish. In your description, use each of the following terms. Underline each term in your answer. (6.5.b)

| | |
|---|---|
| ecosystem | decomposer |
| food web | nitrogen cycle |
| producer | carbon cycle |
| primary consumer | secondary consumer |

## UNIT PROJECTS

If you are doing a unit project, make a folder for your project. Include in your folder a list of the resources you will need, the date on which the project is due, and a schedule to track your progress. Begin gathering data.

For more practice, go to . . .
TEST PRACTICE
CLASSZONE.COM

## Interpreting Graphs

6.5.b, 6.5.d, 6.5.e

*Choose the letter of the best response.*

The graphs below show average monthly temperature and precipitation for one year in Staunton, Virginia, an area located in a temperate deciduous forest biome.

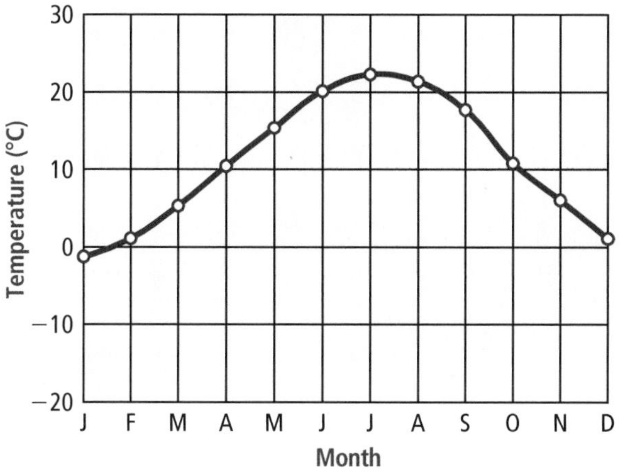


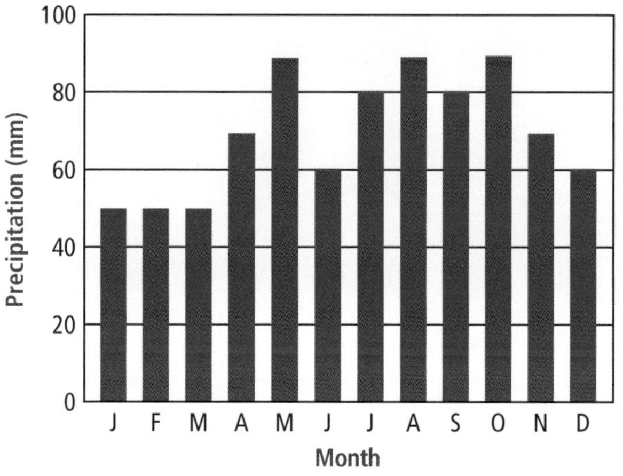


SOURCE: NASA

**1.** What was the average temperature during July?
- **a.** 20°
- **b.** 10°
- **c.** 23°
- **d.** 0°

**2.** Which months had the most precipitation?
- **a.** January, February, March
- **b.** May, August, October
- **c.** July, August, September
- **d.** December, January, February

**3.** What were conditions during May?
- **a.** warm and moist
- **b.** warm and dry
- **c.** cool and moist
- **d.** cool and dry

**4.** Which temperature is closest to the average temperature for the year shown?
- **a.** about 16°
- **b.** about 0°
- **c.** about 20°
- **d.** about 10°

**5.** How much precipitation would you estimate fell as snow in the year shown?
- **a.** less than 10 mm
- **b.** between 50 and 100 mm
- **c.** between 200 and 300 mm
- **d.** more than 400 mm

## Extended Response

**6.** Much of the United States is part of a temperate deciduous forest biome. The deciduous forest biome has seasonal changes. Trees in this biome lose their leaves yearly. Use this information, as well as the information in the graphs, to describe the seasons in the temperate deciduous forest biome.

**7.** Write a paragraph in which you describe a typical ecosystem in your city or town. In your answer include biotic factors such as plants, animals, and other organisms. Also include abiotic factors such as light, temperature, soil, and water. Finish your description by saying how you and other humans affect the ecosystem.

# CHAPTER 12

# Interactions Within Ecosystems

## the BIG idea

**Living things within an ecosystem interact with each other and the environment.**

## Key Concepts

SECTION 1
**Groups of living things interact within ecosystems.**
Learn about how different organisms share living areas, interact in larger communities, and show different patterns within those communities.

SECTION 2
**Organisms can interact in different ways.**
Learn about the different types of interactions in an ecosystem, including competition, cooperation, and symbiosis.

SECTION 3
**Ecosystems are always changing.**
Learn about the limits and boundaries of organisms within an ecosystem and how ecosystems may change over time.

**California ClassZone**

CLASSZONE.COM
Chapter 12 online resources: Content Review, two Resource Centers, Math Tutorial, Test Practice

*How do living things interact?*

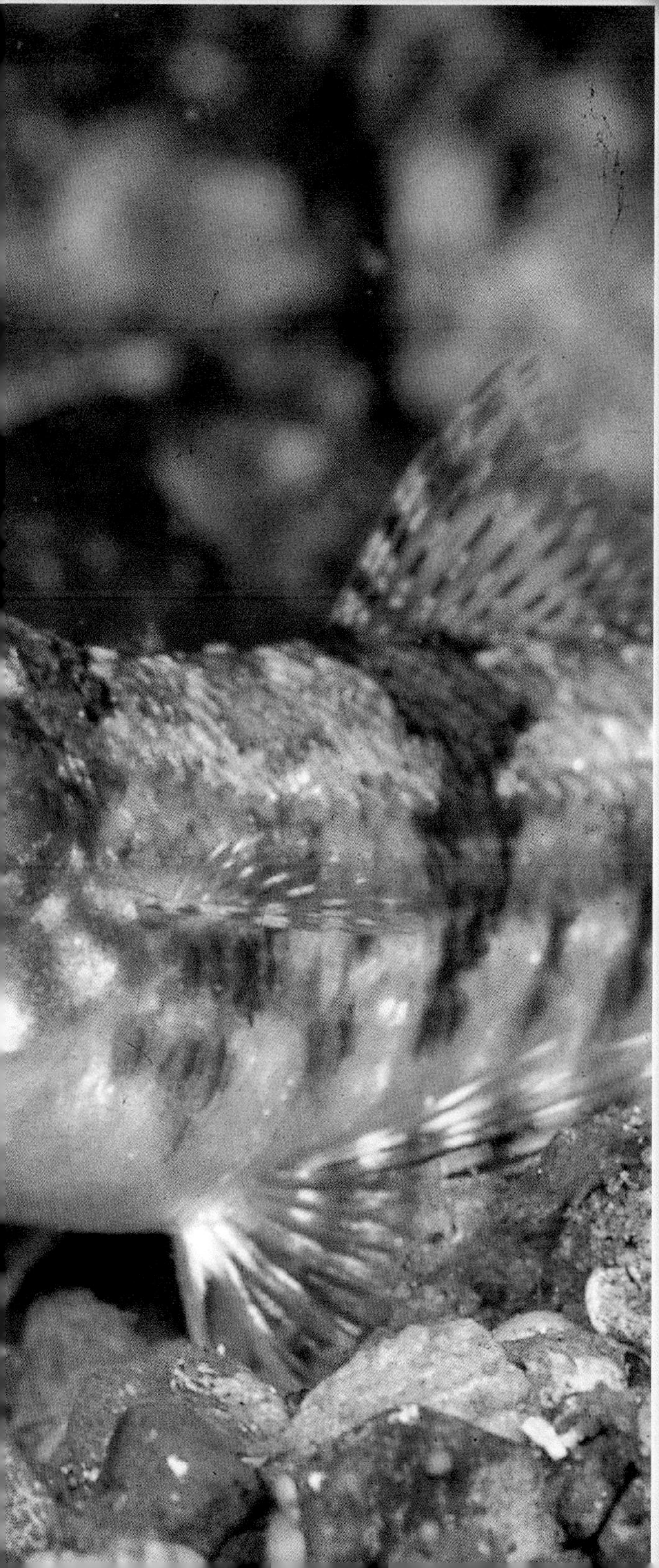

# EXPLORE the BIG idea

## How Do Living Things Interact Where You Live?

6.5.a Students know energy entering ecosystems as sunlight is transferred by producers into chemical energy through photosynthesis and then from organism to organism through food webs.

Take your notebook outside. Observe how different living things interact. Record your observations.

**Observe and Think** Do the interactions you see benefit all the living things involved? Do they involve just animals or plants and animals?

## How Many Roles Can a Living Thing Have in an Ecosystem?

6.5.c Students know populations of organisms can be categorized by the functions they serve in an ecosystem.

While you are outdoors, observe an organism and think about how it fits into the ecosystem.

**Observe and Think** In what way does the organism fit into feeding relationships in the ecosystem? What are some other roles the organism plays?

NSTA scilinks.org SCILINKS
Populations and Communities **Code: MDL002**

CHAPTER 12

# Getting Ready to Learn

## CONCEPT REVIEW

- Ecosystems support life.
- Different ecosystems make up a biome.

## VOCABULARY REVIEW

**producer** p. 391

**consumer** p. 392

**food chain** p. 394

**food web** p. 394

*See Glossary.* **interaction, lichen**

**CONTENT REVIEW**
CLASSZONE.COM

Review concepts and vocabulary.

## TAKING NOTES

### OUTLINE

As you read, copy the headings on your paper in the form of an outline. Then add notes in your own words that summarize what you read.

### VOCABULARY STRATEGY

Write each new vocabulary term in the center of a **four square** diagram. Write notes in the squares around each term. Include a definition, some characteristics, and some examples of the term. If possible, write some things that are not examples of the terms.

See the Note-Taking Handbook on pages R45–R51.

**SCIENCE NOTEBOOK**

I. Groups of living things interact within ecosystems.
   A. Organisms occupy specific living areas.
      1. populations: same species in one area
      2. habitat and niche: place where organisms live; role of organisms
      3. community: several populations living together

| Definition | Characteristics |
|---|---|
| where something lives | supplies shelter and food |
| **Examples** | **Nonexamples** |
| a tree is a habitat for a bird | |

HABITAT

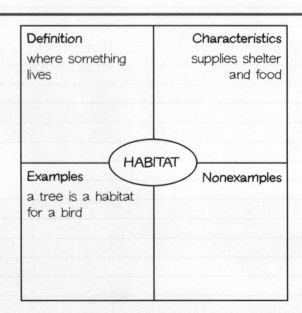

KEY CONCEPT

# 12.1 Groups of living things interact within ecosystems.

**CALIFORNIA Content Standard**

6.5.c Students know populations of organisms can be categorized by the functions they serve in an ecosystem.

**BEFORE, you learned**

- Abiotic and biotic factors interact in an ecosystem
- Matter and energy necessary for life move through ecosystems

**NOW, you will learn**

- How groups of organisms interact in an ecosystem
- About levels of organization in an ecosystem
- About living patterns of different groups of organisms

**VOCABULARY**

**species** p. 413
**population** p. 414
**habitat** p. 414
**niche** p. 415
**community** p. 416

**THINK ABOUT**

***How do California sea lions get the resources they need?***

California sea lions are ocean mammals. Their name comes in part from the loud, roaring noises they make. California sea lions live in large groups along the coasts of California, the Galápagos Islands, and Japan. They are skillful underwater swimmers, and they hunt in the ocean for food. In what ways do California sea lions depend on their environment for survival?

## Organisms occupy specific living areas.

On a walk through the woods, you may see many different plants and animals. These organisms, like all living things, depend on their environment to meet their needs. The particular types of living things you see will depend on the characteristics of the area you are visiting.

Scientists group living things according to their shared characteristics. The smallest grouping is the species. Scientists consider organisms to be members of the same **species** (SPEE-sheez) if the organisms are so similar that they can produce offspring that can also produce offspring. Members of a species can successfully reproduce.

**READING TIP**

The terms *species, specific,* and *special* come from the same Latin root meaning "kind." A species is a kind, or type, of organism.

## Galápagos Island Populations

**A population is a group of organisms of the same species that live in an area.**

**Cacti**

**Crabs**

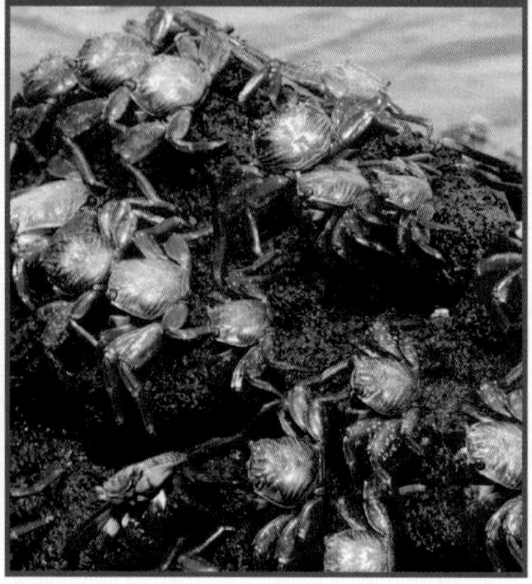

**Iguanas**

## Populations

Scientists use the term **population** to mean a group of organisms of the same species that live in a particular area. This is similar to the population of people who live in a particular city or town. You can then think of people who live in different cities or towns as belonging to different populations. It is the boundary of an area that defines a population. In the study of ecology, members of the same species that live in different areas belong to different populations.

**READING TIP**

Ecology is the study of relationships between organisms and their environment.

A biological population can be a group of animals or a group of plants. It can be a group of bacteria or fungi or any other living thing. Populations of many different species may live in the same area. For example, the photographs above show different populations of organisms that all live in the same place—on one of the Galápagos Islands. The island has a population of cacti, a population of crabs, and a population of iguanas.

**CHECK YOUR READING** What is the difference between a species and a population?

## Habitats and Niches

**VOCABULARY**

Add four square diagrams for *population* and *habitat* to your notebook.

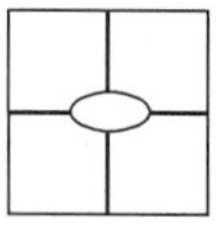

The Galápagos Islands are a small group of volcanic islands off the western coast of South America. The islands are famous for their unusual plant and animal life. They are the **habitat**—the physical location—where these plants and animals live. Island habitats have certain physical characteristics that describe them. These characteristics include the amount of precipitation, the range of temperatures, and the quality of the soil. Different habitats have different characteristics.

## Galápagos Island Habitat

**This island habitat is home to many different populations.**

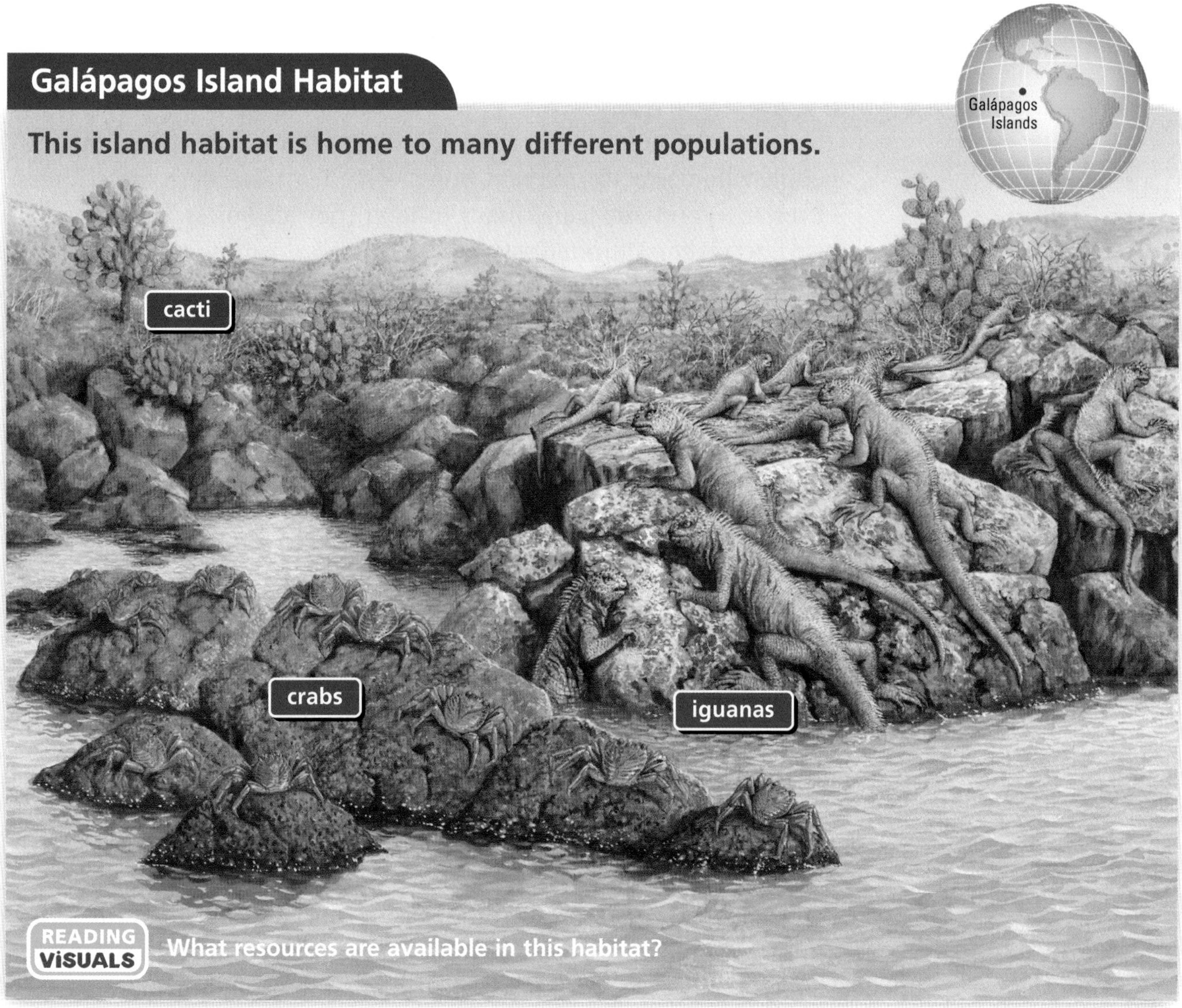


A habitat is filled with different species. Each species depends on the habitat's resources to meet its needs. The characteristics of a habitat determine the species of plants that can grow there. The species of plants that grow determine the species of animals and other organisms that will do well there.

Different populations interact within a habitat. They are part of the flow of energy and matter through an ecosystem. For example, in the Galápagos Island scene above, the cacti capture energy from sunlight and store fresh water. They also provide food for the iguanas, which eat cactus. The cactus is a producer, and the iguana is a primary consumer. The crabs of the Galápagos are secondary consumers that feed on other shellfish. Each of these organisms has a role to play in the habitat. Each organism's role is referred to as its **niche** (nihch).

The niche an organism fills in a habitat is not limited to its place in a food web. Plants provide nesting sites as well as food. The droppings left behind by animals fertilize soil and often spread seeds. Generally, no two species fill the same niche in a habitat.

## Communities

Take a mental tour of your school. Note that you share space with people who do many different things—students, teachers, custodians, librarians, counselors, and many others. They all work together and help each other. We often say that a school is a community.

Scientists use the term *community* in a similar way. A biological **community** is a group of populations that live in a particular area and interact with one another. Cacti, iguanas, and crabs are part of the Galápagos Island community. This community also includes populations of tortoises, finches, flies, bacteria, and many other species.

**CHECK YOUR READING** How is a school community similar to a community of living things in nature?

# The environment can be organized into five levels.

**OUTLINE** Add the different levels of the environment to your outline. Make sure to explain each term in the supporting details.

I. Main idea
  A. Supporting idea
    1. Detail
    2. Detail
  B. Supporting idea

Five terms—biome, ecosystem, community, population, and organism—describe the environment at different levels.

1. **Biome** A biome describes in very general terms the climate and types of plants that are found in similar places around the world.
2. **Ecosystem** Within each biome are many ecosystems. Inside an ecosystem, living and nonliving factors interact to form a stable system. An ecosystem is smaller than a biome and includes only organisms and their local environment.
3. **Community** A community is made up of the living components of the ecosystem. In a community, plants, animals, and other organisms interact with one another.
4. **Population** A population is a group of organisms of the same species that live in the same ecosystem.
5. **Organism** An organism is a single animal, plant, fungus, or other living thing. As the illustration on page 417 shows, an organism plays a part in each level of the environment.

# Patterns exist in populations.

Members of a population settle themselves into the available living space in different ways, forming a pattern. Populations may be crowded together or spread far apart, or they may live in small groups. A population may also show a pattern over time. The number of individuals in the population may rise and fall, depending on the season or other conditions. Numbers may also change as a result of interactions with other organisms.

## Levels in the Environment

**Organisms living in an African savannah illustrate the different levels of the environment.**

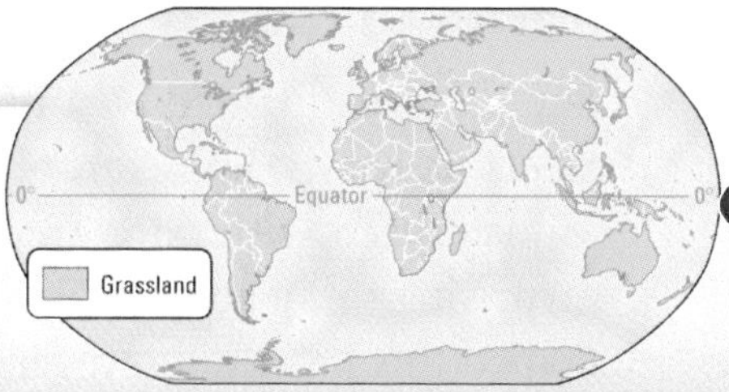

**1 Biome**
The African savannah is part of a grassland biome.

**2 Ecosystem**
The community of organisms, along with water, soil, and other abiotic factors, make up an ecosystem.

**3 Community**
Populations of wildebeests, gazelles, lions, and grasses share the same living areas and resources. These and other populations form a savannah community.

**4 Population**
Gazelles travel together in herds, looking for grazing areas. The total number of gazelles in an ecosystem is called a population of gazelles.

**5 Organism**
The gazelle lives in various grassland habitats in eastern Africa and fills a particular niche.

**READING VISUALS** Describe the gazelle's role in each level of the environment.

## Patterns in Living Space

The patterns formed by a population often show how the population meets its needs. For example, in California's Mojave desert, the pale soil is dotted with dark green shrubs called creosote bushes. A surprising thing about the bushes is their even spacing. No human shaped this habitat, however. The bushes are the same distance from one another because the root systems of mature plants absorb so much water that nearby seeds cannot germinate. This results in a "dead zone" around each plant.

The distribution of animals in a habitat is often related to the availability of resources. Animals must be able to reach their food supply and have places to raise their young. If you put up birdhouses for bluebirds, they should be spaced at least a hundred meters apart. Bluebirds need a large area of their own around their nest in order to collect enough insects to feed their young.

**READING TIP**

As you read this paragraph, note the pattern of wildebeests and elephants in the photograph.

Sometimes, the particular pattern of individuals in a living space helps a population survive. Herring swim in schools, with the individual fish spaced close together. Wildebeests roam African grasslands in closely packed herds. These animals rely on the group for their safety. If one member of the group is attacked, many more will survive.

**CHECK YOUR READING** What are some reasons for the spacing patterns observed in different populations?

**READING VISUALS** What tool might a person use to observe these animals from a distance?

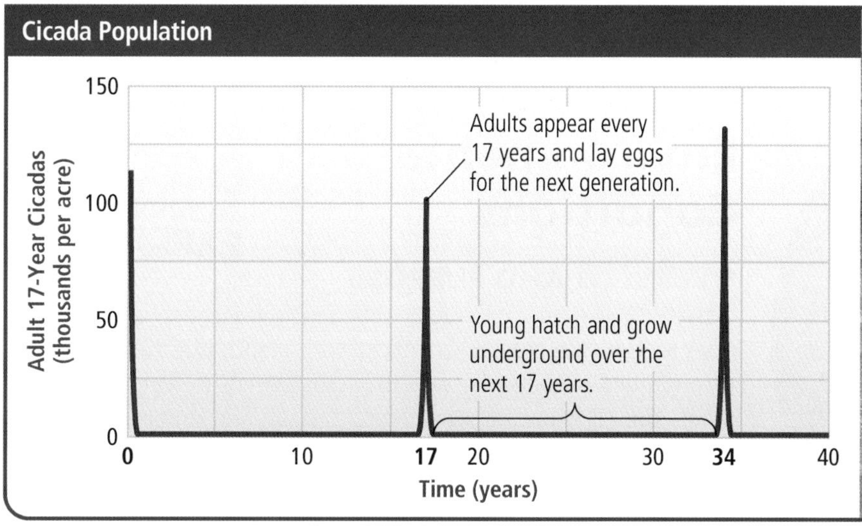

A population of 17-year cicadas increases rapidly each time the adults mature. The adults lay eggs, then die, causing the adult population to fall back to zero.

## Patterns in Time

The graph above shows an unusual pattern of population growth. Certain species of cicadas appear only every 17 years. No other species can rely on these insects as their main source of food, so the cicadas survive long enough to lay eggs when they do appear.

Many birds that nest in North America in the summer fly south to Central and South America in the winter. There, they find enough food and good nesting sites. In North America, this seasonal pattern leads to small bird populations in winter and large ones in summer. You might use binoculars to observe changes in bird populations throughout the year.

Yellow jacket wasps provide another example of a population whose size changes over time. In the spring, the queen wasp lays eggs and new wasps hatch. She continues to lay eggs all summer, and the population grows. When winter comes, all the wasps except the queen die. The population decreases.

## 12.1 Review

### KEY CONCEPTS

1. What are two characteristics of a population? (6.5.c)
2. Order these terms from the simplest to the most complex: biome, community, ecosystem, organism, population. (6.5.c)
3. How do the terms *habitat* and *niche* relate to each other? (6.5.c)

### CRITICAL THINKING

4. **Apply** Choose a biological community in your region. Describe some of the populations that make up that community.
5. **Infer** How might the seasonal patterns of insect populations relate to the seasonal patterns of bird populations?

### CHALLENGE

6. **Synthesize** In some years, California sea lions have trouble finding the types of ocean animals they most like to eat. How is this likely to affect populations of other ocean animals?

# CHAPTER INVESTIGATION

## Environmental Conditions

DESIGN — YOUR OWN — EXPERIMENT

### OVERVIEW AND PURPOSE

Despite their name, pill bugs *(Armadillidium vulgare)* are not insects. They are crustaceans that live on land, but they breathe through gills in the same way that crustaceans in water environments do. Pill bugs are scavengers that depend on decaying plant and animal matter as food sources. In this experiment you will

- observe the behavior of pill bugs
- manipulate a variable of your choice to see which of two environmental conditions pill bugs prefer

### Problem

Write It Up

What environmental conditions do pill bugs prefer?

**MATERIALS**
- shoebox lid
- marker
- 6 pill bugs
- watch or clock with second hand

*Optional Materials*
- paper towel
- water
- black construction paper
- incandescent lamp
- thermometer

**6.5.e, 6.7.b, 6.7.c**

### Procedure

1. Draw a line down the middle of the shoebox lid, as shown. Label the two sides "1" and "2."

step 1

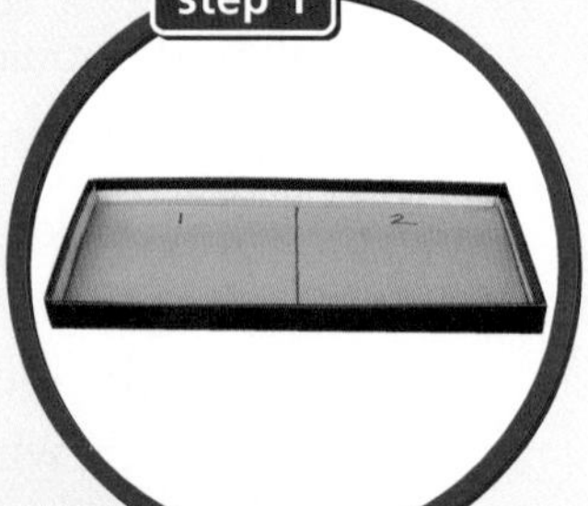

2. Draw a data table like the one shown on page 421.

3. Carefully place three pill bugs on each side of the lid.

4. Observe the behavior of the pill bugs. Count and record the number on each side of the lid after five minutes.

5. Use available materials to alter a condition of your choice on one side of the lid. For example, you could make one side light and the other dark, one dry and the other wet, or one warm and the other cold. The condition you choose is your variable.

6. Repeat step 4.

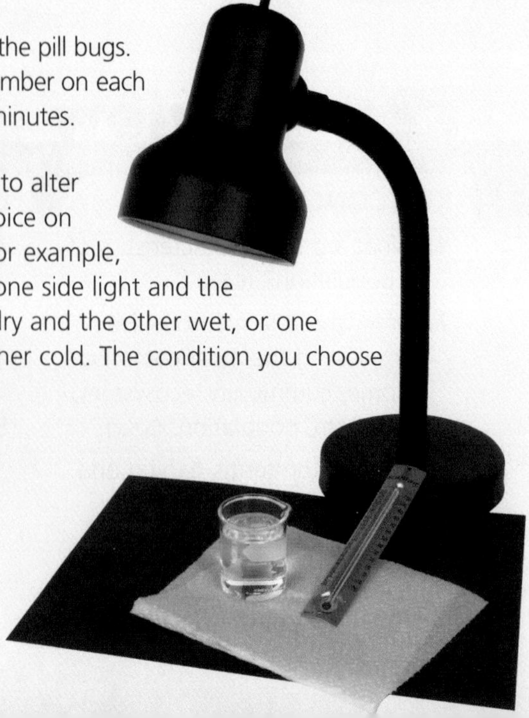

**Content Standard**
6.5.e Students know the number and types of organisms an ecosystem can support depends on the resources available and on abiotic factors, such as quantities of light and water, a range of temperatures, and soil composition.

**Investigation Standard**
6.7.c Construct appropriate graphs from data and develop qualitative statements about the relationships between variables.

## Observe and Analyze

Write It Up

1. **RECORD** Write a narrative about what happened during five minutes of observing. Describe how the pill bugs moved. Use the terms *control group* and *experimental group* in your narrative.
2. **DIAGRAM** Draw your pill-bug environment setup with the altered condition. Make a series of drawings showing the positions of the pill bugs over time. Be sure to label the variables.
3. **IDENTIFY** What was your variable?
4. **IDENTIFY** What did you keep constant in the control group and experimental group?
5. **PRESENT DATA** Look at your drawings. What effect, if any, did the condition you changed have on the movements of the pill bugs?

## Conclude

Write It Up

1. **DRAW CONCLUSIONS** Based on your data, which condition do pill bugs prefer?
2. **COMPARE AND CONTRAST** In what ways is your setup like an environment in nature? In what ways is your setup different?
3. **PRESENT DATA** Combine your data with those of groups who changed other variables. Decide which type of graph would be best for showing your results, how to label each axis, and what units you will use.
4. **PREDICT** Based on your class data, what do you think would happen to pill bugs during a drought?
5. **PREDICT** When would you expect to see pill bugs more active, during the day or at night?

## INVESTIGATE Further

**CHALLENGE** Choose another variable to test the environment that pill bugs prefer. Make sure that your procedure follows the animal safety guidelines in the Lab Handbook on page R11.

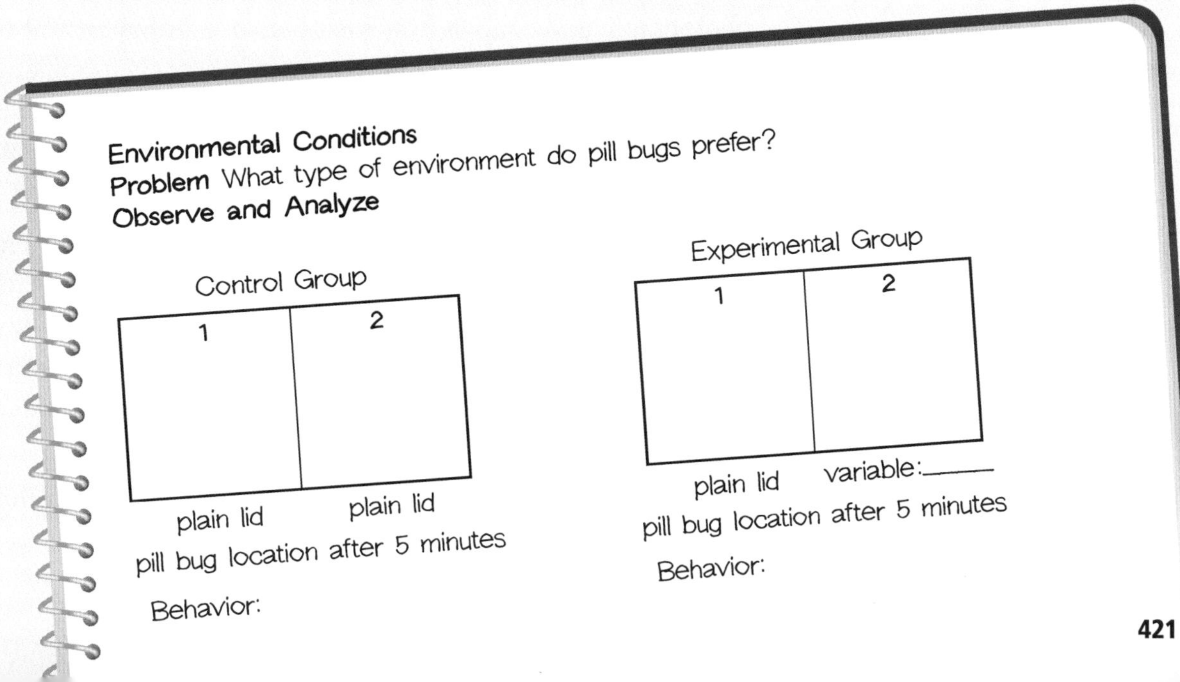

Environmental Conditions
Problem What type of environment do pill bugs prefer?
Observe and Analyze
Control Group
1
2
plain lid
plain lid
pill bug location after 5 minutes
Behavior:
Experimental Group
1
2
plain lid
variable:
pill bug location after 5 minutes
Behavior:

KEY CONCEPT

# 12.2 Organisms can interact in different ways.

**CALIFORNIA Content Standards**

**6.5.c** Students know populations of organisms can be categorized by the functions they serve in an ecosystem.

**6.5.e** Students know the number and types of organisms an ecosystem can support depends on the resources available and on abiotic factors, such as quantities of light and water, a range of temperatures, and soil composition.

**BEFORE, you learned**

- Different populations live together in a habitat
- Different species fill different niches in a habitat
- There are patterns in the ways organisms interact with each other and their environment

**NOW, you will learn**

- About different types of interactions in an ecosystem
- How some species benefit from interactions
- How some species are harmed by interactions

**VOCABULARY**

**predator** p. 423
**prey** p. 423
**competition** p. 423
**cooperation** p. 425
**symbiosis** p. 426
**mutualism** p. 426
**commensalism** p. 427
**parasitism** p. 427

**THINK ABOUT**

***What are some of the ways people interact?***

People in a community interact with one another in many ways. An interaction is the way a person behaves toward or responds to another person. This photograph shows groups of people at a soccer game. There are players from two teams and fans who are watching the game. How would you describe the interactions among the people in this photograph?

## Organisms interact in different ways.

The photograph above shows how members of a human community both compete and cooperate. Different members of the populations of a biological community also compete and cooperate. They not only share a habitat, but they also share the resources in that habitat. How different organisms interact depends on their relationships with one another.

A robin in a meadow finds a caterpillar and swallows it. This is one obvious way organisms in an ecosystem interact—one eats, and the other is eaten. Organisms also compete. The robin may have to compete with a flicker to get the caterpillar. And, just like people, organisms can cooperate. Ants work together to build a nest, collect food, and defend their colony.

**CHECK YOUR READING** Name three ways organisms may interact with each other in an ecosystem.

## Predator and Prey

Many interactions among organisms in an ecosystem involve food. A food chain shows the feeding relationships among different species. Some are producers, and others are consumers. Another way to look at a food chain is through the interactions of predators and prey. A **predator** is an animal that eats another animal. A **prey** is an animal that is eaten by a predator. In a food chain, an organism can be both predator and prey. A meadowlark that eats a grasshopper may, in turn, be eaten by a prairie falcon.

REMINDER

A producer is an organism that makes its own food. A consumer is an organism that eats another organism for food.

Predators can affect how members of their prey populations are distributed. For example, herring move together in a school, and wildebeests travel in a herd, to protect themselves. Sick or older members of the population tend to move more slowly. They are the ones that are most likely to be eaten by predators.

Prey populations affect the location and number of predator populations. For example, some birds are predators that feed on insects. One factor that may affect the movement of these birds from one location to another is the availability of insects.

## Competition

In a team game, two teams compete against each other with the same goal in mind—to win the game. In a biological community, competition is for resources. **Competition** is the struggle between individuals or different populations for a limited resource.

In an ecosystem, competition may occur within the same species. Individual plants compete with each other for light, space, and nutrients. For example, creosote bushes compete with other creosote bushes for the same water supply.

Competition also occurs between members of different species. In the tropical rain forests of Indonesia, vines called strangler figs compete with trees for water, light, and nutrients. The vine attaches itself to a host tree. As it grows, the vine surrounds and eventually kills the tree by blocking out sunlight and using up available water and nutrients.

**INFER** Do you think a strangler fig could survive on its own?

## Competition

**Competition between species** Two different species, hyenas and vultures, compete for the remains of a dead animal.

**Competition within species** Two male deer lock horns as they battle over territory.

Competition occurs between species and within species. For example, vultures and hyenas compete over the food left in the remains of a dead animal. Wolves compete with one another over territory. A wolf marks its territory by urinating on trees. In this way, it warns off other wolves. Animals also compete over territory by fighting or making threatening sounds and displays.

Competition within species often occurs during the mating season. Male birds use special songs and displays of feathers to compete for the attention of females. Male wart hogs fight to attract female wart hogs. Male crickets chirp to attract female crickets.

**CHECK YOUR READING** What types of resources do plants and animals compete for?

**READING TIP**

Compare and contrast the meanings of *competition* and *coexistence*.

Competition does not occur between all populations that share the same resources. Different species can live together in a habitat without causing harm to one another. For example, many different populations of plants coexist in a forest. Maple trees, beech trees, and birch trees can live side by side and still have enough water, nutrients, and sunlight to meet their needs.

# INVESTIGATE Species Interactions

## *How do predator-prey populations interact?*

Use these rules for predator-prey interaction for each round. If a predator card touches three or more prey cards, remove the prey cards that were touched. If the predator card does not touch at least three prey cards, remove the predator card and leave the prey cards.

**SKILL FOCUS**
Analyzing data
(6.5.b)

**MATERIALS**
- 20 10 × 10 cm cardboard squares (predators)
- 200 3 × 3 cm paper squares (prey)
- masking tape

*for Challenge:*
- graph paper
- 2 colored pencils

**TIME**
30 minutes

### PROCEDURE

1. Use masking tape to mark a boundary on a tabletop.
2. Scatter five prey cards into the area. Take a predator card and toss it, trying to get it to land on the prey.
3. According to the rules above, remove the predators and prey that have "died." Record the number of predators and prey that have "survived." This represents one generation.
4. Double the populations of predators and prey—they have "reproduced."
5. Scatter the prey cards into the area and then toss the predator cards as before. Repeat steps 3 and 4 for a total of 15 rounds, or "generations."

### WHAT DO YOU THINK?

- How did the size of the prey population affect the predator population?
- How might the size of a habitat affect the interaction of predators and prey?

**CHALLENGE** Use graph paper and colored pencils to make a graph of your results. Or use a spreadsheet program if one is available to you.

## Cooperation

Not all interactions in an ecosystem involve competition. **Cooperation** is an interaction in which organisms work in a way that benefits them all. Some predators cooperate when they hunt. Although individual lions may hunt on their own, they also hunt in groups to kill large prey.

Killer whales cooperate when they hunt. The whales swim in groups called pods. The pod members swim in circles around a school of fish, forcing the fish close together so they are easier to catch. Pod members may also take turns chasing a seal until it gets tired and is easily killed. The pod may even work together to attack larger species of whales.

Ants, bees, and termites are social insects. Members of a colony belong to different groups, which have different responsibilities. Some groups gather food while others defend the colony. Other animals, such as apes and monkeys, live in family groups. Members of the family cooperate to care for their young.

**Cooperation**
Driver ants work together to bring food to their nest.

## The survival of one species might depend on another species.

**OUTLINE**
Add a sentence about *symbiosis* to your outline and define the three types of symbiosis in the supporting details.

I. Main idea
  A. Supporting idea
    1. Detail
    2. Detail
  B. Supporting idea

You have learned that many different organisms live together in a habitat. Because organisms live together, they must interact in different ways. You have read that an organism might prey upon another for food. Or it might compete or cooperate for resources such as food, water, and territory.

The actions of different organisms can be so closely related that the survival of one species depends on the actions or presence of another. In such a relationship, at least one of the species is getting a resource that it needs to survive. Benefits of the relationship may include food, reproductive help, or protection.

**READING TIP**
*Symbiosis* comes from a Greek word that means "living together."

The relationship between individuals of two different species who live together in a close relationship is called **symbiosis** (SIHM-bee-OH-sihs). A symbiotic relationship may affect the partners in different ways.

- Both species benefit from the relationship.
- One species benefits while the other is not affected.
- One species benefits while the other is harmed.

Here are some examples of each of the three types of symbiosis.

### Both Species Benefit

Stroll through a garden on a sunny day and notice the bees buzzing from flower to flower. Look closely at a single bee and you may see yellow pollen grains sticking to its hairy body. The bee carries these grains of pollen as it goes from flower to flower. The relationship between the flower and the bee is an example of **mutualism** (MYOO-choo-uh-LIHZ-uhm)—an interaction between two species that benefits both. The bee gets food in the form of nectar. The flower gets pollen, which it needs to make seeds.

**Mutualism** The interaction between the hummingbird and the flower benefits both.

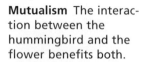

Many plants rely on mutualism to reproduce. The pollen needed to make seeds must be spread from flower to flower. Birds and insects that feed on the nectar in these flowers transfer pollen from one flower to the next. The seeds produced are then moved to other places by animals that eat the seeds or the fruits that hold the seeds. This form of mutualism doesn't benefit the individual flower, but it does ensure the survival of the species.

In some cases, mutualism is necessary for the survival of the organisms themselves. For example, termites are able to eat a food that most animals cannot digest: wood. Termites can't digest wood either, but they have tiny single-celled organisms in their bodies that can break the wood down into digestible parts. The tiny organisms get a safe place to live, and the termites can take advantage of a plentiful food source.

RESOURCE CENTER
CLASSZONE.COM
Explore symbiotic relationships.

CHECK YOUR READING Describe how a bee and a flower benefit from a symbiotic relationship.

## One Species Benefits

**Commensalism** (kuh-MEHN-suh-LIHZ-uhm) is a relationship between two species in which one species benefits while the other is not affected. Orchids and mosses are plants that can have a commensal relationship with trees. The plants grow on the trunks or branches of trees. They get the light they need as well as nutrients from rainwater. As long as these plants do not grow too heavy, the tree is not affected.

READING TIP
*Commensal* means "sharing a meal" in Middle English. Its root is the Latin word *mēnsa*, meaning "table."

Commensal relationships are very common in ocean ecosystems. Small fish called remoras use a type of built-in suction cup to stick to a shark's skin and hitch a ride. When the shark makes a kill, the remora eats the scraps. The shark makes no attempt to attack the remora. The remora benefits greatly from this commensal relationship. The shark is not affected.

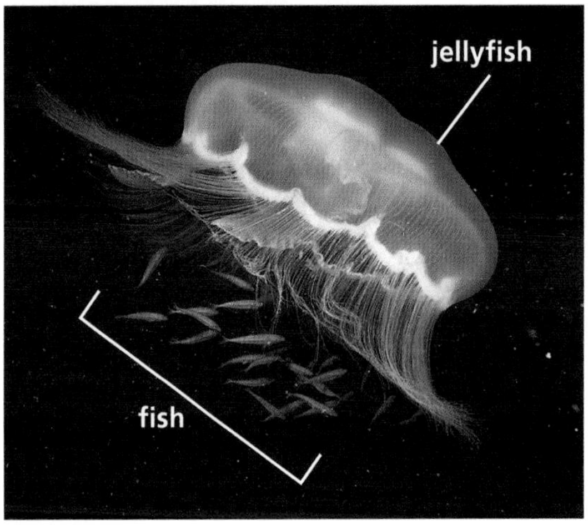

**Commensalism** The interaction between the jellyfish and the fish benefits only the fish.

Not all commensal relationships involve food. Some fish protect themselves by swimming among the stinging tentacles of a moon jellyfish. The fish benefit from the relationship because the tentacles keep them safe from predators. The jellyfish is not helped or hurt by the presence of the fish. As in this example, it is common in commensal relationships for the species that benefits to be smaller than the species that does not.

## One Species Is Harmed

There is one symbiotic relationship in which a smaller organism can harm a much larger organism. **Parasitism** (PAR-uh-suh-TIHZ-uhm) is a relationship between two species in which one species benefits while the species it depends on, the host, is harmed. Parasites are organisms that feed off and weaken their hosts. Ticks, lice, and mites are external parasites that live on or attach to their host's skin. Tapeworms and roundworms are internal parasites that live inside their host.

## Symbiotic Relationships

**Mutualism**
Both species benefit from the relationship.

**Commensalism**
One species benefits while the other is not affected.

**Parasitism**
One species benefits while the other is harmed.

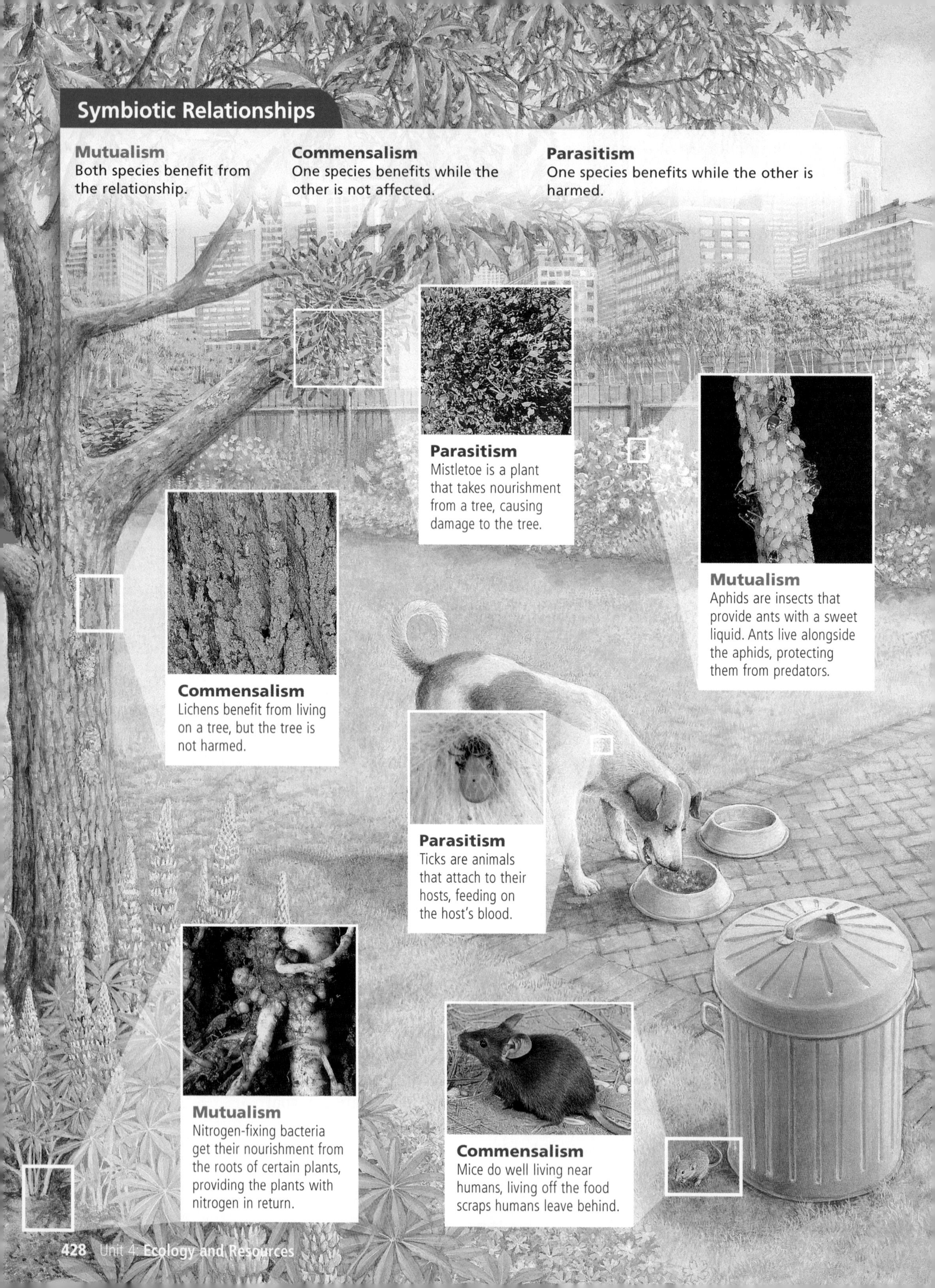

**Parasitism**
Mistletoe is a plant that takes nourishment from a tree, causing damage to the tree.

**Mutualism**
Aphids are insects that provide ants with a sweet liquid. Ants live alongside the aphids, protecting them from predators.

**Commensalism**
Lichens benefit from living on a tree, but the tree is not harmed.

**Parasitism**
Ticks are animals that attach to their hosts, feeding on the host's blood.

**Mutualism**
Nitrogen-fixing bacteria get their nourishment from the roots of certain plants, providing the plants with nitrogen in return.

**Commensalism**
Mice do well living near humans, living off the food scraps humans leave behind.

Cowbirds and warblers have an unusual relationship called nest or brood parasitism. Female cowbirds never build their own nests or raise their own young. Instead, they lay their eggs in warbler nests. Although nest parasitism does not harm the host warbler, it may harm the warbler species. Cowbirds push most warbler eggs from the nest in order to make room for their own eggs. Once the cowbird chicks hatch, they compete with the warbler chicks for food. Because cowbird chicks are larger, the warbler chicks may starve.

**Parasitism** The larger cowbird chick is cared for by a warbler at the expense of the smaller warbler chick.

**CHECK YOUR READING** How is parasitism different from commensalism?

## Interactions in an ecosystem are complex.

Different types of symbiosis occur throughout an ecosystem and often overlap. They may occur in the same locations, and the same species might be involved in more than one symbiotic relationship. The illustration on page 428 shows different symbiotic relationships that may occur in a backyard.

Symbiosis is just one of many interactions that take place in an ecosystem. For example, a garden in the yard may have individual tomato plants that compete for water and nutrients. It may have ants that cooperate to maintain a successful colony. An ecosystem is more than just a collection of biotic and abiotic factors. Interactions within an ecosystem help explain how resources are shared and used up and how energy flows through the system.

# 12.2 Review

### KEY CONCEPTS

1. Name two ways in which members of the same species interact. (6.5.c)
2. In what ways do members of different species interact? (6.5.c)
3. Give an example of each type of symbiotic relationship: mutualism, commensalism, and parasitism. (6.5.c)

### CRITICAL THINKING

4. **Apply** Think of a biological community near you, and give an example of how one population has affected another.
5. **Compare and Contrast** Explain how symbiotic relationships are similar to and different from predator-prey interactions.

### CHALLENGE

6. **Synthesize** Mutualism is more common in tropical ecosystems, such as rain forests and coral reefs, than in other ecosystems. Why do you think this is so?

Think SCIENCE



# Where Are the Salamanders?

6.7.e Recognize whether evidence is consistent with a proposed explanation.

The Cottonwood Lake Study Area is in rural Stutsman County, North Dakota. U.S. Fish and Wildlife Service biologists have been studying wetland ecosystems there for more than 30 years. There are many salamanders in these wetlands. But in May 2000, the researchers started noticing sick salamanders in one wetland. By July, most salamanders had died. What killed them?

This barred tiger salamander can be found in many wetlands in the Great Plains.

## Observations

a. In the past, cold winter weather and food shortages have killed salamanders at Cottonwood Lake.
b. The sick salamanders had discolored skin and enlarged livers.
c. The previous year, leopard frogs in a nearby wetland were found dying from a contagious fungal infection.
d. A viral disease has killed tiger salamanders elsewhere in the western United States.
e. Both large, well-fed salamanders and small, poorly nourished salamanders died.

## Inferences

The following statements are possible inferences.

a. A food shortage caused salamanders to starve.
b. The fungal disease that killed leopard frogs also killed the salamanders.
c. Salamanders were killed by a viral disease.

## Evaluate Inferences

**On Your Own** Which of the inferences are supported by the observations? Write the observations that support each of the inferences you identify.

**As a Group** Discuss your decisions. Come up with a list of reasonable inferences.

**CHALLENGE** What further observations would you make to test any of these inferences?

KEY CONCEPT

# 12.3 Ecosystems are always changing.

**CALIFORNIA Content Standards**

6.5.e Students know the number and types of organisms an ecosystem can support depends on the resources available and on abiotic factors, such as quantities of light and water, a range of temperatures, and soil composition.

6.7.h Identify changes in natural phenomena over time without manipulating the phenomena (e.g., a tree limb, a grove of trees, a stream, a hillslope).

**BEFORE, you learned**

- Populations in an ecosystem interact in different ways
- Organisms can benefit from interactions in an ecosystem
- Organisms can be harmed by interactions in an ecosystem

**NOW, you will learn**

- How different factors affect the size of a population
- How biological communities get established
- How biological communities change over time

**VOCABULARY**

**limiting factor** p. 432
**carrying capacity** p. 433
**succession** p. 434
**pioneer species** p. 434

**EXPLORE Population Growth** (6.5.b, 6.5.e)

***How does sugar affect the growth of yeast?***

**PROCEDURE**

1. Use a marker to label the cups A, B, and C. Pour 150 mL of warm water into each cup. Mark the water level with the marker.
2. Add 1/2 teaspoon of dry yeast to each cup and stir.
3. Add 1/4 teaspoon of sugar to cup B. Add 1 teaspoon of sugar to cup C. Stir.
4. Wait 15 minutes. Measure the height of the foam layer that forms in each cup.

**WHAT DO YOU THINK?**

- Which cup had the most foam? Which cup had the least?
- Describe the effect of sugar on a population of yeast.

**MATERIALS**

- 3 clear plastic cups
- warm water
- sugar
- dry yeast
- measuring spoons
- measuring cup
- stirring rod
- marker
- ruler

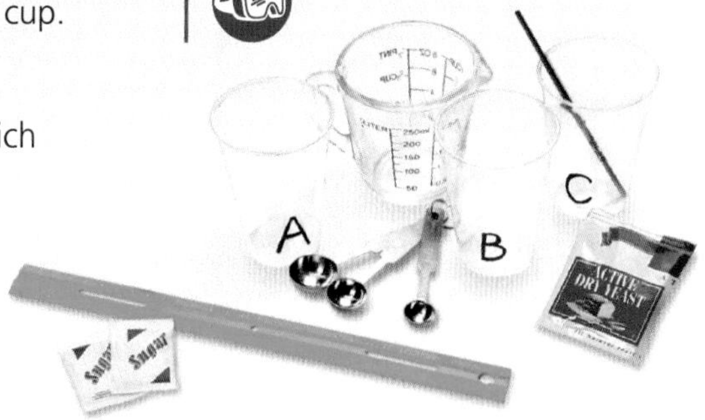


## Populations change over time.

**REMINDER**
A population is a group of organisms of the same species that live together in the same habitat.

You may have a strong memory of a park you visited as a little child. You might remember collecting pine cones, listening to woodpeckers, and catching frogs. Then you visit again, years later, and the park has changed. Maybe more land has been added, and there are more birds and trees. Or maybe the area around the park has been developed. There seem to be fewer woodpeckers, and you can't find any frogs. The community has changed. There are a lot of factors that affect the populations within a biological community. Some have to do with the organisms themselves. Others relate to the habitat.

**CALIFORNIA Focus**

The tule elk is a type of elk that lives only in California. In 1800, large herds of tule elk roamed open grasslands. By 1870, hunting and the development of farms had led to the near extinction of the tule elk. Conservation efforts have increased the population to more than 3000 today.

## Population Growth and Decline

One obvious factor that affects population size is how often organisms reproduce. Birth rate is a measure of the number of births in an animal population. It can also be a measure of changes in an ecosystem. For example, black bears reproduce once every two years. If there is not enough food available, reproduction is delayed. As a result, the bear population does not grow.

Predator-prey interactions also affect population size. Wolves are predators that prey on moose in Isle Royale National Park in Michigan. The graphs show how an increase in the moose population was followed by an increase in the wolf population. The wolves preyed upon the moose, the moose population decreased, and then the wolf population decreased.

**Moose and Wolf Populations, Isle Royale National Park**

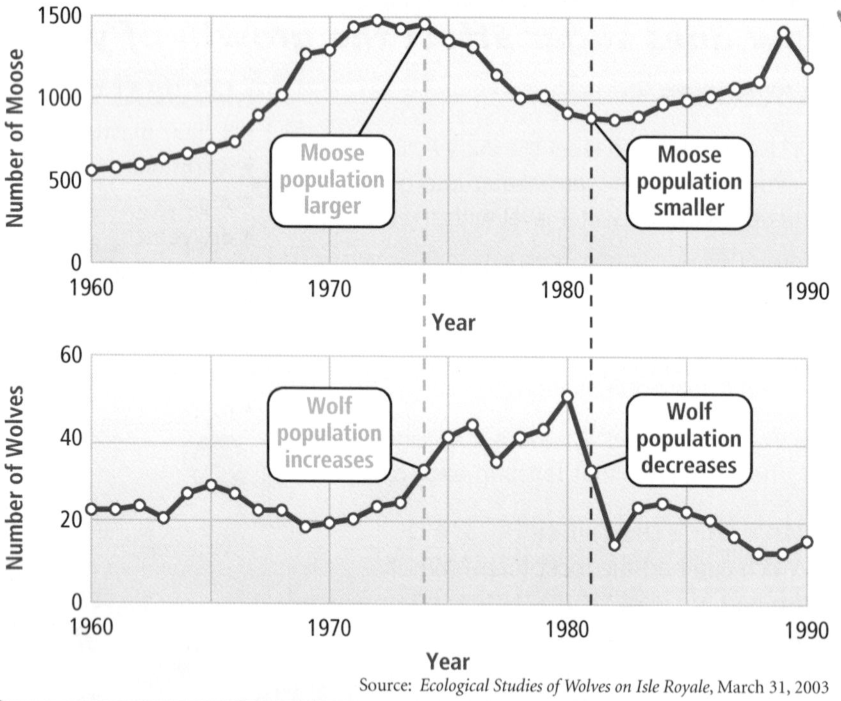


Source: *Ecological Studies of Wolves on Isle Royale*, March 31, 2003

**READING TIP**

Note in the graphs above that it can take some time for the size of one population to affect the size of another.

Any factor or condition that limits the growth of a population in an ecosystem is called a **limiting factor.** A large population of predators will limit the population of prey. A small population of prey will limit the population of predators. Too much or too little of any biotic or abiotic factor—such as food, water, or light—makes an ecosystem unstable and brings about change.

A lack of nutrients in the soil is a limiting factor for plants. That is why farmers fertilize their crops. However, if the fertilizer runs off into a lake, it can increase the population of algae. A large population of algae can cover a lake and use up oxygen needed by fish. This then limits the fish population.

# INVESTIGATE Limiting Factors

## What effect does spacing have on a population of plants?

**DESIGN — YOUR OWN — EXPERIMENT**

Using the materials listed, design an experiment to test this hypothesis: "If plants grow too close together, the health of the population will be affected, because the individual plants do not get enough of the nutrients and water that they need."

### PROCEDURE

1. Decide how to use the seeds, cups, and soil to test the hypothesis.
2. Write up your experimental procedure. Include safety tips.

### WHAT DO YOU THINK?

- What are the variables in your experiment?
- What types of evidence would support your hypothesis?

**CHALLENGE** Conduct your experiment. Note that seeds must be planted near the top of the soil. A good measure for this is the tip of a pencil. Measure and record the growth of the seedlings. Allow the seedlings to grow for two weeks before making your conclusions.

**SKILL FOCUS**
Designing experiments (6.5.e)

**MATERIALS**
- paper cups
- potting soil
- radish seeds
- water
- pencil
- ruler

**TIME**
20 minutes

## Maintaining a Balance

Living things have certain minimum requirements for food, water, and living space. When a population reaches a state where it can no longer grow, the population has reached its **carrying capacity,** the maximum number of individuals that an ecosystem can support. You can see on page 432 that the graph for the moose population appears to peak around 1500. Even if there were no wolves on Isle Royale, the population of moose would still be limited because there is only so much food and space available.

**VOCABULARY**
Remember to make a four square diagram for *carrying capacity* in your notebook. Try to use *limiting factor* in your diagram.

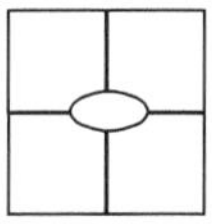

**CHECK YOUR READING** Explain the term *carrying capacity.*

An ecosystem's carrying capacity is different for each population. For example, a meadow ecosystem supports many more bees and ants than bluebirds. Isle Royale supports many more moose than wolves. The moose is a primary consumer of plants. It is at a lower level of the energy pyramid than the wolf, a secondary consumer.

Biotic factors can be limiting factors. These factors include the interactions between populations such as competition, predation, and parasitism. Abiotic factors are also limiting. These include temperature, availability of water or minerals, and exposure to wind.

## Ecosystems change over time.

If you take a walk in a New Hampshire woods, you may see the remains of old stone walls. Once this land was mostly farmland. Then the farms were abandoned. Now, new trees have grown where farm animals once grazed.

**Succession** (suhk-SEHSH-uhn) is the gradual change in an ecosystem in which one biological community is replaced by another. The change from field to forest is an example of succession. Over time the grasses of open farmland are slowly replaced by small plants and shrubs and then by trees.

### Primary Succession

Very few places on Earth are without some form of life. Even when a lava flow covers an area or a glacier melts and leaves behind an empty and barren environment, plants will move into the area and bring it back to life. These are examples of primary succession, the establishment of a new biological community.

**READING TIP**

*Succeed* and *succession* come from the same Latin word, *succedere*, meaning "to go up" or "to follow after."

**Pioneer species** are the first living things to move into a barren environment. In the illustration below, mosses and lichens move in after a glacier retreats. There is little or no topsoil. Lichens are common pioneers because they can grow on bare rock. They hold moisture and add organic matter.

**Primary Succession**

**Primary succession can occur after a glacier retreats, when little topsoil is present.**

1. Mosses and lichens grow on rock with little or no soil. These pioneer species break apart the surface rock.
2. Over time, the rock breaks down further, forming soil. Larger plants take root. These support populations of animals.
3. Coniferous trees take root in a deep layer of soil. Many types of plants and animals are supported in this habitat.

Mosses and other plants join the lichens in the newly forming soil. As these pioneers grow, they gradually weaken the rock surface. The rock breaks down and weathers over time. Decaying plant matter adds nutrients, forming more soil. Now a variety of small plants and shrubs can take root. These plants support insects, birds, and small rodents. Eventually there is enough soil to support coniferous trees. Forests grow, providing a habitat for larger animals.

RESOURCE CENTER
CLASSZONE.COM
Learn more about succession.

## Secondary Succession

Secondary succession takes place after a major disturbance to the biological community in a stable ecosystem. Despite the disturbance, the soil remains. A community can be disturbed by a natural event, such as fire or flood, or it can be disturbed by human activity. A cleared forest or abandoned farmland can lead to secondary succession.

The illustration below shows secondary succession following a forest fire. The damage is bad, but it is surface damage. Below the surface, seeds and plant roots survive. After a time, grasses and small shrubs grow up among the decaying remains of the original plants. Birds, insects, and rodents return. Alder trees take root and put nutrients into the soil. Over time, many types of trees and plants grow, providing food for a variety of animals.

**CHECK YOUR READING** What is the difference between primary and secondary succession?

### Secondary Succession

**Secondary succession occurs if soil remains after a disturbance, such as a forest fire.**

1. Plants at the surface are burned. However, below the surface, seeds and some roots survive.
2. Grasses and small shrubs sprout among the charred trees and vegetation. Small animals return.
3. Deciduous trees, such as elms and maples, grow and mature. A forest habitat is restored. More animals are supported.

## Patterns of Change

All types of ecosystems go through succession. Succession can establish a forest community, a wetland community, a coastal community, or even an ocean community. Succession can happen over tens or hundreds of years. The pattern is the same, however. First a community of producers is established. These are followed by decomposers and consumers, then more producers, and then more decomposers and consumers. Over time, a stable biological community develops.

In a way, establishing a biological community is like planting a garden. To start a garden, you first prepare the soil. Perhaps you add compost. This adds organic matter and nutrients to the soil, which helps the soil hold water. With the right preparation, your vegetables and flowers should grow well.

Pioneer species can function in one of two ways in an ecological succession. They can help other species grow or they can prevent species from getting established.

**READING TIP**

As you read about the two ways plant species function in succession, think in terms of cooperation and competition.

- Some plant species are like gardeners. Trees such as alders have nitrogen-fixing bacteria on their roots that improve the nutrient content of the soil. This allows other tree seedlings to grow. Pioneering species may also stabilize the soil, shade the soil surface, or add nutrients to the soil when they die and decay.
- Some plant species produce conditions that keep out other plants. The plants may release chemicals that keep other plants from taking root. Or a new species may outcompete other species by using up resources or better resisting a disease.

Such interactions between living things help determine the type and rate of succession in an ecosystem.

## 12.3 Review

### KEY CONCEPTS

1. Describe three factors that could limit the size of a population in a habitat. (6.5.e)
2. List two natural disturbances and two human-made disturbances that can lead to succession. (6.7.h)
3. What role do pioneer species play in succession? (6.5.e)

### CRITICAL THINKING

4. **Infer** How and why would secondary succession in a tundra habitat differ from secondary succession in a rainforest habitat?
5. **Predict** Suppose you are clearing an area in your yard to make a small pond. Sketch the stages of succession that would follow this disturbance.

### CHALLENGE

6. **Synthesize** Imagine you are the wildlife manager for a forest preserve that supports both moose and wolves. What types of information should you collect to determine the carrying capacity for each species?

MATH in SCIENCE

**MATH TUTORIAL**
CLASSZONE.COM
Click on Math Tutorial for more help with multiplying fractions and whole numbers.

**Math 6.NS.2.1**
**Science 6.5.e**

## SKILL: MULTIPLYING A FRACTION BY A WHOLE NUMBER

# Number of Births and Populations

Ecologists pay careful attention to the number of offspring born to endangered species. When the number of births is divided by the number of adult females, the result is a fraction. If there are two births for every five adult females in a population, then the fraction is $\frac{2}{5}$.

### Example

Suppose that over time at a national park in Borneo, 2 offspring have been born for every 5 adult female orangutans. There are 150 adult females in the park. Estimate how many young will be born this year. To find out, multiply $\frac{2}{5}$ by the number of adult females.

**(1)** Multiply the numerator of the fraction by the whole number.

$$150 \text{ females} \times \frac{2 \text{ births}}{5 \text{ females}} = \frac{150 \times 2}{5} = \frac{300}{5}$$

**(2)** Divide by the denominator.

$$\frac{300}{5} = 300 \div 5 = 60$$

**ANSWER** 60 young

**Answer the following questions.**

1. In 2001 there were about 72 adult female right whales. Scientists observing the whales reported one birth for every 3 females. About how many right whales were born in 2001?
2. Giant pandas are endangered. Currently only about 140 giant pandas live in captivity in zoos and in parks. About $\frac{3}{5}$ of these were born in captivity. How many is that?
3. The orangutan population of the world has decreased sharply. At one time there were over 100,000 ranging across Asia. Now there may be 25,000, of which $\frac{2}{3}$ live in Borneo. About how many orangutans live in Borneo?

**CHALLENGE** **Suppose 1 birth per year for every 2 adult females is necessary to save an endangered population. There are now 5 births per 20 adult females per year. By what factor does the number of births need to increase?**

# 12 Chapter Review

## the BIG idea

**Living things within an ecosystem interact with each other and the environment.**

**CONTENT REVIEW**
**CLASSZONE.COM**

## KEY CONCEPTS SUMMARY

### 1 Groups of living things interact within ecosystems.

- Members of the same species form a population within a habitat.
- Each species has a distinct role within a habitat. This is its niche.

Population of Crabs

Island Habitat for Crabs

**VOCABULARY**
**species** p. 413
**population** p. 414
**habitat** p. 414
**niche** p. 415
**community** p. 416

### 2 Organisms can interact in different ways.

Some organisms within a community are predators, and some are prey. Some compete with one another, and some cooperate. Some species form symbiotic relationships with other species:

**Mutualism**
benefits both

**Commensalism**
benefits one, other unaffected

**Parasitism**
benefits one, harms other

**VOCABULARY**
**predator** p. 423
**prey** p. 423
**competition** p. 423
**cooperation** p. 425
**symbiosis** p. 426
**mutualism** p. 426
**commensalism** p. 427
**parasitism** p. 427

### 3 Ecosystems are always changing.

**Primary Succession**

In a barren area, a new community is established with pioneer species, such as mosses, that do well with little or no soil. Mosses eventually give way to coniferous trees.

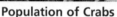

**Secondary Succession**

When a disturbance damages a community but soil remains, the community gets reestablished from seeds and roots left behind. Grasses grow, then small shrubs, and eventually trees.

**VOCABULARY**
**limiting factor** p. 432
**carrying capacity** p. 433
**succession** p. 434
**pioneer species** p. 434

## Reviewing Vocabulary

***Draw a Venn diagram for each pair of terms. Put shared characteristics in the overlap area, put differences to the outside. A sample diagram is provided.***

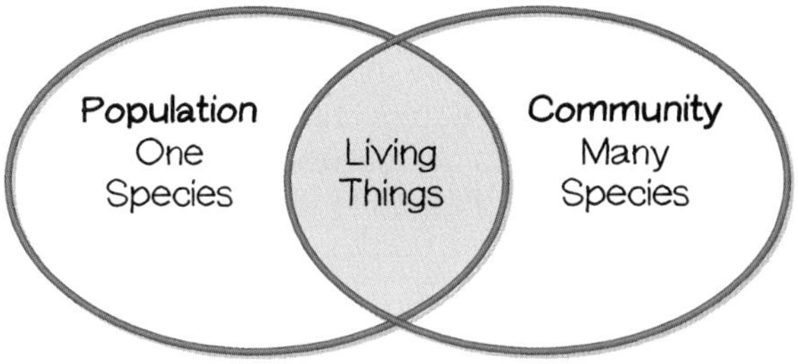


1. habitat, niche
2. mutualism, commensalism
3. mutualism, parasitism
4. competition, cooperation
5. primary succession, secondary succession

## Reviewing Key Concepts

**Multiple Choice** *Choose the letter of the best answer.*

6. What is carrying capacity? (6.5.e)
   - **a.** the largest population an ecosystem can support
   - **b.** the smallest population an ecosystem can support
   - **c.** the number of species an ecosystem can support
   - **d.** the number of habitats in an ecosystem

7. A new species of bird moves into a habitat. The birds feed on a particular caterpillar, so that the resulting population of butterflies is small. What can be said of the relationship between the birds and the butterflies? (6.5.c)
   - **a.** The birds and the butterflies have a commensal relationship.
   - **b.** The birds and butterflies compete.
   - **c.** The birds are a limiting factor for the butterflies.
   - **d.** The birds and butterflies cooperate.

8. Certain types of worms live in the mud at the bottom of lakes. What does the mud represent for the worm? (6.5.e)
   - **a.** an ecosystem
   - **b.** a niche
   - **c.** a community
   - **d.** a habitat

9. What is a pioneer species? (6.5.c)
   - **a.** a species that travels within an ecosystem
   - **b.** a species that is among the first to move into an area after a natural disaster
   - **c.** a species that depends upon animal life
   - **d.** a species that cannot return after a natural disaster

10. The spacing of creosote bushes in a dry area is an example of (6.5.c)
    - **a.** commensalism
    - **b.** parasitism
    - **c.** competition
    - **d.** mutualism

11. Which is an example of parasitism? (6.5.c)
    - **a.** dog and tick
    - **b.** termite and protozoans
    - **c.** shark and remora
    - **d.** flower and hummingbird

12. Which is an example of secondary succession? (6.5.e)
    - **a.** succession after a forest fire
    - **b.** succession after a large volcanic lava flow devastates an area
    - **c.** succession after a glacier retreats, leaving bare rock
    - **d.** succession after a hurricane washes away all the sand from a beach

**Short Answer** *Write a short answer to each question.*

13. Put the terms in order, starting with the term that includes the largest number of individuals and ending with the group containing the fewest individuals: community, population, ecosystem, biome. (6.5.c)
14. List four ways in which members of the same species can cooperate with each other. (6.5.c)
15. Describe three different types of symbiosis. (6.5.c)

## Thinking Critically

*The data in the table below come from the records of a Canadian trading company that, in the late 1800s, bought lynx and hare pelts from hunters and trappers. The Canadian lynx and hare share the same habitat. The lynx relies on the hare as a food source. Use the table to answer the next three questions.*

| Lynx and Hare Pelts | | |
|---|---|---|
| Year | Lynx | Hare |
| 1 | 2 | 30 |
| 2 | 15 | 55 |
| 3 | 65 | 90 |
| 4 | 75 | 160 |
| 5 | 100 | 200 |
| 6 | 95 | 140 |
| 7 | 75 | 80 |
| 8 | 40 | 35 |
| 9 | 20 | 3 |
| 10 | 3 | 4 |
| 11 | 30 | 40 |
| 12 | 55 | 95 |

16. **ANALYZE** How would you describe the pattern that emerges between the two populations in years 1–7? How does the pattern change in years 8–10? (6.5.d)

17. **EVALUATE** The data on the lynx and hare pelts have been used to suggest the sizes of the lynx and hare populations. Is this a reasonable approach to take? Why or why not? (6.5.d)

18. **ANALYZE** Scientists have observed that hare populations will go through cycles of increasing and decreasing populations even when the lynx is not part of the habitat. How would you explain this observation? (6.5.e)

19. **APPLY** A forest has pine trees, along with oak trees and birch trees. All of the trees provide shelter and food for different animals in the habitat. Do these trees occupy the same niche? Explain. (6.5.c)

20. **INFER** Explain why low-growing plants such as mosses are eventually replaced by shrubs, and shrubs are then replaced by trees, in both primary and secondary successions. (6.5.e)

21. **PROVIDE EXAMPLES** List three human activities that could lead to secondary succession.

22. **ANALYZE** Creosote bushes in the Mojave desert are spread out so that each plant is about an equal distance from another. Write a short paragraph to describe the interaction of the creosote bushes, using the terms below. (6.5.c)

| | |
|---|---|
| competition | population pattern |
| limiting factor | community |

23. **APPLY** How might building homes in a wooded area affect carrying capacities of different populations in the area?

## the BIG idea

24. **SUMMARIZE** Look again at the photograph on pages 410–411. How would you change or add details to your answer to the question on the photograph? (6.5.c)

25. **APPLY** Imagine that you are an ecologist from another galaxy who arrives on Earth. Describe a human community using the terms that an Earth ecologist would use to describe a natural community. Your description should include at least three examples of interactions between individuals (whether the same or a different species). Identify the biotic or abiotic factors that serve as limiting factors to human population growth. Also state whether you think the human population is at or below its carrying capacity—and why. (6.5.e)

## UNIT PROJECTS

By now you should have completed the following items for your unit project:

- questions that you have asked about the topic
- schedule showing when you will complete each step of your project
- list of resources including Web sites, print resources, and materials

## Understanding Symbiosis

6.5.c, 6.5.e

*Read the following description of the strangler fig and the relationship it has with other species in a rain forest. Then answer the questions that follow.*

Strangler figs are part of many symbiotic relationships in a rain-forest ecosystem. In some cases, the symbiotic relationship benefits both the fig and an animal. Fig wasps lay their eggs in the fruit of the strangler fig. In turn, the wasps pollinate the fig. Many birds feed on the fruit of the strangler fig. In doing so, they spread the seeds of the plant. The fig does not benefit from its interactions with all species. For example, certain butterflies feed on juice from the fruit without affecting the tree in any way.

The symbiotic relationship that gives the strangler fig its name is between the strangler fig and its host tree. Birds drop seeds onto the top of a tree, and vines of the fig grow downward. Eventually, the vines of the strangler fig touch the ground and join with the roots of the host tree. The host tree is harmed because the leaves of the strangler fig block sunlight. Also, its roots use up nutrients the host tree needs.

**1.** Which feeding relationship is a form of mutualism in which both species benefit?
- **a.** the strangler fig and its host tree
- **b.** the strangler fig and the butterflies
- **c.** the strangler fig and the birds
- **d.** the strangler fig and the fig wasp

**2.** Which symbiotic relationship is a form of parasitism in which one species benefits and the other is harmed?
- **a.** the strangler fig and its host tree
- **b.** the strangler fig and the butterflies
- **c.** the strangler fig and the birds
- **d.** the strangler fig and the fig wasp

**3.** Which symbiotic relationship is a commensal relationship in which one species benefits without affecting the other?
- **a.** the strangler fig and its host tree
- **b.** the strangler fig and the butterflies
- **c.** the strangler fig and the birds
- **d.** the strangler fig and the fig wasp

**4.** Which word best describes the interaction between the strangler fig and its host?
- **a.** coexistence
- **b.** cooperation
- **c.** competition
- **d.** community

## Extended Response

**5.** Strangler figs attach to trees that are sometimes cut for lumber. Write a paragraph that describes how removal of the host trees would affect these populations.
- butterflies
- birds
- wasps
- strangler figs

**6.** Write a paragraph describing some of the different roles played by a strangler fig in a rain forest. Use the terms below in your answer.

| | | |
|---|---|---|
| habitat | niche | populations |
| community | ecosystem | |

# TIMELINES in Science

6.5.c, 6.5.d, 6.5.e

## WILDERNESS CONSERVATION

The idea of wilderness conservation would have seemed strange to anyone living before the 1800s. The wilderness was vast, and much of the wildlife in it dangerous to humans.

In the late 1800s, smoke from railroads and factories rose in American skies. Scientists, artists, and even presidents began the work of setting aside land as parks and reservations to protect natural landscapes. Forestry, new to the U.S. in the 1890s, became a priority of the federal government. Industries learned to harvest and nurture forests rather than clear them. Next came the protection of animal species and a call to control the pollution and depletion caused by human activity.

**1872**

***National Parks Protect Resources***

On March 1, 1872, President Ulysses S. Grant signs a law declaring Yellowstone's 2 million acres in northwest Wyoming as the country's first national park. The law states that the land will forever be "set apart . . . for the benefit and enjoyment of the people."

EVENTS

1870

APPLICATIONS and TECHNOLOGY

### TECHNOLOGY

**Seeing the Wilderness**

Developments in photography in 1839, and its spread during the Civil War, led to adventurous mobile photographers in the late 1800s. In the early 1860s, Mathew Brady and other photographers took mobile studios to the battlefields to bring war news to the public. By the late 1860s and early 1870s, cameras were much smaller. In 1871 William Henry Jackson used a tripod in Yellowstone as the official photographer of the region's first U.S. Geological Survey.

**1898**

### *U.S. Division of Forestry Formed*

Gifford Pinchot becomes the first chief of the Division of Forestry. Pinchot warns lumberers to abandon clear-cutting. He urges them to practice forestry, a more scientific approach. Pinchot instructs lumberers "to have trees harvested when they are ripe."

**1892**

### *Sierra Club Founded*

The Sierra Club is formed to protect California's Yosemite Valley. John Muir is the choice for President. The club's goal is to help people "explore, enjoy, and protect the planet."

**1916**

### *National Park Service (NPS) Founded*

The system of protected forests grows so big that a federal agency is formed to oversee it. Stephen Mather serves as its first director.

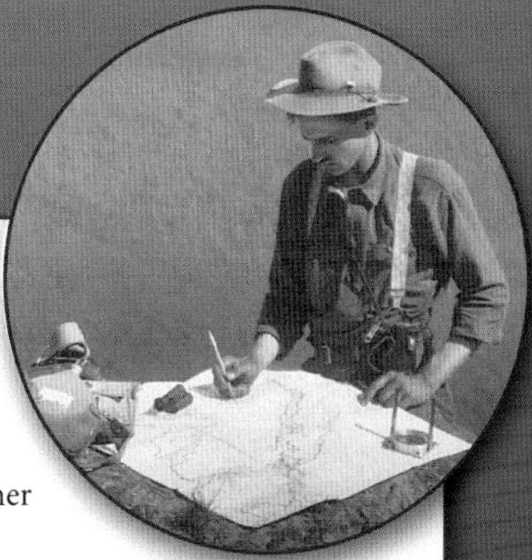

1880 | 1890 | 1900 | 1910

## APPLICATION

### Protecting Animal Species

Fashions of the 1890s used feathers, fur, and even whole birds. Out of concern for the extinction of many birds, a movement to stop wearing rare feathers began. The U.S. Congress enacted the Lacey Act in 1900, which made it illegal to import some birds and mammals. The landmark act became the first in a century of laws protecting animals. The Migratory Bird Treaty of 1918, the Bald Eagle Act of 1940, and the Endangered Species Act of 1973 made animal conservation a national priority. The Endangered Species Act met its strongest test in protecting the northern spotted owl, whose entire range—in California, Oregon, Washington, and Canada—is protected.

**1951**

***Nature Conservancy Established***

The Nature Conservancy is formed to preserve plants, animals, and natural communities that represent Earth's biological diversity.

**1963**

***Glen Canyon Destroyed***

Completion of the Glen Canyon dam causes flooding in Glen Canyon, an immense area north of the Grand Canyon. Many groups fight to close the dam, but it is too late. The canyon is destroyed as Lake Powell forms.

**1962**

**Silent Spring *Breaks Silence***

Biologist and science writer Rachel Carson publishes *Silent Spring.* Chemical pesticides have been widely used and publicized, but Carson uses scientific evidence to show that many of these chemicals harm people and the environment.

**1968**

***Grand Canyon Dam Plans Halted***

Plans to dam the Grand Canyon are withdrawn as a result of public outcry. Recalling what happened to Glen Canyon, organizers ran national newspaper ads in 1966 to make the public aware of plans to dam the canyon.

## TECHNOLOGY

### Maps to Save the Wilderness

Land and wildlife conservation has benefited from computer-based mapping technology called global information systems (GIS). GIS compiles satellite photographs, temperature readings, and other information into a central set of data. Scientists enter distributions of animals and overlay these data on existing maps. The resulting GIS maps show an animal's range and the quality of its habitat. Government efforts to restore the habitat of the endangered San Joaquin kit fox relied on GIS maps.

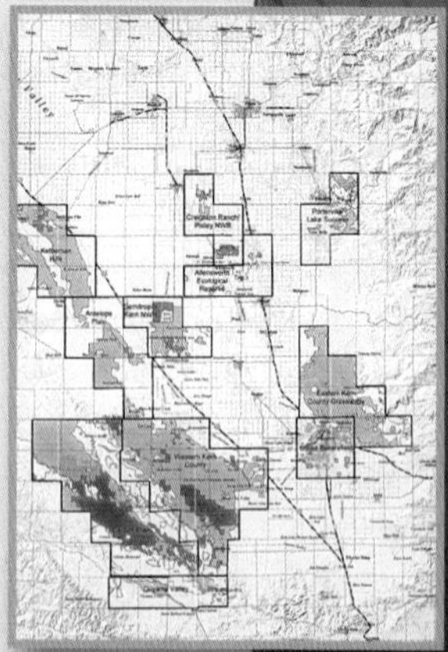

**2001**

***Reservation vs. Resource***

In 1980, Congress expanded the Arctic National Wildlife Refuge (ANWR) to more than twice its size in 1960. In 2001 President George W. Bush proposes limited oil drilling within the range. Debate continues over how to manage its resources and wildlife.

**RESOURCE CENTER**
CLASSZONE.COM

Read more about current conservation efforts.

1990 2000

## APPLICATION

### Selling a Service

In 1996 the New York City water department spent $1.5 billion to protect natural watersheds rather than build a $6 billion water treatment plant. In 2001 a group of scientists met to promote the value that ecosystems bring to society—benefits that include pest control, air purification, and water treatment. For example, dragonflies can eat 300 mosquitoes in a single day. Toads and bats can eat a thousand or more mosquitoes in a single day or night.

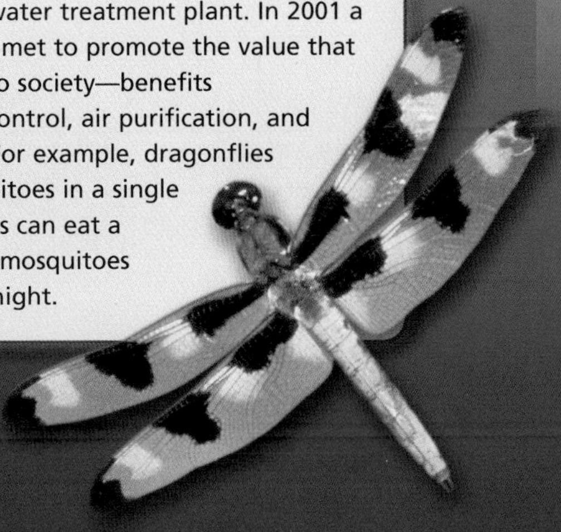

## SPOTLIGHT on

### MARIA MIRITI

Ecologist Maria Miriti studies the interactions of plant populations within a plant community. Her findings have been important for the rapidly growing field of landscape ecology. Knowing how plants interact helps people plan land use, evaluate vegetation changes, and control invasive species.

In 2004 Miriti led a group of researchers in taking a census of desert plants in the Colorado Desert of California's Joshua Tree National Park. They studied the impact of dominant species on plant diversity.

A desert is a harsh environment for plants. Many plants benefit from being close to another plant. Some plants are entirely dependent on other plants for germination, growth, and survival. Miriti thinks deserts are a good model for such studies because all members of the community depend on a scarce water supply.

## ACTIVITIES

### Ecosystem Services Proposal

What services does your local ecosystem provide to the human population? Choose one service and describe how natural processes and interactions within the ecosystem provide the benefits you've identified.

Write a proposal for protecting the ecosystem. Compare the estimated cost of protecting the ecosystem with the cost of human services that provide a similar benefit.

### Writing Project: The Story Behind the News

Research one of the events described on the timeline. Then write the story behind that event.

CHAPTER 13

# Natural Resources

## the BIG idea

**Society depends on natural resources for energy and materials.**

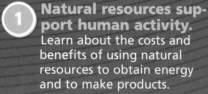

How do people obtain energy from Earth's resources?

## Key Concepts

SECTION 1
**Natural resources support human activity.**
Learn about the costs and benefits of using natural resources to obtain energy and to make products.

SECTION 2
**Minerals and rocks are nonrenewable resources.**
Learn how minerals form, how they are mined, and how they are used.

SECTION 3
**Resources can be conserved and recycled.**
Learn about efforts to conserve and recycle natural resources.

SECTION 4
**Resources can be converted to useful forms.**
Learn how nuclear power and renewable resources can provide energy to the world.

**California ClassZone**

CLASSZONE.COM

Chapter 13 online resources: Content Review, Simulation, Visualization, three Resource Centers, Math Tutorial, Test Practice

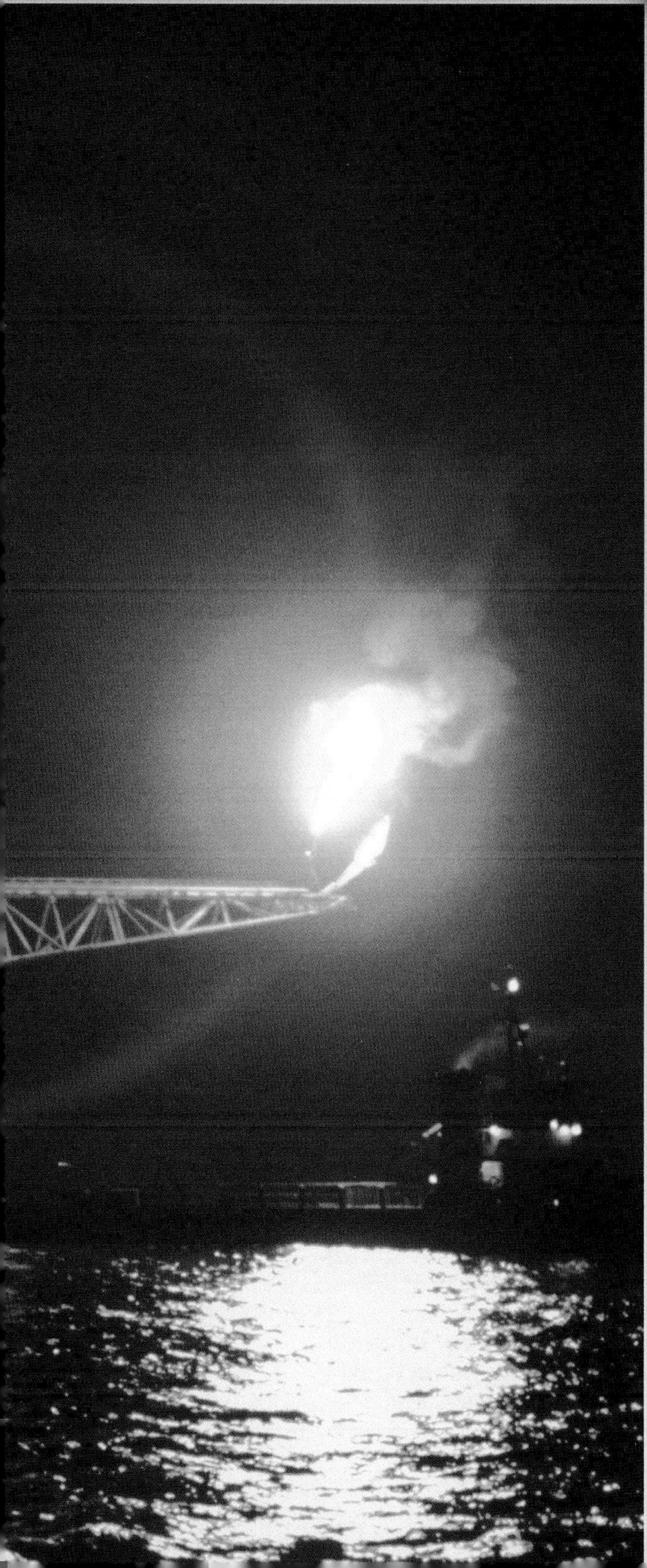

# EXPLORE the BIG idea

## Sunlight as an Energy Source

**6.6.a** Students know the utility of energy sources is determined by factors that are involved in converting these sources to useful forms and the consequences of the conversion process.

Tape black paper around two plastic cups. Half fill the cups with water. Fasten plastic wrap over each top with a rubber band. Place one cup in sunlight and one cup in shade. Wait half an hour. Remove the plastic wrap. Place a thermometer in each cup to measure the water temperature.

**Observe and Think**
What happened to the water temperature in each cup? How do you think people might use sunlight as a source of energy?

## Internet Activity: Resources

**6.6.b** Students know different natural energy and material resources, including air, soil, rocks, minerals, petroleum, fresh water, wildlife, and forests, and know how to classify them as renewable or nonrenewable.

Go to **ClassZone.com** to learn more about natural resources and energy.

**Observe and Think**
What are the most important natural resources in California? How do you use energy from these resources in your daily life?

NSTA scilinks.org SCILINKS

Nonrenewable Resources **Code: MDL056**

CHAPTER 13

# Getting Ready to Learn

## CONCEPT REVIEW

- When fuel is burned, energy is released.
- The Earth system is made up of parts that interact.
- Most rocks are made of minerals.

## VOCABULARY REVIEW

**mineral** p. 184

**fossil, geosphere** *See Glossary.*

**CONTENT REVIEW**
CLASSZONE.COM

Review concepts and vocabulary.

## TAKING NOTES

### SUPPORTING MAIN IDEAS

Make a chart to show each main idea and the information that supports it. Copy each blue heading. Below each heading, add supporting information, such as reasons, explanations, and examples.

### VOCABULARY STRATEGY

Draw a **word triangle** diagram for each new vocabulary term. On the bottom line, write and define the term. Above that, write a sentence that uses the term correctly. At the top, draw a picture to show what the term looks like.

See the Note-Taking Handbook on pages R45–R51.

SCIENCE NOTEBOOK

Natural resources provide materials and energy.

- A natural resource is any energy source, organism, or substance found in nature that people use.
- Four parts of the Earth system provide all the materials needed to support human life.
- There are costs as well as benefits to using natural resources.
- 

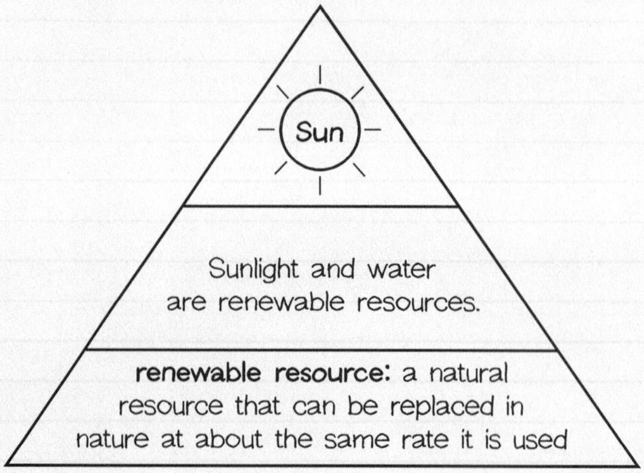

Sun
Sunlight and water are renewable resources.
**renewable resource:** a natural resource that can be replaced in nature at about the same rate it is used

13.1

KEY CONCEPT

# Natural resources support human activity.

**CALIFORNIA Content Standards**

**6.6.a** Students know the utility of energy sources is determined by factors that are involved in converting these sources to useful forms and the consequences of the conversion process.

**6.6.b** Students know different natural energy and material resources, including air, soil, rocks, minerals, petroleum, fresh water, wildlife, and forests, and know how to classify them as renewable or nonrenewable.

**BEFORE, you learned**

- Heat flow transfers energy
- Energy from the Sun heats Earth's surface
- Ecosystems change over time

**NOW, you will learn**

- What makes a natural resource renewable or nonrenewable
- About benefits and costs of using fossil fuels
- How people use natural resources in modern life

**VOCABULARY**

**natural resource** p. 449
**renewable resource** p. 450
**nonrenewable resource** p. 450
**fossil fuel** p. 452

**THINK ABOUT**

***What resources do you need the most?***

Think about all the products you use at school and at home—clothing, books, video games, CDs, backpacks, and other items.

Which ones do you use the most often? What materials are these products made of? Plastic? Cloth? Metal? What would you lose if one of these materials, such as plastic, vanished from Earth overnight?

## Natural resources provide materials and energy.

For thousands of years, people have used natural resources to make tools, build cities, heat their homes, and make their lives more comfortable. A **natural resource** is any energy source, organism, or substance found in nature that people use.

The four parts of the Earth system—atmosphere, hydrosphere, biosphere, and geosphere—provide all the materials needed to support human life. The atmosphere provides the air you breathe and the rain that helps living things grow. The hydrosphere contains all of Earth's waters in rivers, lakes, oceans, and underground. The biosphere and the geosphere are sources of food, fuel, clothing, and shelter.

**VOCABULARY**
Make a word triangle diagram in your notebook for *natural resource.*

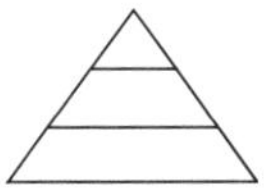

People know that there are costs as well as benefits in using natural resources. For example, burning coal produces heat but also releases smoke that pollutes the air. When forests are cut down, the soil beneath is exposed to the air. Wind and rain can strip away valuable topsoil. This makes it harder for new trees to grow. The soil can choke streams and rivers and kill fish and other animals living in the waters. As you can see, using resources from one part of Earth's system affects all the other parts.

People are also concerned about saving natural resources. Some resources, such as the water in a river or the wind used to turn a windmill, are constantly being replaced. But others, such as oil, take millions of years to form. If these resources are used faster than they are replaced, they will run out. Today, people are more aware of which resources can be renewed and which cannot.

**CHECK YOUR READING** Summarize the costs and benefits of using natural resources.

## Renewable Resources

The charts on page 451 list some of the most common resources people use in modern life. As you might have guessed, sunlight, wind, water, and trees and other plants are renewable. A **renewable resource** is a natural resource that can be replaced in nature at about the same rate it is used.

For example, a lumber company might plant a new tree for each mature tree it cuts down. Over time, the forest will continue to have the same number of trees. However, if the trees are cut down faster than they can be replaced, even a renewable resource will run out.

## Nonrenewable Resources

A **nonrenewable resource** is a natural resource that exists in a fixed amount or that is used up faster than it can be replaced in nature. This means the supply of any nonrenewable resource is limited. In general, all resources produced by geologic forces are nonrenewable. Examples are coal, natural gas, oil, and uranium. These resources form over millions of years.

Today, people are using coal, oil, and natural gas much faster than these resources are forming in nature. As a result, they are becoming more scarce and expensive. Many countries realize that they must conserve their nonrenewable resources. Some, like the United States, are developing alternative energy sources, such as solar and wind energy.

**CHECK YOUR READING** Compare and contrast renewable and nonrenewable resources.

## Natural Resources

**Natural resources can be classified as renewable and nonrenewable.**

**Renewable Resources**

| Resource | Common Uses |
| --- | --- |
| **Sunlight** | power for solar cells and batteries, heating of homes and businesses, and generating electricity |
| **Wind** | power for moving windmills that pump water, grind grain, and generate electricity |
| **Water** | power for generating electricity, transportation by boats and ships, drinking and washing |
| **Trees and other plants** | materials for furniture, clothing, fuel, dyes, medicines, paper, and cardboard |
| **Animal waste** | material for fuels |

**Nonrenewable Resources**

| Resource | Common Uses |
| --- | --- |
| **Coal** | fuel for generating **electricity**, chemicals for medicines and consumer products |
| **Oil** | fuel for cars, airplanes, and trucks; fuel for heating and generating electricity; chemicals for plastics, synthetic fabrics, medicines, grease, and wax |
| **Natural gas** | fuel for heating, cooking, and generating electricity |
| **Uranium** | fuel for generating electricity |
| **Minerals and rocks** | materials for coins, jewelry, buildings, computer chips, lasers, household products, paint, and dyes |

**READING VISUALS** Read the common uses of each resource. Which of these resources are used to generate electricity?

# Fossil fuels supply most of society's energy.

When you turn on an air conditioner, a computer, or a microwave oven, you may use energy from fossil fuels. Billions of people depend on coal, oil, and natural gas for electricity, heat, and fuel.

A **fossil fuel** is a nonrenewable energy resource formed from ancient plants and animals buried in Earth's crust for millions of years. The energy in such a fuel represents a form of stored sunlight, because ancient organisms depended on sunlight. The buried organisms form layers at the bottom of oceans and swamps. Over a long time, this material is compressed and pushed deeper into Earth's crust. High heat and pressure change it chemically into coal, oil, and natural gas.

**CHECK YOUR READING** Explain how fossil fuels are formed from ancient organisms.

## Fossil Fuel Power Station

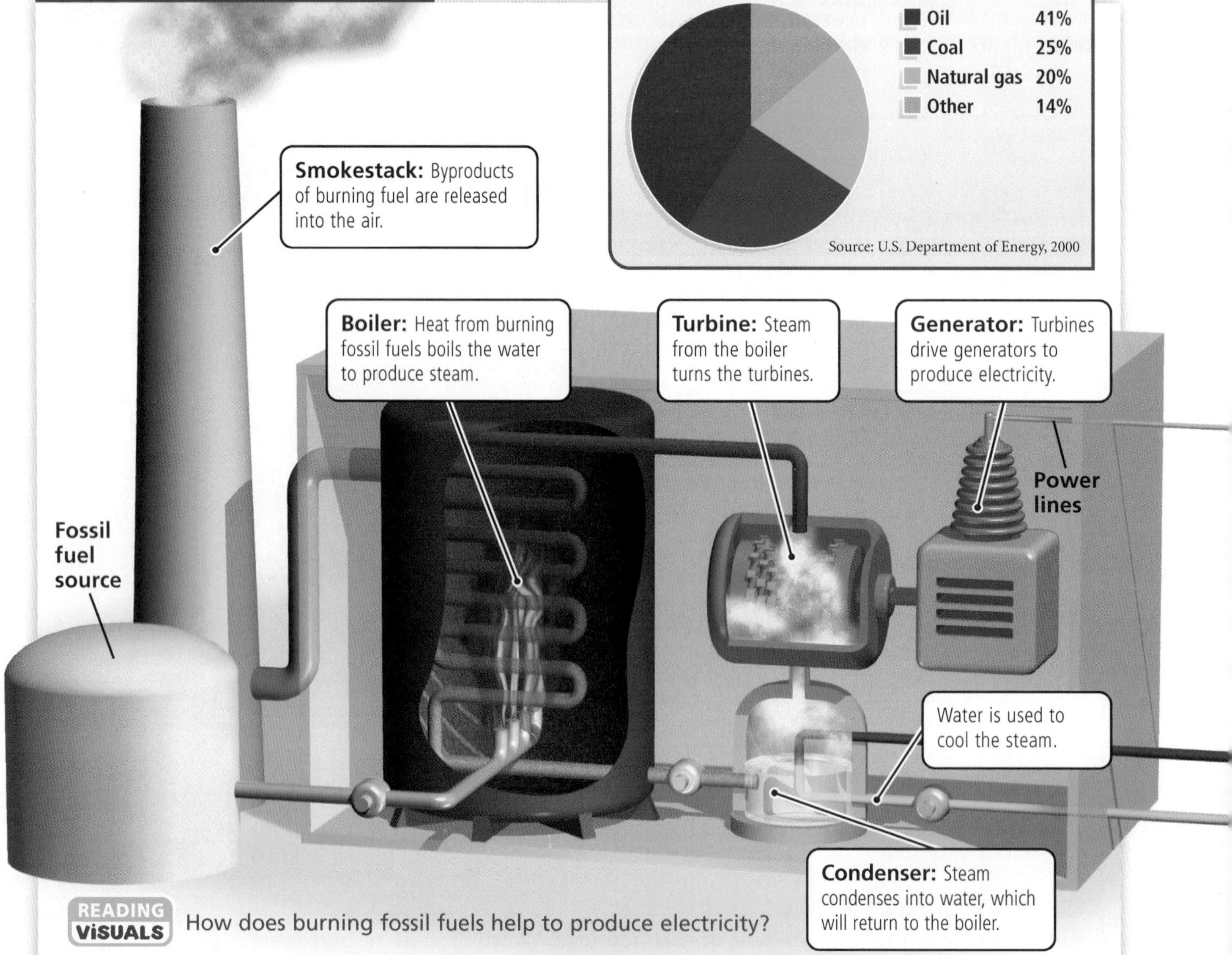

**Smokestack:** Byproducts of burning fuel are released into the air.

Fossil fuel source

**Boiler:** Heat from burning fossil fuels boils the water to produce steam.

**Turbine:** Steam from the boiler turns the turbines.

**Generator:** Turbines drive generators to produce electricity.

**Power lines**

Water is used to cool the steam.

**Condenser:** Steam condenses into water, which will return to the boiler.

### U.S. Energy Sources

| | |
|---|---|
| ■ Oil | 41% |
| ■ Coal | 25% |
| Natural gas | 20% |
| Other | 14% |

Source: U.S. Department of Energy, 2000

**READING VISUALS** How does burning fossil fuels help to produce electricity?

Fossil fuels burn easily and produce a lot of heat. They are used to run most of the power plants that generate electricity in the United States. As shown in the diagram on page 452, heat from a burning fuel is used to change water into steam. The steam turns a turbine. The turbine drives a generator to produce electricity, which is carried through power lines to towns and cities. Electricity is used in many parts of modern life, from running giant factories to the smallest light in your home.

READING TIP

*Turbine* is based on the Latin *turbo,* which means "spinning top." *Generator* is based on the Latin *generāre,* which means "to produce."

But these resources also harm the environment. Burning fossil fuels produces excess carbon dioxide, harmful acids, and other forms of pollution. Most of this pollution comes from power plants and fossil fuels burned by cars and other vehicles.

## Coal

Coal is a solid fossil fuel formed underground from buried and decayed plant material. As shown below, heat and pressure determine the type of coal formed. The hardest coal makes the best energy source. It burns hotter and much cleaner than softer coals. At one time, coal was the main source of energy in the United States.

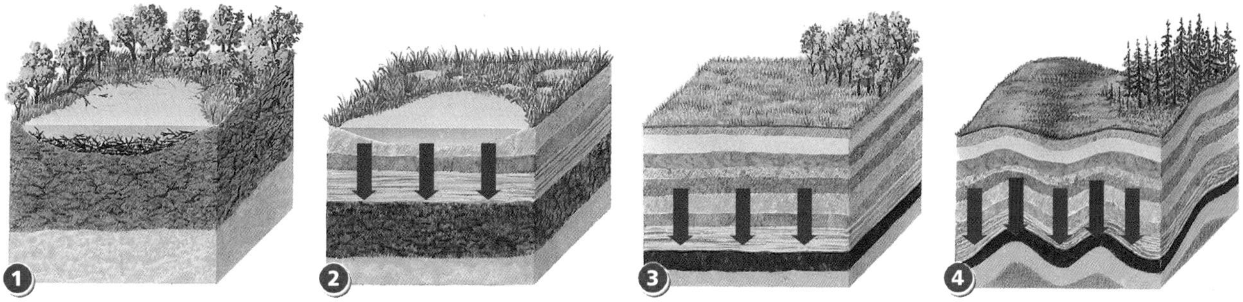

1 Swamp plants decay and are compressed to form peat.

2 Sediments bury the peat. Rising pressure and heat change it into soft coal.

3 Over millions of years, increasing pressure and heat form harder coal.

4 It takes the longest time and the greatest heat and pressure to form the hardest coal.

The United States, Russia, and China are major producers of coal. People use surface mining and deep mining to obtain coal. In surface mines, overlying rock is stripped away to expose the coal. In deep mines, miners must go underground to dig out the coal. Most of the world's coal is used to fuel power plants and to run factories.

When coal is burned as a fuel, it releases byproducts that pollute air and water. Also, surface mining can destroy entire landscapes. Coal dust in mines damages miners' lungs. Yet, reducing pollution, restoring landscapes, and protecting miners cost millions of dollars. Society faces a difficult choice: keep the cost of energy low or raise the price to protect the environment and human health.

CHECK YOUR READING What is the main use of coal?

## Oil and Natural Gas

**READING TIP**

*Non-* is a Latin prefix meaning "not." Porous rock is full of tiny cracks or holes. Therefore, *nonporous* rock is rock that does not have tiny cracks or holes.

Most oil and natural gas are trapped underground in porous rock. Heat and pressure can push the oil and natural gas upward. When they reach a layer of nonporous rock, they are trapped and collect. As shown in the illustration below, wells can be drilled through the nonporous rock to bring the oil and natural gas to the surface. Major oil and natural gas deposits are found under the oceans as well as on land.

**CHECK YOUR READING** How is oil removed from layers of rock?

**CALIFORNIA Focus**

The two main sources of energy in California's energy system are petroleum and natural gas. Second only to Texas, California uses the most natural gas and petroleum per person of the 50 states.

California is also a leader in developing renewable resources, such as solar energy and wind power. It has plans to produce a large amount of its electricity from renewable energy sources.

Recovered oil is transported by ships, trucks, and pipelines from the wells to refineries. Refineries use heat to break down the oil into its different parts. Each part is used to make different products. These include gasoline, jet fuel, cleaning supplies, and plastics. Oil and natural gas burn at high temperatures, releasing energy. They are easily transported, which makes them ideal fuels to heat homes and to power vehicles.

There are costs in using oil. When ships that transport oil are damaged, they can spill millions of gallons into the environment. These spills pollute coastlines and waterways, killing many plants and animals. Cleaning up these spills costs governments millions of dollars each year. Even after the cleanup, some of the oil will remain in the environment for years.

Air pollution is another problem. Waste products from the burning of gasoline, jet fuels, and diesel fuels react with sunlight to produce smog—a foglike layer of air pollution. Some countries have passed clean air laws to reduce this pollution. Yet smog continues to be a problem in most large cities.

**CHECK YOUR READING** What are the benefits and costs of using oil?

### Oil and Natural Gas Wells

Wells are drilled through nonporous rock to bring the oil and gas to the surface.

nonporous shale

Oil and gas are trapped in porous rock layers.

porous sandstone

**Products from a Barrel of Oil**

| | |
|---|---|
| ■ Gasoline | 44% |
| ■ Diesel and heating fuel | 26% |
| ■ Jet fuel | 10% |
| ■ Other products | 9% |
| ■ Gases | 8% |
| ■ Asphalt | 3% |

SOURCE: American Petroleum Institute, 2001

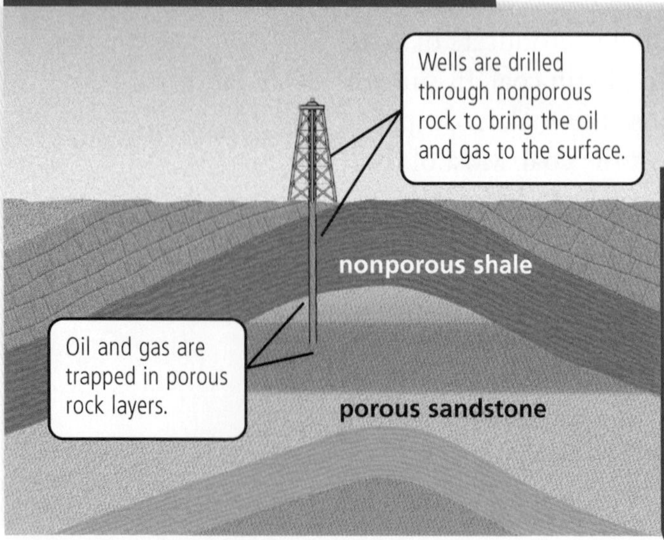

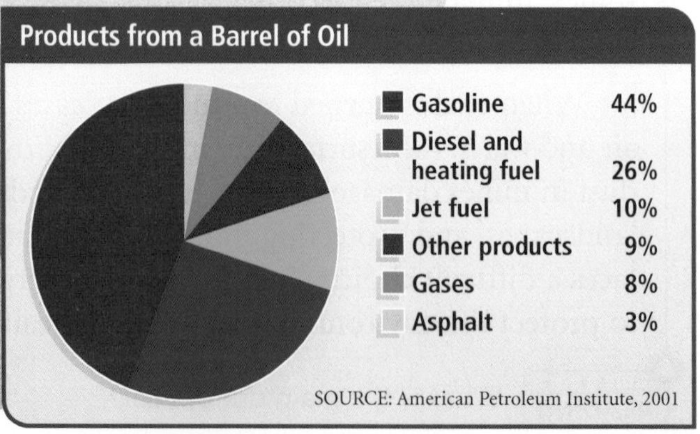

# INVESTIGATE Fossil Fuels Distribution

### *Which fossil fuels are found in California?*

**PROCEDURE**

1. Study the map of U.S. nonrenewable energy resources. Identify the symbols that represent deposits of coal, uranium, natural gas, and oil.
2. Find the state of California on the map. Identify the deposits of nonrenewable resources found in the state of California.
3. Compare the nonrenewable energy resource deposits found in other regions of the United States with those found in California.

**WHAT DO YOU THINK?**

- What types of nonrenewable energy sources shown on the map are found in California?
- How do the types of nonrenewable energy resources in California compare with the types of resources found in the Appalachian region of the United States?

**CHALLENGE** Why do you think the state of California is trying to use more renewable energy resources even though the state is rich in natural gas and oil deposits?

**SKILL FOCUS**
Analyzing data
(6.6.b)

**MATERIALS**
- Map of Fossil Fuels Distribution

**TIME**
15 minutes

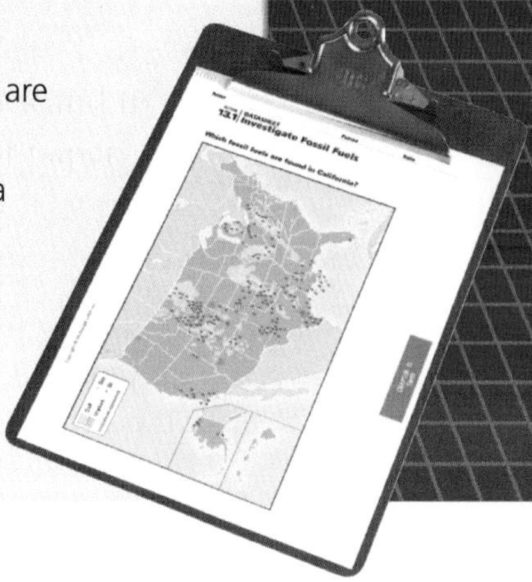

## Fossil fuels, minerals, and plants supply materials for modern products.

Many of the products you use come from fossil fuels. For example, oil is broken down into different chemicals used to make plastics. Plastic materials can be easily shaped, colored, and formed. They are used in electronic and computer equipment, in packaging, in cars and airplanes, and in such personal items as your shoes, toothbrush, and comb.

Minerals are found in cars, airplanes, tools, wires, computer chips, and probably your chair. Minerals such as calcite and gypsum are used to make building materials and cement. In the United States, it takes 9720 kilograms (20,000 lbs) of minerals every year to make the products used by just one person.

Plants are used to make another large group of products. For thousands of years, people have used wood to build homes and to make furniture, household utensils, and different types of paper. Plants are also rich sources of dyes, fibers, and medicines. The plant indigo, for example, has been used to dye fabrics for about 4000 years.

These products benefit people's lives in many important ways, but they also have drawbacks. Fossil fuels must be burned to generate power for the factories and businesses that produce these products.

## Consumer Products

**Thousands of everyday products are made from natural resources.**

### Fossil Fuels

Fossil fuels are used to make thousands of products, from aspirin to zippers. For example, oil-based plastics were used to make this motocross rider's safety helmet, suit, gloves, and boots. Gasoline powers the motorbike.

### Minerals and Rocks

The U.S. Treasury uses zinc, copper, and nickel to mint billions of coins each year. Gold and silver are used in special coins.

### Trees and Other Plants

Each year, the United States produces billions of square meters of corrugated cardboard used to make boxes of all sizes.

Factory waste can pollute air, water, and soil. Even making computer chips can be a problem. A large amount of water is needed to clean the chips during manufacture, which can add to water pollution problems.

To maintain modern life and to protect the planet, people must use natural resources wisely. In the next section, you will read about ways for every person to conserve resources and reduce pollution.

# 13.1 Review

### KEY CONCEPTS

1. Define *renewable resource* and *nonrenewable resource.* Give four examples of each type of resource. (6.6.b)
2. List three advantages and three disadvantages of using fossil fuels. (6.6.a)
3. In what ways are natural resources used to make people's lives more comfortable? (6.6.c)

### CRITICAL THINKING

4. **Infer** Why do you think people are willing to accept the costs as well as the benefits of using fossil fuels?
5. **Predict** If supplies of coal, oil, and natural gas ran out tomorrow, what are some of the ways your life would change?

### CHALLENGE

6. **Apply** Suppose you are lost in the woods, miles from any city or town. You have some dried food and matches but no other supplies. What natural resources might you use to survive until you are found?

California Close-Up

## WATER CONSERVATION

# Feeling Thirsty?

6.6.b Students know different natural energy and material resources, including air, soil, rocks, minerals, petroleum, fresh water, wildlife, and forests, and know how to classify them as renewable or nonrenewable.

Imagine drinking a glass of water. Now imagine millions of people drinking with you. Every day in California more than 35 million people drink water. They also wash, swim, boil pasta, and water their lawns.

Northern California gets plenty of rain and snow. But most Californians live in Southern California, where the climate is dry and hot. The Great Central Valley also gets very little rain. There, huge farms use more than 40 percent of the state's fresh water. All of these numbers add up to one thing: a water problem in California.

Lake Hollywood is a reservoir that was built in 1924 to provide water for the Los Angeles area.

Every winter a lot of snow falls in the Sierra Nevada. When the snow melts, water rushes down the mountainsides. This fresh water is collected in reservoirs. Much of the water used in California is from reservoirs.

California's dry regions get their water from aqueducts. An aqueduct is a human-made pipe or canal that carries water a long way. Aqueducts carry water from the mountains to farms. They bring huge amounts of water from the north to the south. They also bring in more water from Colorado, Oregon, and Mexico.

The California Aqueduct starts at the Sacramento River Delta, east of San Francisco, and continues south a distance of 440 kilometers (273 mi).

Fresh water is a renewable resource as long as there is rain. But because there are so many people in California, fresh water can run out. Therefore, Californians are working to conserve water. Many cities water trees with recycled water. They help people pay for showerheads and toilets that use less water. Other methods for saving water include turning off the tap when brushing teeth and planting gardens that need less water.

Owens Lake was once as large as 280 square kilometers. The city of Los Angeles started using the lake's water in 1913. By 1926 Owens Lake was dry.

### WRITING ABOUT SCIENCE

Write a problem-and-solution essay. Explain some of the water problems in California. Then describe some solutions. Include tips for saving water in daily activities.

KEY CONCEPT

# 13.2 Minerals and rocks are nonrenewable resources.

**CALIFORNIA Content Standards**

**6.6.a** Students know the utility of energy sources is determined by factors that are involved in converting these sources to useful forms and the consequences of the conversion process.

**6.6.b** Students know different natural energy and material resources, including air, soil, rocks, minerals, petroleum, fresh water, wildlife, and forests, and know how to classify them as renewable or nonrenewable.

**6.6.c** Students know the natural origin of the materials used to make common objects.

**VOCABULARY**

**ore** p. 462

**BEFORE, you learned**

- Minerals are classified according to their compositions and crystal structures
- A mineral can be identified by its properties
- Most rocks are made of minerals

**NOW, you will learn**

- How minerals are used in industry and art
- How minerals form
- How minerals are mined

**EXPLORE Minerals at Your Fingertips (6.6.c)**

***What is an everyday use of minerals?***

**PROCEDURE**

1. Observe the core of a wooden pencil. Even though it is called lead, it is made of a mixture of minerals—clay and graphite. A No. 4 pencil has more clay in its lead.
2. Use each pencil to draw something. Notice how each marks the page.

**MATERIALS**

- No. 2 wooden pencil
- No. 4 wooden pencil
- paper

**WHAT DO YOU THINK?**

- Why do pencils have different proportions of clay and graphite?
- When would a No. 4 pencil be more useful than a No. 2 pencil?

## Minerals have many uses in industry.

Minerals are necessary to our modern way of life. Mineral deposits are sources of

- metals for cars and airplanes
- quartz and feldspar for glass
- fluorite and calcite for toothpaste
- silver compounds for photographic film
- mica and talc for paint

These examples illustrate just a few of the many ways we depend on minerals.

**CHECK YOUR READING** Give three examples of the use of minerals in familiar products.

## Minerals have many uses in the arts.

RESOURCE CENTER
CLASSZONE.COM
Learn more about gemstones.

No matter what month you were born in, there is a mineral associated with it—your birthstone. The tradition of birthstones is hundreds of years old. It is one example of the value that people place on the beautiful minerals known as gemstones. In fact, the ancient Egyptians used gems in necklaces and other jewelry at least 4000 years ago.

When gemstones are found, they are usually rough and irregularly shaped. Before a gemstone is used in jewelry, a gem cutter grinds it into the desired shape and polishes it. This process increases the gemstone's beauty and sparkle. The material used to shape and polish a gemstone must be at least as hard as the gemstone itself. Metals, such as gold and silver, also are used in jewelry making and other decorative arts. Both gold and silver are usually combined with copper to increase their hardness.

**CHECK YOUR READING** How are minerals prepared for use in jewelry? What other questions do you have about how minerals are used?

### Uses of Minerals

**Common Uses of Minerals**

| Mineral | Products |
|---|---|
| **Quartz** (source of silicon) | optics, glass, abrasives, gems |
| **Hematite** (source of iron) | machines, nails, cooking utensils |
| **Bauxite** (source of aluminum) | soda cans, shopping carts |
| **Dolomite** (source of magnesium) | insulators, medicines |
| **Chromite** (source of chromium) | automobile parts, stainless steel |
| **Galena** (source of lead) | batteries, fiber optics, weights |
| **Kaolinite** (found in clay) | ceramics, paper, cosmetics |
| **Beryl** (source of beryllium) | computer parts, gems (green form is emerald) |

**Technology**

A clear quartz crystal was sliced to make this computer chip. Minerals such as copper, silver, and gold are commonly used in electronics.

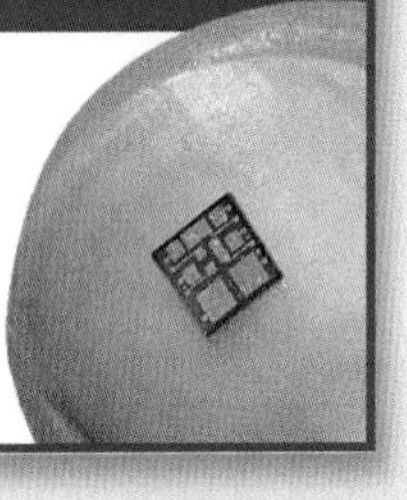

**Industry**

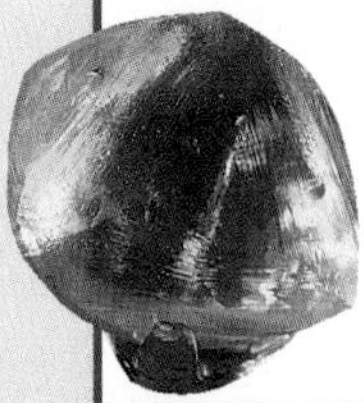

Diamonds are used as abrasives, as in this drill tip. Minerals are also used in such products as insulators and water filters.

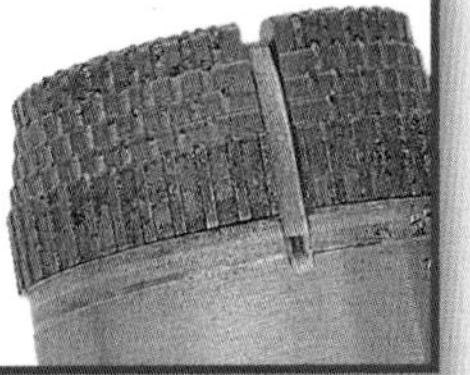

**Arts**

Cinnabar is ground up to make the pigment known as vermilion. Other minerals are also used as pigments in dyes and paints. Gemstones are used in jewelry, as are platinum and gold.

## Minerals form in several ways.

**REMINDER**

An element is a substance that contains only one type of atom. For instance, oxygen is an element. Pure oxygen contains only oxygen atoms.

**SUPPORTING MAIN IDEAS**
Enter each blue heading in a chart and record supporting information.

Minerals form within Earth or on Earth's surface as a result of natural processes. Minerals develop when atoms of one or more elements join together and crystals begin to grow. Recall that each type of mineral has its own chemical makeup. Therefore, what types of minerals form in an area depends in part on which elements are present there. Temperature and pressure also affect which minerals form.

**Water evaporates.** Water usually contains many dissolved substances. Minerals can form when such water evaporates. When salt water evaporates, the atoms that make up halite join to form crystals. Halite is used as table salt. Other minerals form from evaporation too, depending on the substances dissolved in the water. The mineral gypsum often forms as water evaporates.

**Hot water cools.** As hot water within Earth's crust moves through rocks, it can dissolve minerals. When the water cools, the dissolved minerals separate from the water and become solid again. In some cases, minerals are moved from one place to another. Gold can dissolve in hot water that moves through the crust. As the water cools and the gold becomes solid again, it can fill cracks in rocks. In other cases, the minerals that form are different from the ones that dissolved. Lead from the mineral galena can later become part of the mineral wulfenite as atoms join together into new minerals.

**Molten rock cools.** Many minerals grow from magma. Magma—molten rock inside Earth—contains all the types of atoms that are found in minerals. As magma cools, the atoms join together to form different minerals. Minerals also form as lava cools. Lava is molten rock that has reached Earth's surface. Quartz is one of the many minerals that crystallize from magma and lava.

**Heat and pressure cause changes.** Heat and pressure within Earth cause new minerals to form as bonds between atoms break and join again. The mineral garnet can grow and replace the minerals chlorite and quartz as their atoms combine in new ways. The element carbon is present in some rocks. At high temperatures and at high pressure, carbon forms the mineral graphite, which is used in pencils.

**Organisms produce minerals.** A few minerals are produced by living things. For example, ocean animals such as oysters and clams produce calcite and other carbonate minerals to form their shells. Even you produce minerals. Your body produces one of the main minerals in your bones and teeth—apatite.

**CHECK YOUR READING** How is the formation of minerals as molten rock cools similar to the formation of minerals as water evaporates?

## Mineral Formation

**Minerals form at Earth's surface and within Earth.**

**Water evaporates.**

As water evaporates along a shoreline, it leaves behind substances that were dissolved in it. Here, gypsum is forming.

**Hot water cools.**

Gold dissolved in hot water can fill cracks in rocks as the water cools.

**Molten rock cools.**

Minerals such as quartz grow as molten rock cools.

**Heat and pressure cause changes.**

Graphite forms inside Earth when carbon is exposed to great heat and pressure.

**READING VISUALS** Each of the four processes shown involves heat. What is the heat source for quick evaporation of water at Earth's surface?

## Minerals and Ores Around the World

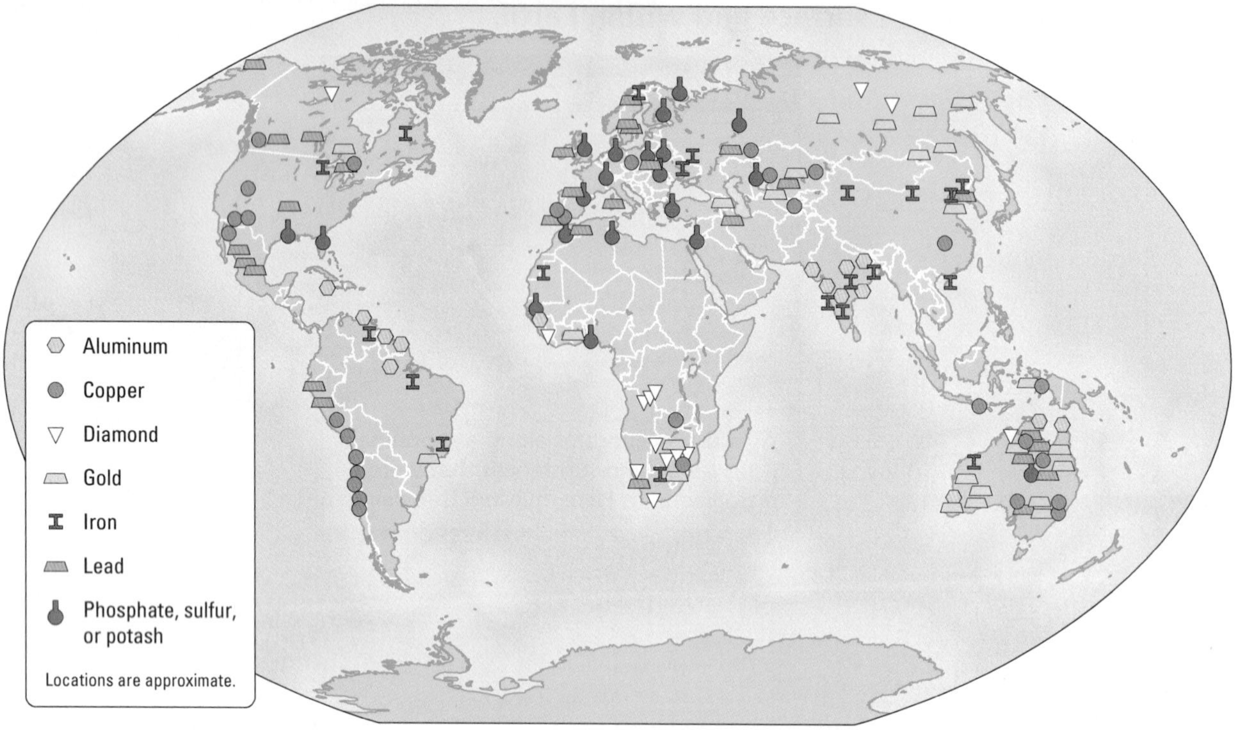


**READING VISUALS** Which mineral resource is most common in the western areas of North America and South America?

## Many minerals are mined.

Before minerals can be used to make products, they must be removed from the ground. Some minerals are found near Earth's surface, while others lie deep underground. Some minerals are found at a wide range of depths, from the surface to deep within Earth.

**READING TIP**
To make a profit, mine owners must be able to sell ores for more than it cost them to dig the ores out.

Most minerals are combined with other minerals in rocks. For any mineral to be worth mining, there must be a fairly large amount of the mineral present in a rock. Rocks that contain enough of a mineral to be mined for a profit are called **ores.**

### Surface Mining

Minerals at or near Earth's surface are recovered by surface mining. Some minerals, such as gold, are very dense. These minerals can build up in riverbeds as less dense minerals are carried away by the water. In a method called panning, a miner uses a pan to wash away unwanted minerals that are less dense. The gold and other dense minerals stay in the bottom of the pan and can then be further separated. In bigger riverbed mining operations, miners use machines to dig out and separate the valuable minerals.

Another method of surface mining is strip mining. Miners strip away plants, soil, and unwanted rocks from Earth's surface. Then they use machines to dig out an ore.

Like strip mining, open-pit mining involves removing the surface layer of soil. Miners then use explosives to break up the underlying rock and recover the ore. As they dig a deep hole, or pit, to mine the ore, they build roads up the sides of the pit. Trucks carry the ore to the surface. Ores of copper and of iron are obtained by open-pit mining.

This open-pit copper mine in Utah is about 4 km wide and 0.8 km deep. For every kilogram of ore removed from the mine, about 5 g of copper is obtained.

**CHECK YOUR READING** How are strip mining and open-pit mining similar? How are they different?

# INVESTIGATE Mining

## *What are the benefits and costs of mining ores?*

**SKILL FOCUS**
Drawing conclusions (6.6.a)

**MATERIALS**
- 1 pound wild-birdseed mix with sunflower seeds
- shallow pan
- 2 small red beads
- 4 small green beads
- 8 small blue beads
- 3 medium yellow beads

**TIME**
25 minutes

### PROCEDURE

1. Put the birdseed into a pan. Add the beads to the birdseed and mix well.
2. Search through the seeds and separate out the beads and sunflower seeds, placing each kind in a different pile. Take no more than 3 minutes.
3. Assign a value to each of the beads and seeds: red bead, $5; green bead, $4; blue bead, $3; sunflower seed, $2. Count up the value of your beads and seeds. For every yellow bead, subtract $100, which represents the cost of restoring the land after mining.

### WHAT DO YOU THINK?

- How does the difficulty of finding the red beads relate to the difficulty of finding the most valuable ores?
- How does the total value of the blue beads and the sunflower seeds compare to the total value of the red and green beads? What can you conclude about deciding which materials to mine?

**CHALLENGE** The sunflower seeds and the red, green, and blue beads could represent minerals that contain copper, gold, iron, and silver. Which bead or seed is most likely to represent each mineral? Explain your choices.

## Deep Mining

Deep-mining methods are needed when an ore lies far below Earth's surface. These methods are used to obtain many minerals. Miners dig an opening to reach a deep ore. When the ore is inside a mountain or hill, miners can cut a level passage to reach the mineral they want. Miners dig a vertical passage to reach an ore that lies underground in a flat area or under a mountain.

From the main passage, miners blast, drill, cut, or dig the ore. If the body of ore is horizontal, miners dig farther and farther into the hill or mountain. If it is vertical, they remove the ore in layers.

These gold miners are working underground near Carlin, Nevada. The world's deepest gold mine is in South Africa and extends almost 4 km (2.5 mi) underground.

# 13.2 Review

### KEY CONCEPTS

1. Give two examples of the use of minerals in industry and two examples of the use of minerals in the arts. (6.6.c)
2. What are the five ways in which minerals form? (6.6.c)
3. What is required for rocks to be considered ores? (6.6.c)

### CRITICAL THINKING

4. **Infer** Would an ore at Earth's surface or an ore deep underground be more expensive to mine? Explain.
5. **Apply** Why do gem cutters usually shape and polish gemstones before using them in jewelry?

### CHALLENGE

6. **Analyze** Both strip mining and open-pit mining are types of surface mining. When might miners choose to use open-pit mining rather than strip mining to obtain an ore?

SCIENCE on the JOB

## GEM CUTTER

# Geometry for Gems

6.6.c Students know the natural origin of the materials used to make common objects.

If you found a gemstone in nature, it would probably look dull and rough. You might want to take it to a gem cutter, who would use a grinding wheel to shape and polish your rough stone into a beautiful gem. You would also discover that a lot of the rough gemstone is ground away into powder.

Gem cutters use geometry to help them choose the best final shapes of gems. Geometry also helps them to shape gems with many small, flat surfaces at specific angles. These surfaces are called facets, and they make the gems sparkle.

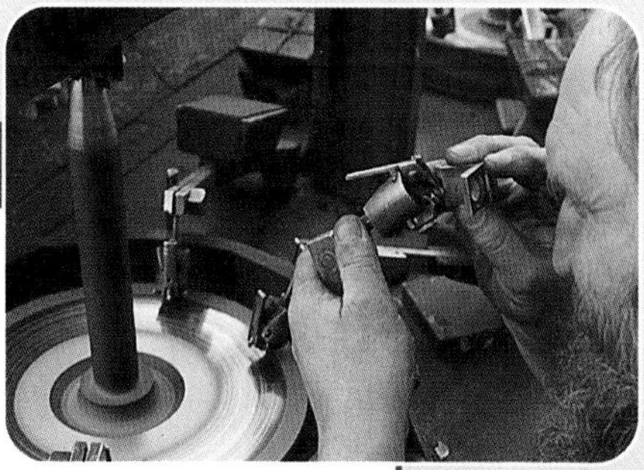

### Starred Gems

Some gems—such as certain rubies, sapphires, and forms of quartz—show a six-pointed star when cut in a rounded shape instead of facets. These gems contain tiny flaws aligned at 120-degree angles. When light hits the flaws, it scatters in a star-shaped pattern. The star ruby shown here is a good example of these beautiful gems.

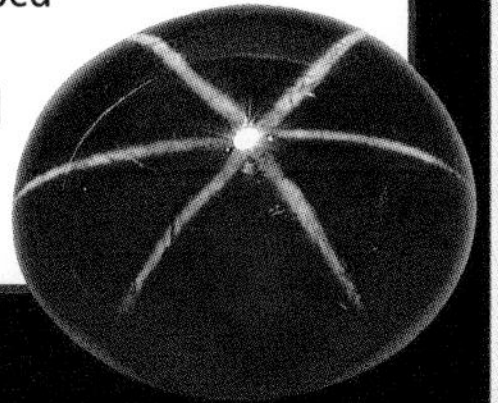

### Sparkling Gems

How much a gem sparkles depends on the geometric angles at which it is cut. If the overall angle of the bottom part of a gem is too shallow **(A)** or too steep **(C)**, light will go through the gem.

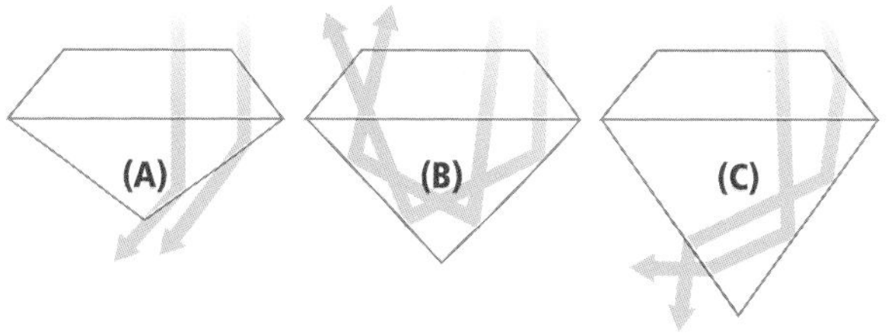


However, if the angles are correct **(B)**, light will bounce around inside the gem as it is reflected to the viewer's eye. The more facets a gem has, the more the light will bounce, and the more the gem will sparkle.

### Deeply Colored Gems

Some gems are shaped to show off their rich colors rather than their sparkle. These gems have fewer and larger facets. Also, many brightly colored gems contain lighter and darker areas of color. The gems are shaped so that the richest color is toward the bottom. Light entering one of these gems strikes the bottom and reflects the rich color to the viewer's eye.

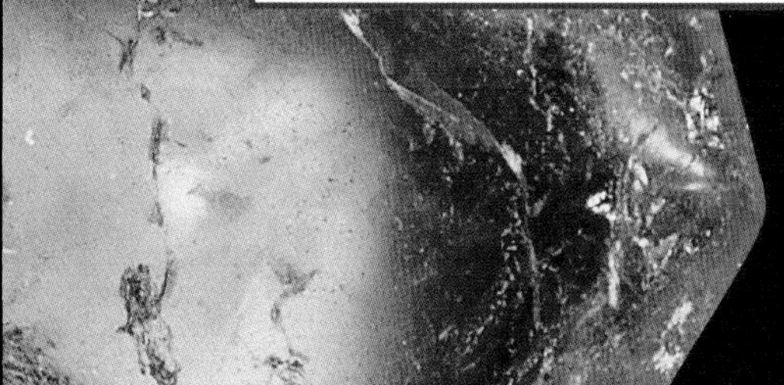

## EXPLORE

1. **COMPARE** Table salt, which is the mineral halite, sparkles as light is reflected from its crystal faces. Snow, which is the mineral ice, also sparkles in sunlight. How are the crystal faces of salt and snow similar to facets? How are they different?
2. **CHALLENGE** When would it be best for a gem cutter to split an irregularly shaped crystal into two or more smaller stones before grinding them into finished gems? Remember, one larger stone is usually more valuable than two smaller ones.

KEY CONCEPT

# 13.3 Resources can be conserved and recycled.

**CALIFORNIA Content Standards**

**6.6.a** Students know the utility of energy sources is determined by factors that are involved in converting these sources to useful forms and the consequences of the conversion process.

**6.6.b** Students know different natural energy and material resources, including air, soil, rocks, minerals, petroleum, fresh water, wildlife, and forests, and know how to classify them as renewable or nonrenewable.

**6.6.c** Students know the natural origin of the materials used to make common objects.

**BEFORE, you learned**

- Natural resources are either renewable or nonrenewable
- Fossil fuels are used to supply most of society's energy and products, but at a cost to the environment

**NOW, you will learn**

- How conservation can help people to reduce waste and reuse natural resources
- How recycling can help people to recover and extend natural resources

**EXPLORE Energy Use (6.6.b)**

***What is your EQ (energy quotient)?***

**PROCEDURE**

1. Think about the electrical appliances you use every day (TV, computer, room lights, microwave, hair dryer). Draw a usage chart like the one in the photo.
2. Estimate the number of hours you use each item every day. Add up all the hours in each column.
3. Multiply the total of each column by 2.5 kilowatts. This is your energy quotient.

**MATERIALS**

- paper
- pen or pencil
- calculator

**WHAT DO YOU THINK?**

- Which item(s) do you use the most? How much of the use is necessary?
- What ways can you think of to conserve electricity each day?

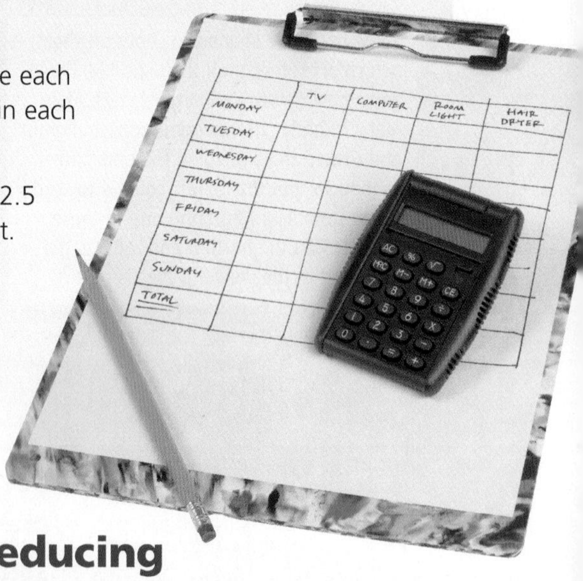


**VOCABULARY**

**conservation** p. 467
**recycling** p. 468

## Conservation involves reducing waste and reusing natural resources.

SUPPORTING MAIN IDEAS
Enter this blue heading in a chart and record supporting information.

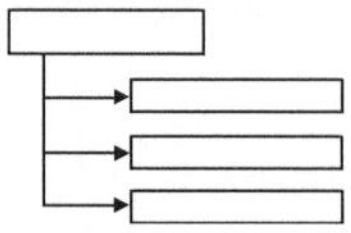

In the 1960s, each person in the United States produced 1.2 kilograms (2.7 lb) of trash a day. Today, that number has more than doubled. All together, the nation's households produce about 236 million tons of trash each year! Over half of this amount is buried in landfills.

Conservation programs can be used to extend natural resources, to protect human health, and to slow the growing mountain of trash. Read on to find out how much your efforts count.

**Conservation** means protecting, restoring, and managing natural resources so that they last as long as possible. Conserving resources can also reduce the amount of pollution released into the air, water, and soil. There are two ways every person can help: reducing and reusing.

**Reduce** You can reduce waste at the source, whether the source is a local store or your own home. Here are a few suggestions:

- When choosing between two similar products, choose the one with less packaging. Product packaging is a major source of paper and plastic waste.
- When brushing your teeth or washing your face, turn the water off until you are ready to rinse. You can save 8 to 23 liters (2 to 6 gal.) of water a day, or 2920 to 8395 liters (730 to 2190 gal.) per year.
- When eating in a restaurant or cafeteria, use only the napkins and ketchup and mustard packets that you really need. The less you throw away, the less garbage will be buried in a landfill.
- Where possible, use energy-efficient light bulbs in your home. Turn off lights and appliances when you are not using them.

**Reuse** Many products can be used more than once. Reusable products and containers conserve materials and resources. Here are some things that you can do:

- Refill plastic water bottles instead of buying new bottles.
- Donate old clothes and other items instead of throwing them away.
- Rinse and reuse plastic sandwich and storage bags.
- Cut the top off a half-gallon container to make a watering can.

**VOCABULARY**
Add a word triangle diagram for *conservation* to your notebook.

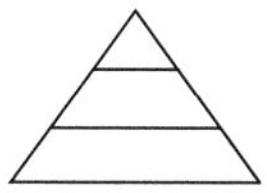

## Reducing Waste

**You can reduce paper and plastic waste by choosing products with the least packaging.**

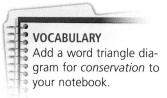

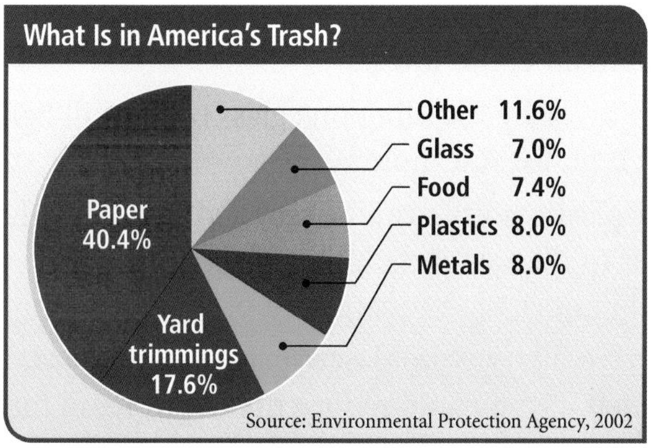


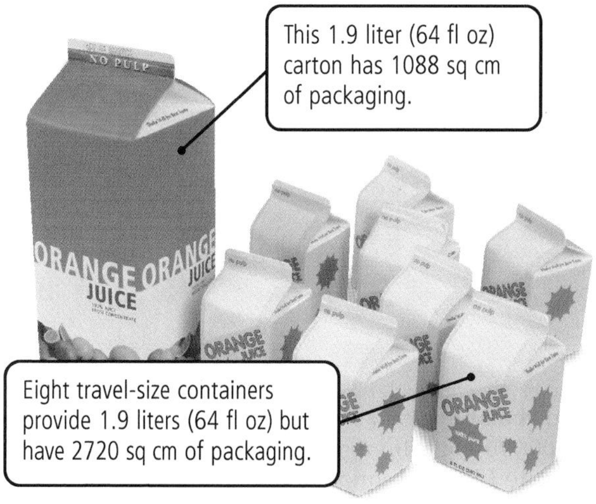

# INVESTIGATE Conservation

## *How can you tell which bulb wastes less energy?*

**DESIGN — YOUR OWN — EXPERIMENT**

The more heat a light bulb gives off, the more energy it wastes. Use what you know about how to measure the temperature of an object to design an experiment that tests which type of light bulb wastes less energy.

**PROCEDURE**

1. Figure out how you are going to test which light bulb—incandescent or fluorescent—wastes less energy.
2. Write up your procedure.
3. Conduct your experiment and record your results.

**WHAT DO YOU THINK?**

- What were the variables in your experiment?
- What were the results of your experiment?
- How does your experiment demonstrate which light bulb is less wasteful?

**SKILL FOCUS**
Designing experiments (6.6.a)

**MATERIALS**
- 2 table lamps
- incandescent light bulb and fluorescent light bulb of same wattage
- 2 thermometers
- pen or pencil

**TIME**
20 minutes

## Recycling involves recovering and extending natural resources.

Did you know that recycling one aluminum can saves enough energy to run a television set for three hours? **Recycling** involves recovering materials that people usually throw away. Some common materials you can recycle are glass, aluminum cans, certain plastics, paper, scrap iron, and such metals as gold, copper, and silver. Here are a few statistics that might encourage you to recycle:

- Recycling 90 percent of the newspapers printed in the United States on just one Sunday would save 500,000 trees, equal to an entire forest.
- The energy saved by recycling one glass bottle will light a 100-watt bulb for four hours.
- Five 2-liter plastic bottles can be recycled into enough plastic fiber to fill a ski jacket. Thirty-six bottles will make enough fiber for a square yard of synthetic carpet.
- If you recycled all household newspapers, cardboard, glass, and metal, you could reduce the use of fossil fuels. It takes less energy to make products from recycled materials than to make new products.

With every item you recycle, you help to recover and extend limited resources.

The average family of four generates about 3000 kilograms (6614 lb) of trash per year. Recycling is catching on, but there is still a long way to go.

It is important to remember that not every item can be recycled or reused. In the photograph above, for instance, only about one-sixth of the family's trash is being recycled. Even some types of plastic and glass items must be thrown away because they cannot be recovered. All the trash in the family's plastic bags will be buried in landfills. You can see why it is important to recycle the items you can and to avoid using items that cannot be recycled.

Recycling is only part of the solution to our resource problems. It takes time, energy, and money to collect waste materials, sort them, remove what can be used, and form new objects. Even with these limitations, recycling can help extend available resources and protect human health and the environment.

**CHECK YOUR READING** What are some of the benefits and drawbacks of recycling?

# 13.3 Review

## KEY CONCEPTS

1. Give examples of ways people can reduce waste and conserve natural resources. (6.6.b)
2. Explain how recycling can help people recover and extend natural resources. (6.6.b)
3. What are some of the limitations of conservation and recycling programs? (6.6.b)

## CRITICAL THINKING

4. **Evaluate** How can conserving or recycling materials help protect the environment?
5. **Calculate** Your city pays $115 per ton to bury an average of 13 tons of garbage a month in a landfill. A recycling program could reduce that number to 8 tons a month. How much would the city save in landfill fees per month? per year?

## CHALLENGE

6. **Synthesize** Work with a group of classmates to list some of the ways in which you could conserve and recycle resources in your home and at school. Create a poster or advertisement to present your ideas to the rest of the class.

MATH in SCIENCE

**MATH TUTORIAL**
CLASSZONE.COM
Click on Math Tutorial for more help with bar graphs.

Math 6.MR.2.4
Science 6.7.c

Machines mounted on boats drill down into the ocean floor to collect sediment cores.

This tube contains a sediment core.

## SKILL: MAKING A DOUBLE BAR GRAPH

# Tracking Contaminants

The layered sediments at the bottom of the ocean have formed over time. The particles in the deeper layers settled to the floor long ago, while those in the top layers settled out of the water more recently. By studying the amounts of pollutants in different layers of sediment, scientists can see how the water quality has changed over time. In 1991 scientists collected sediment cores north of Dash Point in Puget Sound. The table below shows levels of two pollutants, lead and arsenic, in the sediment layers for 1880, 1960, and 1990. The levels are measured in milligrams per kilogram dry weight (mg/kg d.w.).

**Levels of Lead and Arsenic in Sediments**

| Year | Lead (mg/kg d.w.) | Arsenic (mg/kg d.w.) |
|---|---|---|
| 1880 | 10 | 6 |
| 1960 | 62 | 22 |
| 1990 | 45 | 17 |

You can use a double bar graph to analyze the data. A double bar graph shows two sets of data on the same graph. The first two bars of the graph are drawn for you below.

### Example

**(1)** Copy the axes and labels.

**(2)** Draw bars for the lead data. Use the scale to determine the height of each bar, as shown.

**(3)** Draw the arsenic bars next to the lead bars.

**(4)** Shade the bars in different colors. Include a key.

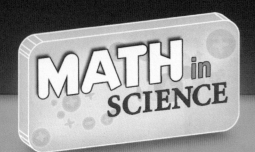

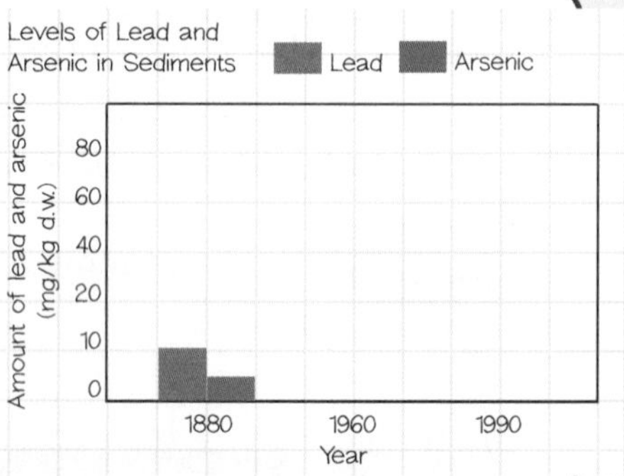


**Make a double bar graph of the data by following the steps above. Use your graph to answer the following questions.**

1. What happened to the levels of lead and arsenic between 1880 and 1960?

2. What happened to the levels of lead and arsenic between 1960 and 1990?

**CHALLENGE** Because lead can be harmful to humans, all new cars were designed to run on unleaded gasoline starting in 1975. The use of lead-based paint in homes was banned in 1978. How might these bans have affected the amount of lead in Puget Sound? Use evidence from your graph to support your answer.

KEY CONCEPT

# 13.4 Resources can be converted to useful forms.

**CALIFORNIA Content Standards**

**6.3.a** Students know energy can be carried from one place to another by heat flow or by waves, including water, light and sound waves, or by moving objects.

**6.6.a** Students know the utility of energy sources is determined by factors that are involved in converting these sources to useful forms and the consequences of the conversion process.

**BEFORE, you learned**

- Conservation helps people reduce waste and reuse natural resources
- Recycling helps people recover and extend natural resources

**NOW, you will learn**

- How renewable resources are used to generate energy
- About the benefits and costs of nuclear power

**VOCABULARY**

**hydroelectric energy** p. 472
**geothermal energy** p. 473
**solar cell** p. 475
**biomass** p. 476
**hydrogen fuel cell** p. 476
**nuclear energy** p. 477

**THINK ABOUT**

***What can the energy of moving water do?***

The flow of water over the upper edge of Yosemite Falls is the greatest in the spring. About 9000 liters (2400 gallons) of water go over the cliff's edge every second. The water flows through a V-shaped cut in the cliff. Where did the energy come from to cut the rock of the cliff?

**SUPPORTING MAIN IDEAS** Enter this blue heading in a chart and record supporting information.

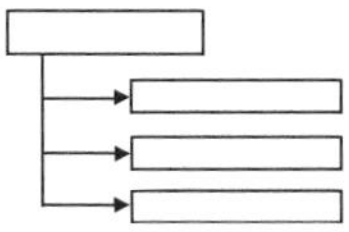

## Renewable resources are used to produce electricity and as fuel.

Sources of renewable energy include moving water, sunlight, and wind. Unlike fossil fuels, many renewable sources of energy are unlimited in supply. These sources can be converted to useful forms such as electricity. The conversion produces little or no air pollution. Using these clean energy sources helps preserve the environment and protect human health.

However, so far these resources cannot produce enough energy to pay for the cost of developing them on a large scale. As a result, only about 6 percent of the total energy used in the United States comes from these resources. Scientists and engineers must improve the necessary technologies before renewable resources can supply more clean energy.

**CHECK YOUR READING** What makes renewable resources attractive as energy sources?

## Hydroelectric Energy

**Hydroelectric energy** is electricity produced by moving water. If you have ever stood near a waterfall or even just turned on a faucet, you have felt the force of moving water. People can use flowing water to generate electricity.

**RESOURCE CENTER**
CLASSZONE.COM
Learn more about the benefits and costs of renewable energy resources.

In most cases, a dam is built across a large river. It blocks the river's flow and creates an artificial lake, or reservoir. As the illustration below shows, water from the reservoir enters the dam through intake gates and flows down a tunnel. The fast-flowing water turns turbines that drive generators, which produce electricity. Because hydroelectric power does not burn any fuel, it produces no air pollution. Dams in the United States generate enough electricity to save 500 million barrels of oil a year.

However, building dams poses problems for the environment. By flooding land to create reservoirs, dams destroy wildlife habitats. In some rivers, such as the Snake and Columbia rivers in the United States, dams interfere with the annual migration of salmon and other fish. Areas near the end of the river may receive less water than before, making it harder to raise crops and livestock.

Areas with large rivers can use their power to produce electricity. The dam in the photo was built on the Yukon River in Alaska.

### Hydroelectric Dam

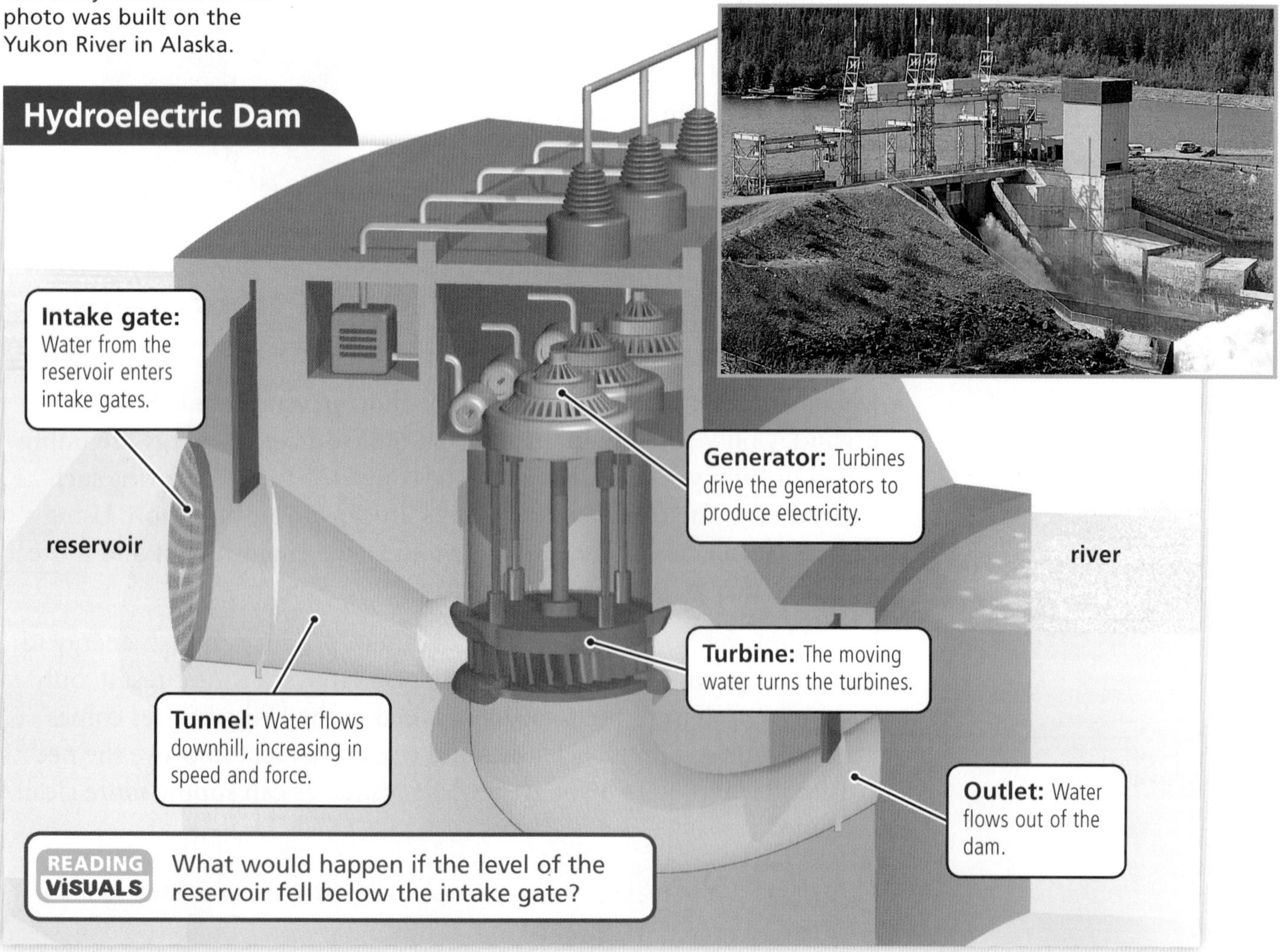

**Intake gate:** Water from the reservoir enters intake gates.
**Generator:** Turbines drive the generators to produce electricity.
reservoir
river
**Turbine:** The moving water turns the turbines.
**Tunnel:** Water flows downhill, increasing in speed and force.
**Outlet:** Water flows out of the dam.

**READING VISUALS** What would happen if the level of the reservoir fell below the intake gate?

## Geothermal Energy

Imagine tapping into Earth's heat to obtain electricity for your home. In some places, that is exactly what people do. They use **geothermal energy,** or energy produced by heat within Earth's crust.

Geothermal energy comes from underground water that is heated by hot rock. The illustration below shows how hot water is piped from a well into a power plant. This superheated water enters a flash tank and produces enough steam to run turbines, which power generators. Excess water is then pumped back into the ground. Some plants also pipe hot water into homes and businesses for heating.

In the United States, geothermal energy provides electricity for more than 3.5 million people. Other major geothermal power plants are in New Zealand and Iceland.

Geothermal energy is clean and renewable. So far, its use is limited to areas where hot water is fairly close to the surface. However, some companies are experimenting with pumping cold water into underground areas of hot rock in Earth's crust. The rock heats the water, which is then pumped back to the surface and used to generate electricity. This new technique may allow more countries to make use of geothermal energy.

**READING TIP**

*Geothermal* combines the Greek prefix *geo-*, meaning "earth," and the Greek word *thermē*, meaning "heat."

**CHECK YOUR READING** What is the source of geothermal energy?

### Geothermal Power Plant

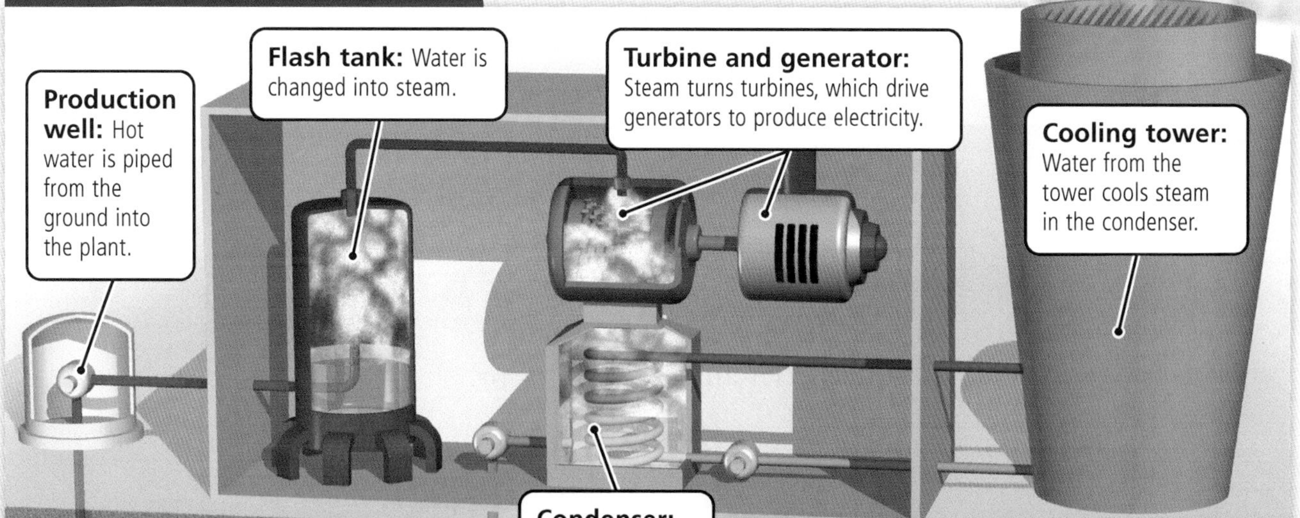
**Production well:** Hot water is piped from the ground into the plant.
**Flash tank:** Water is changed into steam.
**Turbine and generator:** Steam turns turbines, which drive generators to produce electricity.
**Cooling tower:** Water from the tower cools steam in the condenser.
**Condenser:** Steam condenses into water.
**Injection well:** Excess water is pumped back into the ground.

**READING VISUALS** How is this plant similar to a nuclear power plant? How is it different?

In Iceland, geothermal power plants like the one in the photograph supply nearly all of the country's electricity.

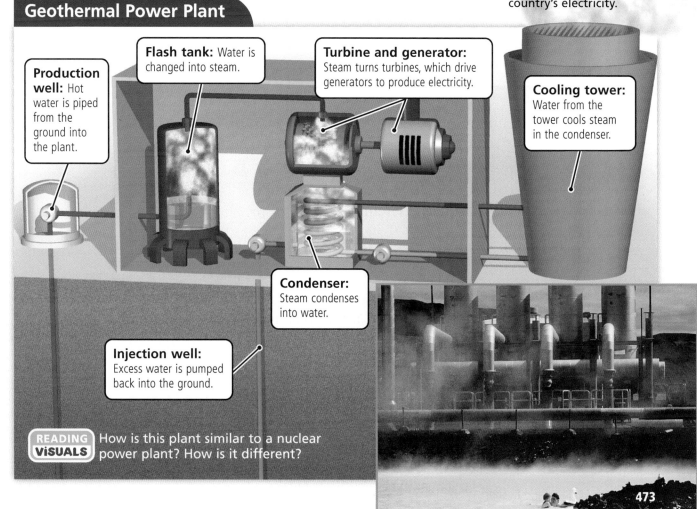

## Wind Energy

For thousands of years, people have captured the tremendous energy of wind to move ships, grind grain, and pump water from underground. Today, people also use wind energy—from the force of moving air—to generate electricity.

REMINDER

The generator is the part that produces the electric current, whether it is driven by turbines or gears.

A modern windmill can stand as tall as a 40-story building. The blades act as a turbine, turning a set of gears that drives the generator. The amount of electricity a windmill produces depends on the speed and angle of the wind across its blades. The faster the blades turn, the more power the windmill produces.

To supply electricity to an area, hundreds of windmills are built on a "wind farm." Wind farms are already producing electricity in California, Hawaii, Texas, and other states. Other countries, such as Denmark and Germany, also use wind farms to supply electricity to some of their cities.

Although wind energy is clean and renewable, it has certain drawbacks. It depends on steady, strong winds blowing most of the time, which are found only in a few places. Wind farms take up a great deal of land, and the turning blades can be noisy. There is also a limit to how much power each windmill can produce. However, in the future, wind farms may become more productive and more widely used.

CHECK YOUR READING What factor determines how much electricity a windmill produces?

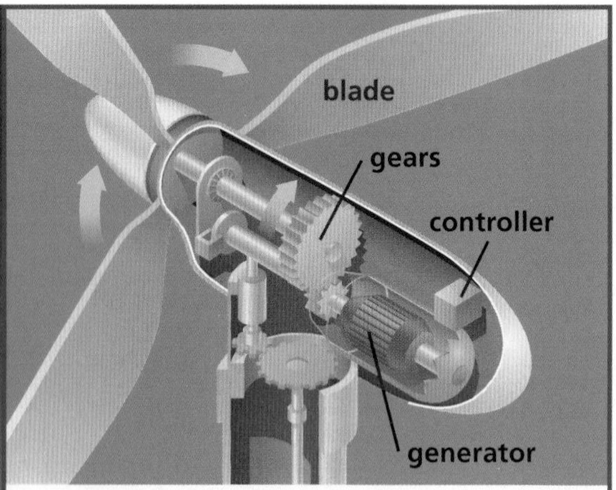


The blades turn the gears, which drive the generator to produce electricity. The controller causes the windmill to operate when wind speeds are about 15 to 100 km/hr.

## Solar Energy

Only a tiny amount of the Sun's energy falls on Earth. Yet even this amount is huge. Enough solar energy strikes the United States each day to supply the country's energy needs for a year and a half. The problem is how to use this abundant resource to produce electricity.

In an effort to solve the problem, scientists developed solar cells. A **solar cell** is a specially constructed sandwich of silicon and other materials that converts light energy to electricity. A single solar cell produces a small amount of electricity. It could be used to power small appliances, such as calculators and watches.

**VOCABULARY**
Add a word triangle diagram for *solar cell* in your notebook.

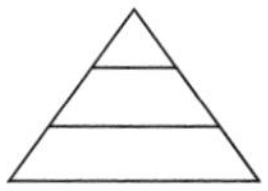

The diagram below shows that many solar cells can be used together. They can be put into solar panels, which provide heat and electricity for homes and businesses. Solar panels are also used to power some spacecraft and space stations once they are in orbit. To meet the energy needs of some cities, hundreds or even thousands of solar panels are built into large structures called arrays. Many cities in the western United States receive part of their electricity from solar arrays.

**READING TIP**
An array is an arrangement of objects in rows and columns.

Sunlight is an unlimited source of clean energy. But current methods of collecting sunlight are expensive and somewhat inefficient. As solar technology improves, sunlight is likely to become an important energy source for the world.

**CHECK YOUR READING** How can people use sunlight to produce electricity?

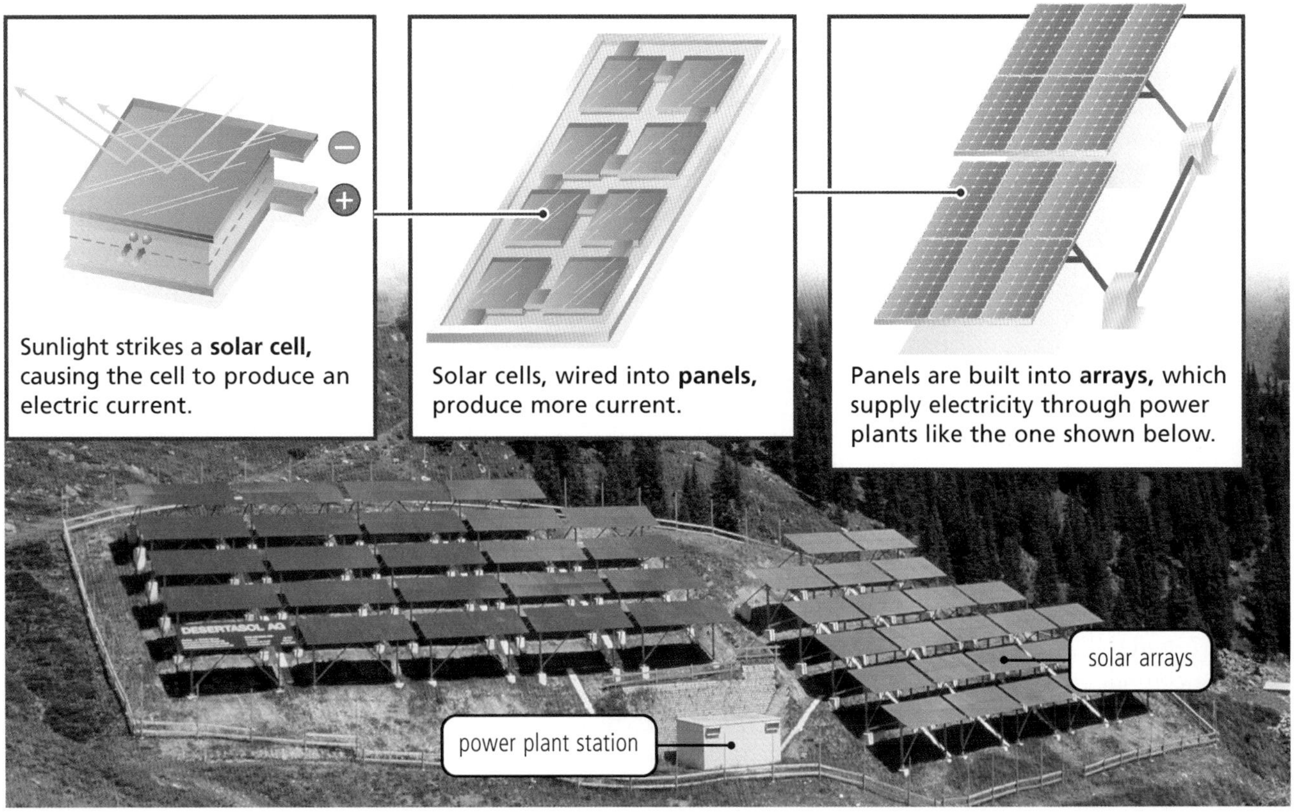


Sunlight strikes a **solar cell,** causing the cell to produce an electric current.

Solar cells, wired into **panels,** produce more current.

Panels are built into **arrays,** which supply electricity through power plants like the one shown below.

## Biomass Energy

**Biomass** is organic matter, such as plant and animal waste, that can be used as fuel. The U.S. Department of Energy works with state and local groups to find ways of converting biomass materials into energy sources.

This wood-burning biomass plant sends electrical energy at a rate of 21 million watts to the San Francisco Bay area. Wood waste products are collected from farms and industries as fuel for the plant.

Each year biomass power stations in the United States burn about 60 million tons of wood and other plant material to generate 40 billion kilowatt hours of electricity. That is similar to the amount of electricity the state of Colorado uses per year. Small biomass stations are used in rural areas to supply power to farms and towns. Fast-growing trees, grasses, and other crops can be planted to supply a renewable energy source that is cheaper than fossil fuels.

Some plant and animal waste can be converted into liquid fuels. For example, the sugar and starch in corn and potatoes are made into a liquid fuel called ethanol. Ethanol can be added to gasoline to form gasohol. This fuel can power cars, farm machinery, and buses. A liquid fuel made from animal waste is used for heating and cooking in many rural areas around the world.

Although biomass is a renewable resource, certain problems limit its use. Burning wood and crops can release as much carbon dioxide into the air as burning fossil fuels does. Biomass crops take up land that could be used to raise food. Also, plant fuels such as ethanol are expensive to produce on a large scale. For now, biomass materials provide only a small part of the world's energy.

**CHECK YOUR READING** What are the advantages and disadvantages of biomass fuels?

## Hydrogen Fuel Cells

**VISUALIZATION**
CLASSZONE.COM
Watch a hydrogen fuel cell in action.

Scientists are also exploring the use of hydrogen gas as a renewable energy source. They have found ways to generate hydrogen from water and from fossil fuels. Hydrogen gas can be set on fire easily and must be handled with care.

Hydrogen is used in a **hydrogen fuel cell,** a device that produces electricity by a chemical reaction between hydrogen and oxygen. Hydrogen enters one side of the cell while oxygen from the air enters the other side. As the reaction happens, electricity flows out of the cell through wires and powers the motor. Water forms as a byproduct of the reaction.

Hydrogen fuel cells are used to supply electrical energy on spacecraft and space stations. Fuel-cell buses are being tested in several countries. Some fuel-cell cars are now available to the public. Storage tanks in these vehicles carry hydrogen fuel for the cells.

A storage tank in the back of this SUV holds hydrogen fuel. Electrical energy from fuel cells powers the motor and a backup battery.

Fuel-cell technology holds great promise for the future. Hydrogen is a clean source of energy, producing only water and heat as byproducts. If every vehicle in the world were powered by hydrogen, the level of air pollution would drop sharply.

However, hydrogen fuel cells are still too expensive to produce in large numbers. Separating hydrogen from water or from fossil fuels takes a great deal of energy, time, and money. Also, there are only a few fueling stations to supply cars and other vehicles that run on hydrogen. The U.S. Department of Energy is working with the automotive industry and other industries to solve these problems.

**CHECK YOUR READING** Why is hydrogen considered a promising alternative energy source?

## Nuclear power is used to produce electricity.

Nuclear energy power plants generate about 20 percent of the total energy used in the United States. **Nuclear energy** is produced by releasing energy contained in the nucleus, or center part, of atoms.

The source of energy in a nuclear power plant is uranium, which is an element. You read in Chapter 6 that an element is a substance that contains only one type of atom. Some elements, such as uranium, are unstable. They change into other elements over time.

An atom of an unstable element has an unstable nucleus. The nucleus gives off particles and energy in a process known as radioactivity. Radioactivity continues until enough particles and energy have been given off to create a new, stable nucleus. In this process, atoms of the original, unstable element can change into atoms of a completely different element.

**READING TIP** *Unstable* means "having a strong tendency to change."

READING TIP
The plural form of the word *nucleus* is *nuclei*.

A nuclear power plant uses uranium atoms as fuel. The atoms' nuclei are made to split, which releases a huge amount of energy. When each atom splits, it produces two smaller atoms. It also releases several tiny particles. The tiny particles hit other uranium nuclei, causing them to split.

A chain reaction happens as particles from each split atom cause other atoms to split. You can think of this process as being similar to shooting one marble into a group of marbles. Every marble that is hit will strike other, nearby marbles.

The power-plant diagram below shows a reactor vessel, which is where the chain reaction takes place. Control rods are used to limit the reaction to provide a safe amount of energy. The chain reaction creates enough heat to produce steam in the reactor vessel. The steam heats a coiled pipe, which is used to boil water in the heat exchanger.

Steam from the exchanger turns the turbines, which drive the generators that produce electricity. The steam condenses into water and is pumped back into the heat exchanger. Water from the cooling tower keeps the equipment from overheating. As you can see, nuclear power plants require a large water supply to produce steam and to stay cool.

## Nuclear Power Plant

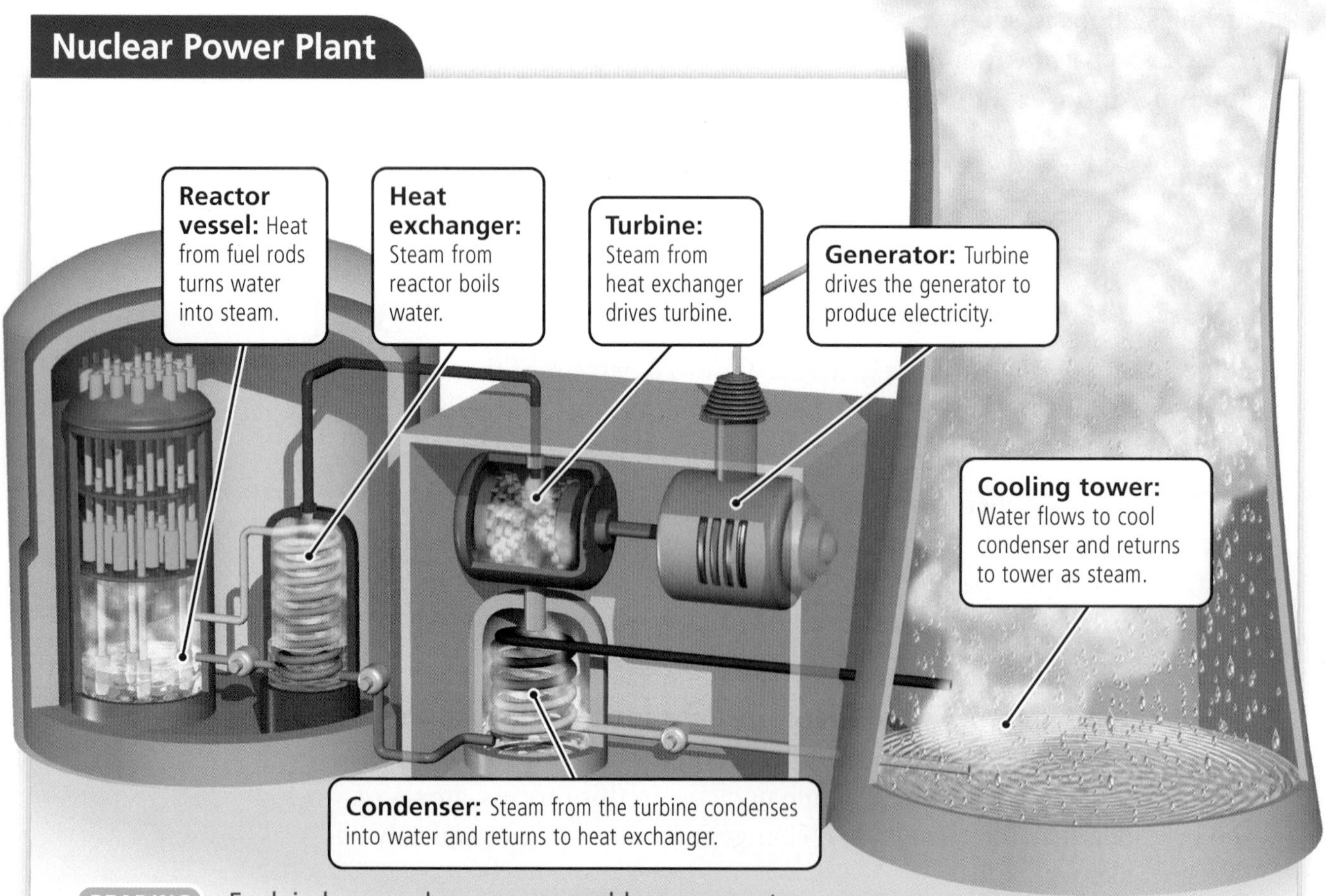
**Reactor vessel:** Heat from fuel rods turns water into steam.
**Heat exchanger:** Steam from reactor boils water.
**Turbine:** Steam from heat exchanger drives turbine.
**Generator:** Turbine drives the generator to produce electricity.
**Cooling tower:** Water flows to cool condenser and returns to tower as steam.
**Condenser:** Steam from the turbine condenses into water and returns to heat exchanger.

**READING VISUALS** Explain how nuclear energy enables a generator to produce electricity.

A nuclear power plant usually has three main sections: reactor buildings, turbine buildings, and cooling towers.

Splitting just one atom of uranium releases millions of times more energy than burning one molecule of natural gas does. However, nuclear power plants also produce radioactive waste. Radioactivity can cause death and disease if living things are exposed to it long enough. Nuclear waste from a power plant will remain radioactive for thousands of years. Countries that use nuclear energy face the challenge of storing this waste safely. The storage sites must keep any radioactivity from escaping until the waste material becomes harmless.

**CHECK YOUR READING** Explain how nuclear energy is used to generate electricity.

**SIMULATION** CLASSZONE.COM

Explore how a nuclear power plant produces energy.

# 13.4 Review

## KEY CONCEPTS

1. Describe the advantages of using sunlight, water, and Earth's heat energy to produce electrical power. (6.3.a)
2. What are some factors that limit the use of biomass, wind, and hydrogen as energy sources? (6.6.a)
3. List the main advantages and disadvantages of nuclear energy as a power source. (6.6.a)

## CRITICAL THINKING

4. **Evaluate** Do you think people would use a clean, renewable fuel that cost twice as much as gasoline? Explain.
5. **Calculate** One acre of corn yields 20 gallons of ethanol. A bus gets 20 miles per gallon and travels 9000 miles in one year. How many acres of corn are needed to fuel the bus for a year?

## CHALLENGE

6. **Synthesize** Review the energy sources discussed in this section. Then think of ways in which one or more of them could be used to supply electricity to a house in Florida and a house in Alaska. Which energy sources would be best in each environment? Describe your ideas in writing, or make sketches of the houses.

# CHAPTER INVESTIGATION

## Wind Power

**OVERVIEW AND PURPOSE** Early windmills were used to pump water and grind flour. In this lab, you will use what you have learned about renewable resources to

- build a model windmill and use it to lift a small weight
- improve its performance by increasing the strength of the wind source

### Problem

Write It Up

What effect will increasing the wind strength have on the lifting power of a model windmill?

### Hypothesize

Write It Up

After completing step 8 of the procedure, write a hypothesis to explain what you think will happen in the next two sets of trials. Your hypothesis should take the form of an "If . . . , then . . . , because . . ." statement.

### Procedure

1. Make a data table in your **Science Notebook,** like the one on page 481.

2. Cut a 15 cm square from a file folder. With a ruler, draw lines from the corners toward the center, forming an X. Where the lines cross, draw a circle around the quarter. Cut inward along the lines from the four corners, stopping at the circle. Punch a hole in each corner, as shown. Also punch a hole in the center of the circle.

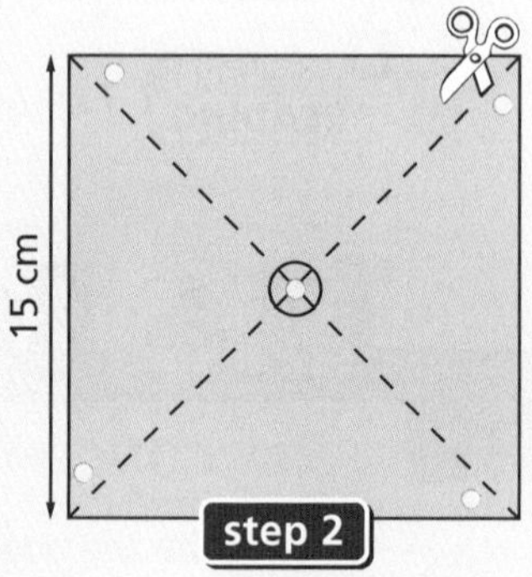


3. Bend the cardboard to align the holes and form a pinwheel. Push a paper fastener through the holes toward the back of the pinwheel. Do not flatten the metal strips of the fastener.

4. Use a pushpin to poke a hole through a straw, about 4 cm from the end. Then push the metal strips through the hole and flatten them at right angles to the straw. Fold the tip of the straw over and tape it to the rest of the straw.

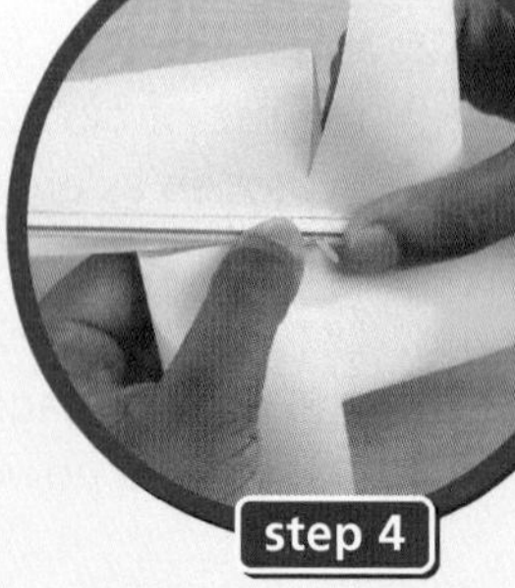


**MATERIALS**
- half of a file folder
- metric ruler
- quarter
- scissors
- paper punch
- brass paper fastener
- drinking straw
- pushpin
- masking tape
- small paper clip
- pint carton
- 30 cm of string
- clock or stopwatch
- small desktop fan

6.6.a, 6.7.a, 6.7.c

**Content Standard**
**6.6.a** Students know the utility of energy sources is determined by factors that are involved in converting these sources to useful forms and the consequences of the conversion process.

**Investigation Standard**
**6.7.a** Develop a hypothesis.

5 Cut the top off the pint carton, as shown. Punch two holes on opposite sides of the carton. Make sure the holes line up and are large enough for the straw to turn easily.

6 Slide the straw through the holes. Tape the string to the end of the straw. Tie a small paper clip (weight) to the other end of the string.

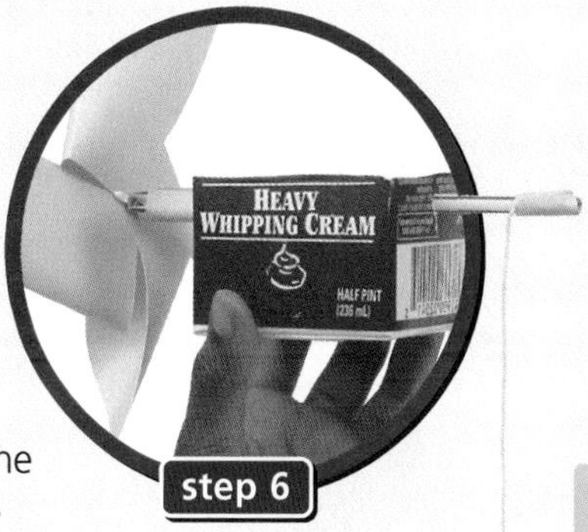


7 Test the model by blowing on the blades. Describe what happens to the weight.

8 Run three trials of the lifting power of the model windmill as you blow on the blades. Keep the amount of force you use constant. Have a classmate use a stopwatch or clock with a second hand to time the trials. Record the results in your data table. Average your results.

9 Vary the strength of the wind by using a small fan at different speeds to turn the windmill's blades. Remember to write a hypothesis explaining what you think will happen in the next two sets of trials.

## Observe and Analyze

Write It Up

1. **MODEL** Draw a picture of the completed windmill. What happens to the weight when the blades turn?
2. **IDENTIFY VARIABLES** What method did you use to increase the wind strength? Add a sketch of this method to your picture to illustrate the experimental procedure.
3. **RECORD OBSERVATIONS** Make sure your data table is completed.
4. **COMPARE** How did the average times it took to raise the weight at different wind strengths differ?

## Conclude

Write It Up

1. **INTERPRET** Answer the question posed under "problem" on page 480.
2. **ANALYZE** Did your results support your hypothesis?
3. **IDENTIFY LIMITS** What limitations or sources of error could have affected your experimental results?
4. **APPLY** Wind-powered turbines are used to generate electricity in some parts of the country. What might limit the usefulness of wind power as an energy source?

## INVESTIGATE Further

**CHALLENGE** How can you get your model windmill to do more work? You might try different weights, or you might build a larger windmill and compare it with your original. Create a new data table. Use a bar graph to compare different weights and wind strengths. How much wind power is needed to lift the additional weight?

Wind Power
Problem
Hypothesize
Observe and Analyze
Table 1. Time to Lift Weight

| Wind Force Used | Trial Number | Time (sec) |
|---|---|---|
| Student powered | 1 | |
| | 2 | |
| | 3 | |
| | Average | |
| Fan on low speed | 1 | |
| | 2 | |
| | 3 | |
| | Average | |
| Fan on high speed | 1 | |
| | 2 | |
| | 3 | |
| | Average | |

Conclude

# 13 Chapter Review

## the BIG idea

**Society depends on natural resources for energy and materials.**

CONTENT REVIEW
CLASSZONE.COM

### KEY CONCEPTS SUMMARY

### 1 Natural resources support human activity.

**Renewable Resources**
- Sunlight
- Wind
- Water
- Trees, other plants
- Plant and animal waste

→ Energy ←

**Nonrenewable Resources**
- Coal
- Oil, natural gas
- Uranium
- Minerals, rocks

**VOCABULARY**
**natural resource** p. 449
**renewable resource** p. 450
**nonrenewable resource** p. 450
**fossil fuel** p. 452

### 2 Minerals and rocks are nonrenewable resources.

Minerals have many uses.

**VOCABULARY**
**ore** p. 462

### 3 Resources can be conserved and recycled.

People can **conserve** natural resources by reducing waste at the source and reusing products.

**Recycling** helps people recover materials, reduce the use of fossil fuels, and protect the environment and human health.

**VOCABULARY**
**conservation** p. 467
**recycling** p. 468

### 4 Resources can be converted to useful forms.

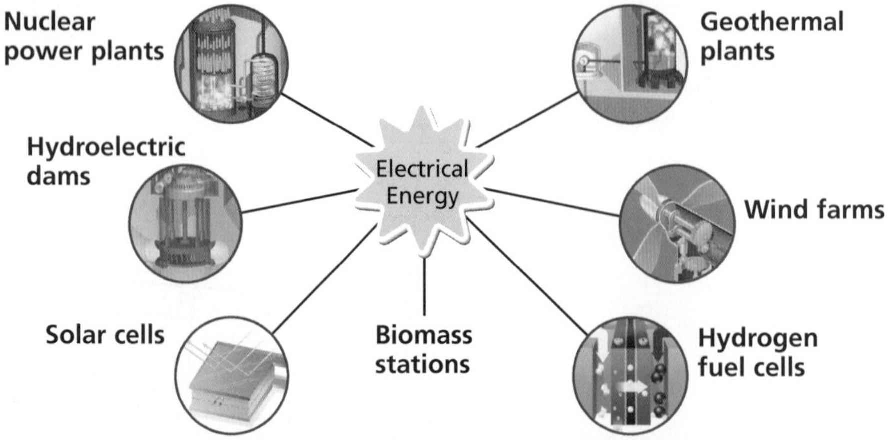


**VOCABULARY**
**hydroelectric energy** p. 472
**geothermal energy** p. 473
**solar cell** p. 475
**biomass** p. 476
**hydrogen fuel cell** p. 476
**nuclear energy** p. 477

## Reviewing Vocabulary

*Copy the chart below, and write each word's definition. Use the meaning of the underlined word part to help you.*

| Word | Meaning of Part | Definition |
|---|---|---|
| **1.** Natural <u>resource</u> | to rise again | |
| **2.** <u>Renew</u>able resource | to refresh | |
| **3.** <u>Nonrenew</u>able resource | not to refresh | |
| **4.** Fossil <u>fuel</u> | material that burns | |
| **5.** <u>Nucle</u>ar energy | nut or kernel | |
| **6.** Geo<u>therm</u>al energy | heat | |

## Reviewing Key Concepts

**Multiple Choice** *Choose the letter of the best answer.*

**7.** What makes wind a renewable resource? (6.6.b)
- **a.** no pollution
- **b.** varied speeds
- **c.** no waste products
- **d.** unlimited supply

**8.** Which of the following is a nonrenewable resource? (6.6.b)
- **a.** trees
- **b.** oil
- **c.** sunlight
- **d.** geothermal energy

**9.** Fossil fuels provide most of the energy used in the United States because they (6.6.a)
- **a.** are found everywhere in the world
- **b.** have no harmful byproducts
- **c.** are easy to transport and burn
- **d.** can be quickly replaced in nature

**10.** Diamonds are often used as (6.6.c)
- **a.** pigments
- **b.** abrasives
- **c.** ores
- **d.** metals

**11.** Which of the following is not a problem associated with the use of fossil fuels? (6.6.a)
- **a.** air pollution
- **b.** explosions
- **c.** limited supply
- **d.** radioactivity

**12.** Which category of products is the most dependent on oil? (6.6.c)
- **a.** pottery
- **b.** coins
- **c.** plastics
- **d.** paper

**13.** How do nuclear power plants generate the heat energy to turn water into steam? (6.3.a)
- **a.** by drawing hot water from Earth's crust
- **b.** by producing an electric current
- **c.** by turning a turbine
- **d.** by splitting uranium atoms

**14.** Hydroelectric energy is produced by using (6.3.a)
- **a.** wind
- **b.** sunlight
- **c.** moving water
- **d.** living matter

**15.** Solar cells produce which of the following? (6.3.a)
- **a.** heat energy
- **b.** steam
- **c.** radioactivity
- **d.** electricity

**16.** What limits the use of biomass liquid fuels? (6.6.a)
- **a.** not enough plant material
- **b.** too expensive to mass-produce
- **c.** not enough energy generated
- **d.** too many harmful byproducts

**17.** Open-pit mining is used to obtain ores that lie (6.6.a)
- **a.** under flat land
- **b.** deep in Earth's crust
- **c.** near the surface of Earth
- **d.** in riverbeds

**Short Answer** *Write a few sentences to answer each question.*

**18.** Why is it important to find renewable sources of energy? (6.6.b)

**19.** Why is conservation of natural resources important? (6.6.b)

**20.** How can recycling help reduce the use of fossil fuels? (6.6.a)

## Thinking Critically

*Use the circle graphs below to answer the following questions.*

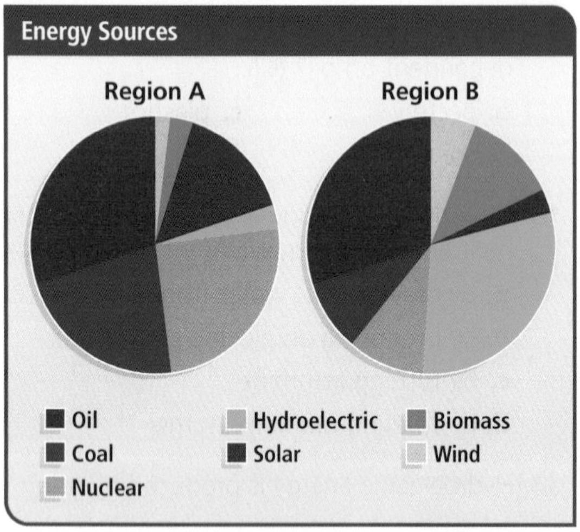


21. **INTERPRET** Which colors represent nonrenewable resources and which ones represent renewable resources? (6.6.b)

22. **CALCULATE** Fossil fuels and nuclear energy together represent about what percentage of the total energy resources in region A? in region B? (6.6.a)

23. **PREDICT** If the price of nonrenewable energy sources rises sharply, which region is likely to be affected more? Why? (6.6.b)

24. **DRAW CONCLUSIONS** What might be one reason that region A uses a greater percentage of fossil fuels and nuclear energy than region B does? (6.6.a)

25. **INFER** Look at the renewable energy sources used in each region. What can you infer about the climate in region A compared with the climate in region B? (6.6.b)

26. **IDENTIFY CAUSES** Why might region B use so much more hydroelectric energy? (6.6.a)

27. **SYNTHESIZE** Region C gets half of its electrical energy from fossil fuels. The region has only 100 days of clear sunlight a year but has abundant plant crops and strong, steady winds. Draw a circle graph for region C, showing the percentage of fossil fuels and the percentage of each renewable energy source the region might use. Explain your choices. (6.6.b)

## Charting Information

*Copy and fill in this chart.*

| Energy Source | Produces Energy From | Byproducts |
|---|---|---|
| **28.** uranium | | radioactive waste |
| **29.** fossil fuel | burning oil, coal | |
| **30.** | moving air | none |
| **31.** river | | |
| **32.** sunlight | | |
| **33.** | burning wood | carbon dioxide |
| **34.** hydrogen | | |

## the BIG idea

35. **APPLY** Look again at the photograph on pages 446–447. Reread the question on the photograph. Now that you have finished the chapter, what would you add to or change about your answer? (6.6.b)

36. **SYNTHESIZE** Imagine that you are a scientist or engineer who is developing a new energy source. What characteristics would you want your energy source to have? List your choices in order of importance, with the most important first—for instance, nonpolluting, inexpensive to mass-produce, and so on. (6.6.a)

37. **APPLY** If you were in charge of your town or city, what measures would you take to conserve natural resources? (6.6.b)

## UNIT PROJECTS

If you need to create graphs or other visuals for your project, be sure you have graph paper, poster board, markers, and other supplies.

# Standards-Based Assessment

For more practice, go to . . .
**TEST PRACTICE**
CLASSZONE.COM

## Analyzing a Graph

6.6.a, 6.6.c

*This graph shows what happens to fuels consumed for energy in the United States. Some of this energy is used and some is lost as heat. Use the graph to answer the questions below.*

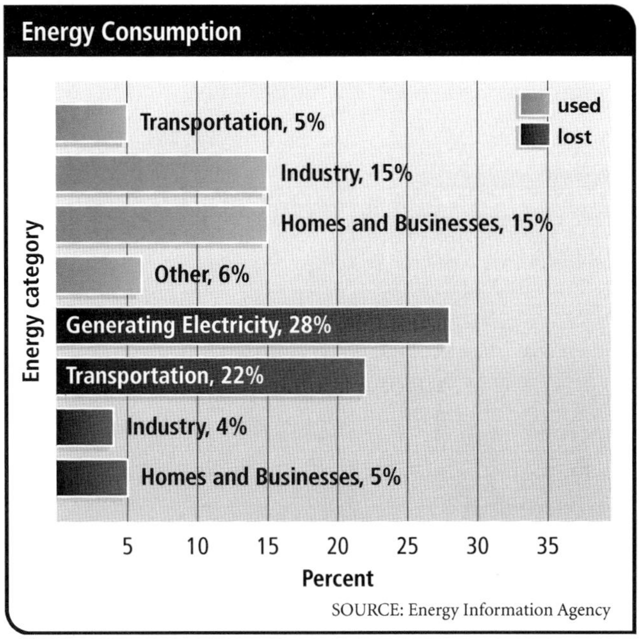


**1.** How much energy is used for transportation and industry?

**a.** 15 percent
**b.** 20 percent
**c.** 30 percent
**d.** 35 percent

**2.** What is the total amount of energy used and lost in industry?

**a.** 4 percent
**b.** 15 percent
**c.** 19 percent
**d.** 28 percent

**3.** What is the largest category of lost energy?

**a.** transportation
**b.** homes and businesses
**c.** generating electricity
**d.** industry

**4.** Which category would include energy used to heat a grocery store?

**a.** used in homes and businesses
**b.** used in industry
**c.** used in transportation
**d.** used in other ways

**5.** If cars burned fuel more efficiently, which category would probably be smaller?

**a.** used in homes and businesses
**b.** used in other ways
**c.** lost in transportation
**d.** lost in industry

**6.** Which statement is true about energy used and lost in transportation?

**a.** The amount lost is greater than the amount used.
**b.** The amount used is greater than the amount lost.
**c.** The amounts used and lost are about the same.
**d.** The amounts used and lost are very low in comparison to the other categories.

## Extended Response

*Answer the two questions below in detail. Include some of the terms in the word box. In your answers, underline each term you use.*

| | | | |
|---|---|---|---|
| reusing | recycling | conserve | extends |
| electricity | hot water | factories | |

**7.** Explain the difference between reusing and recycling products. How does each activity help to reduce the use of natural resources?

**8.** Give three or more examples of ways in which people in the United States use or rely on energy resources every day.

CHAPTER

# 14 Human Impact on Ecosystems

## the BIG idea

**Humans and human population growth affect the environment.**

## Key Concepts

SECTION 1
**Human population growth presents challenges.**
Learn how the increasing human population must share land and resources and dispose of its wastes.

SECTION 2
**Human activities affect the environment.**
Learn how humans may affect natural resources, air and water quality, and biodiversity.

SECTION 3
**People are working to protect ecosystems.**
Learn about federal, local, and scientific efforts to improve resource use and protect ecosystems.

**California ClassZone**

CLASSZONE.COM

Chapter 14 online resources: Content Review, Visualization, four Resource Centers, Math Tutorial, Test Practice

***How have humans affected this landscape in California?***

# EXPLORE the BIG idea

## How Easily Does Polluted Water Move Through Plants?

**6.5.e** Students know the number and types of organisms an ecosystem can support depends on the resources available and on abiotic factors, such as quantities of light and water, a range of temperatures, and soil composition.

Place a few drops of food coloring in a half cup of water. Take a leafy stalk of celery and make a fresh cut across the bottom. Place the celery in the water overnight.

**Observe and Think** What do you observe about the celery and its leaves? What do your observations suggest about plants growing near polluted water?

## Internet Activity: The Environment

**6.5.e** Students know the number and types of organisms an ecosystem can support depends on the resources available and on abiotic factors, such as quantities of light and water, a range of temperatures, and soil composition.

Go to **ClassZone.com** to explore the effects of human activities on the environment.

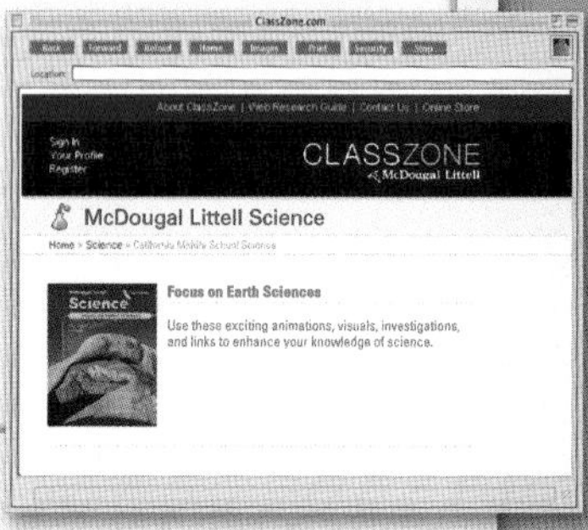


**Observe and Think** How are people working to protect the environment?

NSTA scilinks.org SCiLINKS

Population Growth **Code: MDL003**

CHAPTER 14

# Getting Ready to Learn

## CONCEPT REVIEW

- Both living and nonliving factors affect ecosystems.
- Populations can grow or decline over time.
- Matter and energy move through the environment.

## VOCABULARY REVIEW

**species** p. 413
**habitat** p. 414
**natural resource** p. 449
**conservation** p. 467

*See Glossary for definitions.*
**diversity, urban**

**CONTENT REVIEW**
**CLASSZONE.COM**

Review concepts and vocabulary.

## TAKING NOTES

### CHOOSE YOUR OWN STRATEGY

Take notes using one or more strategies from earlier chapters—**combination notes, outline,** or **supporting main ideas.** You can also use other note-taking strategies that you might already know.

### VOCABULARY STRATEGY

Think about a vocabulary term as a **magnet word** diagram. Write terms or ideas related to that term around it.

See the Note-Taking Handbook on pages R45–R51.

SCIENCE NOTEBOOK

Combination Notes

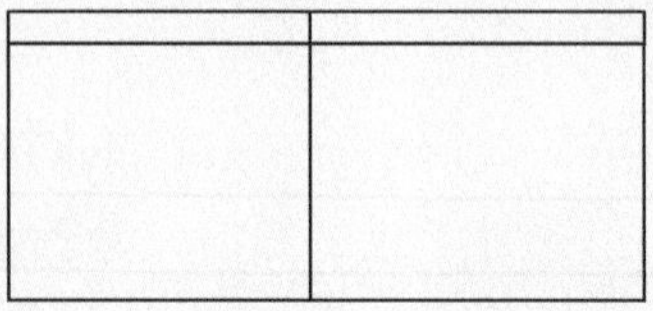

Outline

I. Main Idea
A. Supporting idea
1. Detail
2. Detail
B. Supporting idea

Supporting Main Ideas

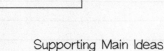

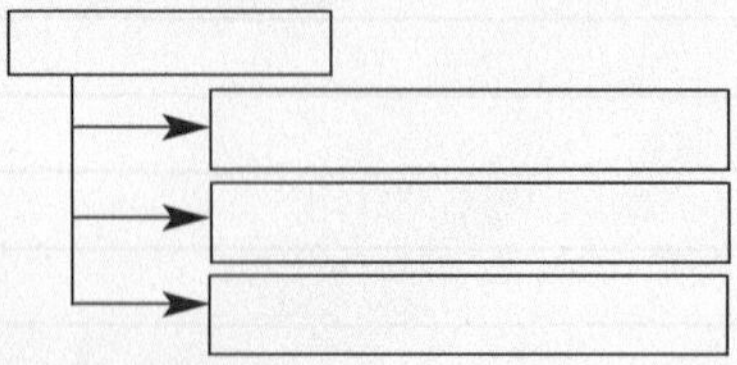

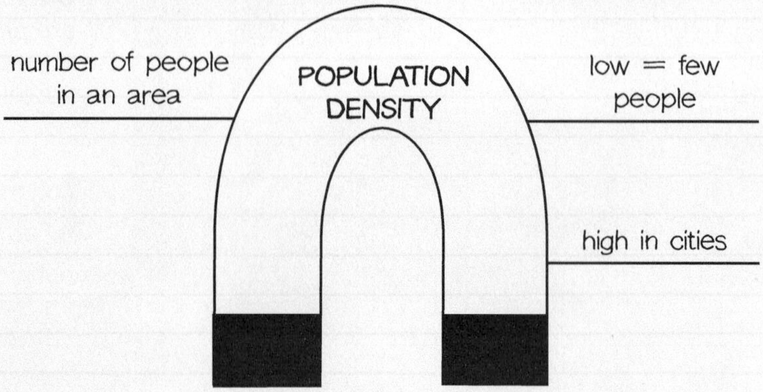

KEY CONCEPT

# 14.1 Human population growth presents challenges.

**CALIFORNIA Content Standards**

**6.5.e** Students know the number and types of organisms an ecosystem can support depends on the resources available and on abiotic factors, such as quantities of light and water, a range of temperatures, and soil composition.

**6.6.b** Students know different natural energy and material resources, including air, soil, rocks, minerals, petroleum, fresh water, wildlife, and forests, and know how to classify them as renewable or nonrenewable.

**BEFORE, you learned**

- Populations have boundaries and are affected by limiting factors
- Living things form communities

**NOW, you will learn**

- How a growing human population puts pressure on ecosystems
- How sharing resources can be difficult

**VOCABULARY**

**population density** p. 494

## EXPLORE Sharing Resources (6.6.b)

### *How can you model resource distribution?*

**PROCEDURE**

1. You will work in a group of several classmates. One member of your group gets a bag of objects from your teacher.
2. Each object in the bag represents a necessary resource. Divide the objects so that each member of the group gets the resources he or she needs.
3. After 10 minutes, you may trade resources with other groups.

**MATERIALS**

bag containing an assortment of objects

**WHAT DO YOU THINK?**

- Did you get a fair share of your group's objects?
- Did the objects represent renewable resources or nonrenewable resources?
- Was the job made easier when trading occurred across groups?

**NOTE-TAKING STRATEGY**
Use a strategy from an earlier chapter to take notes on the main idea: *The human population is increasing.*

## The human population is increasing.

The United Nations reported that on October 12, 1999, Earth's human population reached 6 billion. Until 300 years ago, it had never grown beyond a few hundred million people. Only 200 years ago, the population reached 1 billion. So the increase to 6 billion people has occurred in a very short time. About one-third of all humans alive today are 14 years old or younger. Experts predict that Earth's population will keep growing—to 9 billion or more by the year 2050.

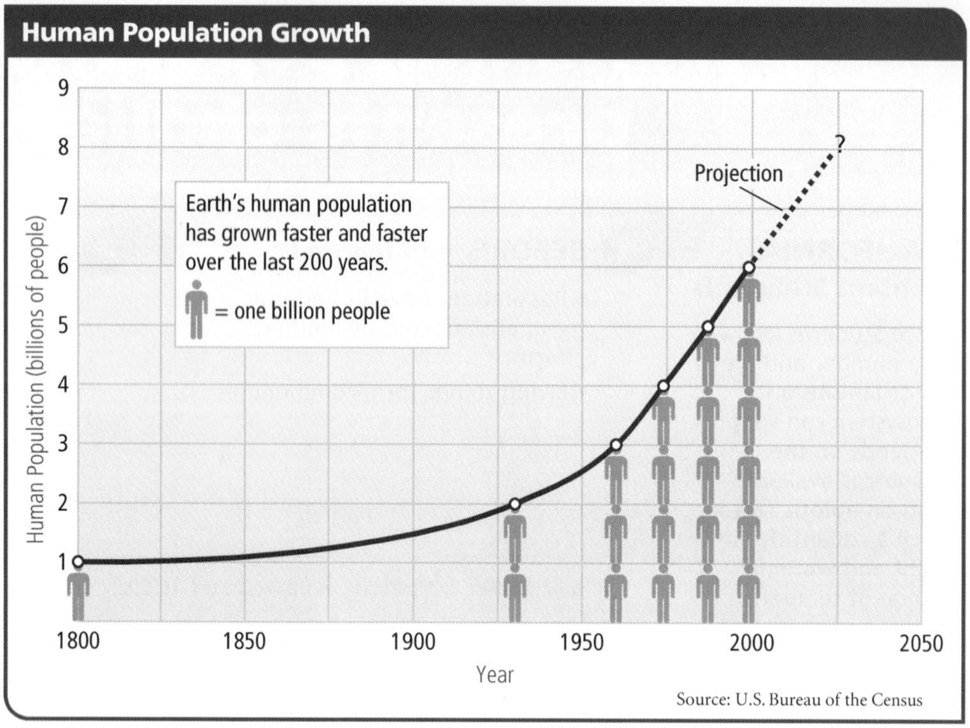


**PREDICT** The graph shows actual population growth through 2000. Predict how the population will grow in the future.

The graph above shows how the human population has grown in the last 200 years. You can see from the way the line gets much steeper after 1950 how quickly the population increased in the 50 years between 1950 and 2000. It is not only the number of babies being born that contributes to Earth's large human population. People are living longer as a result of improving health care and nutrition.

The dotted line on the graph shows a projection that helps us predict what the population would be if it continues to grow at the rate it is growing today. However, remember that an ecosystem has a carrying capacity for any given population. At some point, Earth will reach its carrying capacity for the human population. Today, many people think that our planet is close to—if not already at—its carrying capacity for humans.

**CHECK YOUR READING** How might Earth's carrying capacity affect human population growth?

## Human populations can put pressure on ecosystems.

**VISUALIZATION** CLASSZONE.COM

Examine how the human population has grown.

If your family has guests for the weekend, you may find that you run out of hot water for showers or do not have enough milk for everyone's breakfast. The resources that would ordinarily be enough for your family are no longer enough.

You read in Chapter 12 that resources such as food, water, and space can be limiting factors for biological populations. These same resources limit Earth's human population. As the human population grows, it uses more resources—just as your guests used more of your home's resources. The activities of the growing human population are putting pressure on Earth's ecosystems.

**REMINDER**

A limiting factor is something that prevents a population from continuing to grow.

## Pressures of Waste Disposal

As Earth's human population grows, so does the amount of waste produced by humans. Humans, like all living things, produce natural waste. Often, the water that carries this waste is treated to remove the waste before being cycled back to the environment. However, some of these materials still make it into lakes, rivers, and oceans. This can harm these ecosystems.

Some of the waste produced by humans is garbage, or food waste. The rest of it is trash, or nonfood waste. In the United States, huge amounts of trash are thrown out each year. Most garbage and trash ends up in landfills.

**CALIFORNIA Focus**

Californians have been using methods such as recycling and composting to decrease the percentage of solid waste sent to landfills each year. In 1994 the amount of solid waste sent to landfills was 36.3 million tons, or 75 percent of the total. In 2004 the amount sent to landfills was 37 million tons, or 52 percent of the total.

Landfills can take up a lot of space. The Fresh Kills Landfill in Staten Island, New York, is about 69 meters (225 ft) high in some places. It covers 2200 acres. Decomposing trash and garbage can release dangerous gases into the air as well as harmful chemicals into the ground. Liners made of plastic or packed clay are used to keep chemicals from leaking into the surrounding land and water.

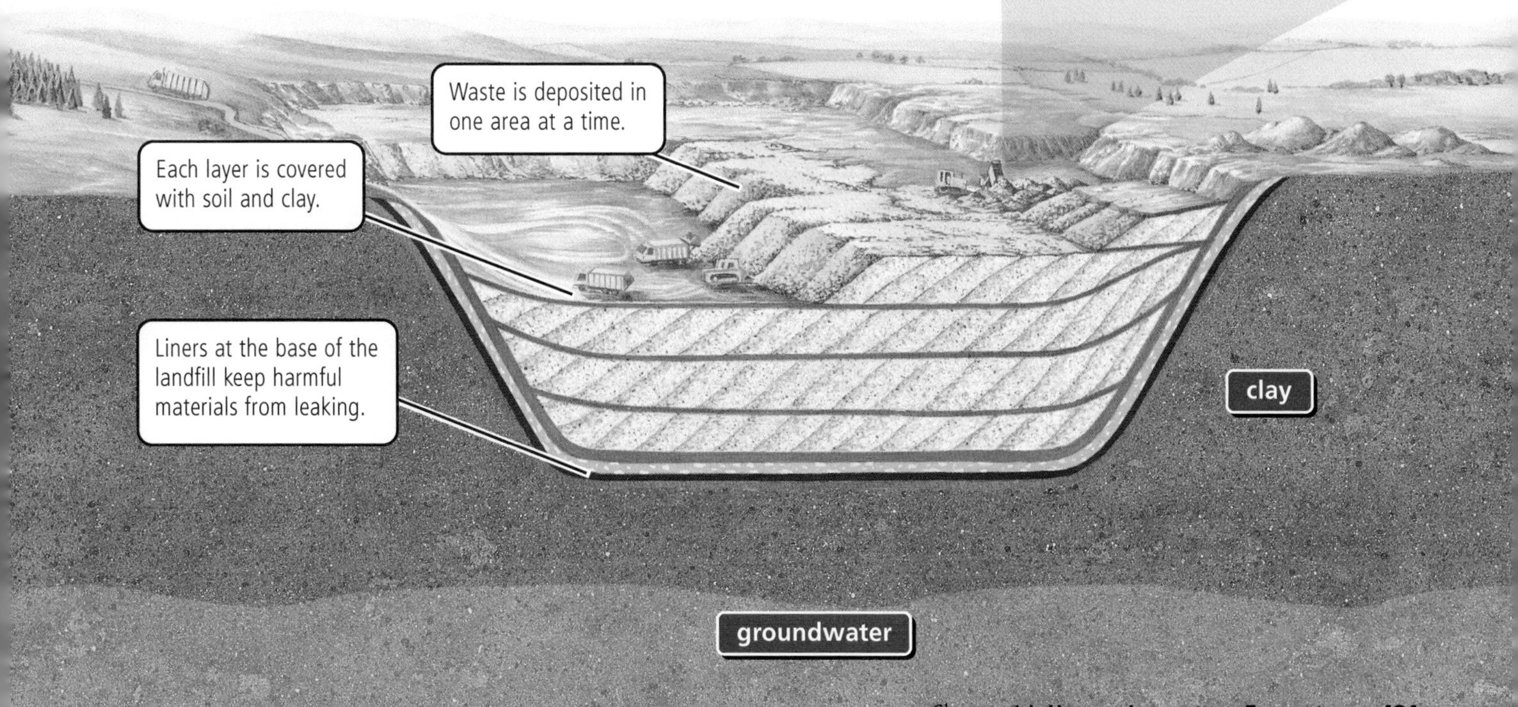

Waste is deposited in one area at a time.
Each layer is covered with soil and clay.
Liners at the base of the landfill keep harmful materials from leaking.
clay
groundwater

Another way to get rid of trash and garbage is to incinerate it—to burn it. The problem with incineration is that it releases harmful gases and chemicals into the air. To prevent the release of these harmful substances, incinerator smokestacks have filters. To prevent further environmental contamination, used filters must be disposed of safely.

## Pressures on Resources

You have seen that a growing human population puts pressure on ecosystems by the amount of waste it leaves behind. Human populations also put pressure on ecosystems by what they take away. Humans depend on the environment for resources. As you recall, a natural resource is any type of material or energy source that humans use to meet their needs. Natural resources that humans take from their environment include water, food, wood, stone, metal, and minerals.

Clean fresh water is an important resource. Only three percent of Earth's water supply is fresh water—and two-thirds of that small amount is contained in polar ice caps, glaciers, and permanent snow. As the human population grows, sharing this important resource will become more difficult.

## INVESTIGATE Water Usage

### *How much water do you use in a week?*

**PROCEDURE**

1. Write down all the ways you use water in a day. Start with the time you get up in the morning. Include activities such as brushing your teeth, flushing the toilet, using ice, and taking a shower.
2. Look at the Water Use datasheet. Identify other ways that you and others in your household use water.
3. Add up how many liters of water you use in a day, and multiply that by seven. This is how much water you use in a week.

**WHAT DO YOU THINK?**

- Which of your activities used the most water?
- What are some ways that you could reduce the amount of water you use weekly?

**CHALLENGE** How is clean drinking water like a nonrenewable resource? a renewable resource?

**SKILL FOCUS**
Analyzing data (6.6.b)

**MATERIALS**
- Water Use datasheet
- calculator

**TIME**
30 minutes

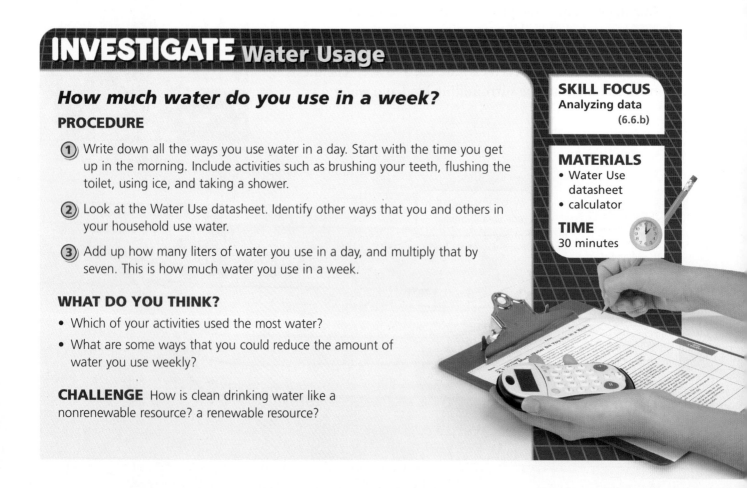

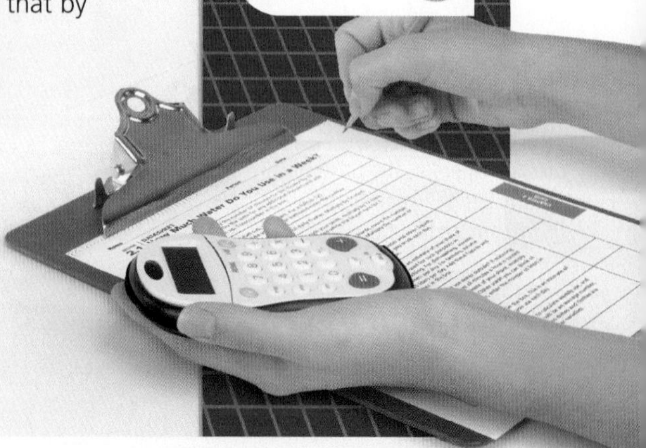

## Case Study: The Colorado River

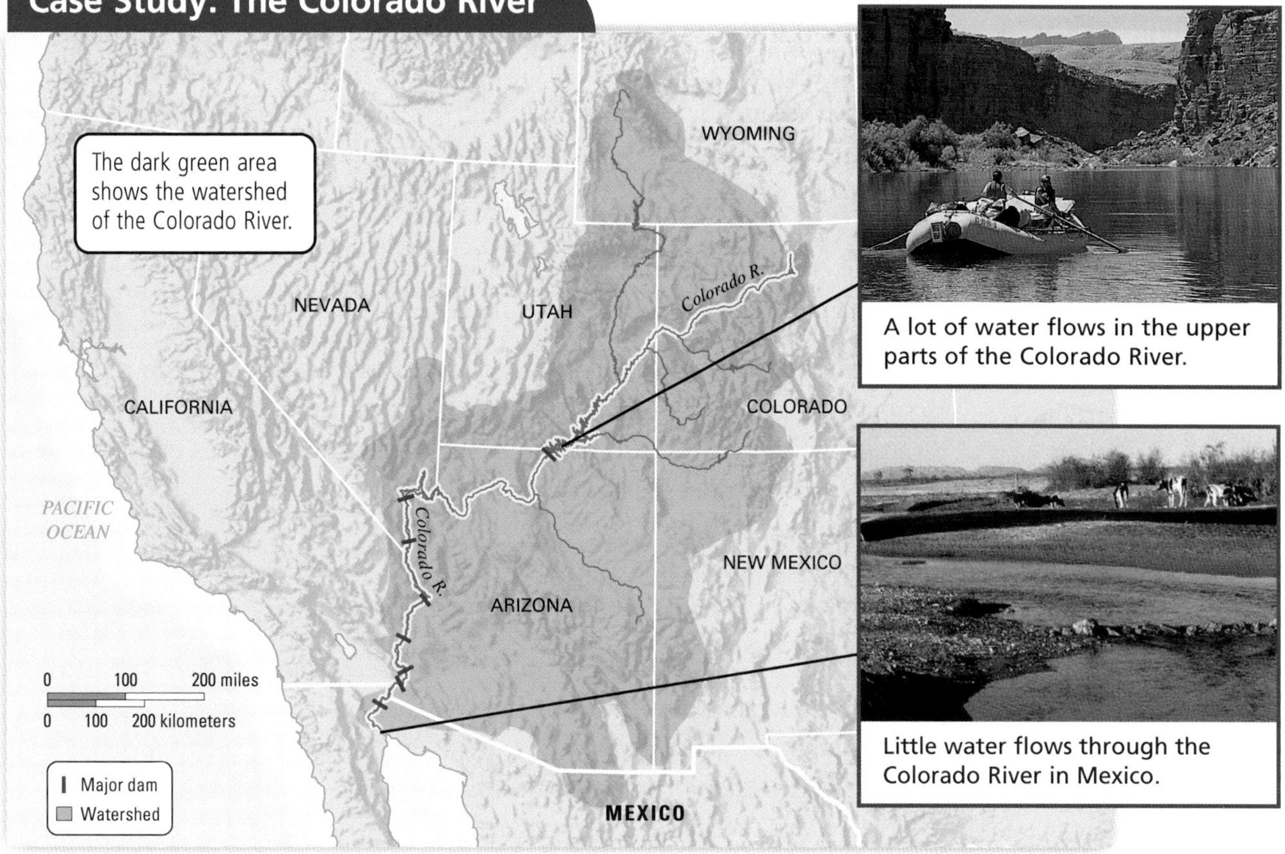


A lot of water flows in the upper parts of the Colorado River.

Little water flows through the Colorado River in Mexico.

A case study that involves the Colorado River shows how a growing human population puts pressures on natural resources. This example also shows that sharing resources isn't easy. The watershed of this major Western river extends into seven U.S. states and parts of Mexico. The watershed includes all the smaller rivers and streams that flow into the Colorado River. In a region where little rain falls each year, these streams and rivers are an important source of water for drinking and agriculture.

**READING TIP**
A watershed is an area of land in which water drains into a stream system. It is also called a drainage basin.

As the West was settled, disagreements about water rights arose between people in the upstream states of Colorado, Utah, Wyoming, and New Mexico and people in the downstream states of California, Arizona, and Nevada. In 1922 the seven states signed an agreement that divided the water between the two groups.

Problems with this agreement soon became apparent. First, the needs of Native American and Mexican populations were not considered. Second, the dams and channels built to prevent floods and transport water harmed river ecosystems. And third, the seven states planned to use more water than the river usually holds. As a result, the river often runs nearly dry at its mouth in Mexico.

**CHECK YOUR READING** List three problems that developed after people made a plan to share Colorado River water.

## Pressures of Urban Growth

RESOURCE CENTER
CLASSZONE.COM
Learn more about urban expansion.

Until recently, the majority of Earth's population was spread out. As a result, the population density was low. **Population density** is the measure of the number of people in a given area. Generally, the lower the population density, the less pressure there is on the environment.

Today, about half of the world's population lives in urban, or city, areas. People are attracted to these areas to live and to work. Over time, suburban areas around a city develop as more and more people look for a place to live. In cities, buildings are spaced close together, so the population density is high. A large number of people in a small area changes the landscape. The local environment can no longer support the number of people living there, so resources must come from outside the environment.

CHECK YOUR READING Why do people who live in a city need to bring in resources from other areas?

In recent years, some people have raised concerns over the dramatic growth in and around urban areas. Los Angeles, Houston, Atlanta, and Washington, D.C., are all cities that have expanded rapidly. Another urban area that has experienced dramatic growth is Las Vegas, Nevada. The images below show the effects of increasing

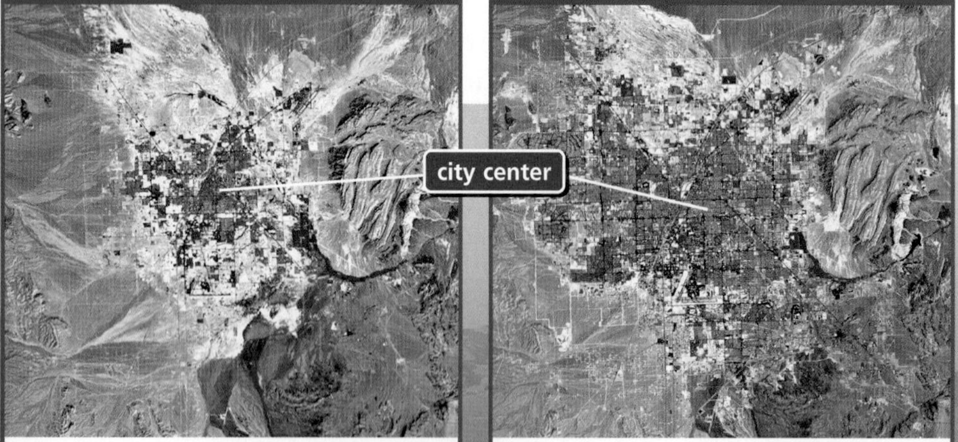

**Las Vegas, 1972**

The darker colors show the developed land of Las Vegas, which is surrounded by desert.

**Las Vegas, 1997**

Over 25 years, the city expanded in all directions. The population rose from 273,000 to 1,124,000.

population density around the city between 1972 and 1997. Located in the middle of a desert, Las Vegas depends on the Colorado River for water and electrical energy. As the population grows, so does the need for natural resources.

INFER What do you think this ecosystem looked like a hundred years ago? two hundred years ago?

## Pressures of Expanding Land Use

One consequence of urban growth is an increasing demand for resources in a particular area. But as communities around cities expand onto surrounding land, the environment is affected. Natural habitats, such as forests, are destroyed. Because forests cycle carbon through the environment, cutting down trees affects the carbon cycle. Soil that was held in place by tree roots may wash into lakes and rivers.

Another consequence of widespread development is the loss of productive farmland. Development replaces more than 2.2 million acres of farmland each year in the United States. This means less land is available locally to produce food for the growing population. The result is that food must be transported over greater distances.

Unlike city development, suburban development increases the need for residents to have cars. This is because most people in suburban areas live farther from where they work, shop, or go to school. A greater number of cars can decrease the air quality. More cars lead to the construction of more roads, which can interrupt natural habitats and endanger wildlife.

**CHECK YOUR READING** Describe some ways that development harms natural ecosystems.

# 14.1 Review

### KEY CONCEPTS

1. Identify four pressures placed on ecosystems by an increasing human population. (6.5.e)
2. Give an example that shows how resources can be difficult to share. (6.5.e)

### CRITICAL THINKING

3. **Apply** Describe an example of sharing resources that occurs in your school.
4. **Infer** How would a city's population density change if the city increased in area and the number of people in it remained the same?

### CHALLENGE

5. **Evaluate** Imagine that you live along the Colorado River. What information would you need to evaluate a water-sharing agreement?

California Close-Up

## ECOSYSTEM MANAGEMENT

# Burn On!

6.5.e Students know the number and types of organisms an ecosystem can support depends on the resources available and on **abiotic factors,** such as quantities of light and water, a range of temperatures, and soil composition.

Sequoias, or redwoods, are tall evergreen trees native to California and Oregon. For many years forest rangers prevented fires in sequoia groves. Surprisingly, the sequoias failed to reproduce. What went wrong? It turned out that to protect the sequoias, rangers needed to let them burn. Fire is essential to sequoia reproduction. It clears the forest floor of debris and smaller trees, making room for new growth. The heat from the fire causes the sequoia cones to dry out and open, releasing the seeds. Fire also creates the necessary soil conditions for the sequoia seeds to germinate.

John Muir (right), shown here with President Theodore Roosevelt, spent his life working for the protection of the natural world. He played a key role in forming many of our national parks, including Yosemite, Sequoia, and Mount Rainier National Parks. In the early 1900s, rangers in Sequoia fought forest fires. They thought that eliminating fires would protect and encourage the growth of giant sequoia trees.

Ferns growing in Yosemite after a forest fire

Fire's role in the history of sequoia ecosystems has literally been burned into the trees. Tree rings tell a story of a region's fires, insect attacks, droughts, and floods. Differences in growing conditions cause the widths of rings to vary in size. Fire scars on the tree rings show scientists when fires occurred and how large the fires were.

Today, National Park Service rangers practice a new kind of ecosystem management that includes controlled burns. With knowledge about the past from the tree rings, we can better care for the places that John Muir fought so hard to protect.

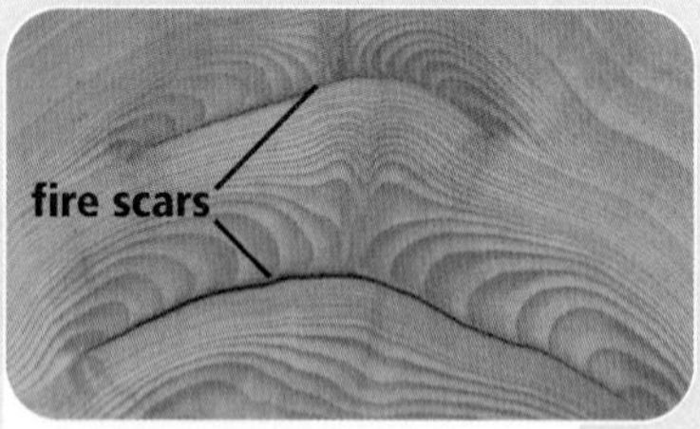


Scientists study tree rings to understand the role that fire plays in forest ecosystems.

### WRITING ABOUT SCIENCE

What other challenges do our national parks face today? Choose one problem, such as overcrowding, and research it. Write a description of the problem and propose your solution to it.

KEY CONCEPT

# 14.2 Human activities affect the environment.

**CALIFORNIA Content Standards**

**6.6.a** Students know the utility of energy sources is determined by factors that are involved in converting these sources to useful forms and the consequences of the conversion process.

**6.6.b** Students know different natural energy and material resources, including air, soil, rocks, minerals, petroleum, fresh water, wildlife, and forests, and know how to classify them as renewable or nonrenewable.

**BEFORE, you learned**

- Human populations are increasing
- Human population growth causes problems

**NOW, you will learn**

- How natural resources are classified
- How pollution affects the environment
- How a loss of diversity affects the environment

**VOCABULARY**

**pollution** p. 498
**biodiversity** p. 498

**THINK ABOUT**

### *How do you use water?*

Think of the number of times you use water every day. Like all living things, you need water. In fact, more than half of the material that makes up your body is water.

Most of the time when you turn on a faucet, clean water flows out. You use water when you take a shower, brush your teeth, or wash a dish. If you've ever lost water service to your home, you've probably been reminded of how much you depend on it. No doubt about it, people need water.

## Humans use many resources.

NOTE-TAKING STRATEGY
Choose a strategy for taking notes about the main idea: *Humans use many resources.*

Throughout history, people around the world have relied on natural resources for survival. Ancient civilizations used stone to create tools and weapons. Wood was an important fuel for cooking and keeping warm. Today, humans continue to rely on the environment and have discovered additional resources to meet their needs. As you read in Chapter 13, people classify these resources into two categories:

- renewable resources
- nonrenewable resources

**RESOURCE CENTER**
CLASSZONE.COM
Find out more about natural resources.

As people use natural resources from one part of the Earth system, they affect other parts of the system. As you read in Chapter 13, there are costs as well as benefits to using natural resources. Some of the costs are described below.

## Pollution endangers biodiversity.

**VOCABULARY**
Remember to add magnet word diagrams to your notebook for *pollution* and *biodiversity.*

As you walk along a city street, you may smell car exhaust or see litter. These are examples of pollution. **Pollution** is the addition of harmful substances to the environment. Many of the ways humans use natural resources cause pollution to be released into soil, air, and water. Pollutants include chemicals, bacteria, and dirt. Even materials that are ordinarily not harmful can cause pollution when they build up in one location.

As pollution becomes common in an ecosystem, living things may be threatened. Plant and animal populations may decrease, and biodiversity may decline. **Biodiversity** is the number and variety of life forms within an ecosystem. Healthy ecosystems support a variety of species. An ecosystem with a variety of organisms can recover more easily from disturbances than an ecosystem that has fewer species.

## INVESTIGATE Particles in the Air

### *Where do you find air pollution?*

**PROCEDURE**

1. Use a hole punch to make a hole at one end of each index card. Cut two pieces of string 30 cm long and tie a string to each card.
2. Choose a different location for each card. Mark the card with its location and the date.
3. Spread a thin film of petroleum jelly about the size of your thumb on each card. Hang the cards at the locations you've chosen.
4. Take down the cards after one week and examine them with a hand lens.

**WHAT DO YOU THINK?**

- Identify the types of particles collected at each location.
- Were all the particles collected the result of pollution?
- Which location had the most pollution?

**CHALLENGE** Hypothesize why certain locations have more particles in the air than others.

**SKILL FOCUS**
Observing (6.5.e, 6.6.b)

**MATERIALS**
- 2 index cards
- marker
- hole punch
- string
- scissors
- petroleum jelly
- hand lens

**TIME**
30 minutes

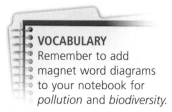

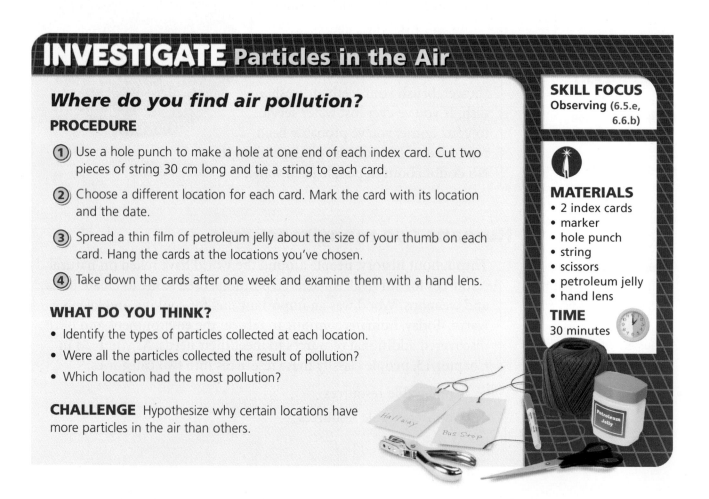

## Air Quality

Air quality affects entire ecosystems. For example, in 1980 Mount St. Helens erupted in Washington state. Hot ash was blown 15 miles up into the air. Three days later some of that ash reached the East Coast. Although natural events like this occasionally release large amounts of air pollutants, human activities pollute every day.

Motor vehicles, factories, and power plants are the main sources of air pollution in the United States today. The fossil fuels they burn release sulfur dioxide, nitrogen dioxide, and carbon monoxide into the air. These pollutants affect humans and animals and are the main cause of acid rain, a serious problem affecting ecosystems.

**READING TIP**

*Pollute* and *pollutant* are in the same word family as *pollution*.

**CHECK YOUR READING** What air pollutants contribute to acid rain problems in the United States?

You read about acid rain in Chapters 3 and 10. Acid rain occurs when air pollutants such as sulfur dioxide and nitrogen dioxide mix with water in the atmosphere to form acid droplets of rain, ice, snow, or mist. Just as wind carried ash from Mount St. Helens, wind can carry these droplets for very long distances before they fall as rain.

Most of the air pollution in urban areas comes from the burning of fossil fuels such as oil, gasoline, and coal. Sunlight causes some of the gases produced by burning fuels to react chemically. The reactions form a type of pollution called smog. Large amounts of smog in the air form a brownish haze. Smog can irritate your eyes, nose, throat, and lungs, and it can cause difficulty in breathing.

**Air Quality** Smog forms in a layer near the ground. The mountains around Los Angeles help trap smog over the city.

## Water Quality

Water quality is another factor that affects biodiversity in ecosystems. In the 1960s, newspaper headlines announced that Lake Erie was "dead" because of pollution. Almost every living thing in the lake had died. Lake Erie suffered for years from pollution from cities, industries, and farms located along its banks. Rivers that emptied into the lake also carried pollution with them.

The pollution found in Lake Erie is common in communities across the United States. Chemicals or wastes that drain off of farm fields, animal feedlots, and landfills all cause water pollution. So do oil spills, soil erosion, and wastewater from towns and industries.

**CHECK YOUR READING** Name four different sources of water pollution.

Like air pollution, water pollution affects entire ecosystems. One river that suffers from heavy pollution is the Duwamish River in Washington. Over 600 million gallons of untreated waste and storm water drain off the land into the river each year. As a result, large amounts of bacteria and harmful chemicals contaminate the water, killing fish and putting humans at risk.

When fish and other animals in aquatic ecosystems are exposed to pollution, the entire food web is affected. If fish become scarce, some birds may no longer find enough food. The bird population may decrease as birds die or move to a new habitat. The result is a decrease in biodiversity in the ecosystem.

**Water Quality** A scientist tests the water of the Duwamish River after chemicals were released into the river.

**Water Pollution**

Pollution that flows into aquatic ecosystems can harm—even kill—organisms such as these fish.

## Sources of Water Pollution

**Human activity can pollute the water supply.**

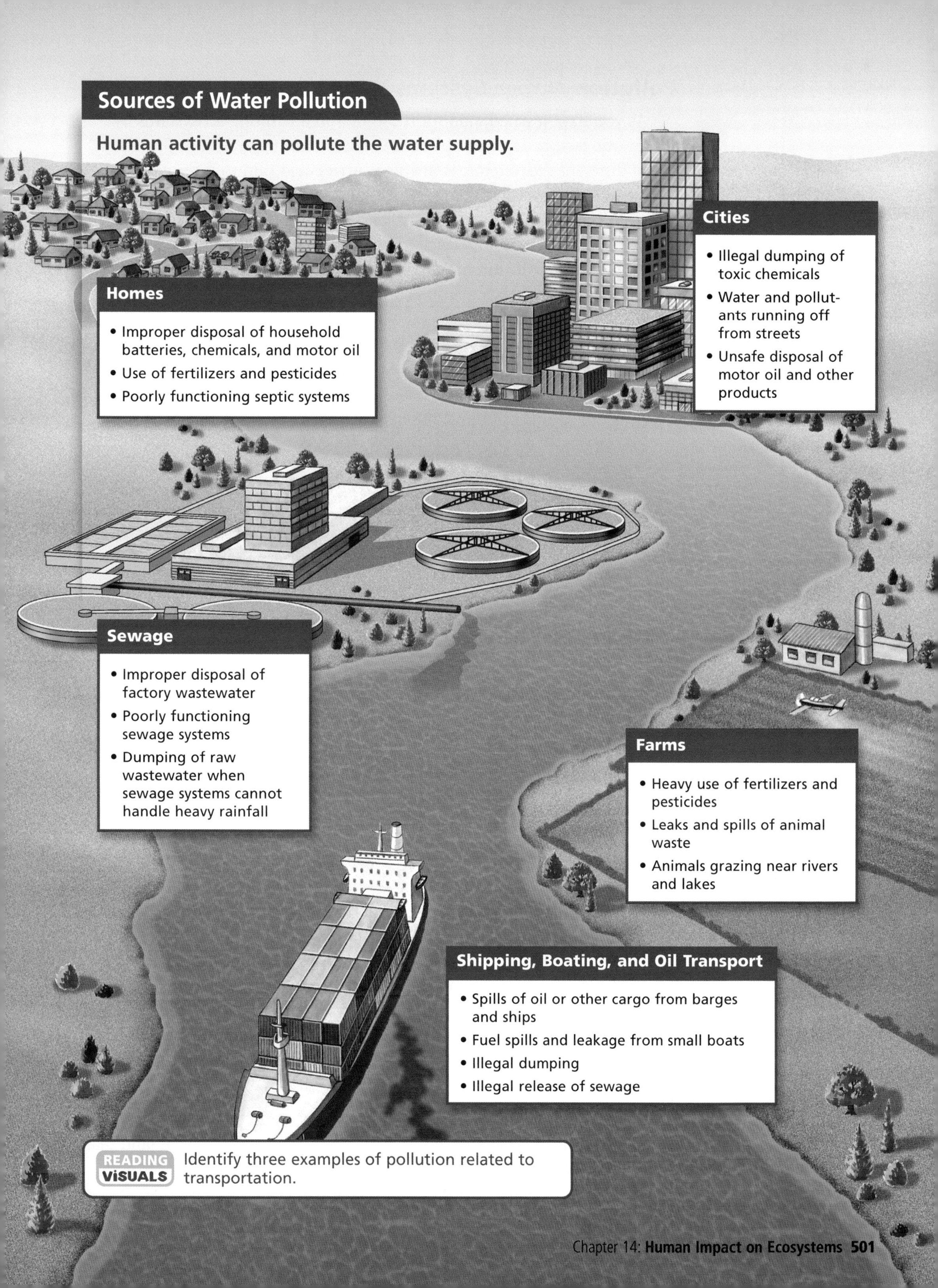

### Homes

- Improper disposal of household batteries, chemicals, and motor oil
- Use of fertilizers and pesticides
- Poorly functioning septic systems

### Cities

- Illegal dumping of toxic chemicals
- Water and pollutants running off from streets
- Unsafe disposal of motor oil and other products

### Sewage

- Improper disposal of factory wastewater
- Poorly functioning sewage systems
- Dumping of raw wastewater when sewage systems cannot handle heavy rainfall

### Farms

- Heavy use of fertilizers and pesticides
- Leaks and spills of animal waste
- Animals grazing near rivers and lakes

### Shipping, Boating, and Oil Transport

- Spills of oil or other cargo from barges and ships
- Fuel spills and leakage from small boats
- Illegal dumping
- Illegal release of sewage

**READING VISUALS** Identify three examples of pollution related to transportation.

### Pollution Across Systems

As you have learned, pollution can be spread among ecosystems by abiotic factors. For example, wind carried ash from Mount St. Helens to different ecosystems. Wind also carries acid rain to forest ecosystems. Pollution can move between air and water. For example, some chemical pollutants can run off land and into a body of water. These pollutants, like the water itself, can evaporate from the water's surface and cycle into the air, moving into the atmosphere.

1 Runoff containing harmful chemicals flows into this pond.

2 The chemicals evaporate into the air from the surface of the water.

## Habitat loss endangers biodiversity.

Scientists know that an ecosystem with many different species of plants and animals can withstand the effects of flooding, drought, and disease more effectively than an ecosystem with fewer species. But a habitat must be able to support a large number of different species for biodiversity to be maintained. If living space is limited or a food source is removed, then the number of species in a biological community will be reduced.

### Removing Habitats

One way human activities affect habitats is by reducing the amounts of natural resources available to other living things. When this occurs, populations that rely on those resources are less likely to survive. For example, if people trim all the dead branches off the trees in a park and remove them, insects that live in rotting wood will not be present in the park. As a result, woodpeckers that may have nested in the area will lose their source of food. By removing this food source, people might affect the biodiversity in the park.

Now consider altering an ecosystem much larger than a park. Instead of removing a single resource, imagine removing a large area of land that is a habitat to many different species. Disturbing habitats removes not only food but space, shelter, and protection for living things.

## Removing Habitat

**A clear-cut forest provides a dramatic example of habitat loss.**

**Forest Habitat** The forest provides food and shelter for many organisms.
**Deforestation** Removing all the trees from an area removes habitats that many species depend on.


Because of land development, forests that once stretched for hundreds of miles have been broken apart into small patches. Organisms that depend on trees cannot live in woods that have large areas that have been clear-cut, or removed all at one time. There is a greater risk of attack by predators such as skunks, raccoons, and crows. These animals eat the eggs of forest songbirds, but will not travel deep into large forests. However, they can reach nests more easily when forests are broken into small areas.

**CHECK YOUR READING** Why is biodiversity important, and how can human activities affect it?

## Changing Habitats

Another kind of habitat loss occurs when humans move species into new habitats, either on purpose or by accident. Some species, when released in a new place, successfully compete against the native species and crowd them out. Over time, the new species, called invasive species, may replace the native species.

One example of an invasive plant is purple loosestrife. In the 1800s loosestrife from Europe was brought to the United States to use in gardens and medicines. One loosestrife plant can produce over 2 million seeds a year. These seeds are carried long distances by wind, water, animals, and humans. Loosestrife sprouts in wetlands, where it can fill in an open-water habitat or replace native plants.

## Changing Habitat

**Habitat loss occurs when purple loosestrife fills in open water or crowds out native plants.**

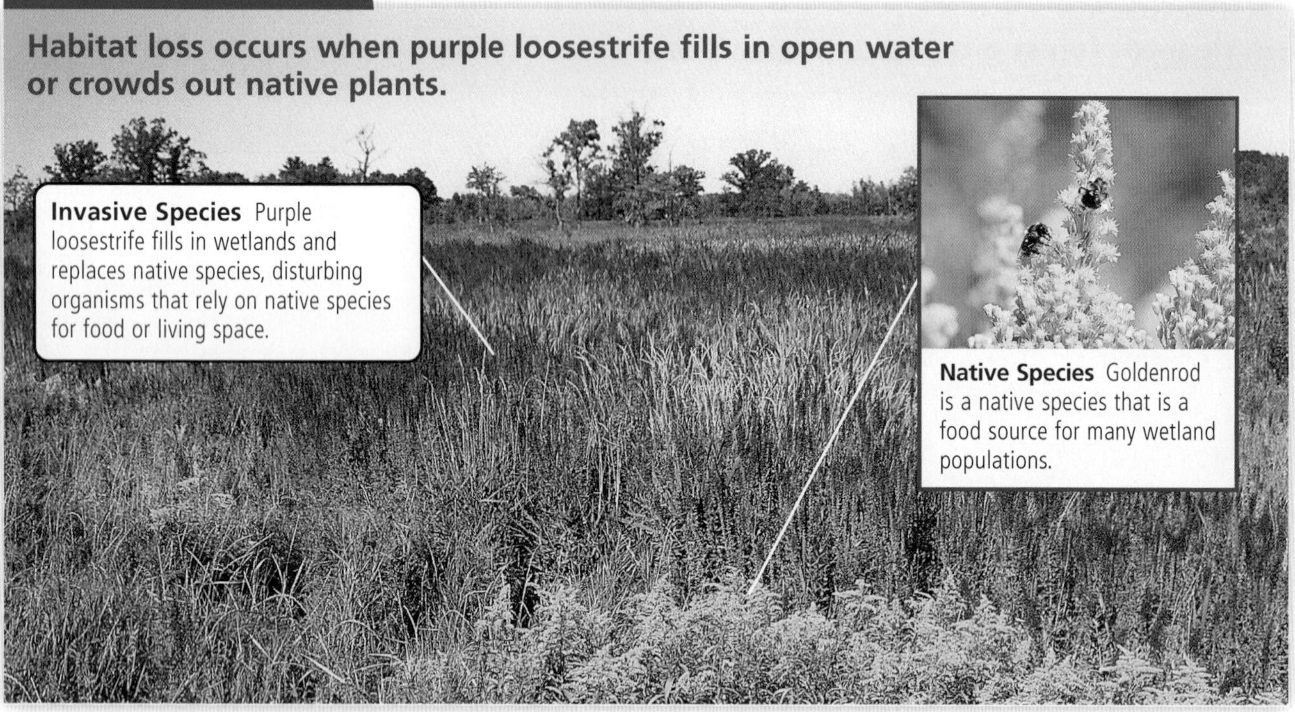

**Invasive Species** Purple loosestrife fills in wetlands and replaces native species, disturbing organisms that rely on native species for food or living space.
**Native Species** Goldenrod is a native species that is a food source for many wetland populations.


Most ducks and fish do not feed on purple loosestrife. When the native plants that wetland animals depend on are replaced by loosestrife, the animals disappear too.

Scientists estimate that Earth supports more than 10 million different species. They also estimate that thousands of species are threatened, and hundreds of species of plants and animals become extinct every year. By protecting biodiversity we can help ecosystems thrive and recover more quickly after a natural disturbance such as a hurricane. Biodiversity benefits humans too. Many medications are based on natural compounds from plants that grow only in certain types of ecosystems.

# 14.2 Review

### KEY CONCEPTS

1. List some renewable and nonrenewable resources that you need in order to survive. (6.6.b)
2. Describe two ways in which pollution can move through ecosystems. (6.6.a)
3. Explain what scientists mean by *biodiversity.* (6.6.b)

### CRITICAL THINKING

4. **Explain** Under some circumstances, valuable natural resources can be considered pollutants. Explain this statement, giving two examples.
5. **Compare** Identify two natural habitats in your area, one with high biodiversity and one with low biodiversity. Describe the biodiversity of each.

### CHALLENGE

6. **Hypothesize** When lakes are polluted by acid rain, the water appears to become clearer, not cloudier. Why do you think this is the case?

MATH in SCIENCE

## SKILL: FINDING VOLUMES

# How Much Water?

When you take a ten-minute shower, you are using about 75 liters of water. How much is that? Liters are a metric unit of volume, the amount of space that matter takes up. One liter is equal to 1000 cubic centimeters.

### Example

A tank in the shape of a cylinder holds enough water for a 10-minute shower. The tank has a radius of 30 cm and a height of 27 cm. What is the volume of a tank?

Volume = area of the base × height

$V = \pi \times r^2 \times h$

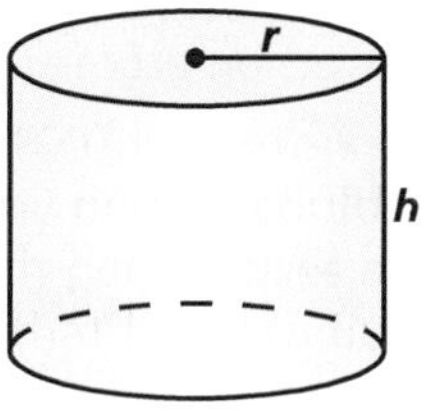


**(1)** Use the formula for volume.
Replace variables with actual dimensions.

$V = 3.14 \times (30 \text{ cm})^2 \times 27 \text{ cm}$

**(2)** Calculate by multiplying.

$3.14 \times 900 \times 27$

$2826 \times 27 = 76{,}302$

**(3)** Check units:

$\text{cm} \times \text{cm} \times \text{cm} = \text{cm}^3$ (cubic centimeters)

**ANSWER** $3.14 \times (30 \text{ cm})^2 \times 27 \text{ cm} = 76{,}302 \text{ cm}^3$

**Find the following volumes.**

1. Brushing your teeth with the water running uses the water in a tank that has a radius of 10 cm and a height of 12 cm. Sketch a tank that holds exactly this amount. Label the dimensions. What is the volume?

2. If you turn off the water while you brush, you use only about half as much water. Sketch a tank that has a radius of 10 cm and a height of 6 cm. Label the dimensions. What is the volume?

3. A toilet flush uses the water in a space with a radius of 10 cm and a height of 37 cm. Find the volume in cubic centimeters. Sketch a model of this volume.

**CHALLENGE** There are approximately 5678 cubic meters of water in the water tower shown. How many people could the tower supply with water for one day if each person uses a volume of water that would fill a cylinder that has a radius of 0.4 m and a height of 0.34 m?

**MATH TUTORIAL**
CLASSZONE.COM
Click on Math Tutorial for more help with finding the volume of a cylinder.

Math 6.MG.1.2, 6.MG.1.3
Science 6.6.b

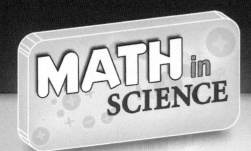

KEY CONCEPT

# 14.3 People are working to protect ecosystems.

**CALIFORNIA Content Standards**

**6.6.a** Students know the utility of energy sources is determined by factors that are involved in converting these sources to useful forms and the consequences of the conversion process.

**6.6.b** Students know different natural energy and material resources, including air, soil, rocks, minerals, petroleum, fresh water, wildlife, and forests, and know how to classify them as renewable or nonrenewable.

**6.6.c** Students know the natural origin of the materials used to make common objects.

**BEFORE, you learned**

- Human activities produce pollutants
- Human activity is depleting some natural resources

**NOW, you will learn**

- About local and federal efforts to protect the environment
- About efforts that are being made to conserve natural resources

**VOCABULARY**

**sustainable** p. 510

**EXPLORE Environmental Impacts (6.5.e)**

***What happens when soil is compressed?***

**PROCEDURE**

1. Fill two pots with 1 cup each of potting soil.
2. Compress the soil in the first pot by pushing down hard on it with your hand.
3. Pour 1 cup of water into the second pot. Start the stopwatch as soon as you start pouring. Stop the watch as soon as all the water has been absorbed. Record the time.
4. Pour 1 cup of water into the first pot. Again record how long it takes for the water to be absorbed. Wash your hands.

**WHAT DO YOU THINK?**

- What effect does compressing the soil have on how quickly the water is absorbed?
- What might happen to water that is not absorbed quickly by soil?

**MATERIALS**

- 2 plant pots with trays
- measuring cup
- potting soil
- water
- stopwatch

## Environmental awareness is growing.

**NOTE-TAKING STRATEGY**
Use a strategy of your choosing to take notes on the main idea.

As pioneers moved westward across the grassy plains and steep mountain ranges of North America, many believed that resources were endless. Midwestern prairies were converted to farmland. Forests were clear-cut for lumber. Mines were dug for coal.

By the 1800s, foresters and naturalists began to take an interest in preserving the wild areas they saw rapidly disappearing. In 1872 Yellowstone was established as the world's first national park. It wasn't long before the conservation of wild places became a goal.

As you read in Chapter 13, conservation is the process of saving or protecting a natural resource.

The movement to protect our environment grew rapidly in the 1960s. In 1962 the book *Silent Spring* raised public awareness of the effects of harmful chemicals on the environment. As local efforts for environmental protection grew, the United States government responded. Throughout the 1970s, far-reaching laws were passed to preserve and protect the environment. Today, local and national government efforts, along with groups of concerned citizens, protect America's natural resources.

**CHECK YOUR READING** List three events in the history of the environmental movement in the United States.

**RESOURCE CENTER** CLASSZONE.COM

Discover how people help ecosystems recover.

Volunteers work to clean up a stream.

## Local Efforts

Maybe you have heard the expression "Think globally, act locally." It urges people to consider the health of the entire planet and to take action in their own communities. Long before federal and state agencies began enforcing environmental laws, people were coming together to protect habitats and the organisms that depend on them. These efforts are often referred to as grassroots efforts. They occur on a local level and are often run by volunteers.

Sometimes the efforts of a few citizens attract the support and interest of so many people that those people form a larger organization. These groups work to bring about change by communicating with politicians, publishing articles, or talking to the news media. Some groups purchase land and set it aside for preservation.

## Federal Efforts

You have probably heard of the Endangered Species Act or the Clean Air Act. You might wonder exactly what these laws do. The United States government works with scientists to write environmental laws. The goal of the laws is for companies and individuals to work together to conserve natural resources and maintain healthy ecosystems.

In 1969 the National Environmental Policy Act (NEPA) made the protection of natural ecosystems a national goal. Several important laws followed. For example, the Clean Air Act and Clean Water Act helped control the kinds and amounts of pollutants that can be released into the air and water. The Environmental Protection Agency (EPA) enforces all federal environmental laws.

**CHECK YOUR READING** Identify two federal environmental laws.

Over the past century, chemical waste from factories has piled up in landfills, and it has polluted water sources. These wastes can threaten ecosystems and human health. In 1980 citizen awareness of the dangers led to the Superfund Program. The goal of the program is to identify dangerous areas and clean up the worst sites.

### Helping Endangered Species

**Government and private groups have helped peregrine falcon populations to recover.**

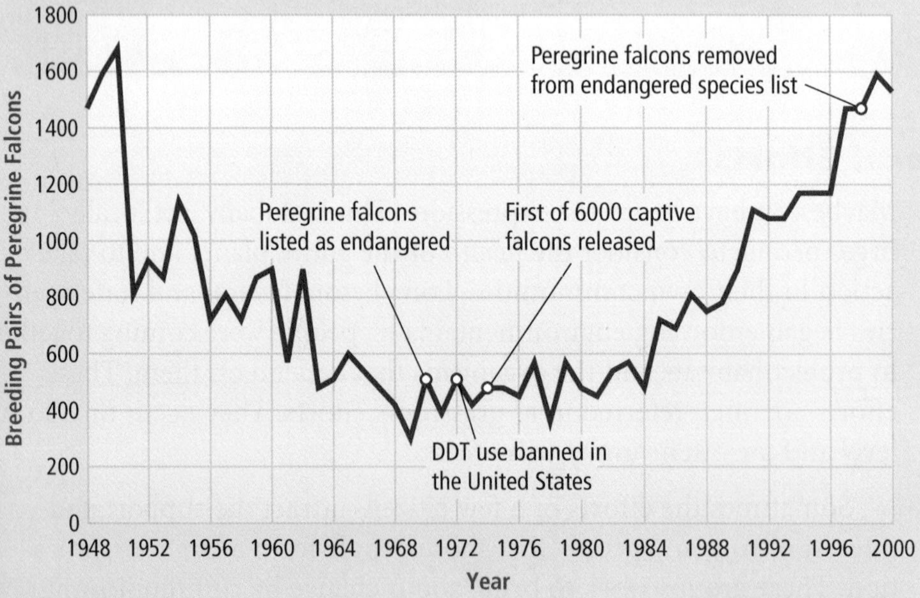


Source: Audubon Society

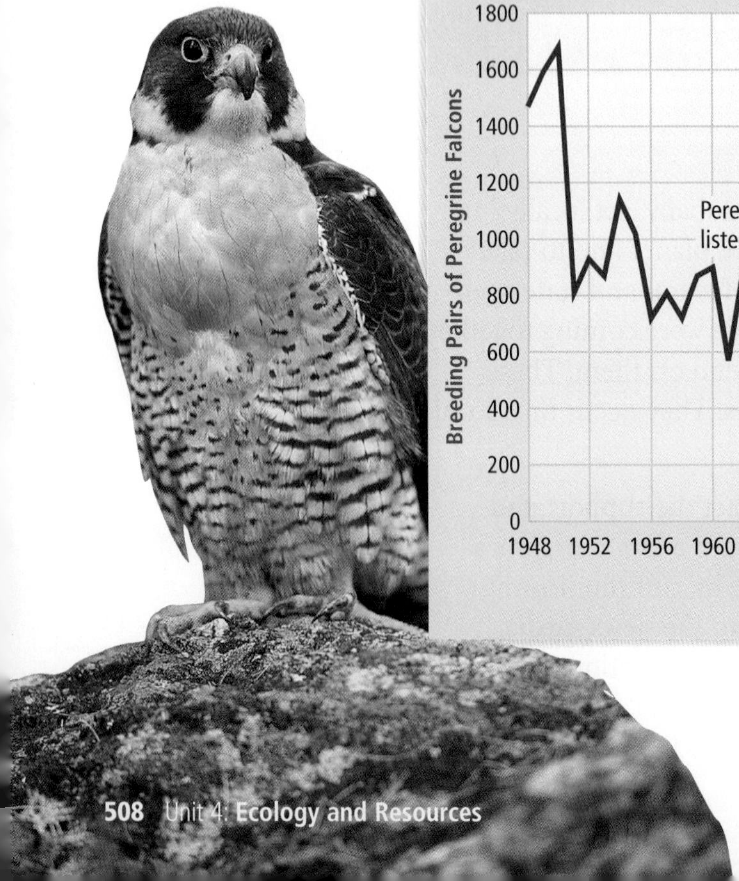

## Ecosystem Recovery

**A growing awareness of the importance of healthy ecosystems is inspiring restoration projects.**

### Wetland

Restoration efforts in Galveston Bay, Texas, focus on bringing back the sea-grass meadows near the coast.

Volunteers help replant sea grass around Galveston Island State Park. Sea grass is a major habitat for birds, fish, and crabs. It helps prevent erosion by holding sediments in place.

### Desert

Members of a restoration group work to restore desert plants and soil in Red Rock Canyon State Park, California.

1 A power auger is used to break up very compacted soil and prepare it for planting.

2 Seedlings of native species, such as the saltbush, are grown elsewhere. Once the plants reach a mature size, they are planted in the park.

3 Plastic cones are used to protect plants from severe weather or predators.

Federal agencies oversee the Superfund Program and other environmental laws. In addition to federal laws protecting the environment, there are state laws. Companies must follow all the laws that apply in each state where they do business. The same company may need to follow different laws in different states.

The United States is just one of many countries learning to deal with the effects of their human population on the environment. Dozens of countries have already met to discuss concerns about clear-cutting, water pollution, and endangered species. At the international level, the United Nations Environment Programme encourages sound environmental practices worldwide.

**INFER** At this Superfund site, the chemical cadmium pollutes the soil. Why does this worker need to wear a face mask?

## Conserving resources protects ecosystems.

Around the world, individuals and companies are expressing more interest in **sustainable** practices—ways of living and doing business that use natural resources without using them up. Sustainable development allows people to enjoy a high quality of life while limiting harm to ecosystems. Developing new technologies, reducing resource use, and creating less waste are three ways to practice sustainability.

**CHECK YOUR READING** What are sustainable practices?

### Improving Resource Use

As you read in Chapter 12, many different interactions take place in ecosystems. Some organisms form close relationships with one another and their environment. Humans are like other organisms. We depend on the environment to help meet our requirements for life. Because many of the resources we rely on are limited, businesses and governments are changing the way they manage farms, forests, and energy resources. They are adopting sustainable practices.

For example, some farmers are practicing sustainable methods that protect soil. Soil conservation is important because soil takes a very long time to form. It can be difficult or impossible to replace once it has been lost. Most soil conservation methods are designed to hold soil in place and keep it fertile. A few of the soil conservation methods that are used by farmers around the world are described on page 511.

**Crop rotation** is the practice of planting different crops on the same field in different years or growing seasons. Grain crops, such as wheat, use up a lot of the nitrogen—a necessary plant nutrient—in the soil. The roots of bean crops, such as soybeans, contain bacteria that restore nitrogen to the soil. By rotating these crops, farmers can help maintain soil fertility.

**Conservation tillage** includes several methods of reducing the number of times fields are tilled, or plowed, in a year. The less soil is disturbed by plowing, the less likely it is to be washed or blown away. In one method of conservation tillage, fields are not plowed at all. The remains of harvested crops are simply left on the fields to cover and protect the soil. New seeds are planted in narrow bands of soil.

**Terraces** are flat, steplike areas built on a hillside to hold rainwater and prevent it from running downhill. Crops are planted on the flat tops of the terraces.

**Contour plowing** is the practice of plowing along the curves, or contours, of a slope. Contour plowing helps channel rainwater so that it does not run straight downhill, carrying away soil with it. A soil conservation method called strip-cropping is often combined with contour plowing. Strips of grasses, shrubs, or other plants are planted between bands of a grain crop along the contour of a slope. These strips of plants also help slow the runoff of water.

**Windbreaks** are rows of trees planted between fields to "break," or reduce, the force of winds that can carry off soil.

Terracing

Contour Plowing

READING VISUALS **COMPARE** Both terracing and contour plowing are soil conservation methods used on sloping land. How does each method help conserve soil?

INFER What benefits do people get from using mass transit? Why might some people be reluctant to use mass transit?

## Reducing Waste and Pollution

Perhaps you take a bus to school. Buses and trains are examples of mass transit, the moving of large groups of people at the same time. When you travel by mass transit, you are working to reduce waste and pollution. The photograph to the left shows a train that carries commuters from downtown Portland, Oregon, to suburbs an hour away. In Portland, mass transit helps reduce traffic congestion, fuel use, air pollution, and noise pollution.

Another way to reduce pollution is by carpooling, or sharing rides. Many states, including California, encourage carpools by reducing tolls or reserving highway lanes for cars carrying more than one person. Traffic is also reduced when workers telecommute, or work from home using computers and telephones. Of course, a telecommuter uses energy at home. But there are many ways to reduce home energy use. You can install compact fluorescent light bulbs, which use less electricity than a regular light bulb. And you can choose energy-efficient appliances.

**CHECK YOUR READING** How does mass transit benefit the environment?

READING TIP
The prefix *re-* means "again," so to recycle a resource is to use it again.

People can conserve water in three ways. The first way is to use less water. A simple way that some cities reduce water use is by repairing leaks in underground pipes. The second way is to reuse water. Many cities reuse treated wastewater for landscaping. The third method is to use water again for the same purpose. Industries can recycle water used to cool machines back through the same system.

The chart below shows how people living in the United States use water in their homes. Note that one way people could conserve water is by repairing leaking toilets.

**U.S. Household Water Usage**

**Americans use an average of 330 liters per person each day.**

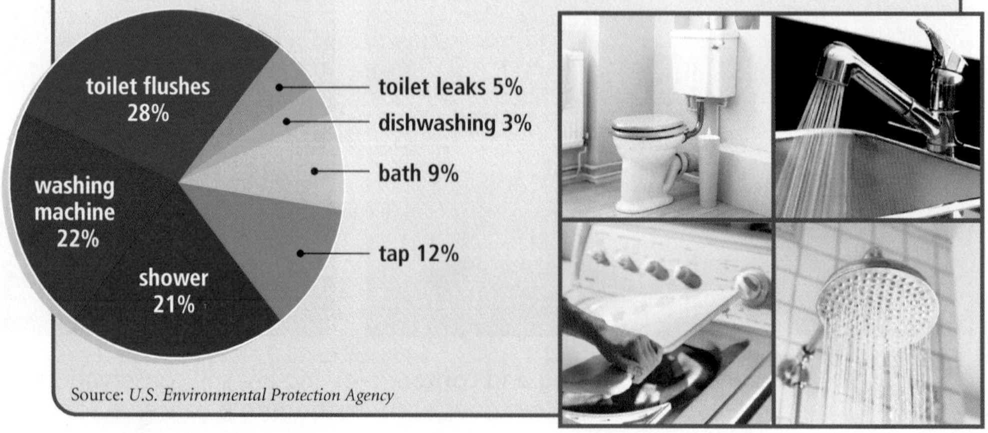


Source: *U.S. Environmental Protection Agency*

Other ways that people can conserve water at home include changes in plumbing and in daily habits. Low-flow toilets and showerheads can cut water use in half. People conserve water by turning off the faucet while brushing their teeth, taking shorter showers, and running the dishwasher only when it is full. Leaking pipes and dripping faucets in homes cause huge amounts of water to be wasted. Regular repair and maintenance of plumbing systems can reduce water use greatly.

**RESOURCE CENTER**
CLASSZONE.COM
Learn more about water conservation.

**CHECK YOUR READING** What are three ways in which people can conserve water at home?

## Think globally, act locally.

Visitors to an ocean beach may find signs like the one on the right. Such signs remind people that small actions, such as protecting the nests of sandpipers, make a difference in the preservation of ecosystems.

The challenges facing society are great. Providing Earth's growing human population with clean water, clean air, and energy for heating, cooling, and transportation are only some of the many tasks. Scientists continue to learn about the interactions in ecosystems and the importance of ecosystems to humans. As you have read about the interactions in ecosystems, you have probably realized that humans—including you—have a large effect on the natural world.

In the coming years, protecting ecosystems will remain a major challenge. By thinking globally, you will be able to understand the effects of society's decisions about resources, development, and transportation. By acting locally, you can become involved in efforts to reduce the use of limited resources and to restore ecosystems.

## 14.3 Review

### KEY CONCEPTS

1. What is meant by the slogan, "Think globally, act locally"?
2. List at least five ways that you can reduce your use of natural resources. (6.6.b)
3. Describe three ways that resources can be managed in a sustainable way. (6.6.b)

### CRITICAL THINKING

4. **Infer** Controlling air and water pollution and protecting endangered species usually require the involvement of the federal government. Why can't state or local governments do this on their own?
5. **Synthesize** How are sustainable practices related to the use of nonrenewable resources?

### CHALLENGE

6. **Apply** Explain how efforts to protect endangered species relate to the restoration of ecosystems.

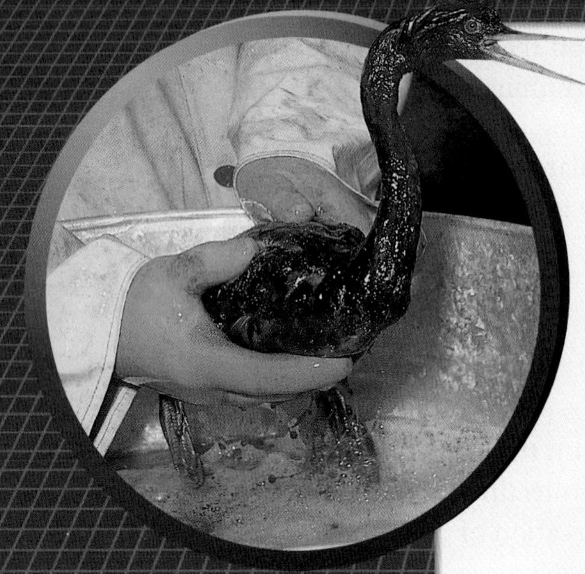

# Cleaning Oil Spills

**DESIGN — YOUR OWN —**

## OVERVIEW AND PURPOSE

One example of a harmful effect of human activity is an oil spill. You've probably heard about oil spills in the news. Damage to an oil-carrying ship or barge can cause thick, black oil to spill into the water. The oil floats on the water, and waves can carry the oil to shore. Oil coats sand and living things that are part of a coastal ecosystem. These spills are especially difficult to clean up. In this investigation you will

- simulate an oil spill and test the effectiveness of various materials used to remove oil
- evaluate materials and processes used to clean up oil spills

## Problem

Write It Up

What materials are effective at removing oil spilled near a coastal ecosystem?

## Hypothesize

Write It Up

Write a hypothesis to propose a material or materials that might best remove oil from a coastal area. Your hypothesis should take the form of an "If . . . , then . . . , because . . ." statement.

## Procedure

1. Make a table in your **Science Notebook** like the one shown on the sample notebook page. Record your observations on the effectiveness of each material.

2. Measure 40 mL of vegetable oil in a small beaker. Stir in a small amount of turmeric to make the oil yellow.

3. Pour sand into one end of the pan, as shown, to model a beach.

4. Carefully pour enough water into the pan so that it forms a model ocean at least 2 cm deep. Try not to disturb the sand pile.

5. Use the yellow-colored oil to model an oil spill. Pour the oil onto the slope of the sand so that it runs off into the water.

step 5

### MATERIALS

- small beaker
- 40 mL vegetable oil
- turmeric
- spoon
- aluminum baking pan
- sand
- large beaker
- water
- sponge
- dish soap
- rubbing alcohol
- paper towels
- cotton balls
- cotton rag
- cornstarch
- yarn
- feather
- seaweed

6.6.a, 6.7.a, 6.7.e

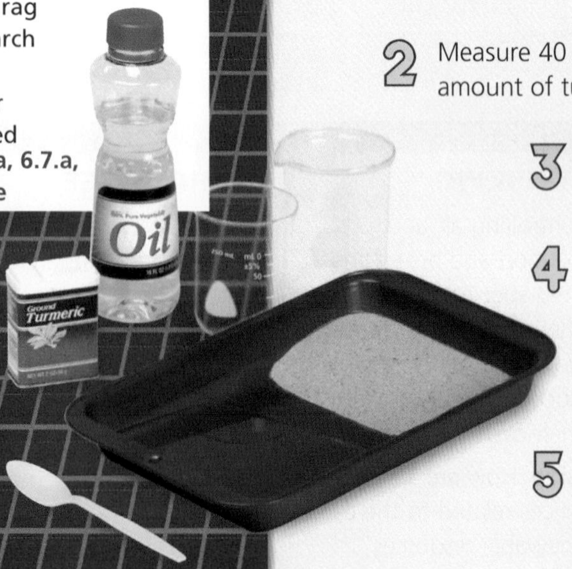

**Content Standard**
6.6.a Students know the utility of energy sources is determined by factors that are involved in converting these sources to useful forms and the consequences of the conversion process.

**Investigation Standard**
6.7.a Develop a hypothesis.

6 Test the materials for effectiveness in removing the oil from the sand and the water. Record your observations on the effectiveness of each material.

7 Place the feather and the seaweed on the beach or in the water, where the oil is. Test materials for effectiveness in removing oil from the feather and seaweed. Record your observations.

8 Using your observations from steps 6 and 7, design a process for removing oil from sand and water. This process may involve several materials and require a series of steps.

## Observe and Analyze

Write It Up

1. **RECORD** Write up your procedure for cleaning oil from sand and water. You may want to include a diagram.
2. **EVALUATE** What, if any, difficulties did you encounter in carrying out this experiment?

## Conclude

Write It Up

1. **INTERPRET** How do your results compare with your hypothesis? Answer the problem question.
2. **EVALUATE** Which materials were most useful for cleaning the water? Were they the same materials that were most useful for cleaning the sand?
3. **EVALUATE** Suppose you are trying to clean oil off of a living thing, such as a bird or seaweed. What process would you use?
4. **IDENTIFY LIMITS** In which ways did this demonstration fail to model a real oil spill?

## INVESTIGATE Further

**CHALLENGE** Explain how the observations you made in this investigation might be useful in cleaning up an actual oil spill.

Cleaning Oil Spills

Problem What materials are effective at removing oil spilled near a coastal ecosystem?

Hypothesis

Observations

| | Water | Sand | Feather | Seaweed |
|---|---|---|---|---|
| Paper towel | | | | |
| Cotton balls | | | | |
| | | | | |
| | | | | |

# 14 Chapter Review

## the BIG idea

**Humans and human population growth affect the environment.**

CONTENT REVIEW
CLASSZONE.COM

### KEY CONCEPTS SUMMARY

#### 1 Human population growth presents challenges.

As the population continues to grow, there is a greater demand for natural resources. Cities and countries share many resources. Increasing populations put pressure on ecosystems.

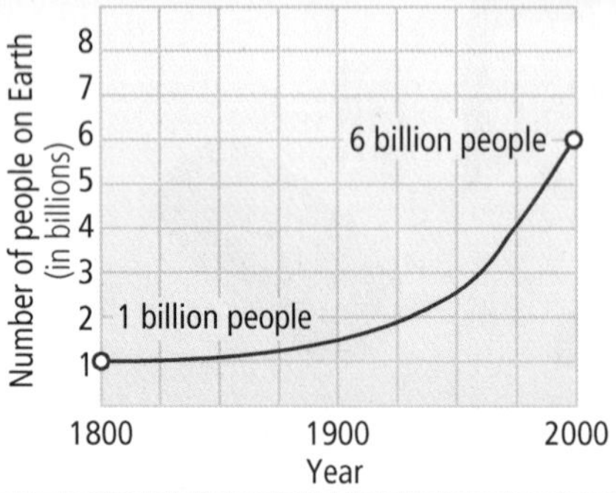


**VOCABULARY**
**population density** p. 494

#### 2 Human activities affect the environment.

Pollution and habitat loss make it difficult for plants and animals to survive. Without the necessary resources, biodiversity decreases, and ecosystems become less stable.

pollution

habitat loss

**VOCABULARY**
**pollution** p. 498
**biodiversity** p. 498

#### 3 People are working to protect ecosystems.

Working at local and governmental levels, people are helping ecosystems recover.

Laws protect endangered species.

People can help clean up the environment.

**VOCABULARY**
**sustainable** p. 510

## Reviewing Vocabulary

*Place each term at the center of a description wheel diagram. Write some words describing it on the spokes.*

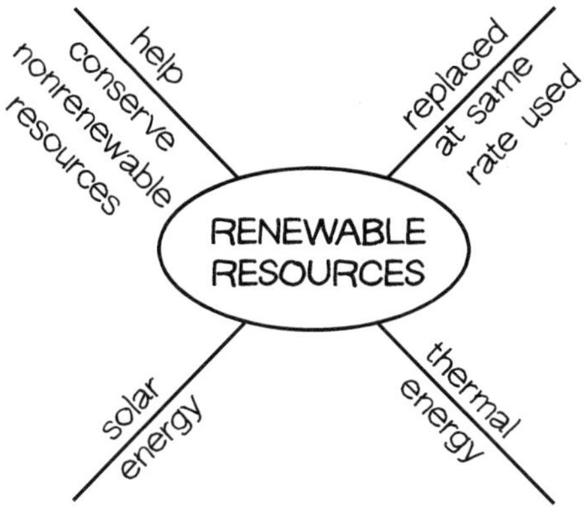


1. population density
2. natural resources
3. pollution
4. biodiversity
5. sustainable
6. conservation

## Reviewing Key Concepts

**Multiple Choice** *Choose the best answer.*

7. What do experts predict will happen to the world population over the next 20 years? (6.5.e)
   - **a.** It will continue to grow rapidly.
   - **b.** It will stay the same.
   - **c.** It will decline sharply.
   - **d.** It will go up and down.

8. Which statement helps explain why Earth's population has grown very rapidly in the last 100 years? (6.5.e)
   - **a.** On average, women are having children at an older age.
   - **b.** People live longer because of improved health care and nutrition.
   - **c.** Global warming has enabled farmers to grow more food.
   - **d.** More land has been developed for housing.

9. Which of the following is an example of increasing biodiversity? (6.6.b)
   - **a.** A forest is clear-cut for its wood, leaving land available for new uses.
   - **b.** New species of animals and plants appear in a wildlife preserve.
   - **c.** A new species of plant outcompetes all of the others around a lake.
   - **d.** A cleared rain forest results in a change to a habitat.

10. Which represents a sustainable practice? (6.6.a)
    - **a.** using conservation tillage and natural fertilizers
    - **b.** removing oil more efficiently
    - **c.** allowing unlimited use of water for higher fees
    - **d.** restocking a lake with fish every year

11. What environmental problem does the Superfund Program address? (6.6.a)
    - **a.** habitat loss
    - **b.** land development
    - **c.** biodiversity
    - **d.** pollution

**Short Answer** *Write a short answer to each question.*

12. List four ways increased human population density affects ecosystems. (6.5.e)

13. Three ways that humans dispose of waste are landfills, incineration, and wastewater treatment plants. List one advantage and one disadvantage of each. (6.6.a)

14. Write a paragraph to describe how an increase in population density affects land development. (6.5.e)

## Thinking Critically

*Use the graph to answer the next three questions.*

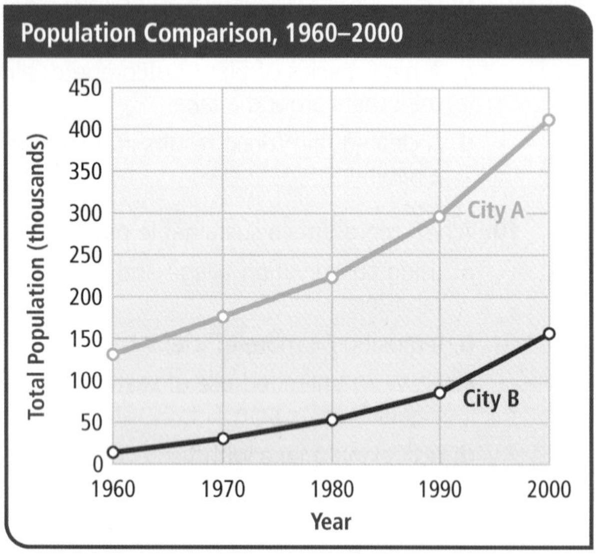


15. **COMPARE AND CONTRAST** Describe the population size and rate of growth for City A and City B. Based on the graph, would you expect the population of City B ever to get bigger than that of City A? (6.5.e)

16. **EVALUATE** Is it possible to determine from the data shown whether the population density is higher in City A than in City B? If not, what other information would you need? (6.5.e)

17. **CONNECT** City A is located in a temperate-forest biome, and City B is located in a desert biome. How might the characteristics of these biomes affect the carrying capacity of the human populations in these cities? (6.5.e)

18. **PREDICT** If the United States used less water from the Colorado River, how would the depth of the river in Mexico be affected? (6.6.b)

19. **COMPARE AND CONTRAST** Explain why trees are generally considered a renewable resource. Describe circumstances under which they could be considered a nonrenewable resource. (6.6.b)

20. **CLASSIFY** Sort the resources below into the correct categories: (6.6.b)

| Resource | Renewable | Nonrenewable |
|---|---|---|
| Water | | |
| Coal | | |
| Soil | | |
| Wood | | |
| Copper | | |
| Petroleum | | |
| Aluminum | | |
| Sunlight | | |

21. **CALCULATE** A compact fluorescent bulb uses less energy than a regular incandescent bulb. It is estimated that a coal-burning power plant would release 72 kilograms more carbon dioxide ($CO_2$) a year to power one regular bulb than it would to power one fluorescent bulb. If you replace five regular bulbs with five compact bulbs, how much less $CO_2$ would be released in a 10-year period? (6.6.a)

## the BIG idea

22. **PROVIDE EXAMPLES** Look again at the photograph on pages 486–487. How would you now change or add details to your initial answer to the question on the photograph? (6.6.a)

23. **APPLY** Suppose that you live in a community located on a small island. Make a brochure that describes the island habitat. Include information about natural resources, such as water and soil. List the plants and animals that live there. Establish four rules that the community should follow to preserve the local habitat. (6.6.b)

## UNIT PROJECTS

Evaluate the materials in your project folder. Finish your project and get ready to present it to your class.

For more practice, go to . . .
TEST PRACTICE
CLASSZONE.COM

## Analyzing Data

6.6.a, 6.7.c

Nowhere is the impact of human population growth more obvious than in the increased size of urban areas. Buildings, parking lots, and roads are replacing forests, farmland, and wetlands. The table below shows the growth of urban areas around 10 cities in the United States over a 20-year period.

**Growth in Land Area, 1970-1990**

| Location | Growth in Land Area ($km^2$) |
|---|---|
| Atlanta, GA | 1817 |
| Houston, TX | 1654 |
| New York City-NJ | 1402 |
| Washington, D.C.-MD-VA | 1166 |
| Philadelphia, PA-NJ | 1068 |
| Los Angeles, CA | 1020 |
| Dallas-Fort Worth, TX | 965 |
| Tampa-St. Petersburg-Clearwater, FL | 929 |
| Phoenix, AZ | 916 |
| Minneapolis-Saint Paul, MN | 885 |

Source: U.S. Bureau of Census Data on Urbanized Areas

**1.** What patterns can you see in the way information is presented from the top of the table to the bottom?

**a.** Cities are arranged alphabetically.
**b.** Cities are arranged by growth in population over 20 years.
**c.** Cities are arranged by the growth in land area over 20 years.
**d.** Cities are arranged by size of urban area.

**2.** How many square kilometers around Philadelphia were affected by urbanization between 1970 and 1990?

**a.** 1020 $km^2$
**b.** 1068 $km^2$
**c.** 1116 $km^2$
**d.** 1166 $km^2$

**3.** How would you describe the change in the land around Atlanta between 1970 and 1990?

**a.** More land was used for farming.
**b.** More land was used for buildings and roads.
**c.** More land was covered with forests.
**d.** Wetland habitats for birds increased.

**4.** Which type of graph would be best for displaying the data in the table?

**a.** bar graph
**b.** circle graph
**c.** line graph
**d.** double bar graph

## Extended Response

**5.** Write a paragraph to describe how a rural area would change if the land were developed and the area became more urban. Use the terms below and underline them in your answer.

| | |
|---|---|
| population density | biodiversity |
| renewable resources | habitat |

**6.** Suppose that you are an urban designer working for a small city that expected to expand rapidly in the next ten years. What recommendations would you make to the city council on how the land should be developed?

# Student Resource Handbooks

## Making Observations

An **observation** is an act of noting and recording an event, characteristic, behavior, or anything else detected with an instrument or with the senses.

Observations allow you to make informed hypotheses and to gather data for experiments. Careful observations often lead to ideas for new experiments. There are two categories of observations:

- **Quantitative observations** can be expressed in numbers and include records of time, temperature, mass, distance, and volume.
- **Qualitative observations** include descriptions of sights, sounds, smells, and textures.

### EXAMPLE

A student dissolved 30 grams of Epsom salts in water, poured the solution into a dish, and let the dish sit out uncovered overnight. The next day, she made the following observations of the Epsom salt crystals that grew in the dish.

To determine the mass, the student found the mass of the dish before and after growing the crystals and then used subtraction to find the difference.

The student measured several crystals and calculated the mean length. (To learn how to calculate the mean of a data set, see page R36.)

Table 1. Observations of Epsom Salt Crystals

| Quantitative Observations | Qualitative Observations |
|---|---|
| • mass = 30 g<br>• mean crystal length = 0.5 cm<br>• longest crystal length = 2 cm | • Crystals are clear.<br>• Crystals are long, thin, and rectangular.<br>• White crust has formed around edge of dish. |

Photographs or sketches are useful for recording qualitative observations.

Epsom salt crystals

### MORE ABOUT OBSERVING

- Make quantitative observations whenever possible. That way, others will know exactly what you observed and be able to compare their results with yours.
- It is always a good idea to make qualitative observations too. You never know when you might observe something unexpected.

# Predicting and Hypothesizing

A **prediction** is an expectation of what will be observed or what will happen. A **hypothesis** is a tentative explanation for an observation or scientific problem that can be tested by further investigation.



### EXAMPLE

Suppose you have made two paper airplanes and you wonder why one of them tends to glide farther than the other one.

1. Start by asking a question.
2. Make an educated guess. After examination, you notice that the wings of the airplane that flies farther are slightly larger than the wings of the other airplane.
3. Write a prediction based upon your educated guess, in the form of an "If . . . , then . . ." statement. Write the independent variable after the word *if,* and the dependent variable after the word *then.*
4. To make a hypothesis, explain why you think what you predicted will occur. Write the explanation after the word *because.*

1. Why does one of the paper airplanes glide farther than the other?

2. The size of an airplane's wings may affect how far the airplane will glide.

3. Prediction: If I make a paper airplane with larger wings, then the airplane will glide farther.

To read about independent and dependent variables, see page R30.

4. Hypothesis: If I make a paper airplane with larger wings, then the airplane will glide farther, because the additional surface area of the wing will produce more lift.

Notice that the part of the hypothesis after *because* adds an explanation of why the airplane will glide farther.

### MORE ABOUT HYPOTHESES

- The results of an experiment cannot prove that a hypothesis is correct. Rather, the results either support or do not support the hypothesis.
- Valuable information is gained even when your hypothesis is not supported by your results. For example, it would be an important discovery to find that wing size is not related to how far an airplane glides.
- In science, a hypothesis is supported only after many scientists have conducted many experiments and produced consistent results.

# Inferring

**An inference is a logical conclusion drawn from the available evidence and prior knowledge. Inferences are often made from observations.**

### EXAMPLE

A student observing a set of acorns noticed something unexpected about one of them. He noticed a white, soft-bodied insect eating its way out of the acorn.

The student recorded these observations.

**Observations**

- There is a hole in the acorn, about 0.5 cm in diameter, where the insect crawled out.
- There is a second hole, which is about the size of a pinhole, on the other side of the acorn.
- The inside of the acorn is hollow.

Here are some inferences that can be made on the basis of the observations.

**Inferences**

- The insect formed from the material inside the acorn, grew to its present size, and ate its way out of the acorn.
- The insect crawled through the smaller hole, ate the inside of the acorn, grew to its present size, and ate its way out of the acorn.
- An egg was laid in the acorn through the smaller hole. The egg hatched into a larva that ate the inside of the acorn, grew to its present size, and ate its way out of the acorn.

When you make inferences, be sure to look at all of the evidence available and combine it with what you already know.

### MORE ABOUT INFERENCES

Inferences depend both on observations and on the knowledge of the people making the inferences. Ancient people who did not know that organisms are produced only by similar organisms might have made an inference like the first one. A student today might look at the same observations and make the second inference. A third student might have knowledge about this particular insect and know that it is never small enough to fit through the smaller hole, leading her to the third inference.

# Identifying Cause and Effect

**In a cause-and-effect relationship, one event or characteristic is the result of another. Usually an effect follows its cause in time.**

There are many examples of cause-and-effect relationships in everyday life.

| Cause | Effect |
|---|---|
| Turn off a light. | Room gets dark. |
| Drop a glass. | Glass breaks. |
| Blow a whistle. | Sound is heard. |

Scientists must be careful not to infer a cause-and-effect relationship just because one event happens after another event. When one event occurs after another, you cannot infer a cause-and-effect relationship on the basis of that information alone. You also cannot conclude that one event caused another if there are alternative ways to explain the second event. A scientist must demonstrate through experimentation or continued observation that an event was truly caused by another event.

**EXAMPLE**

### Make an Observation

Suppose you have a few plants growing outside. When the weather starts getting colder, you bring one of the plants indoors. You notice that the plant you brought indoors is growing faster than the others are growing. You cannot conclude from your observation that the change in temperature was the cause of the increased plant growth, because there are alternative explanations for the observation. Some possible explanations are given below.

- The humidity indoors caused the plant to grow faster.
- The level of sunlight indoors caused the plant to grow faster.
- The indoor plant's being noticed more often and watered more often than the outdoor plants caused it to grow faster.
- The plant that was brought indoors was healthier than the other plants to begin with.

To determine which of these factors, if any, caused the indoor plant to grow faster than the outdoor plants, you would need to design and conduct an experiment.

See pages R28–R35 for information about designing experiments.

# Recognizing Bias

**Television, newspapers, and the Internet are full of experts claiming to have scientific evidence to back up their claims. How do you know whether the claims are really backed up by good science?**

**Bias** is a slanted point of view, or personal prejudice. The goal of scientists is to be as objective as possible and to base their findings on facts instead of opinions. However, bias often affects the conclusions of researchers, and it is important to learn to recognize bias.

When scientific results are reported, you should consider the source of the information as well as the information itself. It is important to critically analyze the information that you see and read.

## SOURCES OF BIAS

There are several ways in which a report of scientific information may be biased. Here are some questions that you can ask yourself:

1. **Who is sponsoring the research?**

   Sometimes, the results of an investigation are biased because an organization paying for the research is looking for a specific answer. This type of bias can affect how data are gathered and interpreted.

2. **Is the research sample large enough?**

   Sometimes research does not include enough data. The larger the sample size, the more likely that the results are accurate, assuming a truly random sample.

3. **In a survey, who is answering the questions?**

   The results of a survey or poll can be biased. The people taking part in the survey may have been specifically chosen because of how they would answer. They may have the same ideas or lifestyles. A survey or poll should make use of a random sample of people.

4. **Are the people who take part in a survey biased?**

   People who take part in surveys sometimes try to answer the questions the way they think the researcher wants them to answer. Also, in surveys or polls that ask for personal information, people may be unwilling to answer questions truthfully.

## SCIENTIFIC BIAS

It is also important to realize that scientists have their own biases because of the types of research they do and because of their scientific viewpoints. Two scientists may look at the same set of data and come to completely different conclusions because of these biases. However, such disagreements are not necessarily bad. In fact, a critical analysis of disagreements is often responsible for moving science forward.

# Identifying Faulty Reasoning

**Faulty reasoning** is wrong or incorrect thinking. It leads to mistakes and to wrong conclusions. Scientists are careful not to draw unreasonable conclusions from experimental data. Without such caution, the results of scientific investigations may be misleading.

### EXAMPLE

Scientists try to make generalizations based on their data to explain as much about nature as possible. If only a small sample of data is looked at, however, a conclusion may be faulty. Suppose a scientist has studied the effects of the El Niño and La Niña weather patterns on flood damage in California from 1989 to 1995. The scientist organized the data in the bar graph below.

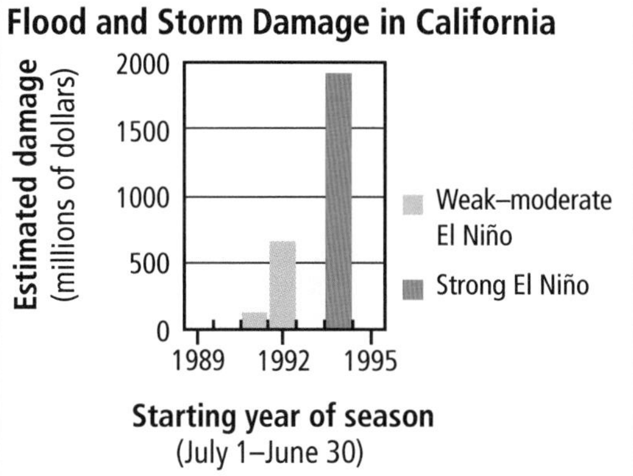

SOURCE: *Governor's Office of Emergency Services, California*

The scientist drew the following conclusions:

1. The La Niña weather pattern has no effect on flooding in California.
2. When neither weather pattern occurs, there is almost no flood damage.
3. A weak or moderate El Niño produces a small or moderate amount of flooding.
4. A strong El Niño produces a lot of flooding.

For the six-year period of the scientist's investigation, these conclusions may seem to be reasonable. However, a six-year study of weather patterns may be too small of a sample for the conclusions to be supported. Consider the following graph, which shows information that was gathered from 1949 to 1997.

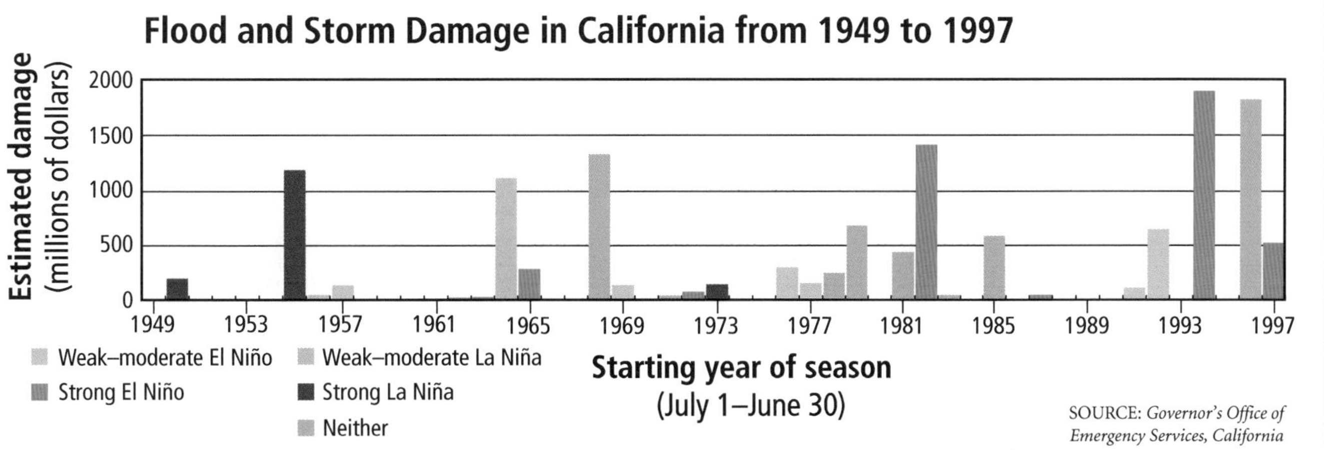

SOURCE: *Governor's Office of Emergency Services, California*

The only one of the conclusions that all of this information supports is number 3: a weak or moderate El Niño produces a small or moderate amount of flooding. By collecting more data, scientists can be more certain of their conclusions and can avoid faulty reasoning.

# Analyzing Statements

To **analyze** a statement is to examine its parts carefully. Scientific findings are often reported through media such as television or the Internet. A report that is made public often focuses on only a small part of research. As a result, it is important to question the sources of information.

## Evaluate Media Claims

To **evaluate** a statement is to judge it on the basis of criteria you've established. Sometimes evaluating means deciding whether a statement is true.

Reports of scientific research and findings in the media may be misleading or incomplete. When you are exposed to this information, you should ask yourself some questions so that you can make informed judgments about the information.

1. **Does the information come from a credible source?**

   Suppose you learn about a new product and it is stated that scientific evidence proves that the product works. A report from a respected news source may be more believable than an advertisement paid for by the product's manufacturer.

2. **How much evidence supports the claim?**

   Often, it may seem that there is new evidence every day of something in the world that either causes or cures an illness. However, information that is the result of several years of work by several different scientists is more credible than an advertisement that does not even cite the subjects of the experiment.

3. **How much information is being presented?**

   Science cannot solve all questions, and scientific experiments often have flaws. A report that discusses problems in a scientific study may be more believable than a report that addresses only positive experimental findings.

4. **Is scientific evidence being presented by a specific source?**

   Sometimes scientific findings are reported by people who are called experts or leaders in a scientific field. But if their names are not given or their scientific credentials are not reported, their statements may be less credible than those of recognized experts.

## Differentiate Between Fact and Opinion

Sometimes information is presented as a fact when it may be an opinion. When scientific conclusions are reported, it is important to recognize whether they are based on solid evidence. Again, you may find it helpful to ask yourself some questions.

1. **What is the difference between a fact and an opinion?**

   A **fact** is a piece of information that can be strictly defined and proved true. An **opinion** is a statement that expresses a belief, value, or feeling. An opinion cannot be proved true or false. For example, a person's age is a fact, but if someone is asked how old they feel, it is impossible to prove the person's answer to be true or false.

2. **Can opinions be measured?**

   Yes, opinions can be measured. In fact, surveys often ask for people's opinions on a topic. But there is no way to know whether or not an opinion is the truth.

**HOW TO DIFFERENTIATE FACT FROM OPINION**

### Human Activities and the Environment

Unfortunately, human use of fossil fuels is one of the most significant developments of the past few centuries. Humans rely on fossil fuels, a nonrenewable energy resource, for more than 90 percent of their energy needs.

This careless misuse of our planet's resources has resulted in pollution, global warming, and the destruction of fragile ecosystems. For example, oil pipelines carry more than one million barrels of oil each day across tundra regions. Transporting oil across such areas can only result in oil spills that poison the land for decades.

**Opinions**
Notice words or phrases that express beliefs or feelings. The words *unfortunately* and *careless* show that opinions are being expressed.

**Facts**
Statements that contain statistics tend to be facts. Writers often use facts to support their opinions.

**Opinion**
Look for statements that speculate about events. These statements are opinions, because they cannot be proved.

SCIENTIFIC THINKING HANDBOOK

# Safety Rules

Before you work in the laboratory, read these safety rules twice. Ask your teacher to explain any rules that you do not completely understand. Refer to these rules later on if you have questions about safety in the science classroom.

## Directions

- Read all directions and make sure that you understand them before starting an investigation or lab activity. If you do not understand how to do a procedure or how to use a piece of equipment, ask your teacher.
- Do not begin any investigation or touch any equipment until your teacher has told you to start.
- Never experiment on your own. If you want to try a procedure that the directions do not call for, ask your teacher for permission first.
- If you are hurt or injured in any way, tell your teacher immediately.



## Dress Code

goggles

apron

gloves

- Wear goggles when
  - — using glassware, sharp objects, or chemicals
  - — heating an object
  - — working with anything that can easily fly up into the air and hurt someone's eye
- Tie back long hair or hair that hangs in front of your eyes.
- Remove any article of clothing—such as a loose sweater or a scarf—that hangs down and may touch a flame, chemical, or piece of equipment.
- Observe all safety icons calling for the wearing of eye protection, gloves, and aprons.

## Heating and Fire Safety

fire safety

heating safety

- Keep your work area neat, clean, and free of extra materials.
- Never reach over a flame or heat source.
- Point objects being heated away from you and others.
- Never heat a substance or an object in a closed container.
- Never touch an object that has been heated. If you are unsure whether something is hot, treat it as though it is. Use oven mitts, clamps, tongs, or a test-tube holder.
- Know where the fire extinguisher and fire blanket are kept in your classroom.
- Do not throw hot substances into the trash. Wait for them to cool or use the container your teacher puts out for disposal.

## Electrical Safety

electrical safety

- Never use lamps or other electrical equipment with frayed cords.
- Make sure no cord is lying on the floor where someone can trip over it.
- Do not let a cord hang over the side of a counter or table so that the equipment can easily be pulled or knocked to the floor.
- Never let cords hang into sinks or other places where water can be found.
- Never try to fix electrical problems. Inform your teacher of any problems immediately.
- Unplug an electrical cord by pulling on the plug, not the cord.

## Chemical Safety

chemical safety

poison

fumes

- If you spill a chemical or get one on your skin or in your eyes, tell your teacher right away.
- Never touch, taste, or sniff any chemicals in the lab. If you need to determine odor, waft. Wafting consists of holding the chemical in its container 15 centimeters (6 in.) away from your nose, and using your fingers to bring fumes from the container to your nose.
- Keep lids on all chemicals you are not using.
- Never put unused chemicals back into the original containers. Throw away extra chemicals where your teacher tells you to.
- Pour chemicals over a sink or your work area, not over the floor.
- If you get a chemical in your eye, use the eyewash right away.
- Always wash your hands after handling chemicals, plants, or soil.

Wafting

## Glassware and Sharp-Object Safety

sharp objects

- If you break glassware, tell your teacher right away.
- Do not use broken or chipped glassware. Give these to your teacher.
- Use knives and other cutting instruments carefully. Always wear eye protection and cut away from you.

## Animal Safety

- Never hurt an animal.
- Touch animals only when necessary. Follow your teacher's instructions for handling animals.
- Always wash your hands after working with animals.

## Cleanup

disposal

- Follow your teacher's instructions for throwing away or putting away supplies.
- Clean your work area and pick up anything that has dropped to the floor.
- Wash your hands.

# Using Lab Equipment

Different experiments require different types of equipment. But even though experiments differ, the ways in which the equipment is used are the same.

## Beakers

- Use beakers for holding and pouring liquids.
- Do not use a beaker to measure the volume of a liquid. Use a graduated cylinder instead. (See page R16.)
- Use a beaker that holds about twice as much liquid as you need. For example, if you need 100 milliliters of water, you should use a 200- or 250-milliliter beaker.

## Test Tubes

- Use test tubes to hold small amounts of substances.
- Do not use a test tube to measure the volume of a liquid.
- Use a test tube when heating a substance over a flame. Aim the mouth of the tube away from yourself and other people.
- Liquids easily spill or splash from test tubes, so it is important to use only small amounts of liquids.

## Test-Tube Holder

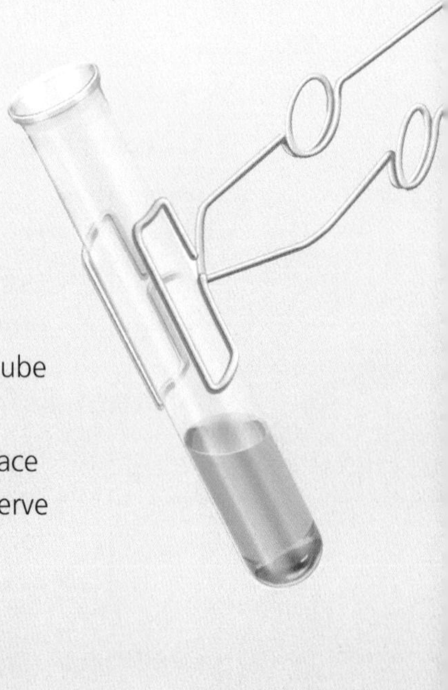

- Use a test-tube holder when heating a substance in a test tube.
- Use a test-tube holder if the substance in a test tube is dangerous to touch.
- Make sure the test-tube holder tightly grips the test tube so that the test tube will not slide out of the holder.
- Make sure that the test-tube holder is above the surface of the substance in the test tube so that you can observe the substance.

LAB HANDBOOK

## Test-Tube Rack

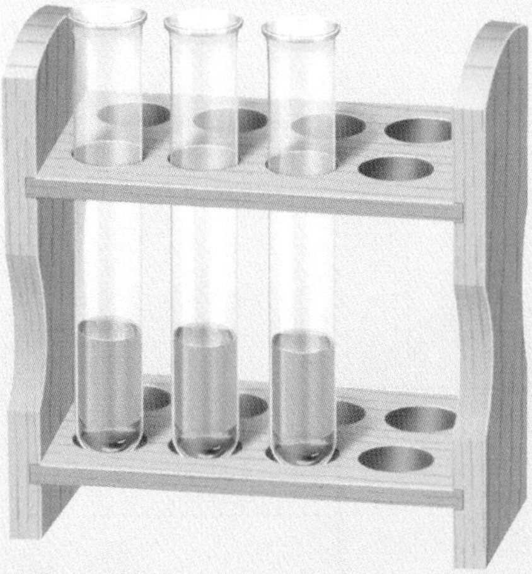

- Use a test-tube rack to organize test tubes before, during, and after an experiment.
- Use a test-tube rack to keep test tubes upright so that they do not fall over and spill their contents.
- Use a test-tube rack that is the correct size for the test tubes that you are using. If the rack is too small, a test tube may become stuck. If the rack is too large, a test tube may lean over, and some of its contents may spill or splash.

## Forceps

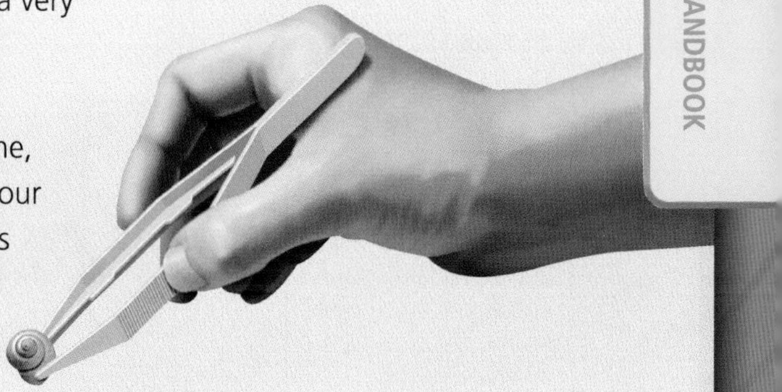

- Use forceps when you need to pick up or hold a very small object that should not be touched with your hands.
- Do not use forceps to hold anything over a flame, because forceps are not long enough to keep your hand safely away from the flame. Plastic forceps will melt, and metal forceps will conduct heat and burn your hand.

## Hot Plate

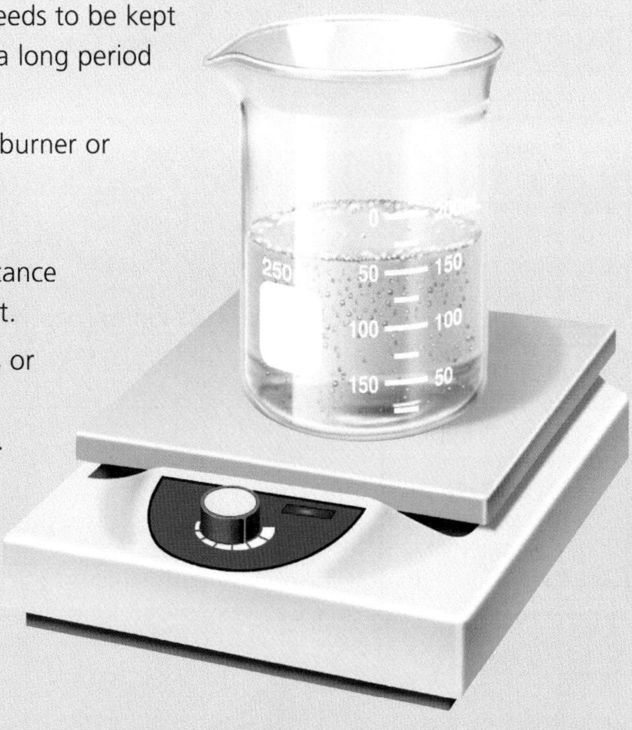

- Use a hot plate when a substance needs to be kept warmer than room temperature for a long period of time.
- Use a hot plate instead of a Bunsen burner or a candle when you need to carefully control temperature.
- Do not use a hot plate when a substance needs to be burned in an experiment.
- Always use "hot hands" safety mitts or oven mitts when handling anything that has been heated on a hot plate.

LAB HANDBOOK

## Microscope

Scientists use microscopes to see very small objects that cannot easily be seen with the eye alone. A microscope magnifies the image of an object so that small details may be observed. A microscope that you may use can magnify an object 400 times—the object will appear 400 times larger than its actual size.

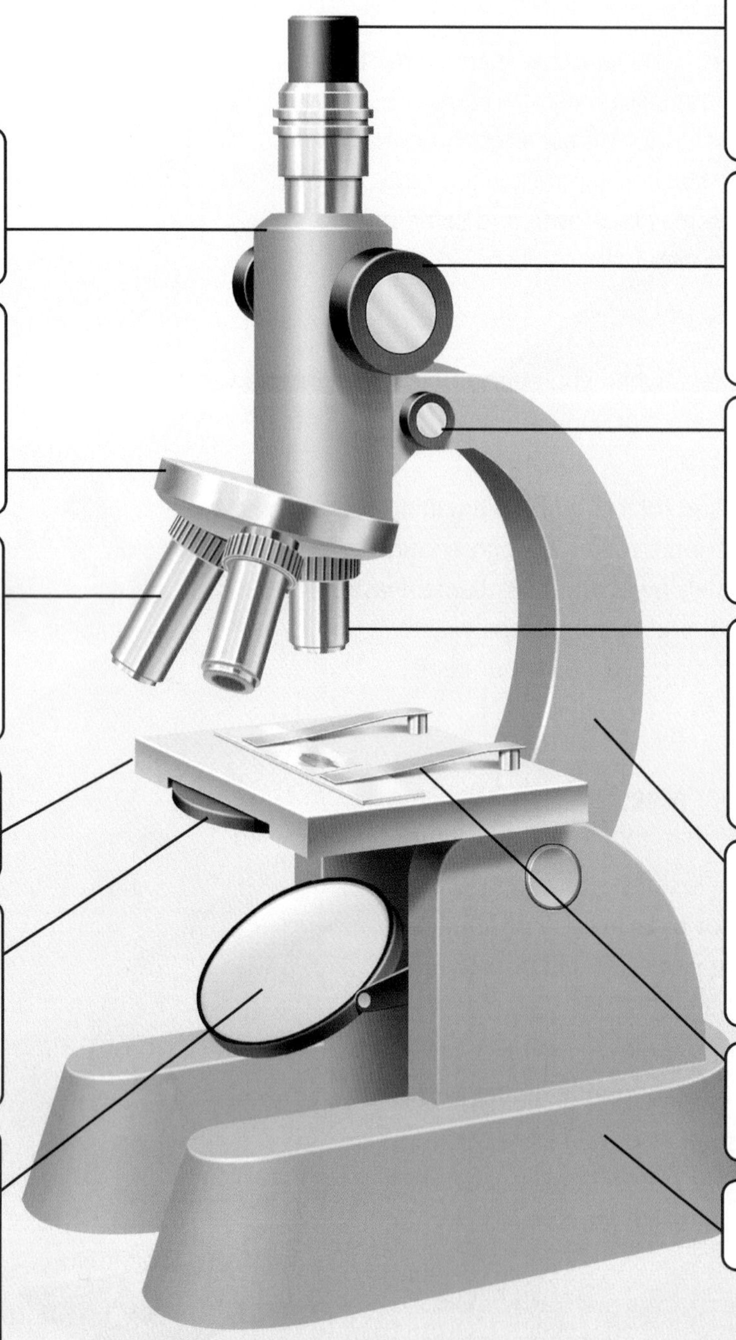
**Body** The body separates the lens in the eyepiece from the objective lenses below.
**Nosepiece** The nosepiece holds the objective lenses above the stage and rotates so that all lenses may be used.
**High-Power Objective Lens** This is the largest lens on the nosepiece. It magnifies an image approximately 40 times.
**Stage** The stage supports the object being viewed.
**Diaphragm** The diaphragm is used to adjust the amount of light passing through the slide and into an objective lens.
**Mirror or Light Source** Some microscopes use light that is reflected through the stage by a mirror. Other microscopes have their own light sources.
**Eyepiece** Objects are viewed through the eyepiece. The eyepiece contains a lens that commonly magnifies an image 10 times.
**Coarse Adjustment** This knob is used to focus the image of an object when it is viewed through the low-power lens.
**Fine Adjustment** This knob is used to focus the image of an object when it is viewed through the high-power lens.
**Low-Power Objective Lens** This is the smallest lens on the nosepiece. It magnifies an image approximately 10 times.
**Arm** The arm supports the body above the stage. Always carry a microscope by the arm and base.
**Stage Clip** The stage clip holds a slide in place on the stage.
**Base** The base supports the microscope.

## VIEWING AN OBJECT

1. Use the coarse adjustment knob to raise the body tube.
2. Adjust the diaphragm so that you can see a bright circle of light through the eyepiece.
3. Place the object or slide on the stage. Be sure that it is centered over the hole in the stage.
4. Turn the nosepiece to click the low-power lens into place.
5. Using the coarse adjustment knob, slowly lower the lens and focus on the specimen being viewed. Be sure not to touch the slide or object with the lens.
6. When switching from the low-power lens to the high-power lens, first raise the body tube with the coarse adjustment knob so that the high-power lens will not hit the slide.
7. Turn the nosepiece to click the high-power lens into place.
8. Use the fine adjustment knob to focus on the specimen being viewed. Again, be sure not to touch the slide or object with the lens.

## MAKING A SLIDE, OR WET MOUNT

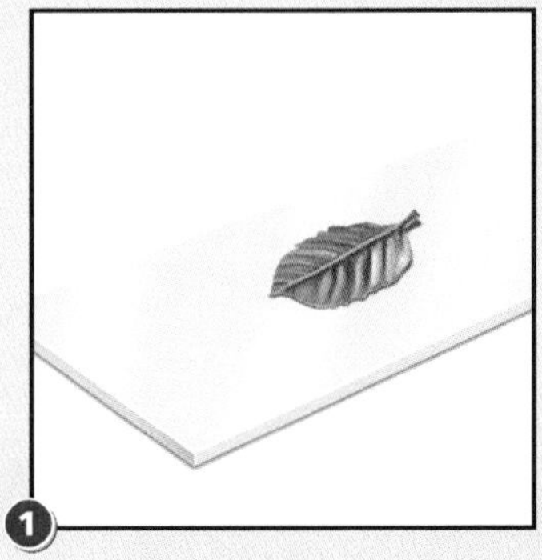

1 Place the specimen in the center of a clean slide.

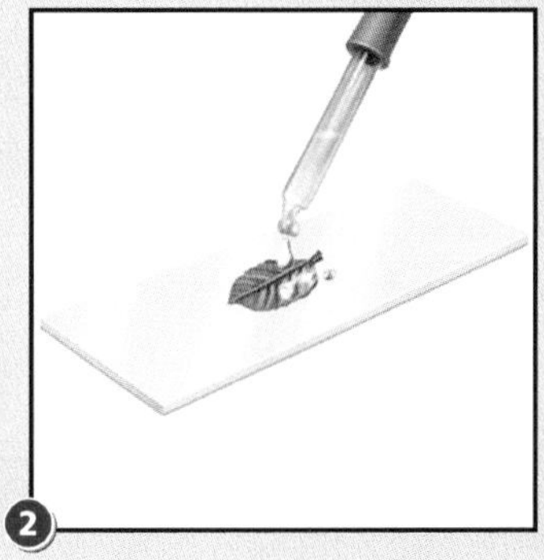

2 Place a drop of water on the specimen.

3 Place a cover slip on the slide. Put one edge of the cover slip into the drop of water and slowly lower it over the specimen.

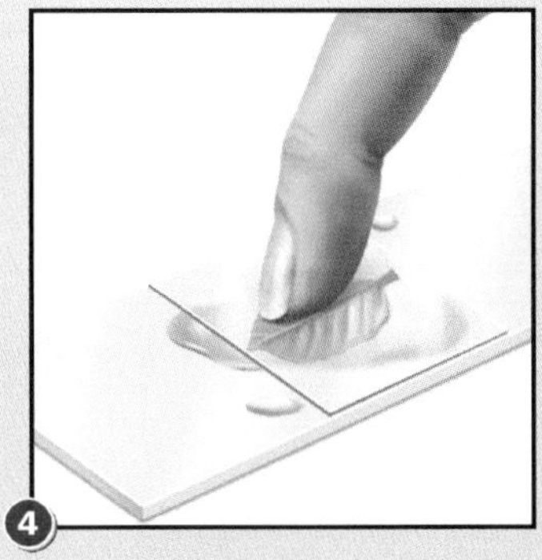

4 Remove any air bubbles from under the cover slip by gently tapping the cover slip.

5 Dry any excess water before placing the slide on the microscope stage for viewing.

## Spring Scale (Force Meter)

- Use a spring scale to measure a force pulling on the scale.
- Use a spring scale to measure the force of gravity exerted on an object by Earth.
- To measure a force accurately, a spring scale must be zeroed before it is used. The scale is zeroed when no weight is attached and the indicator is positioned at zero.
- Do not attach a weight that is either too heavy or too light to a spring scale. A weight that is too heavy could break the scale or exert too great a force for the scale to measure. A weight that is too light may not exert enough force to be measured accurately.

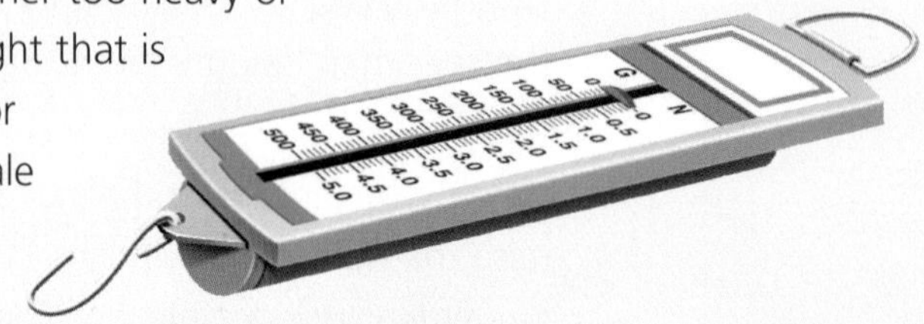

## Graduated Cylinder

- Use a graduated cylinder to measure the volume of a liquid.
- Be sure that the graduated cylinder is on a flat surface so that your measurement will be accurate.
- When reading the scale on a graduated cylinder, be sure to have your eyes at the level of the surface of the liquid.
- The surface of the liquid will be curved in the graduated cylinder. Read the volume of the liquid at the bottom of the curve, or meniscus (muh-NIHS-kuhs).
- You can use a graduated cylinder to find the volume of a solid object by measuring the increase in a liquid's level after you add the object to the cylinder.

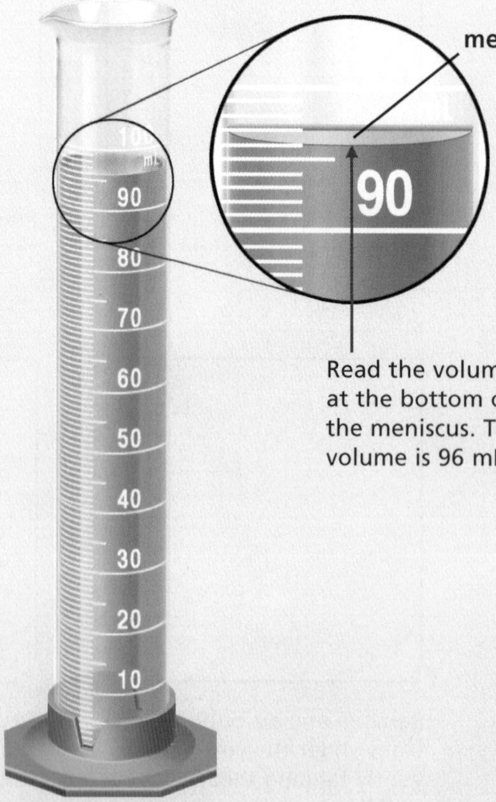

## Metric Rulers

- Use metric rulers or meter sticks to measure objects' lengths.
- Do not measure an object from the end of a metric ruler or meter stick, because the end is often imperfect. Instead, measure from the 1-centimeter mark, but remember to subtract a centimeter from the apparent measurement.
- Estimate any lengths that extend between marked units. For example, if a meter stick shows centimeters but not millimeters, you can estimate the length that an object extends between centimeter marks to measure it to the nearest millimeter.
- **Controlling Variables** If you are taking repeated measurements, always measure from the same point each time. For example, if you're measuring how high two different balls bounce when dropped from the same height, measure both bounces at the same point on the balls—either the top or the bottom. Do not measure at the top of one ball and the bottom of the other.

**EXAMPLE**

### How to Measure a Leaf

1. Lay a ruler flat on top of the leaf so that the 1-centimeter mark lines up with one end. Make sure the ruler and the leaf do not move between the time you line them up and the time you take the measurement.
2. Look straight down on the ruler so that you can see exactly how the marks line up with the other end of the leaf.
3. Estimate the length by which the leaf extends beyond a marking. For example, the leaf below extends about halfway between the 4.2-centimeter and 4.3-centimeter marks, so the apparent measurement is about 4.25 centimeters.
4. Remember to subtract 1 centimeter from your apparent measurement, since you started at the 1-centimeter mark on the ruler and not at the end. The leaf is about 3.25 centimeters long (4.25 cm – 1 cm = 3.25 cm).

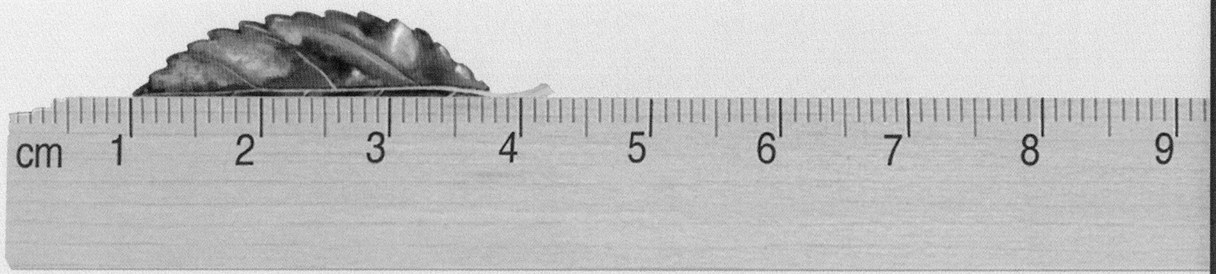


LAB HANDBOOK

## Triple-Beam Balance

This balance has a pan and three beams with sliding masses, called riders. At one end of the beams is a pointer that indicates whether the mass on the pan is equal to the masses shown on the beams.

1. Make sure the balance is zeroed before measuring the mass of an object. The balance is zeroed if the pointer is at zero when nothing is on the pan and the riders are at their zero points. Use the adjustment knob at the base of the balance to zero it.
2. Place the object to be measured on the pan.
3. Move the riders one notch at a time away from the pan. Begin with the largest rider. If moving the largest rider one notch brings the pointer below zero, begin measuring the mass of the object with the next smaller rider.
4. Change the positions of the riders until they balance the mass on the pan and the pointer is at zero. Then add the readings from the three beams to determine the mass of the object.

| | |
|---|---|
| 300 g | position of largest rider |
| 90 g | position of middle rider |
| + 3 g | position of smallest rider |
| 393 g | mass of beaker |

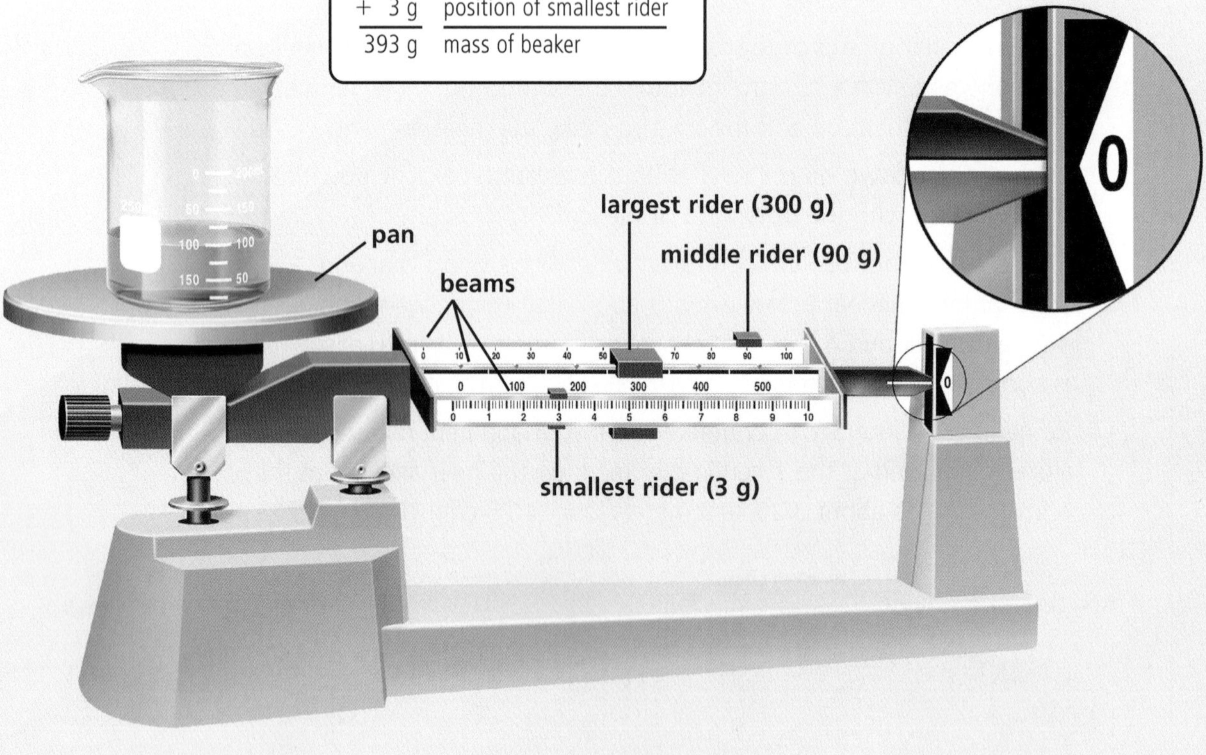

## Double-Pan Balance

This type of balance has two pans. Between the pans is a pointer that indicates whether the masses on the pans are equal.

1. Make sure the balance is zeroed before measuring the mass of an object. The balance is zeroed if the pointer is at zero when there is nothing on either of the pans. Many double-pan balances have sliding knobs that can be used to zero them.
2. Place the object to be measured on one of the pans.
3. Begin adding standard masses to the other pan. Begin with the largest standard mass. If this adds too much mass to the balance, begin measuring the mass of the object with the next smaller standard mass.
4. Add standard masses until the masses on both pans are balanced and the pointer is at zero. Then add the standard masses together to determine the mass of the object being measured.

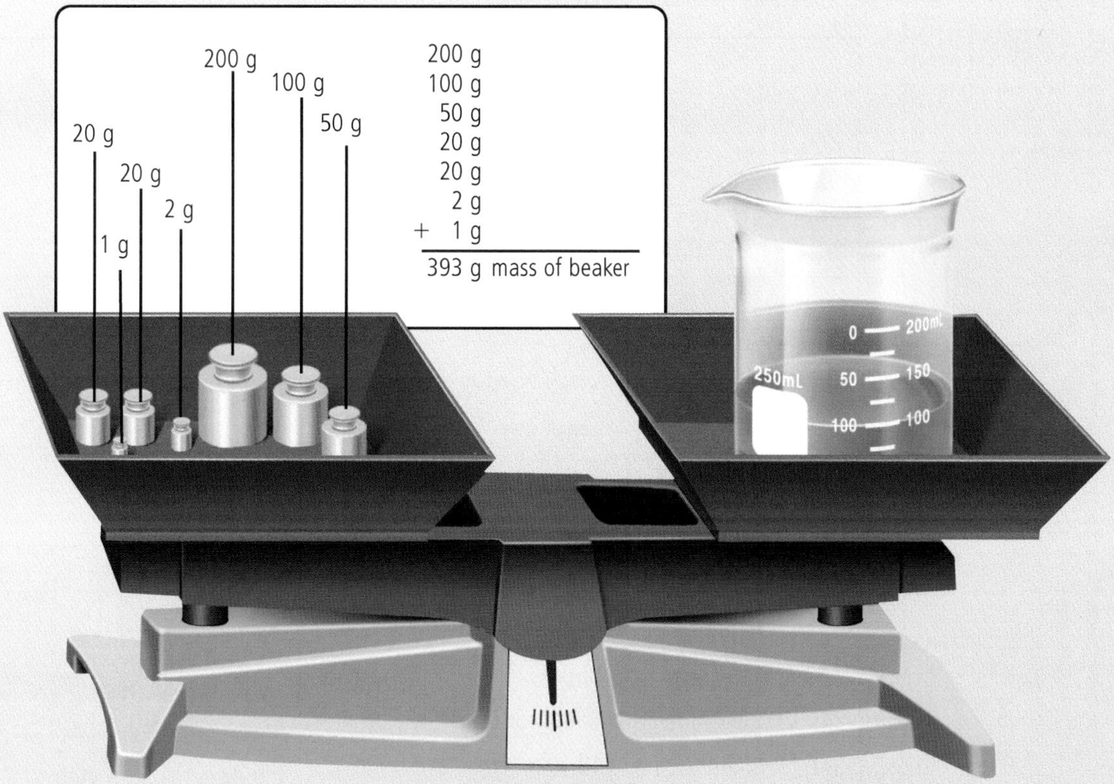


Never place chemicals or liquids directly on a pan. Instead, use the following procedure:

1. Determine the mass of an empty container, such as a beaker.
2. Pour the substance into the container, and measure the total mass of the substance and the container.
3. Subtract the mass of the empty container from the total mass to find the mass of the substance.

# The Metric System and SI Units

Scientists use International System (SI) units for measurements of distance, volume, mass, and temperature. The International System is based on multiples of ten and the metric system of measurement.

**Basic SI Units**

| Property | Name | Symbol |
|---|---|---|
| length | meter | m |
| volume | liter | L |
| mass | kilogram | kg |
| temperature | kelvin | K |

**SI Prefixes**

| Prefix | Symbol | Multiple of 10 |
|---|---|---|
| kilo- | k | 1000 |
| hecto- | h | 100 |
| deca- | da | 10 |
| deci- | d | 0.1 $\left(\frac{1}{10}\right)$ |
| centi- | c | 0.01 $\left(\frac{1}{100}\right)$ |
| milli- | m | 0.001 $\left(\frac{1}{1000}\right)$ |



## Changing Metric Units

You can change from one unit to another in the metric system by multiplying or dividing by a power of 10.

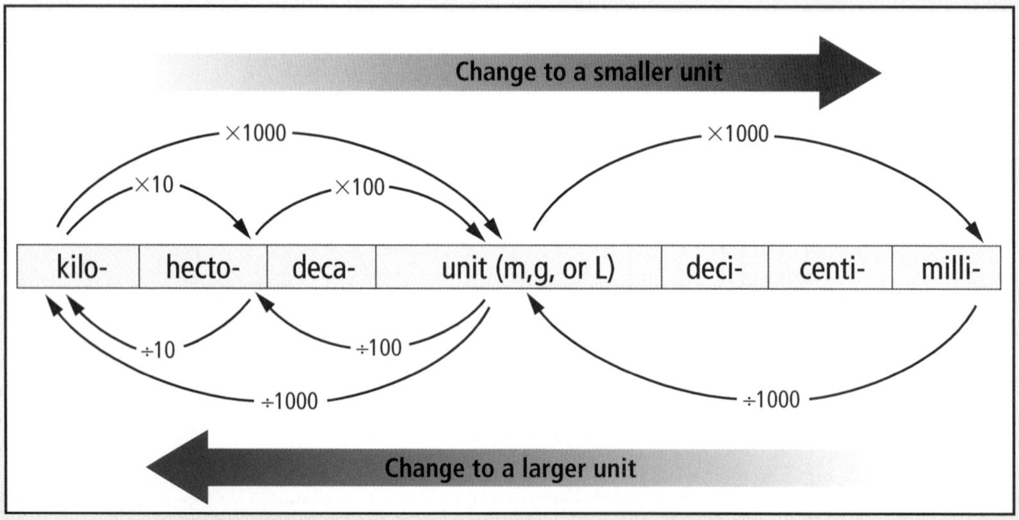


### Example

Change 0.64 liters to milliliters.

**(1)** Decide whether to multiply or divide.

**(2)** Select the power of 10.

**ANSWER** 0.64 L = 640 mL

**Change to a smaller unit by multiplying.**

L —— × 1000 ——→ mL

**0.64** × 1000 = **640.**

### Example

Change 23.6 grams to kilograms.

**(1)** Decide whether to multiply or divide.

**(2)** Select the power of 10.

**ANSWER** 23.6 g = 0.0236 kg

**Change to a larger unit by dividing.**

kg ←—— ÷ 1000 —— g

**23.6** ÷ 1000 = **0.0236**

## Temperature Conversions

Even though the kelvin is the SI base unit of temperature, the degree Celsius will be the unit you use most often in your science studies. The formulas below show the relationships between temperatures in degrees Fahrenheit (°F), degrees Celsius (°C), and kelvins (K).

$$°C = \frac{5}{9}(°F - 32)$$

$$°F = \frac{9}{5}°C + 32$$

$$K = °C + 273$$

See page R42 for help with using formulas.

**Examples of Temperature Conversions**

| Condition | Degrees Celsius | Degrees Fahrenheit |
|---|---|---|
| Freezing point of water | 0 | 32 |
| Cool day | 10 | 50 |
| Mild day | 20 | 68 |
| Warm day | 30 | 86 |
| Normal body temperature | 37 | 98.6 |
| Very hot day | 40 | 104 |
| Boiling point of water | 100 | 212 |

LAB HANDBOOK

## Converting Between SI and U.S. Customary Units

Use the chart below when you need to convert between SI units and U.S. customary units.

| SI Unit | From SI to U.S. Customary | | | From U.S. Customary to SI | | |
|---|---|---|---|---|---|---|
| **Length** | **When you know** | **multiply by** | **to find** | **When you know** | **multiply by** | **to find** |
| kilometer (km) = 1000 m | kilometers | 0.62 | miles | miles | 1.61 | kilometers |
| meter (m) = 100 cm | meters | 3.28 | feet | feet | 0.3048 | meters |
| centimeter (cm) = 10 mm | centimeters | 0.39 | inches | inches | 2.54 | centimeters |
| millimeter (mm) = 0.1 cm | millimeters | 0.04 | inches | inches | 25.4 | millimeters |
| **Area** | **When you know** | **multiply by** | **to find** | **When you know** | **multiply by** | **to find** |
| square kilometer ($km^2$) | square kilometers | 0.39 | square miles | square miles | 2.59 | square kilometers |
| square meter ($m^2$) | square meters | 1.2 | square yards | square yards | 0.84 | square meters |
| square centimeter ($cm^2$) | square centimeters | 0.155 | square inches | square inches | 6.45 | square centimeters |
| **Volume** | **When you know** | **multiply by** | **to find** | **When you know** | **multiply by** | **to find** |
| liter (L) = 1000 mL | liters | 1.06 | quarts | quarts | 0.95 | liters |
| | liters | 0.26 | gallons | gallons | 3.79 | liters |
| | liters | 4.23 | cups | cups | 0.24 | liters |
| | liters | 2.12 | pints | pints | 0.47 | liters |
| milliliter (mL) = 0.001 L | milliliters | 0.20 | teaspoons | teaspoons | 4.93 | milliliters |
| | milliliters | 0.07 | tablespoons | tablespoons | 14.79 | milliliters |
| | milliliters | 0.03 | fluid ounces | fluid ounces | 29.57 | milliliters |
| **Mass** | **When you know** | **multiply by** | **to find** | **When you know** | **multiply by** | **to find** |
| kilogram (kg) = 1000 g | kilograms | 2.2 | pounds | pounds | 0.45 | kilograms |
| gram (g) = 1000 mg | grams | 0.035 | ounces | ounces | 28.35 | grams |

# Precision and Accuracy

When you do an experiment, it is important that your methods, observations, and data be both precise and accurate.

low precision

precision, but not accuracy

precision and accuracy



## Precision

In science, **precision** is the exactness and consistency of measurements. For example, measurements made with a ruler that has both centimeter and millimeter markings would be more precise than measurements made with a ruler that has only centimeter markings. Another indicator of precision is the care taken to make sure that methods and observations are as exact and consistent as possible. Every time a particular experiment is done, the same procedure should be used. Precision is necessary because experiments are repeated several times and if the procedure changes, the results will change.

**EXAMPLE**

Suppose you are measuring temperatures over a two-week period. Your precision will be greater if you measure each temperature at the same place, at the same time of day, and with the same thermometer than if you change any of these factors from one day to the next.

## Accuracy

In science, it is possible to be precise but not accurate. **Accuracy** depends on the difference between a measurement and an actual value. The smaller the difference, the more accurate the measurement.

**EXAMPLE**

Suppose you look at a stream and estimate that it is about 1 meter wide at a particular place. You decide to check your estimate by measuring the stream with a meter stick, and you determine that the stream is 1.32 meters wide. However, because it is hard to measure the width of a stream with a meter stick, it turns out that you didn't do a very good job. The stream is actually 1.14 meters wide. Therefore, even though your estimate was less precise than your measurement, your estimate was actually more accurate.

# Making Data Tables and Graphs

**Data tables and graphs are useful tools for both recording and communicating scientific data.**

## Making Data Tables

You can use a **data table** to organize and record the measurements that you make. Some examples of information that might be recorded in data tables are frequencies, times, and amounts.

### EXAMPLE

Suppose you are investigating photosynthesis in two elodea plants. One sits in direct sunlight, and the other sits in a dimly lit room. You measure the rate of photosynthesis by counting the number of bubbles in the jar every ten minutes.

1. Title and number your data table.
2. Decide how you will organize the table into columns and rows.
3. Any units, such as seconds or degrees, should be included in column headings, not in the individual cells.

Table 1. Number of Bubbles from Elodea

| Time (min) | Sunlight | Dim Light |
|---|---|---|
| 0 | 0 | 0 |
| 10 | 15 | 5 |
| 20 | 25 | 8 |
| 30 | 32 | 7 |
| 40 | 41 | 10 |
| 50 | 47 | 9 |
| 60 | 42 | 9 |

Always number and title data tables.

The data in the table above could also be organized in a different way.

Table 1. Number of Bubbles from Elodea

| Light Condition | Time (min) | | | | | | |
|---|---|---|---|---|---|---|---|
| | 0 | 10 | 20 | 30 | 40 | 50 | 60 |
| Sunlight | 0 | 15 | 25 | 32 | 41 | 47 | 42 |
| Dim light | 0 | 5 | 8 | 7 | 10 | 9 | 9 |

Put units in column heading.

LAB HANDBOOK

## Making Line Graphs

You can use a **line graph** to show a relationship between variables. Line graphs are particularly useful for showing changes in variables over time.

### EXAMPLE

Suppose you are interested in graphing temperature data that you collected over the course of a day.

Table 1. Outside Temperature During the Day on March 7

| | Time of Day | | | | | | |
|---|---|---|---|---|---|---|---|
| | 7:00 A.M. | 9:00 A.M. | 11:00 A.M. | 1:00 P.M. | 3:00 P.M. | 5:00 P.M. | 7:00 P.M. |
| Temp (°C) | 8 | 9 | 11 | 14 | 12 | 10 | 6 |

1. Use the vertical axis of your line graph for the variable that you are measuring—temperature.
2. Choose scales for both the horizontal axis and the vertical axis of the graph. You should have two points more than you need on the vertical axis, and the horizontal axis should be long enough for all of the data points to fit.
3. Draw and label each axis.
4. Graph each value. First find the appropriate point on the scale of the horizontal axis. Imagine a line that rises vertically from that place on the scale. Then find the corresponding value on the vertical axis, and imagine a line that moves horizontally from that value. The point where these two imaginary lines intersect is where the value should be plotted.
5. Connect the points with straight lines.

Be sure to add a number and a title to your graph.

Figure 1. Outside Temperature During the Day on March 7

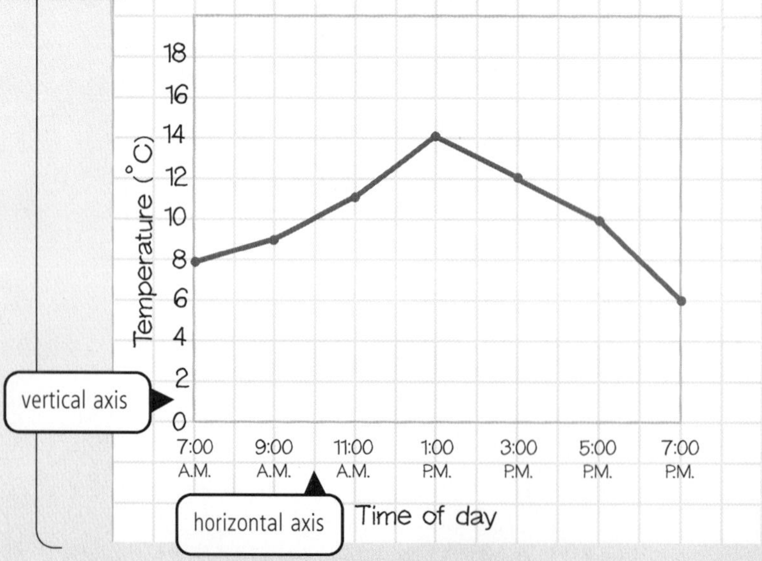

## Making Circle Graphs

You can use a **circle graph,** sometimes called a pie chart, to represent data as parts of a circle. Circle graphs are used only when the data can be expressed as percentages of a whole. The entire circle shown in a circle graph is equal to 100 percent of the data.

### EXAMPLE

Suppose you identified the species of each mature tree growing in a small wooded area. You organized your data in a table, but you also want to show the data in a circle graph.

1. To begin, find the total number of mature trees.

   $56 + 34 + 22 + 10 + 28 = 150$

2. To find the degree measure for each sector of the circle, write a fraction comparing the number of each tree species with the total number of trees. Then multiply the fraction by 360°.

   Oak: $\frac{56}{150} \times 360° = 134.4°$

3. Draw a circle. Use a protractor to draw the angle for each sector of the graph.
4. Color and label each sector of the graph.
5. Give the graph a number and title.

**Table 1. Tree Species in Wooded Area**

| Species | Number of Specimens |
|---|---|
| Oak | 56 |
| Maple | 34 |
| Birch | 22 |
| Willow | 10 |
| Pine | 28 |

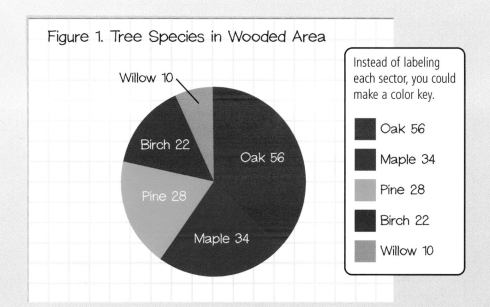

Figure 1. Tree Species in Wooded Area

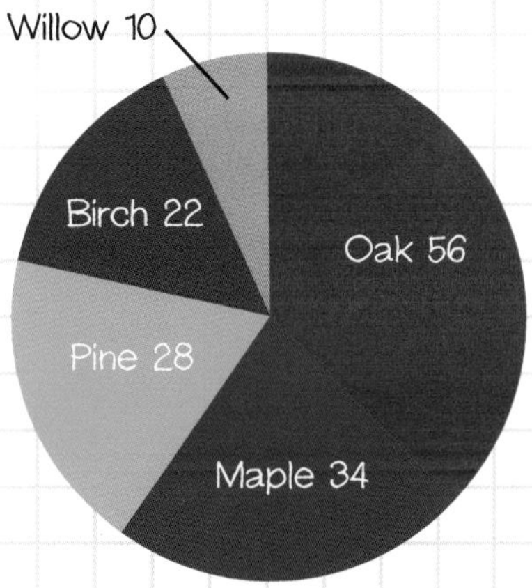


Instead of labeling each sector, you could make a color key.

LAB HANDBOOK

## Bar Graph

A **bar graph** is a type of graph in which the lengths of the bars are used to represent and compare data. A numerical scale is used to determine the lengths of the bars.

### EXAMPLE

To determine the effect of water on seed sprouting, three cups were filled with sand, and ten seeds were planted in each. Different amounts of water were added to each cup over a three-day period.

Table 1. Effect of Water on Seed Sprouting

| Daily Amount of Water (mL) | Number of Seeds That Sprouted After 3 Days in Sand |
|---|---|
| 0 | 1 |
| 10 | 4 |
| 20 | 8 |

1. Choose a numerical scale. The greatest value is 8, so the end of the scale should have a value greater than 8, such as 10. Use equal increments along the scale, such as increments of 2.
2. Draw and label the axes. Mark intervals on the vertical axis according to the scale you chose.
3. Draw a bar for each data value. Use the scale to decide how long to make each bar.

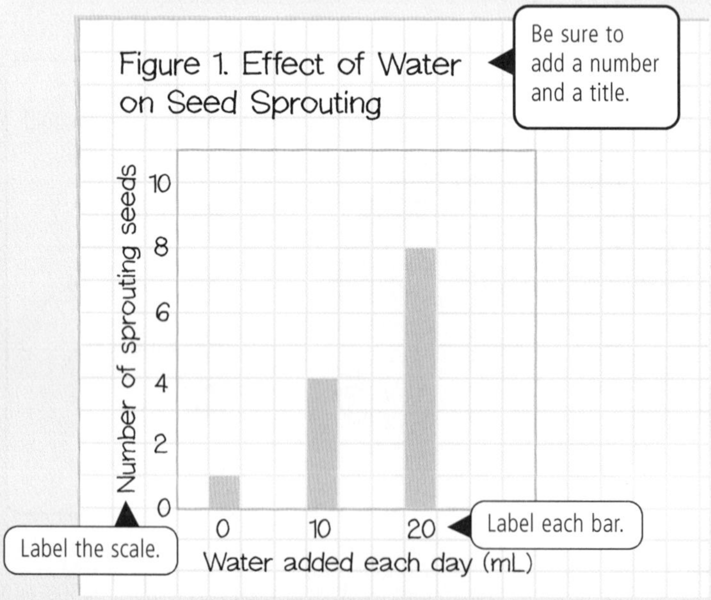

## Double Bar Graph

A **double bar graph** is a bar graph that shows two sets of data. The two bars for each measurement are drawn next to each other.

### EXAMPLE

The seed-sprouting experiment was done using both sand and potting soil. The data for sand and potting soil can be plotted on one graph.

1. Draw one set of bars, using the data for sand, as shown below.
2. Draw bars for the potting-soil data next to the bars for the sand data. Shade them a different color. Add a key.

Table 2. Effect of Water and Soil on Seed Sprouting

| Daily Amount of Water (mL) | Number of Seeds That Sprouted After 3 Days in Sand | Number of Seeds That Sprouted After 3 Days in Potting Soil |
|---|---|---|
| 0 | 1 | 2 |
| 10 | 4 | 5 |
| 20 | 8 | 9 |

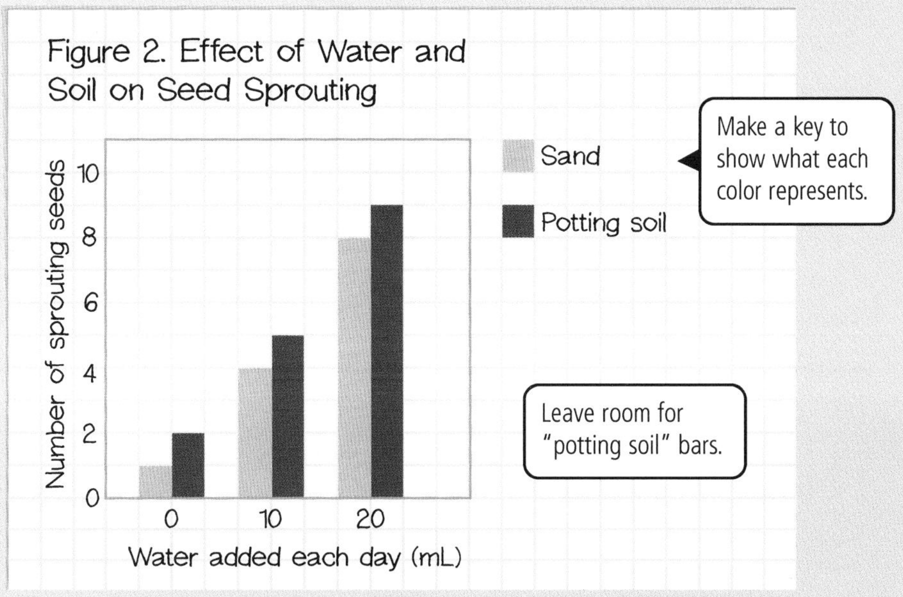


LAB HANDBOOK

# Designing an Experiment

Use this section when designing or conducting an experiment.

## Determining a Purpose

You can find a purpose for an experiment by doing research, by examining the results of a previous experiment, or by observing the world around you. An **experiment** is an organized procedure to study something under controlled conditions.

1. Write the purpose of your experiment as a question or problem that you want to investigate.
2. Write down research questions and begin searching for information that will help you design an experiment. Consult the library, the Internet, and other people as you conduct your research.

Don't forget to learn as much as possible about your topic before you begin.

LAB HANDBOOK

### EXAMPLE

Middle school students observed an odor near the lake by their school. They also noticed that the water on the side of the lake near the school was greener than the water on the other side of the lake. The students did some research to learn more about their observations. They discovered that the odor and green color in the lake came from algae. They also discovered that a new fertilizer was being used on a field nearby. The students inferred that the use of the fertilizer might be related to the presence of the algae and designed a controlled experiment to find out whether they were right.

**Problem**

How does fertilizer affect the presence of algae in a lake?

**Research Questions**

- Have other experiments been done on this problem? If so, what did those experiments show?
- What kind of fertilizer is used on the field? How much?
- How do algae grow?
- How do people measure algae?
- Can fertilizer and algae be used safely in a lab? How?

**Research**
As you research, you may find a topic that is more interesting to you than your original topic, or learn that a procedure you wanted to use is not practical or safe. It is OK to change your purpose as you research.

## Writing a Hypothesis

A **hypothesis** is a tentative explanation for an observation or scientific problem that can be tested by further investigation. You can write your hypothesis in the form of an "If . . . , then . . . , because . . ." statement.

Hypothesis

If the amount of fertilizer in lake water is increased, then the amount of algae will also increase, because fertilizers provide nutrients that algae need to grow.

**Hypotheses**
For help with hypotheses, refer to page R3.

## Determining Materials

Make a list of all the materials you will need to do your experiment. Be specific, especially if someone else is helping you obtain the materials. Try to think of everything you will need.

Materials

- 1 large jar or container
- 4 identical smaller containers
- rubber gloves that also cover the arms
- sample of fertilizer-and-water solution
- eyedropper
- clear plastic wrap
- scissors
- masking tape
- marker
- ruler

# Determining Variables and Constants

## EXPERIMENTAL GROUP AND CONTROL GROUP

An experiment to determine how two factors are related always has two groups—a control group and an experimental group.

1. Design an experimental group. Include as many trials as possible in the experimental group in order to obtain reliable results.
2. Design a control group that is the same as the experimental group in every way possible, except for the factor you wish to test.

**Experimental Group:** two containers of lake water with one drop of fertilizer solution added to each
**Control Group:** two containers of lake water with no fertilizer solution added

Go back to your materials list and make sure you have enough items listed to cover both your experimental group and your control group.

LAB HANDBOOK

## VARIABLES AND CONSTANTS

Identify the variables and constants in your experiment. In a controlled experiment, a **variable** is any factor that can change. **Constants,** or controlled parameters, are all of the factors that are the same in both the experimental group and the control group.

**Hypothesis**
If the amount of fertilizer in lake water is increased, then the amount of algae will also increase, because fertilizers provide nutrients that algae need to grow.

1. Read your hypothesis. The **independent variable** is the factor that you wish to test and that is manipulated or changed so that it can be tested. The independent variable is expressed in your hypothesis after the word *if.* Identify the independent variable in your laboratory report.
2. The **dependent variable** is the factor that you measure to gather results. It is expressed in your hypothesis after the word *then*. Identify the dependent variable in your laboratory report.

Table 1. Variables and Constants in Algae Experiment

| Independent Variable | Dependent Variable | Constants |
|---|---|---|
| Amount of fertilizer in lake water | Amount of algae that grow | • Where the lake water is obtained<br>• Type of container used<br>• Light and temperature conditions where water will be stored |

Set up your experiment so that you will test only one variable.

## MEASURING THE DEPENDENT VARIABLE

Before starting your experiment, you need to define how you will measure the dependent variable. An **operational definition** is a description of the one particular way in which you will measure the dependent variable.

Your operational definition is important for several reasons. First, in any experiment there are several ways in which a dependent variable can be measured. Second, the procedure of the experiment depends on how you decide to measure the dependent variable. Third, your operational definition makes it possible for other people to evaluate and build on your experiment.

### EXAMPLE 1

An operational definition of a dependent variable can be qualitative. That is, your measurement of the dependent variable can simply be an observation of whether a change occurs as a result of a change in the independent variable. This type of operational definition can be thought of as a "yes or no" measurement.

**Table 2. Qualitative Operational Definition of Algae Growth**

| Independent Variable | Dependent Variable | Operational Definition |
|---|---|---|
| Amount of fertilizer in lake water | Amount of algae that grow | Algae grow in lake water |

A qualitative measurement of a dependent variable is often easy to make and record. However, this type of information does not provide a great deal of detail in your experimental results.

### EXAMPLE 2

An operational definition of a dependent variable can be quantitative. That is, your measurement of the dependent variable can be a number that shows how much change occurs as a result of a change in the independent variable.

**Table 3. Quantitative Operational Definition of Algae Growth**

| Independent Variable | Dependent Variable | Operational Definition |
|---|---|---|
| Amount of fertilizer in lake water | Amount of algae that grow | Diameter of largest algal growth (in mm) |

A quantitative measurement of a dependent variable can be more difficult to make and analyze than a qualitative measurement. However, this type of data provides much more information about your experiment and is often more useful.

## Writing a Procedure

Write each step of your procedure. Start each step with a verb, or action word, and keep the steps short. Your procedure should be clear enough for someone else to use as instructions for repeating your experiment.

If necessary, go back to your materials list and add any materials that you left out.

**Procedure**

1. Put on your gloves. Use the large container to obtain a sample of lake water.

2. Divide the sample of lake water equally among the four smaller containers.

3. Use the eyedropper to add one drop of fertilizer solution to two of the containers.

**Controlling Variables**
The same amount of fertilizer solution must be added to two of the four containers.

4. Use the masking tape and the marker to label the containers with your initials, the date, and the identifiers "Jar 1 with Fertilizer," "Jar 2 with Fertilizer," "Jar 1 without Fertilizer," and "Jar 2 without Fertilizer."

5. Cover the containers with clear plastic wrap. Use the scissors to punch ten holes in each of the covers.

6. Place all four containers on a window ledge. Make sure that they all receive the same amount of light.

**Controlling Variables**
All four containers must receive the same amount of light.

7. Observe the containers every day for one week.

8. Use the ruler to measure the diameter of the largest clump of algae in each container, and record your measurements daily.

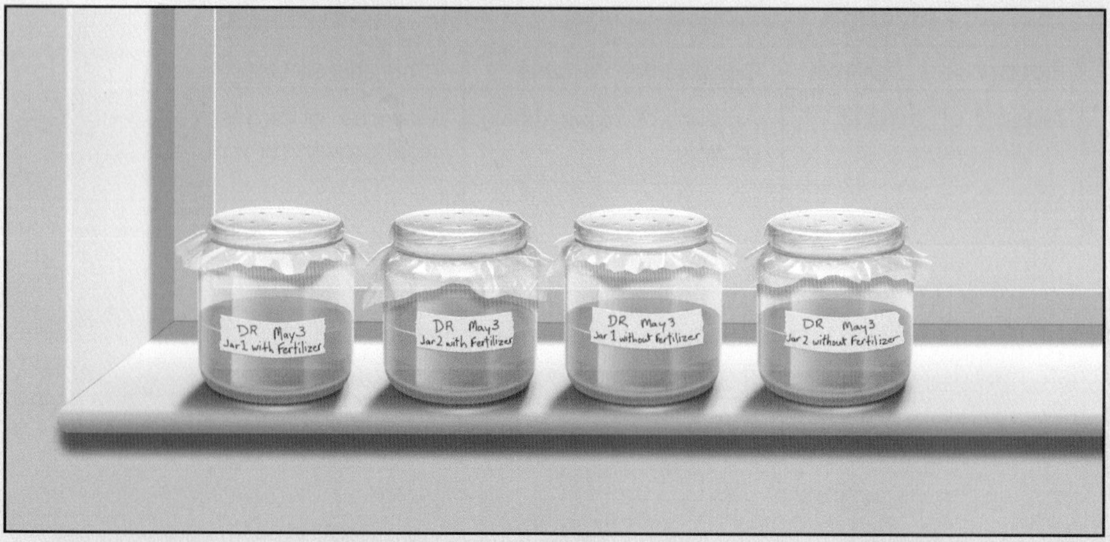

## Recording Observations

Once you have obtained all of your materials and your procedure has been approved, you can begin making experimental observations. Gather both quantitative and qualitative data. If something goes wrong during your procedure, make sure you record that too.

**Observations**
For help with making qualitative and quantitative observations, refer to page R2.

For more examples of data tables, see page R23.

Table 4. Fertilizer and Algae Growth

| | Experimental Group | | Control Group | | |
|---|---|---|---|---|---|
| Date and Time | Jar 1 with Fertilizer (diameter of algae in mm) | Jar 2 with Fertilizer (diameter of algae in mm) | Jar 1 without Fertilizer (diameter of algae in mm) | Jar 2 without Fertilizer (diameter of algae in mm) | Observations |
| 5/3 4:00 P.M. | 0 | 0 | 0 | 0 | condensation in all containers |
| 5/4 4:00 P.M. | 0 | 3 | 0 | 0 | tiny green blobs in jar 2 with fertilizer |
| 5/5 4:15 P.M. | 4 | 5 | 0 | 3 | green blobs in jars 1 and 2 with fertilizer and jar 2 without fertilizer |
| 5/6 4:00 P.M. | 5 | 6 | 0 | 4 | water light green in jar 2 with fertilizer |
| 5/7 4:00 P.M. | 8 | 10 | 0 | 6 | water light green in jars 1 and 2 with fertilizer and in jar 2 without fertilizer |
| 5/8 3:30 P.M. | 10 | 18 | 0 | 6 | cover off jar 2 with fertilizer |
| 5/9 3:30 P.M. | 14 | 23 | 0 | 8 | drew sketches of each container |

Notice that on the sixth day, the observer found that the cover was off one of the containers. It is important to record observations of unintended factors because they might affect the results of the experiment.

Drawings of Samples Viewed Under Microscope on 5/9 at 100x

Use technology, such as a microscope, to help you make observations when possible.

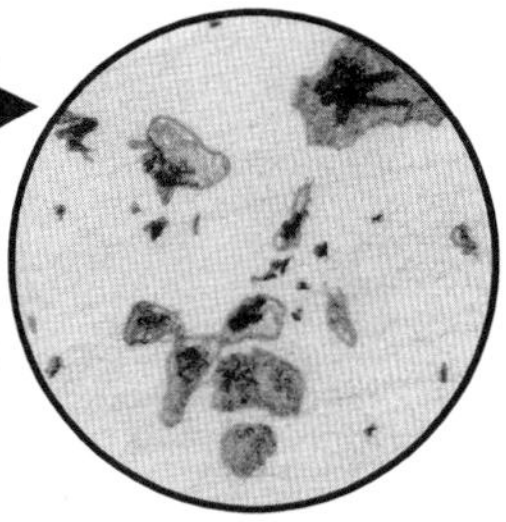

Jar 1 with Fertilizer

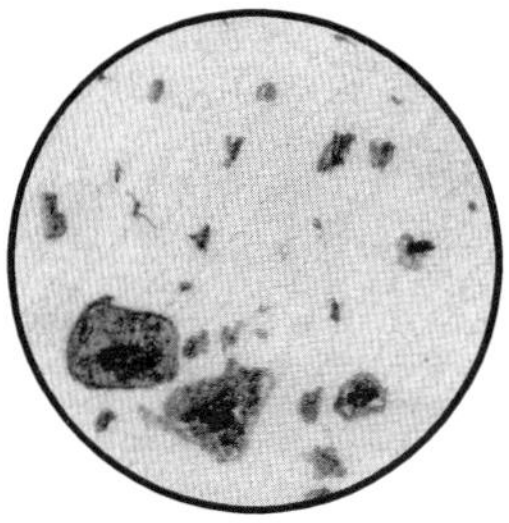

Jar 2 with Fertilizer

Jar 1 without Fertilizer

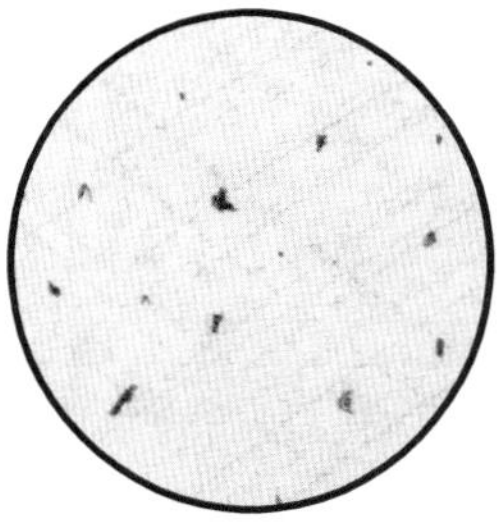

Jar 2 without Fertilizer

## Summarizing Results

To summarize your data, look at all of your observations together. Look for meaningful ways to present your observations. For example, you might average your data or make a graph to look for patterns. When possible, use spreadsheet software to help you analyze and present your data. The two graphs below show the same data.

**EXAMPLE 1**

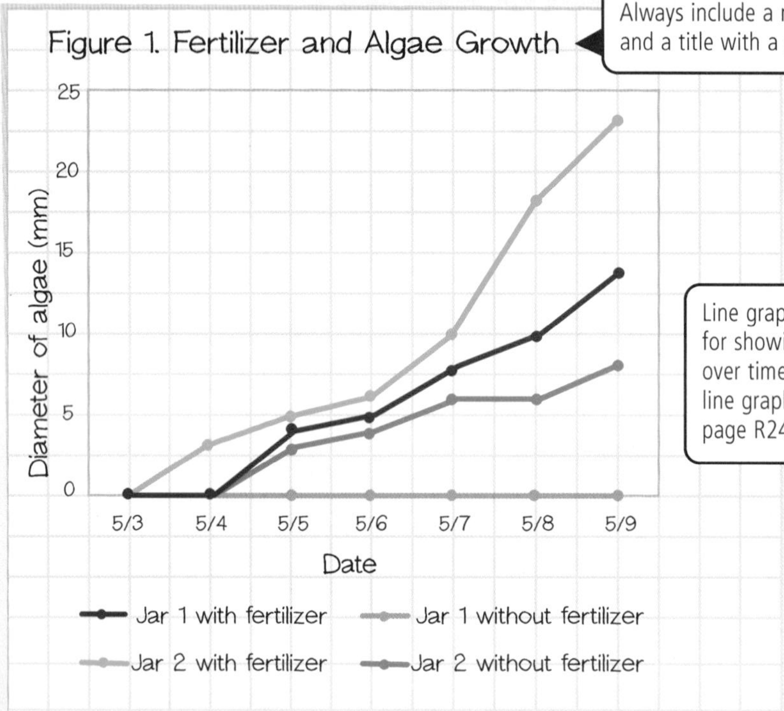


Always include a number and a title with a graph.

Line graphs are useful for showing changes over time. For help with line graphs, refer to page R24.

**EXAMPLE 2**

Bar graphs are useful for comparing different data sets. This bar graph has four bars for each day. Another way to present the data would be to calculate averages for the tests and the controls, and to show one test bar and one control bar for each day.

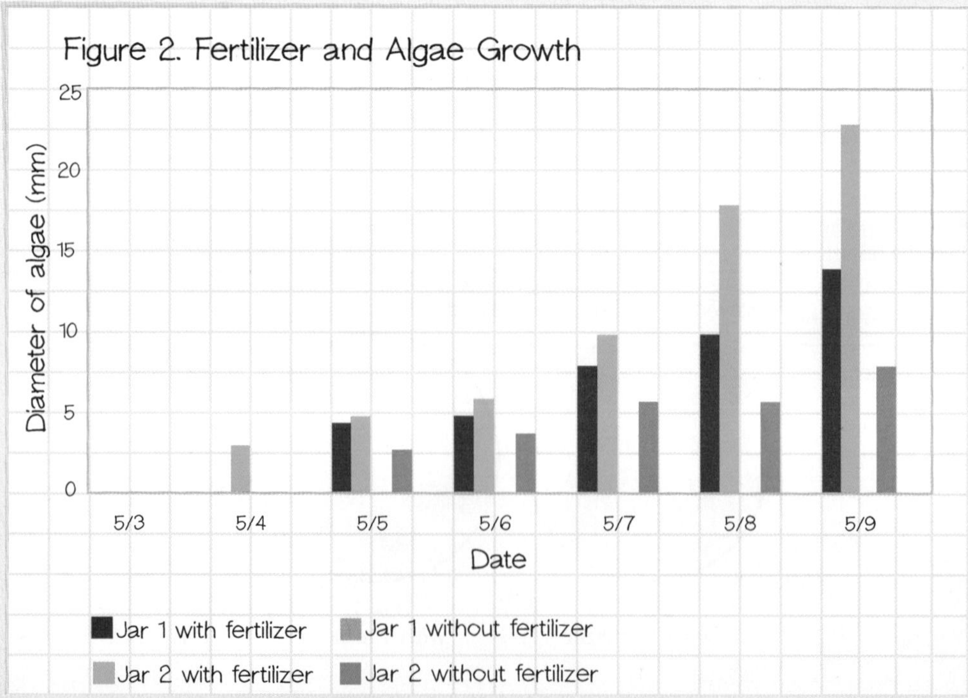


LAB HANDBOOK

## Drawing Conclusions

### RESULTS AND INFERENCES

To draw conclusions from your experiment, first write your results. Then compare your results with your hypothesis. Do your results support your hypothesis? Be careful not to make inferences about factors that you did not test.

For help with making inferences, see page R4.

**Results and Inferences**

The results of my experiment show that more algae grew in lake water to which fertilizer had been added than in lake water to which no fertilizer had been added. My hypothesis was supported. I infer that it is possible that the growth of algae in the lake was caused by the fertilizer used on the field.

Notice that you cannot conclude from this experiment that the presence of algae in the lake was due only to the fertilizer.

### QUESTIONS FOR FURTHER RESEARCH

Write a list of questions for further research and investigation. Your ideas may lead you to new experiments and discoveries.

**Questions for Further Research**

- What is the connection between the amount of fertilizer and algae growth?
- How do different brands of fertilizer affect algae growth?
- How would algae growth in the lake be affected if no fertilizer were used on the field?
- How do algae affect the lake and the other life in and around it?
- How does fertilizer affect the lake and the life in and around it?
- If fertilizer is getting into the lake, how is it getting there?

# Describing a Set of Data

Means, medians, modes, and ranges are important math tools for describing data sets such as the following widths of fossilized clamshells.

**13 mm  25 mm  14 mm  21 mm  16 mm  23 mm  14 mm**

## Mean

The **mean** of a data set is the sum of the values divided by the number of values.

### Example

To find the mean of the clamshell data, add the values and then divide the sum by the number of values.

$$\frac{13\text{ mm} + 25\text{ mm} + 14\text{ mm} + 21\text{ mm} + 16\text{ mm} + 23\text{ mm} + 14\text{ mm}}{7} = \frac{126\text{ mm}}{7} = 18\text{ mm}$$

**ANSWER** The mean is 18 mm.



## Median

The **median** of a data set is the middle value when the values are written in numerical order. If a data set has an even number of values, the median is the mean of the two middle values.

### Example

To find the median of the clamshell data, arrange the values in order from least to greatest. The median is the middle value.

13 mm  14 mm  14 mm  16 mm  21 mm  23 mm  25 mm

**ANSWER** The median is 16 mm.

## Mode

The **mode** of a data set is the value that occurs most often.

### Example

To find the mode of the clamshell data, arrange the values in order from least to greatest and determine the value that occurs most often.

13 mm   14 mm   14 mm   16 mm   21 mm   23 mm   25 mm

**ANSWER** The mode is 14 mm.

A data set can have more than one mode or no mode. For example, the following data set has modes of 2 mm and 4 mm:

2 mm   2 mm   3 mm   4 mm   4 mm

The data set below has no mode, because no value occurs more often than any other.

2 mm   3 mm   4 mm   5 mm

## Range

The **range** of a data set is the difference between the greatest value and the least value.

### Example

To find the range of the clamshell data, arrange the values in order from least to greatest.

13 mm   14 mm   14 mm   16 mm   21 mm   23 mm   25 mm

Subtract the least value from the greatest value.

13 mm is the least value.
25 mm is the greatest value.

25 mm − 13 mm = 12 mm

**ANSWER** The range is 12 mm.

# Using Ratios, Rates, and Proportions

**You can use ratios and rates to compare values in data sets. You can use proportions to find unknown values.**

## Ratios

A **ratio** uses division to compare two values. The ratio of a value $a$ to a nonzero value $b$ can be written as $\frac{a}{b}$.

### Example

The height of one plant is 8 centimeters. The height of another plant is 6 centimeters. To find the ratio of the height of the first plant to the height of the second plant, write a fraction and simplify it.

$$\frac{8 \text{ cm}}{6 \text{ cm}} = \frac{4 \times \overset{1}{\cancel{2}}}{3 \times \underset{1}{\cancel{2}}} = \frac{4}{3}$$

**ANSWER** The ratio of the plant heights is $\frac{4}{3}$.

You can also write the ratio $\frac{a}{b}$ as "a to b" or as $a:b$. For example, you can write the ratio of the plant heights as "4 to 3" or as 4:3.



## Rates

A **rate** is a ratio of two values expressed in different units. A unit rate is a rate with a denominator of 1 unit.

### Example

A plant grew 6 centimeters in 2 days. The plant's rate of growth was $\frac{6 \text{ cm}}{2 \text{ days}}$. To describe the plant's growth in centimeters per day, write a unit rate.

*Divide numerator and denominator by 2:* $\frac{6 \text{ cm}}{2 \text{ days}} = \frac{6 \text{ cm} \div 2}{2 \text{ days} \div 2}$

*Simplify:* $= \frac{3 \text{ cm}}{1 \text{ day}}$

You divide 2 days by 2 to get 1 day, so divide 6 cm by 2 also.

**ANSWER** The plant's rate of growth is 3 centimeters per day.

### Proportions

A **proportion** is an equation stating that two ratios are equivalent. To solve for an unknown value in a proportion, you can use cross products.

#### Example

If a plant grew 6 centimeters in 2 days, how many centimeters would it grow in 3 days (if its rate of growth is constant)?

*Write a proportion:* $\frac{6 \text{ cm}}{2 \text{ days}} = \frac{x}{3 \text{ days}}$

*Set cross products:* $6 \text{ cm} \cdot 3 = 2x$

*Multiply 6 and 3:* $18 \text{ cm} = 2x$

*Divide each side by 2:* $\frac{18 \text{ cm}}{2} = \frac{2x}{2}$

*Simplify:* $9 \text{ cm} = x$

**ANSWER** The plant would grow 9 centimeters in 3 days.

# Using Decimals, Fractions, and Percents

**Decimals, fractions, and percentages are all ways of recording and representing data.**

### Decimals

A **decimal** is a number that is written in the base-ten place value system, in which a decimal point separates the ones and tenths digits. The values of each place is ten times that of the place to its right.

#### Example

A caterpillar traveled from point *A* to point *C* along the path shown.

**ADDING DECIMALS** To find the total distance traveled by the caterpillar, add the distance from *A* to *B* and the distance from *B* to *C*. Begin by lining up the decimal points. Then add the figures as you would whole numbers and bring down the decimal point.

$$\begin{array}{r} 36.9 \text{ cm} \\ +\ 52.4 \text{ cm} \\ \hline 89.3 \text{ cm} \end{array}$$

**ANSWER** The caterpillar traveled a total distance of 89.3 centimeters.

MATH HANDBOOK

## Example *continued*

**SUBTRACTING DECIMALS** To find how much farther the caterpillar traveled on the second leg of the journey, subtract the distance from *A* to *B* from the distance from *B* to *C*.

$$\begin{array}{r} 52.4 \text{ cm} \\ -\ 36.9 \text{ cm} \\ \hline 15.5 \text{ cm} \end{array}$$

**ANSWER** The caterpillar traveled 15.5 centimeters farther on the second leg of the journey.

## Example

A caterpillar is traveling from point *D* to point *F* along the path shown. The caterpillar travels at a speed of 9.6 centimeters per minute.

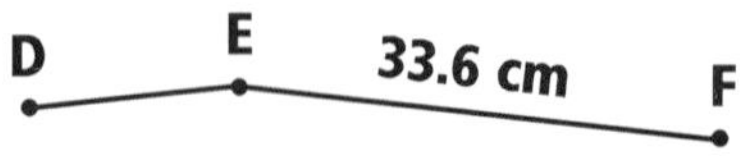


**MULTIPLYING DECIMALS** You can multiply decimals as you would whole numbers. The number of decimal places in the product is equal to the sum of the number of decimal places in the factors.

For instance, suppose it takes the caterpillar 1.5 minutes to go from *D* to *E*. To find the distance from *D* to *E*, multiply the caterpillar's speed by the time it took.

$$\begin{array}{r} 9.6 \\ \times\ 1.5 \\ \hline 480 \\ 96\phantom{0} \\ \hline 14.40 \end{array} \qquad \begin{array}{rl} 1 & \text{decimal place} \\ +\ 1 & \text{decimal place} \\ \hline & \\ & \\ 2 & \text{decimal places} \end{array}$$

Align as shown.

**ANSWER** The distance from *D* to *E* is 14.4 centimeters.

**DIVIDING DECIMALS** When you divide by a decimal, move the decimal points the same number of places in the divisor and the dividend to make the divisor a whole number.

For instance, to find the time it will take the caterpillar to travel from *E* to *F*, divide the distance from *E* to *F* by the caterpillar's speed.

$9.6\overline{)33.6}$

Move each decimal point one place to the right.

$$\begin{array}{r} 3.5 \\ 96\overline{)336.} \\ \underline{288\phantom{.}} \\ 480 \\ \underline{480} \\ 0 \end{array}$$

Line up decimal points.

**ANSWER** The caterpillar will travel from *E* to *F* in 3.5 minutes.

## Fractions

A **fraction** is a number in the form $\frac{a}{b}$, where $b$ is not equal to 0. A fraction is in **simplest form** if its numerator and denominator have a greatest common factor (GCF) of 1. To simplify a fraction, divide its numerator and denominator by their GCF.

### Example

A caterpillar is 40 millimeters long. The head of the caterpillar is 6 millimeters long. To compare the length of the caterpillar's head with the caterpillar's total length, you can write and simplify a fraction that expresses the ratio of the two lengths.

*Write the ratio of the two lengths:* $\frac{\text{Length of head}}{\text{Total length}} = \frac{6 \text{ mm}}{40 \text{ mm}}$

*Write numerator and denominator as products of numbers and the GCF:* $= \frac{3 \times 2}{20 \times 2}$

*Divide numerator and denominator by the GCF:* $= \frac{3 \times \cancel{2}^{1}}{20 \times \cancel{2}_{1}}$

*Simplify:* $= \frac{3}{20}$

**ANSWER** In simplest form, the ratio of the lengths is $\frac{3}{20}$.

## Percents

A **percent** is a ratio that compares a number to 100. The word *percent* means "per hundred" or "out of 100." The symbol for *percent* is %.

For instance, suppose 43 out of 100 caterpillars are female. You can represent this ratio as a percent, a decimal, or a fraction.

| Percent | Decimal | Fraction |
|---|---|---|
| 43% | 0.43 | $\frac{43}{100}$ |

### Example

In the preceding example, the ratio of the length of the caterpillar's head to the caterpillar's total length is $\frac{3}{20}$. To write this ratio as a percent, write an equivalent fraction that has a denominator of 100.

*Multiply numerator and denominator by 5:* $\frac{3}{20} = \frac{3 \times 5}{20 \times 5}$

$= \frac{15}{100}$

*Write as a percent:* $= 15\%$

**ANSWER** The caterpillar's head represents 15 percent of its total length.

MATH HANDBOOK

# Using Formulas

A **formula** is an equation that shows the general relationship between two or more quantities.

The term *variable* is also used in science to refer to a factor that can change during an experiment.

In science, a formula often has a word form and a symbolic form. The formula below expresses Ohm's law.

**Word Form**

$$\text{Current} = \frac{\text{voltage}}{\text{resistance}}$$

**Symbolic Form**

$$I = \frac{V}{R}$$

In this formula, *I*, *V*, and *R* are variables. A mathematical **variable** is a symbol or letter that is used to represent one or more numbers.

### Example

Suppose that you measure a voltage of 1.5 volts and a resistance of 15 ohms. You can use the formula for Ohm's law to find the current in amperes.

*Write the formula for Ohm's law:* $I = \frac{V}{R}$

*Substitute 1.5 volts for* V *and 15 ohms for* R: $I = \frac{1.5 \text{ volts}}{15 \text{ ohms}}$

*Simplify:* $I = 0.1$ amp

**ANSWER** The current is 0.1 ampere.

If you know the values of all variables but one in a formula, you can solve for the value of the unknown variable. For instance, Ohm's law can be used to find a voltage if you know the current and the resistance.

### Example

Suppose that you know that a current is 0.2 amperes and the resistance is 18 ohms. Use the formula for Ohm's law to find the voltage in volts.

*Write the formula for Ohm's law:* $I = \frac{V}{R}$

*Substitute 0.2 amp for* I *and 18 ohms for* R: $0.2 \text{ amp} = \frac{V}{18 \text{ ohms}}$

*Multiply both sides by 18 ohms:* $0.2 \text{ amp} \cdot 18 \text{ ohms} = V$

*Simplify:* $3.6 \text{ volts} = V$

**ANSWER** The voltage is 3.6 volts.

MATH HANDBOOK

# Finding Areas

## The area of a figure is the amount of surface the figure covers.

Area is measured in square units, such as square meters ($m^2$) or square centimeters ($cm^2$). Formulas for the areas of three common geometric figures are shown below.

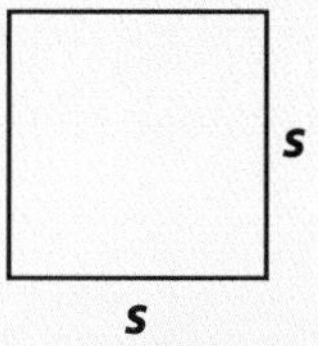


Area = (side length)$^2$
$A = s^2$

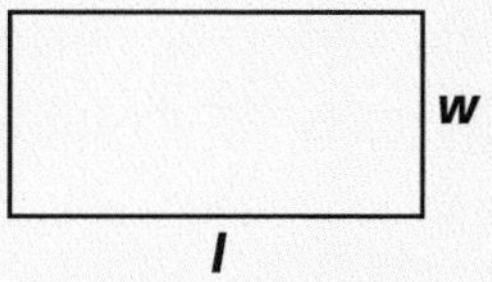


Area = length × width
$A = lw$

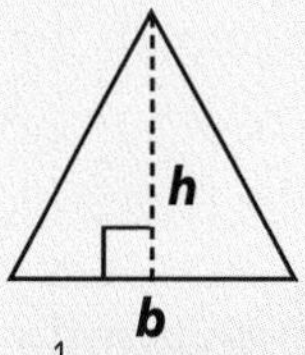


Area = $\frac{1}{2}$ × base × height
$A = \frac{1}{2}bh$

### Example

Each face of a halite crystal is a square like the one shown. You can find the area of the square by using the steps below.

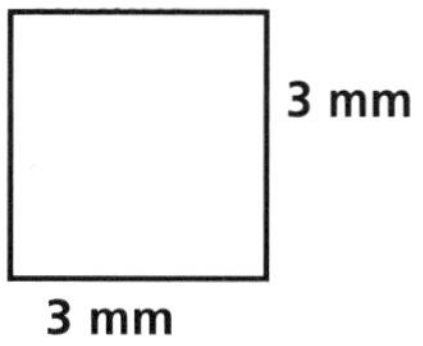


*Write the formula for the area of a square:* $A = s^2$

*Substitute 3 mm for* s: $= (3\text{ mm})^2$

*Simplify:* $= 9\text{ mm}^2$

**ANSWER** The area of the square is 9 square millimeters.

# Finding Volumes

## The volume of a solid is the amount of space contained by the solid.

Volume is measured in cubic units, such as cubic meters ($m^3$) or cubic centimeters ($cm^3$). The volume of a rectangular prism is given by the formula shown below.

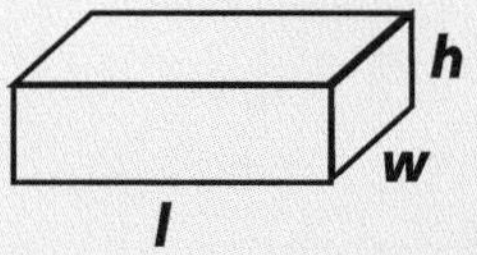


Volume = length × width × height
$V = lwh$

### Example

A topaz crystal is a rectangular prism like the one shown. You can find the volume of the prism by using the steps below.

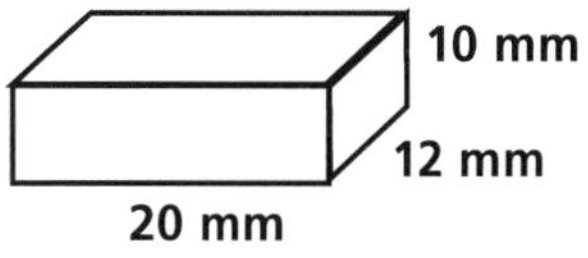


*Write the formula for the volume of a rectangular prism:* $V = lwh$

*Substitute dimensions:* $= 20\text{ mm} \times 12\text{ mm} \times 10\text{ mm}$

*Simplify:* $= 2400\text{ mm}^3$

**ANSWER** The volume of the rectangular prism is 2400 cubic millimeters.

# Using Significant Figures

**The significant figures in a decimal are the digits that are warranted by the accuracy of a measuring device.**

When you perform a calculation with measurements, the number of significant figures to include in the result depends in part on the number of significant figures in the measurements. When you multiply or divide measurements, your answer should have only as many significant figures as the measurement with the fewest significant figures.

### Example

Using a balance and a graduated cylinder filled with water, you determined that a marble has a mass of 8.0 grams and a volume of 3.5 cubic centimeters. To calculate the density of the marble, divide the mass by the volume.

*Write the formula for density:* $\text{Density} = \frac{\text{mass}}{\text{Volume}}$

*Substitute measurements:* $= \frac{8.0\text{ g}}{3.5\text{ cm}^3}$

*Use a calculator to divide:* $\approx 2.285714286\text{ g/cm}^3$

**ANSWER** Because the mass and the volume have two significant figures each, give the density to two significant figures. The marble has a density of 2.3 grams per cubic centimeter.

# Using Scientific Notation

**Scientific notation** is a shorthand way to write very large or very small numbers. For example, 73,500,000,000,000,000,000,000 kg is the mass of the Moon. In scientific notation, it is $7.35 \times 10^{22}$ kg.

### Example

You can convert from standard form to scientific notation.

| **Standard Form** | **Scientific Notation** |
|---|---|
| 720,000 | $7.2 \times 10^5$ |
| 5 decimal places left | Exponent is 5. |
| 0.000291 | $2.91 \times 10^{-4}$ |
| 4 decimal places right | Exponent is –4. |

You can convert from scientific notation to standard form.

| **Scientific Notation** | **Standard Form** |
|---|---|
| $4.63 \times 10^7$ | 46,300,000 |
| Exponent is 7. | 7 decimal places right |
| $1.08 \times 10^{-6}$ | 0.00000108 |
| Exponent is –6. | 6 decimal places left |

MATH HANDBOOK

# Note-Taking Handbook

## Note-Taking Strategies

Taking notes as you read helps you understand the information. The notes you take can also be used as a study guide for later review. This handbook presents several ways to organize your notes.

### Content Frame

1. Make a chart in which each column represents a category.
2. Give each column a heading.
3. Write details under the headings.

| NAME | GROUP | CHARACTERISTICS | DRAWING |
|---|---|---|---|
| snail | mollusks | mantle, shell | 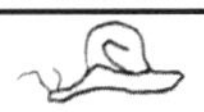 |
| ant | arthropods | six legs, exoskeleton | 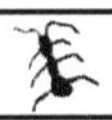 |
| earthworm | segmented worms | segmented body, circulatory and digestive systems |  |
| heartworm | roundworms | digestive system |  |
| sea star | echinoderms | spiny skin, tube feet |  |
| jellyfish | cnidarians | stinging cells |  |

categories

details

### Combination Notes

1. For each new idea or concept, write an informal outline of the information.
2. Make a sketch to illustrate the concept, and label it.

NOTES

Types of forces
- contact force
- gravity
- friction

informal outline

forces on a box being pushed

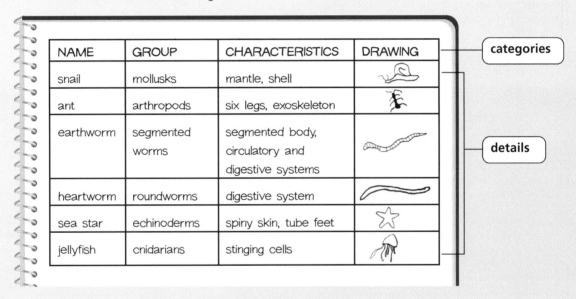

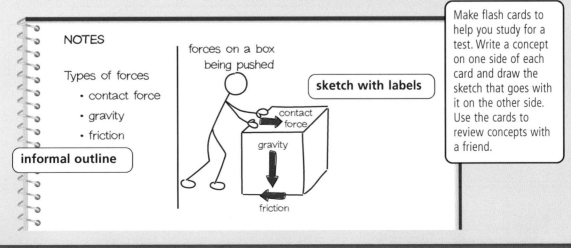

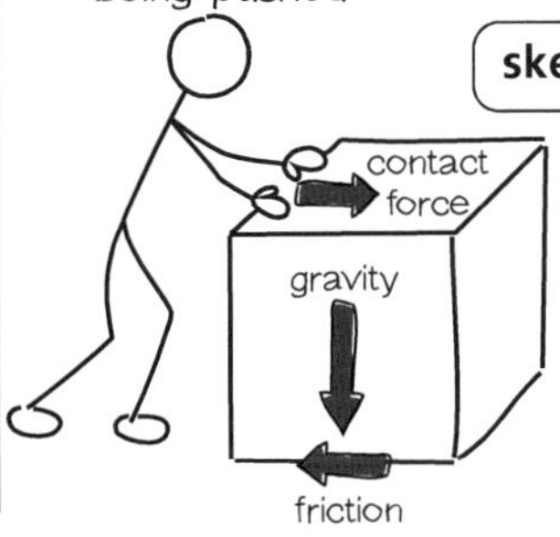


sketch with labels

Make flash cards to help you study for a test. Write a concept on one side of each card and draw the sketch that goes with it on the other side. Use the cards to review concepts with a friend.

NOTE-TAKING HANDBOOK

## Main Idea and Detail Notes

1. In the left-hand column of a two-column chart, list main ideas. The blue headings express main ideas throughout this textbook.
2. In the right-hand column, write details that expand on each main idea.

You can shorten the headings in your chart. Be sure to use the most important words.

When studying for tests, cover up the detail notes column with a sheet of paper. Then use each main idea to form a question—such as "How does latitude affect climate?" Answer the question, and then uncover the detail notes column to check your answer.

| MAIN IDEAS | DETAIL NOTES |
|---|---|
| 1. Latitude affects climate. | 1. Places close to the equator are usually warmer than places close to the poles.<br>1. Latitude has the same effect in both hemispheres. |
| 2. Altitude affects climate. | 2. Temperature decreases with altitude.<br>2. Altitude can overcome the effect of latitude on temperature. |

main idea 1

details about main idea 1

main idea 2

details about main idea 2

## Main Idea Web

1. Write a main idea in a box.
2. Add boxes around it with related vocabulary terms and important details.

You can find definitions near highlighted terms.

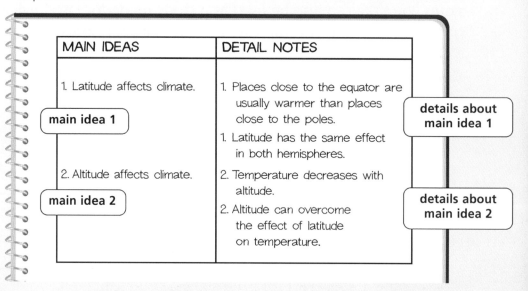

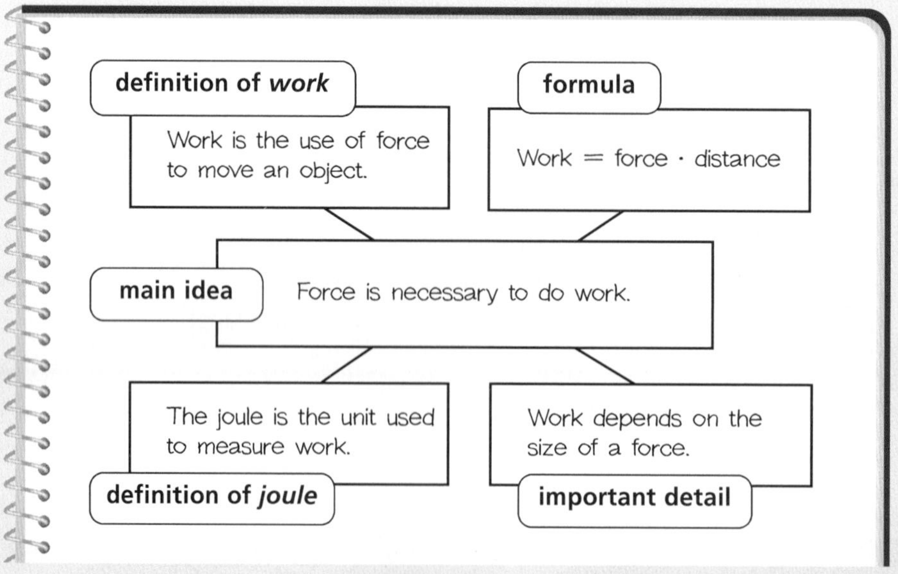
definition of *work*
Work is the use of force to move an object.
formula
Work = force · distance
main idea
Force is necessary to do work.
The joule is the unit used to measure work.
definition of *joule*
Work depends on the size of a force.
important detail

## Mind Map

1. Write a main idea in the center.
2. Add details that relate to one another and to the main idea.

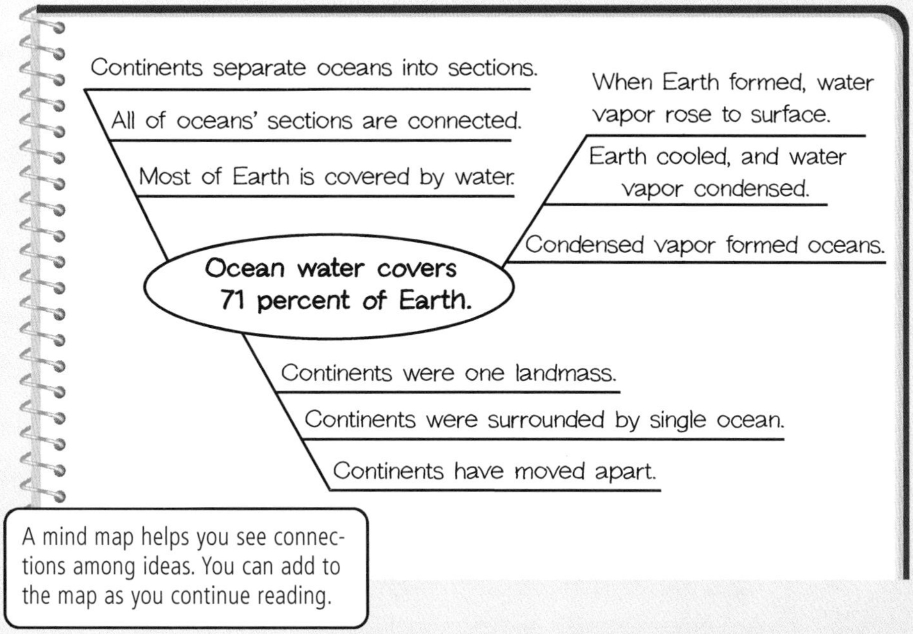


Continents separate oceans into sections.
All of oceans' sections are connected.
Most of Earth is covered by water.
When Earth formed, water vapor rose to surface.

Condensed vapor formed oceans.
Ocean water covers 71 percent of Earth.
Continents were one landmass.
Continents were surrounded by single ocean.

A mind map helps you see connections among ideas. You can add to the map as you continue reading.

## Supporting Main Ideas

1. Write a main idea in a box.
2. Add boxes underneath with information—such as reasons, explanations, and examples—that supports the main idea.

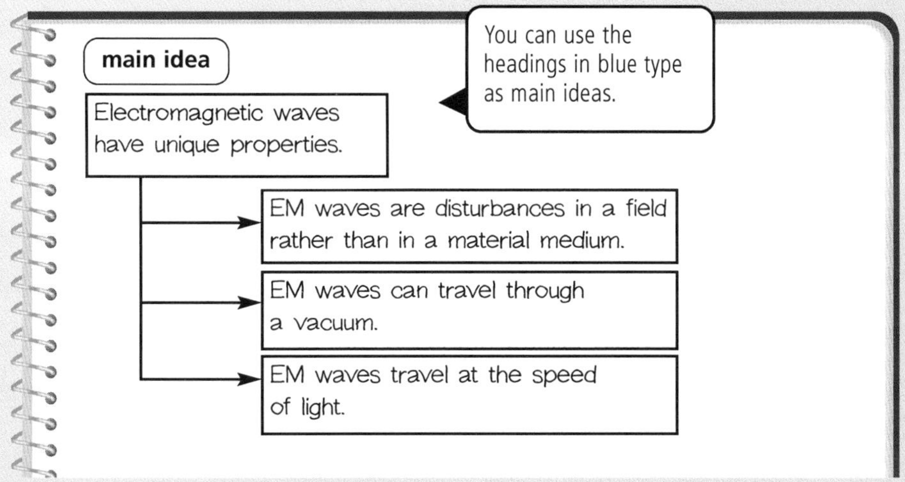

main idea
Electromagnetic waves have unique properties.
You can use the headings in blue type as main ideas.
EM waves are disturbances in a field rather than in a material medium.
EM waves can travel through a vacuum.
EM waves travel at the speed of light.

## Outline

1. Copy the chapter title and headings from the book in the form of an outline.
2. Add notes that summarize in your own words what you read.

Cell Processes

I. Cells capture and release energy. — 1st key idea
   - A. All cells need energy. — 1st subpoint of I
   - B. Some cells capture light energy. — 2nd subpoint of I
     - 1. Process of photosynthesis — 1st detail about B
     - 2. Chloroplasts (site of photosynthesis) — 2nd detail about B
     - 3. Carbon dioxide and water as raw materials
     - 4. Glucose and oxygen as products
   - C. All cells release energy.
     - 1. Process of cellular respiration
     - 2. Fermentation of sugar to carbon dioxide
     - 3. Bacteria that carry out fermentation

II. Cells transport materials through membranes.
   - A. Some materials move by diffusion.
     - 1. Particle movement from higher to lower concentrations
     - 2. Movement of water through membrane (osmosis)
   - B. Some transport requires energy.
     - 1. Active transport
     - 2. Examples of active transport

**Correct Outline Form**

Include a title.

Arrange key ideas, subpoints, and details as shown.

Indent the divisions of the outline as shown.

Use the same grammatical form for items of the same rank. For example, if A is a sentence, B must also be a sentence.

You must have at least two main ideas or subpoints. That is, every A must be followed by a B, and every 1 must be followed by a 2.

## Concept Map

1. Write an important concept in a large oval.
2. Add details related to the concept in smaller ovals.
3. Write linking words on arrows that connect the ovals.

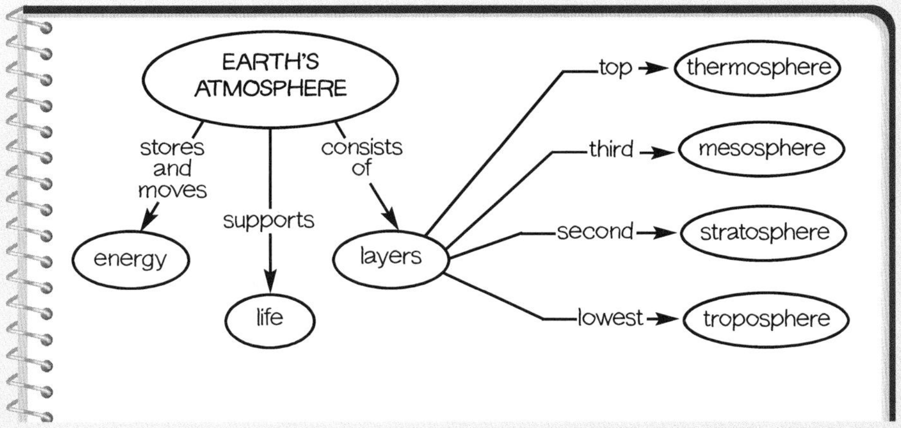


The main ideas or concepts can often be found in the blue headings. An example is "The atmosphere stores and moves energy." Use nouns from these concepts in the ovals, and use the verb or verbs on the lines.

## Venn Diagram

1. Draw two overlapping circles, one for each item that you are comparing.
2. In the overlapping section, list the characteristics that are shared by both items.
3. In the outer sections, list the characteristics that are peculiar to each item.
4. Write a summary that describes the information in the Venn diagram.

characteristics not shared by sound waves

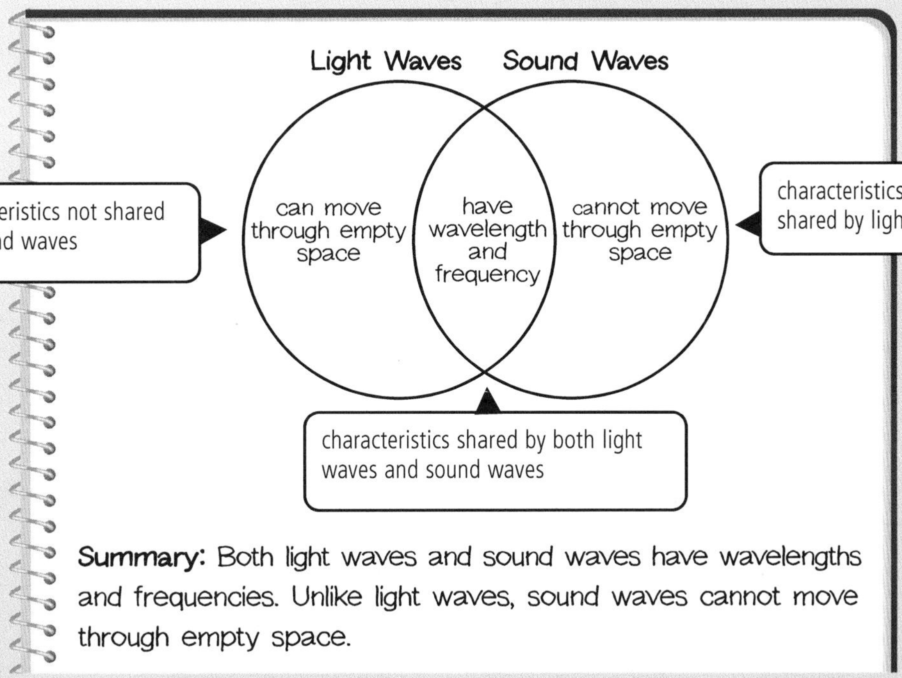


characteristics not shared by light waves

characteristics shared by both light waves and sound waves

NOTE-TAKING HANDBOOK

# Vocabulary Strategies

Important terms are highlighted in this book. A definition of each term can be found in the sentence or paragraph where the term appears. You can also find definitions in the Glossary. Taking notes about vocabulary terms helps you understand and remember what you read.

## Description Wheel

1. Write a term inside a circle.
2. Write words that describe the term on "spokes" attached to the circle.

When studying for a test with a friend, read the phrases on the spokes one at a time until your friend identifies the correct term.

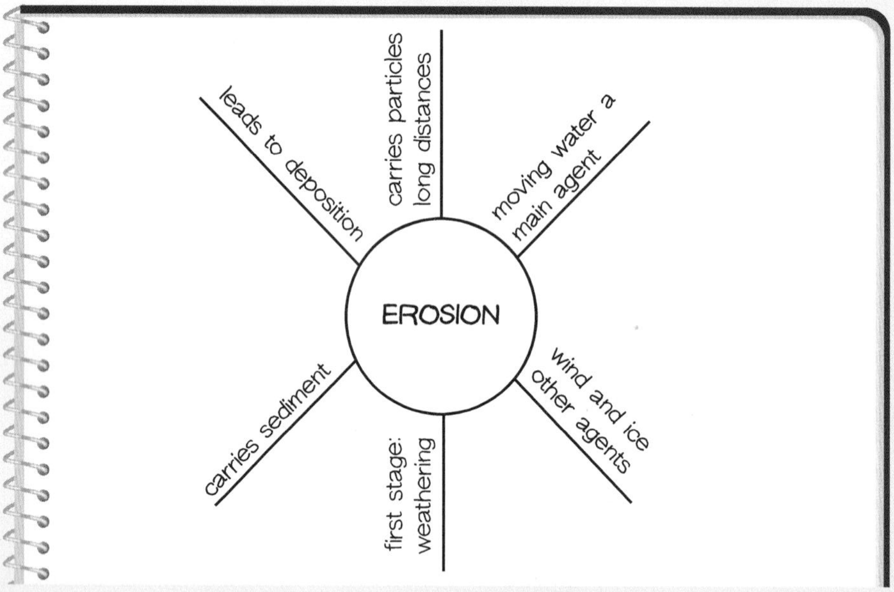


## Four Square

1. Write a term in the center.
2. Write details in the four areas around the term.

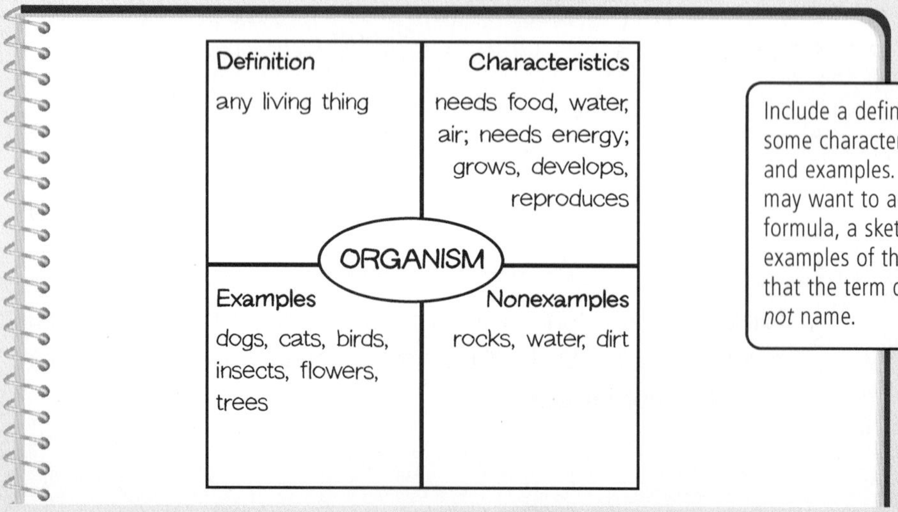


Include a definition, some characteristics, and examples. You may want to add a formula, a sketch, or examples of things that the term does *not* name.

## Frame Game

1. Write a term in the center.
2. Frame the term with details.

Include examples, descriptions, sketches, or sentences that use the term in context. Change the frame to fit each new term.

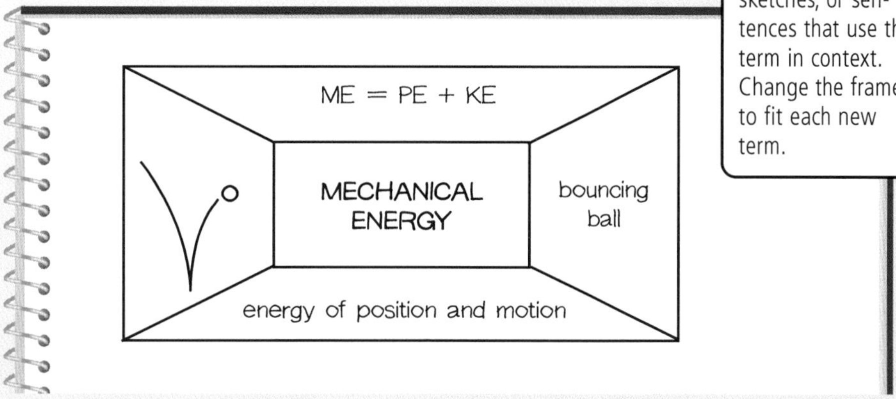


## Magnet Word

1. Write a term on the magnet.
2. On the lines, add details related to the term.

You can also use phrases or sentences on the lines.

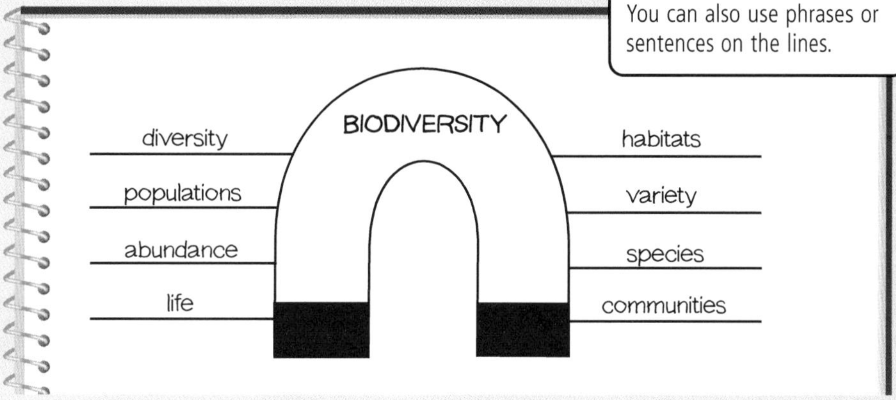


## Word Triangle

1. Write a term and its definition in the bottom section.
2. In the middle section, write a sentence in which the term is used correctly.
3. In the top section, draw a small picture to illustrate the term.

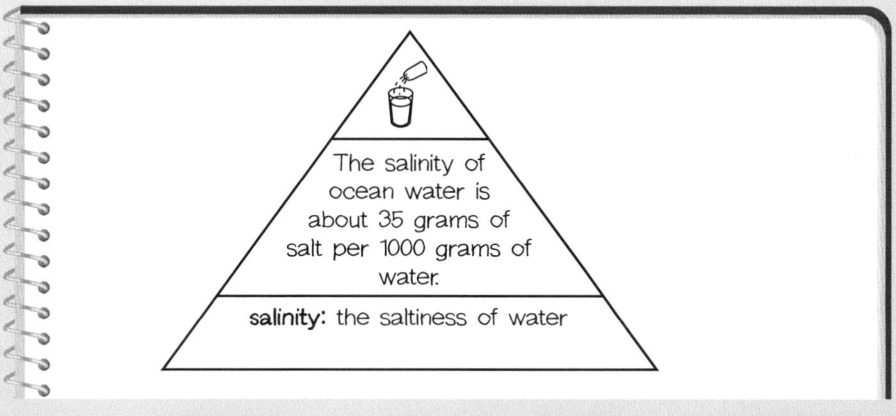

# United States Physical Map

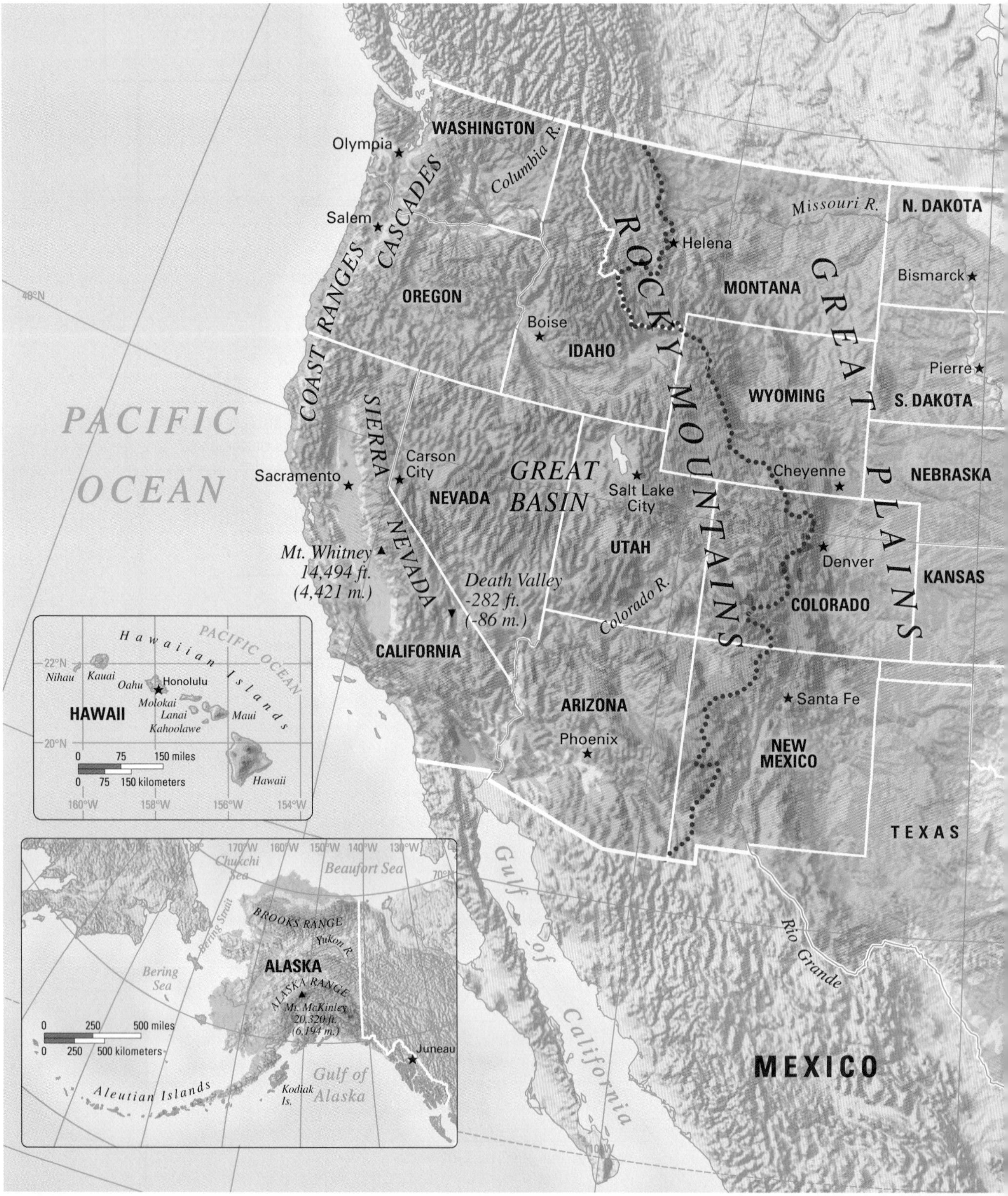

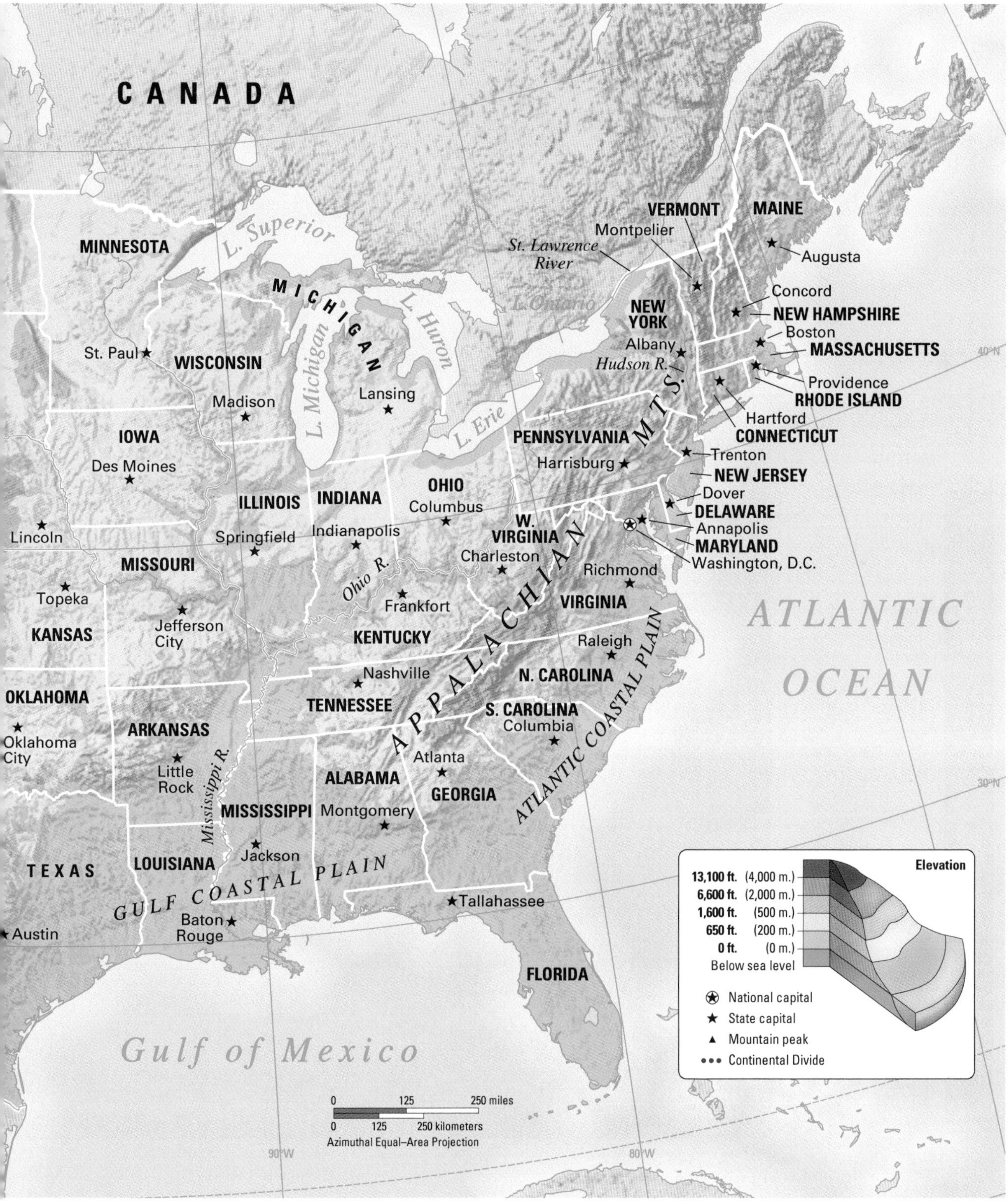
CANADA
MINNESOTA
St. Paul
WISCONSIN
Madison
MICHIGAN
Lansing
L. Superior
L. Michigan
L. Huron
L. Erie
L. Ontario
St. Lawrence River
VERMONT
Montpelier
MAINE
Augusta
Concord
NEW HAMPSHIRE
NEW YORK
Albany
Hudson R.
Boston
MASSACHUSETTS
Providence
RHODE ISLAND
Hartford
CONNECTICUT
PENNSYLVANIA
Harrisburg
Trenton
NEW JERSEY
Dover
DELAWARE
Annapolis
MARYLAND
Washington, D.C.
IOWA
Des Moines
ILLINOIS
Springfield
INDIANA
Indianapolis
OHIO
Columbus
W. VIRGINIA
Charleston
Richmond
VIRGINIA
Lincoln
MISSOURI
Jefferson City
Topeka
KANSAS
Ohio R.
Frankfort
KENTUCKY
APPALACHIAN MTS.
Raleigh
N. CAROLINA
Nashville
TENNESSEE
OKLAHOMA
Oklahoma City
ARKANSAS
Little Rock
Mississippi R.
S. CAROLINA
Columbia
Atlanta
GEORGIA
ALABAMA
Montgomery
MISSISSIPPI
Jackson
ATLANTIC COASTAL PLAIN
TEXAS
Austin
LOUISIANA
Baton Rouge
GULF COASTAL PLAIN
Tallahassee
FLORIDA
ATLANTIC OCEAN
Gulf of Mexico
40°N
30°N
90°W
80°W
0 125 250 miles
0 125 250 kilometers
Azimuthal Equal–Area Projection
Elevation
13,100 ft. (4,000 m.)
6,600 ft. (2,000 m.)
1,600 ft. (500 m.)
650 ft. (200 m.)
0 ft. (0 m.)
Below sea level
National capital
State capital
Mountain peak
Continental Divide

APPENDIX

# World Physical Map

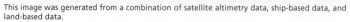

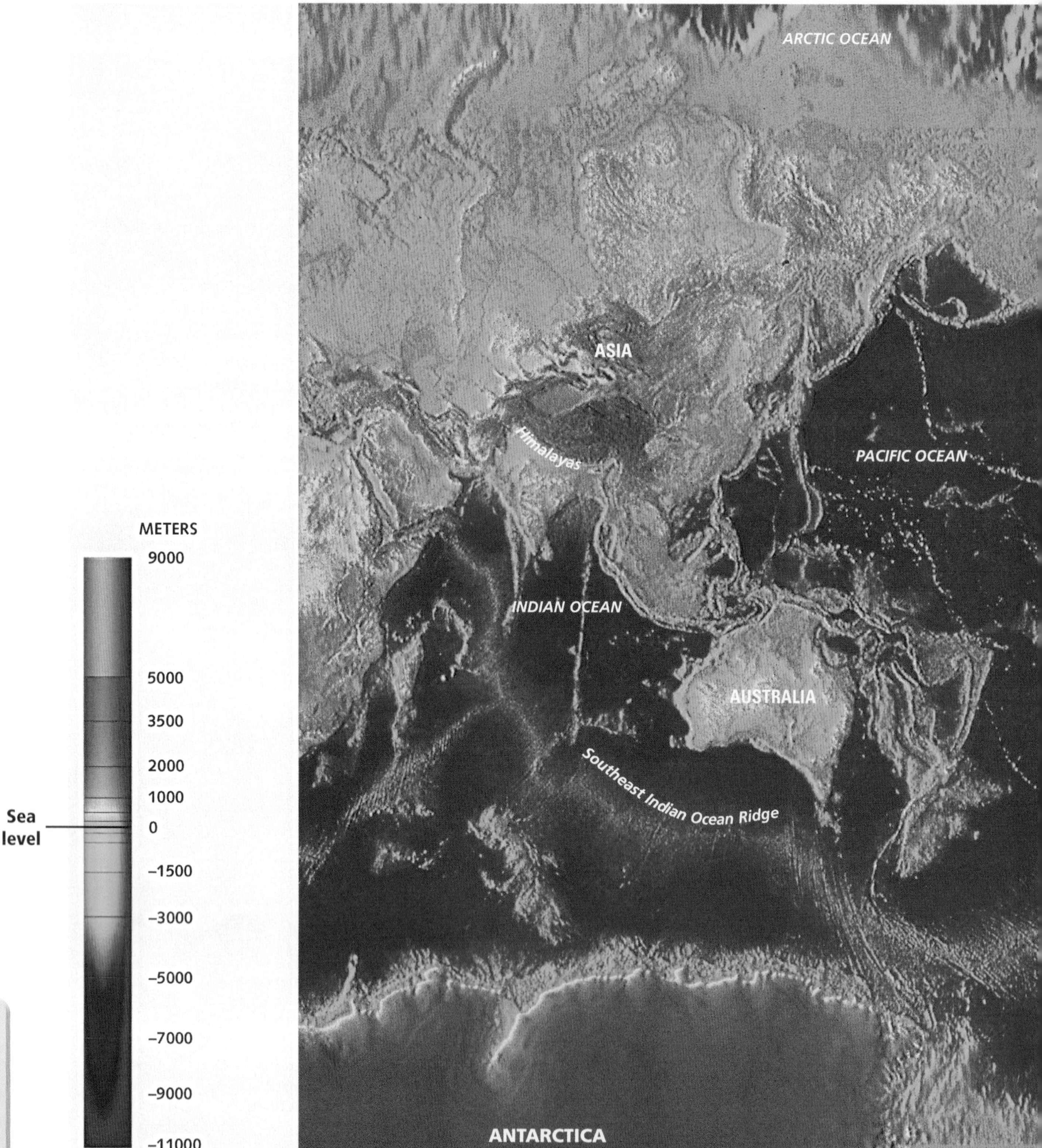


This image was generated from a combination of satellite altimetry data, ship-based data, and land-based data.

APPENDIX

GREENLAND
NORTH AMERICA
Rocky Mountains
Appalachian Mts.
EUROPE
Alps
ATLANTIC OCEAN
Atlas Mts.
Mid-Atlantic Ridge
AFRICA
PACIFIC OCEAN
SOUTH AMERICA
INDIAN OCEAN
East Pacific Rise
Andes
Southwest Indian Ocean Ridge
ANTARCTICA
ANTARCTICA

APPENDIX

# Tectonic Plates

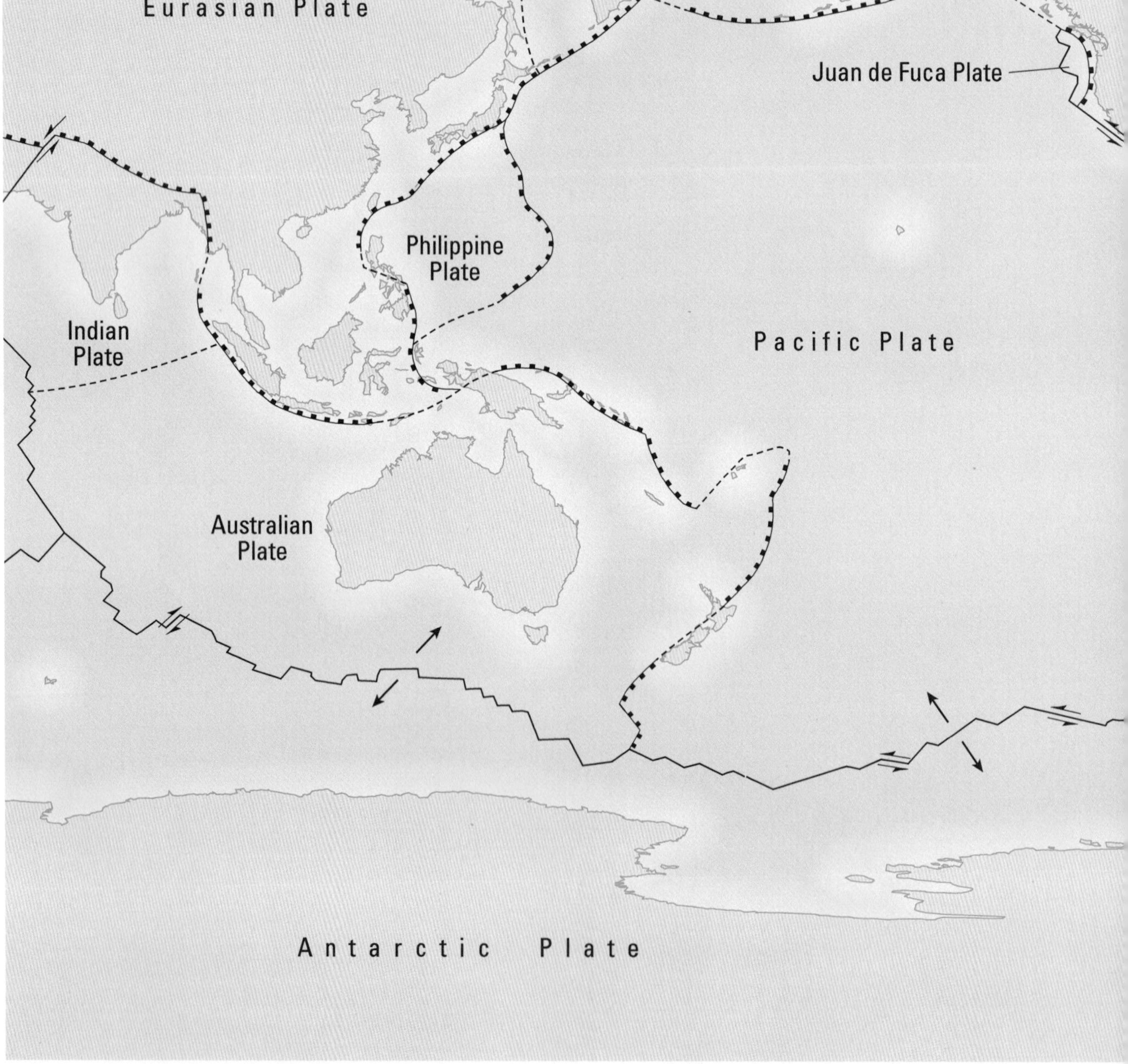

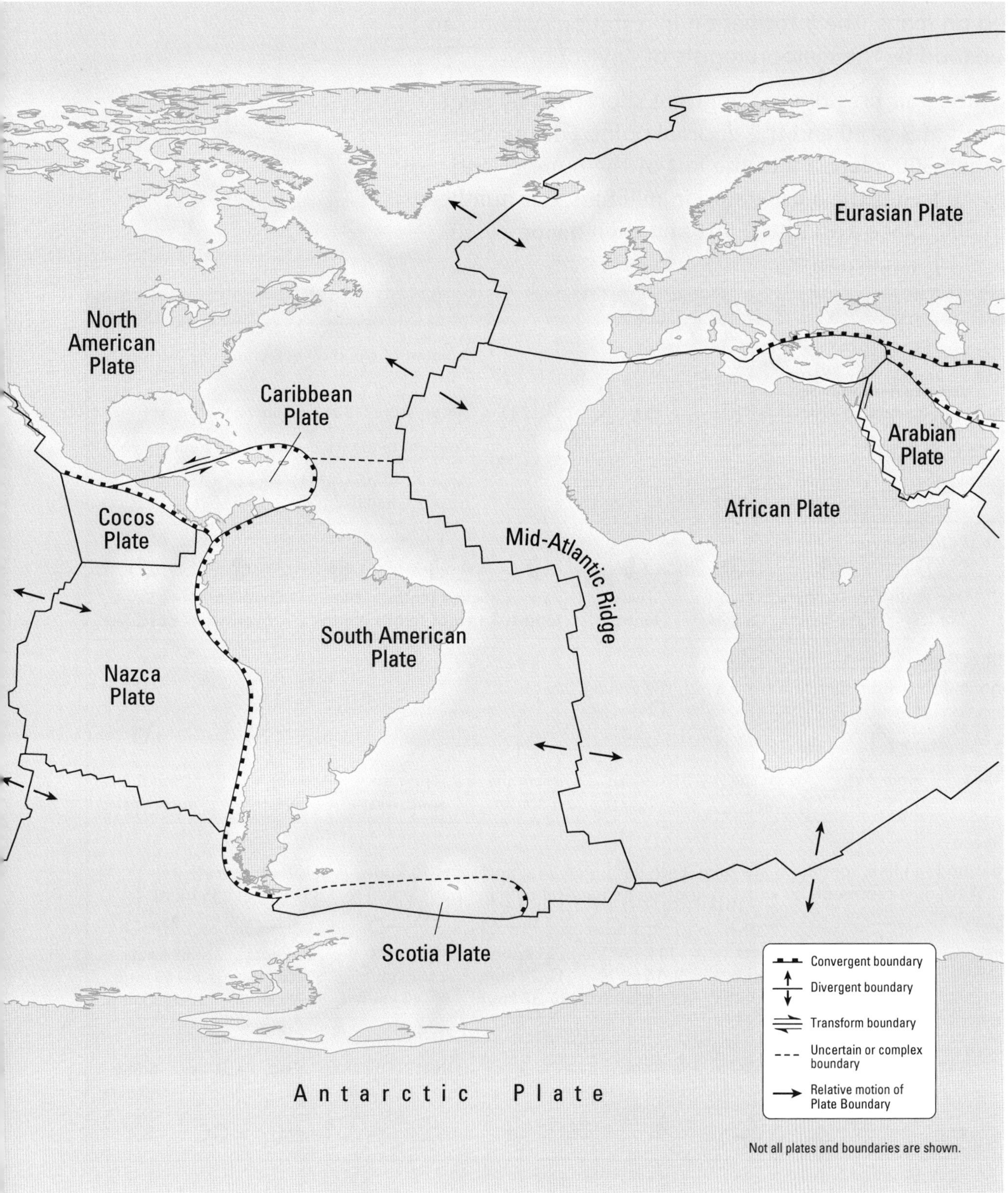
Eurasian Plate
North American Plate
Caribbean Plate
Arabian Plate
African Plate
Cocos Plate
Mid-Atlantic Ridge
South American Plate
Nazca Plate
Scotia Plate
Convergent boundary
Divergent boundary
Transform boundary
Uncertain or complex boundary
Relative motion of Plate Boundary
Antarctic Plate
Not all plates and boundaries are shown.

APPENDIX

# Station Symbols

Meteorologists use station symbols to condense the weather data they receive from ground stations. The symbols are displayed on maps. The information in a station symbol can be understood by the meteorologists of any country.

In the symbol, air pressure readings are shortened by omitting the initial 9 or 10 and the decimal point. For numbers greater than 500, place a 9 to the left of the number and divide by 10 to get the air pressure in millibars. For numbers less than 500, place a 10 to the left and then divide by 10.

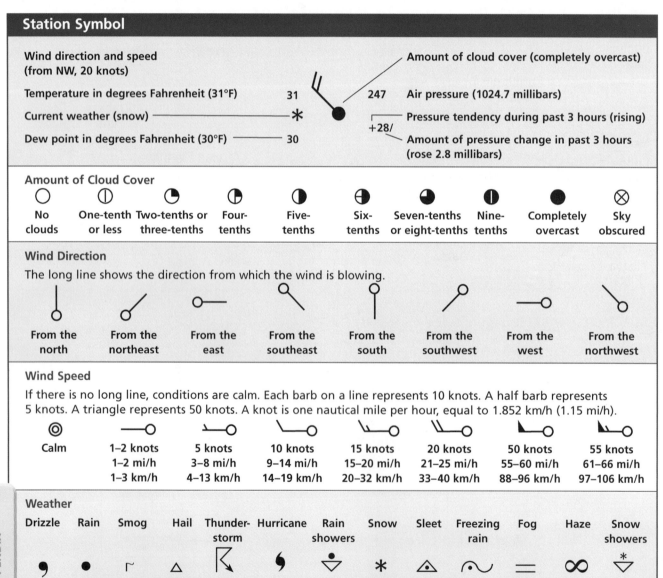

## Station Symbol

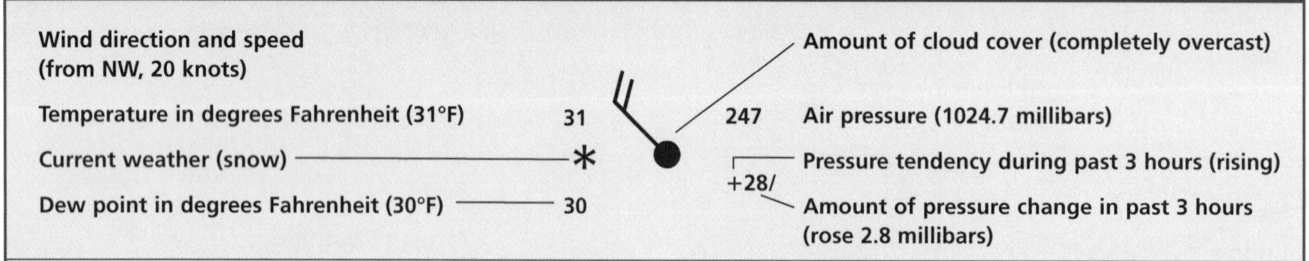


### Amount of Cloud Cover

| No clouds | One-tenth or less | Two-tenths or three-tenths | Four-tenths | Five-tenths | Six-tenths | Seven-tenths or eight-tenths | Nine-tenths | Completely overcast | Sky obscured |
|---|---|---|---|---|---|---|---|---|---|

### Wind Direction

The long line shows the direction from which the wind is blowing.

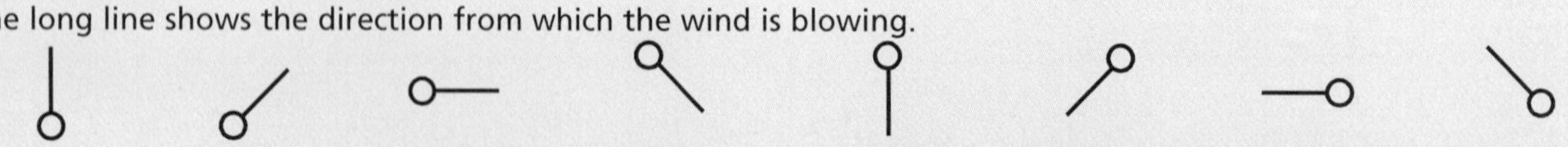

| From the north | From the northeast | From the east | From the southeast | From the south | From the southwest | From the west | From the northwest |
|---|---|---|---|---|---|---|---|

### Wind Speed

If there is no long line, conditions are calm. Each barb on a line represents 10 knots. A half barb represents 5 knots. A triangle represents 50 knots. A knot is one nautical mile per hour, equal to 1.852 km/h (1.15 mi/h).

| Calm | 1–2 knots | 5 knots | 10 knots | 15 knots | 20 knots | 50 knots | 55 knots |
|---|---|---|---|---|---|---|---|
| | 1–2 mi/h | 3–8 mi/h | 9–14 mi/h | 15–20 mi/h | 21–25 mi/h | 55–60 mi/h | 61–66 mi/h |
| | 1–3 km/h | 4–13 km/h | 14–19 km/h | 20–32 km/h | 33–40 km/h | 88–96 km/h | 97–106 km/h |

### Weather

| Drizzle | Rain | Smog | Hail | Thunderstorm | Hurricane | Rain showers | Snow | Sleet | Freezing rain | Fog | Haze | Snow showers |
|---|---|---|---|---|---|---|---|---|---|---|---|---|

APPENDIX

# Relative Humidity

You can find the relative humidity by calculating the difference between the two readings on a psychrometer. First look up the dry-bulb temperature in the left-hand column of the relative humidity chart. Then find in the top line the difference between the wet-bulb temperature and the dry-bulb temperature.

**Relative Humidity (%)**

| Dry-Bulb Temperature (°C) | Difference Between Wet-Bulb and Dry-Bulb Temperatures (°C) | | | | | | | | | | | | | | | |
|---|---|---|---|---|---|---|---|---|---|---|---|---|---|---|---|---|
| | 0 | 1 | 2 | 3 | 4 | 5 | 6 | 7 | 8 | 9 | 10 | 11 | 12 | 13 | 14 | 15 |
| **−20** | 100 | 28 | | | | | | | | | | | | | | |
| **−18** | 100 | 40 | | | | | | | | | | | | | | |
| **−16** | 100 | 48 | | | | | | | | | | | | | | |
| **−14** | 100 | 55 | 11 | | | | | | | | | | | | | |
| **−12** | 100 | 61 | 23 | | | | | | | | | | | | | |
| **−10** | 100 | 66 | 33 | | | | | | | | | | | | | |
| **−8** | 100 | 71 | 41 | 13 | | | | | | | | | | | | |
| **−6** | 100 | 73 | 48 | 20 | | | | | | | | | | | | |
| **−4** | 100 | 77 | 54 | 32 | 11 | | | | | | | | | | | |
| **−2** | 100 | 79 | 58 | 37 | 20 | 1 | | | | | | | | | | |
| **0** | 100 | 81 | 63 | 45 | 28 | 11 | | | | | | | | | | |
| **2** | 100 | 83 | 67 | 51 | 36 | 20 | 6 | | | | | | | | | |
| **4** | 100 | 85 | 70 | 56 | 42 | 27 | 14 | | | | | | | | | |
| **6** | 100 | 86 | 72 | 59 | 46 | 35 | 22 | 10 | | | | | | | | |
| **8** | 100 | 87 | 74 | 62 | 51 | 39 | 28 | 17 | 6 | | | | | | | |
| **10** | 100 | 88 | 76 | 65 | 54 | 43 | 33 | 24 | 13 | 4 | | | | | | |
| **12** | 100 | 88 | 78 | 67 | 57 | 48 | 38 | 28 | 19 | 10 | 2 | | | | | |
| **14** | 100 | 89 | 79 | 69 | 60 | 50 | 41 | 33 | 25 | 16 | 8 | 1 | | | | |
| **16** | 100 | 90 | 80 | 71 | 62 | 54 | 45 | 37 | 29 | 21 | 14 | 7 | 1 | | | |
| **18** | 100 | 91 | 81 | 72 | 64 | 56 | 48 | 40 | 33 | 26 | 19 | 12 | 6 | | | |
| **20** | 100 | 91 | 82 | 74 | 66 | 58 | 51 | 44 | 36 | 30 | 23 | 17 | 11 | 5 | | |
| **22** | 100 | 92 | 83 | 75 | 68 | 60 | 53 | 46 | 40 | 33 | 27 | 21 | 15 | 10 | 4 | |
| **24** | 100 | 92 | 84 | 76 | 69 | 62 | 55 | 49 | 42 | 36 | 30 | 25 | 20 | 14 | 9 | 4 |
| **26** | 100 | 92 | 85 | 77 | 70 | 64 | 57 | 51 | 45 | 39 | 34 | 28 | 23 | 18 | 13 | 9 |
| **28** | 100 | 93 | 86 | 78 | 71 | 65 | 59 | 53 | 47 | 42 | 36 | 31 | 26 | 21 | 17 | 12 |
| **30** | 100 | 93 | 86 | 79 | 72 | 66 | 61 | 55 | 49 | 44 | 39 | 34 | 29 | 25 | 20 | 16 |

APPENDIX

# Wind Speeds

Descriptive names, such as *fresh gale,* were used by sailors and other people to describe the strength of winds. Later, ranges of wind speeds were determined. The table below lists the wind speeds and conditions you might observe around you on land.

| Beaufort Scale of Wind Speeds | | |
|---|---|---|
| **Beaufort Number** | **Wind Speed** | **Description** |
| 0 | 0 km/h (0 mi/h) | **Calm or Still** Smoke will rise vertically |
| 1 | 2–5 km/h (1–3 mi/h) | **Light Air** Rising smoke drifts, weather vane is inactive |
| 2 | 6–12 km/h (4–7 mi/h) | **Light Breeze** Leaves rustle, can feel wind on your face, weather vane moves |
| 3 | 13–20 km/h (8–12 mi/h) | **Gentle Breeze** Leaves and twigs move around, lightweight flags extend |
| 4 | 21–30 km/h (13–18 mi/h) | **Moderate Breeze** Thin branches move, dust and paper raised |
| 5 | 31–40 km/h (19–24 mi/h) | **Fresh Breeze** Small trees sway |
| 6 | 41–50 km/h (25–31 mi/h) | **Strong Breeze** Large tree branches move, open wires (such as telegraph wires) begin to "whistle," umbrellas are difficult to keep under control |
| 7 | 51–61 km/h (32–38 mi/h) | **Moderate Gale** Large trees begin to sway, noticeably difficult to walk |
| 8 | 62–74 km/h (39–46 mi/h) | **Fresh Gale** Twigs and small branches are broken from trees, walking into the wind is very difficult |
| 9 | 75–89 km/h (47–54 mi/h) | **Strong Gale** Slight damage occurs to buildings, shingles are blown off of roofs |
| 10 | 90–103 km/h (55–63 mi/h) | **Whole Gale** Large trees are uprooted, building damage is considerable |
| 11 | 104–119 km/h (64–72 mi/h) | **Storm** Extensive, widespread damage. These typically occur only at sea, rarely inland. |
| 12 | 120 km/h or more (74 mi/h or more) | **Hurricane** Extreme damage, very rare inland |

# Tornado Intensities

The Fujita scale describes the strength of a tornado based on the damage it does. The scale is useful for classifying tornadoes even though it is not exact. For example, a tornado can strengthen and then weaken before it dies out. The wind speeds are estimates of the strongest winds near the ground. Most tornadoes are F0 or F1. One-quarter to one-third of tornadoes are F2 or F3. Only a few percent of tornadoes are F4 or F5.

**Fujita Scale for Tornadoes**

| F-Scale | Wind Speed | Type of Damage |
|---|---|---|
| F0 | 64–116 km/h (40–72 mi/h) | **Light Damage** Some damage to chimneys; branches broken off trees; shallow-rooted trees pushed over; sign boards damaged |
| F1 | 117–180 km/h (73–112 mi/h) | **Moderate Damage** Surface peeled off roofs; mobile homes pushed off foundations or overturned; moving autos blown off roads |
| F2 | 181–253 km/h (113–157 mi/h) | **Considerable Damage** Roofs torn off frame houses; mobile homes demolished; boxcars overturned; large trees snapped or uprooted; light-object missiles generated; cars lifted off ground |
| F3 | 254–332 km/h (158–206 mi/h) | **Severe Damage** Roofs and some walls torn off well-constructed houses; trains overturned; most trees in forest uprooted; heavy cars lifted off the ground and thrown |
| F4 | 333–418 km/h (207–260 mi/h) | **Devastating Damage** Well-constructed houses leveled; structures with weak foundations blown away some distance; cars thrown and large missiles generated |
| F5 | 419–512 km/h (261–318 mi/h) | **Incredible Damage** Strong frame houses leveled off foundations and swept away; automobile-sized missiles fly through the air in excess of 100 meters (109 yds); trees debarked; incredible phenomena will occur |

# Geologic Time Scale

| Eon | Era | | Period | MYA* <br>*Millions of years ago | Epoch |
|---|---|---|---|---|---|
| Phanerozoic | **Cenozoic** "Age of Mammals" 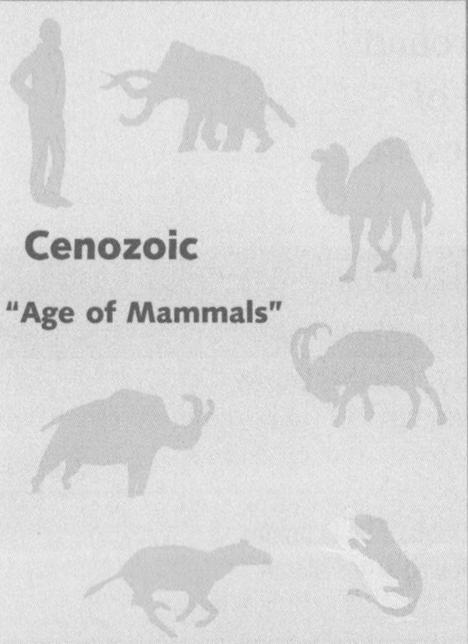 | | Quaternary | 0.01 (10,000 yrs) | Holocene or Recent |
| | | | | 2 | Pleistocene |
| | | Tertiary | Neogene | 5 | Pliocene |
| | | | | 24 | Miocene |
| | | | Paleogene | 34 | Oligocene |
| | | | | 55 | Eocene |
| | | | | 65 | Paleocene |
| | **Mesozoic** "Age of Reptiles"  | | Cretaceous | 144 | |
| | | | Jurassic | 206 | |
| | | | Triassic | 248 | |
| | **Paleozoic** "Age of Invertebrates" 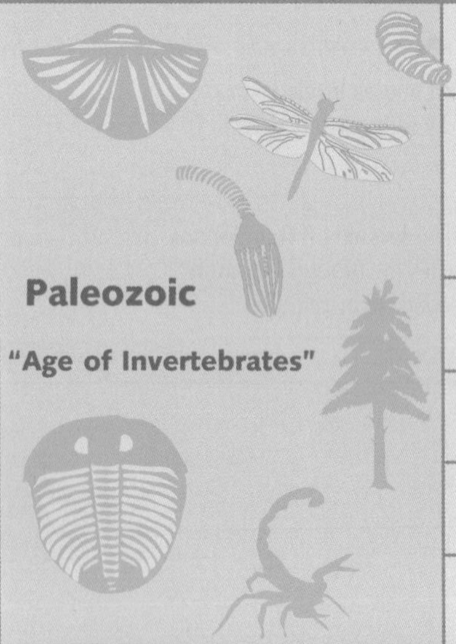 | | Permian | 290 | |
| | | Carboniferous | Pennsylvanian | 323 | |
| | | | Mississippian | 354 | |
| | | | Devonian | 417 | |
| | | | Silurian | 443 | |
| | | | Ordovician | 490 | |
| | | | Cambrian | 543 | |
| Proterozoic | | | | 2,500 | |
| Archean | | | | 3,800? | |

| MYA | Life | North American Rock Record |
|---|---|---|
| 0.01 (10,000 yrs) | Humans dominant. Domestic animal species develop. | West Coast uplift continues in U.S.; Great Lakes form. |
| 2 | Hominids develop. Elephants flourish in North America, then die out. | Ice Age. Raising of mountains and plateaus in western U.S. |
| 5 | Hominids appear. Modern horse, camel, elephant develop. Sequoias decline; tropical trees driven south. | North America joined to South America. Sierras and Appalachians re-elevated by isostatic rebound. |
| 24 | Horse migrates to Asia, elephant to America. Grasses, grazing animals thrive. | North America joined to Asia. Volcanism in northwestern U.S., Columbia Plateau. |
| 34 | Mammals progress. Cats and dogs develop and diverge. Elephants in Africa. | Volcanism in western U.S. as Alps and Himalayas forming. |
| 55 | Pygmy ancestors of modern horse, other mammals. First whales. Diatoms, flowering plants thrive. | Coal forming in western U.S. |
| 65 | Many new mammals appear. | Uplift in western U.S. continues. |
| 144 | Dinosaurs, ammonites die out. Mammals, birds show new adaptations. Flowering plants, hardwoods rise. | Uplift of Rockies begins. Colorado Plateau raised. Coal swamps in western U.S. Intrusion of Sierra Nevada batholith. |
| 206 | Giant dinosaurs. First birds. Conifers and cycads abundant. Earliest mammals. | West-central North America under huge sea. Gulf of Mexico, Atlantic Ocean begin to form. |
| 248 | Reptiles thrive. Forests of conifers and cycads. | Volcanism and faulting along East Coast. Palisades of the Hudson River formed. |
| 290 | Mass extinction of existing species. Trilobites, seed ferns, scale trees die out. Corals abundant. | Final uplift in Appalachians. Salt-forming deserts in western U.S. while an ice age in South America. |
| 323 | First reptiles. Many giant insects. Spore-bearing plants, amphibians flourish. | Great coal-forming swamps in North America (and Europe). |
| 354 | Sharks, amphibians, and crinoids flourish. Seed ferns, conifers abundant. | Extensive submergence of continents. |
| 417 | First amphibians; fishes abound. First forests. | Mountain building continues in New England and Canada. White Mountains raised. |
| 443 | First land plants and animals (spiders, scorpions). Fishes develop; marine invertebrates thrive. | Salt and gypsum deserts forming in eastern U.S. |
| 490 | Marine invertebrates thrive: mollusks, trilobites, graptolites. | Beginning of Appalachian mountain building. Taconic and Green Mountains form. Half of North America submerged. |
| 543 | First vertebrates (fish). Many marine invertebrates (first trilobites, shelled animals). Many seaweeds. | Extensive deposition of sediments in inland seas. |
| 2,500 | No life on land. Simple marine organisms (algae, fungi, worms). Stromatolites dominant. Other life probably existed, but fossil evidence is lacking. | Great volcanic activity, lava flows, metamorphism of rocks. Formation of iron, copper, and nickel ores. |
| 3,800? | | Formation of Earth's crust. |

# Properties of Rocks and Earth's Interior

## Scheme for Sedimentary Rock Identification

| TEXTURE | GRAIN SIZE | COMPOSITION | COMMENTS | ROCK NAME | MAP SYMBOL |
|---|---|---|---|---|---|
| Clastic (fragmental) | Pebbles, cobbles, and/or boulders embedded in sand, silt, and/or clay | Mostly quartz, feldspar, and clay minerals; may contain fragments of other rocks and minerals | Rounded fragments | Conglomerate | |
| | | | Angular fragments | Breccia | |
| | Sand (0.2 to 0.006 cm) | | Fine to coarse | Sandstone | |
| | Silt (0.006 to 0.0004 cm) | | Very fine grain | Siltstone | |
| | Clay (less than 0.0004 cm) | | Compact; may split easily | Shale | |

**CHEMICALLY AND/OR ORGANICALLY FORMED SEDIMENTARY ROCKS**

| TEXTURE | GRAIN SIZE | COMPOSITION | COMMENTS | ROCK NAME | MAP SYMBOL |
|---|---|---|---|---|---|
| Crystalline | Varied | Halite | Crystals from chemical precipitates and evaporites | Rock Salt | |
| | Varied | Gypsum | | Rock Gypsum | |
| | Varied | Dolomite | | Dolostone | |
| Bioclastic | Microscopic to coarse | Calcite | Cemented shell fragments or precipitates of biologic origin | Limestone | |
| | Varied | Carbon | From plant remains | Coal | |

## Scheme for Metamorphic Rock Identification

| TEXTURE | | GRAIN SIZE | COMPOSITION | TYPE OF METAMORPHISM | COMMENTS | ROCK NAME | MAP SYMBOL |
|---|---|---|---|---|---|---|---|
| FOLIATED | MINERAL ALIGNMENT | Fine | MICA, QUARTZ, FELDSPAR, AMPHIBOLE, GARNET, PYROXENE | Regional | Low-grade metamorphism of shale | Slate | |
| | | Fine to medium | | (Heat and pressure increase with depth) | Foliation surfaces shiny from microscopic mica crystals | Phyllite | |
| | | | | | Platy mica crystals visible from metamorphism of clay or feldspars | Schist | |
| | BAND-ING | Medium to coarse | | | High-grade metamorphism; some mica changed to feldspar; segregated by mineral type into bands | Gneiss | |
| NONFOLIATED | | Fine | Variable | Contact (Heat) | Various rocks changed by heat from nearby magma/lava | Hornfels | |
| | | Fine to coarse | Quartz | Regional or Contact | Metamorphism of quartz sandstone | Quartzite | |
| | | | Calcite and/or dolomite | | Metamorphism of limestone or dolostone | Marble | |
| | | Coarse | Various minerals in particles and matrix | | Pebbles may be distorted or stretched | Metaconglomerate | |

APPENDIX

## Scheme for Igneous Rock Identification

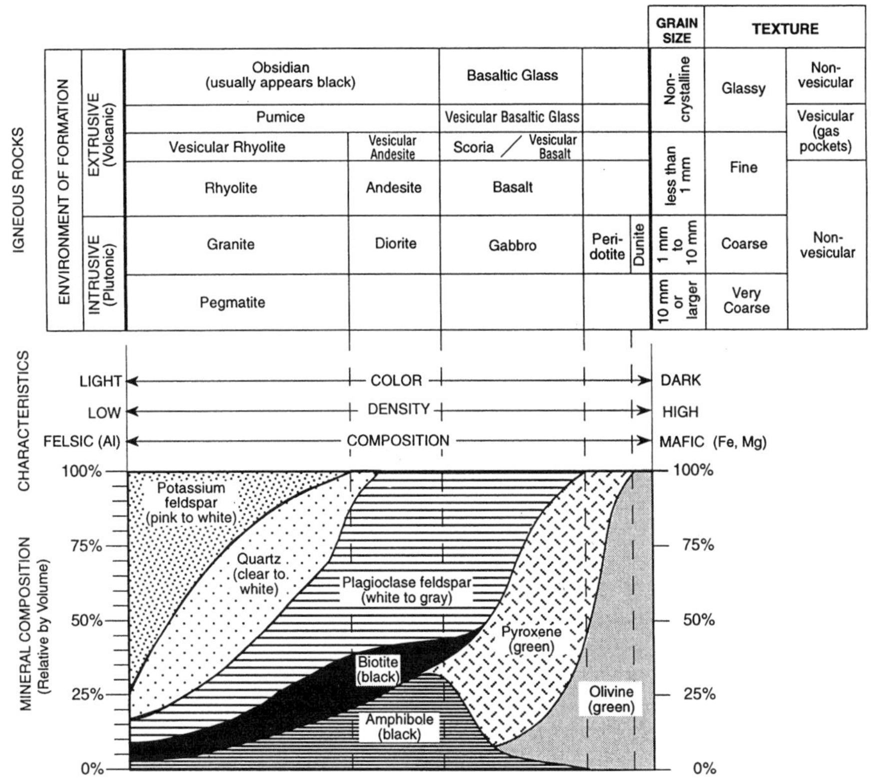

IGNEOUS ROCKS
ENVIRONMENT OF FORMATION
EXTRUSIVE (Volcanic)
INTRUSIVE (Plutonic)
Obsidian (usually appears black)
Basaltic Glass
Pumice
Vesicular Basaltic Glass
Vesicular Rhyolite
Vesicular Andesite
Scoria / Vesicular Basalt
Rhyolite
Andesite
Basalt
Granite
Diorite
Gabbro
Peri-dotite
Dunite
Pegmatite
GRAIN SIZE
TEXTURE
Non-crystalline
Glassy
Non-vesicular
Vesicular (gas pockets)
less than 1 mm
Fine
1 mm to 10 mm
Coarse
Non-vesicular
10 mm or larger
Very Coarse
CHARACTERISTICS
LIGHT
COLOR
DARK
LOW
DENSITY
HIGH
FELSIC (Al)
COMPOSITION
MAFIC (Fe, Mg)
MINERAL COMPOSITION (Relative by Volume)
100%
75%
50%
25%
0%
Potassium feldspar (pink to white)
Quartz (clear to white)
Plagioclase feldspar (white to gray)
Biotite (black)
Amphibole (black)
Pyroxene (green)
Olivine (green)


## Inferred Properties of Earth's Interior

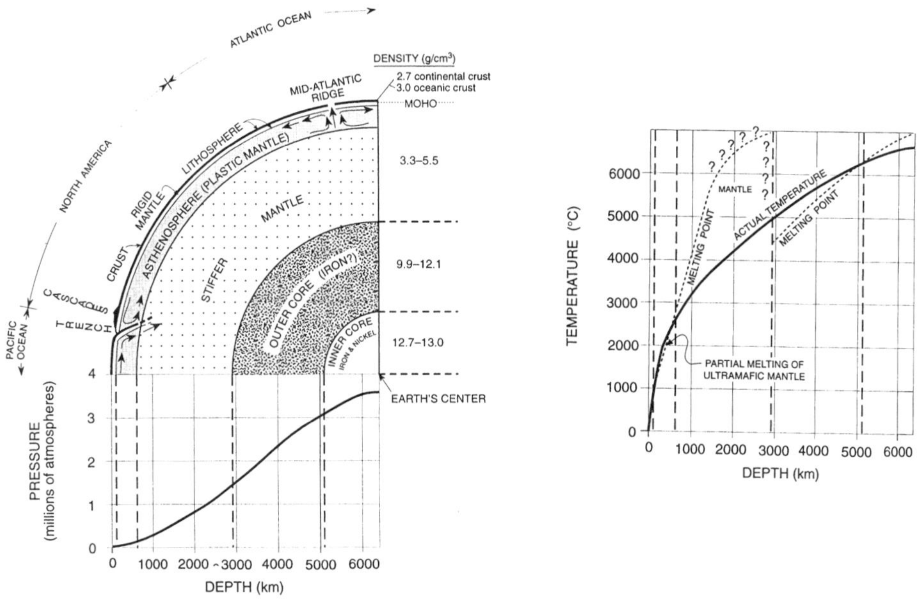



APPENDIX

# Properties of Common Minerals

In this table, minerals are arranged alphabetically, and the most useful properties for identification are printed in *italic* type. Most minerals can be identified by means of two or three of the properties listed below. For some minerals, density is important; for others, cleavage is characteristic; and for others, the crystal shapes identify the minerals. The colors listed are the most common for each mineral.

| Name | Hardness | Color | Streak | Cleavage | Remarks |
|---|---|---|---|---|---|
| Apatite | 5 | Green, brown | White | Poor in one direction | Nonmetallic (glassy) luster. Sp. gr. 3.1 to 3.2. |
| Augite | 5–6 | Dark green to black | Greenish | *Two directions, nearly at 90°* | Nonmetallic (glassy) luster. *Stubby four- or eight-sided crystals.* Common type of pyroxene. Sp. gr. 3.2 to 3.4. |
| Beryl | 7.5–8 | *Bluish-green, yellow, pink, colorless* | White | Imperfect in one direction | Nonmetallic (glassy) luster. *Hardness, greenish color, six-sided crystals.* Aquamarine and emerald are gem varieties. Sp. gr. 2.6 to 2.8. |
| Biotite mica | 2.5–3 | Black, brown, dark green | White | *Perfect in one direction* | Nonmetallic (glassy) luster. *Thin elastic films peel off easily.* Sp. gr. 2.8 to 3.2. |
| Calcite | *3* | White, colorless | White | *Perfect, three directions, not at 90° angles* | Nonmetallic (glassy to dull) luster. *Fizzes in dilute hydrochloric acid.* Sp. gr. 2.7. |
| Chalcopyrite | 3.5–4 | *Golden yellow* | Greenish black | Poor in one direction | Metallic luster. *Hardness distinguishes from pyrite.* Sp. gr. 4.1 to 4.3. |
| Chlorite | 2–2.5 | *Greenish* | Pale green to gray or brown | Perfect in one direction | Nonmetallic (glassy to pearly) luster. *Nonelastic flakes.* Sp. gr. 2.6 to 3.3. |
| Copper | 2.5–3 | *Copper red* | Copper | None | *Metallic luster on fresh surface. Dense.* Sp. gr. 8.9. |
| Corundum | 9 | Brown, pink, blue | White | None, parting resembles cleavage | Nonmetallic (glassy to brilliant) luster. *Barrel-shaped, six-sided crystals with flat ends.* Sp. gr. 4.0. |
| Diamond | 10 | Colorless to pale yellow | White | Perfect, four directions | Nonmetallic (brilliant to greasy) luster. *Hardest of all minerals.* Sp. gr. 3.5. |

Sp. gr. = specific gravity

| Name | Hardness | Color | Streak | Cleavage | Remarks |
|---|---|---|---|---|---|
| Dolomite | 3.5–4 | Pinkish, colorless, white | White | *Perfect, three directions, not at 90° angles* | Nonmetallic luster. *Scratched surface fizzes in dilute hydrochloric acid. Cleavage surfaces curved. Sp. gr. 2.8 to 2.9.* |
| Feldspar (Orthoclase) | *6* | *Salmon pink, red,* white, light gray | White | *Good, two directions, 90° intersection* | Nonmetallic (glassy) luster. *Hardness, color, and cleavage taken together are diagnostic.* Sp. gr. 2.6. |
| Feldspar (Plagioclase) | 6 | *White to light gray,* can be salmon pink | White | *Good, two directions, about 90°* | Nonmetallic (glassy to pearly) luster. *If striations are visible, they are diagnostic.* Sp. gr. 2.6 to 2.8. |
| Fluorite | 4 | Varies | White | *Perfect, four directions* | Nonmetallic (glassy) luster. In cubes or octahedrons as crystals. Sp. gr. 3.2. |
| Galena | 2.5 | *Lead gray* | Lead gray | *Perfect, three directions, at 90° angles* | *Metallic luster.* Occurs as crystals and masses. *Dense.* Sp. gr. 7.4 to 7.6. |
| Gold | 2.5–3 | *Gold* | Gold | None | Metallic luster. *Dense.* Sp. gr. 15.0 to 19.3. |
| Graphite | 1–2 | *Dark gray to black* | Grayish black | *Perfect in one direction* | Metallic or nonmetallic (earthy) luster. *Greasy feel, marks paper.* This is the "lead" in a pencil (mixed with clay). Sp. gr. 2.2. |
| Gypsum | *2* | Colorless, white, gray, yellowish, reddish | White | *Perfect in one direction* | Nonmetallic (glassy to silky) luster. *Can be scratched easily by a fingernail.* Sp. gr. 2.3. |
| Halite | 2–2.5 | Colorless, white | White | *Perfect, three directions, at 90° angles* | Nonmetallic (glassy) luster. *Salty taste.* Sp. gr. 2.2. |
| Hematite | 5–6 (may appear softer) | *Reddish-brown, gray, black* | *Reddish* | None | Metallic or nonmetallic (earthy) luster. *Dense.* Sp. gr. 5.3. |
| Hornblende | 5–6 | *Dark green to black* | Brown to gray | *Perfect, two directions at angles of 56° and 124°* | Nonmetallic (glassy to silky) luster. Common type of amphibole. Long, slender, six-sided crystals. Sp. gr. 3.0 to 3.4. |
| Kaolinite | 2 | White, gray, yellowish | White | *Perfect in one direction* | Nonmetallic (dull, earthy) luster. Claylike masses. Sp. gr. 2.6. |
| Limonite group | 4–5.5 | *Yellow, brown* | *Yellowish brown* | None | Nonmetallic (earthy) luster. Rust stains. Sp. gr. 2.9 to 4.3. |
| Magnetite | 5.5–6.5 | *Black* | Black | None | Metallic luster. Occurs as eight-sided crystals and granular masses. *Magnetic. Dense.* Sp. gr. 5.2. |

Sp. gr. = specific gravity

# Properties of Common Minerals *continued*

| Name | Hardness | Color | Streak | Cleavage | Remarks |
|---|---|---|---|---|---|
| Muscovite mica | 2–2.5 | Colorless in thin films; silvery, yellowish, and greenish in thicker pieces | *White* | Perfect in one direction | Nonmetallic (glassy to pearly) luster. *Thin elastic films peel off readily.* Sp. gr. 2.8 to 2.9. |
| Olivine | 6.5–7 | *Yellowish, greenish* | White | *None* | *Nonmetallic (glassy) luster. Granular.* Sp. gr. 3.3 to 4.4. |
| Opal | 5–6.5 | Varies | White | None | *Nonmetallic (glassy to pearly) luster. Conchoidal fracture.* Sp. gr. 2.0 to 2.2. |
| Pyrite | *6–6.5* | *Brass yellow* | Greenish black | None | Metallic luster. *Cubic crystals* and granular masses. *Dense.* Sp. gr. 5.0 to 5.1. |
| Quartz | *7* | *Colorless, white; varies* | White | None | Nonmetallic (glassy) luster. *Conchoidal fracture. Six-sided crystals common.* Many varieties. Sp. gr. 2.6. |
| Serpentine | 3–5 | *Greenish (variegated)* | White | None or good in one direction, depending on variety | *Nonmetallic (greasy, waxy, or silky) luster. Conchoidal fracture.* Sp. gr. 2.5 to 2.6. |
| Sphalerite | *3.5–4* | *Yellow, brown, black* | Yellow to light brown | *Perfect, six directions* | *Nonmetallic (brilliant to resinous) luster.* Sp. gr. 3.9 to 4.1. |
| Sulfur | 1.5–2.5 | *Yellow* | Yellow | Poor, two directions | Nonmetallic (glassy to earthy) luster. Granular. Sp. gr. 2.0 to 2.1. |
| Talc | *1* | Apple-green, gray, white | White | Perfect in one direction | Nonmetallic (pearly to greasy) luster. Nonelastic flakes, *greasy feel.* Sp. gr. 2.7 to 2.8. |
| Topaz | *8* | Varies | White | Perfect in one direction | Nonmetallic (brilliant to glassy) luster. *Crystals commonly striated length-wise.* Sp. gr. 3.4 to 3.6. |
| Tourmaline | 7–7.5 | *Black; varies* | White | None | Nonmetallic (glassy) luster. *Crystals often have triangular cross sections. Conchoidal fracture.* Sp. gr. 3.0 to 3.3. |

Sp. gr. = specific gravity

# Mineral Identification

To identify a mineral, you need to observe its properties—characteristic features that identify it. Usually it is necessary to observe several different properties of a mineral before being able to determine its identity.

Sometimes the shape of a mineral's crystals can help you identify the mineral. The photographs below show examples of well-formed crystals. But although all minerals have an internal crystal structure, crystals with well-formed outer shapes are not particularly common.

As you begin the process of identifying a mineral, you might look at its color. However, many minerals occur in more than one color. You would need to examine other properties as well. Some of these properties are related to the appearance of the mineral, such as how shiny or dull its surface is. Others, such as hardness and density, are related to the mineral's composition and internal structure.

## Crystal Groups

**Crystal groups are named by their shapes and the angles formed by imaginary lines through their centers. Crystals take many shapes, but all belong to these six groups.**

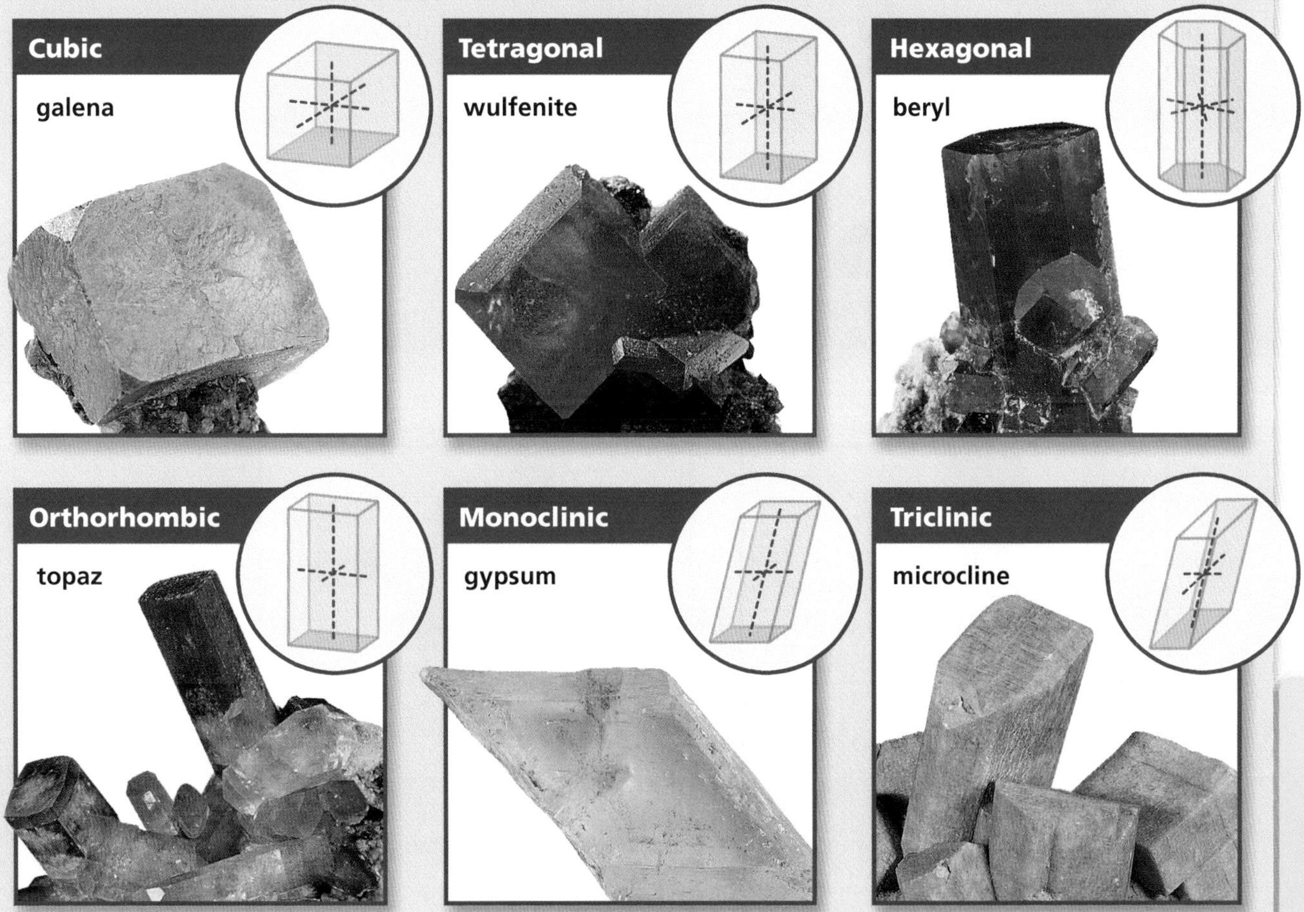

## Color and Streak

Some minerals can be almost any color, but most minerals have a more limited color range. For example, a particular mineral may almost always be brown to black.

Three main factors cause minerals to vary in color. First, a mineral may get its color from tiny amounts of an element that is not part of its normal chemical makeup. For example, a sample of pure quartz is clear and colorless, but tiny amounts of iron can give quartz a violet color. This violet variety of quartz is called amethyst. Second, a mineral's color can change when it is at or near Earth's surface and is in contact with the atmosphere or water. Third, mineral crystals can have defects in their crystal structures that change their color.

Some minerals have a different color when they are ground into a fine powder than when they are left whole. A mineral's streak is the color of the powder left behind when the mineral is scraped across a surface. Geologists use a tile of unglazed porcelain, called a streak plate, as a tool to identify minerals by their streaks. Streak is a better clue to a mineral's identity than surface color is. Look at the photographs of hematite below. Even though the mineral samples are different colors, both leave a reddish brown streak when scraped across a streak plate. All samples of the same mineral have the same streak.

### Streak

**These samples are of the mineral hematite. They are different colors, but they have the same streak.**

This hematite looks dull because it has tiny crystals that reflect light in all directions.

This hematite looks shiny because it has larger crystals.

APPENDIX

### Luster

A mineral's luster is the way in which light reflects from its surface. The two major types of luster are metallic and nonmetallic. The mineral pyrite has a metallic luster. It looks as if it were made of metal. A mineral with a nonmetallic luster can be shiny, but it does not appear to be made of metal. An example of a nonmetallic luster is the glassy luster of garnet. Compare the lusters of pyrite and garnet in the photographs below.

Pyrite has a metallic luster.

Garnet crystals in this rock have a nonmetallic luster.

Like a mineral's color, its luster may vary from sample to sample. If a mineral has been exposed to the atmosphere or to water, its surface luster can become dull. However, if the mineral is broken to reveal a fresh surface, its characteristic luster can be seen.

## The way a mineral breaks helps identify it.

If you hit a piece of calcite with a hammer, the calcite will break into tilted blocks. You can peel off layers of mica because it splits into thin, flat sheets. Each kind of mineral always breaks in the same way, and this property can help identify a mineral. In fact, the way a mineral breaks is a better clue to its identity than are its color and luster.

#### Cleavage

**Cleavage is a tendency to break along flat surfaces.**

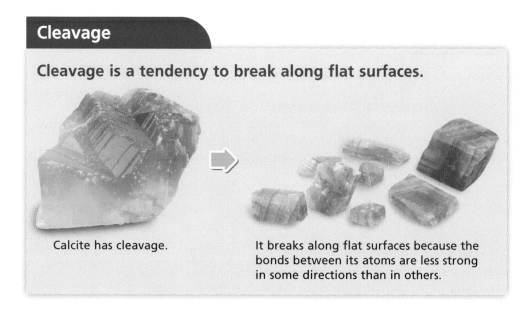

Calcite has cleavage.

It breaks along flat surfaces because the bonds between its atoms are less strong in some directions than in others.

## Cleavage

Cleavage is the tendency of a mineral to break along flat surfaces. The way in which a mineral breaks depends on how its atoms are bonded, or joined together. In a mineral that displays cleavage, the bonds of the crystal structure are weaker in the directions in which the mineral breaks.

**Carbon Bonds in Graphite**

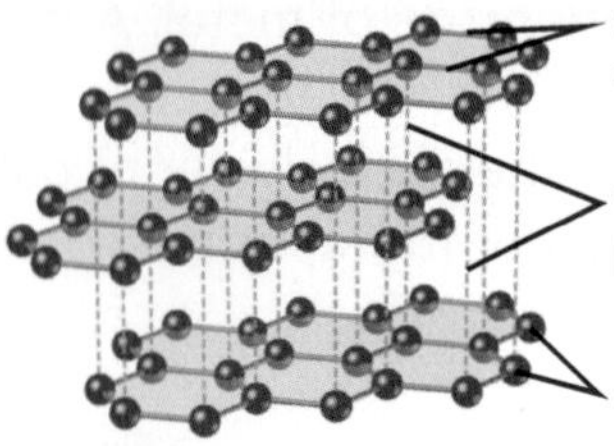


In graphite, carbon atoms are arranged in layers. Graphite has cleavage because the weak bonds between the layers break easily.

When geologists describe the cleavage of a mineral, they consider both the directions in which the mineral breaks and the smoothness of the broken surfaces. Mica has cleavage in one direction and breaks into sheets. The photographs on page R71 show that calcite has cleavage in three directions and breaks into tilted blocks. Because the broken surfaces of both mica and calcite are smooth, these minerals are said to have perfect cleavage.

## Fracture

Fracture is the tendency of a mineral to break into irregular pieces. Some minerals such as quartz break into pieces with curved surfaces, as shown below. Other minerals may break differently—perhaps into splinters or into rough or jagged pieces.

In a mineral that displays fracture, the bonds that join the atoms are fairly equal in strength in all directions. The mineral does not break along flat surfaces because there are no particular directions of weakness in its crystal structure.

### Fracture

**Fracture is a tendency to break into irregular pieces.**

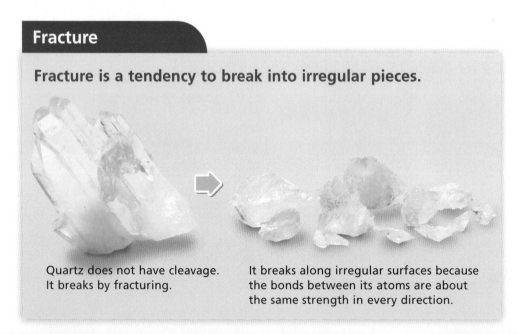

Quartz does not have cleavage. It breaks by fracturing.

It breaks along irregular surfaces because the bonds between its atoms are about the same strength in every direction.

APPENDIX

## A mineral's density and hardness help identify it.

A tennis ball is not as heavy or as hard as a baseball. You would be able to tell the two apart even with your eyes closed by how heavy and hard they feel. You can identify minerals in a similar way.

### Density

Even though a baseball and a tennis ball are about the same size, the baseball has more mass and so is more dense. A substance's density is the amount of mass in a given volume of the substance. For example, 1 cubic centimeter of the mineral pyrite has a mass of 5.1 grams, so pyrite's density is 5.1 grams per cubic centimeter.

Density is very helpful in identifying minerals. For example, gold and pyrite look very similar. Pyrite is often called fool's gold. However, you can tell the two minerals apart by comparing their densities. Gold is much denser than pyrite. The mass of a piece of gold is almost four times the mass of a piece of pyrite of the same size. A small amount of a very dense mineral, such as gold, can have more mass and be heavier than a larger amount of a less dense mineral, such as pyrite. A mineral's density is determined by the kinds of atoms that make up the mineral, as well as how closely the atoms are joined together. An experienced geologist can estimate the density of a mineral by lifting it. But to get an exact measurement, geologists use special scales.

#### Comparing Densities

**Differences in density can be used to tell minerals apart.**

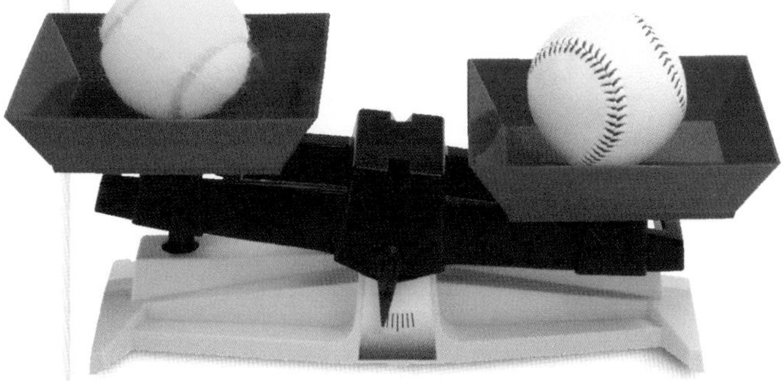

The baseball on the right has more mass, and so is denser, than a tennis ball that is about the same size.

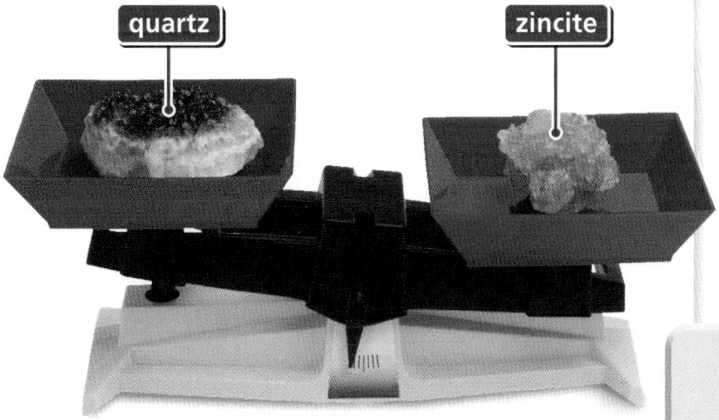


The zincite sample on the right is about twice as dense as the quartz sample.

APPENDIX

## Hardness

One way to tell a tennis ball from a baseball without looking at them is to compare their densities. Another way is to test which one is harder. Hardness is another dependable clue to a mineral's identity.

A mineral's hardness is its resistance to being scratched. Like a mineral's cleavage, a mineral's hardness is determined by its crystal structure and the strength of the bonds between its atoms. Harder minerals have stronger bonds.

A scale known as the Mohs scale is often used to describe a mineral's hardness. This scale is based on the fact that a harder mineral will scratch a softer one. As you can see in the chart at the right, ten minerals are numbered in the scale, from softest to hardest. Talc is the softest mineral and has a value of 1. Diamond, the hardest of all minerals, has a value of 10.

A mineral can be scratched only by other minerals that have the same hardness or are harder. To determine the hardness of an unknown mineral, you test whether it scratches or is scratched by the minerals in the scale. For example, if you can scratch an unknown mineral with apatite but not with fluorite, the mineral's hardness is between 4 and 5 in the Mohs scale.

In place of minerals, you can use your fingernail, a copper penny, and a steel file to test an unknown mineral. To avoid damage to the minerals, you can test whether the mineral scratches these items. When using a penny to test hardness, make sure its date is 1982 or earlier. Only older pennies are made mainly of copper, which has a hardness of about 3.

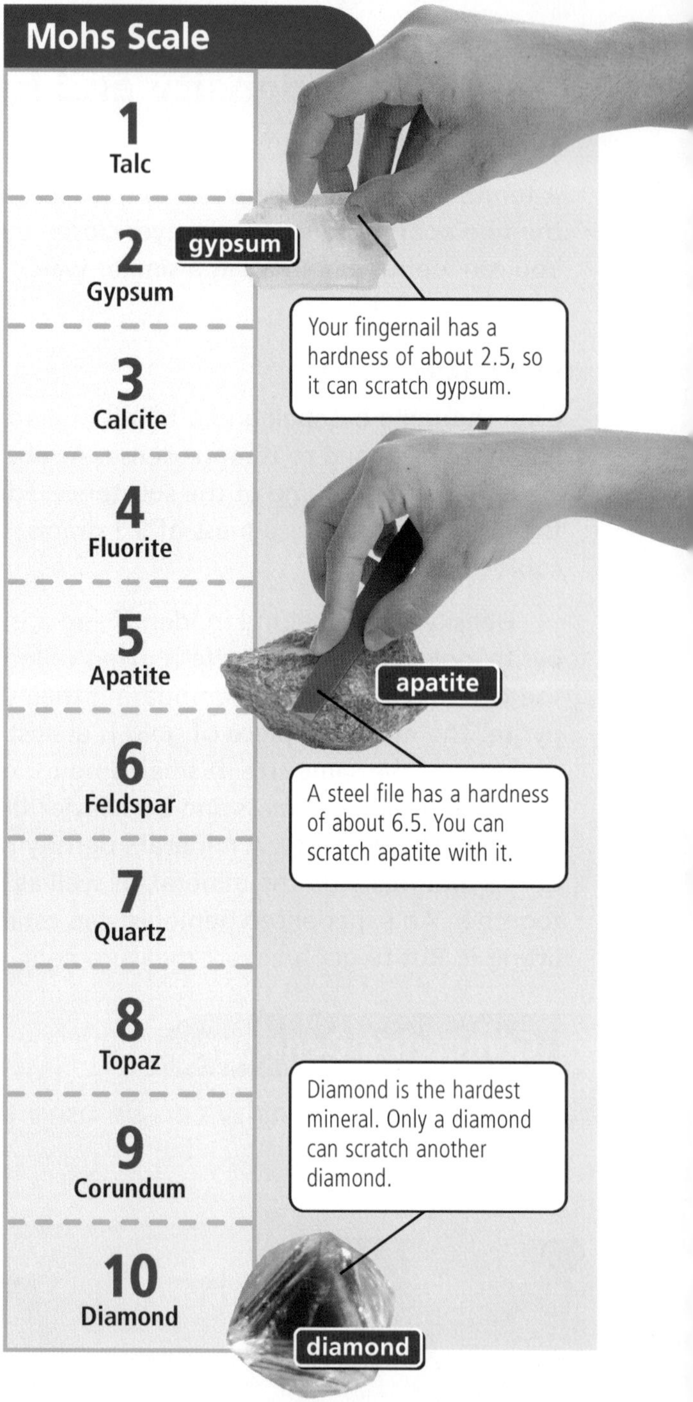
Mohs Scale
1
Talc
2
Gypsum
3
Calcite
4
Fluorite
5
Apatite
6
Feldspar
7
Quartz
8
Topaz
9
Corundum
10
Diamond
gypsum
Your fingernail has a hardness of about 2.5, so it can scratch gypsum.
apatite
A steel file has a hardness of about 6.5. You can scratch apatite with it.
Diamond is the hardest mineral. Only a diamond can scratch another diamond.
diamond

## Some minerals have special properties.

The photographs below show tests that help identify minerals that have unusual properties. Minerals in the carbonate group, such as calcite, react with acid. Chalk is a familiar item that is made up of carbonate minerals. The test consists of putting a drop of a weak solution of hydrochloric acid on a mineral sample. If the acid reacts with the mineral, carbon dioxide gas will form and bubble out of the acid. The bubbles show that the mineral is a carbonate.

Some minerals have a property known as fluorescence (flu-REHS-uhns). Fluorescent minerals glow when they are exposed to ultraviolet (UHL-truh-VY-uh-liht) light. The word *fluorescence* comes from the name of the mineral fluorite, which has this property. Other minerals that display fluorescence include calcite and willemite. Although fluorescence is an interesting and sometimes dramatic property, it has limited value in mineral identification. Different samples of the same mineral may or may not display fluorescence, and they may glow in different colors.

A few minerals respond to magnets. A magnet is pulled toward these minerals. The mineral magnetite strongly attracts magnets, and some other minerals weakly attract magnets. To test a mineral, hold a magnet loosely and bring it close to the mineral. You will be able to notice if there is even a small pull of the magnet toward the mineral. Magnets are commonly used in laboratories and industries to separate magnetic minerals from other minerals.

Some rare minerals have a property known as radioactivity. They contain unstable elements that change into other elements over time. As this happens, they release energy. Geologists can measure this energy and use it to identify minerals that contain unstable elements.

### Special Properties

**Acid Test**

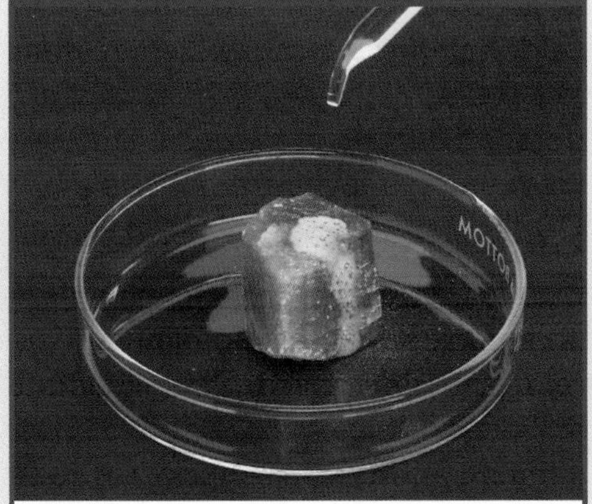

Acid in contact with carbonate minerals, such as calcite, forms bubbles.

**Fluorescence**

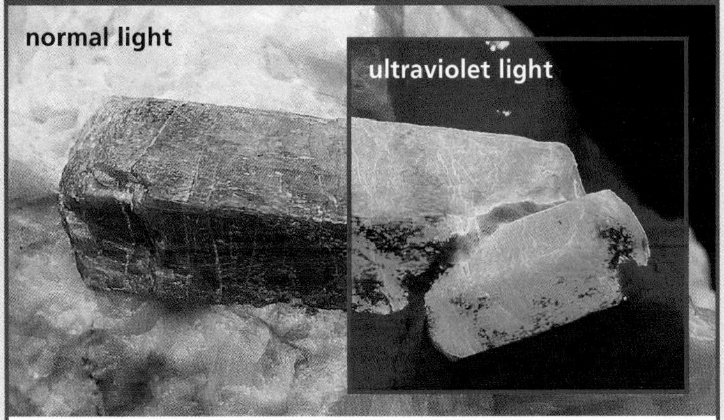


These minerals look ordinary in normal light but display red and green fluorescence under ultraviolet light.

APPENDIX

# Topographic Map Symbols

The U.S. Geological Survey uses the following symbols to mark human-made and natural features on all of the topographic maps the USGS produces.

Primary highway, hard surface ..........................
Secondary highway, hard surface .................
Light-duty road, hard or improved surface...
Unimproved road ..........................................
Trail ...............................................................
Railroad: single track ...................................
Railroad: multiple track ................................
Bridge ...........................................................
Drawbridge ...................................................
Tunnel ..........................................................
Footbridge ....................................................
Overpass—Underpass ....................................
Power transmission line with located tower ..
Landmark line (labeled as to type)................ TELEPHONE

Dam with lock ...............................................
Canal with lock .............................................
Large dam .....................................................
Small dam: masonry—earth...........................
Buildings (dwelling, place of employment, etc.)..
School—Church—Cemeteries.........................
Buildings (barn, warehouse, etc.)..................
Tanks; oil, water, etc. (labeled only if water)... • ● ● Water Tank
Wells other than water (labeled as to type).. ○ Oil  ○ Gas
U.S. mineral or location monument—Prospect ... ▲ .......... X
Quarry—Gravel pit ........................................ ⚒ .......... ×
Mine shaft—Tunnel or cave entrance........... ◘ ......... Y
Campsite—Picnic area.................................. ⚑ ............ ⚟
Located or landmark object—Windmill......... ⊙ ............ ✖
Exposed wreck...............................................
Rock or coral reef..........................................
Foreshore flat ...............................................
Rock: bare or awash......................................

Benchmarks................................................... BM ×671   ×672
Road fork—Section corner with elevation ... ⟋⟍429   +58
Checked spot elevation.................................. × 5970
Unchecked spot elevation.............................. × 5970

Boundary: national.....................................
  State .....................................................
  county, parish, municipio.........................
  civil township, precinct, town, barrio ....
  incorporated city, village, town, hamlet.
  reservation, national or state ..................
  small park, cemetery, airport, etc. .........
  land grant ..............................................
Township or range line, U.S. land survey .....
Section line, U.S. land survey ......................
Township line, not U.S. land survey ........
Section line, not U.S. land survey............
Fence line or field line .................................
Section corner: found—indicated.............. + ............ +
Boundary monument: land grant—other... ▢ ............ ▢

| | | | |
|---|---|---|---|
| Index contour | | Intermediate contour | |
| Supplementary cont | | Depression contours | |
| Cut—Fill......... | | Levee ............ | |
| Mine dump ..... | | Large wash ...... | |
| Dune area........ | | Distorted surface | |
| Sand area ........ | | Gravel beach ... | |

| | | | |
|---|---|---|---|
| Glacier............. | | Intermittent streams | |
| Seasonal streams | | Aqueduct tunnel | |
| Water well—Spring ○ ...... | | Falls................ | |
| Rapids............ | | Intermittent lake | |
| Channel......... | | Small wash ... | |
| Sounding—Depth curve .. | 10 | Marsh (swamp) | |
| Dry lake bed ... | | Land subject to controlled flooding | |

| | | | |
|---|---|---|---|
| Woodland...... | | Mangrove........ | |
| Submerged marsh | | Scrub ............ | |
| Orchard ......... | | Wooded marsh | |
| Vineyard........ | | Many buildings ...... | |
| Areas revised since previous edition ........... | | | |

**Source: U.S. Geological Survey**

APPENDIX

# Time Zones

Because Earth rotates, noon can occur in one location at the same moment that the Sun is setting in another location. To avoid confusion in transportation and communication, officials have divided Earth into 24 time zones. Within a time zone, clocks are set to the same time of day.

Time zones are centered on lines of longitude, but instead of running straight, their boundaries often follow political boundaries. The starting point for the times zones is centered on the prime meridian (0°). The time in this zone is generally called Greenwich Mean Time (GMT), but it is also called Universal Time (UT) by astronomers and Zulu Time (Z) by meteorologists. The International Date Line is centered on 180° longitude. The calendar date to the east of this line is one day earlier than the date to the west.

In the map below, each column of color represents one time zone. The color beige shows areas that do not match standard zones. The labels at the top show the times at noon GMT. Positive and negative numbers at the bottom show the difference between the local time in the zone and Greenwich Mean Time.

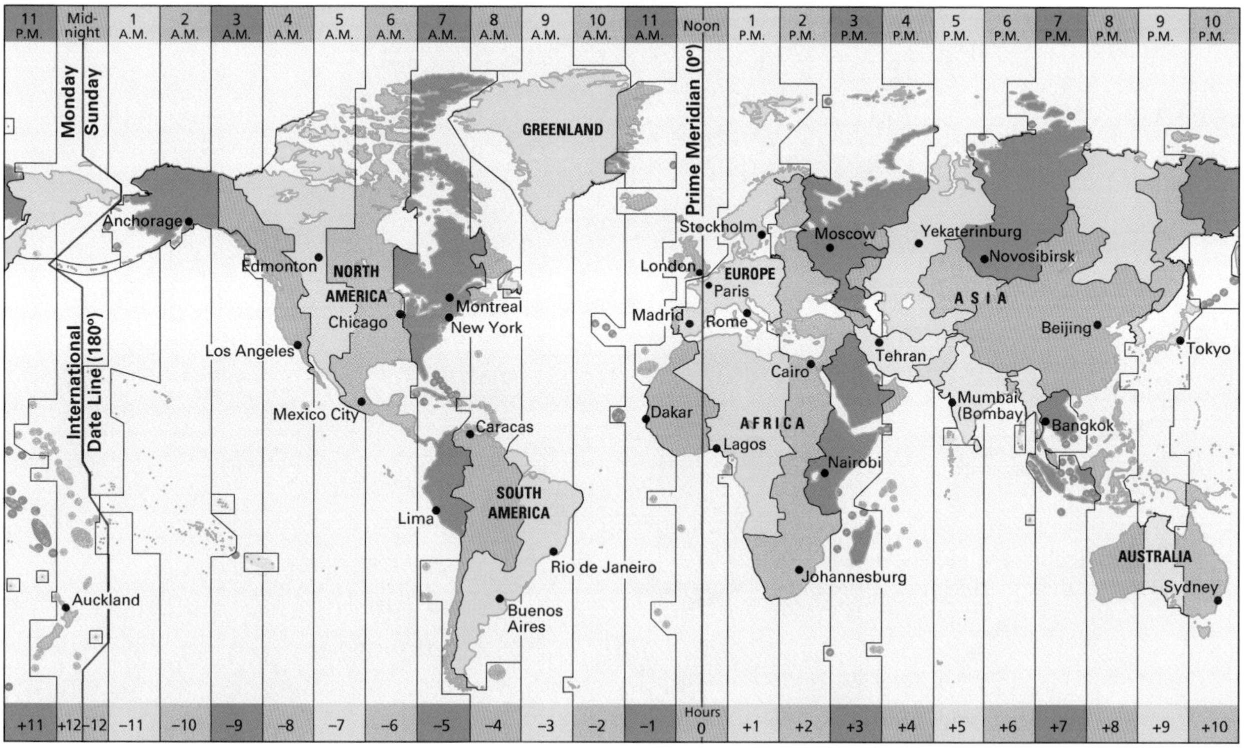

# California Physical Map

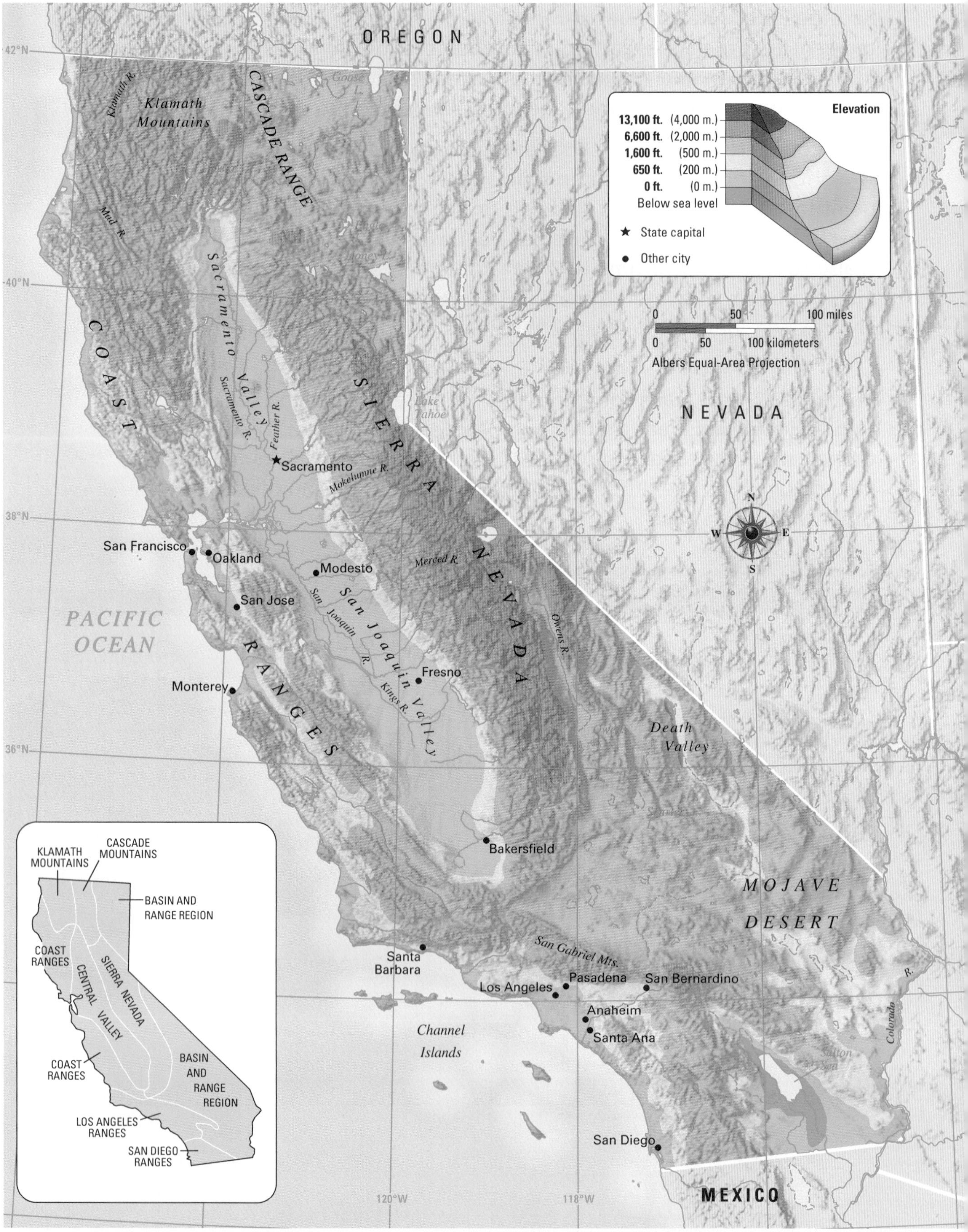

OREGON
NEVADA
MEXICO
PACIFIC OCEAN
42°N
40°N
38°N
36°N
120°W
118°W
Klamath R.
Klamath Mountains
CASCADE RANGE
Mad R.
Sacramento Valley
Sacramento R.
Feather R.
COAST RANGES
SIERRA NEVADA
Lake Tahoe
Goose L.
Honey L.
Sacramento
Mokelumne R.
San Francisco
Oakland
Modesto
Merced R.
San Jose
San Joaquin R.
San Joaquin Valley
Fresno
Kings R.
Monterey
Owens R.
Death Valley
Bakersfield
MOJAVE DESERT
San Gabriel Mts.
Santa Barbara
Los Angeles
Pasadena
San Bernardino
Anaheim
Santa Ana
Channel Islands
Salton Sea
Colorado R.
San Diego
Elevation
13,100 ft. (4,000 m.)
6,600 ft. (2,000 m.)
1,600 ft. (500 m.)
650 ft. (200 m.)
0 ft. (0 m.)
Below sea level
State capital
Other city
0 50 100 miles
0 50 100 kilometers
Albers Equal-Area Projection
N
S
E
W
KLAMATH MOUNTAINS
CASCADE MOUNTAINS
BASIN AND RANGE REGION
COAST RANGES
SIERRA NEVADA
CENTRAL VALLEY
COAST RANGES
BASIN AND RANGE REGION
LOS ANGELES RANGES
SAN DIEGO RANGES

# Glossary



## A

**abiotic factor** (AY-by-AHT-ihk)
A nonliving physical or chemical part of an ecosystem. (p. 378)

**factor abiótico** Una parte física o química sin vida de un ecosistema.

**acid rain**
Rain that has become more 'acidic' than normal due to pollution. (pp. 106, 360)

**lluvia ácida** Lluvia que se ha vuelto más ácida de lo normal debido a la contaminación.

**adaptation**
A characteristic, a behavior, or any inherited trait that makes a species able to survive and reproduce in a particular environment. (p. CA17)

**adaptación** Una característica, un comportamiento o cualquier rasgo heredado que permite a una especie sobrevivir o reproducirse en un medio ambiente determinado.

**aftershock**
A smaller earthquake that follows a more powerful earthquake in the same area. (p. 318)

**réplica** Un terremoto más pequeño que ocurre después de uno más poderoso en la misma área.

**air mass**
A large volume of air that has nearly the same temperature and humidity at different locations at the same altitude. (p. 115)

**masa de aire** Un gran volumen de aire que tiene casi la misma temperatura y humedad en distintos puntos a la misma altitud.

**air pressure**
The force of air molecules pushing on an area. (p. 79)

**presión de aire** La fuerza de las moléculas de aire empujando sobre un área.

**alluvial fan** (uh-LOO-vee-uhl)
A fan-shaped deposit of sediment at the base of a slope, formed as water flows down the slope and spreads out at the bottom. (p. 233)

**abanico aluvial** Un depósito de sedimentos en forma de abanico situado en la base de una pendiente; se forma cuando el agua baja por la pendiente y se dispersa al llegar al pie de la misma.

**altitude**
The distance above sea level.

**altitud** La distancia sobre el nivel del mar.

**asthenosphere** (as-THEHN-uh-SFEER)
The layer in Earth's upper mantle and directly under the lithosphere in which rock is soft and weak because it is close to melting. (p. 267)

**astenosfera** La capa del manto superior de la Tierra situada directamente bajo la litosfera en la cual la roca es blanda y débil por encontrarse próxima a su punto de fusión.

**atmosphere** (AT-muh-SFEER)
The outer layer of gases of a large body in space, such as a planet or star; the mixture of gases that surrounds the solid Earth; one of the four parts of the Earth system. (p. CA15)

**atmósfera** La capa externa de gases de un gran cuerpo que se encuentra en el espacio, como un planeta o una estrella; la mezcla de gases que rodea la Tierra sólida; una de las cuatro partes del sistema terrestre.

**atom**
The smallest particle of an element that has the chemical properties of that element. (p. CA19)

**átomo** La partícula más pequeña de un elemento que tiene las propiedades químicas de ese elemento.

**axis**
An imaginary line about which a turning body, such as Earth, rotates. (pp. 52, 684)

**eje** Una línea imaginaria alrededor de la cual gira un cuerpo, como lo hace la Tierra.

## B

**barometer**
An instrument that measures air pressure in the atmosphere. (p. 82)

**barómetro** Un instrumento que mide la presión del aire en la atmósfera.

### barrier island
A long, narrow island that develops parallel to a coast as a sandbar builds up above the water's surface. (p. 240)

**isla barrera** Una isla larga y angosta que se desarrolla paralelamente a la costa al crecer una barra de arena hasta rebasar la superficie del agua.

### biodiversity
The number and variety of living things found on Earth or within an ecosystem. (p. 498)

**biodiversidad** La cantidad y variedad de organismos vivos que se encuentran en la Tierra o dentro de un ecosistema.

### biomass
Organic matter that contains stored energy from sunlight and that can be burned as fuel. (p. 476)

**biomasa** Materia orgánica que contiene energía almacenada proveniente de la luz del Sol y que puede ser usada como combustible.

### biome (BY-OHM)
A region of Earth that has a particular climate and certain types of plants. Examples are tundra, taiga, desert, grassland, temperate forest, and tropical forest. (p. 398)

**bioma** Una región de la Tierra que tiene un clima particular y ciertos tipos de plantas. La tundra, la taiga, el desierto, la estepa, la selva tropical y el bosque templado son ejemplos de biomas.

### biosphere (BY-uh-SFEER)
All living organisms on Earth in the air, on the land, and in the waters; one of the four parts of the Earth system. (p. CA15)

**biosfera** Todos los organismos vivos de la Tierra, en el aire, en la tierra y en las aguas; una de las cuatro partes del sistema de la Tierra.

### biotic factor (by-AHT-ihk)
A living thing in an ecosystem. (p. 378)

**factor biótico** Un organismo vivo en un ecosistema.

### blizzard
A blinding snowstorm with winds of at least 56 kilometers per hour (35 mi/h), usually with temperatures below –7°C (20°F). (p. 126)

**ventisca** Una cegadora tormenta de nieve con vientos de por lo menos 56 kilómetros por hora (35 mi/h), usualmente con temperaturas menores a –7°C (20°F).

## C

### carbon cycle
The continuous movement of carbon through Earth, its atmosphere, and the living things on Earth. (p. 386)

**ciclo del carbono** El movimiento continuo del carbono en la Tierra, su atmósfera y todos los seres vivos en ella.

### carrying capacity
The maximum sustainable size that a population can reach in an ecosystem. (p. 433)

**capacidad de carga** El tamaño máximo sostenible que una población puede alcanzar en un ecosistema.

### cell
The smallest unit that is able to perform the basic functions of life. (p. CA17)

**célula** La unidad más pequeña capaz de realizar las funciones básicas de la vida.

### chemical weathering
The breakdown or decomposition of rock that takes place when minerals change through chemical processes. (p. 202)

**meteorización química** La descomposición de las rocas que ocurre cuando los minerales cambian mediante procesos químicos.

### climate
The characteristic weather conditions in an area over a long period of time. (p. 65)

**clima** Las condiciones meteorológicas características de un lugar durante un largo período de tiempo.

### commensalism (kuh-MEHN-suh-LIHZ-uhm)
An interaction between two species in which one species benefits without harming the other; a type of symbiosis. (p. 427)

**comensalismo** Una interacción entre dos especies en la cual una especie se beneficia sin causar daño a la otra; un tipo de simbiosis.

### community
All the populations that live and interact with each other in a particular place. The community can live in a place as small as a pond or a park, or it can live in a place as large as a rain forest or the ocean. (p. 416)

**comunidad** Todas las poblaciones que viven e interactúan entre sí en un lugar. La comunidad puede vivir en un lugar tan pequeño como una laguna o un parque o en un lugar tan grande como un bosque tropical o el océano.

### competition
The struggle between two or more living things that depend on the same limited resource. (p. 423)

**competencia** La lucha entre dos o más organismos vivos que dependen del mismo recurso limitado.

### compound
A substance made up of two or more different types of atoms bonded together.

**compuesto** Una sustancia formada por dos o más diferentes tipos de átomos enlazados.

### condensation
The process by which a gas changes into a liquid. (p. 92)

**condensación** El proceso por el cual un gas se transforma en líquido.

### conduction
The process by which energy is transferred from a warmer object to a cooler object by means of physical contact. (p. 27)

**conducción** El proceso mediante el cual se transfiere energía de un objeto más caliente a un objeto más frío por medio de contacto físico.

### coniferous (koh-NIHF-uhr-uhs)
A term used to describe cone-bearing trees and shrubs that usually keep their leaves or needles during all the seasons of the year; examples are pine, fir, and spruce trees. (p. 400)

**conífero** Un término usado para describir a los árboles y los arbustos que producen conos o piñas y que generalmente conservan sus hojas o agujas durante todas las estaciones del año; el pino, el abeto y la picea son ejemplos de coníferas.

### conservation
The process of saving or protecting a natural resource. (p. 467)

**conservación** El proceso de salvar o proteger un recurso natural.

### conservation of energy
A law stating that no matter how energy is transferred or transformed, it continues to exist in one form or another (p. 14)

**conservación de la energía** Una ley que establece que no importa cómo se transfiere o transforma la energía, toda la energía sigue en alguna forma u otra.

### consumer
A living thing that gets its energy by eating other living things in a food chain; consumers are also called heterotrophs. (p. 392)

**consumidor** Un organismo vivo que obtiene su energía alimentándose de otros organismos vivos en una cadena alimentaria; los consumidores también son llamados heterótrofos.

### continental-continental collision
A boundary along which two tectonic plates carrying continental crust push together. (p. 287)

**colisión continente-continente** Un límite a lo largo del cual dos placas tectónica de corteza continental empujan contra sí.

### continental drift
The hypothesis that Earth's continents move on Earth's surface. (p. 270)

**deriva continental** La hipótesis que postula que los continentes de la Tierra se mueven sobre la superficie del planeta.

### contour interval
On a topographic map, the difference in elevation from one contour line to the next. (p. 166)

**equidistancia entre curvas de nivel** En un mapa topográfico, la diferencia en elevación de una curva de nivel a la siguiente.

### contour line
A line on a topographic map that joins points of equal elevation. (p. 165)

**curva de nivel** Una línea en un mapa topográfico que une puntos de igual elevación.

### convection
The transfer of energy from place to place by the motion of heated gas or liquid; in Earth's mantle, convection is thought to transfer energy by the motion of solid rock, which when under great heat and pressure can move like a liquid. (pp. 28, 273)

**convección** La transferencia de energía de un lugar a otro por el movimiento de un líquido o gas calentado; se piensa que en el manto terrestre la convección transfiere energía mediante el movimiento de roca sólida, la cual puede moverse como un líquido cuando está muy caliente y bajo alta presión.

### convection current
A circulation pattern in which material is heated and rises in one area, then cools and sinks in another area, flowing in a continuous loop. (pp. 30, 273)

**corriente de convección** Un patrón de circulación en el cual el material se calienta y asciende en un área, luego se enfría y se hunde en otra área, fluyendo en un circuito contínuo.

**convergent boundary** (kuhn-VUR-juhnt)
A boundary along which two tectonic plates push together, characterized either by subduction or a continental collision. (p. 278)

**límite convergente** Un límite a lo largo del cual dos placas tectónicas se empujan mutuamente; este límite se caracteriza por una zona de subducción o una colisión entre continentes.

**cooperation**
A term used to describe an interaction between two or more living things in which they are said to work together. (p. 425)

**cooperación** Un término que describe la interacción entre dos or más organismos vivos en la cual se dice que trabajan juntos.

**Coriolis effect** (KAWR-ee-OH-lihs)
The influence of Earth's rotation on objects that move over Earth. (p. 85)

**efecto Coriolis** La influencia de la rotación de la Tierra sobre objetos que se mueven sobre la Tierra.

**crust**
A thin outer layer of rock above a planet's mantle, including all dry land and ocean basins. Earth's continental crust is 40 kilometers thick on average and oceanic crust is 7 kilometers thick on average. (p. 267)

**corteza** Una delgada capa exterior de roca situada sobre el manto de un planeta que incluye toda la tierra seca y todas las cuencas oceánicas. La corteza continental de la Tierra tiene un grosor promedio de 40 kilómetros y la corteza oceánica tiene un grosor promedio de 7 kilómetros.

**crystal**
A solid substance in which the atoms are arranged in an orderly, repeating, three-dimensional pattern. (p. 185)

**cristal** Una sustancia sólida en la cual los átomos están organizados en un patrón tridimensional y ordenado que se repite.

**cycle**
***n.*** A series of events or actions that repeat themselves regularly; a physical and/or chemical process in which one material continually changes locations and/or forms. Examples include the water cycle, the carbon cycle, and the rock cycle.

***v.*** To move through a repeating series of events or actions. (pp. 44, 384)

**ciclo *s.*** Una serie de eventos o acciones que se repiten regularmente; un proceso físico y/o químico en el cual un material cambia continuamente de lugar y/o forma. Ejemplos: el ciclo del agua, el ciclo del carbono y el ciclo de las rocas.

# D

**data**
Information gathered by observation or experimentation that can be used in calculating or reasoning. *Data* is a plural word; the singular is *datum.*

**datos** Información reunida mediante observación o experimentación y que se puede usar para calcular o para razonar.

**deciduous** (dih-SIHJ-oo-uhs)
A term used to describe trees and shrubs that drop their leaves when winter comes; examples are maple, oak, and birch trees. (p. 401)

**caducifolio** Un término usado para describir árboles y arbustos que dejan caer sus hojas cuando llega el invierno; el arce, el roble y el abedul son ejemplos de árboles caducifolios.

**decomposer**
An organism that feeds on and breaks down dead plant or animal matter. (p. 393)

**descomponedor** Un organismo que se alimenta de y degrada materia vegetal o animal.

**delta**
An area of land at the end, or mouth, of a river that is formed by the buildup of sediment. (p. 233)

**delta** Un área de tierra al final, o en la desembocadura, de un río y que se forma por la acumulación de sedimentos.

**density**
A property of matter representing the mass per unit volume. (p. 28)

**densidad** Una propiedad de la materia que representa la masa por unidad de volumen.

**deposition** (DEHP-uh-ZIHSH-uhn)
The process in which transported sediment is laid down. (p. 225)

**sedimentación** El proceso mediante el cual se deposita sedimento que ha sido transportado.

**dew point**
The temperature at which air with a given amount of water vapor will reach saturation. (p. 94)

**punto de rocío** La temperatura a la cual el aire con una cantidad determinada de vapor de agua alcanzará la saturación.

**divergent boundary** (dih-VUR-juhnt)
A boundary along which two tectonic plates move apart, characterized by either a mid-ocean ridge or a continental rift valley. (p. 278)

**límite divergente** Un límite a lo largo del cual dos placas tectónicas se separan; este límite se caracteriza por una dorsal oceánica o un valle de rift continental.

### diversity
A term used to describe the quality of having many differences. Biodiversity describes the great variety and many differences found among living things.

**diversidad** Un término usado para describir la cualidad de tener muchas diferencias. La biodiversidad describe la gran variedad y las muchas diferencias encontradas entre organismos vivos.

### divide
A continuous high line of land—or ridge—from which water drains to one side or the other. (p. 231)

**línea divisoria de aguas** Una línea continua de tierra alta, o un cerro, desde donde el agua escurre hacia un lado o hacia el otro.

### drainage basin
An area of land in which water drains into a stream system. The borders of a drainage basin are called divides. (p. 231)

**cuenca tributaria** Un área de tierra en la cual el agua escurre a un sistema de corrientes. Los límites de una cuenca tributaria se denominan líneas divisorias de aguas.

### dune
A mound of sand built up by wind. (p. 241)

**duna** Un montículo de arena formado por el viento.

# E

### earthquake
A shaking of the ground caused by the sudden movement of large blocks of rocks along a fault. (p. 301)

**terremoto** Un temblor del suelo ocasionado por el movimiento repentino de grandes bloques de rocas a lo largo de una falla.

### ecology
The scientific study of how living things interact with each other and their environment. (p. 377)

**ecología** El estudio científico de cómo interactúan los organismos vivos entre sí y con su medio ambiente.

### ecosystem
All the living and nonliving things that interact in a particular environment. An ecosystem can be as small as a rotting log or as large as a forest or a desert. (p. 377)

**ecosistema** Todos los organismos vivos y las cosas que interactúan en un medio ambiente específico. Un ecosistema puede ser tan pequeño como un tronco podrido, o tan grande como un bosque o un desierto.

### electromagnetic spectrum
The range of all electromagnetic frequencies, including the following types (from lowest to highest frequency): radio waves, microwaves, infrared light, visible light, ultraviolet light, x-rays, and gamma rays. (p. 21)

**espectro electromagnético** La gama de todas las frecuencias electromagnéticas, incluyendo los siguientes tipos (de la frecuencia más baja a la más alta): ondas de radio, microondas, luz infrarroja, luz visible, luz ultravioleta, rayos X y rayos gamma.

### element
A substance that cannot be broken down into a simpler substance by ordinary chemical changes. An element consists of atoms of only one type. (p. 184)

**elemento** Una sustancia que no puede descomponerse en otra sustancia más simple por medio de cambios químicos normales. Un elemento consta de átomos de un solo tipo.

### elevation
A measure of how high something is above a reference point, such as sea level. (p. 165)

**elevación** Una medida de lo elevado que está algo sobre un punto de referencia, como el nivel del mar.

### energy
The ability to do work or to cause a change. For example, the energy of a moving bowling ball knocks over pins; energy from food allows animals to move and to grow; and energy from the Sun heats Earth's surface and atmosphere, which causes air to move. (p. 9)

**energía** La capacidad para trabajar o causar un cambio. Por ejemplo, la energía de una bola de boliche en movimiento tumba los pinos; la energía proveniente de su alimento permite a los animales moverse y crecer; la energía del Sol calienta la superficie y la atmósfera de la Tierra, lo que ocasiona que el aire se mueva.

### energy pyramid
A model used to show the amount of energy available to living things in an ecosystem. (p. 396)

**pirámide de energía** Un modelo usado para mostrar la cantidad de energía disponible para organismos vivos en un ecosistema.

GLOSSARY

### environment
Everything that surrounds a living thing. An environment is made up of both living and nonliving factors. (p. CA17)

**medio ambiente** Todo lo que rodea a un organismo vivo. Un medio ambiente está compuesto de factores vivos y factores sin vida.

### epicenter (EHP-ih-SEHN-tuhr)
The point on Earth's surface directly above the focus of an earthquake. (p. 308)

**epicentro** El punto en la superficie de la Tierra situado directamente sobre el foco sísmico.

### equator
An imaginary east-west line around the center of Earth that divides the planet into the Northern Hemisphere and the Southern Hemisphere; a line set at 0° latitude. (p. 158)

**ecuador** Una línea imaginaria de este a oeste alrededor del centro de la Tierra y que divide al planeta en hemisferio norte y hemisferio sur; la línea está fijada a latitud 0°.

### erosion
The process in which sediment is picked up and moved from one place to another. (p. 225)

**erosión** El proceso en el cual el sedimento es recogido y transportado de un lugar a otro.

### estuary
The lower end of a river where it meets the ocean and fresh and salt waters mix. (p. 401)

**estuario** La parte baja de un río donde desemboca en el océano y donde el agua dulce del río se mezcla con el agua salada del mar.

### evaporation
The process by which liquid changes into gas. (p. 92)

**evaporación** El proceso por el cual un líquido se transforma en gas.

### experiment
An organized procedure to study something under controlled conditions. (pp. CA22, R28)

**experimento** Un procedimiento organizado para estudiar algo bajo condiciones controladas.

### extinction
The permanent disappearance of a species. (p. CA17)

**extinción** La desaparición permanente de una especie.

## F

### false-color image
A computer image in which the colors are not what the human eye would see. A false-color image can assign different colors to different types of radiation coming from an object to highlight its features. (p. 171)

**imagen de color falso** Una imagen computacional en la cual los colores no son los que el ojo humano observaría. Una imagen de color falso puede asignar diferentes colores a los diferentes tipos de radiación que provienen de un objeto para hacer destacar sus características.

### fault
A fracture in Earth's lithosphere along which blocks of rock move past each other. (p. 301)

**falla** Una fractura en la litosfera de la Tierra a lo largo de la cual bloques de roca se mueven y pasan uno al lado de otro.

### fault-block mountain
A mountain that forms as blocks of rock move up or down along normal faults in areas where the lithosphere is being pulled apart. (p. 342)

**montaña de bloques de falla** Una montaña que se forma cuando bloques de roca se mueven hacia arriba o hacia abajo a lo largo de fallas normales en las áreas donde la litosfera está siendo separada.

### floodplain
A flat area of land on either side of a stream that becomes flooded when a river overflows its banks. (p. 232)

**planicie de inundación** Un área plana de tierra en cualquier costado de un arroyo que se inunda cuando un río se desborda.

### focus
In an earthquake, the point underground where the rocks first begin to move. (p. 308)

**foco sísmico** En un terremoto, el punto subterráneo donde comienza el movimiento de las rocas.

### folded mountain
A mountain that forms as continental crust is compressed and rocks bend into large folds. (p. 340)

**montaña plegada** Una montaña que se forma cuando la corteza continental es comprimida y las rocas se doblan en grandes pliegues.

### food chain
A model used to show the feeding relationship between a single producer and a chain of consumers in an ecosystem. In a typical food chain, a plant is the producer that is eaten by a consumer, such as an insect; then the insect is eaten by a second consumer, such as a bird. (p. 394)

**cadena alimenticia** Un modelo usado para mostrar la relación de ingestión entre un solo productor y una cadena de consumidores en un ecosistema. En una cadena alimenticia típica, una planta es la productora que es ingerida por un consumidor como un insecto, y luego el insecto es ingerido por un segundo consumidor como un pájaro.

### food web
A model used to show a feeding relationship in which many food chains overlap in an ecosystem. (p. 394)

**red trófica** Red de cadenas alimenticias de un ecosistema.

### force
A push or a pull; something that changes the motion of an object. (p. CA12)

**fuerza** Un empuje o un jalón; algo que cambia el movimiento de un objeto.

### fossil
A trace or the remains of a once-living thing from long ago. (p. CA15)

**fósil** Un rastro o los restos de un organismo que vivió hace mucho tiempo.

### fossil fuel
Fuel formed from the remains of prehistoric organisms that is burned for energy. (p. 452)

**combustibles fósiles** Combustibles formados a partir de los restos de organismos prehistóricos que son consumidos para obtener energía.

### freezing rain
Rain that freezes when it hits the ground or another surface and coats the surface with ice. (p. 104)

**lluvia helada** Lluvia que se congela cuando cae a la tierra o cualquier otra superficie y cubre la superficie con hielo.

### friction
A force that resists the motion between two surfaces in contact. (p. CA19)

**fricción** Una fuerza que resiste el movimiento entre dos superficies en contacto.

### front
The boundary between air masses. (p. 118)

**frente** El límite entre masas de aire.

## G

### geographic information systems GIS
Computer systems that can store, arrange, and display geographic data in different types of maps. (p. 173)

**sistemas de información geográfica** Sistemas computarizados que pueden almacenar, organizar y mostrar datos geográficos en diferentes tipos de mapas.

### geologic cycle
All the processes by which Earth's features are worn down and built up. (p. 199)

**ciclo geológico** Todos los procesos por medio de los cuales los rasgos de la Tierra son desgastados y construidos.

### geologic map
A type of map that shows the locations of geologic features at and near Earth's surface. (p. 206)

**mapa geológico** Un tipo de mapa que muestra el lugar de los rasgos geológicos en y cerca de la superficie de la Tierra.

### geosphere (JEE-uh-SFEER)
All the features on Earth's surface—continents, islands, and seafloor—and everything below the surface—the inner and outer core and the mantle; one of the four parts of the Earth system. (p. CA15)

**geosfera** Todas las características de la superficie de la Tierra, es decir, continentes, islas y el fondo marino, y de todo bajo la superficie, es decir, el núcleo externo e interno y el manto; una de las cuatro partes del sistema de la Tierra.

### geothermal energy
Heat energy that originates from within Earth and drives the movement of Earth's tectonic plates. Geothermal energy can be used to generate electricity. (p. 473)

**energía geotérmica** Energía calorífica que se origina en el interior de la Tierra y que impulsa el movimiento de las placas tectónicas de planeta. La energía geotérmica puede usarse para generar electricidad.

### geyser
A type of hot spring that shoots water into the air. (p. 361)

**géiser** Un tipo de fuente termal que dispara agua al aire.

### glacier (GLAY-shuhr)
A large mass of ice that exists year-round and moves over land. (p. 245)

**glaciar** Una gran masa de hielo que existe durante todo el año y se mueve sobre la tierra.

GLOSSARY

### global winds
Winds that travel long distances in steady patterns over several weeks. (p. 84)

**vientos globales** Vientos que viajan grandes distancias en patrones fijos por varias semanas.

### gravity
The force that objects exert on each other because of their mass. (pp. CA13, CA19)

**gravedad** La fuerza que los objetos ejercen entre sí debido a su masa.

### greenhouse effect
The process by which certain gases in a planet's atmosphere absorb and emit infrared radiation, resulting in an increase in surface temperature. (p. 63)

**efecto invernadero** El proceso mediante el cual ciertos gases en la atmósfera de un planeta absorben y emiten radiación infrarroja, resultando en un incremento de la temperatura superficial del planeta.

## H

### habitat
The natural environment in which a living thing gets all that it needs to live; examples include a desert, a coral reef, and a freshwater lake. (p. 414)

**hábitat** El medio ambiente natural en el cual un organismo vivo consigue todo lo que requiere para vivir; ejemplos incluyen un desierto, un arrecife coralino y un lago de agua dulce.

### hail
Layered lumps or balls of ice that fall from cumulonimbus clouds. (p. 104)

**granizo** Trozos de hielo que caen de nubes cumulonimbos.

### heat energy
The total energy of the motion of particles in an object; also called thermal energy. (p. 10)

**energía calórica** La energía total del movimiento de partículas en un objeto, también llamado energía térmica.

### heat flow
The movement of heat energy. (p. 11)

**flujo de calor** El movimiento de energía calórica.

### high-pressure system
A generally calm and clear weather system that occurs when air sinks down in a high-pressure center and spreads out toward areas of lower pressure as it nears the ground. (p. 120)

**sistema de alta presión** Un sistema climático generalmente claro y calmo que se presenta cuando el aire desciende en un centro de alta presión y se esparce hacia áreas de baja presión conforme se acerca al suelo.

### hot spot
An area where a column of hot material rises from deep within a planet's mantle and heats the lithosphere above it, often causing volcanic activity at the surface. (p. 283)

**punto caliente** Un área donde una columna de material caliente surge del interior del manto de un planeta y calienta la litosfera situada sobre él, con frecuencia ocasionando actividad volcánica en la superficie.

### humidity
The amount of water vapor in air. (p. 94)

**humedad** La cantidad de vapor de agua en el aire.

### hurricane (HUR-ih-KAYN)
A tropical low-pressure system with sustained winds of 120 kilometers per hour (74 mi/h) or more. (p. 123)

**huracán** Un sistema tropical de baja presión con vientos sostenidos de 120 kilómetros por hora (74 mi/h) o más.

### hydroelectric energy
Electricity that is generated by the conversion of the energy of moving water. (p. 472)

**energía hidroeléctrica** Electricidad que se genera por la conversión de la energía del agua en movimiento.

### hydrogen fuel cell
A device that uses hydrogen and oxygen to produce electricity. The byproducts are heat and water. (p. 476)

**celda de combustible de hidrógeno** Un aparato que usa hidrógeno y oxígeno para producir electricidad. Los subproductos son calor y agua.

### hydrosphere (HY-druh-SFEER)
All water on Earth—in the atmosphere and in the oceans, lakes, glaciers, rivers, streams, and underground reservoirs; one of the four parts of the Earth system. (p. CA15)

**hidrosfera** Toda el agua de la Tierra: en la atmósfera y en los océanos, lagos, glaciares, ríos, arroyos y depósitos subterráneos; una de las cuatro partes del sistema de la Tierra.

### hypothesis
A tentative explanation for an observation or phenomenon. A hypothesis is used to make testable predictions. (p. CA22)

**hipótesis** Una explicación provisional de una observación o de un fenómeno. Una hipótesis se usa para hacer predicciones que se pueden probar.

# I

**igneous rock** (IHG-nee-uhs)
Rock that forms as molten rock cools and becomes solid. (p. 191)

**roca ígnea** Roca que se forma al enfriarse la roca fundida y hacerse sólida.

**inner core**
A solid sphere of metal, mainly nickel and iron, at Earth's center. (p. 266)

**núcleo interno** Una esfera sólida de metal, principalmente níquel y hierro, que se encuentra en el centro de la Tierra.

**interaction**
The condition of acting or having an influence upon something. Living things in an ecosystem interact with both the living and nonliving parts of their environment.

**interacción** La condición de actuar o influir sobre algo. Los organismos vivos en un ecosistema interactúan con las partes vivas y las partes sin vida de su medio ambiente.

**isobar** (EYE-suh-BAHR)
A line on a weather map connecting places that have the same air pressure. (p. 137)

**isobara** Una línea en un mapa climático que conecta lugares que tienen la misma presión de aire.

# J

**jet stream**
A fast-moving wind that flows from west to east around Earth generally at altitudes of 10 to 15 kilometers. (p. 88)

**corriente de chorro** Vientos de alta velocidad que giran alrededor de la Tierra de oeste a este, generalmente a una altitud de 10 a 15 kilómetros.

# K

**kettle lake**
A bowl-shaped depression that was formed as sediment built up around a block of ice left behind by a glacier and later filled with water. (p. 249)

**lago de la caldera** Una depresión que se formó al acumularse sedimento alrededor de un bloque de hielo que quedó como resultado de una acción glacial. Luego, al derretirse el hielo, la caldera se llena de agua.

# L

**latitude**
The distance in degrees north or south from the equator. (p. 158)

**latitud** La distancia en grados norte o sur a partir del ecuador.

**lava**
Molten rock that reaches a planet's surface through a volcano. (pp. 191, 347)

**lava** Roca fundida que llega a la superficie de un planeta a través de un volcán.

**law**
In science, a rule or principle describing a physical relationship that always works in the same way under the same conditions. The law of conservation of energy is an example.

**ley** En las ciencias, una regla o un principio que describe una relación física que siempre funciona de la misma manera bajo las mismas condiciones. La ley de la conservación de la energía es un ejemplo.

**lichen** (LY-kuhn)
An organism that results from a close association between single-celled algae and fungi.

**liquen** Un organismo que resulta de una asociación cercana entre algas unicelulares y hongos.

**limiting factor**
A factor or condition that prevents the continuing growth of a population in an ecosystem. (p. 432)

**factor limitante** Un factor o una condición que impide el crecimiento contínuo de una población en un ecosistema.

**liquefaction**
A process in which the shaking of ground causes loose, wet soil to act like a liquid. (p. 318)

**licuefacción** Un proceso en el cual el temblor del suelo ocasiona que la tierra húmeda y suelta actúe como un líquido.

**lithosphere** (LIHTH-uh-SFEER)
The layer of Earth made up of the crust and the rigid rock of the upper mantle, averaging about 40 kilometers thick and broken into tectonic plates. (p. 267)

**litosfera** La capa de la Tierra compuesta por la corteza y la roca rígida del manto superior, con un promedio de 40 kilómetros de grosor y fracturada en placas tectónicas.

### loess (LOH-uhs)
Deposits of fine-grained, wind-blown sediment. (p. 242)

**loess** Depósitos de sedimento de grano fino transportado por el viento.

### longitude
The distance in degrees east or west of the prime meridian. Longitude lines are numbered from 0° to 180°. (p. 159)

**longitud** La distancia en grados al este o al oeste del primer meridiano. Las líneas de longitud están numeradas de 0° a 180°.

### longshore current
The overall direction and movement of water as waves strike the shore at an angle. (p. 239)

**corriente litoral** La dirección y el movimiento general del agua conforme las olas golpean la costa en ángulo.

### longshore drift
The zigzag movement of sand along a beach, caused by the action of waves. (p. 239)

**deriva litoral** El movimiento en zigzag de la arena a lo largo de una playa, ocasionado por la acción de las olas.

### low-pressure system
A large and often stormy weather system that occurs when air moves around and into a low-pressure center, then moves up to higher altitudes. (p. 121)

**sistema de baja presión** Un sistema climático grande y usualmente lluvioso que se presenta cuando el aire se mueve alrededor de y hacia un centro de baja presión, y luego se mueve hacia mayores altitudes.

## M

### magma
Molten rock beneath Earth's surface. (p. 191)

**magma** Roca fundida que se encuentra bajo la superficie de la Tierra.

### magnetic reversal
A switch in the direction of Earth's magnetic field so that the magnetic north pole becomes the magnetic south pole and the magnetic south pole becomes the magnetic north pole. (p. 280)

**inversión magnética** Un cambio en la dirección del campo magnético de la Tierra, de modo que el polo norte magnético se convierte en el polo sur magnético y el polo sur magnético se convierte en el polo norte magnético.

### mantle
The layer of rock between Earth's outer core and crust, in which most rock is hot enough to flow in convection currents; Earth's thickest layer. (p. 267)

**manto** La capa de roca situada entre el núcleo externo y la corteza de la Tierra, en la cual la mayor parte de la roca es lo suficientemente caliente para fluir en corrientes de convección; la capa más gruesa de la Tierra.

### map legend
A chart that explains the meaning of each symbol used on a map; also called a key. (p. 157)

**clave del mapa** Una tabla que explica el significado de cada símbolo usado en un mapa.

### map scale
The comparison of distance on a map with actual distance on what the map represents, such as Earth's surface. Map scale may be expressed as a ratio, a bar scale, or equivalent units. (p. 157)

**escala del mapa** La comparación de la distancia en un mapa con la distancia real en lo que el mapa representa, como la superficie de la Tierra. La escala del mapa puede expresarse como una azón, una barra de escala o en unidades equivalentes.

### mass
A measure of how much matter an object is made of.

**masa** Una medida de la cantidad de materia de la que está compuesto un objeto.

### mass wasting
The downhill movement of loose rock or soil. (p. 227)

**movimiento de masa** El desplazamiento cuesta abajo de suelo o de roca suelta.

### matter
Anything that has mass and volume. Matter exists ordinarily as a solid, a liquid, or a gas. (p. CA13)

**materia** Todo lo que tiene masa y volumen. Generalmente la materia existe como sólido, líquido o gas.

### mechanical weathering
The breakdown of rock into smaller pieces of the same material without any change in its composition. (p. 200)

**meteorización mecánica** El desmoronamiento de las rocas en pedazos más pequeños del mismo material, sin ningún cambio en su composición.

**metamorphic rock** (MEHT-uh-MAWR-fihk)
Rock formed as heat or pressure causes existing rock to change in structure, texture, or mineral composition. (p. 194)

**roca metamórfica** Roca formada cuando el calor o la presión ocasionan que la roca existente cambie de estructura, textura o composición mineral.

**meteorologist** (MEE-tee-uh-RAHL-uh-jihst)
A scientist who studies weather. (p. 134)

**meteorólogo** Un científico que estudia el clima.

**mid-ocean ridge**
A long line of sea-floor mountains where new ocean crust is formed by volcanic activity along a divergent boundary. (p. 272)

**dorsal oceánica** Una larga línea de montañas en el fondo marino donde se forma nueva corteza oceánica debido a la actividad volcánica a lo largo de un límite divergente.

**mineral**
A substance that forms in nature, is a solid, has a definite chemical makeup, and has a crystal structure. (p. 184)

**mineral** Una sustancia sólida formada en la naturaleza, de composición química definida y estructura cristalina.

**molecule**
A group of atoms that are held together by covalent bonds so that they move as a single unit.

**molécula** Un grupo de átomos que están unidos mediante enlaces covalentes de tal manera que se mueven como una sola unidad.

**monsoon**
A wind that changes direction with the seasons. (p. 90)

**monzón** Un viento que cambia de dirección con las estaciones.

**moraine** (muh-RAYN)
A deposit of till left behind by a retreating glacier. Moraines can form along a glacier's sides and at its end. (p. 248)

**morrena** Un depósito de sedimentos glaciares dejado por un glaciar que retrocede. Las morrenas pueden formarse en los costados de un glaciar o en su extremo.

**mutualism** (MYOO-choo-uh-LIHZ-uhm)
An interaction between two species in which both benefit; a type of symbiosis. (p. 426)

**mutualismo** Una interacción entre dos especies en la cual ambas se benefician; un tipo de simbiosis.

# N

**natural resource**
Any type of matter or energy from Earth's environment that humans use to meet their needs. (p. 449)

**recurso natural** Cualquier tipo de materia o energía del medio ambiente de la Tierra que usan los humanos para satisfacer sus necesidades.

**niche** (nihch)
The role a living thing plays in its habitat. A plant is a food producer, whereas an insect both consumes food as well as provides food for other consumers. (p. 415)

**nicho** El papel que juega un organismo vivo en su hábitat. Una planta es un productor de alimento mientras que un insecto consume alimento y a la vez sirve de alimento a otros consumidores.

**nitrogen cycle**
The continuous movement of nitrogen through Earth, its atmosphere, and the living things on Earth. (p. 387)

**ciclo del nitrógeno** El movimiento continuo de nitrógeno por la Tierra, su atmósfera y los organismos vivos de la Tierra.

**nonrenewable resource**
A resource that exists in a fixed amount or is used up more quickly than it can be replaced in nature. (p. 450)

**recurso no renovable** Un recurso que existe en una cantidad fija o se consume más rápidamente de lo que puede reemplazarse en la naturaleza.

**nuclear energy**
The energy released by a nuclear reaction. (p. 477)

**energía nuclear** La energía liberada por una reacción nuclear.

**nutrient** (NOO-tree-uhnt)
A substance that an organism needs to live. Examples include water, minerals, and materials that come from the breakdown of food particles.

**nutriente** Una sustancia que un organismo necesita para vivir. Ejemplos incluyen agua, minerales y sustancias que provienen de la descomposición de partículas de alimento.

# O

**ocean current**
A mass of moving ocean water. (p. 62)

**corriente oceánica** Una masa de agua oceánica en movimiento.

GLOSSARY

### oceanic-continental subduction
A boundary along which a tectonic plate carrying oceanic crust sinks beneath a plate with continental crust. (p. 289)

**subducción océano-continente** Un límite a lo largo del cual una placa tectónica de corteza oceánica se hunde bajo una placa de corteza continental.

### oceanic-oceanic subduction
A boundary along which a tectonic plate carrying oceanic crust sinks beneath another plate with oceanic crust. (p. 288)

**subducción de placas oceánica-oceánica** Un límite a lo largo del cual una placa tectónica de corteza oceánica se hunde bajo otra placa de corteza oceánica.

### ore
A rock that contains enough of a valuable mineral to be mined for a profit. (p. 462)

**mena** Una roca que contiene suficiente mineral valioso para ser extraído con fines lucrativos.

### organism
An individual living thing, made up of one or many cells. (p. CA17)

**organismo** Un individuo vivo, compuesto de una o muchas células.

### outer core
A layer of molten metal, mainly nickel and iron, that surrounds Earth's inner core. (p. 266)

**núcleo externo** Una capa de metal fundido, principalmente níquel y hierro, que rodea al núcleo interno de la Tierra.

# P, Q

### Pangaea (pan-JEE-uh)
A supercontinent that included all of the landmasses on Earth. It began breaking apart about 200 million years ago. (p. 272)

**Pangea** Un supercontinente que incluía todas las masas continentales de la Tierra. Empezó a fracturarse aproximadamente hace 200 millones de años.

### parasitism (PAR-uh-suh-TIHZ-uhm)
A relationship between two species in which one species is harmed while the other benefits; a type of symbiosis. (p. 427)

**parasitismo** Una relación entre dos especies en la cual una especie es perjudicada mientras que la otra se beneficia; un tipo de simbiosis.

### photosynthesis (FOH-toh-SIHN-thih-sihs)
The process by which green plants and other producers use simple compounds and energy from light to make sugar, an energy-rich compound.

**fotosíntesis** El proceso mediante el cual las plantas verdes y otros productores usan compuestos simples y energía de la luz para producir azúcares, compuestos ricos en energía.

### pioneer species
The first species to move into a lifeless environment. Lichens are typical pioneer species on land. (p. 434)

**especie pionera** La primera especie que ocupa un medio ambiente sin vida. Los lichens son típicas especies pioneras terrestres.

### pollution
The release of harmful substances into the air, water, or land. (p. 498)

**contaminación** La descarga de sustancias nocivas al aire, al agua o a la tierra.

### population
A group of organisms of the same species that live in the same area. For example, a desert will have populations of different species of lizards and cactus plants. (p. 414)

**población** Un grupo de organismos de la misma especie que viven en la misma área. Por ejemplo, un desierto tendrá poblaciones de distintas especies de lagartijas y de cactus.

### population density
A measure of the number of organisms that live in a given area. The population density of a city may be given as the number of people living per square kilometer. (p. 494)

**densidad de población** Una medida de la cantidad de organismos que viven un área dada. La densidad de población de una ciudad puede expresarse como el número de personas que viven en un kilómetro cuadrado.

### precipitation
Any type of liquid or solid water that falls to Earth's surface, such as rain, snow, or hail. (p. 93)

**precipitación** Cualquier tipo de agua líquida o sólida que cae a la superficie de la Tierra, como por ejemplo lluvia, nieve o granizo.

**predator**
An animal that hunts other animals and eats them. (p. 423)

**predador** Un animal que caza otros animales y se los come.

**prey**
An animal that other animals hunt and eat. (p. 423)

**presa** Un animal que otros animales cazan y se comen.

**prime meridian**
An imaginary north-south line that divides the planet into the Eastern Hemisphere and the Western Hemisphere. The prime meridian passes through Greenwich, England. (p. 159)

**primer meridiano** Una línea imaginaria de norte a sur que divide al planeta en hemisferio oriental y hemisferio occidental. El primer meridiano pasa a través de Greenwich, Inglaterra.

**producer**
An organism that captures energy from sunlight and transforms it into chemical energy that is stored in energy-rich carbon compounds. Producers are a source of food for other organisms. (p. 391)

**productor** Un organismo que capta energía de la luz solar y la transforma a energía química que se almacena en compuestos de carbono ricos en energía. Los productores son una fuente de alimento para otros organismos.

**projection**
A representation of Earth's curved surface on a flat map. (p. 160)

**proyección** Una representación de la superficie curva de la Tierra en un mapa plano.

**pyroclastic flow** (PY-roh-KLAS-tihk)
A dense cloud of superheated gases and rock fragments that moves quickly downhill from an erupting volcano. (p. 348)

**corriente piroclástica** Una nube densa de gases sobrecalentados y fragmentos de rocas que desciende rápidamente de un volcán en erupción.

# R

**radiation** (RAY-dee-AY-shuhn)
Energy that travels across distances as electromagnetic waves. (p. 18)

**radiación** Energía que viaja a través de la distancia en ondas electromagnéticas.

**recrystallization**
The process by which bonds between atoms in minerals break and re-form in new ways during metamorphism. (p. 195)

**recristalización** El proceso mediante el cual los enlaces entre los átomos de los minerales se rompen y se vuelven a formar de diferentes maneras durante el metamorfismo.

**recycling**
The reusing of materials that people would otherwise throw away, such as paper, glass, plastics, and certain metals. (p. 468)

**reciclaje** El reutilizar los materiales que la gente de otra forma desecharía, como el papel, el vidrio, los plásticos y ciertos metales.

**relative humidity**
The comparison of the amount of water vapor in air with the maximum amount of water vapor that can be present in air at that temperature. (p. 94)

**humedad relativa** La comparación entre la cantidad de vapor de agua en el aire y la cantidad máxima de vapor de agua que puede estar presente en el aire a esa temperatura.

**relief**
In geology, the difference in elevation between an area's high and low points. (p. 165)

**relieve** En geología, la diferencia en elevación entre los puntos altos y bajos de un área.

**relief map**
A map that shows the differences in elevation in an area. Relief maps can show elevations through the use of contour lines, shading, colors, and, in some cases, three-dimensional materials. (p. 156)

**mapa de relieve** Un mapa que muestra las diferencias en elevación de un área. Los mapas de relieve pueden mostrar elevaciones mediante del uso de curvas de nivel, sombreado, colores y, en algunos casos, materiales tridimensionales.

**remote sensing**
A method of using scientific equipment to gather information about something from a distance. Most remote-sensing methods make use of different types of electromagnetic radiation. (p. 170)

**teledetección** Un método de reunir información sobre algo a distancia usando equipo científico. La mayoría de los métodos de sensoramiento remoto hacen uso de diferentes tipos de radiación electromagnética.

GLOSSARY

### renewable resource
A natural resource that can be replaced in nature at about the same rate as it is used. (p. 450)

**recurso renovable** Un recurso natural que puede reemplazarse en la naturaleza casi al mismo ritmo al que es utilizado.

### respiration
The physical and chemical processes by which a living thing exchanges gases with the environment. In cellular respiration, cells take in oxygen and release the energy stored in carbon compounds.

**respiración** Los procesos físicos y químicos mediante los cuales un organismo vivo toma oxígeno y libera energía. En la respiración celular, las células absorben oxígeno y liberan la energía almacenada en compuestos de carbono.

### rift valley
A deep valley formed as tectonic plates move apart, such as along a mid-ocean ridge. (p. 279)

**valle de rift** Un valle profundo formado cuando las placas tectónicas se separan, como a lo largo de una dorsal oceánica.

### rock
A naturally formed solid that is usually made up of one or more types of minerals. (p. 187)

**roca** Un sólido formado de manera natural y generalmente compuesto de uno o más tipos de minerales.

### rock cycle
The set of natural, repeating processes that form, change, break down, and re-form rocks. (p. 196)

**ciclo de las rocas** La serie de procesos naturales y repetitivos que forman, cambian, descomponen y vuelven a formar rocas.

# S

### sandbar
A ridge of sand built up by the action of waves and currents. (p. 240)

**barra de arena** Una colina de arena que se forma por la acción de las olas y las corrientes.

### satellite
An object that orbits a more massive object.

**satélite** Un objeto que orbita un objeto de mayor masa.

### saturation
A condition of the atmosphere in which the rates of evaporation and condensation are equal. (p. 94)

**saturación** Una condición de la atmósfera en la cual las tasas de evaporación y condensación son iguales.

### sediment
Solid materials such as rock fragments, plant and animal remains, or minerals that are carried by water or by air and that settle on the bottom of a body of water or on the ground.

**sedimento** Materiales sólidos como fragmentos de rocas, restos de plantas y animales o minerales que son transportados por el agua o el aire y que se depositan en el fondo de un cuerpo de agua o en el suelo.

### sedimentary rock (SEHD-uh-MEHN-tuh-ree)
Rock formed as pieces of older rocks and other loose materials get pressed or cemented together or as dissolved minerals re-form and build up in layers. (p. 192)

**roca sedimentaria** Roca que se forma cuando los pedazos de rocas más viejas y otros materiales sueltos son presionados o cementados o cuando los minerales disueltos vuelven a formarse y se acumulan en capas.

### seismic wave (SYZ-mihk)
The vibrations caused by an earthquake. (p. 307)

**onda sísmica** Las vibraciones ocasionadas por un terremoto.

### seismograph (SYZ-muh-GRAF)
An instrument that constantly records ground movements. (p. 312)

**sismógrafo** Un instrumento que registra constantemente los movimientos del suelo.

### sensor
A mechanical or electronic device that receives and responds to a signal, such as light. (p. 171)

**sensor** Un dispositivo mecánico o electrónico que recibe y responde a una señal, como la luz.

### sinkhole
An open basin that forms when the roof of a cavern becomes so thin that it falls in. (p. 235)

**sumidero** Una cuenca abierta que se forma cuando el techo de una caverna se vuelve tan delgado que se desploma.

### sleet
Small pellets of ice that form when rain passes through a layer of cold air and freezes before hitting the ground. (p. 104)

**aguanieve** Pequeñas bolitas de hielo que se forman cuando la lluvia pasa a través de una capa de aire frío y se congela antes de caer al suelo.

**slope**
A measure of how steep a landform is. Slope is calculated as the change in elevation divided by the distance covered. (p. 165)

**pendiente** Una medida de lo inclinada de una formación terrestre. La pendiente se calcula dividiendo el cambio en la elevación por la distancia recorrida.

**soil**
The top layer of Earth's surface, consisting of rock and mineral particles mixed with organic matter.

**suelo** La capa superior de la superficie de la Tierra, que consiste de rocas y partículas minerales mezcladas con material orgánico.

**solar cell**
A device that converts the energy of sunlight into electrical energy. (p. 475)

**celda solar** Un aparato que convierte la energía de la luz del Sol en energía eléctrica.

**species**
A group of living things so closely related that they can breed with one another and produce offspring that can breed as well. (p. 413)

**especie** Un grupo de organismos que están tan estrechamente relacionados que pueden aparearse entre sí y producir crías que también pueden aparearse.

**storm surge**
A rapid rise in water level in a coastal area that occurs when a hurricane pushes a huge mass of ocean water, often leading to flooding and widespread destruction. (p. 125)

**marea de tormenta** Un rápido aumento del nivel del agua en un área costera que ocurre cuando un huracán empuja una gran masa de agua oceánica, muchas veces provocando inundaciones y destrucción extensa.

**stress**
The force applied by an object pressing on, pulling on, or pushing against another object. (p. 301)

**tensión** La fuerza aplicada por un objeto que presiona, jala o empuja contra otro objeto.

**subduction**
The process by which an oceanic tectonic plate sinks under another plate into Earth's mantle. (p. 286)

**subducción** El proceso mediante el cual una placa tectónica oceánica se hunde bajo otra placa y entra al manto de la Tierra.

**succession** (suhk-SEHSH-uhn)
A natural process that involves a gradual change in the plant and animal communities that live in an area. (p. 434)

**sucesión** Un proceso natural que involucra un cambio gradual en las comunidades de plantas y animales que viven en un área.

**sustainable**
A term that describes the managing of certain natural resources so that they are not harmed or used up. Examples include maintaining clean groundwater and protecting topsoil from erosion. (p. 510)

**sostenible** Un término que describe el manejo de ciertos recursos naturales para que no se deterioren o se terminen. Ejemplos incluyen mantener limpia el agua subterránea y proteger de la erosión a la capa superficial del suelo.

**symbiosis** (SIHM-bee-OH-sihs)
The interaction between individuals from two different species that live closely together. (p. 426)

**simbiosis** La interacción entre individuos de dos especies distintas que viven en proximidad.

**system**
A group of objects or phenomena that interact. A system can be as simple as a rope, a pulley, and a mass. It also can be as complex as the interaction of energy and matter in the four parts of the Earth system. (p. 41)

**sistema** Un grupo de objetos o fenómenos que interactúan. Un sistema puede ser algo tan sencillo como una cuerda, una polea y una masa. También puede ser algo tan complejo como la interacción de la energía y la materia en las cuatro partes del sistema de la Tierra.

# T

**technology**
The use of scientific knowledge to solve problems or engineer new products, tools, or processes.

**tecnología** El uso de conocimientos científicos para resolver problemas o para diseñar nuevos productos, herramientas o procesos.

**tectonic plate** (tehk-TAHN-ihk)
One of the large, moving pieces into which Earth's lithosphere is broken and which commonly carries both oceanic and continental crust. (p. 268)

**placa tectónica** Una de las grandes piezas en movimiento en las que la litosfera de la Tierra se rompe y que comúnmente lleva corteza oceánica y continental.

GLOSSARY

**temperature**
A measure of the average amount of the energy of motion of the particles in an object. (p. 10)

**temperatura** Una medida de la cantidad promedio de energía de movimiento de las partículas en un objeto.

**theory**
In science, a set of widely accepted explanations of observations and phenomena. A theory is a well-tested explanation that is consistent with all available evidence.

**teoría** En las ciencias, un conjunto de explicaciones de observaciones y fenómenos que es ampliamente aceptado. Una teoría es una explicación bien probada que es consecuente con la evidencia disponible.

**theory of plate tectonics**
A theory stating that Earth's lithosphere is broken into huge plates that move and change in size over time. (p. 274)

**teoría de la tectónica de placas** Una teoría que establece que la litosfera de la Tierra está formada por enormes placas que se mueven y cambian de tamaño con el tiempo.

**thunderstorm**
A storm with lightning and thunder. (p. 128)

**tormenta eléctrica** Una tormenta con relámpagos y truenos.

**till**
Sediment of different sizes left directly on the ground by a melting, or retreating, glacier. (p. 248)

**sedimentos glaciares** Sedimentos de diferentes tamaños depositados directamente en el suelo por un glaciar que se derrite o retrocede.

**topography**
All natural and human-made surface features of a particular area. (p. 164)

**topografía** Todas las características de superficie de origen natural y humano en un área particular.

**tornado**
A violently rotating column of air stretching from a cloud to the ground. (p. 131)

**tornado** Una columna de aire que gira violentamente y se extiende desde una nube hasta el suelo.

**transform boundary**
A boundary along which two tectonic plates scrape past each other, and crust is neither formed nor destroyed. (p. 278)

**límite transcurrente** Un límite a lo largo del cual dos placas tectónicas se rozan y no se forma corteza ni se destruye.

**tropical storm** (TRAHP-ih-kuhl)
A low-pressure system that starts in the tropics with winds of at least 65 kilometers per hour (40 mi/h) but less than 120 kilometers per hour (74 mi/h). (p. 123)

**tormenta tropical** Un sistema de baja presión que inicia en los trópicos con vientos de por lo menos 65 kilómetros por hora (40 mi/h) pero menores a 120 kilómetros por hora (74 mi/h).

**tsunami** (tsu-NAH-mee)
A water wave caused by an earthquake, volcanic eruption, or landslide. (p. 318)

**tsunami** Una ola de agua ocasionada por un terremoto, erupción volcánica o derrumbe.

## U

**urban**
A term that describes a city environment.

**urbano** Un término que describe el medio ambiente de una ciudad.

## V

**variable**
Any factor that can change in a controlled experiment, observation, or model.

**variable** Cualquier factor que puede cambiar en un experimento controlado, en una observación o en un modelo.

**volcano**
An opening in the crust through which molten rock, rock fragments, and hot gases erupt; a mountain built up from erupted materials. (p. 346)

**volcán** Una abertura en la corteza a través de la cual la roca fundida, fragmentos de roca y gases calientes hacen erupción; una montaña formada a partir de los materiales que surgen de una erupción.

**volume**
An amount of three-dimensional space, often used to describe the space that an object takes up.

**volumen** Una cantidad de espacio tridimensional; a menudo se usa este término para describir el espacio que ocupa un objeto.

# W, X, Y, Z

### water cycle

The continuous movement of water on Earth, through its atmosphere, and in the living things on Earth. (p. 60)

**ciclo del agua** El movimiento continuo de agua sobre la Tierra, por su atmósfera y dentro de los organismos vivos de la Tierra.

### wave

A disturbance that transfers energy from one place to another. (p. 19)

**onda** Una perturbación que transfiere energía de un lugar a otro.

### wavelength

The distance from one wave crest to the next crest; the distance from any part of one wave to the identical part of the next wave. (p. 20)

**longitud de onda** La distancia de una cresta de onda a la siguiente cresta; la distancia de cualquier parte de una onda a la parte idéntica de la siguiente onda.

### weather

The condition of Earth's atmosphere at a particular time and place. (pp. 62, 83)

**estado del tiempo** La condición de la atmósfera terrestre en un lugar y momento particular.

### weathering

The process by which natural processes break down rocks. (p. 199)

**meteorización** El proceso por el cual los procesos naturales fragmentan las rocas.

### wind

The horizontal movement of air caused by differences in air pressure. (p. 83)

**viento** El movimiento horizontal de aire provocado por diferencias en la presión de aire.

### work

The use of force to move an object over a distance. (p. 15)

**trabajo** El uso de fuerza para mover un objeto una distancia.

# Index

Note: The page numbers for definitions are printed in **boldface** type.
The page numbers for illustrations, maps, and charts are printed in *italic* type.

## A

# B



INDEX

# C



INDEX

INDEX

# D

# E



INDEX

INDEX

# F



INDEX

# G



INDEX

# H



# I



INDEX

# J, K



# L



INDEX

INDEX

# M



INDEX

# N



INDEX

# O

# P



INDEX

# Q



# R



INDEX

INDEX

INDEX

# T



INDEX

# U



# V

# W



INDEX

# X, Y, Z



INDEX

# Acknowledgments



## Photography

**Cover** © Garry Black/Masterfile; **i** © Garry Black/Masterfile; **iii** *top to bottom left* Photograph of James Trefil by Evan Cantwell; Photograph of Rita Ann Calvo by Joseph Calvo; Photograph of Linda Carnin by Amilcar Cifuentes; Photograph of Sam Miller by Samuel Miller; *top to bottom right* Photograph of Kenneth Cutler by Kenneth A. Cutler; Photograph of Donald Steely by Marni Stamm; Photograph of Vicky Vachon by Redfern; **v** *left top to bottom* © William M. Bruce; © Jack Castro; Dr. Bernice Filerman - ; © Mark Handwerker; ca-s6pe-000000-009 **004–v** Sandy Steinburg - ; **viii** AP/Wide World Photos; **x** © Steve Starr/ Stock Boston Inc./PictureQuest; **xii** © Orion Press/Corbis; **xiv** © William Stevenson/Alamy Images; **xx, xxi** Photograph by Sharon Hoogstraten; **CA12–CA13** © Roger Ressmeyer/Corbis; **CA14–CA15** AP/Wide World Photos; **CA16–CA17** © Ron Sanford/ Corbis; **CA18–CA19** © Galen Rowell/Corbis; **CA20** © Vince Streano/Corbis; **CA21** © Roger Ressmeyer/Corbis; **CA22** *top left* University of Florida Lightning Research Laboratory; *center* © Roger Ressmeyer/Corbis; **CA23** *center* © Mauro Fermariello/Science Researchers; *bottom right* © Alfred Pasieka/Photo Researchers; **CA24–CA25** *background* © Stocktrek/Corbis; *center* NOAA; **CA25** *left* © Alan Schein; *center right* Vaisala Oyj, Finland.

## Unit 1

**1** © Bill Ross/Corbis; **2–3** © Bruce Byers/Getty Images; **3** *top right* © The Chedd-Angier Production Company; *bottom left* © D. Faulkner/Photo Researchers; **4** *top left* © Luiz C. Marigo/Peter Arnold, Inc.; *top center* Image courtesy Norman Kuring/ SeaWiFS Project, NASA; *top right* © Norbert Wu; *bottom* © The Chedd-Angier Production Company; **6–7** AP/Wide World Photos; **7** Photograph by Sharon Hoogstraten; **9** © Peter J. Bryant/Biological Photo Service; **10** *top* © Patrick Ward/Corbis; *bottom* © H. David Seawell/Corbis; **12** © Larry Lee Photography/ Corbis; **14** Photograph by Frank Siteman; **15** © Digital Vision; **16** *top* © Grant Klotz/Alaska Stock Images/PictureQuest; *bottom* Photograph by Sharon Hoogstraten; **17, 18** Photograph by Sharon Hoogstraten; **20** *left* © Jeremy Hoare/Alamy Images; *center* © Mark Clarke/Science Photo Library/Photo Researchers; *right* © Russ Widstrand/Alamy Images; **21** © Alfred Pasieka/Science Photo Library/Photo Researchers; **23** Photograph by Sharon Hoogstraten; **24** © Sally A. Morgan/Ecoscene/Corbis; **25** *left* © Pulse Productions/SuperStock/PictureQuest; **26** Photograph by Sharon Hoogstraten; **27** © Brand X Pictures/Alamy; **28, 29** Photograph by Sharon Hoogstraten; **32** © SuperStock; **33** *top left* © Jeremy Samuelson/FoodPix; *right* © Martin Jacobs/FoodPix; *bottom left* © William Reavell/StockFood Munich/StockFood; **38–39** hanglider - © Joson/Getty Images; **39, 41** Photograph by Sharon Hoogstraten; **42–43** NASA; **42** *left* © David Parker/ Photo Researchers; *right* © Chuck Davis/Getty Images; **43** *bottom center* © Dr. Neville Winchester/University of Victoria, British Columbia, Canada; *bottom right* © Peter and Georgina Bowater/Stock Connection/ PictureQuest; **44** © Carol Polich/Lonely Planet Images; **45** Photograph by Sharon Hoogstraten; **46** AP/Wide World Photos; **47** *left* AP/Wide World Photos; *right* © Sue Ellen Hirschfeld/Department of Geological Sciences, California State Unviversity, East Bay; **48** © David Young-Wolff/ PhotoEdit; **49** © Joson/Corbis; **50** *top* © Lauri Nykopp/Alamy Images; *bottom* © Sergio Pitamitz/ Alamy Images; **51** Photograph by Sharon Hoogstraten; **55** © Thomas Hallstein/Alamy Images; **56** *top* © Michael Kevin Daly/Corbis; *bottom* Photograph by Sharon Hoogstraten; **58** © Martin Rietze/Alamy Images; **61** © MedioImages/Alamy Images; **63** © AFP/ Corbis; **65** Photo by Sharon Hoogstraten; **67** *left* © Simon Fraser/Mauna Loa Observatory/Photo Researchers; *bottom right* Photograph by Sharon Hoogstraten; **72** © Don Farrall/Getty Images; **73** *top left* © Sheila Terry/Photo Researchers; *top right, center* © Dorling Kindersley; *bottom* © SEF/Art Resource, New York; **74** *top left* Mary Evans Picture Library; *top right, bottom* © Dorling Kindersley; **75** *right* © Mark Wiens/ Masterfile; *left* © 1913 Debris Yearbook, Purdue University; **76–77** AP/Wide World Photos; **77, 79, 81, 83, 85** Photograph by Sharon Hoogstraten; **90** Earth Vistas; **91** *left* © Lester Lefkowitz/Corbis; *inset* NASA/Corbis; **92** *center right* Photograph by Sharon Hoogstraten; *bottom left* © Japack Company/Corbis; **93** © Kristi Bressert/Index Stock Imagery/PictureQuest; **95** *bottom right* Photograph by Sharon Hoogstraten; **96** © Grant Heilman/Grant Heilman Photography, Inc.; **98** *top* © John Mead/Photo Researchers; *center* © Corbis; *bottom* © Fred Whitehead/Animals Animals/Earth Scenes; **99** © Mark E. Gibson/Corbis; **100** *top* © Gunter Marx Photography/Corbis; *bottom* Photograph by Sharon Hoogstraten; **102** *top* © Stockbyte/PictureQuest;

**105** *left* © Larry West/Photo Researchers; *right* © Astrid & Hanns-Frieder Michler/Photo Researchers, Inc.; **106** © Will McIntyre/Photo Researchers; **107** *left* ©1990 Warren Faidley/Weatherstock; *right* Global Atmospherics, Inc; **110** © Dorling Kindersley; **112–113** AP/Wide World Photos; **113, 115, 117** Photograph by Sharon Hoogstraten; **119** © Photodisc/Getty Images; **120** *bottom right* University of Wisconsin-Madison Space Science and Engineering Center; **122** © Stephen J. Krasemann/Photo Researchers; **123** Photograph by Sharon Hoogstraten; **124** NASA Goddard Space Flight Center/Image by Marit Jentoft-Nilsen; **125** © Smiley N. Pool/The Dallas Morning News/Corbis; **126** Photograph by Sharon Hoogstraten; **127** AP/Wide World Photos; **128** © William James Warren/Corbis; **130** *top* Photograph by Sharon Hoogstraten; *bottom* © Photodisc/Getty Images; **131** © David K. Hoadley; **132** © Reuters/Corbis; **133** *top left inset, top right* © Fletcher & Baylis/Photo Researchers; *background* © Waite Air Photos, Inc.; **134** Used with permission © January 9, 2003 Chicago Tribune Company, Chicago, Illinois. Photograph by Sharon Hoogstraten; **136, 137, 138** Provided by the Space Science and Engineering Center, University of Wisconsin-Madison; **139** Courtesy Bob Werner/ WSBT-TV, South Bend, Indiana; **140** *top left* © Mary Kate Denny/PhotoEdit; *bottom* Photograph by Sharon Hoogstraten; **140–141** Photograph by Sharon Hoogstraten; **142** *center* NASA Goddard Space Flight Center/Image by Marit Jentoft-Nilsen; *bottom* Provided by the Space Science and Engineering Center, University of Wisconsin-Madison; **144** Used with permission © January 9, 2003 Chicago Tribune Company, Chicago, Illinois. Photograph by Sharon Hoogstraten.

## Unit 2

**147** © Per Breiehagen/Getty Images; **148–149** Courtesy of NASA/Jet Propulsion Lab/Caltech; **149** *top* NASA/Carla Thomas; *bottom* Courtesy Diamonds North Resources, Ltd.; **150** *top* NASA/Carla Thomas; *bottom* © The Chedd-Angier Production Company; **151** © William Whitehurst/Corbis; **152–153** NASA; **153** *top left* National Air & Space Museum, Smithsonian Institution, Washington, D.C.; *top right* Courtesy of L. Sue Baugh; *center left* NASA/Goddard Space Flight Center/SeaWiFS Project; *bottom left* National Air & Space Museum, Smithsonian Institution, Washington, D.C.; *bottom right* NASA/Goddard Space Flight Center; **155** Photograph by Sharon Hoogstraten; **156** U.S. Geological Survey; **159** © David Parker/Photo Researchers; **160** Photograph by Sharon Hoogstraten; **163** © Jerry Driendl/Getty Images; **164** Photograph by Sharon Hoogstraten; **165** *top* © Stan Osolinski/Getty Images; *bottom* U.S. Geological Survey; **166** U.S. Geological Survey; **168** *top left* U.S. Geological Survey; *center, bottom* Photograph by Sharon Hoogstraten; **170** © Space Imaging; **171** *top* © Space Imaging; *bottom background* © Paul Morrell/Stone/Getty Images; *left, inset* National Oceanic and Atmospheric Administration/Department of Commerce; **172** NASA/MODIS Land Rapid Response Team; **174** © 1997 John D. Rogie; **175** *background* NASA/Goddard Space Flight Center/SeaWiFS Project and ORBIMAGE; *top inset* Library of Congress; *right* NASA/Jet Propulsion Lab/National Imagery and Mapping Agency; **176** *center* U.S. Geological Survey; *bottom left* © Paul Morrell/Stone/Getty Images; *inset* National Oceanic and Atmospheric Administration/ Department of Commerce; **178** U.S. Geological Survey; **179** © National Park Service; **180–181** Panning for gold - © Steve Starr/Stock Boston Inc./PictureQuest; **181** *center* Photograph by Sharon Hoogstraten; *bottom* Courtesy of L. Sue Baugh; **183** Photograph by Sharon Hoogstraten; **185** *center* © Charles D. Winters/Photo Researchers; *bottom* © Astrid & Hanns-Freider/Photo Researchers; **186** Photograph by Sharon Hoogstraten; **187** © Andrew J. Martinez/Photo Researchers; **188** *top left* © Dorling Kindersley; *top right, bottom right* © Doug Martin/Photo Researchers; **189** *left* © Joyce Photographics/ Photo Researchers; *right* © Dorling Kindersley; **190** Photograph by Sharon Hoogstraten; **191** © James Lyon/Lonely Planet Images; **192** *center* © Arthur R. Hill/Visuals Unlimited; *bottom* © Mark Schneider/ Visuals Unlimited; **194** Photograph by Sharon Hoogstraten; **195** *top to bottom* © Gerald & Buff Corsi/Visuals Unlimited; © 1995 Andrew J. Martinez/ Photo Researchers; The Boltin Picture Library; © Breck P. Kent; © 1996 Andrew J. Martinez/Photo Researchers; **196** *top left, bottom left* © Andrew J. Martinez/Photo Researchers; *right* © Arthur R. Hill/Visuals Unlimited; **198** *background* © Nobert Wu/Norbert Wu Productions/PictureQuest; *inset* National Oceanic and Atmospheric Administration *right* © Corbis; **199** Photograph by Sharon Hoogstraten; **201** *background* © Photodisc/Getty Images; *top right* © Susan Rayfield/ Photo Researchers; *center right*, *bottom left* Photograph courtesy of Sara Christopherson; *bottom right* © Kirkendall-Spring Photographers; **202** © Cheyenne Rouse/Visuals Unlimited; **204** *top* © image100/Alamy Images; *bottom* Photograph by Sharon Hoogstraten; **206** © Richard Cummins/ SuperStock; **209** *background* © PhotoBliss/Alamy Images; *center right* © Alamy Images; *bottom left* © W. Perry Conway/Corbis; *bottom right* © Ruaridh Stewart/ZUMA/Corbis; **212** U.S. Geological Survey;

**213** *background* AP/Wide World Photos; *left* © Science Photo Library/Photo Researchers; *right* The Granger Collection, New York; **214** *right, center* © Andrew J. Martinez/Photo Researchers; *left* © Arthur R. Hill/ Visuals Unlimited; **218** *top* The Granger Collection; *bottom* © Tom Bean/Corbis; **219** *top* © Gianni Dagli Orti/Corbis; *center* The Natural History Museum, London; *bottom* Courtesy British Geological Survey; **220** *top* © Sally A. Morgan/Ecoscene/ Corbis; *bottom* © James King-Holmes/Photo Researchers; **221** *top* © Sherwin Crasto/Corbis; *center* © Mark A. Klinger/ Carnegie Museum of Natural History; *bottom* © The Field Museum; **222–223** © A.C. Waltham/Robert Harding Picture Library/Alamy Images; **223** *top* Photograph by Mike Mulligan; *bottom* Photograph by Sharon Hoogstraten; **225** © Bernhard Edmaier/Photo Researchers; **226** Photograph by Sharon Hoogstraten; **227** AP/Wide World Photos; **228** *top* Photograph by L.M. Smith, Waterways Experiment Station, U.S. Army Corps of Engineers. Courtesy, U.S. Geological Survey; *bottom* © Thomas Rampton/Grant Heilman Photography, Inc.; **229** © Troy and Mary Parlee/Alamy Images; **230** Photograph by Sharon Hoogstraten; **231** © Bill Ross/Corbis; **232** *top* © Kevin Horan/Stock Boston/ PictureQuest; *bottom* © Yann Arthus-Bertrand/Corbis; **233** *top* © 1992 Tom Bean; **234** © Charles Kennard/ Stock Boston/PictureQuest; **235** *top* © Reuters/Corbis; **236** *top* © Peter Bowater/Alamy Images; *bottom* Photograph by Sharon Hoogstraten; **238** © Craig Lovell/Corbis; **239** © Robert Perron; **240** Photograph by Sharon Hoogstraten; **241** © Tim Barnwell/Picturesque/ PictureQuest; **242** © John Shaw/Bruce Coleman, Inc.; **243** *top* © 1994 Tom Bean; *bottom* © Goodshoot/Alamy Images; **244** *background* © ImageState/ PictureQuest; *inset* © Santa Barbara County Flood Control District; **245** Photograph by Sharon Hoogstraten; **247** *left* © Bernard Edmaier/Photo Researchers; *right* © ImageState-Pictor/PictureQuest; **248** *top* © Norman Barett/Bruce Coleman, Inc.; *bottom* © Jim Wark/Airphoto; ca-s6pe-020704=007 **249** *top* © 1990 Tom Bean; *bottom* Photograph by Sharon Hoogstraten; **250** Mapquest-Source: U.S. Army Corps of Engineers/Great Lakes Commission; **251** © Chuck Pefley/Alamy Images; **252** *top* © Bernhard Edmaier/Photo Researchers; *center* © Craig Lovell/Corbis; *bottom* © John and Lisa Merrill/Getty Images; **254** © Tom Bean.

## Unit 3

**257** © Roger Ressmeyer/Corbis; **258–259** © Stephen and Donna O'Meara/Photo Researchers; **259** NASA Goddard Space Flight Center/METI/ERSDAC/JAROS, and U.S./Japan ASTER Science Team; **260** *top left* Photograph by T. Miller/U.S. Geological Survey; *inset* U.S. Geological Survey; *bottom* © The Chedd-Angier Production Company; **261** NASA Goddard Space Flight Center/METI/ERSDAC/JAROS, and U.S./Japan ASTER Science Team; **262–263** © Tony Waltham/Geophotos; **263, 265, 268, 270** Photograph by Sharon Hoogstraten; **271** © 1995–2002 Geoclassics. All rights reserved.; **276** *top* © Worldsat International/ Photo Researchers; *bottom* Photograph by Sharon Hoogstraten; **278, 281** Photograph by Sharon Hoogstraten; **283** *top* © Christophe Ratier/NHPA/Photo Researchers; *bottom* © NASA/Photo Researchers; ca-s6pe-0308mf=001 **285** *left* © Dr. John Brackenbury/Photo Researchers; *right* NASA; **286** Photograph by Sharon Hoogstraten; **287** © John Coletti/Stock Boston/PictureQuest; **289** Photograph by Sharon Hoogstraten; **290** © Lloyd Cluff/Corbis; **291** © Paul Chesley/Getty Images; **293** *left* © Albrecht G. Schaefer/ Corbis; *right* © Mitch Diamond/Index Stock/PictureQuest; **298–299** AP/Wide World Photos; **299, 301, 303** Photograph by Sharon Hoogstraten; **304** *top, bottom* © Martin Miller/University of Oregon, Eugene, Oregon; **305** NOAA/National Geophysical Data Center; **306** *top* U.S. Geological Survey; *bottom* © Bettmann/Corbis; **307, 309** Photograph by Sharon Hoogstraten; **315** AP Wide World Photos; **316** Photograph by Sharon Hoogstraten; **317** © Mark Downey; **318** U.S. Geological Survey; **319** © AFP/Getty Images; **322** © Roger Ressmeyer/Corbis; **324** *top* © Michael S. Yamashita/Corbis; *bottom* Photograph by Sharon Hoogstraten; **325** Photograph by Sharon Hoogstraten; **330** *top* © Chris Butler/Photo Researchers; *bottom* © Detlev van Ravenswaay/Photo Researchers; **331** *top* © Jim Brandenburg/Minden Pictures; *center* Courtesy of J.W. Schopf/University of California, Los Angeles; *bottom* Japan Meteorological Agency; **332** *top left* © Simon Fraser/Photo Researchers; *top right* © Chase Studio/Photo Researchers; *bottom* Courtesy of the Ocean Drilling Program; **333** *top left* NASA/Goddard Space Flight Center; *top right* © Brooks Kraft/Corbis; *bottom* NASA/ STS-113 Shuttle Crew; **334–335** Volcanic Eruptions - © Douglas Peebles; **335, 337** Photograph by Sharon Hoogstraten; **338** U.S. Department of the Interior; **339, 340** © Martin Miller/University of Oregon, Eugene, Oregon; **341** © Tim Hauf Photography/Visuals Unlimited; **342** Photograph by Sharon Hoogstraten; **343** © Martin Miller/University of Oregon, Eugene, Oregon; **344** © Phil Schermeister/Corbis; **345** © William Ervin/Photo Researchers; **346, 348** Photograph by Sharon Hoogstraten; **350** © G.R. Roberts Photo Library; **351** *left* © Tom Bean/Corbis; *right* © Krafft-Explorer/SS/Photo Researchers; **352** © F. Gohier/Photo Researchers;

**353** NASA/Carnegie Mellon University; **354** *top* © Krafft-Explorer/Photo Researchers; *bottom* Photograph by Sharon Hoogstraten; **356** *top* © James A. Sugar/Corbis; *bottom* © Mark E. Gibson/Corbis; **357** *top* © Stephen and Donna O'Meara/Volcano Watch International/Photo Researchers; *bottom* © Sid Balatan/Black Star Publishing/PictureQuest; **358** U.S. Geological Survey; **360** © The Image Bank/Getty Images; **361** © Simon Fraser/Photo Researchers; **362** © Peter Ryan/Photo Researchers; **363** *background* © Russ Bishop/Age Fotostock; *left* © Hulton-Deutsch Collection/Corbis; *right* © QT Luong/terragalleria.com; *right inset* © Dave G. Houser/Corbis; **364** *left* © Sid Balatan/Black Star Publishing/PictureQuest; *center* © The Image Bank/Getty Images; *right* © Simon Fraser/Photo Researchers; **366** © Roger Ressmeyer/Corbis.

## Unit 4

**370–371** © Mark Thiessen/National Geographic Image Collection; **371** *top* © Frank Oberle/Getty Images; *bottom* © Hal Horwitz/Corbis; **372** *top left, top right* © Lawrence J. Godson; *bottom* © Chedd-Angier Production Company; **374–375** © William Stevenson/Alamy Images; **375, 377** Photograph by Ken O'Donoghue; **378** © Mark Allen Stack/Tom Stack & Associates; **379** *left* © Jim Brandenburg/Minden Pictures; *right* © Ted Kerasote/Photo Researchers, Inc.; **380** © Grant Heilman Photography; **381** © Frans Lemmens/Getty Images; **382** *top* © Larry Lefever/Grant Heilman Photography, Inc.; *bottom* Photograph by Sharon Hoogstraten; **384** Photograph by Ken O'Donoghue; **387** Photograph by Frank Siteman; **389** © Randy Wells/Corbis; **390** Photograph by Frank Siteman; **391** *left* © Eric Crichton/Corbis; *top right* © E.R. Degginger/Color-Pic, Inc.; *bottom right* © T.E. Adams/Visuals Unlimited; **392** © Anthony Mercieca Photo/Photo Researchers, Inc.; **393** *top* © Fred Bruemmer/DRK Photo; *bottom* Photograph by Ken O'Donoghue; **395** *background* © Raymond Gehman/Corbis; **397** *left* © Arthur Gurmankin and Mary Morina/Visuals Unlimited; *right* © Carmela Leszczynski/Animals Animals; **398** © Charles Melton/Visuals Unlimited; **399** © Michio Hoshino/Minden Pictures; **400** *top left* © Tom Bean; *top right* © E.R. Degginger/Color-Pic, Inc.; *bottom* © Joe McDonald/Visuals Unlimited; **401** *left* © David Wrobel/Visuals Unlimited; *right* © Tom Bean; **402** *left* © Owaki-Kulla/Corbis; *right* © Frans Lanting/Minden Pictures; **403** *top* Photograph by Sharon Hoogstraten; *bottom* © Stephen Dalton/Photo Researchers, Inc.; **404** *left* © Aaron Horowitz/Corbis; *center* © Hans Pfletschinger/Peter Arnold, Inc.; *right* © Arthur Gurmankin and Mary Morina/Visuals Unlimited; **405** *left* © Paul Rezendes; *center* © Richard Herrmann/Visuals Unlimited; *right* © Norbert Wu; **410–411** © Wolcott Henry/National Geographic Image Collection; **411** Photograph by Frank Siteman; **413** © Kevin Schafer/Corbis; **414** *left, center* © Frans Lanting/Minden Pictures; *right* © Robin Karpan/Visuals Unlimited; **418** © Walt Anderson/Visuals Unlimited; **419** © Alan & Linda Detrick/Photo Researchers, Inc.; **420** *top* © Frank Awbrey/Visuals Unlimited; *bottom* Photograph by Sharon Hoogstraten; **422** © Spencer Grant/PhotoEdit; **423** © Gary Braasch; **424** *top* © Joe McDonald/Visuals Unlimited; *bottom* © Stephen J. Krasemann/Photo Researchers, Inc.; **425** *top* Photograph by Ken O'Donoghue; *bottom* © Michael Fogden/Bruce Coleman, Inc.; **426** © Michael & Patricia Fogden/Minden Pictures; **427** © Bradley Sheard; **428** *top left* © Phil Degginger/Color-Pic, Inc.; *top center* © S.J. Krasemann/Peter Arnold, Inc.; *top right* © Ray Coleman/Visuals Unlimited; *center* © Astrid & Hanns-Frieder Michler/Science Photo Library; *bottom left* © Dwight R. Kuhn; *bottom right* © E.R. Degginger/Color-Pic, Inc.; **429** © Arthur Morris/Visuals Unlimited; **430** *background* © Kevin Fleming/Corbis; *top* © David M. Dennis/Animals Animals; **431** Photograph by Ken O'Donoghue; **432** *top* © Shin Yoshino/Minden Pictures; *bottom* © Tim Fitzharris/ Minden Pictures; **433** Photograph by Frank Siteman; **434** © Leo Collier/Getty Images; **435** © David R. Frazier/Getty Images; **437** © A. & J. Visage/Peter Arnold, Inc.; **438** © Frans Lanting/Minden Pictures; **442** *left* Denver Public Library, Western History Collection, call # F-4659; *top right* © James Randklev/Getty Images; *bottom right* Library of Congress, Prints and Photographs Division; **443** *top left* © H.H. French/Corbis; *top right* © Bill Ross/Corbis; *center left* The Bancroft Library, University of California, Berkeley; *center right* © Corbis; *bottom* © Michael Sewell/Peter Arnold, Inc.; **444** *top* © Tom Bean/DRK Photo; *center left* © Alfred Eisenstaedt/Getty Images; *center right* © David Muench/Corbis; *bottom left* © Kevin Schafer/Corbis; *bottom right* Habitat Quality for San Joaquin Kit Fox on Managed and Private Lands reprinted from ESRI Map Book, Vol. 16 and used herein with permission. Copyright © 2001 ESRI. All rights reserved.; **445** *top left* © Tom Soucek/AlaskaStock.com; *top right* © Ohio State University; *bottom* © Richard Galosy/Bruce Coleman, Inc.; **446–447** © Richard Folwell/Photo Researchers; **447** Photograph by Sharon Hoogstraten; **449** © Corbis; **451** *top* © SuperStock; *bottom* © Gunter Marx Photography/Corbis; **455** Photograph by Sharon Hoogstraten; **456** *left* Diane Moore/Icon SMI; *top right* © Corbis; *bottom right* © Photodisc/Getty Images; **457** *background* © Pauline Horton/Corbis; *left* © Craig Aurness/Corbis; *right* © Peter Essick/Getty Images; **458** Photograph by Sharon Hoogstraten; **459** *top left* © Geoff Tompkinson/Photo Researchers; *top right* © Charles Falco/

Photo Researchers; *center left* © A.J. Copely/ Visuals Unlimited; *center right* © Dorling Kindersley; *bottom left* © Charles D. Winters/Photo Researchers; *bottom right* © Dorling Kindersley; **461** *top* © Mark A. Schneider/ Photo Researchers; *center left* © Mark A. Schneider/Photo Researchers; *center right* © Andrew J. Martinez/ Photo Researchers; *bottom* © M. Claye/ Photo Researchers; **463** *top* © Mervyn P. Lawes/Corbis; *bottom* Photograph by Sharon Hoogstraten; **464** Courtesy of Newmont Mining Corp.; **465** *top left, center left, bottom left* © Dorling Kindersley; *right* © Louis Goldman/Photo Researchers; **466, 467** Photograph by Sharon Hoogstraten; **468** *top* Photograph by Sharon Hoogstraten; *bottom* © David Young-Wolff/PhotoEdit; **469** © Jose Azel/Aurora; **470** *left, inset* © Lowell Georgia/Corbis; **471** © Donald C. & Priscilla Alexander Eastman/Lonely Planet Images; **472** © Beth Davidow/Visuals Unlimited; **473** © James Stilling/Getty Images; **474** © Lynne Ledbetter/Visuals Unlimited; **475** © Martin Bond/Photo Researchers; **476** Andrew Carlin/ Tracy Operators; **477** © California Fuel Cell Partnership; **479** © Steve Allen/Brand X Pictures/PictureQuest; **480** *top* © M.L. Sinibald/Corbis; *bottom* Photograph by Sharon Hoogstraten; **481** Photograph by Sharon Hoogstraten; **482** *upper left-top* © SuperStock; *upper left, bottom* © Gunter Marx Photography/Corbis; *center* © Jose Azel/Aurora; *bottom left* © Astrid & Hanns-Freider/ Photo Researchers; *bottom right, top to bottom* © Photodisc/Getty Images; © Dorling Kindersley; © Photodisc/ Getty Images; **486–487** highways © Alex Maclean/Photonica; **487** Photograph by Ken O'Donoghue; **489** Photograph by Frank Siteman; **491** © Ray Pfortner/Peter Arnold, Inc.; **492** Photograph by Ken O'Donoghue; **493** *top* © John Elk III; *bottom* © Ted Spiegel/Corbis; **494** *top left, top right* U.S. Geological Survey/EROS Data Center; *bottom* © ChromoSohm/ Sohm/Photo Researchers, Inc.; **495** © Mark E. Gibson/Visuals Unlimited; **496** *background* © John M. Roberts/Corbis; *left inset* © Bettmann/Corbis; *top right* © Dewitt Jones/Corbis; *bottom right* © Dr. Henri Grissno-Mayer, Department of Geography, University of Tennessee; **497** © David Young-Wolff/ PhotoEdit; **498** Photograph by Ken O'Donoghue; **499** *left* © Jenny Hager/The Image Works; *right* © Tom Bean/DRK Photo; **500** *left* © Natalie Fobes/Corbis; *right* © Natalie Fobes/Getty Images; **503** © Kent Foster Photgraphs/ Visuals Unlimited; **504** *top* © Andrew J. Martinez/Photo Researchers, Inc.; *inset* © D. Cavagnaro/Visuals Unlimited; **505** © Tom Edwards/Visuals Unlimited; **506** *top* Photograph by Ken O'Donoghue; *bottom* Photograph by Frank Siteman; **507** © Frank Pedrick/The Image Works; **508** © Joe McDonald/Visuals Unlimited; **509** *background* © Tom Bean/Corbis; *top left inset* © Jim Wark/Airphoto; *top right inset* © Scott Williams/U.S. Fish and Wildlife Service; *bottom insets* Courtesy of San Diego State University, Soil Ecology and Restoration Group; **510** © Melissa Farlow/National Geographic Image Collection; **511** *top left* © Charles O'Rear/Corbis; *top right* © Larry Lefever/Grant Heilman Photography, Inc.; **512** *top* © Janis Miglavs; *bottom, clockwise from top left* © Digital Vision; © Bob Melnychuk/ Getty Images; © Digital Vision; © Photodisc/Getty Images; **513** © Kevin Schafer/Corbis; **514** *top* © Tom Myers/ Photo Researchers, Inc.; *bottom* Photograph by Frank Siteman; **515** Photograph by Frank Siteman; **516** *top left* © Natalie Fobes/Corbis; *top right* © Kent Foster Photographs/Visuals Unlimited; *bottom left* © Joe McDonald/Visuals Unlimited; *bottom right* © Klein/Hubert/Peter Arnold, Inc.; **R54–R55** NOAA/National Geophysical Data Center; **R69** *top left* © Charles D. Winters/Photo Researchers; *top right* Photograph by Malcolm Hjerstedt. Courtesy of F. John Barlow/SANCO Publishing; *center* © Charles D. Winters/Photo Researchers; *bottom left* © Biophoto Associates/ Photo Researchers; *bottom center* © Dorling Kindersley; *bottom right* © Phil Degginger/ Color-Pic, Inc.; **R70** Photograph by Sharon Hoogstraten; **R71** *top left* © Charles D. Winters/Photo Researchers; *top right* © Mark A. Schneider/Photo Researchers; *bottom* Photograph by Sharon Hoogstraten; **R72, R73** Photograph by Sharon Hoogstraten; **R74** *top left, top right,* Photograph by Sharon Hoogstraten; *top center* © Mark A. Schneider/Visuals Unlimited; *center right* Photograph by Sharon Hoogstraten; *bottom right* © Thomas Hunn/Visuals Unlimited.

## Illustration and Maps

Accurate Art, Inc. **145, 255**
Ampersand Design Group **33, 502**
Argosy **66, 82, 474, 475**
Richard Bonson/Wildlife Art Ltd. **60, 70, 80, 108, 266, 267, 294, 296, 328, 339, 341, 343, 347, 361, 364, 396, 415, 417, 428, 438**
Peter Bull **135, 142, 240, 242, 247, 249, 252, 273, 308, 314, 326, 501**
Steve Cowden **11**
Sandra Doyle/Wildlife Art Ltd. **395**
Stephen Durke **13, 59, 64, 185, 280, 321, 323, 326, R72**
Chris Forsey **195, 311**
Luigi Galante **434, 435, 438**
David A. Hardy **44**
Garry Hincks **84, 87, 197, 229, 233, 279, 280, 282, 284, 287, 288, 290, 291, 294, 350–351, 364, 385, 386, 388, 404, 482, 491**
Mapquest.com, Inc. **50, 53, 54, 62, 85, 88, 90, 91, 103, 116, 119, 120, 121, 122, 124, 129, 133, 138, 157, 158, 159, 161, 162, 163, 174, 176, 207, 209, 210, 211, 231, 235, 246, 269, 271, 272, 275, 279, 283, 284, 287, 291, 292, 294, 302, 313, 319, 320, 326, 332, 338, 341, 349, 359, 399, 415, 462, 493, R52–R53, R56–R57**
Martin Macrae/nbIllustration.co.uk **380**
Janos Marffy **193, 453**
Laurie O'Keefe **397**
Precision Graphics **89, 95, 108, 304, 305, 326, 352, 454**
Mike Saunders **97, 105, 108, 201, 203, 214**
SlimFilms **452, 472, 473, 478**
Raymond Turvey **119, 142, 239**
NOAA/National Geophysical Data Center **R54–R55**
Rob Wood/Wood Ronsaville Harlin **201, 234, 252**